Development of Concepts of Physics

To Charles W. Cole,
former president of Amherst College,
whose enthusiastic, articulate,
and unstinted support made possible
the development of the course
on which this book is based

W9-BQY-915

Development of

FROM THE RATIONALIZATION OF MECHANICS

PHYSICS DEPARTMENT

OHIO NORTHERN UNIVERSITY

A. B. ARONS, *Amherst College*

Concepts of Physics

TO THE FIRST THEORY OF ATOMIC STRUCTURE

Chapters 10–15 are from
Introduction to Concepts and Theories in Physical Science
by **GERALD HOLTON,** Harvard University

 **ADDISON-WESLEY** READING, MASSACHUSETTS

This book is in the
ADDISON-WESLEY SERIES IN PHYSICS

Copyright © 1965

Philippines Copyright 1965

ADDISON-WESLEY PUBLISHING COMPANY, INC.

Printed in the United States of America

ALL RIGHTS RESERVED. THIS BOOK, OR PARTS THEREOF,
MAY NOT BE REPRODUCED IN ANY FORM
WITHOUT WRITTEN PERMISSION OF THE PUBLISHERS.

Library of Congress Catalog Card No. 65-10924

Chapters 10–15 are from
Introduction to Concepts and Theories in Physical Science,
by GERALD HOLTON
Copyright Addison-Wesley Publishing Company, Inc.

ADDISON-WESLEY PUBLISHING COMPANY, INC.
READING, MASSACHUSETTS · Palo Alto · London
NEW YORK · DALLAS · ATLANTA · BARRINGTON, ILLINOIS

530
A769d
c. 2

Preface

The course on which this textbook is based is part of a required core curriculum* instituted at Amherst College in 1947. It has the dual objective of developing the student's knowledge of physical phenomena, concepts, and theories, and of setting this technical content in historical and philosophic perspective. The course was designed both as a terminal one for students not planning further study of physics and as an introductory one for students intending to take more physics courses. Although principal emphasis is on the subject matter of physics itself, attention is given to questions of epistemology and philosophy; to the origin and significance of physical concepts; to the way in which conceptual insights produce unification of our view of apparently unrelated phenomena; to the provisional nature of the "understanding" provided by scientific theory; to the impact of science on intellectual history and the way in which growing factual and theoretical scientific knowledge has altered man's view of himself and of the universe; to aspects of sociology as reflected in the motivation and behavior of scientists; and so forth. Discussion of these ideas is distributed throughout the text and is not confined to isolated sections.

Implicit throughout is the fundamental assumption that one of the basic criteria of knowledge and understanding is the student's capability to deal with verbally expressed ideas as well as the solution of problems. He is expected to cultivate the ability to discuss definitions of physical concepts, to analyze the structure of a theory, to identify idealizations, assumptions, and approximations in the solution of a physical problem, to interpret the results of a mathematical analysis, pursuing on his own initiative the interpretation of limiting cases, and to ask additional critical questions of his own.

The text presents many problems explicitly designed to elicit this type of performance. The problems dispersed through the text are meant to be study guides. They direct the student into the questions and exercises he should set for himself in order to develop an understanding of what he has just read and of what is coming next. To save space, the text contains few routine, repetitive exercises. Different groups of students need such exercises in varying degree, and teachers should plan to supplement the text in this regard whenever desirable.

Many of the problems are sequential, leading the student, by a series of questions, to consider various facets of a given physical situation. Some students may need more detailed guidance than others, and teachers may add such guidance when they wish. Many questions and problems are open-ended, or are deliberately placed ahead of the game, and do not have pat answers. In fact, some do not have "answers" at all, in the ordinary unequivocal sense. These questions are meant to invite speculation—however fanciful—to excite imagina-

---

* The rationale behind the core curriculum is described in *Education at Amherst*, by Gail Kennedy (New York: Harper, 1955). The course itself is described in "Structure, Methods, and Objectives of the Required Freshman Calculus–Physics Course at Amherst College," by A. B. Arons [*Am. J. Phys.*, **27**, 658 (1959)].

tion, to stir wonder and even worry in the student. It is hoped that he will begin to see that physics does not have pat answers for everything, and that there are many interesting questions that must be discussed, looked at from alternative points of view, and left open—as are many questions encountered in humanistic and social studies.

In order to cultivate such attitudes in the student, considerable pains have been taken to motivate each conceptual development and show how various elements of knowledge were acquired: how we know what we think we know; why we accept a given conceptual or theoretical structure. In particular, effort has been made to develop ideas first, describe them in simple words having prior definition, and give them names only after the ideas themselves are securely established.

In the course on which this text is based, students are expected to penetrate several areas through independent study, coupled with laboratory work but without extended classroom instruction. These areas include: (1) the slide rule, (2) concepts of calorimetry, (3) Ohm's law and simple series and parallel d-c circuits, (4) image formation by thin lenses. Items (2) and (3) are discussed briefly in the body of the text. Item (4) is relegated to an outline in Appendix H. No attempt has been made to treat the dynamics of oscillations and waves, sound, fluids, a-c circuits, and nuclear physics. These omissions reflect lack of space and time rather than a denial of the importance of the subject matter.

The text is self-contained mathematically. Just enough calculus is developed to make possible the consideration of problems involving continuous change. An effort has been made to state mathematical ideas with some precision and to indicate where proofs have been given and where they are lacking. The Fundamental Theorem of Integral Calculus, for example, is presented on the basis of plausible argument and is not accorded rigorous arithmetical proof.

Teachers may wish to omit certain chapters and to take material in a variety of different orders. For students who have a reasonable preparation in calculus, Chapters 3, 8, and 16 can be omitted entirely. Chapters 10–15 and also 19 and 20 are readily adaptable as outside-reading assignments and can be by-passed so far as formal classroom treatment is concerned. Chapter 21 on rigid-body motion and 30 on kinetic theory can be omitted without breaking the logical sequence of the other chapters. One could very well start by studying Chapters 28 and 29 on the atomic-molecular theory first, and then going back to Chapter 1 and the study of mechanics. The atomic-molecular ideas could then be referred to during subsequent study, and could be invoked in discussion of collisions, energy concepts, etc.

Readers will easily discern my indebtedness to some of the fine physics texts published in recent years, in particular the pioneering text of L. W. Taylor and the books by Sears, Ingard and Kraushaar, Resnick and Halliday, Rogers, and the Physical Science Study Committee. Professor Dudley Towne gave valuable criticism and suggestions on certain portions of the manuscript. Mrs. Jean Arons contributed countless hours of typing, proofreading, checking, and indexing. Numerous excellent illustrations were made available through the courtesy of Educational Services, Inc. A National Science Foundation faculty fellowship in 1962 permitted me to improve my background in the history and philosophy of science.

Above all, however, I wish to acknowledge my debt to Professor Gerald Holton. The influence of his fine text is obvious not only in the chapters reprinted herein but in the structure and spirit of the course. He read and criticized major portions of the manuscript, and his encouragement played a major role in my undertaking the entire task.

Amherst, Massachusetts   A.B.A.
November 1964

Contents

Introduction

"It stands to the everlasting credit of science that by acting on the human mind it has overcome man's insecurity before himself and before nature."—Albert Einstein

"To judge by all available evidence, the rise of civilization was not a gift of the gods or a tribute to them. It was a technological affair, an economic enterprise inspired by practical motives. Through inventions and discoveries, men were able to take care of their physical wants more efficiently; in the leisure, comfort, and relative security thus achieved, they were able to develop social graces, fine arts, literate learning, and higher religions."—H. J. Muller (in *Uses of the Past*)

Of the numerous ways in which science and its daughter, technology, have influenced our lives, values, views, and attitudes, the two remarked on by Einstein and Muller are among the deepest and most indelible. Science has freed us from ancient tyrannies and fears; it has revealed to us a rational physical universe characterized by symmetry and mathematical order; it has given us deep insights into the regularities to be discovered in that range of physical phenomena directly perceivable by our senses—motion, force, gravitation, wave behavior, light; it has given us an equally deep insight into an amazing range of phenomena not directly perceivable—electricity, magnetism, electromagnetic waves, the structure of matter, atoms, molecules, electrons, nuclei, elementary particles, anti-particles, the dual (corpuscular and wave) behavior of both material particles and light.

However, the knowledge which science has placed at our disposal is double-edged: on one side its implementation has the capacity for unbounded good and on the other side for incalculable evil. Through the influence of technology much has been done to improve the physical well-being of humankind. But we stand at this point fully able to destroy life on earth by radioactive contamination, and even short of such total obliteration, we are only just beginning to guess at the appalling damage that we might be inflicting by radioactive and chemical poisons on those large and complicated molecules which are our genes—the molecules which continue to determine the genetic heritage and the course of evolution of the human race.

Here in the second half of the twentieth century, scientists find themselves a new social, professional class. They, who have always been particularly sensitive to the manner in which their activity has played a role in liberating humanity from irrational fears, discover that they have become a new priesthood, in possession of words and incantations not understood by the uninitiated populace, a priesthood holding a strange new alliance with military power. At the same time, men who are not professional scientists, but who in government or industrial or public life find themselves in positions of decision-making responsibility, are forced to contend with the consequences of scientific knowledge which they are ill equipped to comprehend.

Our endeavor in this book will be to develop some understanding of the enterprise that has brought about our insights and our dilemmas. What are scientific concepts? How are they devised? What do we mean by "understanding" natural phenomena? What are the roles played by discovery, by theory, by mathematics, by inductive and deductive thought? What are the successful concepts and theories that characterize our present knowledge? By what criteria are they validated and judged successful? How have they altered in the course of time? What kinds of alteration might we at least intelligently speculate about for the future? What limitations have we learned to discern in scientific knowledge?

These and related questions we shall examine by studying the science of physics. We shall deal with important concepts, with problems, with mathematical theory and formulation; we shall follow the mainstream of physical thought, from the elucidation by Galileo and Newton of the nature of motion and of the laws that govern motion of physical objects on the earth and in the cosmos, to our present view of the structure of matter and the laws that govern the microcosm of molecules, atoms, and subatomic particles—a microcosm that we comprehend only by indirect inference and by subtle analogy and mathematical theory.

CHAPTER 1

Motion of Particles

1.1 INTRODUCTION

In *The Origins of Modern Science*, the historian Herbert Butterfield remarks,

"Of all the intellectual hurdles which the human mind has confronted and has overcome in the last fifteen hundred years, the one which seems to me to have been the most amazing in character and the most stupendous in the scope of its consequences is the one relating to the problem of motion."

In Greek philosophy the concept of motion embraced virtually everything that involved change: birth, growth, decay, displacement of objects, alterations in quality. Displacement of an object (falling of a stone, flight of an arrow, sailing of a ship) came to be denoted by the special term "local" motion. The conceptual revolution referred to by Butterfield reached a climax in Europe at the turn of the 17th century and was characterized in part by a deliberate stripping away of much of the allegorical connotation previously attached to the concept of motion. Attention was focused on the description and understanding of local motion, and the modern conception emerged at a pace that, in the perspective of history, seems extremely rapid.

The change was characterized not only by clearer definition of concepts but also by a heightened self-consciousness on the part of natural philosophers concerning the nature of their activity: the process of scientific inquiry, the role of mathematics in the analysis and description of natural phenomena, the logic and limitations of scientific concepts and theories.

Prominent among the names we shall encounter in discussing these events and ideas is that of the Italian Galileo Galilei (1564–1642), among whose influential writings was the synthesis of a new science—*kinematics*, or the description of local motion. In subsequent sections and chapters we shall refer to Galileo's work and insights, as well as to the wider historical background. First, however, we shall develop the basic concepts in modern terms and symbols.

1.2 RECTILINEAR MOTION OF A PARTICLE: POSITION AND CHANGE OF POSITION

Motions that we discern in the world around us are, in general, incredibly complex: three-dimensional motion of changing cloud shapes in the sky; sinuous, bobbing motion of grass in the wind; chaotic, turbulent, fluid motions of air and water; even the spinning, curving motion of a thrown object or the weaving motion, on a winding road, of a car, with its body vibrating and its wheels rotating. What is it that we mean when we talk about an object which moves "at so many meters per second or miles per hour"? Consciously or unconsciously, in our usual discourse on such matters we have made an abstraction which focuses our attention on some interesting aspect of the motion and which helps us neglect the infinity of complex detail which, at the moment, is irrelevant.

Thus in some cases we select an abstraction in which we regard both the cloud and the car as "particles," ignoring the fuzzy changing shape of one and the vibrating body and rotating wheels of the other. We may also ignore the geometrical complexities of the paths followed by the bodies and view the motion as though it were in a straight line. Such abstractions from physical reality lie at the very core of science. Successful scientific inquiry almost invariably starts with an examination of the very simplest abstractions, building up to more complex situations as insights are deepened by the initial steps.

FIG. 1.2.1. Position numbers *s* along a path of rectilinear motion. Spacing between integers is determined by selection of an arbitrary unit of length, such as meter, centimeter, foot, mile, etc.

To create a numerical description of position of a particle along a straight line, we set up a series of numerical markers, as illustrated in Fig. 1.2.1. Denoting an arbitrarily chosen "origin" point by 0, we mark other points $+1$, $+2$, -1, -2, etc., laying off a coordinate scale of the kind the reader has encountered in elementary algebra. The size of the spacing between integer numbers along the line is arbitrary, and we might adopt any of the standard units of length available to us through national or international definition. Along a road we might wish to use a spacing measured in miles; on a laboratory table we might wish to use meters or centimeters, feet or inches. For positions in between those marked by integers, we use appropriate fractional values; thus, at some instant of time, a car on the road may be at position 2.86 on a scale determined by a spacing in miles.* (Such a reference line or coordinate

---

* It is significant to note that the spacing of integer positions need not be uniform; we could still describe positions on a line by specifying numerical values for points on a highly irregular scale. We invariably choose a uniform scale, however, because we seek a simple description, easily reproduced by other individuals, readily comparable with other physical situations, and revealing of any simplicity or orderliness in the motions we attempt to describe.

axis is sometimes called a "frame of reference." To describe positions in two- or three-dimensional space, we erect two or three such axes, usually perpendicular to each other, to obtain two- or three-dimensional frames of reference.)

We shall use the symbol s to denote any individual position, and symbols with subscripts (s_0, s_1, s_2, etc.) to denote particular positions we wish to distinguish from each other. It must be carefully noted that these symbols are *not* being used to denote distances traversed by the body; they will be used to represent *positions only*. Thus numbers such as $s_1 = +8.63$ or $s_2 = -3.40$ will indicate locations of a car on the road and *not* distances traveled over some period of time.

We are aware of motion of a particle along our reference line when we find its position changing from instant to instant. Let us denote its position at some first, or initial, instant of time by s_1 and its position at a later instant by s_2. The number $s_2 - s_1$ gives us information about what we might call "change of position." For example, in the case cited in the preceding paragraph,

$$s_2 - s_1 = -3.40 - 8.63 = -12.03 \text{ mi}$$

(if the spacing between integer markers is in miles). We shall frequently use the symbol Δs (read "delta s") as a shorthand for the number $s_2 - s_1$; that is,

$$\Delta s \equiv s_2 - s_1,^* \tag{1.2.1}$$

where Δs is called "displacement" or "change in position." In mathematics it is usually referred to as "directed distance." Note that Δs has algebraic properties; i.e., it may be positive, negative, or zero depending on the numerical values and algebraic signs of s_2 and s_1. This property requires interpretation; see Problem 1.1.

PROBLEM 1.1. (a) Describe in your own words how algebraic signs became associated with values of s in the first place. What do the signs mean?

(b) In the light of your answer to part (a), interpret the significance of positive and negative values of Δs.

(c) Make up some numerical cases to illustrate your answer to (b). Include situations such as: s_2 and s_1 both negative but Δs positive; s_2 and s_1 both positive but Δs negative; etc.

(d) Considering that the particle might move back and forth along the line in either a regular or erratic way, does Δs necessarily represent a distance traversed by the particle between the two positions s_2 and s_1? Explain your answer with specific illustrations. Describe a case for which $\Delta s = 0$ but the distance traversed is not zero.

A remark concerning mathematical terminology: A number b is said to be greater than number a if $a + x = b$, where x is a positive number. This in turn implies that the quantity $(b - a)$ is positive. The symbols $>$ and $<$ are a shorthand for

---

* Read the symbol $\equiv$ as "is defined by" or "is identical with." Note that statement (1.2.1) is not an equation in the sense that $y = 3x^2 - 2x + 1$ is an equation; Δs is simply a name for $s_2 - s_1$.

the phrases "greater than" and "less than," respectively. Thus

$b > a$ means that $(b - a)$ is positive, or $(b - a) > 0$;

$a < b$ means that $b > a$.

In this sense $+7 > +2$; $+2 > -5$; $-1 > -3$; $+3 < +4$; $-5 < +1$; and $-8 < -3$. Prompted by this standard mathematical terminology, we shall always speak of the numbers in Fig. 1.2.1 as increasing toward the right and decreasing toward the left, regardless of whether we are dealing with positive or negative values; i.e., the numbers increase as we go from -8 to -3, since, in accordance with our definition, $-3 > -8$. Furthermore it is consistent with this terminology to speak of the "positive direction" as toward the right in Fig. 1.2.1 and the "negative direction" as toward the left.

The symbol $|x|$ (read "absolute value of x" or "magnitude of x") stands for the positive number associated with x. That is,

$|x| = x$ if x is positive, $|x| = -x$ if x is negative.

Thus $|+4| = 4$ and $|-4| = -(-4) = 4$.

1.3 INSTANTS AND INTERVALS OF TIME

We measure intervals of time as arbitrarily as we measure distances in space, but fortunately there are fewer conventional units. The most widely used unit, the "second," is defined as 1/86,400th part of a mean solar day. (A mean solar day is the average time between successive crossings by the sun of the meridian plane at a point on the earth. An average must be taken because this interval varies slightly but systematically during the course of a year, with the systematic variation of the earth's orbital velocity around the sun.) Intervals of time are then measured by observing the displacement of some object which, in effect, counts a regular variation or oscillation: Displacement of the hand of a clock counts oscillations of a pendulum or of a balance wheel. Concerning his experiments with motion on an inclined plane, Galileo says,

> "For the measurement of time, we employed a large vessel of water placed in an elevated position; to the bottom of this vessel was soldered a pipe of small diameter giving a thin jet of water, which we collected in a small glass during each time of descent . . .; the water thus collected was weighed, after each descent, on a very accurate balance."

Of course, many variations on this theme are possible, but, in effect, we associate "instants of time" with positions of the hand of a clock (or an amount of water in Galileo's glass), and we associate "intervals of time" with changes in position (or changes in amount of water). Again, we can number instants of time in sequence, and associate our representation with the number line in Fig. 1.3.1, as we did for position in Fig. 1.2.1.

To this representation we bring our intuitive conception of the natural "flow" of time, and we adopt the convention of labeling succeeding instants with increasingly positive numbers. The instant we denote by $t = 0$ is arbitrarily selected. The negative numbers in Fig. 1.3.1 contain no implication whatsoever of time running backward, or negative time intervals. The instant $t = -3$ simply refers to an instant which precedes $t = 0$ by 3 units; the sequence of positions of the hands of the clock (and therefore of instants) went $-3, -2, -1, 0, +1$, etc.

FIG. 1.3.1.   Representation of instants of time t along a number line. Spacing between integers is determined by selection of an arbitrary time unit such as second, hour, year, etc., and representation of this unit on a scale.

As in the case of position symbols s, we shall use "instant of time" symbols t, t_0, t_1, t_2, etc. These symbols do *not* denote *intervals* of time. To calculate an interval of time, we must take a difference:

$$\Delta t \equiv t_2 - t_1, \tag{1.3.1}$$

where t_2 is always taken as the instant *later* in the sequence than t_1. Thus we define time interval, Δt, as an intrinsically positive quantity.

1.4   DISPLACEMENT AND CORRESPONDING TIME INTERVAL

In talking about the speed or rapidity of motion of a particle we say, for example, that the position of the particle changed by 85 mi in a time interval of 2.4 hr. Let us connect this statement with the concepts defined above.

We observe that the particle is located at some position s_1 when the hand of the clock is at "position" or instant t_1. Thus we observe the simultaneous occurrence of a pair of events—position of the particle and position of the hand of our clock. Similarly we observe the coincidence of a second pair of events which we associate with the symbols t_2 and s_2. Now, having the pairs of numbers (t_1, s_1) and (t_2, s_2), we calculate the displacement Δs and the corresponding time interval Δt.

1.5   s-VERSUS-t "HISTORIES" OF MOTION

A particularly simple way of presenting information about the motion of a particle is to make a graph of position versus time. We set up a pair of coordinate axes as illustrated in Fig. 1.5.1, and, instead of labeling them y and x as we did in elementary algebra, we label them s and t.

In this representation, each "event" in the rectilinear motion of a particle (position s occupied at instant t) becomes associated with a point in the s-t plane defined by the two coordinate lines. An accumulation of data—corresponding values of t and s—can then be "plotted" in such a diagram to give a visual picture of the history of an observed motion; or, conversely, a line or curve drawn on an s-t diagram can be interpreted as the history of an hypothetical motion. In coordinate representations of this kind the horizontal coordinate, in this case t, is called the *abscissa*, and the vertical is called the *ordinate*.

PROBLEM 1.2.   Figure 1.5.1 shows the plot of a sequence of observations made on the rectilinear motion of a particle, starting at instant $t = -3$ sec and ending at $t = +9$ sec.

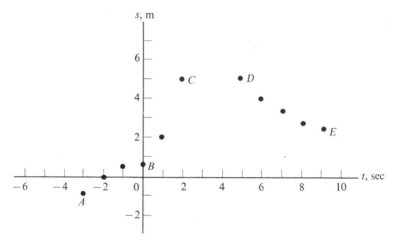

FIG. 1.5.1. Plot of a sequence of observations of positions occupied by a particle at successive instants of time.

(a) Suppose we had been watching the particle and had the sense that the motion was smooth and regular rather than jerky. How would we be inclined to fill in the history between the given points? Would this filling-in be entirely reliable?

(b) Suppose we had no information at all besides the plotted points. What possibilities do you see in the way of intermediate events or histories?

(c) If on subsequent occasions we elect to draw continuous lines or curves through a graph of experimental points, what kinds of knowledge or suppositions must we invoke besides the numerical data themselves?

(d) Write a table of numerical values of Δs and the corresponding time intervals Δt for the following pairs of points in Fig. 1.5.1: A, C; B, D; C, D; C, E.

PROBLEM 1.3.   Figure 1.5.2 shows a number of s-versus-t diagrams representing hypothetical histories of straight-line motion of a particle. Pretend you are in a car which is executing these motions, and describe each history in words. In each case, execute with your hand the motion you have described. For each diagram, describe in words the significance of the lettered points. (Remain alert to the possibility that at least one of them might not have any interpretable significance.)

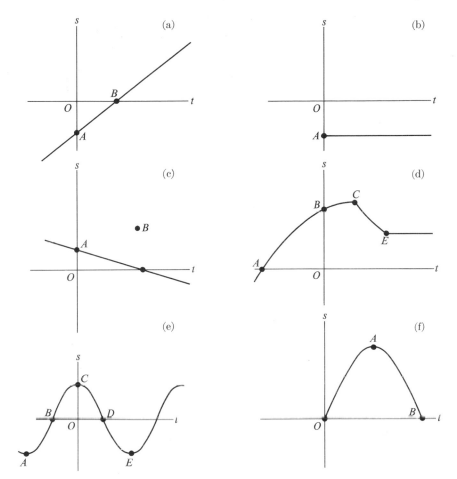

Fɪɢ. 1.5.2. Hypothetical s-versus-t diagrams for rectilinear motion of a particle (Problem 1.3).

1.6 THE NUMBER $\Delta s/\Delta t$

From the concepts of displacement, Δs, and corresponding time interval, Δt, we now proceed to generate a new concept, one that is intended to give information concerning the rapidity of the motion. We calculate the number denoted by

$$\frac{\Delta s}{\Delta t} \quad \text{or} \quad \frac{s_2 - s_1}{t_2 - t_1}.$$

What significance does this number have? How is it related to our intuitive perceptions about the motion? What interpretations are to be placed on its algebraic properties? What information does it *fail* to convey about the motion? (Even though the basic idea may be familiar, these are sophisticated questions which are worth careful thought and consideration. Forming the habit of asking oneself such questions in the initial stages of studying science leads to a quicker and deeper grasp of unfamiliar concepts later on. In many cases this is the kind of question a working scientist asks himself almost instinctively as he progresses through a line of analysis or inquiry.)

Examination of the behavior of the number $\Delta s/\Delta t$ in various circumstances leads to the following statements about its properties:

(1) If the motion is monotonic (takes place in one direction), the size of the number, regardless of algebraic sign, gives some sense of the rapidity with which distance was traversed—so many meters/second, miles/hour, etc. Note that there is nothing inevitable about this; we might have elected to calculate $\Delta t/\Delta s$, and the size of the number would then have been a measure of slowness rather than rapidity.

(2) Since Δt has been defined to be intrinsically positive, the algebraic sign of $\Delta s/\Delta t$ is determined by the *direction* of the displacement. (Review the interpretations made in Problem 1.1.) Positive values indicate motion in the direction of increasing position numbers; negative values indicate motion in the direction of decreasing position numbers.

(3) For monotonic motion, except for the additional ingredient of the algebraic sign, $\Delta s/\Delta t$ is the number which we use when we talk about a trip by car in which we "averaged so many miles per hour."

(4) If the motion is not monotonic, but reverses itself one or more times during the time interval Δt, the displacement Δs no longer represents a distance traversed by the particle (Problem 1.1). In this case $\Delta s/\Delta t$ is to be interpreted as the number of miles per hour which would have been associated with a direct displacement from the initial to the final position, regardless of the complexity of the actual motion. If at t_2 the particle has returned to its initial position, $\Delta s/\Delta t$ will come out to be zero, regardless of how fast the particle moved in executing its trip back and forth.

(5) Since the number of miles per hour may well be different for different portions of a trip, one immediately has the sense that the single number $\Delta s/\Delta t$ is some sort of "lumped" or "smeared out" measure of rapidity. One senses the need for a more refined calculation and more detail if he is to describe variations in rapidity during a particular displacement. Such a motion is described as "nonuniform." An important and interesting special case of motion is one that we would describe as "uniform": a motion in which equal displacements occur in successive equal intervals of time. Note that this is the character of the motions illustrated in Figs. 1.5.2(a) and (b).

PROBLEM 1.4. Support the preceding five assertions about the character of $\Delta s/\Delta t$ by making up specific numerical illustrations for each case and explaining them in your own words. Relate your illustrations to relevant diagrams in Fig. 1.5.2.

The preceding discussion of $\Delta s/\Delta t$ has been carried out without giving this number a name in order to dramatize the point that a name is not essential; the ideas of interest reside in the definition of how the number is to be calculated and how it is to be interpreted. But the absence of a name for a frequently used concept is cumbersome, and we now produce a name and a symbol: average velocity, $\bar{v}$ (read as "v bar").

$$\text{Average velocity:} \quad \bar{v} \equiv \frac{\Delta s}{\Delta t} \quad \text{or} \quad \frac{s_2 - s_1}{t_2 - t_1}. \quad (1.6.1)$$

We speak of a number calculated this way as having units or dimensions—in this case length/time such as meters/second, miles/hour, etc. If we were to compare two velocities by forming a ratio such as $\bar{v}_A/\bar{v}_B$ and speak of one average velocity as being so many times another, we would speak of the resulting number as a "pure number" or "dimensionless number."

The use of a bar over a symbol is a conventional mathematical notation for an average of some sort. Although we are giving $\Delta s/\Delta t$ the name of average velocity, we have not made clear whether the word "average" used in this context is in any way related to the familiar arithmetical process of finding an average by adding up a group of values and dividing by the number of them. Such a connection does indeed exist, but it involves ideas more subtle than might be apparent at first glance. We shall return to this question later in the text.

For the special case of motion in which equal distances are traveled in successive equal intervals of time, we obtain the same number for $\Delta s/\Delta t$ regardless of time interval and corresponding displacement (motion at uniform velocity). Thus it is convenient to drop the bar notation and write simply

$$\text{Uniform velocity:} \qquad v \equiv \frac{\Delta s}{\Delta t} \qquad \text{or} \qquad \frac{s_2 - s_1}{t_2 - t_1}. \qquad (1.6.2)$$

Flash photographs of rectilinear motions at uniform velocity are shown in Fig. 1.6.1.

(a)   (b)

FIG. 1.6.1.   (a) Flash photographs of successive positions of a frictionless puck moving at uniform velocity along a glass plate.   (b) Translational motion of a rigid body at uniform velocity.   (There is no rotation until puck strikes obstacle at right of picture.)

PROBLEM 1.5.   Suppose we made our calculations by taking the quotient:

$$\frac{s_1 - s_2}{t_1 - t_2}.$$

What effect would this have on the ideas and interpretations advanced in Section 1.6? Why? (We do *not* use the Δ symbol with differences such as $s_1 - s_2$. This is reserved for *final* minus *initial* values; that is, $s_2 - s_1$.)

1.7   GRAPH OF s-VERSUS-t FOR MOTION AT UNIFORM VELOCITY

Let us denote by the symbol s_0 the position of a moving particle when the hand of the clock is at 0, that is, at $t = 0$, and think of this as an initial point corresponding to t_1, s_1, in the calculation $v \equiv \Delta s/\Delta t$. Similarly, let us denote by t, s some later instant and position, corresponding to the combination t_2, s_2. Substituting the new symbols into Eq. (1.6.2), we write:

$$v = \frac{s - s_0}{t - 0}$$

and, rearranging terms, we obtain

$$s = vt + s_0. \tag{1.7.1}$$

Statement (1.7.1) has a very different logical connotation from that of (1.6.2), the *definition* from which it was derived. Statement (1.7.1) is an *equation;* it specifies a way of calculating the position s associated with an arbitrary instant of time t, providing the values of v and s_0 are known. We are considering a case of uniform motion, and therefore v stands for a particular number, such as 3 m/sec; s_0 also stands for a particular number—the position of the particle at $t=0$. Equation (1.7.1) has a general form corresponding to

$$y = 3x + 2 \qquad \text{or} \qquad y = mx + b,$$

where m and b are constants. This form is familiar from elementary algebra; its graph is a straight line. (Note that the straight line we are now talking about is a graph; it is a *picture* in an s-t system of coordinates or in the so-called "s-t plane." It is *not* the straight-line path along which the particle moves and along which we have marked position numbers s.)

PROBLEM 1.6.   Plot the graph of $s = vt + s_0$ for the case $v = +3$ m/sec, $s_0 = +2$ meters. What happens to the graph if v remains unchanged but s_0 is successively considered to be $+5$, -2, 0? What happens to the graph if s_0 remains unchanged but v has the values $+5$, or -2, or 0? Generalize in your own words the regularities you perceive in the results: What are the effects of different numerical values of s_0 and v on the position and character of the straight line?

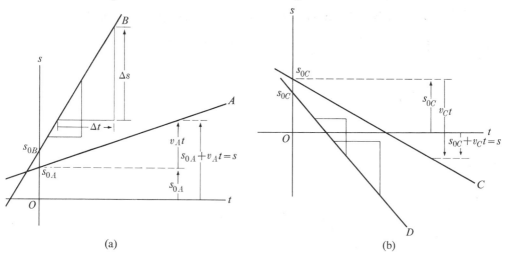

(a)   (b)

FIG. 1.7.1. Graphs of Eq. (1.7.1) for rectilinear motion at uniform velocity of different positive and negative values. The various terms of Eq. (1.7.1) are interpreted as directed distances on each diagram.

Figure 1.7.1 provides additional interpretation and illustration of the significance of Eq. (1.7.1). Note the following features:

(1) The straight-line s-t history indicates that equal displacements occur in equal intervals of time; this is essentially what we *mean* by uniform velocity. For any given line we obtain the same value of $\Delta s/\Delta t$ regardless of what time interval is taken. (Note the similar triangles indicated by light lines in the figure.)

(2) The constant ratio $\Delta s/\Delta t$ is called the "slope" of the straight line. For the lines in Fig. 1.7.1(a), Δs is always positive, and the "slope" (or velocity) is positive. This means that the particle in question moves at uniform velocity in the direction we defined to be positive. Similarly, Fig. 1.7.1(b) shows graphs of motions at uniform *negative* velocities. The negative slope (negative velocity) simply indicates motion in the direction we called negative on the original reference line. A steep slope indicates a large magnitude of velocity.

(3) Using the mathematical terminology defined in Section 1.2, let us compare the velocities of the various motions pictured in Fig. 1.7.1:

$$v_B > v_A, \qquad v_C > v_D, \qquad |v_C| < |v_D|,$$

where the subscripts refer to the various lines in the figure.

(4) The terms s_0 and vt appearing in Eq. (1.7.1) are given a geometrical interpretation in each figure.

The number $|v|$ is frequently referred to as the "speed" of the moving particle. We shall not make extensive use of this concept, but it is the number we usually think of in our first intuitive attempts to describe the rapidity of a motion. Velocity, as we have defined it, is a more sophisticated concept; it can be generalized and extended to apply to more complicated motions—nonuniform and multidimensional.

1.8   EXTENSION AND REDEFINITION OF THE CONCEPT OF VELOCITY

Consider the two histories of rectilinear motion A and B shown in Fig. 1.8.1. Case A is now familiar as that of uniform velocity, but in case B we find a different average velocity for each different Δt and corresponding Δs. For the interval ab, $\bar{v}$

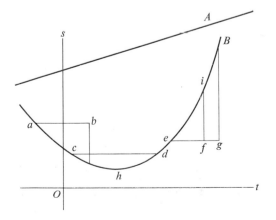

FIG. 1.8.1. These diagrams show s-versus-t motion at uniform velocity (A) and at nonuniform velocity (B).

is negative; for *cd* it is zero; for *ef* it is positive; for *eg* it is positive and greater than for *ef*. There is clearly no one number which can characterize velocity in case *B*, and we are led to say that the velocity was changing. As a matter of fact we sense that the velocity was systematically *increasing* throughout the indicated history. This sense is reinforced by the geometrical character of curve *B*, in which we note that the "average slope" of succeeding sections is increasing with time. (We have not defined "slope" properly in this new context, but we can nevertheless make a rough intuitive connection with the definition in Section 1.7.)

Is it possible under these circumstances to use the idea embodied in $\Delta s/\Delta t$ and give it unique and unequivocal meaning? The answer turns out to be yes, and constitutes one of the great triumphs in the application of mathematical thought to physical science. We shall discuss the concept at this point in an elementary and nonrigorous way and return to it for more careful discussion in subsequent chapters.

Imagine the curve in the neighborhood of point *e* in Fig. 1.8.1 to be magnified or blown up to successively larger scales, with *e* itself located at $t = 4$, $s = 3$, as in Fig. 1.8.2.

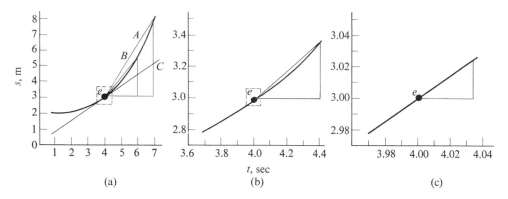

Fig. 1.8.2. Successively expanded plots of the region near point *e* in Fig. 1.8.1. The curve appears flatter, more and more nearly like a straight line as one examines a smaller segment on a larger scale. Figure (b) is plotted to ten times the scale of (a); (c) is plotted to ten times the scale of (b). Dashed boxes block out region which is shown on next figure. Note that slope of line segment in (c) is approximately 0.75 m/sec.

Let us imagine making calculations of $\Delta s/\Delta t$ with *e* as the initial point, corresponding to t_1, s_1, in each case. If we take $\Delta t = 3$; that is, $t_2 = 7$, we would obtain a value of $\Delta s/\Delta t$ corresponding to the slope of the chord marked *A* in Fig. 1.8.2(a). If we take $\Delta t = 2$, we would get a value corresponding to the slope of chord *B*. What are we to expect if we continue this process, taking smaller and smaller values of Δt and dividing them into the ever smaller values of corresponding displacement Δs? At first, as we see in Fig. 1.8.2(a), the values decrease somewhat; but as we take $\Delta t = 0.3, 0.2, 0.1$ in Fig. 1.8.2(b), the successive values of $\Delta s/\Delta t$ will change very little; and by the time we take Δt's of the order of 0.02, 0.01 [Fig. 1.8.2(c)] we are dealing with a section of curve that is so nearly a straight line that we keep getting the same number to the first few figures of the calculation regardless of what value of Δt is selected. This "final" value of $\Delta s/\Delta t$ is the slope of the straight line which is a very good representation of the expanded section of curve in Fig. 1.8.2(c). Furthermore, intuition about the geometrical relationships involved suggests that this straight line is what, in geometry, we would call the tangent to the curve at point e. Note that tangent line C in part (a) is parallel to the segment in part (c).

An exactly similar process of calculation could be carried out for other points in Fig. 1.8.1. Visualize the results: at i we would obtain a larger positive value than at e; at d a smaller positive value; at h we would expect to get zero; at c and a a negative values.

PROBLEM 1.7. Take an s-t curve the equation of which is $s = 3 - (t^3/8)$, and examine it in the neighborhood of $t = 1$ by making graphs such as those in Fig. 1.8.2 (s is in meters; t in seconds). Verify that the slope of the final, expanded, very nearly straight segment is about -0.38 m/sec.

Since we shall repeatedly refer to the idea of a "final" value of $\Delta s/\Delta t$ at a point in an s-t diagram, it becomes highly desirable to have a shorthand notation to denote it. A conventional shorthand is

$$\lim_{\Delta t \to 0} \frac{\Delta s}{\Delta t},$$

(read "limit as Δt approaches zero of $\Delta s/\Delta t$"). A still shorter conventional form is

$$\frac{ds}{dt}.$$

The d's in this case are part of the notation and are *not* arithmetical symbols which may be canceled out.

Our investigation suggests certain interesting possibilities and interpretations:

(1) The number

$$\lim_{\Delta t \to 0} \frac{\Delta s}{\Delta t}$$

has the character of velocity as previously defined. For each point in an s-versus-t history of motion there seems to be a single, unique value obtained from this calculation. Obtaining a unique value for a given instant of time suggests the interpretation of this number as a velocity associated with the particular instant! Hence the name "instantaneous velocity." We take the symbol v to denote instantaneous velocity (this is still applicable to uniform motion, since the instantaneous velocity is then always the same):

$$v \equiv \lim_{\Delta t \to 0} \frac{\Delta s}{\Delta t} \equiv \frac{ds}{dt}. \tag{1.8.1}$$

(2) The result of the limit calculation can always be thought of as a velocity associated with some uniform motion, represented by a straight line on the diagram, the velocity being the slope of the line. What line is this? Since our calculation is

intrinsically *arithmetical* (as opposed to geometrical), this line might possibly be regarded as the arithmetical definition of "a line tangent to the curve at the point in question."

(3) Both instantaneous and average velocities can be viewed as slopes of straight lines in an *s-t* diagram: instantaneous velocity in the sense suggested in the preceding paragraph, and average velocity as the slope of the chord connecting the two points between which the average velocity is calculated. This view suggests a simple additional interpretation for each number: Average velocity may be described as that *uniform* velocity at which a given displacement would occur in the same time interval that was required under the actual, varying conditions. Instantaneous velocity might be interpreted as that uniform velocity at which the motion would continue if all *change* were stopped at the given instant. It should be carefully noted that these statements are *interpretations* of the numbers we have created and not definitions. The definitions are contained in statements (1.6.1) and (1.8.1), which prescribe the specific arithmetical operations which must be carried out to obtain the number we call "velocity."

Now, having pointed to some of the attractive and interesting implications that stem from the "limit" calculation based on taking ever smaller Δt's, let us look at the other side of the ledger and sound some warnings (or some encouragement for the critical student who did not feel at ease about the arithmetical logic and validity of all the steps and phrases of the preceding discussion):

(1) The concept we are generating is exceedingly subtle—so much so that it was never invented or mastered by the great Greek scientists and mathematicians. Among other things, they lacked the powerful diagrammatic representation and the modern forms of algebra and arithmetic, all of which we glibly put to our advantage in this section, but they also had great difficulty with the fundamental notion itself. Had this been otherwise, there might have existed a highly developed theory of motion prior to the seventeenth century.

(2) A host of critical questions should be asked about the proposed definition: Precisely what are we to understand by phrases such as "Δt is made smaller and smaller" or "Δt approaches zero"? How small is "small enough"? *Is* there a small enough Δt? What are we to understand by the terms "limit" or "final value"? Can such limits be shown to exist in the sense of being unique and unequivocal, precisely defined? Are there circumstances under which the proposed calculation is meaningless or impossible or does not give a unique result? If so, how does one predict or recognize the breakdown?

(3) The answer to the latter questions is that breakdowns indeed do occur: consider Fig. 1.8.3. This figure shows an hypothetical *s-t* history with abrupt changes at *A* and *B*. With actual physical objects *instantaneously* abrupt changes are, of course, not possible, but it is entirely possible for changes to be so abrupt that they *appear* to be instantaneous on the scale of time which, in the particular case, we are capable of discriminating. Suppose, for example, that we were observing, with a timing device having smallest intervals of 0.2 sec, the motion of a baseball before and after it had been struck by a bat. If we then plotted our diagram on a scale that showed several seconds on either side of the encounter between bat and ball, we would have a pic-

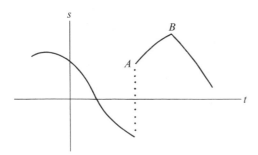

Fig. 1.8.3. Hypothetical *s-t* history of a motion in which changes at *A* and *B* take place so abruptly that, on the scales of time and position measurement observable in the given circumstances, the changes appear to occur instantaneously. Calculation of

$$\lim_{\Delta t \to 0} \Delta s / \Delta t$$

at such points may be ambiguous or meaningless.

ture very much like the region on either side of *B* in Fig. 1.8.3, and the encounter would appear instantaneous within the basic coarseness or "graininess" of our time measurements. Suppose we tried to evaluate

$$\lim_{\Delta t \to 0} \frac{\Delta s}{\Delta t}$$

at *A* and *B* in Fig. 1.8.3. What point should we take at *A*? Which curve should we consider at *B*?

Thus, although the utility of the notion of instantaneous velocity (and other concepts based on similar limit calculations) came to be appreciated during the seventeenth century, questions concerning the logic, validity—the mathematical rigor and meaning—of these calculations troubled the greatest mathematicians for the next 250 years. We shall return to consider some of these questions in Chapter 3. In the meantime we shall use the concepts as did seventeenth-century scientists—on faith, deepening our insights and understanding through the acquaintance and familiarity which come through repeated use of an idea in different contexts.

In retrospect, note how our idea of velocity has evolved. We started with a simple notion of uniform velocity, ignoring the complexity associated with variation from instant to instant. We then *redefined* the concept, deepening and extending it to clarify a distinction between average and instantaneous velocities. The process of redefinition of terms, ideas, and concepts lies at the heart of *all* inquiry—in history, social studies, criticism, natural science—wherever careful analytical thinking is done. We shall encounter such evolution and redefinition continually, with practically every idea we discuss; it is well to become explicitly conscious of the process, note it when it occurs, and take repeated stock of the level attained. The evolution of our concept of velocity is still far from complete; we have created an idea in the context of rectilinear motion only, and have yet to examine the modifications and generalizations which might be needed to extend the concept to a description of motion in two or three dimensions.

1.9 v-VERSUS-t "HISTORIES" OF MOTION

Now that we have established a way of calculating velocity at an instant of time, we have an association of a pair of numbers, *v* and *t*, just as we had an association between *s* and *t*. Velocity-time diagrams are just as instructive as are the *s-t* diagrams we used in the preceding sections.

PROBLEM 1.8. Remembering that when we deal with an *s-t* diagram, instantaneous velocity *v* may be calculated as the slope of the straight line tangent to the curve at the instant in question, sketch *v-t* curves for the motions shown in Figs. 1.5.2, 1.8.1, and 1.8.3. (In making such sketches, it is good practice to draw the *v-t* diagram directly below a reproduction of the *s-t* diagram so that corresponding instants of time match up along vertical lines. Then one can clearly sense the relation between the two figures.) In each case describe what you would be doing with brake pedal and accelerator if you were executing the given motion in a car.

PROBLEM 1.9. Consider again the diagrams in Fig. 1.5.2, but change the symbol designating the ordinate from *s* to *v*; i.e., regard them as *v-t* histories. Interpret each *v-t* diagram in words, describing the motion which is executed; state carefully the direction of motion, whether or not the direction changes during the time sketched, whether the velocity is increasing or decreasing. Sketch *s-t* curves which would correspond to these *v-t* curves. What information is lacking as far as positioning the *s-t* curves is concerned? (Sketch the *s-t* diagrams directly above or below the *v-t* diagrams so that corresponding times match up on vertical coordinate lines.)

If we know the instantaneous velocities, v_1 and v_2, of a particle at any two instants or positions, we can calculate the corresponding change of velocity $\Delta v \equiv v_2 - v_1$. For example: (1) If the velocity is -3.2 m/sec initially and $+1.3$ m/sec finally, $\Delta v = +1.3 - (-3.2) = +4.5$ m/sec. (2) If the velocity is $+2.1$ m/sec initially and -4.2 m/sec finally, $\Delta v = -4.2 - (+2.1) = -6.3$ m/sec. The algebraic sign associated with Δv indicates whether the velocity has become more positive or more negative; i.e., it indicates the *direction* in which the change has occurred. A positive Δv (velocity change in the positive direction) may actually be associated with a decrease in speed, as illustrated in the first example.

1.10 DESCRIBING RATE OF CHANGE OF VELOCITY

Now that we have established a way of calculating velocity of a particle at an instant of time, and therefore at a position in space, it becomes meaningful to consider creating a numerical description of how fast velocity itself is changing. It is apparent that there are at least two simple ways of calculating a relevant measure:

(1) We might determine the velocity change Δv over an interval of displacement Δs, and calculate the change of velocity for every meter, foot, etc., of displacement; that is, $\Delta v/\Delta s$ [(m/sec)/m].

(2) Alternatively, we might determine Δv for an interval of time Δt and calculate the velocity change for every second, hour, etc., of time; that is, $\Delta v/\Delta t$ [(m/sec)/sec].

We are now confronted with the necessity of making a conscious and deliberate choice in the creation of a scientific concept. Neither of the proposed alternatives is "right" or "wrong" in some absolute sense; both offer possible ways of describing how velocity is changing. The reader is undoubtedly aware that $\Delta v/\Delta t$ is selected in preference to $\Delta v/\Delta s$. Why is this done?

Let us anticipate two ideas that will be subjected to more detailed examination later on: First, we shall see that the concept $\Delta v/\Delta t$ gives us a simpler way of describing the motion of free fall than does $\Delta v/\Delta s$, because $\Delta v/\Delta t$ is *uniform* in free fall while $\Delta v/\Delta s$ is not. Second, we shall see that the concept $\Delta v/\Delta t$ plays a pivotal role in the science of "dynamics"—the definition of the concepts of force and mass and the description of how changes in motion are produced.

Galileo was among the first to give an explicit discussion of the problem we have posed. In his very influential book, *Discourses Concerning Two New Sciences,** written shortly before his death, he summarized the views and attitudes apparent in his day.

This treatise is couched in the form of a discussion among three individuals: Salviati, the spokesman for Galileo; Simplicio, who holds the Aristotelian view which Salviati attacks; and Sagredo, a well-informed, open-minded friend of the other two. The three friends are discussing a manuscript by "our Academician" (Galileo himself). The manuscript reads:

"The properties belonging to uniform motion have been discussed . . . , but accelerated motion remains to be considered. And first of all it seems desirable to find and explain a definition best fitting natural phenomena. For anyone may invent an arbitrary type of motion and discuss its properties . . .; but we have decided to consider the phenomena of bodies falling with an acceleration such as actually occurs in nature and to make this definition of accelerated motion exhibit the essential features of accelerated motions . . . . Finally in the investigation of naturally accelerated motion we were led, by the hand as it were, in following the habit and custom of nature herself, in all her various other processes, to employ only those means which are most common, simple and easy.

". . . If we now examine the matter carefully, we find no addition or increment more simple than that which repeats itself always in the same manner. This we readily understand when we consider the intimate relationship between time and motion; for just as . . . we call a motion uniform when equal distances are traversed during equal time intervals, so also we may . . . picture to our mind a motion as uniformly and continuously accelerated when, during any equal interval of time whatever, equal increments of speed are given to it . . . ."

Thus the author suggests defining a uniformly changing motion as one for which $\Delta v/\Delta t$ is constant. Then the discussion begins:

Sagredo: "Although I can offer no rational objection to this or indeed any other definition, devised by any author whomsoever, since all definitions are arbitrary, I may nevertheless without offence be allowed to doubt whether such a definition as the above, established in an abstract manner, corresponds to and describes

---

* Translation by Crew and deSalvio, Dover Publications, New York, 1952.

that kind of accelerated motion which we meet in nature in the case of freely falling bodies . . . . So far as I see at present, the definition might have been put a little more clearly perhaps without changing the fundamental idea, namely, uniformly accelerated motion is such that its speed increases in proportion to the space traversed; so that, for example, the speed acquired by a body falling four cubits would be double that acquired in falling two cubits and this latter would be double that acquired in the first cubit . . . ."

This incorrect conception of the nature of free fall (i.e., that $\Delta v/\Delta s$ is constant) was a legacy of Aristotelian physics and was one of the principal targets of Galileo's polemic. Galileo proceeds to argue that $\Delta v/\Delta t$ is the preferable definition, and adduces experimental evidence to support his position. We shall return to his argument in Chapter 2. (For a visual presentation of the accelerated motion of free fall, turn to the modern flash photograph shown in Fig. 2.12.1 in the next chapter.)

To the idea represented by the calculation $\Delta v/\Delta t$ we give the name acceleration and the symbol a. We then have the statements:

$$\text{Average acceleration:} \qquad \bar{a} \equiv \frac{\Delta v}{\Delta t}, \qquad\qquad (1.10.1)$$

$$\text{Instantaneous acceleration:} \qquad a \equiv \lim_{\Delta t \to 0} \frac{\Delta v}{\Delta t} \equiv \frac{dv}{dt}. \qquad\qquad (1.10.2)$$

The dimensions of acceleration are (length/time)/time; in abbreviated notation this is usually written length/(time)^2 and in specific units: m/sec^2; mi/hr^2; (m/sec)/hr; (mi/hr)/sec; etc.

Statements (1.10.1) and (1.10.2) are meant to convey the idea that all the things we said about average and instantaneous velocities in Sections 1.6, 1.7, and 1.8 are to be repeated in the new context for the ideas of average and instantaneous acceleration. Note in particular that acceleration, like velocity, is an algebraic quantity with plus and minus signs which arise in the calculation and which must be given a physical interpretation. Review the comment about the sign of Δv at the end of Section 1.9.

PROBLEM 1.10.   Use Problems 1.7, 1.8, and 1.9 as a pattern of suggestions as to how to study the concept of acceleration. Make up your own exercises, particularly some very simple ones in which you know the answer to begin with; apply the language and concepts of definitions (1.10.1) and (1.10.2) to these situations rigorously and carefully. Give particular attention to providing a complete verbal description for cases of uniform acceleration such as those illustrated in Fig. 1.10.1. Describe at least two simple physical situations in which you might see a car or a thrown object executing the kind of motion suggested in Fig. 1.10.1. Sketch s-t diagrams for the motion.

It is to be very strongly emphasized that we are establishing only one single definition for acceleration—not separate definitions for motions which are speeding up or

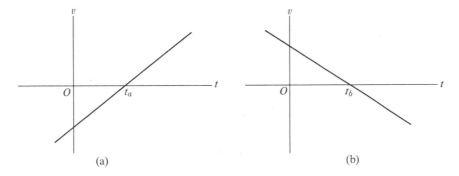

(a)   (b)

FIG. 1.10.1. These two diagrams show v-t histories of uniformly accelerated rectilinear motions, with positive and negative accelerations, respectively (Problem 1.10).

slowing down. Statements 1.10.1 and 1.10.2 are *algebraic*, as were our statements about velocity; how are plus and minus signs to be interpreted? Note that a will be a positive number if $v_2 > v_1$, regardless of whether the velocities are positive, negative, or change signs in the interval; similarly a will be a negative number if $v_2 < v_1$ algebraically, regardless of the absolute values of v_2 and v_1. In the motion suggested by Fig. 1.10.1(a), acceleration is at every instant uniform and positive despite the fact that in the interval between $t = 0$ and t_a the motion is slowing down, and, after t_a, is speeding up, and despite the fact that the direction of motion is reversed at the instant t_a. Make a similar statement of your own about the motion suggested in Fig. 1.10.1(b).

1.11   THE "KINEMATIC EQUATIONS" FOR UNIFORMLY ACCELERATED MOTION: ALGEBRAIC RELATIONS AMONG s, v, a, AND t

Statements (1.6.1), (1.8.1), (1.10.1), and (1.10.2) are algebraic statements which create meaning for the symbols v and a. These statements are *definitions;* they are not derived by mathematical manipulation from prior connections or relationships. Once we have expressed these definitions in symbols, however, algebraic manipulation leads to the expression of other relationships among the symbols—a simple and more or less obvious equation such as (1.7.1), and rather more sophisticated and less obvious equations which we shall now proceed to derive.

Consider the case to which Galileo points so forcefully in the quotations in the preceding section: uniformly accelerated, rectilinear motion. Figure 1.11.1(a) is an a-t diagram for such a motion, with positive acceleration. Figure 1.11.1(b) is a corresponding v-t diagram; the equation of the straight line on this diagram stems from the definition of acceleration [exactly as Eq. (1.7.1) followed from the definition of velocity]:

$$a \equiv \frac{\Delta v}{\Delta t} = \frac{v - v_0}{t - 0},$$

$$v = at + v_0. \qquad\qquad (1.11.1)$$

Note some mathematical vocabulary: we think of Eq. (1.11.1) as an expression for the *dependent variable v* in terms of the *independent variable t* and the constants or *parameters a* and v_0.

Figure 1.11.1(c) is an *s-t* diagram corresponding to the *v-t* history of 1.11.1(b). An equation of the chord $s_0 A$ can be obtained as follows:

$$\bar{v} \equiv \frac{\Delta s}{\Delta t} = \frac{s - s_0}{t - 0},$$

$$s = \bar{v}t + s_0, \qquad (1.11.2)$$

where the value of $\bar{v}$ will be different for every different time interval t.

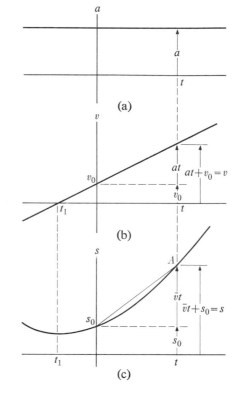

FIG. 1.11.1. (a) An *a-t* diagram for uniformly accelerated rectilinear motion with positive acceleration a. (b) A *v-t* diagram corresponding to acceleration diagram (a); $v = v_0$ at $t = 0$; $v = v$ at $t = t$. (c) An *s-t* diagram corresponding to velocity diagram (b); $\bar{v}$ denotes average velocity for time interval between $t = 0$ and $t = t$; that is, $\bar{v} = (s - s_0)/(t - 0)$, where s_0 denotes position at $t = 0$.

Although the equation $v = at + v_0$ is a perfectly satisfactory description of Fig. 1.11.1(b)—a and v_0 are considered to be known numbers, and the equation gives us a value of instantaneous velocity v at any instant of time t—Eq. (1.11.2) is hardly an adequate description of the *s-t* curve in Fig. 1.11.1(c); $\bar{v}$ is *not* a single, constant value, and therefore Eq. (1.11.2) does *not* establish values of s uniquely in terms of instantaneous values of t. In particular, the equation of the *s-t* curve must depend somehow on the value of a, but a does not appear explicitly in Eq. (1.11.2). Progress in the derivation requires a deeper examination of $\bar{v}$ and its relation to instantaneous velocities such as v_0 and v. Recall our interpretation, in Section 1.8, of $\bar{v}$ as that uniform velocity at which a given displacement (with varying velocity) would have taken place in the same time interval, and consider the *v-t* histories represented in Fig. 1.11.2.

In Figs. 1.11.2(a) and (b), the instantaneous velocity is shown to change from a given initial value v_0 at $t = 0$ to the same final value v at instant t in each case. In case (a), the velocity increases rapidly at first, and then changes slowly, most of the time interval being spent at velocities near v. In case (b), the velocity changes slowly at first, most of the interval being spent at velocities near v_0, and then increases rapidly to the final value v. We certainly do not expect $\bar{v}$ to be the same for both cases; we would expect $\bar{v}$ to be closer in numerical value to v than to v_0 in case (a) and vice versa in case (b). Since the motion is all in the same direction in each case,

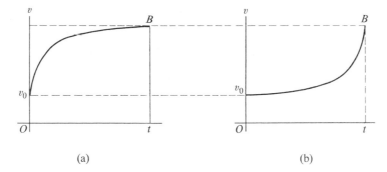

(a)   (b)

FIG. 1.11.2. These are v-versus-t histories of rectilinear motion, in which velocity changes from given initial value v_0 at $t = 0$ to same final value v at $t = t$ in two different ways.

we would also expect Δs in case (a) to be greater than Δs in case (b), and this is consistent with our sense of the difference between the two average velocities. Note again that all these statements are based on our *interpretation* of $\bar{v}$ as that *uniform* velocity at which a given displacement will be executed in the same time interval.

If we now imagine deforming the v-t histories of Fig. 1.11.2 so that each curve becomes straighter and both approach the straight line connecting the points marked v_0 and B, we can imagine the value of $\bar{v}$ for case (a) decreasing and that for (b) increasing until the two values become identical for the straight-line history, and take on a numerical value exactly halfway between v_0 and v, i.e., for the straight-line v-t history we expect the value of $\bar{v}$ to be equally spaced between v_0 and v and not to be closer to one or the other, as it is in the situations of Fig. 1.11.2. From this argument it follows that for a uniformly accelerated motion (straight-line v-t history) we might expect that:

$$\bar{v} = \frac{v + v_0}{2} \tag{1.11.3}$$

or, substituting $v = at + v_0$:

$$\bar{v} = \tfrac{1}{2}at + v_0. \tag{1.11.4}$$

Note carefully that these statements are *not* valid for the motions represented in Fig. 1.11.2; they apply *only* to uniformly accelerated motion such as that of Fig. 1.11.1.

It is worth stopping for a moment to give thought to the logical status of the argument which led us to Eqs. (1.11.3) and (1.11.4). We might have glibly asserted that $\bar{v} = (v_0 + v)/2$ for Fig. 1.11.1(b) "because the velocity is increasing uniformly"; this may sound reasonable, but it glosses over a significant logical issue. Equation (1.11.3) is *not* a definition of $\bar{v}$; $\bar{v}$ is defined as $\Delta s/\Delta t$. If our reasoning is to be sound and careful, we must establish a clear and logical connection between the idea of average velocity $\Delta s/\Delta t$ and the idea we articulate in Eq. (1.11.3). The verbal argument of the preceding paragraph was introduced to make this connection reasonable and plausible. It must be recognized that, although plausible, this argument is not rigorous; it is far from constituting a mathematically satisfactory proof. We have not established a clear arithmetical definition of the process of averaging; we have not shown that arithmetically and unambiguously the number calculated from

$\Delta s/\Delta t$ must be identical with the number obtained by averaging up the sequence of uniformly changing velocities in Fig. 1.11.1(b). Lack of *complete* rigor or logical precision will not prevent us from going ahead with our line of reasoning; this is characteristic of physical science. Galileo and his contemporaries erected a very useful and fruitful conceptual structure in just the manner we are illustrating. But logical difficulties should not be glibly glossed over; they should be pointed to and acknowledged; reasonable, plausible connections must still be established.

A rather different approach to the justification of Eqs. (1.11.3) and (1.11.4) is presented in the next section by developing an argument about the interpretation of "area" under v-t curves. Although providing an interesting alternative, and therefore support, for the argument used in this section, it is also just a reasonable and plausible development rather than a rigorous proof. As in other instances to which we have alluded, these issues are to be treated rigorously and unambiguously only with sufficiently sophisticated mathematical tools; these tools we shall develop and examine later.

Suppose we now eliminate $\bar{v}$ from Eq. (1.11.2) by using Eq. (1.11.4). Algebraic manipulation gives:

$$s = (\tfrac{1}{2}at + v_0)t + s_0,$$
$$s = \tfrac{1}{2}at^2 + v_0t + s_0. \tag{1.11.5}$$

Since a, v_0, and s_0 are implied to be constants in the context of our problem—numbers about which we have prior information—Eq. (1.11.5) can now be identified as the equation of the s-t graph in Fig. 1.11.1(c); we now have a direct connection between position values s and instants of time t in terms of fixed numbers a, v_0, and s_0; such a direct connection was not available in Eq. (1.11.2). In Eq. (1.11.5) we have an expression for the dependent variable s in terms of the independent variable t and the constants or parameters a, v_0, and s_0.

There remains one more connection between pairs of variables; we obtain an equation relating v and s by eliminating t from (1.11.1) and (1.11.5), obtaining:

$$v^2 - v_0^2 = 2a(s - s_0). \tag{1.11.6}$$

PROBLEM 1.11.   Derive Eq. (1.11.6) by solving for t in Eq. (1.11.1) and substituting this expression into (1.11.5).

1.12   INTERPRETATION AND USE OF THE KINEMATIC EQUATIONS

Summarizing results, we have three equations describing various aspects of uniformly accelerated rectilinear motion; these are frequently referred to as the "kinematic relations" for such motion:

$$v = at + v_0, \tag{1.12.1}$$
$$s = \tfrac{1}{2}at^2 + v_0t + s_0, \tag{1.12.2}$$
$$v^2 - v_0^2 = 2a(s - s_0). \tag{1.12.3}$$

(The term "kinematic" as used in this context refers to description of motion only, without reference to effects which produce or alter the motion. Contrasting terms would be "dynamic" or "kinetic," and would imply reference to ideas such as laws of force, effects of inertia—ideas concerning causes of motion which have been deliberately excluded from the initial discussion.)

The kinematic relations give a *complete* description of any uniformly accelerated rectilinear motion. For example, if the motion reverses direction at some instant, the equations say so directly; the *same* equations describe the motion on either side of the reversal of direction, and we do *not* resort to two sets of equations, with one set for one direction of the motion and one for the other.

PROBLEM 1.12. Verify the fact that Eqs. (1.12.1) and (1.12.3), exactly as they stand, with a and v_0 as positive numbers, describe Figs. 1.11.1(a) and (b), respectively, with reversal of direction of motion at the instant $t = t_1$, where t_1 is a negative number and is equal to $-v_0/a$.

In solving numerical and algebraic problems using the kinematic equations, the student is advised to adopt a careful systematic approach. Adopt a convention for positive direction and for origin of position. Write down algebraic statements of the known values (such as "given: $v_0 = -3.25 \text{ m/sec}$"). Translate the verbal requirements into symbols (i.e., "How high does a stone rise when thrown vertically into the air?" is translated as $s = ?$ when $v = 0$). Select the equation which connects the known and unknown quantities in the most direct way, and calculate the unknown. An example worked out in this style follows; work it through carefully, and then use a similar approach in problems at the end of the chapter.

Example 1.1. Consider a case in which a stone is thrown vertically upward with an initial velocity of 60.0 ft/sec from the edge of a 250-ft cliff, so that it rises and falls along a straight line which misses the edge of the cliff. (a) If one applies the kinematic equations (1.12.1, 2, 3) to this physical situation, what assumption about the character of the motion is implied? (b) Sketch rough a-t, v-t, and s-t diagrams based on this assumption. (c) Apply the equations to obtain numerical values for the following particular points, taking the acceleration to have a magnitude of 32.2 ft/sec^2:

(1) How high does the stone rise?
(2) At what instant does it arrive at its highest point?
(3) What velocity does it have when it returns past the edge of the cliff?
(4) At what instant does it strike the ground at the foot of the cliff?
(5) Where is it located 10.0 sec after it is thrown?

Solution: (a) If one applies the kinematic equations to the case cited, he assumes that not only is the motion rectilinear, as stated, but that it is also uniformly accelerated.

(b) Let us adopt a convention in which positive direction is vertically upward, and $s = 0$ at the top of the cliff. Take $t = 0$ at instant of throwing the stone. Since we have taken positive direction upward, v_2 will always be less than v_1 at successive instants of time (thus, on the way up $v_1 = 5 \text{ m/sec}$ may be followed by $v_2 = 2$

m/sec, and $\Delta v = -3$ m/sec; on the way down $v_1 = -3$ m/sec may be followed by $v_2 = -7$ m/sec at a later instant and $\Delta v = -4$ m/sec) and the acceleration a will be a negative quantity. Figure 1.12.1 shows the kinematic diagrams of this motion.

We have given:

$$a = -32.2 \text{ ft/sec}^2,$$

since positive direction is taken upward;

$$v_0 = +60.0 \text{ ft/sec},$$

$$s_0 = 0 \text{ by convention adopted.}$$

Question 1. Translation: $s = ?$ when $v = 0$. The connection between s and v is given directly by Eq. (1.12.3):

$$v^2 - v_0^2 = 2a(s - s_0).$$

Substituting given values, we have

$$0 - (60.0)^2 = 2(-32.2)(s - 0),$$

$$s = \frac{(60.0)^2}{2(32.2)} = +56.0 \text{ ft}.$$

Thus the stone rises to a height of 56.0 ft above the edge of the cliff. If the initial velocity were larger, the stone would rise higher in proportion to the *square* of the velocity.

Question 2. Translation: $t = ?$ when $v = 0$. The connection between v and t is given directly by Eq. (1.12.1):

$$v = at + v_0,$$

$$0 = -32.2t + 60.0,$$

$$t = \frac{60.0}{32.2} = +1.86 \text{ sec}.$$

The stone attains its highest position 1.86 sec after it is thrown. (Note that at this instant, as well as at all others, it has an acceleration of -32.2 ft/sec^2; that is, the stone is accelerating even at the instant it has zero velocity.)

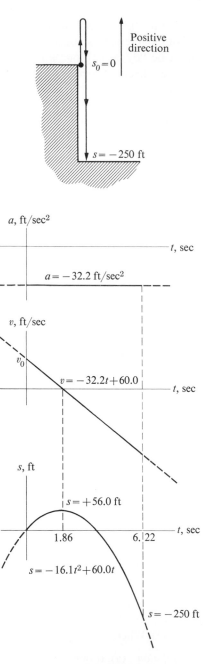

Fig. 1.12.1. Diagrams accompanying Example 1.1. (Dashed sections of curves do not have physical significance in the problem, but are nevertheless described by the kinematic equations.)

Question 3. Translation: $v = $? when $s = 0$. (Note that we do *not* make the intuitive guess that the velocity will have the same magnitude as the initial velocity and an opposite direction. Let us *prove* this. To do so we do *not* break the motion up into an upward phase and a downward phase.) The connection between s and v is given by (1.12.3):

$$v^2 - v_0^2 = 2a(s - s_0),$$

$$v^2 - (60.0)^2 = 2(-32.2)(0 - 0) = 0,$$

$$v^2 = (60.0)^2,$$

$$v = \pm 60.0 \text{ ft/sec.}$$

There are two values for v when $s = 0$, and they must be interpreted: $+60.0$ ft/sec is the *initial* velocity of the stone when it leaves $s = 0$ on the upward path; therefore -60.0 ft/sec must be its velocity on its *return* to the position $s = 0$. The body returns to $s = 0$ with a velocity equal in magnitude but opposite in direction to v_0.

Question 4. Translation: $t = $? when $s = -250$ ft. The connection between s and t is given by Eq. (1.12.2):

$$s = \tfrac{1}{2}at^2 + v_0t + s_0,$$

$$-250 = \tfrac{1}{2}(-32.2)t^2 + 60.0t + 0,$$

$$16.1t^2 - 60.0t - 250 = 0,$$

$$t^2 - 3.73t - 15.5 = 0.$$

Applying the formula for the solution of a quadratic equation, we obtain:

$$t = \frac{3.73 \pm \sqrt{(3.73)^2 + 4(15.5)}}{2} = \begin{cases} +6.22 \text{ sec} \\ -2.50 \text{ sec} \end{cases} \quad \text{for} \quad s = -250 \text{ ft.}$$

Equation (1.12.2), like the other kinematic equations, is a general algebraic relation which describes any uniformly accelerated motion *for all values of t* from left to right on the t-line. The result $t = -2.50$ sec refers to the time at which the body would have passed $s = -250$ ft on the way up so as to have an upward velocity of 60.0 ft/sec at $t = 0$; this result is irrelevant in the physical situation described; $t = +6.22$ sec is the time (after throwing) at which the stone arrives at the foot of the cliff.

Question 5. It is clear from the result just obtained that by $t = 10.0$ sec the stone lies on the ground at the foot of the cliff. Let us verify this from the equations: We are looking for $s = $? when $t = 10.0$, and this is given by Eq. (1.12.2). Thus

$$s = \tfrac{1}{2}at^2 + v_0t + s_0,$$

$$= \tfrac{1}{2}(-32.2)(10.0)^2 + 60.0(10.0) + 0,$$

$$= -1610 + 600 = -1010 \text{ ft.}$$

Therefore $s = -1010$ ft is where the stone would be at $t = 10.0$ sec if the foot of the cliff were sufficiently far away. With the ground at $s = -250$ ft, the physical interpretation is that the stone lies on the ground at $t = 10.0$ sec.

1.13   ALTERNATIVE VIEW OF THE RELATION AMONG $\bar{v}$, v_0, AND v: "AREA" UNDER v-VERSUS-t GRAPH

Consider the v-t diagram of a motion at uniform velocity v_0 (Fig. 1.13.1); any arbitrary time interval $t_2 - t_1$, however large or small, forms the base of a rectangle with altitude v_0. The "area" of this rectangle is $v_0(t_2 - t_1)$ which we recognize, from our definition of velocity, to be Δs or $s_2 - s_1$. (We have put the word area in quotation marks because we are not talking about surface area in the familiar sense of square feet, square meters, acres, etc.; we are multiplying velocity along one axis by time along the other to obtain a number which is like an area in the sense of being an altitude times a base, but which has the dimensions of distance or displacement. The quotation marks will be dropped in the following discussion, but this qualification should be kept in mind.)

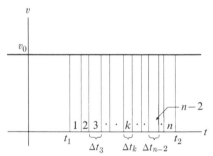

FIG. 1.13.1.   A v-t diagram for rectilinear motion at uniform velocity v_0. Note that "area" of rectangle with base $(t_2 - t_1)$ is $v_0(t_2 - t_1)$, and is equal to the displacement $s_2 - s_1$ associated with this time interval.

Thus the area of the rectangle corresponding to any arbitrary time interval in a v-t diagram of uniform velocity is equal to the displacement which occurs in that time interval. Furthermore, we can consider the large rectangle in Fig. 1.13.1 as being made up of any number of smaller rectangles; the bases of these rectangles are small time intervals which all add up to $t_2 - t_1$, and the areas are small successive displacements which add up to $s_2 - s_1$.

We shall develop a mathematical notation to describe this simple case—a notation which will be of great service later when it is necessary to deal with continuously varying quantities in a more general way: Divide the time interval $t_2 - t_1$ into n segments (these need not be of equal size, although equal size would be a perfectly acceptable special case) and number the segments in sequence from 1 to n. We shall use the letter k to denote any one of the numbers between 1 and n. For example, we shall use subscripts to denote the various small time intervals: the first segment Δt_1, the second Δt_2, the kth segment Δt_k, the last segment Δt_n. To denote adding up all the n segments in succession from the first to the last, we write:

$$t_2 - t_1 = \Delta t_1 + \Delta t_2 + \cdots + \Delta t_k + \cdots + \Delta t_n \qquad (1.13.1)$$

and, as a shorthand, we denote the sum on the right-hand side of (1.13.1) by

$$\sum_{k=1}^{n} \Delta t_k,$$

(read as "summation from $k = 1$ to $k = n$ of Δt sub k"). The symbol $\sum$ (Greek capital letter sigma) is a conventional mathematical symbol for "summation."

Similarly in this notation we would describe the kth displacement (the area of the kth little rectangle) as

$$\Delta s_k = v_0 \, \Delta t_k,$$

and the total displacement in $t_2 - t_1$ as

$$s_2 - s_1 = \sum_{k=1}^{n} v_0 \, \Delta t_k. \tag{1.13.2}$$

Note that this sum is positive and corresponds to a positive displacement if v_0 is positive (i.e., if the rectangle lies above the t-axis); the displacement is negative if the rectangle lies below the t-axis.

PROBLEM 1.13. As an exercise in the use of the summation notation, write out expressions for the sums represented by the following:

(a) $\displaystyle\sum_{k=1}^{5} k$ (b) $\displaystyle\sum_{k=1}^{4} x_k^2$ (c) $\displaystyle\sum_{k=1}^{n} \frac{1}{k^2}$ (d) $\displaystyle\sum_{k=1}^{3} 2k \, \Delta t_k$ (e) $\displaystyle\sum_{k=1}^{n} v_k \, \Delta t_k$

[*Answer to* (d): $2 \, \Delta t_1 + 4 \, \Delta t_2 + 6 \, \Delta t_3$.]

The sum in Eq. (1.13.2) suggests an interesting notion: Suppose we keep cutting $t_2 - t_1$ into more and more segments (i.e., we keep making all the segments smaller and smaller and n larger and larger); as n increases indefinitely and as the segments become indefinitely small, does the sum described in (1.13.2) still have significance? Does it still refer to a particular number, $s_2 - s_1 = v_0(t_2 - t_1)$? This is not a trivial question regardless of what our intuition suggests. We are asking whether the sum of an infinitely* large number of terms yields a simple, finite number. The answer in this case is yes, but proving this by rigorous mathematical argument from the laws of arithmetic is a rather complicated problem.

The Greeks experienced great trouble with ideas of this kind—ideas that involved the indefinitely large, the indefinitely small, continuity of subdivision, and infinite sums. The philosopher Zeno sounded a warning about careless thinking in this sphere by propounding a famous set of paradoxes, one of which, concerning Achilles and the tortoise, runs as follows: "Achilles, the fleet runner, can never overtake the slow-moving tortoise who gets a head start in a race, because by the time Achilles gets to the point at which the tortoise started, the latter has moved on; and by the time Achilles reaches the new position the tortoise has moved on again; and so forth indefinitely." The paradox is resolved by the demonstration that one is dealing here

---

* The words "infinite" or "infinity" are not used to denote a number; they refer to the idea of a numerical value which has no upper bound; for any number, however large, one can specify a larger number.

with the sum of an infinite number of terms and that this sum does indeed have a perfectly definite value.

We shall leave these mathematical questions for subsequent study, and tentatively accept the assertion that the sum in Eq. (1.13.2) has a definite and unambiguous value as the intervals are made indefinitely small in size and indefinitely large in number. Our mathematical notation for this will be:

$$s_2 - s_1 = \lim_{\substack{||\Delta|| \to 0 \\ n \to \infty}} \sum_{k=1}^{n} v_0 \, \Delta t_k. \tag{1.13.3}$$

The symbol $||\Delta|| \to 0$ is to be read "the norm becomes indefinitely small"—the "norm" being the largest of the n intervals in any arbitrary subdivision of $t_2 - t_1$. The symbol $n \to \infty$ is to be read "n becomes indefinitely large or 'infinite'."

1.14   AREA UNDER A v-VERSUS-t CURVE

Consider now a motion in which velocity varies with time (Fig. 1.14.1). Is the shaded area (bounded by the curve, the t-axis, and t_1 and t_2) equal to the displacement in the interval $t_2 - t_1$ as was the case in Fig. 1.13.1? Still more significantly: What meaning should we assign to the whole idea of "area under the curve"? The area of figures bounded by straight lines was an unambiguous concept—one can count the squares—but the area of figures bounded by curves is a more subtle notion. This will require a bit of investigation.

Let us again divide our figure into n small intervals and consider the rectangles we might erect on these intervals, the area of each small rectangle representing a small displacement. In each instance we have two extreme choices for the "altitude" or velocity characterizing the rectangle. One extreme is represented by the smallest value of v in the interval and is illustrated by the series of "steps" which lie below the curve. Let us denote the altitude of this rectangle for the kth interval by $v_k^{(s)}$; $v_1^{(s)}$ is marked as an example. The other extreme is represented by the largest value of v in the interval and is illustrated by the series of steps which lie *above* the curve. Let us denote the altitude of this rectangle in the kth interval by $v_k^{(l)}$; $v_1^{(l)}$ is marked as an example.

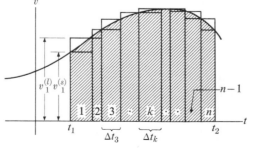

FIG. 1.14.1.   Rectilinear motion in which velocity varies with time. Is shaded area equal to displacement $(s_2 - s_1)$ during time interval $(t_2 - t_1)$, as is the case in Fig. 1.13.1?

We can now add up our two sets of rectangles to obtain two different areas—a larger area denoted by $A^{(l)}$, and a smaller area by $A^{(s)}$:

$$A^{(l)} = \sum_{k=1}^{n} v_k^{(l)} \, \Delta t_k, \tag{1.14.1}$$

$$A^{(s)} = \sum_{k=1}^{n} v_k^{(s)} \, \Delta t_k. \tag{1.14.2}$$

It is clear from the geometry of Fig. 1.14.1 that $A^{(l)} > A^{(s)}$, and that the difference between $A^{(l)}$ and $A^{(s)}$ must be the sum of the areas of the small blocks which lie partly below and partly above the curve. We can interpret $A^{(l)}$ as a displacement taking place at velocities systematically greater than ones which actually obtained in the motion, and therefore $A^{(l)}$ must be greater than the actual displacement $s_2 - s_1$. Similarly, $A^{(s)}$ represents a displacement less than $s_2 - s_1$. In summary:

$$A^{(l)} > (s_2 - s_1) > A^{(s)}. \tag{1.14.3}$$

What happens to these numbers as the Δt's are made indefinitely small; that is, as $\|\Delta\| \to 0$? We would expect the little blocks to become smaller and smaller and $A^{(l)}$ and $A^{(s)}$ to become more and more nearly equal. Thus our intuition suggests that the numbers

$$\lim_{\|\Delta\| \to 0} \sum_{k=1}^{n} v_k^{(l)} \, \Delta t_k \qquad \text{and} \qquad \lim_{\|\Delta\| \to 0} \sum_{k=1}^{n} v_k^{(s)} \, \Delta t_k$$

should be equal to each other, and that the resulting number is to be interpreted as the "area under the curve" and as the displacement $s_2 - s_1$:

$$s_2 - s_1 = \lim_{\|\Delta\| \to 0} \sum_{k=1}^{n} v_k \, \Delta t_k. \tag{1.14.4}$$

The superscript notation on v has been dropped because, hopefully, the limit does not depend on what value of v we use in each interval, so long as it is a value for some point on the section of curve which lies in that interval.

Again leaving the mathematical subtleties for a later inquiry, let us try out our tentative conclusion on a simple specific case: uniformly accelerated motion (Fig. 1.14.2).

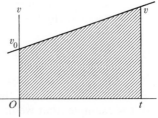

FIG. 1.14.2. A v-t history of uniformly accelerated rectilinear motion. Shaded trapezoidal area is $[(v_0 + v)/2]t$.

The area of the shaded trapezoid in **Fig.** 1.14.2 is

$$\frac{v_0 + v}{2} t.$$

Our preceding arguments suggest that this is equal to the displacement occurring in the interval between $t = 0$ and $t = t$:

$$s - s_0 = \frac{v_0 + v}{2} t. \tag{1.14.5}$$

In Eq. (1.14.5) we recognize $(v_0 + v)/2$ as that uniform velocity at which the displacement $s - s_0$ would have taken place in the time interval $t - 0$. Furthermore

$$\frac{s - s_0}{t - 0} = \frac{\Delta s}{\Delta t} = \frac{v_0 + v}{2} = \bar{v}. \tag{1.14.6}$$

Thus, from this rather different point of view concerning the interpretation of areas under v-t curves, we have found support for the argument that led to Eq. (1.11.3). This should lead us to expect an intimate connection between the two arguments and points of view.

PROBLEM 1.14. (a) In this section it has been argued that the area under a portion of v-t curve is to be interpreted as the displacement occurring in the given time interval. Arguing by analogy, what would you expect to be the interpretation of area under a portion of acceleration-versus-time curve? Draw some a-t diagrams analogous to the v-t diagrams used in this section, and practice using the summation notation by writing expressions for the areas as limits of sums.

(b) What interpretation, if any, would you give the area under a portion of s-t curve?

PROBLEM 1.15. Measuring areas from $t = 0$ as the initial instant in Fig. 1.14.3, describe and interpret the way in which the calculated numbers would behave as the value of t for the final instant increased progressively. Pay particular attention to the instants t_a and t_b. [Recall that negative values of area go with negative values of v: see Eqs. (1.13.2) and (1.14.4).]

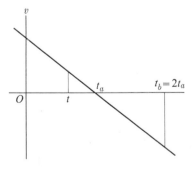

FIG. 1.14.3. Rectilinear motion with uniform negative acceleration (Problem 1.15).

1.15 COMMENTS ON CONCEPTS AND DEFINITIONS

Now that we have devised a description of rectilinear motion, it will pay us to pause and take stock of some of the things that we have done and *not* done. It may be noticed, for example, that we have made no attempt to define either space or time as entities. We have specified how we would *measure* space intervals and time intervals by comparing them with arbitrary standards such as meters or seconds, but this is very different from making statements asserting what space "is" and what time "is." We are treating both space and time as undefined elements, in a manner similar to that in which mathematicians view ideas such as "number," "point," "line." They are undefined elements which we work into a conceptual structure by describing the rules which they obey and the manipulations we impose on them.

Our whole approach to definition has been one that is described as "operational"; we specify very carefully all the actions of measurement and calculation which we perform in order to arrive at a number to which we give a name such as "instantaneous velocity" or "average acceleration." For this reason the student must not expect pat phrases of definition that he can memorize as an end result. The definition of each of the concepts we have successively created out of the notions of displacement and time interval consists of some sentences of description of the numbers used, calculations made, and the explanation of the symbols involved; i.e., a description of the actions or operations we must perform to end up with the number we call "velocity" or "acceleration."

Finally, concepts such as velocity and acceleration are not "objects" which are bodily present in the physical world, awaiting discovery by a great investigator. They are abstractions, created by the human intellect, based on certain specific calculations with numbers denoting intervals of space and time, and the calculations which are christened "velocity" and "acceleration" are selected from among *alternative possibilities* of calculation, for reasons of simplicity or convenience or elegance.

1.16 QUESTIONS AND PROBLEMS

1.16. At various points in this chapter the following words have been used: "implication," "assertion," "assumption," "paradox," "rigorous," "intuitive," "plausible." Define these terms in the appropriate context.

1.17. Suppose you were in possession of observations of a particular motion. How would you determine whether or not the motion was uniformly accelerated if (a) the observations consist of a set of values of instantaneous velocity and corresponding times? (b) the observations consist of a set of values of position and corresponding values of time? In each case take into account the fact that observational data always have some scatter and a range of uncertainty.

1.18. Suppose you wished to introduce the term "average speed" into the vocabulary of this chapter. How would you define the term? Do the phrases "average magnitude of instantaneous velocity" and "magnitude of the average velocity" denote the same number? Cite specific examples in your discussion.

1.19. Describe some motions encountered in common experience which you have reason to believe are not uniformly accelerated. Sketch v-t and s-t diagrams.

1.20. Consider again the problem of the stone thrown up into the air (Example 1.1 worked out in the text), but this time from the point of view of an observer in a helicopter rising at a uniform velocity of 60.0 ft/sec. Suppose this observer passes the edge of the cliff at the instant the stone is thrown; what will he say about the motion of the stone relative to him? Will it appear to be accelerated? If so, in what direction? Will it appear to go up and then down *relative to the helicopter*? What will the stone appear to be doing relative to the observer in the helicopter at the instant the observer on the cliff says it has reached the top of its flight? What fundamental assumptions are you making about agreement between measurements of displacement and time intervals made by the two observers? [*Note to teacher and student:* This question is meant to plant the seeds for subsequent study of relativity concepts and theory. It contains many philosophical subtleties and deserves reconsideration from time to time as the course progresses.]

1.21. The velocity of sound in air varies somewhat with temperature, but under ordinary conditions it is about 1100 ft/sec.

(a) Look up the relation between feet and meters in Appendix C and calculate the velocity of sound in m/sec.

(b) If you watch a man at a distance swinging a hammer, you hear the hammer strike some interval of time after you see it fall. If this time interval is 1.5 sec, how far away is the man?

(c) Suppose you are able to count to between 4 and 5 sec after a lightning flash before you hear the thunderclap; about how far away was the lightning?

(d) In (b) and (c), what assumption have you been making about the velocity of light?

(e) A cliff which gives a good echo is located at some distance from you; you start clapping at regular intervals and adjust the interval so that you no longer hear the echo because it arrives simultaneously with the next clap. Under these conditions, your friend with a stop watch determines that in Δt seconds you clap N times (not counting the first clap which starts the timing period). How far away is the cliff? Make up some reasonable numerical cases. Over what range (i.e., how close to a wall

and how far away) is this likely to be a useful method for estimating distance?

1.22. The velocity of light and of radio waves in vacuum is very nearly 186,000 mi/sec or 3.00×10^8 m/sec. (It is very slightly less than this in air, but the latter effect is to be considered negligible for present purposes.)

(a) Looking up appropriate distances: calculate the time of travel of a radar wave from the earth to the moon and back to the receiver; calculate the time of travel of light from the sun to the earth. (See Appendix B.)

(b) Calculate how far a pulse of light will travel in one year (in miles and in meters). This distance is called "one light year," and astronomical distances beyond the solar system are usually measured in this unit. Compare it numerically (find ratios) with some large distances which you think you have a "feeling for" or comprehension of.

1.23. Suppose you and a friend are making a trip in separate cars. You start off and travel at a constant speed of 40 mi/hr. Your friend starts a half hour later (i.e., you have a lead time of one half hour) and travels at 60 mi/hr. How long will it take him to overtake you?

(Do not just tinker with the numbers given in the above statement. Solve this first as a general algebraic problem, adopting symbols for the two different velocities and the lead time. Examine your algebraic solution: Does it behave properly; i.e., does the time to overtake increase or decrease as it should if one or the other velocity is changed? What does your solution say happens as the velocities are taken to be more and more nearly equal? Does this make sense? What other questions can you ask?)

After making this general investigation, obtain a numerical solution for the particular case described in the original statement of the problem.

1.24. Problems 1.21 and 1.22 suggest ways in which one might use time intervals traversed by sound or light at uniform velocity to estimate distances. Assuming a stone to be accelerated at about 32 ft/sec^2 (approximately 10 m/sec^2) in free fall; how would you use the time interval between dropping a stone from rest and seeing it strike the water below to estimate the height of the bridge? Give a general algebraic discussion and then make up some reasonable numerical examples. Suppose you were trying to estimate such a distance in the dark and could only hear the splash rather than see it; would the delay due to the time of travel of sound have to be considered? (Make your answer specific and *numerical* by calculating the effect.)

1.25. A body slides along a level surface, the motion being governed by friction. An experiment is made in which instantaneous velocities are determined at the beginning and end of a known time interval, and a value of acceleration is calculated from these numbers.

(a) If you are to use the kinematic equations and the acceleration calculated in the above experiment to predict the behavior of the same body in future instances of sliding on the same surface, what idealizations, assumptions, or limitations must you invoke? Does the presence of friction make application of the kinematic relations to this problem invalid? Justify your answer.

Suppose the results of the experiment are the following: The body is observed to change its velocity from 2.65 to 1.23 m/sec in an interval of 0.36 sec.

(b) Use the kinematic relations to predict how far the body will slide if it is given an initial velocity of 5.80 m/sec. (*Note:* State explicitly the sign convention you adopt.)

(c) For the same case (initial velocity 5.80 m/sec), calculate the location of the body at $t = 10$ sec. Interpret the result.

(d) How long does the body remain in motion?

1.26. (a) Figure 1.16.1 represents the v-t history of a rectilinear motion. By drawing appropriate rectangles, calculate and add their areas to obtain a numerical estimate of the area between $t = -10$ and $t = +40$ sec. Does this value make sense as a magnitude of the displacement traversed under velocities of the size indicated? How would you evaluate the average velocity for the time interval in question? How would you represent this velocity in Fig. 1.16.1?

(b) Draw straight lines tangent to the curve at two or three points in Fig. 1.16.1 and calculate accelerations at these instants by calculating the slopes of the lines from appropriate Δv and Δt intervals measured on the diagram.

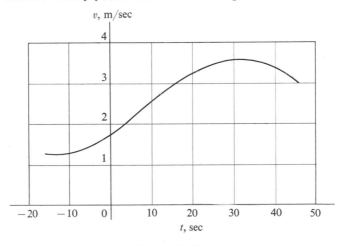

FIGURE 1.16.1

1.27. A body rolled down an inclined plane is observed to have a uniform acceleration of about 14 ft/sec². Suppose the same body is given an initial velocity *up* the plane of 18 ft/sec from a starting position at the foot of the plane.

(a) How far up the plane will it roll? (Assume the plane to be long enough so that the object does not fall off the upper end.) How long will this take?

(b) When will the body return to the foot of the plane?

(c) When will it be located 6 ft up the plane from the starting point?

(d) What velocity will it have 6 ft up the plane from the starting point? 20 ft from the starting point?

(e) Where will the body be at t = 10 sec?

Problem for More Advanced Work

1.28. Two thin wires are located, one above the other, a known distance Δs apart. A heavy object is dropped from rest at some distance above the wires. As it falls, it breaks the wires, causing electrical signals separated by a time interval Δt which is measured electronically. Assuming that the falling motion is uniformly accelerated and that the acceleration is known, is it possible from the above data to calculate the position (relative to the wires) from which the object is dropped? Analyze the problem algebraically, and present an algebraic formula as your solution. Solve the problem numerically for the particular case in which the wires are 5.00 ft apart and the time interval is measured to be 0.21 sec. It should be apparent that if Δs is "small enough," the average velocity $\Delta s/\Delta t$ is so little different from the instantaneous velocity at either wire that the height of fall can be calculated directly from $v^2/2a$. How small is "small enough"; i.e., how small does Δs have to be relative to the height of fall to make $v^2/2a$ in error by less than 10%? 5%? 1%? Present a general algebraic solution!

ANSWERS TO PROBLEMS

1.21. (a) about 330 m/sec   (b) about 1600 ft
       (c) between 4400 and 5500 ft   (e) $\Delta s = 1100\,\Delta t/2N$

1.22. (b) 5.86×10^{12} mi; 9.45×10^{15} m; that is, about 10^{16} m

1.23. $t = v_B t_0/(v_A - v_B)$; 1.0 hr

1.25. Assuming acceleration uniform and reproducible: $a = -3.9$ m/sec²;   (b) 4.3 m
       (c) $s = -137$ m, meaningless since body stops at $t = 1.5$ sec

1.27. (a) 11.6 ft; 1.3 sec   (b) 2.6 sec   (c) 0.39 sec and 2.2 sec   (d) $v = \pm 12.5$ ft/sec
       (going up and coming down, respectively)

1.28. 6.5 ft above upper wire

SUPPLEMENTARY READING AND STUDY

For treatment and problems at a somewhat more elementary level:
  Physics, Physical Science Study Committee. Boston: D. C. Heath, 1960, Chapter 5

For a somewhat more advanced treatment:
  Physics for Students of Science and Engineering, R. Resnick and D. Halliday. New York: John Wiley & Sons, 1960, Chapters 1–3

CHAPTER 2

Gravity, Levity, and Free Fall

2.1 INTRODUCTION

The preceding chapter presented a few glimpses of Galileo's attitudes and a few snatches of his rhetoric, but emphasis was placed on the science of kinematics as we see and talk about it now, after three hundred years of "modern" scientific thought. Intellectual involvement in a discipline, however, is not just a matter of mastering and applying its language and its concepts. The latter mastery is essential if one is to understand the discipline at all, but depth of insight is lost if one does not stand back and look at what has been done—at the context in which new ideas arose; at what made these ideas successful; at their limitations and range of applicability; at their influence, inhibiting or fruitful, in the subsequent courses of discovery; at their significance in influencing our outlook toward the universe in which we live. These insights are essentially philosophical and historical in character and are a vital, living part of any study, be it natural science, literature, government, economics, sociology, history, or mathematics.

It is by no means easy to ask oneself critical, embarrassing questions about what he knows and what he does not know, to maintain an articulate, explicit awareness of philosophical facets and epistemology* of a discipline which he is studying or in which he is doing research. For the most part, the greatest investigators and creators of new ideas have been keenly sensitive to philosophical aspects of their achievements and make lucid statements about them in their writings. Then disciples of more limited intellectual range confine themselves to analysis and mastery of the end results, ignoring or overlooking the master's warnings and admonitions, endowing the original conceptual scheme with a rigidity its creator never intended and the creator with an inflexible authority to which he did not pretend. Few of us will be great innovators or synthesizers, but we can be more intelligent, perceptive disciples.

With this motivation, let us stand back and look at the science of kinematics, at Galileo's contribution to the history of ideas. No innovator, however original or profound, has created ideas out of a void; he starts with a body of thought, knowl-

---

* This term refers to theory or examination of knowledge—with particular reference to its limits and validity.

edge, and achievement built up by predecessors and contemporaries. Frequently, discovery is almost at hand in many places, among many individuals, and the discoverer cuts through some obstacle of language or attitude, failure of perception, or deference to outmoded authority. Newton once said that if he had seen further than others "it is by standing on ye shoulders of Giants." Among these giants was Galileo, and Galileo in turn stood on other shoulders. A brief narrative sketch is necessary to set the perspective.

2.2 ROOTS OF NATURAL SCIENCE IN WESTERN CIVILIZATION

The beginnings of arithmetic, geometry, physics, and astronomy are shrouded in prehistory. Chaldeans, Babylonians, Egyptians, Chinese—motivated most probably by needs of commerce, agriculture, religion, and war—had developed elaborate systems of counting and calculation; they were aware of geometrical relationships such as important constructions and the Pythagorean theorem (at least for certain special right triangles); they accumulated extensive records of astronomical observations which were available to, and played an important role in, the later astronomy of the Alexandrian Greeks, Hipparchus, and Claudius Ptolemy. The marvelous detective work of archeology keeps revealing more and more of the knowledge of the ancients and serves only to augment our respect for their achievements.

This body of prehistorical, essentially empirical and un-unified knowledge was well disseminated throughout the Mediterranean world at the beginning of historical times. With the rise of Greek civilization, there came a conscious, imaginative effort to incorporate the knowledge into a general view of the world, into the unending speculative search for principles of unity in nature and their relation to human life. In this way mathematical and scientific knowledge became undissociably connected with philosophical speculation concerning the nature of life, of the soul, of good and evil, of beauty and art, and of thought itself.

In the course of six centuries, to the advent of the Christian era, Hellenic and Hellenistic thinkers asked and discussed a major portion of the fundamental questions of logic, science, mathematics, and philosophy that concern western civilization to this day. Their conscious goal was to achieve a unity of knowledge—an explanation of the universe, of natural phenomena, and of the place and state of humankind. They wondered about numbers and infinity, about discreteness and continuity, about infinity in the large and infinity in the small, about patterns and symmetry, about regular figures and regular solids, about music and harmony and their relation to numbers, about force and motion, winds and tides, planets and stars, about the structure of matter, about the structure and life cycles of biological organisms, about the structure and physiological processes of the human body. To give the reader a sense of chronology, the dates of life and work of a number of leading Hellenic and Hellenistic thinkers are given in Table 2.1.1.

Among the early pre-Socratic philosophical schools, one of the most influential is that of the Pythagoreans. All of Greek philosophy has been strongly stamped by the Pythagorean tradition, and, through what seems to have been a very profound influence on Plato among others, the tradition was passed on into the European Ren-

TABLE 2.1.1

DATES OF A FEW OF THE GREAT PHILOSOPHERS,
MATHEMATICIANS, AND ASTRONOMERS OF ANTIQUITY

	Hellenic era		
Pythagoras	6th century	B.C.	Samos and Croton
Zeno of Elea	5th century	B.C.	Athens
Socrates	470–399	B.C.	Athens
Democritus	ca. 460–370	B.C.	Abdera
Plato	429–348	B.C.	Athens
Eudoxus	ca. 408–355	B.C.	Cnidos
Aristotle	384–322	B.C.	Athens
	Hellenistic era		
Euclid	ca. 300	B.C.	Alexandria
Archimedes	287–212	B.C.	Syracuse (Sicily)
Aristarchos of Samos	ca. 280–260	B.C.	Samos
Hipparchus	ca. 130	B.C.	Alexandria
Ptolemy	ca. 130–150	A.D.	Alexandria

aissance and into our own literary heritage. Pythagoras is a semi-legendary character about whom very little is known. It is likely that Pythagoras himself, or one of his followers, discovered a general *proof* of the relation between the hypotenuse and the legs of a right triangle; the relation itself was known prior to that time. Euclid in his *Elements* labels this theorem the "Theorem of Pythagoras" and thus transmits the name to us. In their search for unity of knowledge of nature, the Pythagoreans created the idea that nature is somehow constructed, dominated, and governed by number. They endowed numbers with shape and with sacred properties; they saw the world as made of lines, triangles, circles, squares, and regular solids; they saw perfection in the regularity of circles and spheres; they saw in numbers the clear, immutable perfection of underlying structure—the ideal beneath the gross realities of everyday appearance.

The Pythagoreans apparently discovered the simple numerical ratios existing between lengths of strings that produce musical scales and pleasing harmonies. To them this must have been a profound and thrilling confirmation of the primacy they ascribed to number and numerical idealization. Out of such combinations of insight and superstition, they fashioned a cult—a phenomenon not unknown even in this day. When someone among the Pythagoreans discovered the incommensurability of the side and diagonal of a square,* the cult was horrified by what was deemed an

---

* This refers to the discovery of what we now call *irrational numbers*, the particular "number" in question being $\sqrt{2}$. In our day, when we glibly learn in grade school to write endless fractions (without comprehending in our own words the logic of what we are doing), we lose sight of the deep problem that disturbed the Greeks and which was, in fact, not satisfactorily solved until the second half of the nineteenth century. The only numbers con-

ceived by the ancients were what we now call the "natural" numbers, 1, 2, 3, 4, etc. Quantities such as lengths, areas, or volumes were compared with each other as ratios of whole numbers q/p. A ratio was not thought of as a fraction or mixed number in the sense of being a new number in its own right. It was intuitively supposed that any two quantities could be compared with each other as a ratio of whole numbers simply by making the numbers sufficiently large. Thus the ratio of the diagonal of a square to the side, q/p, should be expressible as a ratio of whole numbers q and p if one simply adopts a small enough unit of length; i.e., cuts the lengths in question into a sufficiently large integral number of small segments. This is by no means a strange or unreasonable notion, and the fact that it is impossible, *in principle*, to achieve such a ratio comes as a shock of insight to many people even now. The argument runs as follows: Assume that a unit of measurement is selected so that q and p are both whole numbers and that the ratio q/p is in its most reduced form with no further common divisors (a ratio such as 27/19 or 10/7 or 511/361). Under these circumstances not more than one of the numbers, p or q, can be even; if both are even, they have a common divisor of 2 and are not in reduced form. The Pythagorean Theorem requires: $q^2 = 2p^2$, and we write $q/p = \sqrt{2}$. We know that q^2 must be an even number, since it is twice p^2. But q^2 can be even only if q itself is even. Therefore, if an unreducible ratio of integers q/p exists as assumed, p *cannot* be even because q *must* be even. Let us examine p. Since q is shown to be necessarily even, we can express it as twice some other number; $q = 2r$. Then

$$p^2 = \frac{q^2}{2} = \frac{4r^2}{2} = 2r^2,$$

from which it follows that p must also be even, but this contradicts the assumption of an irreducible ratio. From this we are forced to conclude that such an irreducible ratio *does not exist* and that if the side of the square is divided into an integral number of units, *however small*, the diagonal will never contain an integral number of the same units. Mathematical science now recognizes objects such as $\sqrt{2}$ as a class of numbers within the overall number system, and, retaining a note from ancient tradition, calls such numbers "irrational." It was this discovery of the irrational that was such a shock to Pythagorean superstition. (Suggested problem: Prove that $\sqrt{3}$ is also irrational. Start with $q^2/p^2 = 3$. See *Numbers, Rational and Irrational*, by I. Niven. New York: Random House, 1961.)

---

imperfection or flaw in the creed, and it is said that an attempt was made to keep the knowledge secret from the uninitiated, it being referred to as the "unutterable."

In one line of inheritance from Pythagorean philosophy lies numerological superstition; in another line lie Galileo and the modern field of mathematical physics.

2.3   HELLENIC PHILOSOPHY

The full flowering of Hellenic philosophy is associated with the Athenean schools of Socrates, Plato, and Aristotle (the period 470–322 B.C.), and with other great names such as Eudoxus (408–355 B.C.), Democritus (460–370 B.C.), Epicurus (340–270 B.C.), and Zenon of Cition (about 300 B.C., founder of the Stoic school). Three centuries of evolution of Hellenic thought were marked by a slow, profound departure from a primitive, animistic view of nature to a more sophisticated, "causal" view. With the development of mechanical techniques in agriculture, commerce, and medicine, there came a stronger awareness of a distinction between inanimate and living matter, a gradual atrophy of the animistic view that endowed sticks and stones, water and air with soul, spirit, and capricious volition; there came a more conscious tendency to seek for "causes" and regular processes, for rational explanation of physical events in terms of systematic properties of inanimate matter. Some of the properties with which Greek philosophy endowed inanimate matter may sound highly animistic to us today, but this should not becloud the magnitude of the step. The process was a long and slow one; it did not attain full maturity until the seventeenth century.

As C. C. Gillispie says,*

"Albert Einstein once remarked that there is no difficulty in understanding why China or India did not create science. The problem is why Europe did, for science is a most arduous and unlikely undertaking. The answer lies in Greece. Ultimately science derives from the legacy of Greek philosophy. The Egyptians, it is true, developed surveying techniques and conducted certain surgical operations with notable finesse. The Babylonians disposed of numerical devices of great ingenuity for predicting the patterns of planets. But no Oriental civilization graduated beyond technique to curiosity about things in general. Of all the triumphs of the speculative genius of Greece, the most unexpected, the most truly novel was precisely its rational conception of the cosmos as an orderly whole, working by laws discoverable in thought. The Greek transition from myth to knowledge was the origin of science as of philosophy. . . ."

There were numerous schools of philosophy with differing views of ethics and morality, different theories of the structure of the universe, of the existence or nonexistence of atoms and a "void," but underlying these differences was a common tradition. Time and space, however, do not allow us to delve adequately into the history of classical philosophy. The most powerful impact on subsequent European thought came from the works of Plato and Aristotle, and we shall try to adumbrate enough of the character of their views and theories to make intelligible the context in which we perceive Galileo.

2.4 PLATONIC "IDEALISM"

In Plato (429–348 B.C.) one finds a strong strain of mysticism and continuity of the Pythagorean tradition. He found "reality" only in the pure ideas captured in abstract thought; behind each imperfect form that one actually perceives in nature— lines, triangles, circles, horses, trees—lies the perfect "idea" of the form itself. Mathematical relations are eternal and ideal and therefore founded in truth and reality not attainable to the world of mundane things. "That which is apprehensible by thought with a rational account," he says, "is the thing which is always unchangeably real;

---

* *The Edge of Objectivity*, C. C. Gillispie, Princeton, N. J.: Princeton University Press, 1960. A discussion of the history of a number of crucial scientific ideas.

whereas that which is the object of belief together with unreasoning sensation is the thing that becomes and passes away but never has real being. Again, all that becomes must needs become by the agency of some cause; for without a cause nothing can come to be."

Plato saw little relevance of mathematics to physics, and would never have embarked on what we now view as a modern line of scientific thought. For him, uncertain physics was too far removed from the pure, abstract truth and reality of mathematical relationship. One can conceive of a line tangent to a circle, but the finest compass and straightedge will not construct a circle and line with but one point in common.

Plato was profoundly impressed by the arithmetical regularities the Pythagoreans had discovered in musical intervals, and injected similar regularities of harmonic interval and perfect number into mystical surmises concerning proportions which the World Artificer (Demiurge) had used in constructing the World Soul, and into a vision of astronomy and the structure of the universe. Since neither Soul nor heavenly bodies were made of mundane earth, but of perfect "quintessences," they did not partake of the unreality of physical things and could be conceived in mathematical purity, the orbits of the heavenly bodies being necessarily associated with circles or with rotating spheres. Plato's cosmology is set forth in *The Timaios*. George Sarton, a leading historian of ancient science,* comments: "The astrologic nonsense that has done so much harm in the Western world and is still poisoning weak-minded people today was derived from the *Timaios*, and Plato's astrology was itself an offshoot of the Babylonian one. In justice to Plato it must be added that his own astrology remained serene and spiritual and did not degenerate into petty fortune-telling. To his contemplative mind the planets are like perfect clocks which reveal the march of time, the rhythms of the universal soul."

Unsound and unscientific though much of Plato's edifice may be, his philosophy was nevertheless in the tradition of viewing the "cosmos as an orderly whole, working by laws discoverable in thought." It seems probable that his own teaching, and that of the great academy he founded, played a significant role in the development of geometrical analysis preceding the monumental synthesis by Euclid. And, for a time, Plato was a teacher of Aristotle, through whom the bulk of Hellenic science was transmitted to later generations.

2.5   ARISTOTLE

Aristotle was born in 384 B.C. in Macedonia, the son of a physician. At the age of 17 he went to Athens to complete his education and became a disciple of Plato at the academy. He stayed at the academy for twenty years, left it in 347 shortly after Plato's death, was tutor of the young Alexander from 343 to 340 when the latter acceded to Philip's throne, returned to Athens in 335 to found a new school, the Lyceum, and died in 322 shortly after the death of his patron Alexander.

---

* *A History of Science*, George Sarton. Cambridge, Mass.: Harvard University Press, 1952. Subsequent quotations from Sarton are taken from the same source.

Aristotle could not long have been a disciple of Plato in any subservient sense. Despite their similar points of departure, and similar intellectual goals, Aristotle's scientific philosophy is fundamentally different, in some respects directly opposite to the Platonic. To him, reality lay in physics—in forms, processes, qualities that could never be completely described in terms of the precise, abstract, unreal truths of mathematics. He thus agreed with Plato on the irrelevance of mathematics to physics but differed as to the reason.

Aristotle's writings are encyclopedic in scope. He set as his goal a synthesis of the knowledge of his time, and into his works he distills the entire philosophical heritage of his day, reinforced and refined by his own insights and observations. The corpus of Aristotelian writings covers logic, mechanics, physics, astronomy, meteorology, botany, zoology, psychology, ethics, economics, politics, metaphysics, and literature. Mathematical discussion is scattered in various relevant places; and he gives a cautious, penetrating discussion of continuity and infinity. Biologists still marvel at the accuracy and perceptiveness of some of his zoological descriptions and wonder at the credulity he exhibits in others. He wrote the first treatise on logic, clarifying the nature of proof by deduction (*if . . . then* reasoning), forms of the syllogism, statements of propositions.

Aristotle's fundamental view toward the properties of inanimate matter and the behavior of living organisms derived from Plato and also reflected the prevailing conception of the time: all processes and properties of matter, all natural phenomena, were conceived as being shaped by an innate purpose and directed toward an end or goal. Objects of various kinds held "natural places" in the order of the universe and tended toward those places if allowed to do so: earth and water seek positions closer to the center of the earth; air and fire move upward; things change because of inherent purposes—a striving to approach or attain some predestined consummation or perfection. In philosophical terminology this view is called *teleological.* Although teleology has long since ceased to play a serious role in the physical sciences, many of our locutions, ways of saying things about physical situations, bear a teleological cast; and in the biological sciences some groups still tend to take a teleological view of biological processes, of the development and function of physiological organs, and of the nature of organisms themselves.

Sarton, ending his paragraph with tongue in cheek, describes Aristotle as believing

"that mechanism and purpose are complementary and inseparable aspects; in the study of nature one must seek for a mechanical explanation or for the leading reason; sometimes the mechanism is clearer, sometimes the reason. In his time practically no mechanism (for example, a physiologic mechanism) was conceivable; hence there remained only the teleologic explanation. To a hard-boiled man of science of today such an explanation is mere verbiage. It is futile to ask the 'why' of things, he would say, it suffices to answer as carefully as possible the question 'how?'. Aristotle was trying prematurely to answer the question 'why' and was giving that question first place. Was he all wrong? The question might be premature, but it was not futile; it had in a first approximation a guiding value . . . teleologic explanations, even if insufficient, are yet very useful; every man of science uses them wittingly or unwittingly; the purpose of an organ helps us to understand and remember its anatomy and physiology. . . . The teleological point of view implied the concept of evolution, evolution toward an ideal, progress. To understand things we must penetrate their purpose, their genesis and growth. Aristotle applied these ideas to natural history, rather than to human history; otherwise he would have been one of the ancestors of the historians of science."

2.6 ARISTOTELIAN PHYSICS

In subsequent chapters we shall have occasion to trace some of the influences of Aristotelian cosmology, the model of the universe of earth, planets, suns, and stars; but our present concern is with Aristotelian physics—in particular its conception of motion. Earthly substances, located beneath the sphere of the moon, were viewed as consisting of four elements: fire, air, water, and earth. The changeless heavenly bodies were made of a fifth element not associated with the earth—an incorruptible quintessence or ether. Water and earth were endowed with "gravity," an innate tendency to move toward the center of the universe; fire and air were endowed with "levity," a tendency to move away from the center.* Materials in general are made of mixtures of the four elements in various proportions: fire on being added to water is seen to produce "air"; when ordinary water is boiled away, there is always to be found a residue of "earth," etc. Bodies move in a direction determined by the element that dominates the composition. "All bodies both rest and move naturally and by constraint," writes Aristotle. "A body moves naturally to that place where it rests without constraint, and rests without constraint in that place to which it naturally moves. It moves by constraint to that place in which it rests by constraint. . . . Further, if a certain movement is enforced, then its opposite is natural." The earth must be at the center of the universe since that is where earth rests naturally, and its tendency toward such rest must long since have been accomplished. There can be no other worlds, because if there were, earth and fire would not be able to find one natural place, and the organized world as we know it could not exist. (These tenets subsequently proved very congenial to medieval Christian theology.)

Motion of a projected stone or of an arrow was viewed as a combination of "forced" or "violent" motion and "natural" motion of earthly material toward the "center."

---

* Note how gravity and levity are treated as *intrinsic properties* of particular materials, and not as "interactions" between bodies, and sense how profoundly modern science has altered this view, among other things completely eliminating the concept of "levity." Note also how the words gravity and levity have analogous meanings, in an entirely different context, as sobriety and frivolity. Such analogies, or allegories, in scientific and everyday language are very common and by no means accidental; one usage illuminates the other and gives us a deeper perception of the language that we use. In many instances the evolution of a clear, new scientific concept has been characterized by the stripping away of most of the allegory surrounding a particular term.

All motion was seen to encounter resistance, from rubbing of solid bodies against each other and from the surrounding medium of air and water. Resistance to motion was thus seen to be a fundamental, all-pervasive property. Aristotle, without the tools for making quantitative observations and probably without the conception of such a possibility, conjectured that the *speed* of any body is directly proportional to the "force" pushing or pulling it and inversely proportional to the resistance of the medium. In our algebraic notation we would translate this statement into the symbols

$$v \propto \frac{F}{R} \quad \text{or} \quad v = k\frac{F}{R}. \tag{2.6.1}$$

(Read the symbol $\propto$ as "proportional to." The letter k denotes a "proportionality constant.")

Thus, in the absence of a resisting medium, the resistance R would be zero and the speed of a motion infinite. This suited Aristotle's preconceptions perfectly. Motion in complete emptiness is inconceivable in any case (since a stone would not "know" which way to go); infinite speed is impossible; therefore an empty void or vacuum cannot exist. With this argument Aristotle joined Plato in rejecting the speculations of Democritus concerning a structure of matter based on arrangements and motion of invisibly small, discrete "atoms" in a void. With this argument he also justified the famous doctrine of *horror vacui* ("Nature abhors a vacuum") that left another conceptual obstacle to be overcome in seventeenth-century science.

Aristotle concluded that the speed of a falling body should be proportional to its weight and that the speed should increase as it came closer to its natural place. Hence he supposed that in free fall the speed should be proportional to the distance fallen. (See the quotations from Galileo's *Two New Sciences* in Section 1.10.)

Without a driving force F in Eq. (2.6.1), a body would have zero speed, and therefore Aristotle was left with the sticky point* as to what keeps the stone and arrow moving in flight. To explain the obvious fact that they do move, he invoked the observation that moving bodies are able to impart motion to each other on collision and suggested that "violent" motion of an object through a resisting medium had some of the aspects of a collision, in that the medium (air) was set in motion by being pushed aside and then returned this motion to the stone by closing in and "colliding" or pushing it from behind. One must admire the ingenuity of the conception even if, from an unfair modern vantage point, he finds it unpersuasive. Although Aristotle's conception turns out to be fundamentally incorrect, his appeal to the phenomenon of collision foreshadows later developments. In the seventeenth century, clarification of the "laws of motion" came largely through experimental study of collisions or "percussion."

---

* Sticky points have been present in practically every great conceptual development of modern science—in Newton's theory, in nineteenth-century views of electricity and magnetism, in atomic physics, etc. In retrospect, it has repeatedly been shown that these gnawing, bothersome issues should have received more critical attention and less glossing over. As a result, present-day physical science has become very much more sensitive to delicate logical, epistemological issues than was science of an earlier day.

As a final note in our sketch of the two towering figures who projected separate traditions into subsequent European philosophy, we have this pungent assessment of George Sarton's:

"Aristotle was sound but dull; Plato was more attractive but as unsound as could be. Aristotle and his contemporaries built the best foundation for the magnificent achievements of Euclid, Archimedes, and Apollonius, while Plato's seductive example encouraged all the follies of arithmology and induced other superstitions. Aristotle was the honest teacher, Plato the magician, the Pied Piper; it is not surprising that the followers of the latter were far more numerous than those of the former. But we should always remember with gratitude that many mathematicians owed their vocation to Plato; they obtained from him the love of mathematics, but they did not otherwise follow him, and their own genius was their salvation."

From a perspective of twenty-three centuries it is temptingly easy to view Plato, Aristotle, and their successors as credulous, painfully naïve individuals who theorized wildly from inadequate premises, endowed matter with fantastic properties, prematurely asked impossible questions, and set unattainable philosophical goals. But we must remember that Plato and Aristotle had certain definite objectives: They were attempting to organize a qualitative synthesis of all human experience, to view such experience as an organic whole—a much more complex and ambitious undertaking than that assumed by the enterprise we now call "science." We must also remember that our present insights came slowly; that in societies lacking the Greek heritage they did not come at all; and finally we should ask ourselves what naïveté future generations, given still deeper knowledge and perspective of time, will find in our own vaunted sophistication.

2.7 TRANSMISSION OF GREEK LEARNING TO RENAISSANCE EUROPE

During his short, brilliant reign, Alexander founded the city of Alexandria in Egypt. This polyglot, cosmopolitan city became in the following centuries the intellectual and commercial capital of the Mediterranean world. The library and center of scholarly research called the Museum, stimulated, in men of diverse origins and races, a productivity as rich and brilliant as that of Athens in its prime. Historians refer to this as the Hellenistic era, the adjective indicating that, although influenced by Greece, it was no longer purely Greek.

In the centuries between 300 B.C. and 200 A.D., Hellenistic science produced some of the greatest mathematicians and astronomers of all time. Euclid wrote his deeply influential synthesis of geometry in which, refining the experience of past ages, he selected a small number of fundamental axioms and postulates as a starting point and then rigorously deduced all remaining geometrical knowledge in the form of theorems arranged in invincibly logical order. Eratosthenes estimated the radius of the earth. Hipparchus, having calculated the first trigonometric tables from arithmetical-geometrical considerations, had available with high numerical precision the trigonometric properties of very small angles and angles very close to 90°. With this information at his disposal, he measured the size of the earth and the size and distance of the moon.* Hipparchus formalized existing astronomical observations by assigning combinations of various circular motions to the heavenly bodies, with the earth as a primary center. He borrowed the model from Hellenic tradition but endowed it with numbers and hence with numerical *predictability*. This work was later refined, elaborated and expanded by Claudius Ptolemy in the *Almagest*, and became the astronomy of medieval Europe.

But it would be illusory to view the Hellenic and Hellenistic eras as periods of unalloyed beauty and enlightenment. Savagery and war prevailed on many levels. This was a slave-owning society, with masses of people living in abject poverty and disease. Enlightenment and release from superstition were available only to the intellectual rich. Sarton writes of the kindly efforts of the philosopher Epicurus:

"In spite of Epicurean efforts, the pagan superstitions did not decrease; the lack of political and economic stability tended, on the contrary, to increase them. The best of ancient religion was being gradually debased, corrupted; its poetry was lost. . . . There remained only rituals, processions, pilgrimages, and superstitions of every kind. The religious vacuum was filled with fantastic ideas borrowed from Europe and other parts of the Near East. . . . The plain people were so deeply afflicted, their miseries were so many and so complex, that they abandoned rational improvement and thought only of 'salvation'—a kind of mystical salvation in another world."

Roman conquest, the rise of Christianity, and subsequent Moslem invasions finally destroyed the intellectual flowering of the Hellenistic world. The library at Alexandria was burned several times. Stories of the survival of certain crucial manuscripts, such as those of Aristotle, read like Sindbad's adventures.

Greek learning was preserved and reintroduced into Europe indirectly by the rise of a great new tradition of Arab scholarship during the ninth and tenth centuries A.D. Works of Aristotle and of other philosophers were available in Arabic and were accompanied by extensive commentaries and extensions by scholars such as Ibn Rushd (known as Averroes) and many others. During the twelfth century, European scholars became acquainted with Greek works in translation from Arabic into Latin. The Church was inclined to suppress what it viewed as a revival of paganism, but some of its greatest scholars, such as St. Augustine and St. Thomas Aquinas, found in Greek thought much that was congenial and transposable into Christian doctrine. St. Thomas in particular (thirteenth century), approaching theology in almost Euclidean fashion, wove Aristotle's cosmology into a proof of the existence of God.

---

* For a simple, exciting description of Hipparchus' achievements, see Chapter 5 of *Mathematics in Western Culture*, by Morris Kline. New York: Oxford University Press, 1953.

Aristotle became the supreme authority in matters of philosophy and science, and Ptolemy's *Almagest* became the sanctioned view of the organization of the universe.

Intellectual followers of Thomas Aquinas became the recognized scholars of medieval Europe. They occupied professorial chairs in the universities and wrote extensively on theological, philosophical, and scientific subjects within the framework of Aristotelian logic and physics and of Ptolemaic cosmology. These scholars are usually referred to as "scholastics" or "school men," and their doctrines and teachings as "scholastic thought." University influence in Galileo's day (sixteenth and early seventeenth century) was still primarily scholastic. His teachers, and subsequently his colleagues, were of this tradition, and he spent much time in his mature years debating and attacking scholastic conceptions which resisted change when change was clearly overdue.

2.8 GALILEO'S PRECURSORS

We should not acquire the impression, however, that Galileo single-handedly, in shining armor, slew the dragon of scholasticism; revolutions in conceptual thought do not occur in so simple a fashion. Criticism of Aristotelian concepts of motion can be traced at least as far back as Hipparchus. Modern historical research has revealed a continuous thread of thought, from early times, questioning the assertion embodied in Eq. (2.6.1). One of the first Christian philosopher-scientists, John Philoponus of the sixth-century Alexandrian school, proposed that velocity depends on the *difference* between driving and resisting effects rather than on the ratio, as in Eq. (2.6.1). He also suggested that throwing or projection endows the body with a property which tends to keep it going. This property came to be called *impetus*. Both these ideas strike deeply at Aristotelian conceptions: the first undermines the argument against motion in a void; the second endows the object *itself* with a property that keeps it moving rather than assigning this function to collision of the surrounding medium.

Historians trace these notions through the medieval Arab commentators and find them re-emerging in Europe in fourteenth-century schools at Oxford and at the University of Paris, with which are associated the names of William of Ockham, Jean Buridan, Nicholas of Oresme, and others. Ockham is noted for his adherence to a philosophical doctrine that it is inadvisable, in lines of thought and explanation, to postulate any more entities, properties, or tendencies than absolutely necessary, and that one should cut away superfluous assumptions and attributes. This doctrine is usually called "Ockham's razor"; in a day of numerous assumptions of occult qualities and arbitrary properties, it struck directly at the very foundations of scholasticism and Aristotelian teleology. For this reason many writers regard Ockham as among the first precursors of modern scientific thought.

Followers of the impetus school, somewhat more quantitative than Philoponus in their theorizing, visualized impetus as a product of the mass of the moving body and some function of its velocity, not being clear as to the precise character of the latter. (This idea contains the seeds of the modern concept of momentum, eventually clearly defined as a vector quantity by John Wallis and used mathematically by Newton.)

The impetus school followed a rule for describing uniformly accelerated motion, originally formulated at Merton College in Oxford. This rule held that "a uniformly accelerated or retarded movement is equivalent, so far as space traversed in given time is concerned, to a uniform movement of which the velocity is equal throughout to the instantaneous velocity possessed by the uniformly accelerated or retarded movement at the middle instant of time."[*] This rule is, of course, equivalent to

$$\bar{v} = \frac{v_0 + v}{2},$$

which played so crucial a role in our derivation of the kinematic equations in Chapter 1. Lacking an algebraic formulation, Oresme expressed the concept in geometric form in terms of half the altitude of a triangle, as illustrated in Fig. 2.8.1. Eventually we find essentially the same triangle appearing in Theorem I, Proposition I in the Third Day of Galileo's *Two New Sciences*.

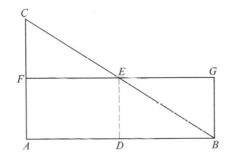

Fig. 2.8.1. Oresme's geometrical representation of the "Merton Rule."

Triangle *ABC* represents the displacement occurring in a uniformly changing motion, while the rectangle *ABGF* represents displacement in a motion at constant velocity. If the rectangle is drawn so as to have an area equal to that of the triangle, the altitude *ED* of the rectangle is half the altitude *AC* of the triangle. With altitude taken to represent "intensity" or velocity of the motion, the uniform motion described by the rectangle will achieve the same result as the changing motion described by the triangle.

Rapid growth of printing after the middle of the fifteenth century distributed the writings of the "impetus" schools throughout Europe. They influenced the scientific views of men like Leonardo da Vinci and were well known in the universities of Italy, where Galileo subsequently studied and taught. Galileo frequently uses the word impetus, and early papers from his days at Pisa have been shown to reflect the influence of Philoponus and the Paris school.

---

* *Robert Grosseteste and the Origins of Experimental Science*, A. C. Crombie. New York: Oxford University Press, 1953, page 93. See also *The Science of Mechanics in the Middle Ages*, Marshall Clagett. Madison, Wis.: University of Wisconsin Press, 1959, Chapters 5 and 6.

FIGURE 2.9.1

2.9   GALILEO GALILEI (1564–1642): BIOGRAPHICAL NOTE

Galileo Galilei (Fig. 2.9.1) was born in Pisa in 1564. His father was a poor but well-born and cultivated Florentine who communicated to his son a love of poetry and music and a knowledge of the classics. He started as a student of medicine at the University of Pisa, but his discovery and reading of Euclid and Archimedes attracted him into mathematics and natural philosophy. His originality and unusual capacity for knowledge were obviously respected; at the age of 26 he was appointed to the chair of mathematics at Pisa. Here he discovered the isochronism* of the pendulum; here also he began his attacks on the entrenched Aristotelian conceptions of his scholastic colleagues. One of Galileo's students, Vincenzo Viviani, was responsible many years later for the famous story, now somewhat discredited by modern historical criticism, concerning an experiment of dropping unequal weights from the Leaning Tower to demonstrate that they fell with equal speeds, contrary to Aristotle's assertion. Galileo's few writings dating from that time seem to indicate that although he had reached the point of questioning Aristotle's assertion of the infinite velocity in a vacuum he was still visualizing a force as necessary for the maintenance of uniform velocity, and expected objects of different weight to fall at different speeds if air resistance were unimportant.

---

* The fact that the time of a complete cycle or swing is the same regardless of the amplitude of the swing.

In 1592 Galileo moved to the University of Padua where the great anatomist Vesalius had lectured and where Copernicus and Harvey studied. While at Padua he invented a primitive thermometer and began his epoch-making researches in astronomy which later brought him trouble with the Inquisition. In 1610 he returned to Florence as mathematician and philosopher to the Grand Duke. During this remaining period of his life, he published many papers on physics and astronomy and his two successful and deeply influential books: *Dialogue Concerning the Two Chief World Systems* (1632) and *Discourses Concerning Two New Sciences* (1638), from which we have already quoted. The latter volume, written while he was going blind, was surreptitiously sent out of Italy and published in Holland while Galileo was under technical arrest by the Inquisition. The poet John Milton, who visited him in 1638, wrote, "There it was I found and visited the famous Galileo, grown old, a prisoner of the Inquisition for thinking in Astronomy otherwise than the Franciscan and Dominican licensers of thought." Galileo died at the age of 78 on January 8, 1642, the year of Newton's birth.

2.10 GALILEO'S INFLUENCE

In view of the significant achievements of Galileo's precursors, how is it that he, in particular, has become the widely accepted symbol of the end of scholastic domination and the beginning of modern science?

Galileo had a great literary gift, profound physical intuition, imaginative originality, a lucidly clear philosophical view of what his ideas implied. He was a great polemicist and propagandist; he wrote brilliantly and persuasively, sometimes with vitriolic humor. He was, intentionally, a popularizer of science: In a letter to a friend concerning his book on sunspots published in 1613, Galileo says, "I wrote in the colloquial tongue because I must have everyone able to read it . . . I am induced to do this by seeing how young men are sent through the universities at random to be made physicians, philosophers, and so on; thus many of them are committed to professions for which they are unsuited while other men who would be fitted for these are taken up by family cares and other occupations. . . .   The latter are furnished with horse sense, but because they are unable to read things which are 'Greek' to them, they become convinced that in those big books are great new things of logic and philosophy and still more that is way over their heads. Now I want them to see that just as nature has given to them, as well as to philosophers, eyes with which to see her works, so she has also given them brains capable of penetrating and understanding them." (His objective was not in conflict with that of modern courses in science for nonscience students.)

Long before publication of the *Two New Sciences*, Galileo's work and discoveries, particularly in astronomy, had made him famous throughout Europe. His view of motion was published at the height of his fame, in the mature period of the Renaissance, at a time ripe for a *coup de grace* to reactionary scholasticism.

In the following sections we shall discuss some facets of Galileo's philosophy that make his work and influence distinct from that of his predecessors.

2.11   LIMITATION OF THE SCOPE OF INQUIRY

Galileo very consciously and explicitly restricted the *scope* of his inquiry in order to master and clarify one significant issue at a time.   After some discussion of the definition of acceleration and of instantaneous velocities of bodies in free fall, Sagredo suggests,

> "From these considerations it appears to me that we may obtain a proper solution of the problem discussed by philosophers, namely, what causes the acceleration in the motion of heavy bodies?"

and Salviati stops this line with,

> "The present does not seem to be the proper time to investigate the cause of acceleration of natural motion concerning which various opinions have been expressed by various philosophers, some explaining it by attraction to the center, others to repulsion between the very small parts of the body, while still others attribute it to a certain stress in the surrounding medium which closes in behind the falling body and drives it from one of its positions to another.   Now, all these fantasies and others too, ought to be examined; but it is not really worth while.   At present it is the purpose of our Author merely to investigate and to demonstrate some of the properties of accelerated motion (whatever the cause of this acceleration may be) . . . and if we find the properties of accelerated motion . . . are realized in freely falling bodies, we may conclude that the assumed definition includes such a motion of falling bodies. . . ."

In other words Galileo firmly rejects an Aristotelian move to provide a complete explanation of all aspects of falling motion right from the beginning of the inquiry. Salviati's statement has a very modern stance.

As we shall repeatedly illustrate, there exists no one method of modern science which can be made into a formula or prescription for an infallible procedure which unerringly leads to truth.   But fruitful and successful steps in the winning of new knowledge sometimes have broad characteristics in common.   One of the most clearly notable characteristics of modern scientific investigation is the art of limiting the scope of inquiry in such a way as to ensure winning of one step of understanding at a time, avoiding the distraction and confusion introduced by premature or irrelevant questions.   But this procedure is not foolproof, and in some cases may serve to conceal important issues and inhibit solution of a problem.   Deciding when and to what extent to restrict an inquiry is still the hallmark of individual genius.

2.12   IDEALIZATION AND THE ROLE OF EXPERIMENT

Galileo was well versed in Aristotelian conceptions concerning universal resistance to motion and the necessity of applying a force to maintain a given velocity.   He performed experiments with bodies falling through liquids, and must have been keenly sensitive to his inability to make direct observations of displacements, velocities, and

time intervals in free fall. In the face of these difficulties, he apparently became aware
of the immensely powerful tool that resides in "thinking away" interfering effects.
It occurred to him to ask what natural motion would be like in the absence of resistance, even if such a physical condition could not be attained in full purity. In
the steps of Philoponos and the impetus school, he was not hampered by an Aristotelian misconception of impossibility of motion in a vacuum. And it further occurred to him that falling motion could be studied *indirectly* by "diluting" or slowing
it down on an inclined plane.

Galileo convinced himself that gravitationally governed motion on an inclined
plane was uniformly accelerated in the sense defined in Chapter 1. His attitude toward experiment is clearly revealed in this context. He anticipated that such motion
is uniformly accelerated only in an ideal limit in which rubbing against the plane and
air resistance are "thought away." Therefore, to test the idea experimentally, he
made his plane as smooth as possible and used a bronze ball sufficiently heavy to
minimize the effects of air resistance. Salviati says,

> "So far as experiments go they have not been neglected by the Author; and
> often, in his company I have attempted in the following manner to assure myself
> that the acceleration experienced by falling bodies is that above described.
>
> "A piece of wooden scantling, about 12 cubits* long, half a cubit wide, and
> three finger-breadths thick, was taken; on its edge was cut a channel a little more
> than one finger in breadth; having made this groove very straight, smooth and pol-
> ished, and having lined it with parchment, also as smooth and polished as pos-
> sible, we rolled along it a hard, smooth, and very round bronze ball. Having
> placed this board in a sloping position, by lifting one end some one or two cubits
> above the other, we rolled the ball along the channel, noting in a manner pres-
> ently to be described, the time required to make the descent. We repeated this
> experiment more than once in order to measure the time with an accuracy such
> that the deviation between two observations never exceeded one tenth of a
> pulse beat. Having performed this operation and having assured ourselves of
> its reliability, we now rolled the ball only one quarter the length of the channel;
> and having measured the time of descent, we found it precisely one half the
> former. Next we tried other distances, comparing the time for the whole length
> with that for the half, or two thirds, or three fourths, or indeed for any fraction;
> in such experiments, repeated a full hundred times, we always found that the
> spaces traversed were to each other as the square of the times, and this was true
> for all inclinations of the plane." [Salviati then describes the running-water
> system for measuring time intervals which has already been quoted in Section 1.3.]

PROBLEM 2.1. Galileo obviously could not measure acceleration directly at various
instants and show that it was always the same. If we translate the quotation given above
into algebraic form, Galileo says that the displacements from rest of the ball rolling
down the plane conform to the relation $\Delta s \propto t^2$.

* One cubit is equivalent to about 18 to 20 inches.

Explain in your own words the several steps of reasoning that are involved. How does Galileo's result support the hypothesis that the rolling motion is uniformly accelerated? What kind of result might have necessitated a conclusion that the motion is not uniformly accelerated? Refer back at this point to your discussion of Problem 1.17 at the end of Chapter 1.

Again Galileo exhibits a very modern stance. He describes an experiment conceived according to a particular logical plan—a strategy, designed to test, in *mathematical* form, a particular, preconceived hypothesis. The hypothesis is confirmed, and then further inferences are drawn from it as a basis for subsequent thought. The experiment is addressed to an idealized situation—motion in the absence of resistive interference and along a straight line. In actuality a real straight line does not exist, and resistance is not zero, but this does not vitiate the significance of the results.

The remark to the effect that "this was true for all inclinations of the plane" is crucial. Galileo extrapolates* this result: He argues that the acceleration will be uniform for *any* inclination of the plane, including the steep inclinations at which he can no longer make observations because of the excessive speed of the motion; he argues that the same characteristic must persist into the limiting situation in which the plane is vertical and the motion freely falling. This arguing to a limiting case, unattainable by direct means, is again part of the process of idealization, of "thinking away" of obstacles, and has a very modern tone.

Putting together all his evidence and idealizations, Galileo drew the inference that not only is free fall uniformly accelerated, but all bodies in free fall have the same acceleration—the same, that is, in the absence of rubbing and resistance. (See Fig. 2.12.1 on opposite page.) He foresaw what is certainly not obvious to common-sense experience, that a feather, a piece of paper, a grain of sand, and a cannonball would all fall together in a vacuum. But he had to discern this in an act of imagination and not in physical reality. Not until the invention of the vacuum pump about 12 years after Galileo's death was it possible to show directly that disparate chunks of matter indeed do fall together in a vacuum.

Galileo attacks the Aristotelian disputations on this matter:

Simplicio: "Your discussion is really admirable; yet I do not find it easy to be-believe that a bird shot falls as swiftly as a cannon ball."

Salviati: "Why not say a grain of sand as rapidly as a grindstone? But, Simplicio, I trust you will not follow the example of many others who divert the discussion from its main intent and fasten upon some statement of mine which lacks a hairbreadth of the truth and, under this hair, hide the fault of another which is as big as a ship's cable. Aristotle says that an iron ball of 100 pounds falling

---

* *Extrapolation* implies the act of extending an idea or a curve of data into a range in which the idea has not been tested and observations have not been made. This is a vitally important and notoriously dangerous procedure. It leads on various occasions to useful results, imaginative discoveries, and sometimes to abysmal errors.

from a height of 100 cubits reaches the ground before a one-pound ball has fallen a single cubit. I say that they arrive at the same time. You find, on making the experiment, that the larger outstrips the smaller by two finger breadths . . . , now you would not hide behind these two fingers the ninety-nine cubits of Aristotle, nor would you mention my small error and at the same time pass over in silence his very large one."

Galileo did not invent the art of experiment or a mythical "experimental method." Other men of his day rolled spheres down inclined planes and dropped objects from heights (among them was the Dutch mathematician and engineer, Stevinus of Bruges), but Galileo saw more clearly the character of the question he was asking and the perspective in which it should be held. He used his experiment to verify a mathematical theory; in the appropriate context, he saw experimental discrepancies as minor errors instead of major truths. Galileo had many predecessors in criticism of Aristotle, but he was the one who put together the final, complete and correct mathematical description of free fall; he was the one who arrived at the revolutionary idea of treating time as a *physical variable* in the mathematical formulation. (Figure 2.12.1 shows a modern flash photograph of two ball bearings falling together in air; frictional effects on these objects are negligible.)

In the process of his thought about motion, resistance, and fall, and in the tradition of Ockham's razor, he eliminated the concept of levity from physics. He clearly saw the meaning of the hydrostatic principle of Archimedes, and associated the rise of heated gases with gravity and difference in density, rather than with still another *ad hoc* property.

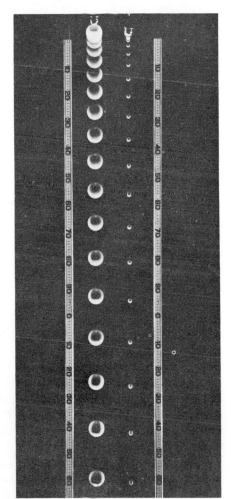

FIG. 2.12.1. Flash photograph (at successive uniform time intervals) of two steel balls simultaneously released from rest. Note the regular increase in spacing, indicating a linear increase in speed. Note also how the balls stay together, as they might have in the apocryphal Leaning Tower experiment. (Courtesy Educational Services, Inc.)

2.13   HOW NEARLY UNIFORM IS ACCELERATION OF FREE FALL?

As a footnote, illuminating the character of scientific knowledge, it is now appropriate to remark that, in a certain sense, Galileo was wrong: free fall is *not* uniformly accelerated. When Newton finally asked and found a solution to the question Galileo consciously put aside—what causes the acceleration?—he showed it to be a consequence of the law of gravitation that the acceleration of free fall should vary inversely as the square of the distance from the center of the earth. Let us translate this statement into algebraic form. A conventional symbol for acceleration due to gravity is g. Denote the radius of the earth by R_0 and the acceleration at the surface of the earth by g_0; similarly denote by R any arbitrary radial distance from the center of the earth and the acceleration at that distance by g. Then, according to Newton,

$$g \propto \frac{1}{R^2},\tag{2.13.1}$$

or

$$\frac{g}{g_0} = \frac{R_0^2}{R^2}.\tag{2.13.2}$$

If we let h denote height above the surface of the earth, so that $R = R_0 + h$, Eq. (2.13.2) becomes

$$\frac{g}{g_0} = \frac{R_0^2}{(R_0 + h)^2} = \frac{1}{[1 + (h/R_0)]^2}.\tag{2.13.3}$$

Applying the binomial theorem or simply carrying out the algebraic long division on the right-hand side of Eq. (2.13.3), we obtain

$$\frac{g}{g_0} = 1 - \frac{2h}{R_0} + 3\left(\frac{h}{R_0}\right)^2 - \cdots,\tag{2.13.4}$$

$$\frac{g - g_0}{g_0} = -\frac{2h}{R_0} + 3\left(\frac{h}{R_0}\right)^2 - \cdots.\tag{2.13.5}$$

PROBLEM 2.2.   Derive Eq. (2.13.5) from (2.13.3). Then interpret Eq. (2.13.5).

Note the strategy which has been used in extracting the information in which we are interested. Calculations of this kind are frequently used in scientific thinking. The quantity $(g - g_0)/g_0$ is directly the fractional change in acceleration associated with a change in height h. We say this quantity has been *expanded* in terms of ascending powers of h/R_0. This algebraic form is particularly useful when h/R_0 is fairly small because $(h/R_0)^2$ and higher terms are then completely negligible in comparison with the first-order term h/R_0. Since R_0 is about 4000 mi, g decreases by about 1% if we go to a height of about 20 mi.

PROBLEM 2.3.   Verify the last assertion. Is the term $3h^2/R_0^2$ significant in this calculation? What is the value of acceleration due to gravity at the orbit of a satellite 100 mi above the surface of the earth? Is the term $3h^2/R_0^2$ significant in this calculation?

PROBLEM 2.4. A good modern gravimeter can readily detect changes in g of one part per million; i.e., a fractional variation of 10^{-6}. How many feet change in altitude at the surface of the earth would this variation correspond to? On this scale of sensitivity, g varies markedly from place to place on the earth: It varies with local geological structure, with the presence of bodies of ore, with variations in the earth's crust at the boundaries of continents. It increases systematically as one goes north, because of the flattening of the earth at the poles. In the light of your calculations and of these remarks, in what sense was Galileo right? In what sense was he wrong?

2.14 APPLICATION OF MATHEMATICS TO PHYSICS

In his attitude toward mathematics, his regard for its beauty and order and in the primacy he accorded it, Galileo moved in a Platonic tradition. (Modern historians classify him as a neo-Platonist, using the latter term to designate a very widespread persistence and revival of Platonic attitudes and ideas which can be followed through the dark ages and medieval times despite the dominance of Aristotelian scholasticism.) But unlike both Plato and Aristotle, he saw mathematics, in all its idealization, to be directly relevant to the description of nature. He avoided the superstitious, numerological branch of Pythagorean-Platonic tradition; he borrowed the best from the Platonic and Aristotelian wellsprings of classical thought. As Sarton remarks (in the quotation cited at the end of Section 2.6), his genius was his salvation. Galileo repeatedly exhibits the mathematical ignorance of poor Simplicio and has him make admissions such as, "I am quite convinced; and believe me, if I were again beginning my studies, I should follow the advice of Plato and start with mathematics, a science which proceeds very cautiously and admits nothing as established until it has been rigidly demonstrated."

But it is only fair to note that had Aristotle himself been reincarnated in Tuscany in Galileo's day, it is unlikely that he would have espoused scholastic conservatism. Second-rate disciples were deferring to obsolete and outmoded authority; the creative thinker himself would more probably have been at the van of synthesis of new ideas rather than at the rear of defensive rationalization.

Galileo, in his utilization of mathematics for the description of nature, initiated the prodigiously fruitful line of mathematical physics which reached towering peaks in Newton, Laplace, Maxwell, Einstein, and Schrödinger and which plays a major role in present-day scientific thought.

2.15 THE LAW OF INERTIA

We have repeatedly pointed to the Aristotelian idea that continual application of a driving action is essential to maintain constant velocity of a body. This is a highly plausible generalization of everyday experience; yet it contains profound misinterpretation of the character of motion and the laws governing its change. Development of a science of dynamics was blocked until this misconception was corrected. Although Galileo never developed a successful dynamics himself, one of his most fundamental and influential contributions lay in starting the science on the right track by beginning to correct the misconception.

Galileo marshaled his evidence: First, from the studies with inclined planes:

"... any velocity once imparted to a moving body will be rigidly maintained as long as the external causes of acceleration and retardation are removed, a condition which is found only on horizontal planes; for in the case of planes which slope downwards there is already present a cause of acceleration, while on planes sloping upward there is retardation; from this it follows that motion along a horizontal plane is perpetual; for if velocity be uniform, it cannot be diminished or slackened. ..."

Here he again reasons toward one of the limits. To argue about free fall, he extrapolated to the expected behavior of the moving body as the plane was elevated to vertical position. Now he argues what will happen as the angle of inclination is made smaller and the plane approaches a horizontal orientation.

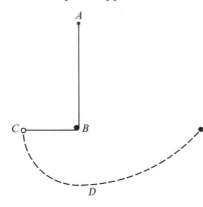

FIG. 2.15.1. Pendulum with point of suspension at A, fixed peg at B. Bob is released at C and swings along arcs CD and DE, returning to its original level at E.

Time and again in his writings Galileo refers to the behavior of pendulums, which he studied throughout his life. He had noted that in its swing a pendulum always tends to rise on one side of the vertical to the same height from which it was let go on the other, even in cases such as that illustrated in Fig. 2.15.1. If the bob is let go at C, the swing takes place along arcs CD and DE. If we visualize point A as being raised higher and higher, and the string made longer and longer without limit with positions C and B remaining unchanged, point E recedes to the right, arc DE becomes more and more nearly a horizontal line. Thus, after falling to D, the bob moves to the right indefinitely at uniform velocity if the string has unlimited length.

In our day, with blocks of dry ice or "frictionless pucks" floating on cushions of gas over smooth horizontal surfaces, we can dramatically reduce resistance to motion and give a direct, visual impression of the tendency of bodies to move indefinitely with uniform velocity. But, as in the case of conceiving all bodies to have the same acceleration in free fall, Galileo had to arrive at this conception by an act of imagination, by thinking away the resistance. Beyond this, he had to have the still more subtle idea that the primary physical principles are to be discovered in the fictitious frictionless domain, that what we finally observe in real situations consists of the superposition of frictional effects on the more fundamental, frictionless behavior.

This is a complete and revolutionary departure from Aristotelian conceptions. In the latter, all motion requires continual action of a "mover" (including the motion of the heavenly bodies). With Galileo, motion does not require a mover; it is the natural state, and only ever-present friction causes it to run down.

Galileo's perception is the first articulation of what we now call the "law of inertia." It is curious to note that he never got it completely right. In his conception the center of the earth remained a natural center for all earthly motion. He was so sensitive to the point that a "horizontal" plane is in reality a spherical surface and a "horizontal" line a circle on the earth, that he never shook off the idea that inertial motion is essentially *circular* in character. Apparently because of this, he continued to think of the motion of the planets around the sun as being similar to that of the rolling ball on the horizontal plane, and never realized the necessity of a central force to keep them in their curved orbits. In many ways he remained an Aristotelian while breaking some of the shackles of Aristotelian thought!

In Descartes the statement of the law of inertia later became: "Every individual body remains in the same state so far as possible and changes its state only by impact with other bodies. Every body tends to continue its motion in a straight line, not a curved line, and all curvilinear motion is motion under some constraint." In Newton it took the form: "Every body continues in its state of rest or of uniform motion in a straight line, unless it is compelled to change that state by forces impressed upon it."

For his profoundly original philosophical perceptions and conceptual insights, for his description of motion, for his persuasively successful application of mathematics to physics, for his contributions to astronomy, for the law of inertia, Galileo is justly known as the father of modern science.

2.16　QUESTIONS AND PROBLEMS

2.1. In this chapter we have used a substantial number of words not normally part of the vocabulary of a young student. This is not a failure on the part of the student but reflects an encounter with a new level of ideas. Can you now define and explain the following terms in your own words: epistemology, empirical, cosmology, syllogism, teleogical, extrapolate?

2.2. In the last section of this chapter we discussed the law of inertia, which forms the cornerstone of the successful theory of dynamics. The word inertia is our own name for the tendency or property of bodies to continue in motion. In Chapter 5 we shall see how this concept, interpreted as a resistance to acceleration, is given numerical values by operational definition and is, in the science of physics, more commonly called *mass*. In the light of your reading and experience up to this point, do you see, in a philosophical sense, any vestiges of Aristotelianism about some of our uses of the word inertia? Do you see the manner in which our usage is definitely *not* Aristotelian? Can you spot vestiges of Aristotelianism in other scientific jargon which might be known to you?

2.3. Following are some facts about the behavior of objects rolling down inclined planes:

(1) Homogeneous spheres of different sizes all have exactly the same acceleration regardless of size.

(2) Similarly, homogeneous cylinders all have exactly the same acceleration regardless of size, but spheres always have a larger acceleration than cylinders; i.e., if a cylinder and sphere are started from rest at the top of the plane, the sphere always arrives first at the bottom.

Galileo was apparently quite unaware of the latter phenomenon. (Its explanation is to be arrived at only in a more highly developed theory of dynamics.) At this stage of your knowledge, how does the fact that cylinders and spheres roll with different accelerations strike you? How would this affect your attitude toward the extrapolation to increasing angle of inclination of the plane and conclusions about free fall as the plane approached the vertical? Speculate on how this fact might have affected Galileo had he been aware of it. What is your guess concerning the behavior of a frictionless puck *sliding* down the plane, relative to the rolling sphere and cylinder? (You might construct some interesting laboratory experiments around an investigation of this problem.)

2.4. See if you can make some reasonable guesses as to how the acceleration of a rolling sphere would vary with angle of inclination of the plane. (It is obvious that it will be greater for greater inclinations; this is not the point. The point is to discover the *algebraic relation*. No method of approach to such a problem is unfair. A scientist tries to discover the correct answer by hook or crook or guesswork or any other stratagem he can devise. Subsequently he will work it into an elegant and logical scheme, consistent with other facts he has already learned.) Galileo asked himself this question, arrived at a theoretical answer, and verified the result experimentally. [*Note:* Given a very small amount of ingenuity, relevant experiments can be readily performed with modest lengths of board, a marble, etc. This is eminently fair game!]

2.5. For those interested in athletics and athletic records: A substantial amount of rather bad physics has entered into the recognition and assessment of athletic records. Some of the errors and lack of understanding are centered around the fact that g is not the same in different geographical locations. Look up the paper by Prof. Paul Kirkpatrick of Stanford University in the February 1944 issue of the *American Journal of Physics*, entitled "Bad physics in athletic measurements," and identify which measurements are affected by lack of understanding of acceleration due to gravity, and how they are affected.

2.6. In the first paragraph of the discussion of motion (Third Day) in the *Two New Sciences*, Galileo refers to aspects of "natural motion" which have only been superficially studied, and asserts that he has discovered "some properties of it which are worth knowing and which have not hitherto been either observed or demonstrated. Some superficial observations have been made, as, for instance, that the natural motion of a heavy falling body is continuously accelerated; but to just what extent this acceleration occurs has not yet been announced; for so far as I know, no one has yet pointed out that the distances traversed during equal intervals of time, by a body falling from rest, stand to one another in the same ratio as the odd numbers beginning with unity." This remark is strongly in Pythagorean–Platonic tradition in its concern with numerical regularities. To Galileo this was a triumph of Platonism; here was a specific instance in which a terrestrial phenomenon was described by integer numbers.

(a) What Galileo means is that, if $s_1 - s_0$, $s_2 - s_1$, $s_3 - s_2$, etc., denote *successive* displacements occurring in *equal* intervals of time, then, if $s_1 - s_0$ is set equal to 1 unit of length, we find that $s_2 - s_1 = 3$ units, $s_3 - s_2 = 5$ units, $s_4 - s_3 = 7$ units, etc. Demonstrate that this relation among successive displacements follows from Eq. (1.12.2) when $v_0 = 0$, and would thus be true for any uniformly accelerated motion *starting from rest*. [You may wish to start with specific calculations which lead you successively to the ratios 1, 3, 5, 7, . . . , but eventually try to present a completely general analysis; i.e., formulate an analysis which expresses the ratio of the nth interval to the first interval, $(s_n - s_{n-1})/(s_1 - s_0)$, in terms of n, and show that this gives the sequence of odd numbers starting with unity.]

(b) If one ties a series of metal chunks uniformly spaced along a string, holds the entire "chain" vertically suspended above the floor and lets it drop, he hears a clatter as the successive chunks hit the floor. This clatter increases in "frequency" (time intervals between successive thuds decrease) as the chain falls. Why? How would you space the metal chunks along the string in order to get a clatter of uniform frequency (equal time intervals between the thuds)? Why?

2.7. Table 2.16.1 shows data recorded for two different motions, designated A and B. Examine these data from the standpoint of determining whether or not the motions can be described as uniformly accelerated. Note that there is not necessarily an unequivocal, pat answer to this question. It is indicated that the data are subject to a large uncertainty; therefore it may only be possible to give an answer qualified within certain limits. If a motion is uniformly accelerated, determine the numerical value of the acceleration; if a motion is not uniformly accelerated, deduce qualitatively whatever you can about the way in which acceleration varies. [*Hint concerning the analysis:* The clearest and most powerful way of dealing with data of this kind is to present the analysis graphically so that an entire pattern can be judged or assimilated by eye. Plotting a graph of s-versus-t cannot be informative, however, since the eye cannot judge whether a set of points falls on a parabola or some other curve. Therefore a more subtle strategy is required. A very widely used method is to plot the data in such a way that the points would fall on a straight line if the acceleration were uniform and would depart from the straight line if the acceleration were not uniform. Obviously this tech-

TABLE 2.16.1

POSITION-TIME DATA FOR TWO MOTIONS (A AND B).
EACH MOTION STARTS FROM REST AT $s = 0$ WHEN $t = 0$.

Motion A		Motion B	
Time, t, sec	Position, s, m	Time, t, sec	Position, s, m
0.0	0.0	0.0	0.0
1.0	2.0	1.2	8.4
1.8	7.1	2.6	28
2.5	12	3.3	34
3.3	21	5.1	73
4.6	48	6.3	100
5.2	54	8.0	115
6.2	80	9.2	136
7.4	120	10.3	140

Time readings uncertain to about ±0.1 sec.
Position readings uncertain to ±10% of indicated values.

nique is applicable to any situation in which adherence to a mathematical formula is being tested and is not limited to an inquiry about uniformity of acceleration. Suppose that a set of points lies on a curve defined by the equation $s = \frac{1}{2}at^2$; suppose you calculate the value of s/t^2 for each point and plot the resulting number against its corresponding value of t; how will your new graph appear? Suppose you calculate s/t and plot the resulting numbers against t; how will this graph appear? Suppose you plot $\sqrt{s}$ against t? Utilize at least one of these ideas in analyzing the data of Table 2.16.1, draw your conclusions, and explain the logic of your reasoning in full detail.]

2.8. Table 2.16.2 shows data recorded for a motion which does *not* start from rest; that is, $v_0 \neq 0$, although $s = 0$ at $t = 0$.

If this motion is uniformly accelerated, it must satisfy the equation $s = \frac{1}{2}at^2 + v_0t$. Following up one of the hints listed in Problem 2.7, how would you graph the data so that the points would fall on a straight line if the motion were uniformly accelerated? What would be the physical significance of the slope of this line? of the intercept on the vertical axis? Analyze the data of Table 2.16.2, extracting all the numerical information possible about the character of the motion.

TABLE 2.16.2

POSITION-TIME DATA FOR AN ACCELERATED MOTION;
$s = 0$ AT $t = 0$; $v_0 \neq 0$

Time, t, arbitrary units, "ticks"	Position, s, cm	Time, t, "ticks"	Position, s, cm
0	0	9	17.2
1	0.77	10	20.2
2	1.85	11	24.0
3	3.18	12	27.6
4	4.77	13	31.9
5	6.60	14	36.2
6	8.72	15	40.7
7	11.1	16	45.8
8	14.0		

SUPPLEMENTARY READING AND STUDY

For Galileo's writings concerning motion:

Dialogue Concerning the Two Chief World Systems (First Day), Galileo Galilei. Translated by Stillman Drake. Berkeley, Calif.: University of California Press, 1953

Dialogues Concerning Two New Sciences (First and Third Days), Galileo Galilei. Translated by H. Crew and A. de Salvio. New York: Dover Publications, Inc., 1952

For background material on ancient science:

The Origins of Scientific Thought, Giorgio de Santillana. Chicago: University of Chicago Press, 1961; also Mentor paperback MQ 336

A History of Science: Ancient Science Through the Golden Age of Greece, George Sarton. Cambridge, Mass.: Harvard University Press, 1952

The Physical World of the Greeks, Samburski. New York: Macmillan, 1956

Biographical material on Galileo:

Galileo, His Life and Work, J. J. Fahie. New York: James Pott & Co., 1903

The Crime of Galileo, Giorgio de Santillana. Chicago: University of Chicago Press, 1955

See also the preface to *Dialogues Concerning Two Chief World Systems*.

For material on European science prior to Galileo:

Science of Mechanics in the Middle Ages, Marshall Clagett. Madison, Wis.: University of Wisconsin Press, 1959

Origins of Modern Science, H. Butterfield. London: G. Bell & Sons, 1949, Chapters 1 and 5; also New York: Collier Books, AS 259V, 1962

Medieval and Early Modern Science, A. C. Crombie. New York: Doubleday Anchor Book A167a, 1959

The Mechanization of the World Picture, E. J. Dijksterhuis. Oxford: Clarendon Press, 1961

Roots of Scientific Thought: A Cultural Perspective, edited by P. P. Wiener and A. Noland. New York: Basic Books, 1957

CHAPTER 3

Mathematics I:* Cartesian Geometry; Functions and Limits

In generating the concepts of kinematics in Chapter 1, we made extensive use of mathematical ideas and representations, but it was necessary to point out repeatedly that important issues were being glossed over or treated casually. In Chapter 2 we heard something of Galileo's impassioned plea for the use of mathematics in describing the physical universe and saw some of the evidence leading to the conviction that nature is essentially mathematical in the order and organization of phenomena; this conviction will be enormously strengthened as we follow the evolution of physical thought through the concepts of dynamics, the discovery of the conservation laws, and the study of electricity and light and the structure of matter. To this end it will be necessary to forge and refine some of our mathematical tools; we begin the process in this chapter.

3.1 THE BASIC CONCEPT OF CARTESIAN GEOMETRY

Mathematics, to the ancient Greeks, was essentially geometry; they dealt with points, lines, and figures which they could draw (or visualize drawing) mechanically. Arithmetic or number entered this science through relations of proportion, one length to another for example, as in theorems concerning the sides of similar tri-

---

* *Note to teacher and student:* In order to avoid fragmenting mathematical ideas and dispersing them in small sections throughout the text, mathematical concepts are being presented in several self-contained chapters, of which this is the first. These chapters need not, and probably should not, be studied in uninterrupted sequence. Depending on the nature of a particular course, teachers may find it advisable to weave back and forth between the mathematics and physics chapters. For example, after studying sections 3.1–3.5, one might go on to projectile motion in Chapter 4, returning afterward to the concepts of function and limit. The chapters on Newtonian mechanics could then be interposed before beginning the calculus in Chapter 8. Study of the ellipse in Section 3.6 or the hyperbola in Section 3.7 could be undertaken in conjunction with the discussion of Kepler's laws (Chapter 13), or the two-source interference pattern (Chapter 22), respectively. (If students have had an introductory course in analytic geometry and calculus, Chapters 3, 8, and 16 can readily be omitted without a break in the physics sequence.)

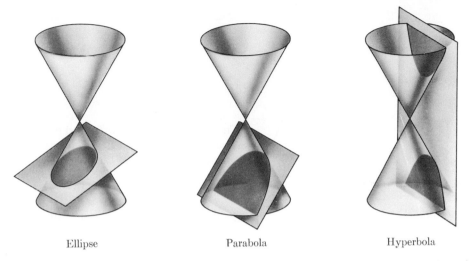

Ellipse   Parabola   Hyperbola

FIG. 3.1.1. Generation of conic sections by passing planes at various angles to the axis of a right circular cone. A circle is generated by passing the plane perpendicular to the axis.

angles. Properties of curved figures such as the circle, ellipse, parabola, and hyperbola were known only in terms of proportions between various characteristic lines which could be drawn on the figure; these figures were (and still are) known as *conic sections*, or simply "conics," because the shapes are generated by passing planes at various angles to the axis of a right circular cone (Fig. 3.1.1). Properties of these figures were then studied geometrically through proportionality relations among various tangent lines and other segments. When a figure was found in a new context, satisfying the same proportionality conditions, it would be recognized as a parabola, ellipse, etc., as the case might be. Proofs of theorems about these figures are lengthy and complicated; for this reason they are rarely encountered, or even hinted at, in elementary courses in plane geometry. Discovery of theorems and their proofs involved creative mathematical thought and genius of a very high order. Among the principal contributors in this field were Apollonius of Perga and Archimedes—two of the greatest mathematicians of the Alexandrian era.

When Galileo in the *Two New Sciences* discusses the path followed by a projectile, he first reviews the proof of a theorem from the books of Apollonius. Apollonius proved* that for the parabola (Fig. 3.1.2)

$$\frac{(\overline{bd})^2}{(\overline{fe})^2} = \frac{\overline{da}}{\overline{ea}}. \tag{3.1.1}$$

Galileo then shows that the lines on the figure of the trajectory of a projectile exhibit the same proportionality and concludes that the trajectory must therefore be a

---

* For Galileo's version of the Apollonius proof see page 246 of the Crew and de Salvio translation of the *Two New Sciences*. New York: Dover Publications, 1952.

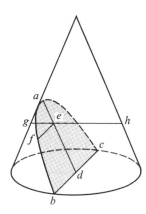

FIG. 3.1.2. Parabola *bfac* formed by plane passed through right circular cone parallel to an element, or line, of the cone.

parabola. During the seventeenth century, these ideas were put more directly into the language of algebra and arithmetic.

In 1637 the French philosopher Descartes (Fig. 3.1.3) published, as an appendix to his *Discourse on Method*, a treatise on geometry in which he explored the connection between geometrical figures and proportionalities on one hand and algebraic equations on the other. He showed that one could write algebraic equations representing relationships contained in geometrical constructions and, conversely, that geometrical constructions could be devised to represent certain algebraic equations. Oresme's triangle, described in Section 2.8, is regarded by some historians as one of several precursors of Descartes' discovery.

FIG. 3.1.3. René Descartes (1596–1650).

The time was ripe for this synthesis, which we now call *analytic geometry*. It was being independently explored by Descartes' contemporary, the mathematician Pierre de Fermat; it was quickly assimilated into current mathematical thought and developed far beyond the level of Descartes' original treatise.

In several analyses performed in his treatise, Descartes obtained algebraic equations of geometrical loci by measuring lengths x and y in directions established by two mutually perpendicular reference lines. The usefulness of this idea was immediately appreciated, and it soon evolved into the system of rectangular or *Car-*

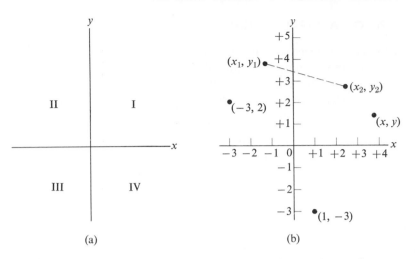

(a)   (b)

FIG. 3.1.4. (a) Numbering of quadrants in the Cartesian plane. (b) Notation representing points in the plane: (abscissa, x; ordinate, y).

tesian coordinates which the reader has utilized in elementary algebra and which we have already employed in our description of motion in Chapter 1. Descartes actually confined his own analyses to what we now call the "positive quadrant" (Quadrant I in Fig. 3.1.4a) of the coordinate system. Newton, some years later, pointed out the meaning and utility of the negative extensions of the axes.

In this and the following few sections we become acquainted with several fundamental results and methods of analytic or Cartesian geometry. First a review of the conventional terminology:

Axes which are not associated with physically interpreted quantities are usually labeled x (abscissa) and y (ordinate). The quadrants into which the axes divide a plane are numbered as in Fig. 3.1.4(a).

The location of a point (Fig. 3.1.4b) is specified by notation such as $(-3, 2)$, with the abscissa always understood to be the first of the pair of numbers. Such a set of numbers is frequently called an "ordered pair." The notation (x_1, y_1), (x_2, y_2), etc., as in Chapter 1, will be used to indicate *particular* points in the sense of a fixed value of x and corresponding fixed value of y. The notation (x, y) will denote any *general* point with abscissa x and corresponding ordinate y. Point $(0, 0)$ is called the *origin* of the system.

Numbers such as $(x_2 - x_1)$ and $(y_2 - y_1)$ are called *directed distances*, parallel to the respective axes.

Invoking the Pythagorean theorem, we can obtain the distance between two points $P_1(x_1, y_1)$ and $P_2(x_2, y_2)$ by:

$$\overline{P_1P_2} = \sqrt{(x_2 - x_1)^2 + (y_2 - y_1)^2}.^* \tag{3.1.2}$$

(See Fig. 3.1.4b.)

---

* We shall systematically follow the widespread mathematical convention of using the radical sign $\sqrt{}$ to denote the positive value of the square root of a number.

3.2 SLOPE OF A STRAIGHT LINE

In view of the experience the student has already had with representation of straight lines, this section will be more of an outline, setting the concepts in logical perspective, than an explanatory discourse.

(1) The straight line is an undefined or "primitive" element in geometry. We do not attempt to organize a circular verbalization to define it; we *draw* the object— examples *A, B, C* in Fig. 3.2.1.

(2) We recognize that straight lines can be differently *oriented* with respect to the coordinate axes, and we introduce a geometrical description of this orientation by referring to the angle α (Fig. 3.2.1) as the *inclination* of the line relative to the axes. This definition confines α to the range of values from 0° to 180°. A more convenient description of the orientation is discovered in a number which is more directly con-

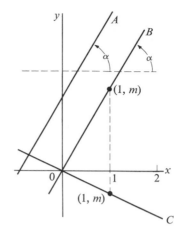

FIG. 3.2.1. Straight lines oriented in various ways relative to Cartesian axes. Line *B*, parallel to line *A*, passes through the origin. Angle α is called "inclination" of the line; $0 \leq \alpha \leq 180°$. Ordinate *m* of point where line *B* crosses the *x* = 1 coordinate line is called slope of line *B* (geometrical definition of slope).

nected to numbers along the coordinate axes: In Fig. 3.2.1, line *B* is drawn through the origin of coordinates parallel to line *A*. The slope of line *B* is defined as the ordinate *m* of point (1, *m*) as shown; *m* is then also the slope of the parallel line *A* or of any other line parallel to *A* or *B*. While the value of *m* is positive for lines oriented as *A* and *B* are, *m* has a negative value for line *C* and for lines parallel to *C*. This gives us a numerical definition of slope *m* in purely *geometrical* language. In *trigonometrical* language, from the definition of "tangent of an angle," it follows that

$$m = \tan \alpha. \tag{3.2.1}$$

This provides us with a geometrical description of the orientation of the line, the "locus" of points in which we are interested. In the next paragraph, we shall connect this description with the algebraic (*x, y*) symbols of our system of coordinates. Note that *m* has positive values for $\alpha < 90°$ and negative values for $\alpha > 90°$, and that it has the value zero for lines parallel to the *x*-axis. For lines parallel to the *y*-axis, *m* is undefined, since the calculation of tan α involves division by zero. Mathematical language refers to lines parallel to the *y*-axis as having "no slope." This does *not* mean that they have zero slope; it means that the slope is undefined.

(3) The slope of a line, defined geometrically in the preceding paragraph, can be calculated from the values of the coordinates of any two points on the line; this establishes the connection between the geometrical concept and the numerical properties of the coordinate system.

Consider the points P_1 and P_2 on a straight line, as in Fig. 3.2.2, taking P_2 to the right of P_1 (that is, $x_2 > x_1$). Using the laws of similar triangles (or the definition of tan α), we can show by reference to the definition of m that

$$m = \frac{y_2 - y_1}{x_2 - x_1}. \tag{3.2.2}$$

PROBLEM 3.1. Show that Eq. (3.2.2) follows from the definition of m in the preceding paragraph. Then show also that

$$m = \frac{y_2 - y_1}{x_2 - x_1}$$

for the case in which P_2 lies to the *left* of P. (This step is necessary to complete a demonstration that Eq. (3.2.2) is indeed a perfectly general expression for m in terms of the coordinates of a pair of points on the line.)

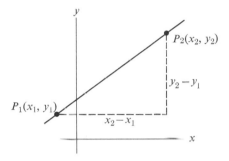

FIG. 3.2.2. P_1 and P_2 are points on a straight line. P_2 is taken to the right of P_1.

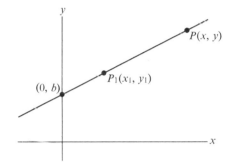

FIG. 3.3.1. Straight line of given slope m, passing through a particular point $P_1(x_1, y_1)$. Point $P(x, y)$ denotes any general point located on the given line. Point $(0, b)$ is called the "y-intercept."

3.3 EQUATION OF A STRAIGHT LINE

Now, recognizing that the location and orientation of a line on a set of Cartesian axes is completely determined by specification of its slope and of the coordinates of one particular point through which the line passes, we couch our analytic-geometrical problem in our newly defined terms: We seek the locus of all points $P(x, y)$ so located with respect to $P_1(x_1, y_1)$ that the line connecting the points P and P_1 has a particular numerical value of slope m. (The word locus has the meaning that it contains every point which satisfies the given description and no other points.)

Figure 3.3.1 shows a straight line of prescribed slope m, passing through the particular point $P_1(x_1, y_1)$. The point $P(x, y)$ represents *any* other point on the line; this point may lie to the left or right of P_1 and anywhere on the extensions of the line. It follows from Eq. (3.2.2) and the solution to Problem 3.1 that point $P(x, y)$ lies on the locus just described only if:

$$m = \frac{y - y_1}{x - x_1}, \qquad y - y_1 = m(x - x_1). \tag{3.3.1}$$

Equation (3.3.1) is also satisfied if point P is identified with P_1, since both sides then take the value 0. Therefore Eq. (3.3.1) is satisfied by the coordinates of every point on the prescribed straight line. We must now give attention to the simple, but far from trivial, converse question: If the coordinates of a point satisfy Eq. (3.3.1), does the point necessarily lie on the prescribed straight line? The answer in this case is yes, and the proof is outlined in the following problem.

PROBLEM 3.2. Explain and justify the following steps: (a) If the coordinates of an arbitrarily chosen point $P(x, y)$, not identical with P_1, satisfy Eq. (3.3.1), the slope of line PP_1 must equal the slope of the prescribed line. (b) Then PP_1 must be parallel to the prescribed line or identical with it. (c) Since PP_1 and the prescribed line have the point P_1 in common, they must be identical. (d) Therefore any point whose coordinates satisfy Eq. (3.3.1) must lie on the straight line prescribed by m and $P_1(x_1, y_1)$.

In summary then: Eq. (3.3.1) establishes a numerical connection between ordinate and abscissa values for any point $P(x, y)$ lying on a straight line of slope m, passing through point $P_1(x_1, y_1)$. The coordinates of every point on the line satisfy this equation; every point whose coordinates satisfy the equation lies on the line. Given these properties, Eq. (3.3.1) is called "the equation of the prescribed straight line"— in particular, the *point-slope* form of the equation, referring to the prescribed quantities.

An alternative, very useful form is obtained by taking P_1 to be the y-intercept point $(0, b)$ rather than an arbitrarily located point (x_1, y_1). In this case, show that Eq. (3.3.1) takes the form:

$$y = mx + b. \qquad (3.3.2)$$

Equation (3.3.2) is called the *slope-intercept* form; compare it directly with equations such as (1.7.1), (1.11.1), and (1.11.2) in Chapter 1 and with Problem 1.6.

3.4 GENERAL EQUATION OF THE FIRST DEGREE

Consider the equation

$$Ax + By + C = 0, \qquad (3.4.1)$$

where A, B, and C are numbers. This is known as the general equation of the first degree in x and y, if A and B are not both zero. It is obviously related to Eqs. (3.3.1) and (3.3.2); let us explore the connection.

If $B \neq 0$ (read "B is not equal to zero"), it is permissible to divide Eq. (3.4.1) by B, giving, on solving for y,

$$y = \frac{-Ax}{B} + \frac{-C}{B}. \qquad (3.4.2)$$

Comparing Eqs. (3.4.2) and (3.3.2), we immediately identify $-A/B$ with the slope m and $-C/B$ with the y-intercept of a straight line.

If $A = 0$, Eq. (3.4.2) takes the form

$$y = \frac{-C}{B},$$

which we recognize to represent a line of zero slope, parallel to the x-axis.

In the remaining case, when $B = 0$, we have

$$Ax + C = 0, \qquad x = \frac{-C}{A}. \tag{3.4.3}$$

We identify the significance of Eq. (3.4.3) in the following way: Every point on the line parallel to the y-axis and passing through $(-C/A, 0)$ satisfies this equation, and every point with coordinates $(-C/A, y)$ lies on this line. Therefore (3.4.3) is the equation of a straight line parallel to the y-axis (and having no slope).

Thus we have shown, in effect, that every straight line is represented by an equation of the first degree, and every equation of the first degree represents a straight line. For this reason equations of the first degree between pairs of quantities, x and y, s and t, are also called *linear equations*.

A statement of direct proportionality between two quantities, $y \propto x$ (read "y is directly proportional to x"), can always be cast in the form

$$\frac{y}{y_1} = \frac{x}{x_1}, \qquad y = \left(\frac{y_1}{x_1}\right)x = kx, \tag{3.4.4}$$

where k is a constant representing the numerical value of the ratio y_1/x_1. Thus a statement of direct proportionality is a special case of the general linear relation—the one corresponding to a straight line which passes through the origin; i.e., with y-intercept zero. The more general linear relation (3.4.1), on the other hand, is *not* a statement of direct proportionality.

The symbols x and y in Eqs. (3.3.1), (3.3.2), and (3.4.1) are referred to as "variables." (Compare with the use of symbols s, v, t in equations developed in Chapter 1.) We might think of x as assuming any of the infinity of numerical values along the x-axis, and the corresponding value of y on a particular straight line being determined by Eq. (3.3.2). In such a case we speak of x as the independent variable and y as the dependent variable in the equation. Our equation, in terms of variables, manages, in principle, to describe a straight line in its infinite entirety!

The Greeks, apparently inhibited by the discovery of irrational numbers (see footnote in Section 2.2), had hesitated to pursue the connection between numbers and points on a line, fearing perhaps that a correspondence might not exist. The Cartesian system assumed, without further inquiry, that there is a simple and direct correspondence.

To see that there may be more here than meets the eye, consider Figs. 1.2.1 and 1.3.1, where we have already associated numbers with points on a line: Suppose we increase the scale in Fig. 1.2.1; i.e., increase the separation between integers. We seem to have increased the number of points between successive integers, but we cannot change the number of numbers between 1 and 2; do we still have a correspondence between numbers and points? This naïvely stated question touches on deep issues of continuity and infinity; mathematical science did not provide a clear resolution, with rigorous treatment of the number system and its relation to the geometry of points on a line, until the end of the nineteenth century. Much of what is associated with modern mathematics, or the modern view toward the structure of mathematical thought, has its roots in this inquiry.*

Mathematics, however, like the natural sciences, is frequently found to transcend gaps, jumping to new insights and achievements before older ones have been completely secured and consolidated. The full armory of tools and understanding which followed from the introduction of Cartesian geometry ultimately played a role in clearing up ambiguity in the initial conception.

3.5 LOCUS OF POINTS EQUIDISTANT FROM A FIXED POINT

Let us now apply the general attitude and logic of the preceding sections to obtain equations of a few figures of interest and importance other than straight lines:

The locus of all points in a plane equidistant from a fixed point is the curve we call a circle. Figure 3.5.1 shows a circle of radius r and center at point (a, b). Our analytic-geometric description of the circle is: the locus of all points $P(x, y)$ at fixed distance r from (a, b). This can be immediately translated into an algebraic statement by recourse to Eq. (3.1.2), which gives, in the present symbols:

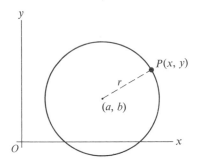

$$r = \sqrt{(x - a)^2 + (y - b)^2}. \quad (3.5.1)$$

In the very useful special case where the center point (a, b) is placed at the origin of coordinates $(0, 0)$, Eq. (3.5.1) reduces to:

$$x^2 + y^2 = r^2. \quad (3.5.2)$$

FIG. 3.5.1. Geometrical figure: circle with radius r and center at (a, b). Analytical problem: find locus of points $P(x, y)$ lying at fixed distance r from point (a, b).

Every point on the circle of radius r has coordinates which satisfy (3.5.1); every point whose coordinates satisfy (3.5.1) lies at a distance r from (a, b), and therefore lies on the circle. Thus, in the sense defined in Section 3.2, Eq. (3.5.1) is the equation of a circle. Note that this is the simplest of the conic sections.

3.6 LOCUS OF POINTS EQUIDISTANT FROM A FIXED POINT AND A LINE

Consider the locus of all points in a plane equidistant from a given point, called the focus, and a given straight line, called the directrix. To investigate this locus, let us deliberately position our coordinate axes in a simple way relative to focus and

---

* A lively narration of the genesis and history of these ideas is given by Tobias Dantzig in *Number, the Language of Science.* New York: Doubleday, Anchor Book No. A67, 1956.

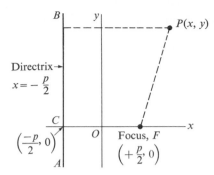

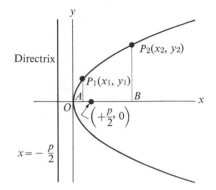

FIG. 3.6.1. *Problem*: to find analytical expression for locus of points equidistant from a given point F ("focus") and a given line AB ("directrix"). For simplicity and convenience, Cartesian axes are located so that x-axis passes through F perpendicular to directrix AB, and y-axis is perpendicular bisector of FC. The x-coordinates of F and C are denoted by $+p/2$ and $-p/2$, respectively. The directed distance from directrix to focus is denoted by p.

FIG. 3.6.2. Graph of Eq. (3.6.1) with p taken positive. For each positive value of x there are two symmetrically placed points with positive and negative values of y. No values of y exist for negative values of x.

directrix, say as shown in Fig. 3.6.1, so as to ensure that the locus we seek passes through the origin of coordinates and so that the distances from the directrix are easily expressed. (Note that Fig. 3.6.1 is not unique; we might equally well have made the directrix parallel to the x-axis and placed the focus on the y-axis; we might also have placed the focus to the left of the directrix instead of to the right, etc.)

The geometrical definition of the locus says: $\overline{PF} = \overline{PB}$. Translated into algebraic symbols by the use of Eq. (3.1.2), this becomes, after squaring both sides:

$$\left(x - \frac{p}{2}\right)^2 + y^2 = \left(x + \frac{p}{2}\right)^2,$$

$$x^2 - px + \frac{p^2}{4} + y^2 = x^2 + px + \frac{p^2}{4},$$

$$y^2 = 2px, \tag{3.6.1}$$

or

$$y = \pm\sqrt{2px}.$$

Equation (3.6.1) is satisfied by the coordinates of all points equidistant from focus F and line AB. Furthermore, all points whose coordinates satisfy (3.6.1) must be equidistant from F and AB, since we can reverse the sequence of calculation carried out above and show that $\overline{PF} = \overline{PB}$ if $y^2 = 2px$ for the coordinates y and x of a particular point. Hence Eq. (3.6.1) is the equation of the curve sought; the curve is sketched in Fig. 3.6.2 for the case of positive value of p (positive directed distance from directrix to focus).

Consider any two particular points $P_1(x_1, y_1)$ and $P_2(x_2, y_2)$ lying on the curve in Fig. 3.6.2. Since the coordinates of these points must satisfy Eq. (3.6.1), we have

$$y_2^2 = 2px_2, \qquad y_1^2 = 2px_1,$$

and, dividing one by the other, we obtain

$$\frac{y_2^2}{y_1^2} = \frac{x_2}{x_1}. \tag{3.6.2}$$

From Eq. (3.6.2), we have the following statement about lengths:

$$\frac{(\overline{P_2B})^2}{(\overline{P_1A})^2} = \frac{(\overline{BO})}{(\overline{AO})}. \tag{3.6.3}$$

Compare Eq. (3.6.3) with the relation proved by Apollonius for the curve in Fig. 3.1.2. From this relation, we recognize our new locus to be identical with the one in Fig. 3.1.2, and we now call it *parabola*. (Up to this point, use of the name "parabola" for the curve represented by Eq. (3.6.1) was inappropriate and was avoided, because the name had already been pre-empted for that of a particular conic section.) In the orientation of Fig. 3.6.2, the x-axis is said to coincide with the axis of the parabola.

PROBLEM 3.3.   If in Eq. (3.6.1) we take p to be negative (i.e., negative directed distance from directrix to focus), there are no values of y corresponding to positive values of x, but there do exist values of y corresponding to *negative* values of x. How is this to be interpreted? Where are the focus and directrix located? Argue that in this case Eq. (3.6.1) represents a parabola which "opens" toward the left instead of toward the right as in Fig. 3.6.2.

PROBLEM 3.4.   Show that if the directrix is taken to be the line $y = -p/2$, parallel to the x-axis, and if the focus is located on the y-axis at $(0, +p/2)$, then the equation takes the form

$$x^2 = 2py, \qquad y = \frac{1}{2p}x^2. \tag{3.6.4}$$

Sketch the graphs of Eq. (3.6.4) for p positive and p negative, showing that the parabola opens upward in the former case and downward in the latter.

PROBLEM 3.5.   Sketch on numbered axes, with a few strategically chosen points, graphs of the equations:

$$y^2 = 8x, \tag{3.6.5}$$

$$y = \tfrac{1}{2}x^2, \tag{3.6.6}$$

$$y = -16x^2. \tag{3.6.7}$$

Note that the *s*-versus-*t* equation for uniformly accelerated motion [Eq. (1.12.2)] takes the form

$$s = \tfrac{1}{2}at^2 \tag{3.6.8}$$

if v_0 and s_0 are taken to be zero. Thus, in the light of Problems 3.4 and 3.5 if a is positive, we have a parabola on the s-versus-t axes opening upward, as sketched for Eq. (3.6.6). If a is negative, we have a parabola opening downward, as sketched for Eq. (3.6.7). If, in the physical case under consideration, the motion starts from rest at $t = 0$, and there is no description of motion prior to $t = 0$, we are interested, from the standpoint of physical interpretation, only in the "branch" of the curve lying to the right of the s-axis. Equation (3.6.8) might perfectly well, however, describe a motion that was in process prior to $t = 0$, and both branches of the parabola become relevant to a description of the history of the motion for whatever time interval Eq. (3.6.8) is physically meaningful.

Since Eq. (3.6.8) appears to be a special case with v_0 and s_0 both equal to zero, there remains the question as to whether Eq. (1.12.2) in its original form,

$$s = \tfrac{1}{2}at^2 + v_0t + s_0, \qquad (1.12.2)$$

also represents a parabola. The answer is that it does—a parabola with focus, vertex, and axis displaced from the simple locations afforded them in our first analysis. The more complex form of the equation is simply the price paid for greater generality of position with respect to the axis of coordinates.

It must be noted that the parabola referred to in the above discussion is the shape of the *history* of a uniformly accelerated motion as sketched in a system of s-t coordinates. It must not be confused with a *path* followed by a moving particle in space. It will be discovered in Chapter 4 that the path in space (called "trajectory") swept out by a particle projected horizontally and falling freely is also a parabola, but here we shall be referring the discussion to two axes representing space coordinates, and not s-versus t.

3.7   ELLIPSE

Another curve, interesting because of its physical occurrence as the form of planetary and satellite orbits, is the ellipse, defined as a conic section in Section 3.1. An alternative description of the ellipse as a locus is demonstrated by a particularly simple and elegant geometrical analysis discovered in 1822 by a Belgian mathematician, G. P. Dandelin.

Consider Fig. 3.7.1 in which spheres S_1 and S_2 have been inscribed in the cone,

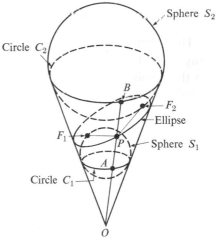

FIG. 3.7.1. Dandelin's construction. Spheres S_1 and S_2 are inscribed in the cone; they are tangent to the plane of the ellipse at F_1 and F_2 and touch the cone along circles C_1 and C_2, respectively. Line $OAPB$ is an element of the cone through any point P on the ellipse. (From *Calculus*, Volume I, T. M. Apostol. New York: Blaisdell Publishing Co., 1961.)

as explained in the caption. Take P as any point on the ellipse; draw lines PF_1 and PF_2. Line OP is a line on the cone from vertex O to point P, and A and B are intersections of this line with circles C_1 and C_2. Since lines PF_2 and PB are both tangent to sphere S_2 and originate at the same point, $\overline{PF_2} = \overline{PB}$, and similarly $\overline{PF_1} = \overline{PA}$. Then

$$\overline{PF}_1 + \overline{PF}_2 = \overline{PA} + \overline{PB} = \overline{AB}, \tag{3.7.1}$$

but $\overline{AB}$ is a fixed length, the distance between the parallel circles C_1 and C_2. Thus we can translate Eq. (3.7.1) into the verbal statement that the ellipse is the locus of all points P such that the sum of the distances of P from two other fixed points is constant. The two fixed points are called the *foci* of the ellipse.

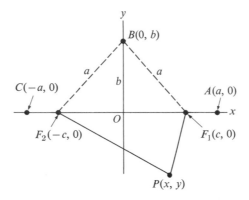

FIG. 3.7.2. A string of total length $2a$ and with ends fixed at F_1 and F_2 is held taut by a pencil at B. Length $\overline{F_1B} = a$; length $\overline{OB} = \sqrt{a^2 - c^2} \equiv b$; length $CA = 2c + 2(a - c) = 2a$.

This condition can be set up mechanically and the curve drawn in a very simple way: Take foci at fixed points F_1 and F_2 (Fig. 3.7.2), fastening the ends of a string to these points. Take a length of string greater than $2c$, the distance between the points. Keeping the string taut by pressing the pencil against it from inside the figure, run the pencil around the circuit, tracing out the elliptical curve. The curve will pass through points A, B, C, P. If $\overline{F_1B}$ is denoted by a, the length of string must be $2a$. Point B is located at (O, b) where $b \equiv \sqrt{a^2 - c^2}$ from the right triangle OF_1B. Point A must be located at (a, O) since the entire distance CA must also be equal to $2a$, the length of the string.

Applying the definition of the locus, in the symbols of Fig. 3.7.2, we have

$$\overline{PF}_1 + \overline{PF}_2 = 2a,$$

and applying the distance formula (3.1.2), we obtain

$$\sqrt{(x - c)^2 + y^2} + \sqrt{(x + c)^2 + y^2} = 2a,$$

$$\sqrt{(x - c)^2 + y^2} = 2a - \sqrt{(x + c)^2 + y^2}, \qquad \text{etc.} \tag{3.7.2}$$

Equation (3.7.2) is simplified by transposing one radical, squaring, transposing the remaining radical and squaring again. The steps will not be indicated here, but are exactly similar to those carried out for the hyperbola in Section 3.8. The reader should show that (3.7.2) reduces to:

$$\frac{x^2}{a^2} + \frac{y^2}{a^2 - c^2} = 1.$$

Using $b \equiv \sqrt{a^2 - c^2}$, as motivated by Fig. 3.7.2, we have

$$\frac{x^2}{a^2} + \frac{y^2}{b^2} = 1, \qquad y^2 = b^2\left(1 - \frac{x^2}{a^2}\right). \tag{3.7.3}$$

Thus we have shown that every point (x, y) on the ellipse satisfies Eq. (3.7.3), and by retracing the steps, we can show that every point $P(x, y)$ which satisfies (3.7.3) must have $\overline{PF_1} + \overline{PF_2} = 2a$. This qualifies Eq. (3.7.3) as the equation of an ellipse with foci symmetrically positioned about the origin on the x-axis. The lengths $2a$ and $2b$ are called the major and minor axes of the ellipse, respectively.

Verify the fact that the form

$$\frac{y^2}{a^2} + \frac{x^2}{b^2} = 1 \tag{3.7.4}$$

with $a > b$ represents an ellipse with foci on the y-axis.

3.8   HYPERBOLA

The last conic section, the hyperbola, can be shown to be identical with the locus of points $P(x, y)$ such that the absolute value of the *difference* between distances to two foci F_1 and F_2 has a fixed value (less than $\overline{F_1F_2}$) (Fig. 3.8.1). In physics this curve is encountered in the interference patterns formed by waves from two point sources (Section 22.14) and in the trajectory of a particle repelled from a fixed point by an inverse-square law force (Section 33.13).

If we represent the difference in distances by $2a$, this requirement leads to the equation

$$\sqrt{(x + c)^2 + y^2} - \sqrt{(x - c)^2 + y^2} = \pm 2a. \tag{3.8.1}$$

We reduce this to a simpler form by the following operations:

$$\sqrt{(x + c)^2 + y^2} = \pm 2a + \sqrt{(x - c)^2 + y^2}.$$

Squaring both sides, we have

$$(x + c)^2 + y^2 = 4a^2 \pm 4a\sqrt{(x - c)^2 + y^2} + (x - c)^2 + y^2,$$

$$x^2 + 2cx + c^2 + y^2 = 4a^2 \pm 4a\sqrt{(x - c)^2 + y^2} + x^2 - 2cx + c^2 + y^2,$$

$$4cx = 4a^2 \pm 4a\sqrt{(x - c)^2 + y^2}.$$

Dividing both sides by $4a$ and transposing one term, we obtain

$$\frac{cx}{a} - a = \pm\sqrt{(x - c)^2 + y^2}.$$

Squaring both sides again, we have

$$\frac{c^2}{a^2}x^2 - 2cx + a^2 = x^2 - 2cx + c^2 + y^2,$$

$$\frac{c^2}{a^2}x^2 - x^2 - y^2 = c^2 - a^2,$$

$$(c^2 - a^2)\frac{x^2}{a^2} - y^2 = c^2 - a^2,$$

$$\frac{x^2}{a^2} - \frac{y^2}{c^2 - a^2} = 1,$$

providing $c^2 - a^2 \neq 0$.

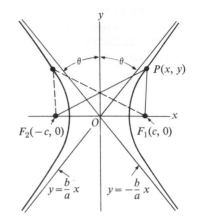

FIG. 3.8.1.   Hyperbola, with foci at F_1 and F_2, defined by locus of points P such that: $|\overline{PF_2} - \overline{PF_1}| = 2a$, with $2a < 2c$.

Introducing the symbol b, defined by $b^2 \equiv c^2 - a^2$, we obtain

$$\frac{x^2}{a^2} - \frac{y^2}{b^2} = 1, \qquad y^2 = b^2\left(\frac{x^2}{a^2} - 1\right). \qquad (3.8.2)$$

The curve described by this equation has two branches, symmetrically positioned on either side of the y-axis, as sketched in Fig. 3.8.1.

The second form of Eq. (3.8.2) might be written

$$y = \pm b\sqrt{(x^2/a^2) - 1}. \qquad (3.8.3)$$

For $|x/a| \gg 1$ (read "absolute value of x/a very much greater than 1"), y in Eq. (3.8.3) takes on values very close to $\pm bx/a$, but is always slightly less than this value because of the -1 within the radical. We immediately recognize

$$y = +\frac{bx}{a}, \qquad (3.8.4)$$

$$y = -\frac{bx}{a}, \qquad (3.8.5)$$

as straight lines passing through the origin with slope $+b/a$ and $-b/a$, respectively, as shown in Fig. 3.8.1. These lines are *not* part of the curve we are studying. They are mathematically distinct, but they bear a special relation to the "wings" of the curve. They are called the *asymptotes* of the hyperbola. For large values of $|x/a|$ it becomes difficult or impossible to distinguish the curve from these lines in a drawing or representation. (We shall have occasion to make use of this idea in dealing with the physical problem of interference of waves from two small sources.)

If we denote by θ the angles between the asymptotes and the y-axis, as indicated in Fig. 3.8.1, it follows from the fact that the *slopes* have magnitude b/a that

$$\tan \theta = \frac{a}{b}. \qquad (3.8.6)$$

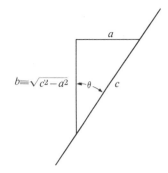

A right triangle with θ as one angle is shown in Fig. 3.8.2. Since $b^2 \equiv c^2 - a^2$, we have $c^2 = a^2 + b^2$, and c is the length of the hypotenuse when the legs of the right triangle are b and a, as shown. From Fig. 3.8.2, it follows that

FIG. 3.8.2. A right triangle, with $\tan \theta = a/b$, $\sin \theta = a/c$.

$$\sin \theta = \frac{a}{c} = \frac{2a}{2c}. \qquad (3.8.7)$$

Translated into words, Eq. (3.8.7) says that the sine of the angle between an asymptote and the y-axis (in the case of an hyperbola oriented as in Fig. 3.8.1) is given by the ratio of the fixed difference of distances which defines the locus to the separation between the foci. It is this property of the asymptotes which will prove particularly useful in physical problems later on.

3.9 CURVES AND EQUATIONS

In the preceding sections we have shown that equations of the first degree always represent straight lines in a Cartesian system of coordinates. In examining the group of curves called conic sections, we have found a second-degree equation in each case. As a matter of fact, it can be shown that the general second degree equation

$$Ax^2 + By^2 + Cxy + Dx + Ey + F = 0$$

represents various conic sections in different locations and orientations relative to the axes, depending on the relative values and algebraic signs of the coefficients. Straight lines are, of course, included among the special cases. (The analysis of the second-degree equation is time-consuming and will not be undertaken here.) Third-degree equations form a next level of study in their own right, and so on. A vast variety of equations can be invented and studied. Equations which arose in the solution of physical problems frequently motivated mathematical study of the type illustrated in this chapter. In other cases, curiosity about certain kinds of equations led to insights and relationships which unexpectedly illuminated physical problems. Such interaction between the sciences is characteristic, and is historically significant.

Two simple equations which we have not discussed in the preceding sections will arise repeatedly in our study of physics:

$$y = \frac{a}{x}, \qquad (3.9.1)$$

$$y = \frac{a}{x^2}. \qquad (3.9.2)$$

Equation (3.9.2) arises in the description of the variation of electric or gravitational forces between particles—the so-called "inverse square" laws of force. Equation (3.9.1) arises in the description of variation of potential energy quantities associated with these forces. Equation (3.9.1) is a special case of the second-degree equation, with coefficients A, B, D, E equal to zero; it is a conic section—an hyperbola whose asymptotes are the x- and y-axes themselves!

> PROBLEM 3.6.   Sketch graphs of Eqs. (3.9.1) and (3.9.2) for both positive and negative values of x. Describe and comment on the symmetry of each graph relative to the coordinate axes.

3.10   STATEMENTS OF CORRESPONDENCE OR ASSOCIATION: THE CONCEPT OF FUNCTION

Many results of experience, observation, deduction, and mathematical invention are couched in the form of statements of "correspondence" or "association." Consider the contrasting list of examples collected in Table 3.10.1.

These diverse statements form a pattern: In each one we imply the existence of a collection or set of objects, numbers, or characteristics X and another collection Y, and we give a statement of correspondence which associates with each object in the collection X one and only one object in the collection Y. This may involve all the objects in Y, but not necessarily. Such a correspondence is called a *function;* the collection X is called the "domain of the function"; the subset of those objects in Y which are associated with objects in X is called the "range of the function."

A conventional shorthand has been evolved for this context: Functions, or statements of association, are frequently denoted by letters such as f, g, h, F, ϕ, etc. Objects in the domain of the function are frequently denoted by letters such as x, z, u, v, t, etc. The symbols $f(x)$ (read "f of x"), $g(t)$, $F(u)$ are then used to denote in general that object in the range of the function which is associated with the object x, t, or u in the domain. If the domain consists of all real numbers x, for example, as implied in statement 9 of Table 3.10.1, we have the general statement:

$$f(x) = 4x^3 + 3,$$

and for the particular value $x = -2$ in the domain, we write the corresponding value in the range as

$$f(-2) = 4(-2)^3 + 3 = -29.$$

For the particular value $x = 0$ in the domain we have $f(0) = 4(0) + 3 = 3$ in the range. For the value u in the domain, $f(u) = 4(u)^3 + 3$. For the value $-z$ in the domain, $f(-z) = 4(-z)^3 + 3$. For the value $-x$ in the domain, $f(-x) = 4(-x)^3 + 3$. Thus if we have a general algebraic formula for $f(x)$, we obtain an expression for any particular case $x = w$ by replacing x by w in the formula; the resulting value in the range is denoted by $f(w)$.

TABLE 3.10.1

EXAMPLES OF STATEMENTS OF ASSOCIATION

1. The growth of capitalism is associated with the growth of industrial technology.

2. Frequency of incidence of disease corresponds to level of sanitation.

3. In a table showing the distribution of expenditures of tax funds, each category of expenditure has associated with it a percentage of the funds.

4. Each acidity of a chemical solution, containing an indicator, has associated with it a particular color of the solution.

5. Each particular level of roughness of the sea surface corresponds to a velocity of wind.

6. The maximum height of tide on any given day is associated with the relative positions of sun and moon.

7. Each distance fallen by an object dropped from rest is associated with a particular time of fall.

8. A particular value of force is associated with each distance of separation between two magnets.

9. If x denotes a number, each value of x has associated with it a particular value of $4x^3 + 3$.

10. In a table of sines of angles, each value of the angle has associated with it a particular value of the sine.

11. Each value of abscissa x, defining the location of a point on a curve, has associated with it a value of the slope of the line tangent to the curve at that point, as shown on the left below

12. Each value of $(x - a)$ along the abscissa has associated with it a particular value of area between the curve and the x-axis, as shown on the right above.

Some statements of functional connection, as in the preceding illustration, can be written out as algebraic equations, and such equations are called *formulas*. All the equations we dealt with in Chapter 1 and in the preceding sections of this chapter can be interpreted to be formulas in this sense. They are particular statements of functional correspondence between sets of numbers, and they illustrate a very important special class of functions with which we shall be concerned throughout this book. It should be clearly understood, however, that the concept of function is far broader than that encompassed by the algebraic formulas to which we have just alluded. By no means all functions can be expressed as algebraic formulas; even many statements about *numbers* cannot be put into this form!

PROBLEM 3.7. To the best of your *present* knowledge, assess the statements in Table 3.10.1 from the standpoint of whether or not they are expressible as algebraic formulas. Statements 11 and 12 merit particularly thoughtful attention; they deal with the two aspects of "calculus" which underlie most of the physics we shall study in this text.

In Chapter 1 we established definitions of velocity and acceleration which made s a particular function of t. We would now express this in the following symbols:

$$s = f(t) \quad \text{or} \quad s = s(t),$$

(read "s is a function of t"), and in the special case of uniformly accelerated motion, $f(t)$ was shown to be expressed by the algebraic formula $(\frac{1}{2})at^2 + v_0t + s_0$.

In studying analytic geometry, we described certain loci (straight lines and conic sections) so that for values, x, of the abscissa there were defined corresponding values of the ordinate, y; that is, it would seem that we have established statements of correspondence denoted by

$$y = f(x),$$

(read "y is a function of x"). We had better examine this statement a little more closely, however: In Eq. (3.6.1) for the parabola we have

$$y^2 = 2px, \quad y = \pm\sqrt{2px} \tag{3.10.1}$$

(as indicated previously, we adhere to the convention that the radical $\sqrt{}$ denotes the positive value of a square root). Thus for each positive x we have not one, but two, values of y. In older literature one sees such cases referred to as "double-valued functions," but modern mathematical terminology has abandoned such locutions and adheres to the usage that the word function denotes *one and only one* corresponding

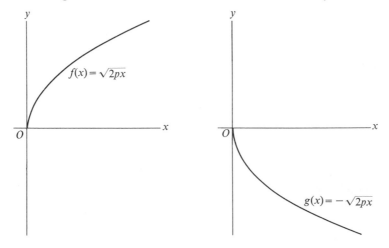

FIG. 3.10.1. Graphs of the two separate functions representing the parabola $y^2 = 2px$. Domain of each function is $x \geq 0$.

object. We handle the situation of Eq. (3.10.1) by saying that the parabola is made up of two separate functions or branches. One branch (the upper one) is denoted by

$$y = f(x) = +\sqrt{2px} \qquad (3.10.2)$$

and the other by

$$y = g(x) = -\sqrt{2px}. \qquad (3.10.3)$$

We are now permitted to use the word function, since in each branch a value of x has associated with it one and only one value of y. (See Fig. 3.10.1.) The domain of each function is the set of all positive real numbers and zero; that is, $x \geq 0$.

A description in our new language of the system of plotting curves on Cartesian axes: In Fig. 3.10.1 we plot the domain X along the x-axis of coordinates, and the value $f(x)$ of the range Y along the y-axis. We deal with functions, $y = f(x)$, such that lines parallel to the y-axis cut the graph of the function once and only once.

PROBLEM 3.8. Identify the separate functions which describe the circle [Eq. (3.5.2)] and the ellipse [Eq. (3.7.3)]. What points of view are possible with respect to the parabola of Problem 3.4 [Eq. (3.6.4)]?

3.11 EXAMPLES OF FUNCTIONS AND FUNCTIONAL NOTATION

Our interest will be principally focused on functions the domain and range of which are sets of real numbers. It must be strongly emphasized that this category of functions is entirely arithmetical in conception and definition, and not geometrical; the relations, stated as algebraic formulas or in words, are connections between *numbers*. We shall make extensive use of graphs and diagrams to assist us in visualizing the character and properties of various functions, but these geometrical devices are only aids which help us *display* functions of real numbers visually. Geometrical diagrams are not the functions themselves.

Some functions are directly expressible as algebraic formulas in terms of the independent variable; others are not, and must remain described in words or by verbal specification of rules of calculation. The following examples are introduced in order to help the reader improve his facility with language and notation. (Graphs of the functions referred to are sketched in Fig. 3.11.1. Verify each one as you go along.)

(1) A very special case, the constant function (Fig. 3.11.1a):

$$f(x) = a, \qquad (3.11.1)$$

where a is a constant. A particular instance would be $f(x) = -2$.

(2) The absolute value function (Fig. 3.11.1b):

$$g(x) = |x|. \qquad (3.11.2)$$

(3) The sine function (Fig. 3.11.1c):

$$h(x) = \sin x. \qquad (3.11.3)$$

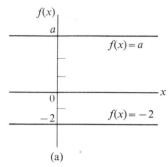

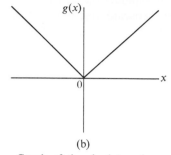

(a)

Graphs of the constant functions $f(x) = a$; $f(x) = -2$.

(b)

Graph of the absolute value function $g(x) = |x|$.

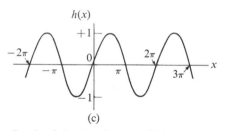

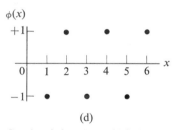

(c)

Graph of the sine function $h(x) = \sin x$.

(d)

Graph of function which is $+1$ when x is an even positive integer, -1 when x is an odd positive integer, elsewhere undefined.

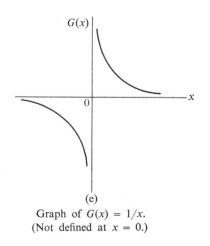

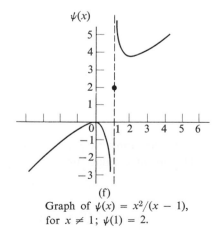

(e)

Graph of $G(x) = 1/x$.
(Not defined at $x = 0$.)

(f)

Graph of $\psi(x) = x^2/(x - 1)$, for $x \neq 1$; $\psi(1) = 2$.

FIGURE 3.11.1

Note that this is not an algebraic formula. The symbol "sin" is not essentially different from "h"; it simply refers to a particular correspondence which we call the *sine function*. Our calculation of $h(x)$ must be made from the specified definition of sinc. Numbers in a table of sines are calculated in the same way. (A summary of definitions of trigonometric functions is given in Appendix I.)

(4) A function $\phi(x)$ such that

$$\phi(x) = \begin{cases} +1 \text{ if } x \text{ is an even positive integer,} \\ -1 \text{ if } x \text{ is an odd positive integer.} \end{cases}$$

(See Fig. 3.11.1d.) This function must remain described in words; it cannot be written out as an algebraic formula. The domain of the function is that of positive integers only; it is not defined for 0, negative numbers, or noninteger positive numbers such as 0.5, π, 2.7, etc. The range of the function is confined to the numbers $+1$ and -1.

(5) The function $G(x) = 1/x$ (Fig. 3.11.1e; see Problem 3.6). This function has the domain of all numbers $x \neq 0$ (read "x not equal to zero"); it is not defined for $x = 0$.

(6) The function

$$\psi(x) = \frac{x^2}{x - 1} \quad \text{for } x \neq 1, \qquad \psi(1) = +2 \quad \text{(by fiat).}$$

(See Fig. 3.11.1f.) This function has the domain of all real numbers, since a value of $\psi(1)$ has been specified.

PROBLEM 3.9. Given $f(x) = x^2 - 2x + 3$.
   (a) Find numerical values of $f(1)$, $f(-2)$, $f(0)$. [*Answer:* $f(-2) = 11$.]
   (b) Write expressions for $f(a)$, $f(u + v)$, $f(x + h)$, $f(x - 1)$. [*Answer:* $f(x + h) = x^2 + 2hx + h^2 - 2x - 2h + 3$.]
   (c) What is the domain of the function?

PROBLEM 3.10. Given $g(x) = \sqrt{x^2 - 1}$.
   (a) Find $g(3)$, $g(1)$.
   (b) What is the domain of the function? The range? [*Answer:* Domain: $x \leq -1$; $x \geq +1$.]

PROBLEM 3.11. Given $G(x) = x^2$; $f(x) = 1/\sqrt{x + 2}$.
   (a) What is the domain of $f(x)$? [*Answer:* $x > -2$.]
   (b) Write expressions for $G(f(x))$ and $f(G(x))$. [*Answer:* $G(f(x)) = 1/(x + 2)$.]

3.12 INTRODUCTION TO THE CONCEPT OF LIMIT

In Chapter 1 we used the word *limit* several times in a preliminary way. We spoke of instantaneous velocity and instantaneous acceleration as "limits of the ratios $\Delta s/\Delta t$ and $\Delta v/\Delta t$ as Δt approaches zero." We then seized upon the plausible geometrical interpretation of these quantities as the slopes of tangents to the s-versus-t and v-versus-t graphs, respectively. This is not unlike the manner in which the inventors of the calculus— Newton, Leibniz, and their followers—thought about such problems. If the student has been bothered by the vagueness of the limit concept, if he has been concerned about the meaning of "approaches," if he has wondered whether the "limit" is a definable, single, unique number or just a fuzzy range of numbers, he has sensed the questions that eighteenth-century mathematicians felt to be of prime importance in establishing sound, logical foundations for this newly invented branch of mathematics. Central to the problem is the necessity of devising a rigorous, *arithmetical* definition of "limit." Such an unambiguous, mathematically useful definition was provided in 1821 by the French mathematician Augustin Louis Cauchy (1789–1857). We shall first illustrate the basic concept involved and then state the definition itself.

Consider first the very simple example: $f(x) = 3x^2 + 2$. If we set $x = +1$, we obtain $f(+1) = 3 + 2 = 5$; that is, the function is defined at $x = +1$ and has the value $+5$. Suppose, however, that we refrain from setting x *equal* to $+1$, but ask ourselves about the values assumed by $f(x)$ when x is assigned values *close* to $+1$. It is easy to see that if x is taken very close to $+1$ (say values such as $+1.01$, $+0.9995$, etc.), the value of $f(x)$ will be very close (but not exactly equal) to $+5$. We also feel that we can make $f(x)$ as close as we please to $+5$ (say no further away than 0.01 or 0.0001 or 0.0000001, etc.) if we take x "sufficiently close" to $+1$. This is a highly simplified illustration of the manner in which we shall build up a definition of what we mean by the assertion that the "limit of $(3x^2 + 2)$ as x approaches $+1$ is $+5$." Our notation for this assertion is

$$\lim_{x \to +1} (3x^2 + 2) = +5. \tag{3.12.1}$$

Note that this is *not* the same as saying that $f(+1) = 5$. In the latter case we actually *set* $x = +1$; in the former case we specifically refrain from doing so.

As another illustration, consider the function

$$f(x) = \frac{3(x^2 - 1)}{(x - 1)}. \tag{3.12.2}$$

In this case we cannot evaluate $f(+1)$ at all; it is undefined because the denominator of the expression becomes zero, and division by zero is undefined. (Actually, *both* the numerator and denominator of this function take on values very close to zero when x is taken close to $+1$. In this sense the behavior of the function is similar to that of the quantities $\Delta s/\Delta t$ and $\Delta v/\Delta t$ as Δt is taken close to zero.) If we agree not to set x equal to $+1$, we can simplify expression (3.12.2) by dividing out $(x - 1)$:

$$f(x) = \frac{3(x + 1)(x - 1)}{x - 1} = 3(x + 1). \tag{3.12.3}$$

When x is very close to $+1$, we see that $f(x)$ must be very close to 6. This suggests the possibility that the limit exists and the $\lim_{x \to +1} f(x)$ is 6 while $f(+1)$ remains *undefined!* Let us examine the problem more formally. The quantity $|f(x) - 6|$ measures how far $f(x)$ is from $+6$, either above or below. From (3.12.3) we have

$$|f(x) - 6| = |3(x + 1) - 6| = |3x - 3| = 3|x - 1|. \tag{3.12.4}$$

The quantity $|x - 1|$ measures how far x is from $+1$; note that this quantity has made its appearance in (3.12.4).

Suppose we arbitrarily choose a small positive number, say 0.01 (we shall denote such numbers by the symbol ϵ). Can we find values of x such that $|x - 1|$ is small enough to make $|f(x) - 6|$ smaller than 0.01? Equation (3.12.4) tells us that we can: we must take values of x such that $|x - 1|$ is smaller than 0.01/3, providing $|x - 1|$ is not allowed to become zero (that is, x may be any number between 0.997 and 1.003 except exactly $+1$). We shall denote numbers (such as 0.01/3) that establish the allowable range of x by the symbol δ.

If we choose ϵ to be 0.0001, we can make $|f(x) - 6| < 0.0001$ if we take $0 < |x - 1| < 0.0001/3$. In general, we can make $|f(x) - 6|$ less than *any* arbitrarily small number ϵ (less than a millionth or a billionth, etc.) by taking $|x - 1|$ greater than zero but less than δ, where the value of δ depends upon our choice of ϵ; in the case illustrated above $\delta = \epsilon/3$. Note that in each instance $|f(x) - 6|$ is smaller than ϵ, not for just a single value of x but for an entire *range* of values defined by $0 < |x - 1| < \epsilon/3$.

Observe that, for the case with which we are working, the numbers $+6$ for the function and $+1$ for x form a unique combination. Let us emphasize this by noting what we can*not* do. It is *not* possible to make $|f(x) - 6|$ arbitrarily small by bringing x closer and closer to some number *different* from $+1$, even slightly different, say 1.01. Equation (3.12.4) indicates that if we bring x close to 1.01, $|f(x) - 6|$ gets stuck near 0.03, and we cannot make it as small as we please. Similarly, although 5.99 is a number quite close to $+6$, we cannot make $|f(x) - 5.99|$ arbitrarily small by bringing x closer and closer to $+1$; as x gets very close to $+1$, $|f(x) - 5.99|$ gets stuck near 0.01 and does not become smaller.

Our investigation indicates that we can associate a single, unique number (namely $+6$) with the function $3(x^2 - 1)/(x - 1)$ as x approaches $+1$—even though the numerator and denominator of the function both get closer and closer to zero, and even though $f(+1)$ is undefined. We are *not* confronted by a fuzzy, ill-defined range of values, but a single number, $+6$; no other one will do, and this number is the one we call the "limit" in the given circumstances. (Note that this result offers encouragement concerning the possible uniqueness and definability of

$$\lim_{\Delta t \to 0} \frac{\Delta s}{\Delta t} ;$$

we shall consider this specific problem in Chapter 8.)

PROBLEM 3.12. Examine the behavior of

$$f(x) = \frac{1}{x - 3} \quad \text{as} \quad x \to 5$$

and the behavior of

$$g(x) = \frac{3(x^2 - 1)}{x + 1} \quad \text{as} \quad x \to -1$$

in a manner exactly parallel to that illustrated in the preceding paragraphs, deducing what the respective limits seem to be and testing them by showing that ϵ can be made as small as you please, providing δ is made small enough. Be specific concerning how δ is related to the ϵ you chose in any particular test. Then argue in the case of the first function that the limit as $x \to 5$ cannot be 0.49, since under these circumstances ϵ cannot be made as small as you please by making x closer and closer to 5.

3.13 FORMAL DEFINITION OF LIMIT

Cauchy's rigorous definition of limit, which we have been illustrating discursively in the preceding section, can be stated formally as follows (as you read each part of the statement, compare it with the corresponding steps taken in the example developed in Section 3.12):

Definition: The statement that

$$\lim_{x \to a} f(x) = b$$

shall mean that for each arbitrarily chosen positive number ϵ there exists a positive number δ, depending on ϵ, such that:

$$\text{if } 0 < |x - a| < \delta, \qquad \text{then } |f(x) - b| < \epsilon,$$

where x is any number for which $f(x)$ is defined.

Let us apply the definition in making a formal test of an assertion concerning a limit. Consider the function

$$f(x) = \frac{x^2 - 4}{5(x - 2)}. \tag{3.13.1}$$

Providing $x \neq 2$, we can simplify the expression by dividing out $(x - 2)$:

$$f(x) = \frac{(x + 2)(x - 2)}{5(x - 2)} = \frac{x + 2}{5}, \qquad \text{providing } x \neq 2. \tag{3.13.2}$$

In the light of (3.13.2), is it correct to assert that

$$\lim_{x \to 2} \frac{x^2 - 4}{5(x - 2)} = \frac{4}{5}? \tag{3.13.3}$$

The quantity that corresponds to $|f(x) - b|$ is

$$\left| \frac{x^2 - 4}{5(x - 2)} - \frac{4}{5} \right| = \left| \frac{x + 2}{5} - \frac{4}{5} \right| = \frac{1}{5}|x - 2|. \tag{3.13.4}$$

If we take $\delta = 5\epsilon$, we have

$$0 < |x - 2| < 5\epsilon. \tag{3.13.5}$$

From (3.13.4), we have

$$\left| \frac{x^2 - 4}{5(x - 2)} - \frac{4}{5} \right| = \frac{1}{5}|x - 2| < \epsilon. \tag{3.13.6}$$

Therefore, for any arbitrarily chosen positive number ϵ, there *does* exist a positive number δ (δ being equal to 5ϵ) such that if $0 < |x - 2| < \delta$, then

$$\left| \frac{x^2 - 4}{5(x - 2)} - \frac{4}{5} \right| < \epsilon,$$

and (3.13.3) is demonstrated to be a correct assertion, satisfying our formal definition of limit.

As a final illustration, consider the example proposed in Section 3.12:

$$f(x) = 3x^2 + 2.$$

Is it correct that $\lim_{x \to +1} (3x^2 + 2) = 5$?
  Analysis:

$$|3x^2 + 2 - 5| = |3x^2 - 3| = 3|x + 1| \cdot |x - 1|. \tag{3.13.7}$$

In this case the quantity $|x - 1|$ is multiplied by $3|x + 1|$, rather than by a constant as in our preceding examples, and we must take this into account in expressing the dependence of δ on ϵ. If we agree to restrict x to values that will not exceed 2 (i.e., will remain within ± 1 of $+1$), then $3|x + 1|$ will not exceed 9. Then we will be sure that $|3x^2 + 2 - 5|$ will always be less than $9|x - 1|$. Now, if we take $\delta = \epsilon/9$ so that $0 < |x - 1| < \epsilon/9$, it follows that $|3x^2 + 2 - 5| < \epsilon$, and our assertion that the limit is 5 is verified.

Having given these illustrations, let us summarize remarks that help make clear the "stance" and character of the formal definition of limit:

(1) The concept of limit is defined solely in terms of numbers. The verbal idea of closeness is made numerical, and no use is made of diagrams or geometrical analogies or words like "moving" or "changing."

(2) The definition involves values of x *different* from a. x is never set equal to a, and nothing is said about $f(a)$. $f(x)$ must be defined for all the values of x considered, but $f(a)$ need not be defined since $x = a$ is not included in the discussion.

(3) As indicated in the illustrative examples, it *may* be that $\lim_{x \to a} f(x)$ exists, and at the same time $f(a)$ may not exist. If $f(a)$ exists, it may be equal to $\lim_{x \to a} f(x)$ or it may be different from the limit.

(4) No locutions are used in the definition to the effect that a "limit approaches some value" or that the "function approaches such and such a value as a limit." The statement made is that the "limit *is* such and such a value." This is the accepted verbalization; other phrases should not be used.

(5) In order to answer some of the questions raised about the concepts of instantaneous velocity and acceleration in Chapter 1, it will eventually be necessary to examine

$$\lim_{\Delta t \to 0} \frac{\Delta s}{\Delta t} \qquad \text{and} \qquad \lim_{\Delta t \to 0} \frac{\Delta v}{\Delta t}$$

in the light of Cauchy's definition.

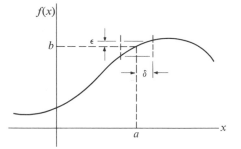

Fig. 3.13.1. Diagram giving geometrical interpretation of the definition of limit. As ϵ is assigned smaller values, giving $f(x)$ values closer to b, δ must be assigned smaller values, giving x values closer to a. If a sequence of such steps is continued indefinitely, the box surrounding point (a, b) in the diagram "tightens down" around this point. (This diagram illustrates the arithmetical definition of limit, but is not at all part of the definition.)

PROBLEM 3.13. Applying Cauchy's definition, test the following statements concerning limits:

(a) $\lim\limits_{x \to 3} 5x^2 = 45,$

(b) $\lim\limits_{x \to 3} \dfrac{2x^2 - 18}{x - 3} = 12,$

(c) $\lim\limits_{x \to -2} x^2 - 4 = 0.$

Now that we have emphasized the purely numerical nature of the rigorous definition of limit, it may be useful to help visualize the idea by means of a diagram. The diagram, however, plays no role in the definition. Figure 3.13.1 illustrates b, a, ϵ, and δ in a simple, "nonpathological" case and suggests how the box defined by ϵ and δ would "tighten down" around the point (a, b) as ϵ and the corresponding δ are made smaller and smaller.

3.14 LIMIT THEOREMS

Many functions which we encounter are combinations of simpler functions, formed by sums, differences, quotients, etc. By using the ϵ, δ definition, we can prove a number of very useful theorems which in turn permit us to establish the limits of the composite functions once we know the limits of the parts. For example, it can be shown that the limit of a sum of two functions is the sum of the limits. Let us see how this structure is built up.

We first consider two very simple "degenerate" cases represented by the constant function $f(x) = k$, where k is a constant (see Fig. 3.11.1a), and the linear function $g(x) = x$. For the constant function $|f(x) - k|$, being zero, is certainly less than any arbitrarily chosen ϵ when x is close to a but not equal to a. Thus the limit definition is formally satisfied, and we can write

$$(1) \ \lim_{x \to a} f(x) = k \quad \text{when } f(x) = k, \quad \text{or simply:} \quad \lim_{x \to a} k = k.$$

For the function $g(x)$, we note that $|g(x) - a|$ is actually equal to $|x - a|$, and we can certainly make $|g(x) - a| < \epsilon$ by taking $|x - a|$ greater than zero but less than $\delta = \epsilon$. Therefore, we have

$$(2) \ \lim_{x \to a} x = a.$$

In the following cases it is given that

$$\lim_{x \to a} f(x) = b \quad \text{and} \quad \lim_{x \to a} g(x) = c.$$

Let us outline the proof of the following theorem:

$$(3) \ \lim_{x \to a} [f(x) + g(x)] = b + c.$$

That is, the limit of a sum is equal to the sum of the limits.

Examine the quantity

$$|f(x) + g(x) - (b + c)| = |f(x) - b + g(x) - c| \le |f(x) - b| + |g(x) - c|.$$

(The last statement of inequality follows from the fact that the algebraic sum of two numbers, in this case the numbers $[f(x) - b]$ and $[g(x) - c]$, can never be greater than the sum of their absolute values. This is a theorem concerning numbers which we would have to prove at an early stage of study of the number system. We shall accept it here as a plausible statement.)

Since we know b and c to be limits of $f(x)$ and $g(x)$, respectively, it follows that we can select a value of δ small enough to make each of the quantities $|f(x) - b|$ and $|g(x) - c|$ smaller than some value $\epsilon/2$. Then the sum of the quantities will be less than ϵ, and $|f(x) + g(x) - (b + c)|$ will certainly be less than ϵ.

It is thus shown to be possible to select δ so as to make $|f(x) + g(x) - (b + c)|$ smaller than any preassigned number ϵ, and theorem (3) is therefore proved.

In an exactly similar fashion it can be shown that

$$(4) \ \lim_{x \to a} [f(x) - g(x)] = b - c.$$

The proof is left to the reader.

Theorem:

$$(5) \ \lim_{x \to a} [k \cdot f(x)] = k \cdot \lim_{x \to a} f(x).$$

Since it is given that $\lim_{x \to a} f(x) = b$, we examine the quantity

$$|k \cdot f(x) - k \cdot b| = k \cdot |f(x) - b|.$$

Since we know that we can select a δ that makes $|f(x) - b|$ as small as we please, we can select a δ making $|f(x) - b| < \epsilon/k$. Then $k \cdot |f(x) - b|$ is less than ϵ, and Theorem (5) is proved.

Theorem:

(6) **If** $\lim\limits_{x \to a} F(x) = 0$ **and if** $\lim\limits_{x \to a} G(x) = 0$,   **then** $\lim\limits_{x \to a} [F(x) \cdot G(x)] = 0$.

From the definitions given, it follows that we can always make $|F(x) - 0| < \epsilon_1$ for a suitably chosen δ_1, and we can make $|G(x) - 0| < \epsilon_2$ for a suitably chosen δ_2. Therefore, we can always make $|F(x) \cdot G(x) - 0| < \epsilon$ by selecting a δ such that ϵ_1 and ϵ_2 are both less than $\sqrt{\epsilon}$, and Theorem (6) is proved.

If we now define the functions $F(x) = f(x) - b$ and $G(x) = g(x) - c$, by applying Theorems (4) and (1) we have

$$\lim_{x \to a} F(x) = \lim_{x \to a} f(x) - \lim_{x \to a} b = b - b = 0.$$

Similarly: $\lim_{x \to a} G(x) = c - c = 0$.

We now evaluate

$$\lim_{x \to a} [F(x) \cdot G(x)] = \lim_{x \to a} \{[f(x) - b] \cdot [g(x) - c]\}$$

$$= \lim_{x \to a} [f(x)g(x) - cf(x) - bg(x) + bc].$$

Applying Theorems (1), (3), (4), (5), (6), we obtain

$$\lim_{x \to a} [f(x) \cdot g(x)] - cb - bc + bc = 0,$$

(7) $\lim\limits_{x \to a} [f(x) \cdot g(x)] = b \cdot c.$

That is, the limit of a product equals the product of the limits.

We assert two more theorems without giving the proofs:*

(8) $\lim\limits_{x \to a} \dfrac{f(x)}{g(x)} = \dfrac{b}{c}$,   providing $c \neq 0$.

(9) $\lim\limits_{x \to a} [f(x)]^n = b^n$,   if $b > 0$ and n is any real number.

Following is an example of how these theorems are used in evaluating limits: Consider

$$\lim_{x \to +2} \frac{3x}{x^2 - 2}.$$

---

* For proofs, see a more advanced calculus text; e.g., *Calculus*, by T. M. Apostol. New York: Blaisdell Publishing Co., 1961, Section 2.29, pages 165–167.

By (5) and (2): $\lim_{x\to+2} 3x = 6$; by (9), (4), and (1): $\lim_{x\to+2}(x^2 - 2) = 2$; by application of (8):

$$\lim_{x\to+2} \frac{3x}{x^2 - 2} = 3.$$

The reader should make up several examples like the one just illustrated and work them out, citing relevant theorems as he goes along.

3.15   LIMITS INVOLVING INFINITY

Consider the function $f(x) = 1/(x - 3)$ cited in Problem 3.12. Here $f(3)$ is undefined; what can be said about $\lim_{x\to 3} 1/(x - 3)$? If x is closer to 3 than 2.99 or 3.01, $|x - 3| < 0.01$ and $|1/(x - 3)| > 100$. If $|x - 3| < 0.0001$, $|1/(x - 3)| > 10,000$, and so forth. By making x sufficiently close to 3, we can make $|1/(x - 3)|$ as large as we please; i.e., for any positive number N, however large, we can always find a value of $|x - 3|$ small enough to make $|1/(x - 3)|$ larger than N. Under such circumstances we say that a limit does not exist and that $|1/(x - 3)|$ becomes arbitrarily large when $|x - 3|$ is made sufficiently small. In symbols we write:

$$\lim_{x\to 3} \frac{1}{x - 3} = \infty \text{ (read "infinity"),}$$

but this is not a statement of equality or of existence of a limit; ∞ is *not* a number, and the existence of a limit is defined by Cauchy's condition, which is clearly not satisfied in this instance. The illustrative example is translated into a general definition as follows.

Definition:

$$\lim_{x\to a} f(x) = \infty$$

means that for any positive number N, however large, there exists a sufficiently small positive number δ such that $|f(x)| > N$ whenever $0 < |x - a| < \delta$. In such a case we say that a limit does not exist.

A formal example: Investigate $f(x) = k/(x - 1)$ in the neighborhood of $x = 1$; k is a constant not equal to zero.

(1) $f(1)$ is undefined, since its calculation involves division by zero.

(2) $|k/(x - 1)|$ can be made $> N$ if $|x - 1| < |k|/N$. Thus by taking δ smaller than $|k|/N$, $f(x)$ can be made larger than N, regardless of how large N is taken to be.

(3) Hence:

$$\lim_{x\to 1} \frac{k}{x - 1} = \infty$$

and a limit does not exist.

One final contingency is again illustrated by $f(x) = 1/(x - 3)$. We can make $|f(x)|$ as small as we please by making $|x|$ sufficiently large. This can be defined as follows.

Definition:

$$\lim_{x \to \infty} f(x) = b$$

means that for any arbitrarily chosen positive number ϵ, however small, there exists a sufficiently large positive number M such that $|f(x) - b| < \epsilon$ whenever $|x| > M$.

A formal example: Investigate

$$f(x) = \frac{3x + 2}{x - 1} \qquad \text{as} \quad x \to \infty.$$

(1) As x becomes very large, the influence of $+2$ and -1 in numerator and denominator becomes negligible. The numerator will then always be very nearly three times the denominator. This suggests testing the hypothesis that

$$\lim_{x \to \infty} \frac{3x + 2}{x - 1} = 3.$$

(2) $\left| \dfrac{3x + 2}{x - 1} - 3 \right| = \left| \dfrac{3x + 2 - 3x + 3}{x - 1} \right| = \left| \dfrac{5}{x - 1} \right|.$

We can make $|5/(x - 1)| < \epsilon$ by making $|x|$ sufficiently larger than $5/\epsilon$, say $1 + (5/\epsilon)$. Thus for every positive number ϵ, however small, there exists a sufficiently large positive number $M = 1 + 5/\epsilon$ such that

$$\left| \frac{3x + 2}{x - 1} - 3 \right| < \epsilon$$

whenever $|x| > M$. Hence it is proved that

$$\lim_{x \to \infty} \frac{3x + 2}{x - 1} = 3.$$

PROBLEM 3.14. Investigate the following cases in the light of the two definitions developed in this section: (a) The function illustrated in Fig. 3.11.1(f) in the neighborhood of $x = 1$. (How would you analyze the behavior as $x \to \infty$?); (b) $f(x) = k/x$ as $x \to \infty$ and near $x = 0$; (c) $f(x) = (-x + 7)/(4x - 3)$ as $x \to \infty$ and near $x = \frac{3}{4}$.

3.16 THE CONCEPT OF CONTINUITY

Having created a clear-cut, arithmetical notion of limit, and definitions of when a limit is said to exist or not exist, it is now possible to generate a similarly clear-cut concept of the "continuity of a function." Cauchy's definition is as follows: A func-

tion $f(x)$ will be called *continuous* at $x = a$ if the following conditions are satisfied:
(1) $f(a)$ is defined; (2) $\lim_{x \to a} f(x)$ exists; (3) $\lim_{x \to a} f(x) = f(a)$.

In one of the illustrative examples of Section 3.13, we showed that

$$\lim_{x \to +1} (3x^2 + 2) = f(+1),$$

and we would now say that the function $3x^2 + 2$ is continuous at $x = +1$. As a matter of fact it is continuous for all values of x. In another illustrative example in Section 3.13 we showed that

$$\lim_{x \to 2} \frac{x^2 - 4}{5(x - 2)} = \frac{4}{5},$$

but since $f(2)$ is not defined, this function is described as not continuous at $x = 2$; we could make it continuous by specifying separately that $f(2) = +2$. The function $\psi(x)$ shown in Fig. 3.11.1(f) is discontinuous at $x = 1$, because, although $\psi(2)$ is defined to be $+2$, the limit does not exist. The function shown in Fig. 3.11.1(d) is discontinuous, since the function is not defined for any but integer values of x, and limits can therefore not be defined or evaluated, since $f(x)$ is not defined for values of x close to the integers. The function shown in Fig. 3.11.1(e) is discontinuous at $x = 0$, since $f(0)$ is not defined, and the limit does not exist. The function shown in Fig. 3.11.1(b) is everywhere continuous, even at $x = 0$.

PROBLEM 3.15. Examine the following functions for points of discontinuity. In each instance, specify which continuity conditions are violated.

(a) $\dfrac{4x}{x^2 - 9}$ 　　　　(b) $\dfrac{x - 2}{x^2 + x - 6}$ 　　　　(c) $3x^2 - 2x + 1$

(d) $f(x) = \begin{cases} x^2 + 3 & \text{for } x < 1 \\ 2x + 2 & \text{for } x > 1 \end{cases}$

3.17 QUESTIONS AND PROBLEMS

3.16. Given a line with slope m_1. Find the slope m_2 of a line perpendicular to the given line.

Outline of solution:

(a) For simplicity, draw line OA through the origin, parallel to the given line. Draw OB perpendicular to OA (Fig. 3.17.1).

(b) Since AOB is a right triangle:

$$\overline{BA}^2 = \overline{AO}^2 + \overline{OB}^2.$$

(c) From the distance formula [Eq. (3.1.2)]:

$$\overline{BA}^2 = (1 - 1)^2 + (m_1 - m_2)^2,$$

etc., for OA and OB.

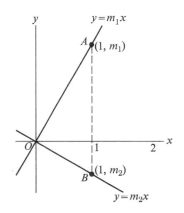

FIGURE 3.17.1

(d) Substituting into the equation in (b) and simplifying the algebraic expression leads to

$$m_1 m_2 = -1 \quad \text{or} \quad m_2 = -1/m_1.$$

Interpret this result. Is it restricted to lines passing through the origin because the lines were so taken in the derivation?

(e) What is the slope of lines perpendicular to the following:

$$y = -3x + 5; \qquad y = \tfrac{5}{2}x - 6;$$

$$\frac{y - 3}{x - 2} = \frac{-3}{5} ?$$

[*Answer*: $\tfrac{1}{3}, -\tfrac{2}{5}, \tfrac{5}{3}$.] What is the equation of the perpendicular line in each of the preceding cases if it goes through the points

$$(0, 0); \quad (4, -1); \quad (-2, 3), \text{ respectively?}$$

3.17. In the light of the study of conics in Sections 3.5, 3.6, 3.7, and 3.8, identify and sketch on numbered axes the following curves. Where relevant, show distances a, b, c, and asymptotes on the sketch. Note that an ellipse "fits" into a rectangle the sides of which have lengths $2a$ and $2b$.

(a) $x^2 + y^2 = 9$ (b) $y^2 + 20x = 0$

(c) $\dfrac{x^2}{25} + \dfrac{y^2}{9} = 1$ (d) $x^2 + \dfrac{y^2}{4} = 1$

(e) $5x^2 + 3y^2 = 30$ (f) $\dfrac{x^2}{25} - \dfrac{y^2}{9} = 1$

(g) $\dfrac{y^2}{4} - \dfrac{x^2}{9} = 1$

(h) $x^2 - y^2 - 1 = 0$

(i) $x^2 - 2y^2 + 4 = 0$

3.18. Find the equations of the following parabolas:

(a) Vertex at origin, focus $(0, -4)$
(b) Vertex at origin, directrix $y = -2$
(c) Vertex at origin; y-axis is axis of parabola; parabola passes through point $(3, 2)$. [*Answer*: $x^2 = \tfrac{9}{2}y$.]

3.19. Find equations of the following ellipses:

(a) Foci at $(\pm 2, 0)$ and vertices at $(\pm 3, 0)$
(b) Foci at $(0, \pm 5)$ and endpoints of minor axis at $(\pm 5, 0)$
(c) Ellipse with "center" at the origin, touching the sides of a rectangle whose vertices have the coordinates $(\pm 3, \pm 4)$
(d) Vertices of ellipse at $(0, \pm 6)$ and distance between vertex and nearest focus is 2

3.20. Find equations of the following hyperbolas:

(a) Foci at $(\pm 3, 0)$ and vertices at $(\pm 2, 0)$
(b) Vertices at $(0, \pm 5)$, and passing through $(7, 10)$
(c) Vertices at $(\pm 3, 0)$; asymptotes $y = \pm x$
(d) Coordinate axes as axes of symmetry; foci on the x-axis, and passing through $(-3, 2)$ and $(5, 4)$

3.21. An hyperbola is called equilateral when its asymptotes are perpendicular to each other. Using the results of Problem 3.16, show that the equation $x^2 - y^2 \pm a^2 = 0$ ($a \neq 0$) always represents an equilateral hyperbola.

3.22. The number $e \equiv c/a$ is called the *eccentricity* of a conic section.

(a) What is the range of values of e for ellipses? What is the character of the figure if e is very close to zero? equal to zero? very close to 1?
(b) What is the range of values of e for hyperbolas? What is e for an equilateral hyperbola (Problem 3.21)?
(c) The orbit of the earth around the sun is an ellipse of $e \sim \tfrac{1}{60}$ (the symbol $\sim$ is read "approximately equal to") with the sun at one focus. The semimajor axis of the earth's orbit is $\sim 93 \times 10^6$ mi. What is the greatest distance between the centers of earth and sun? The least distance?
(d) What is the eccentricity of a satellite orbit which has its perigee (distance of closest approach) 200 mi above the surface of the earth and apogee (greatest distance) 800 mi above the surface? The radius of the

earth is ~ 4000 mi, and a satellite orbit is an ellipse with the center of the earth at one focus.

3.23. (a) If $f(x) = \sqrt{x+1}$, what are the domain and range of the function? What are $f(3)$, $f(-1)$, $f(1+a)$, $f(x^2+2)$, $f(-3)$?

(b) If $g(u) = 2^u$, what are the domain and range of the function? What are $g(3)$, $g(-1)$, $g(b)$, $g(\tfrac{1}{2})$, $g(2x)$?

(c) If $f(x) = a^x$, express in functional notation the fact that $a^m \cdot a^n = a^{m+n}$.

3.24. For the following functions write expressions for the "area" between the curve and the x-axis corresponding to the sectioned area in item 12 of Table 3.10.1.

(a) $f(x) = 2$, taking $a = 1$
(b) $f(x) = b$, taking $a = a$
(c) $f(x) = 3x + 4$, taking $a = -1$
(d) $f(x) = kx$, taking $a = 0$

3.25. Sketch the functions

(a) $\cos x$,   (b) $\tan x$,   (c) $\log x$.

3.26. Apply the limit theorems of Section 3.14 to evaluate the limits of the following expressions; indicate which theorem you use at each step. (Remember that $f(a)$ and $\lim_{x \to a} f(x)$ are two entirely different ideas.)

(a) Given

$$f(x) = \frac{x^2 - 1}{x + 1}.$$

Find

$$\lim_{x \to 2} f(x); \quad \lim_{x \to 1} f(x); \quad \lim_{x \to -1} f(x).$$

(b) Given

$$g(x) = \frac{x^2 - 5x + 6}{x^2 - 9}.$$

Find

$$\lim_{x \to 1} g(x); \quad \lim_{x \to 3} g(x).$$

(c) $\lim_{h \to 0} \dfrac{(4+h)^2 - 16}{h}$;

$$\lim_{x \to 0} \frac{x}{\sqrt{x + a^2} - a},$$

for $a > 0$. (Rationalize denominator.)

(d) In a few cases test your evaluations rigorously by the ϵ and δ proof.

3.27. By examination of the character of the function, make an intelligent guess as to the value of

$$\lim_{x \to \infty} \frac{x}{x + 1}.$$

Then, using the concepts of Section 3.15, test your conclusion rigorously.

3.28. In the definitions of Section 3.15, we made no effort to distinguish between concepts of $+\infty$ and $-\infty$. It is entirely possible to give meaning to these symbols. How would you modify the definitions to do so? What meaning (expressed in a notation similar to that of Section 3.15) would you give to statements such as

$$\lim_{x \to -\infty} f(x) = k; \quad \lim_{x \to a} f(x) = -\infty ?$$

3.29. Two somewhat more sophisticated problems for special work:

(a) Find

$$\lim_{x \to 1} \frac{x - 1}{\sqrt{x} - 1}$$

and test the result rigorously by means of an ϵ, δ proof.

(b) Show that if $f(x) > 0$ for every x with $0 < |x - a| < \delta$, then $\lim_{x \to a} f(x) \geq 0$ (provided that the limit exists); i.e., show that the limit cannot be negative.

SUPPLEMENTARY READING AND STUDY

For a less detailed discussion of analytic geometry and functions:

Mathematics: A Cultural Approach, Morris Kline.   Reading, Mass.: Addison-Wesley, 1962, Chapters 13 and 15

For more detailed discussion of analytic geometry, functions, and limits:

University Calculus with Analytic Geometry, C. B. Morrey, Jr. Reading, Mass.: Addison-Wesley, 1962, Chapters 2–5

Calculus: Introduction, with Vectors and Analytic Geometry, Volume I, Tom M. Apostol. New York: Blaisdell Publishing Co., 1961

For properties of numbers and numerical relations:

Numbers: Rational and Irrational, Ian Niven. New York: Random House (New Mathematical Library), 1961

An Introduction to Inequalities, E. Beckenbach and R. Bellman. New York: Random House (New Mathematical Library), 1961

Historical material:

The Geometry of René Descartes. New York: Dover Publications (S68), 1954

The World of Mathematics, J. R. Newman. New York: Simon and Schuster, 1956

"The Invention of Analytic Geometry," C. B. Boyer. *Scientific American*, January 1949

A Source Book in Mathematics, Volume II, D. E. Smith. New York: Dover Publications (S553), 1959

CHAPTER 4

Superposition of Velocities;
Projectile Motion

4.1 INTRODUCTION

Having developed a description of rectilinear motion, including a concept of acceleration which deals with the natural phenomenon of free fall in a simple and powerful way, we are automatically confronted with a next level of inquiry: Are the concepts created for description of rectilinear motion adaptable to the description of motion in a plane or in three dimensions? Can we extend the ideas already at hand, or is it necessary to make a fresh start with new constructs? In such an inquiry we must again make reasonable guesses, select extensions of our definitions, and test their applicability to observable phenomena. Two particularly simple and widely encountered two-dimensional cases present themselves for consideration in extending our conceptual structure: circular motion such as that of a point on a rotating wheel or a bob on a string, and projectile motion such as that of a thrown ball or fired missile or projectile. The former motion we shall investigate in due course, but the latter motion, which still involves the effects of free fall, commends itself particularly strongly to our attention. This is the problem which Galileo builds toward in the *Two New Sciences*, and finally considers in the last part of the dialogues, the Fourth Day:

> "In the preceding pages we have discussed the properties of uniform motion and of motion naturally accelerated.... I now propose to set forth those properties which belong to a body whose motion is compounded of two other motions, namely, one uniform and one naturally accelerated.... This is the kind of motion seen in a moving projectile; its origin I conceive to be as follows: Imagine any particle projected along a horizontal plane without friction.... This particle will move along this same plane with a motion which is uniform and perpetual, provided the plane has no limits. But if the plane is limited and elevated, then the moving particle, which we imagine to be a heavy one, will on passing over the edge of the plane, acquire, in addition to its previous uniform and perpetual motion, a downward propensity due to its own weight; so that the resulting motion ... is compounded of one which is uniform and horizontal and of another which is vertical and naturally accelerated."

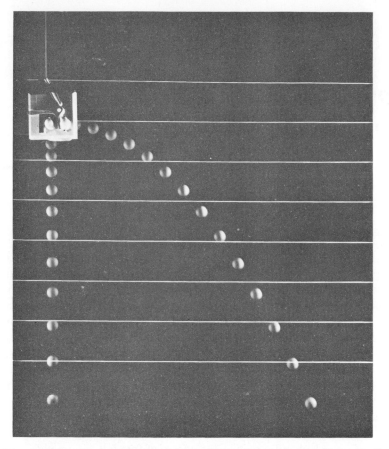

FIG. 4.2.1. Multiexposure photograph at uniform time intervals of two balls released simultaneously, one projected with initial horizontal velocity. Note that balls are at same level on each successive exposure. (Courtesy Educational Services, Inc.)

4.2   SUPERPOSITION OF MOTIONS

The key phrases in the preceding quotation are "resulting motion" and "compounded of." With these deceptively simple terms, Galileo reveals how far he has shifted from the scholastic point of view, in which motion was seen only as a whole and never conceived as compounded. These phrases also articulate his inductive guess that the horizontal and vertical motion of a stone or projectile do not influence each other, that they behave as though each alone were present, and that the net effect is a simple combination of the two independent motions calculated separately. This is an hypothesis about *physics*, and is not just a matter of definition; verification is required just as with the hypothesis that free fall is uniformly accelerated.

Galileo could only verify the idea indirectly, by deducing consequences concerning ranges and trajectories of projectiles, and checking these deduced consequences against observations. Such an investigation requires a measure of self-confidence and intellectual fortitude. One is not initially sure that he has the proper solution, and he must be willing to pursue a sequence of reasoning, through many steps, not knowing what results will emerge or what the right answer is. His only recourse is to careful checking—for internal consistency, and for reasonable results in limiting cases.

In our present age of high-speed photography and electronic techniques, it is relatively easy to present direct, persuasive evidence for the independence of the two motions at right angles, but before doing so, let us be clear as to the precise nature of the logical problem. We must know the answers to two separate questions: (1) Does imparting a horizontal velocity to a particle in any way alter the vertical acceleration and velocities which it acquires in free fall along a straight line? (2) Conversely, does the presence of vertical acceleration and velocity alter the horizontal velocity which a particle might initially have? These are two *separate* questions, and an answer to one does not automatically supply the answer to the other.

These questions are answered by two experiments illustrated in Figs. 4.2.1 and 4.2.2. In Fig. 4.2.1, one ball is projected horizontally while the other is dropped from rest; since the balls occupy identical levels at corresponding times, we infer that the horizontal velocity of the projected ball has not altered the vertical motion it would have had in the absence of horizontal velocity. In Fig. 4.2.2, we observe the motion of a ball which is dropped from a rigid standard moving at uniform horizontal velocity. Since the ball falls but also remains in line with the standard at each succeeding instant, we infer that the initial horizontal velocity is not altered by the vertical effects of free fall.

Our conclusion from these experiments is that motions at right angles to each other are *independent*; i.e., one does not influence or alter the other. It should therefore be possible to use separate numerical knowledge of such motions and to "compound" or "superpose" the numbers into a description of the combined two-dimensional effect. This is precisely what Galileo proposed to do.

The experiments cited and the success of the theory we shall derive are so persuasive that it is a chastening experience to be confronted with the fact that motions at right angles to each other are independent only to a certain degree of precision and only over a limited range of observation. This was not understood or even dreamt of until the beginning of this century, with the advent of the Theory of Relativity. It is now understood that in experiments of the type illustrated in Fig. 4.2.1, for example, the horizontal velocity indeed does have an influence on our observations of the falling motion in the following sense: If the horizontal velocity v_x of the falling particle is made very large relative to us, the acceleration a_y would appear to be smaller than it would from a frame of reference in which the horizontal velocity relative to us is very small or zero. The ratio of the two values of acceleration is $1 - (v_x^2/c^2)$, where c is the velocity of light (186,000 mi/sec or 3×10^8 m/sec). This fraction does not differ from unity by as much as one hundredth of one percent until v_x is of the order of 2000 mi/sec. Since we do not encounter situations in which objects of ordinary size move at such fantastic velocities, our ordinary range of physical experience does not prepare us for this phenomenon; it is even less detectable than the nonuniformity of g was to Galileo. However, such effects become not only observable, but quite pronounced, when in large accelerators one deals with subatomic particles

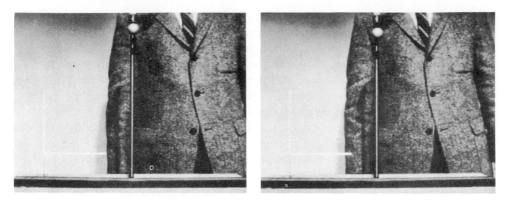

(a)   (b)

(c)   (d)

Fig. 4.2.2. Successive exposures at uniform time intervals of moving standard from which ball is released electromagnetically. (Courtesy Educational Services, Inc.)

moving at velocities approaching that of light. In this new range of physical experience, there is no question but that motions at right angles to each other are *not* independent. Our conclusion as to their independence, based on observations such as those of Figs. 4.2.1 and 4.2.2, reflects the fact that under ordinary circumstances the dependence is unobservably small. In the appropriate range of experience, the assumption of their independence is very precise and extremely useful.

Galileo's assumption became deeply embedded in scientific theory; it seemed so reasonable and proved so successful in its consequences that no challenge of its verity or accuracy was made for 250 years, until very fundamental problems of a new era—problems concerning electricity, magnetism, and light—led Einstein to reexamine systematically our conceptions of space and time, and our procedures for measuring these quantities. Thus the challenge to the idea of independence of the motions came not by direct observation of a dependence, but from an entirely new and different range of experience and theory.

(e)   (f)

(g)   (h)

FIGURE 4.2.2 (*continued*)

For future reference, it will be useful to note the role played by light in the experiments of Figs. 4.2.1 and 4.2.2. The observations utilize light in a very direct way, and the inferences we draw from the photographs implicitly utilize the idea that light propagates so rapidly that, in the given physical circumstances, no account whatever need be taken of time intervals involved in its propagation. The same would be true of other versions of these experiments—even ones which did not utilize a photographic technique. If we were, however, observing motions of objects very far apart or if the objects moved at velocities comparable with that of light, we would no longer be able to forget so casually the time intervals associated with propagation of light from one point to another in our system!

4.3   PROJECTILE MOTION: INITIAL VELOCITY HORIZONTAL

Limiting ourselves to an appropriate range of velocities, let us investigate the arithmetical consequences of the statements: (1) that each motion in the projectile case (horizontal and vertical) behaves as though it alone were present, and (2) that the horizontal motion remains uniform and unaccelerated. Consider the projection of a ball with initial horizontal velocity as in Fig. 4.2.1; refer positions of the ball to a set of coordinate axes y and x as in Fig. 4.3.1, with the initial position at the origin of co-ordinates. Using g to denote the absolute value of acceleration due to gravity, v_{0x} to denote the uniform horizontal velocity, and measuring t from the instant of projec-tion, kinematic equations (1.12.1) and (1.12.2) give:

For the horizontal motion:

$$v_x = v_{0x}, \quad \text{constant}, \quad (4.3.1)$$

$$x = v_{0x}t. \quad (4.3.2)$$

For the vertical motion:

$$v_y = -gt, \quad (4.3.3)$$

$$y = -\tfrac{1}{2}gt^2. \quad (4.3.4)$$

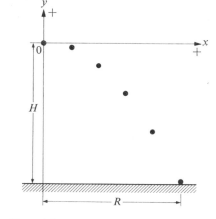

Thus, at any instant of time t, we would claim to know the separate values of both coordinates x and y, and we could locate the position of the projectile in the plane. This is what is meant by a simple *superposi-tion* of the two motions; while the particle

FIG. 4.3.1.   Position axes positive to right and upward. Particle projected hori-zontally from (0, 0).

undergoes a horizontal displacement from 0 to x, it simultaneously undergoes a ver-tical displacement from 0 to y. The total or resultant displacement is from point (0, 0) in Fig. 4.3.1 to (x, y). Since for any value of x there is a corresponding value of y, we note that y can be regarded as a function of x, and this function can be ob-tained by eliminating t from Eqs. (4.3.2) and (4.3.4): From Eq. (4.3.2), we have $t = x/v_{0x}$.

Substituting this equation for t into (4.3.4), we obtain

$$y = -\frac{1}{2}g\left(\frac{x}{v_{0x}}\right)^2 = -\left(\frac{g}{2v_{0x}^2}\right)x^2. \quad (4.3.5)$$

Comparing this result with the discussion in Section 3.6 and Problem 3.4, we recog-nize Eq. (4.3.5) as that of a parabola,

$$y = \frac{1}{2p}x^2, \quad (4.3.6)$$

with p negative; i.e., a parabola, passing through the origin, opening downward, its axis coincident with the y-axis. Since the physical phenomenon described by Eq. (4.3.5) begins at the origin, the left-hand branch of the parabola in quadrant III is not relevant, and our concern is with the branch in quadrant IV. Equation (4.3.5) represents the *path* or trajectory of the projectile in space, and predicts this path to be a semi-parabola.

Galileo obtained this same result through the more involved and cumbersome geometrical analysis alluded to in connection with Fig. 3.1.2, and his writing reveals something of the excitement and triumph he experienced in establishing this connection between the trajectory of a physical object and that mathematical abstraction—a parabola—whose properties and characteristics were already thoroughly known and explored. Simple physical theory produces a mathematical result which illuminates and orders a whole class of events: With larger initial velocity v_{0x}, p is larger and the parabola is broader; a larger vertical acceleration, if it were still uniform, would simply produce a narrower parabola; if the ground is a distance H below the point of projection, the horizontal range of motion R is given by the amplitude of the parabola at a distance H from its vertex:

$$R = v_{0x}\sqrt{2H/g}. \tag{4.3.7}$$

(See Fig. 4.3.1 for geometrical interpretation of R and H.)

PROBLEM 4.1. (a) Derive Eq. (4.3.7) by rearranging (4.3.5).

(b) If an object is rolled or slid off the edge of a table, it is very easy to determine its initial horizontal velocity from measurements of R and H. Perform such an experiment, and calculate the horizontal velocity.

(c) Suppose you were standing on a bluff; stones and a stop watch are available, but the bluff slopes sufficiently so that it is impossible to drop a stone vertically to the foot. Is it still possible to determine the height of the bluff? How? What conditions must be satisfied?

In any other circumstance where a particle is projected at uniform velocity in one direction and is uniformly accelerated at right angles, we immediately recognize that its trajectory must be a parabola. We shall encounter exactly this situation with tiny, electrically charged particles moving between the charged plates of a capacitor, under circumstances where gravitational effects are entirely negligible, but the mathematical description remains unaltered. This ordering of broad classes of events and of entirely different phenomena under one mathematical representation is characteristic of science, and we shall see many additional examples, far broader in scope than this one.

4.4 IDEALIZATIONS IN THE DESCRIPTION OF PROJECTILE MOTION

Galileo was fully aware of the objections and criticisms which scholastic science would voice toward his idealizations:

Sagredo: "The axis of the parabola along which we imagine the natural motion of a falling body to take place stands perpendicular to a horizontal surface and ends at the center of the earth; and since the parabola deviates more and more from its axis no projectile can ever reach the center of the earth or, if it does, as seems necessary, then the path of the projectile must transform itself into some other curve very different from the parabola."

Simplicio: "To these difficulties, I may add others. One of these is that we suppose the horizontal plane, which slopes neither up nor down, to be represented by a straight line . . . as one starts from the middle of the line and goes toward either end, he departs farther and farther from the center of the earth and is therefore constantly going up hill. Whence it follows that the motion cannot remain uniform for any distance whatever, but must continually diminish. Besides, I do not see how it is possible to avoid the resistance of the medium which must destroy the uniformity of the horizontal motion and change the law of acceleration. These various difficulties render it highly improbable that a result derived from such unreliable hypotheses should hold true in practice."

And Galileo answers in a very modern way, taking exactly the stance which any scientist now assumes in his day-to-day work:

Salviati: "All these difficulties and objections which you urge are so well founded . . . I am ready to admit them all, which indeed I think our author would also do. I grant . . . that neither will the horizontal motion be uniform nor the natural acceleration be in the ratio assumed, nor the path of the projectile be a parabola. . . .

"In his *Mechanics,* Archimedes takes for granted that the beam of a balance is a straight line, every point of which is equidistant from the center [of the earth], and that the cords by which heavy bodies are suspended are parallel to each other. Some consider this assumption permissible because, in practice, our instruments and the distances involved are so small in comparison with the enormous distance from the center of the earth that we may consider a minute of arc on a great circle as a straight line, and may regard the perpendiculars let fall from its two extremities as parallel. For if in actual practice one had to consider such small quantities, it would be necessary first of all to criticise the architects who presume, by use of a plumbline, to erect high towers with parallel sides. . . .

"When we wish to apply our proven conclusions to distances which, though finite, are very large, it is necessary for us to infer . . . what correction is to be made. . . . The range of our projectiles . . . will never exceed four of those miles of which many thousands separate us from the center of the earth, and since these paths terminate upon the surface of the earth, only very slight changes can take place in their parabolic figure. . . .

"As to the perturbation arising from the resistance of the medium, this is more considerable and does not, on account of its manifold forms, submit to fixed laws and exact description. Thus if we consider only the resistance which the air offers to the motions studied by us, we shall see that it disturbs them all and disturbs them in an infinite variety of ways corresponding to the infinite variety in the form, weight, and velocity of the projectiles. . . .

"Of these properties . . . infinite in number . . . it is not possible to give any exact description; hence in order to handle this matter in a scientific way, it is necessary to cut loose from these difficulties; and having discovered and demonstrated the theorems in the case of no resistance, to use them and apply them with such limitations as experience will teach."

It is for the crystal-clear articulation of such attitudes and working policy, as well as for the results and insights he published, that Galileo is frequently called the father of modern science.

The modern scientist follows this advice by training and habit. The first, idealized result in an investigation is frequently referred to as a *first-order* theory or analysis. If higher precision is required, a *second-order* theory or calculation provides small corrections which are applied to the first-order results. (The terms "first and second order" refer to relative size and to the fact that correction terms are small.) The correction terms may not demand high accuracy within themselves: If the correction can be estimated roughly to within 20% of its value, and if the correction is about 10% of the first-order term, the final uncertainty is only 2%!

In the case of projectile motion, tables are computed which correct the first-order theory for effects of varying air resistance, wind and even (for very long-range projectiles) for the rotation of the earth.

Our first-order analysis of projectile motion now leaves us with the view that the moving particle simultaneously possesses two instantaneous velocities v_x and v_y as given by Eqs. (4.3.1) and (4.3.3). It is natural to raise the questions: Can we think of the particle as having a single, resultant, instantaneous velocity, varying in direction as well as magnitude, "compounded" of v_x and v_y? What extension or modification of our conception of velocity might this imply? These questions and their consequences are dealt with in the following sections.

4.5   VECTORS AND ORDERED PAIRS OF NUMBERS

In creating a kinematics of rectilinear motion we had at our disposal the entire apparatus of ordinary arithmetic—positive and negative numbers; axioms of commutation and association; rules of addition, subtraction, and other operations. We invoked this apparatus by connecting positions in rectilinear motion with points on the number line. In the problem which now confronts us—motion in a plane—we have already invoked the Cartesian scheme of representing positions by an *ordered pair* of numbers (x, y), the "coordinates" of a point. (See Section 3.1.)

Since the arithmetic of ordered pairs is not as familiar as ordinary arithmetic, we shall proceed to build up a few of its definitions, axioms, and theorems, using our physical problem as the basic motivation. We shall make no attempt to carry out an exhaustive treatment of this mathematical subject. The student would do well to take advantage of the logical sequence presented to test, in parallel, his understanding of the basic structure of ordinary arithmetic. He should remember that the physical motivations and interpretations are being invoked only to help him visualize the new arithmetic more quickly and easily; they are not necessary to the abstract development.

Our first concern, as in Chapter 1, is with change in position. Consider a displacement from 1 to 2 as shown in Fig. 4.5.1. The displacement is made up of horizontal and vertical projections which have been labeled A_x and A_y. We denote the line

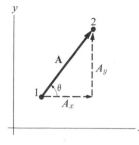

FIG. 4.5.1. "Change-of-position vector" A: $A = [A_x, A_y]$. Horizontal projection A_x and vertical projection A_y are called "components." Direction is defined by $\tan \theta = A_y/A_x$.

connecting points 1 and 2 by the symbol **A**,* and we place an arrow on the line indicating the direction of the displacement. The symbol **A** is called a displacement *vector*, and is defined by the ordered pair of numbers A_x and A_y which are called its horizontal and vertical "components," respectively. We state this definition by the following symbols:

$$A \equiv [A_x, A_y]. \tag{4.5.1}$$

A_x and A_y can, of course, be either positive or negative, and correspond to the rectilinear displacements we dealt with in Chapter 1 and the directed distances referred to in Chapter 3.

The direction of the vector is defined by the angle θ (as in the case of the inclination of a straight line in Section 3.2), and

$$\tan \theta = \frac{A_y}{A_x}. \tag{4.5.2}$$

The total size of the displacement, regardless of direction, is clearly the length of **A** which is related to A_x and A_y by the Pythagorean Theorem, so long as the space in which we apply these ideas is one obeying Euclidean geometry. Therefore the absolute value of **A**, denoted by $|A|$, is taken to be the length of **A** and is defined by

$$|A| = \sqrt{A_x^2 + A_y^2}. \tag{4.5.3}$$

It then follows that the vector itself can always be "resolved" back into its components:

$$A_x = |A| \cos \theta, \tag{4.5.4}$$

$$A_y = |A| \sin \theta. \tag{4.5.5}$$

To summarize: Eqs. (4.5.1) through (4.5.5) have been connected with the definition of a displacement vector. The vector need *not* be interpreted as a displacement, however, and the equations would in any case be connected with the vector **A** defined by the uninterpreted ordered number pair $[A_x, A_y]$.

———————

* In handwritten or typewritten work, it is customary to use arrows over letters, or wiggles under them, as $\vec{A}$ or $\underset{\sim}{A}$, to indicate vectors. In printed material, vectors are commonly indicated by boldface letters, as **A**.

4.6 ADDITION OF VECTORS

Next, consider a succession of displacements: 1 to 2 followed by 2 to 3, as illustrated in Fig. 4.6.1. The overall result is equivalent to a direct displacement **C** from 1 to 3 with components $[(A_x + B_x), (A_y + B_y)]$, the plus sign referring to ordinary arithmetic of addition of numerical values of the respective components. We are thus motivated to define a new concept—that of *vector addition*—by saying that result **C** is what we mean by **A** + **B**:

$$C = A + B \equiv [(A_x + B_x), (A_y + B_y)]. \qquad (4.6.1)$$

The notation **A** + **B** is called a *vector sum,* and means something quite different from the plus sign of ordinary arithmetic; it refers to addition of components and an overall result such as that illustrated in Fig. 4.6.1. The length of **C** is not equal to the arithmetical sum of the lengths of **A** and **B**, for example. The concept is clearly *related* to ordinary addition, however, and rather than use a different symbol, we use the convention of the plus sign, understanding the sign to mean different things in the two separate contexts.

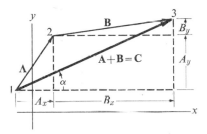

FIG. 4.6.1. Successive displacements from 1 to 2 to 3 are equivalent to a single direct displacement from 1 to 3. Components of the direct displacement are $[(A_x + B_x), (A_y + B_y)]$; $\tan \alpha = (A_y + B_y)/(A_x + B_x)$.

It then follows from Eqs. (4.5.2) through (4.5.5) that:

$$\tan \alpha = \frac{A_y + B_y}{A_x + B_x}, \qquad (4.6.2)$$

$$|C| = |A + B| = \sqrt{(A_x + B_x)^2 + (A_y + B_y)^2}, \qquad (4.6.3)$$

$$C_x = |C| \cos \alpha, \qquad (4.6.4)$$

$$C_y = |C| \sin \alpha. \qquad (4.6.5)$$

Thus, in general, the sum of two vectors is a third vector with magnitude and direction different from the first two. Definition (4.6.1) is an *arithmetical* representation of what we mean by addition of vectors; Fig. 4.6.1 is a *geometrical* representation. The geometrical equivalent of the calculation in definition (4.6.1) is the graphical operation of placing the arrows representing the two vectors **A** and **B** head to tail and drawing the third arrow **C** connecting the first tail with the last head. The process of addition can, of course, be applied to 3, 4, 5, or any number of vector terms, and an exercise to this effect is suggested in Problems 4.3 and 4.4.

The sum of two or more vectors is called a resultant vector or simply a *resultant*. The "zero vector" is, of course, one with components [0, 0]. A group of vectors might very well add up to zero; this would be illustrated geometrically when the head of the last arrow fell back on the tail of the first.

PROBLEM 4.2.   By virtue of definition (4.6.1) of vector addition, it follows that vector addition is commutative:

$$A + B = B + A.$$

That is, the order of addition does not alter the final result. Using your knowledge of ordinary arithmetic, show how this assertion follows from (4.6.1). Then illustrate the same idea geometrically by adding appropriate lines to Fig. 4.6.1, carrying out the other possible order of addition of the vectors.

PROBLEM 4.3.   The associative rule of vector addition is stated:

$$A + (B + C) = (A + B) + C.$$

Show that it must follow from the similar associative property of numbers in ordinary arithmetic.

PROBLEM 4.4.   Generalize definition (4.6.1) by writing out what would be meant by $A + B + C + D + \cdots$ in the form of (4.6.1). Then illustrate the same idea geometrically by adding the following vectors head to tail (Fig. 4.6.2):

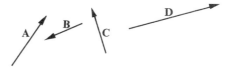

FIGURE 4.6.2

Having defined the concept of vector addition, we can now go back to vector **A** and the following simple idea: We can treat components as themselves being special-case vectors, parallel to the axes

$$A_x = [A_x, 0], \tag{4.6.6}$$

$$A_y = [0, A_y], \tag{4.6.7}$$

and it then follows that

$$A = A_x + A_y, \tag{4.6.8}$$

which is simply another view of a vector and its components—any vector can be thought of as the vector sum of its components.

PROBLEM 4.5.   Give the geometrical illustration of (4.6.8) with appropriate arrows.

4.7 MULTIPLYING A VECTOR BY A SCALAR

Definition of equality: Two vectors **A** and **B** (Fig. 4.7.1) are said to be equal if their respective components are equal. That is, $\mathbf{A} = \mathbf{B}$ if $A_x = B_x$ and $A_y = B_y$.

If we add two equal vectors $\mathbf{A} + \mathbf{A}$ (Fig. 4.7.2), it follows from the definition of addition that

$$\mathbf{A} + \mathbf{A} = [2A_x, 2A_y]. \tag{4.7.1}$$

This is a vector having the same direction as **A** (why?), and twice the length. Thus we are led to say that $\mathbf{A} + \mathbf{A} = 2\mathbf{A} = [2A_x, 2A_y]$, and to generalize this idea by defining multiplication of a vector by a scalar number k:

$$k\mathbf{A} \equiv [kA_x, kA_y]. \tag{4.7.2}$$

If k is a positive number, the direction of $k\mathbf{A}$ is identical with that of **A**; if k is a negative number, the direction of $k\mathbf{A}$ is directly opposite to that of **A**. The symbol k denotes any number (not necessarily an integer) and is without directional properties. It is conventional to distinguish k from a vector by use of the contrasting term *scalar*. Definition (4.7.2) is called "the rule of multiplication of a vector by a scalar." Since k might be a fraction, say $1/b$, definition (4.7.2) also includes the division of a vector by a scalar.

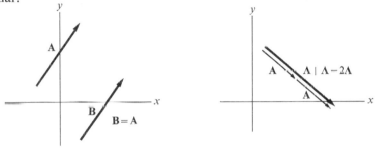

FIGURE 4.7.1   FIGURE 4.7.2

4.8 SUBTRACTION OF VECTORS

In order to define "subtraction," we should first define what we mean by the negative of a vector; i.e., by the symbol $-\mathbf{A}$. In arithmetic we define the negative of a number x as that number which, when added to x, gives zero; that is, $x + (-x) = 0$. We follow exactly the same pattern with vectors, defining:

$$-A \equiv [-A_x, -A_y], \tag{4.8.1}$$

and it is clear from the rule of addition (4.6.1) that:

$$\mathbf{A} + (-\mathbf{A}) = 0.$$

The concept is illustrated in Fig. 4.8.1.

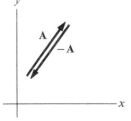

FIGURE 4.8.1

PROBLEM 4.6.   (a) Using a copy of Fig. 4.6.1, sketch the vector $-\mathbf{B}$. Using the graphical representation, find $\mathbf{A} + (-\mathbf{B})$, written $\mathbf{A} - \mathbf{B}$ for short, as in arithmetic.

(b) Assuming in Fig. 4.6.1 that $\mathbf{C}$ and $\mathbf{B}$ are given initially, find (in a graphical sketch) $\mathbf{C} - \mathbf{B}$.

(c) Generalize the ideas developed above to give the arithmetical rule for subtraction of vectors:

$$\mathbf{A} - \mathbf{B} = [(A_x - B_x), (A_y - B_y)]. \qquad (4.8.2)$$

Note that the meaning of the minus sign on the left of (4.8.2) differs from the meaning on the right, just as with the plus sign discussed earlier.

4.9 DISPLACEMENT, VELOCITY, AND ACCELERATION VECTORS

Having established these necessary basic operations, let us return to the original question of displacements and velocities in two dimensions by referring to displacement from point (x_1, y_1) to another point (x_2, y_2) along the trajectory shown in Fig. 4.9.1. The vectors $\mathbf{s}_1$ and $\mathbf{s}_2$ from the origin to position points 1 and 2, respectively, are called *position vectors*. They locate points 1 and 2 relative to the origin and can be thought of as equivalent displacements from the origin to the points in question. From our definition of subtraction, we have

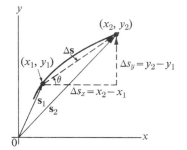

FIG. 4.9.1. Position vectors s_1 and s_2 and displacement vector $\Delta s = s_2 - s_1$ between two points on a trajectory: $\tan \theta = (y_2 - y_1)/(x_2 - x_1).$

$$\Delta \mathbf{s} = \mathbf{s}_2 - \mathbf{s}_1 = [(x_2 - x_1), (y_2 - y_1)]$$

$$= [\Delta x, \Delta y] = \Delta \mathbf{x} + \Delta \mathbf{y}, \qquad (4.9.1)$$

and the direction of $\Delta \mathbf{s}$ is determined by

$$\tan \theta = \frac{\Delta y}{\Delta x}, \qquad (4.9.2)$$

where $\Delta \mathbf{s}$ is called the displacement vector from point 1 to point 2. (The fact that the particle in question moved along the curved path and not along the arrow $\Delta \mathbf{s}$ is not material; recall again that the displacement Δs in rectilinear motion is not necessarily equal to the distance traversed by the particle but is just $s_2 - s_1$.) If we make Δx smaller and smaller, we bring point 2 closer to point 1 and the inclination θ of $\Delta \mathbf{s}$ keeps changing. If the appropriate limits exist, the limit of the inclination of $\Delta \mathbf{s}$ is determined by

$$\lim_{\Delta x \to 0} \tan \theta = \lim_{\Delta x \to 0} \frac{\Delta y}{\Delta x}. \qquad (4.9.3)$$

We recognize in the right-hand side of (4.9.3) the number we intuitively associated with the slope of a tangent to a curve in our discussions of Chapter 1. Here the slope has meaning as an actual direction in space—the "instantaneous direction" of motion at any point along a trajectory is therefore conceivable as being in the direction of the tangent to the trajectory at that point.

Now we can reexamine our measure of rate of change of position, starting as we did in Chapter 1 with average velocity. Referring again to Fig. 4.9.1 and Eq. (4.9.1), we would write

$$\frac{\Delta \mathbf{s}}{\Delta t} = \left[\frac{\Delta x}{\Delta t}, \frac{\Delta y}{\Delta t}\right] = \frac{\Delta \mathbf{x}}{\Delta t} + \frac{\Delta \mathbf{y}}{\Delta t}. \tag{4.9.4}$$

Since the time interval Δt is a scalar quantity, Eq. (4.8.4) follows directly from rule (4.7.2). Our new terms have all the vector properties previously associated with displacement; recall that division by a scalar gives a new vector, parallel to the first one.

Translating Eq. (4.9.4) into words, we note that we can define an average velocity between positions 1 and 2 which has the magnitude $|\Delta \mathbf{s}|/\Delta t$ and the direction of $\Delta \mathbf{s}$. The components of this velocity are $\Delta x/\Delta t$ and $\Delta y/\Delta t$, which we recognize as $\bar{v}_x$ and $\bar{v}_y$ in the system of symbols used in Chapter 1.

Now, providing limits exist in the sense discussed in Section 3.13:

$$\lim_{\Delta t \to 0} \frac{\Delta \mathbf{s}}{\Delta t} = \left[\left(\lim_{\Delta t \to 0} \frac{\Delta x}{\Delta t}\right), \left(\lim_{\Delta t \to 0} \frac{\Delta y}{\Delta t}\right)\right]$$

$$= \lim_{\Delta t \to 0} \frac{\Delta \mathbf{x}}{\Delta t} + \lim_{\Delta t \to 0} \frac{\Delta \mathbf{y}}{\Delta t},$$

which we would translate into the shorthand of velocity symbols as

$$\mathbf{v} = [v_x, v_y] = \mathbf{v}_x + \mathbf{v}_y. \tag{4.9.5}$$

We use vector symbols because the ordered pair of numbers in (4.9.5) must have all the vector properties associated with displacements, being derived from the latter by scalar multiplication by $1/\Delta t$.

Since $\mathbf{v}$ is simply a shorthand for

$$\lim_{\Delta t \to 0} \frac{\Delta \mathbf{s}}{\Delta t},$$

we expect the direction of this vector to be the limiting direction of $\Delta \mathbf{s}$ as given by Eq. (4.9.3); i.e., we expect $\mathbf{v}$ to be tangent to the trajectory at point 1. (We assert this plausible result without taking time for a rigorous proof.) We then also have that $|\mathbf{v}| = \sqrt{v_x^2 + v_y^2}$, and the angle of inclination θ of the velocity vector $|\mathbf{v}|$ is determined by $\tan \theta = v_y/v_x$.

These results answer the questions raised at the end of Section 4.4. With any point along a trajectory, we can associate an instantaneous velocity *vector* $\mathbf{v}$ which is tangent to the trajectory at that point. The components of this resultant vector are the instantaneous velocities v_x and v_y, which we already used in our discussion of projectile motion but did not put together into a resultant velocity; we are now justified in doing so. Figure 4.9.2 shows the vector $\mathbf{v}$ and its components at various points on the trajectory of projectile motion discussed in Section 4.3.

In Section 1.8 we remarked that the velocity concept would be subjected to further evolution and extension. Note how this has now been achieved.

Since acceleration is derived from velocity changes (that is, $\Delta \mathbf{v}$) by another operation of multiplication by the scalar quantity $1/\Delta t$, acceleration in two dimensions must

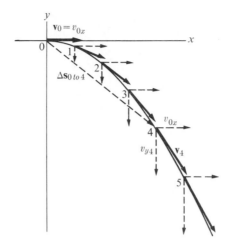

Fɪɢ. 4.9.2. Projectile motion. Resultant velocity $\mathbf{v} = \mathbf{v}_{0x} + \mathbf{v}_y$, and $|\mathbf{v}| = \sqrt{v_{0x}^2 + v_y^2}$. As motion proceeds along the trajectory, v_{0x} remains constant but v_y becomes more negative; therefore $\mathbf{v}$ changes in magnitude and direction. Acceleration $\mathbf{a}$ has horizontal component 0 and vertical component $-g$; $\mathbf{a} = [0, -g]$. $\Delta\mathbf{s}_{0\,to\,4}$ is displacement vector from origin to point 4; direction of $\Delta\mathbf{s}_{0\,to\,4}$ is *not* tangent to trajectory at point 4, but instantaneous velocity $\mathbf{v}_4$ *is* tangent to the trajectory at that point.

have the same vector properties as displacement and velocity:

$$\mathbf{a} \equiv \lim_{\Delta t \to 0} \frac{\Delta\mathbf{v}}{\Delta t} = [a_x, a_y] = \mathbf{a}_x + \mathbf{a}_y. \tag{4.9.6}$$

The direction of instantaneous acceleration, however, need not be tangent to the trajectory; in the projectile motion of Fig. 4.9.2 the acceleration vector has constant magnitude and would be drawn directed downward at every instantaneous position. In this case $\mathbf{a} = [0, -g]$.

PROBLEM 4.7. A particle at some instant of time has a horizontal component of velocity of $+3$ m/sec and a vertical component of $+4$ m/sec. (a) What is the magnitude and direction of the resultant velocity? (b) Answer the same question for the case $v_x = +42$ ft/sec; $v_y = -21$ ft/sec. [*Answer:* (a) 5 m/sec; tan $\theta = \frac{4}{3}$.]

PROBLEM 4.8. What are the horizontal and vertical components of a resultant velocity of 25 m/sec (a) directed at 38° above the horizontal? (b) directed at 20° below the horizontal? [*Answer:* (b) $+24$ m/sec; -8.6 m/sec.]

Any ordered pair of numbers obeying the arithmetic defined in the preceding sections is called a vector. The vectors **A** and **B** may represent mathematical constructs defined by ordered pairs of numbers without any physical interpretation whatever, or they may be *interpreted* to represent displacements or velocities or accelerations, depending on the context in which they are applied. Any physical quantity which is so defined that it must obey vector arithmetic is called a *vector quantity*.

4.10 PROJECTILE MOTION: INITIAL VELOCITY NOT HORIZONTALLY DIRECTED

In Section 4.3 we started investigation of projectile motion with a simple special case: the initial motion of the projectile was horizontal. This investigation, however, has led us to refine and extend our ideas, and the refinement now feeds back to the starting point. The newly developed concept of obtaining a resultant velocity by adding components and the reverse process of resolving a velocity *into* its components gives us a method for dealing with the general case of projectile motion, in which the particle is given an initial velocity v_0 at some angle α to the horizontal (Fig. 4.10.1). This is precisely the sequence of reasoning adopted by Galileo in the Fourth Day of *Two New Sciences*, except that we are using more modern vocabulary and symbols.

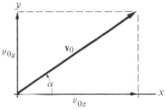

FIG. 4.10.1. Initial velocity vector for general case of projectile motion. Angle α may be above or below the horizontal; in the latter case it may be considered negative. Components: $v_{0x} = v_0 \cos \alpha$, $v_{0y} = v_0 \sin \alpha$, where $v_0 \equiv |\mathbf{v}_0|$.

Denoting the magnitude of the velocity vector by the simple notation v_0 (rather than the more cumbersome $|\mathbf{v}_0|$), we see that the new motion should consist of the superposition of a horizontal part with uniform velocity component $v_{0x} = v_0 \cos \alpha$ and a vertical part with uniform acceleration and an initial vertical velocity $v_{0y} = v_0 \sin \alpha$. If the initial vertical component is directed upward, the projectile must describe a trajectory in which it rises and then falls, as in the cases dealt with in Chapters 1 and 2 without simultaneous horizontal motion.

In order to make a systematic investigation of the predictions which can be drawn from the kinematic relations, let us write down the relations relevant to our new case, taking the origin of the motion at the origin of (x, y)-coordinates:

HORIZONTAL MOTION

Initial velocity component:	$v_{0x} = v_0 \cos \alpha.$	(4.10.1)
Velocity component at time t:	$v_x = v_{0x} = v_0 \cos \alpha \quad$ (constant).	(4.10.2)
Position at time t:	$x = (v_0 \cos \alpha)t.$	(4.10.3)
Velocity-position relation:	——	

VERTICAL MOTION

Initial velocity component:	$v_{0y} = v_0 \sin \alpha.$	(4.10.4)
Velocity component at time t:	$v_y = -gt + v_0 \sin \alpha \quad$ [from Eq. (1.12.1)].	(4.10.5)
Position at time t:	$y = -\tfrac{1}{2}gt^2 + (v_0 \sin \alpha)t \quad$ [from Eq. (1.12.2)].	(4.10.6)
Velocity-position relation:	$v_y^2 - v_{0y}^2 = -2gy \quad$ [from Eq. (1.12.3)].	(4.10.7)

COMBINED MOTION

Equation of trajectory:
solve for t in (4.10.3) and substitute into (4.10.6); valid providing $\cos \alpha \neq 0$;

$$y = -\frac{g}{2v_0^2 \cos^2 \alpha} x^2 + (\tan \alpha)x. \qquad (4.10.8)$$

Magnitude v of resultant velocity **v** at any instant:

$$v = \sqrt{v_x^2 + v_y^2}. \qquad (4.10.9)$$

Direction θ of **v** at any instant:

$$\tan \theta = \frac{v_y}{v_x}. \qquad (4.10.10)$$

4.11 ANALYSIS OF THE PROJECTILE EQUATIONS

Equation (4.10.8) is the equation of the trajectory, valid for $\cos \alpha \neq 0$, obtained by eliminating t from (4.10.3) and (4.10.6); that is, it is the counterpart of Eq. (4.3.5). It should contain most of the story of general projectile motion; let us subject it to complete analysis and interpretation in a manner illustrative of that utilized by a theoretical physicist:

(1) Does Eq. (4.10.8) make sense in what it says about special cases to which we already know the answer?

Suppose $\alpha = 0$; this corresponds to the special case dealt with in Section 4.3. Since $\cos 0 = 1$ and $\tan 0 = 0$, Eq. (4.10.8) then reduces to

$$y = -\frac{g}{2v_0^2} x^2,$$

which corresponds exactly to Eq. (4.3.5) and provides a check and reinforcement of our ideas. If this reduction to the special case had not worked, we would look for an algebraic error in our analysis.

Suppose $\alpha = +(\pi/2)$ or $90°$; we can no longer refer to Eq. (4.10.8), since $\cos (\pi/2) = 0$, and (4.10.8) was obtained by taking $t = x/v_0 \cos \alpha$ from (4.10.3). We can go back to (4.10.3) and (4.10.6), however. Since $\cos (\pi/2) = 0$ and $\sin (\pi/2) = 1$, we obtain

$$x = 0; \qquad y = -\tfrac{1}{2}gt^2 + v_0 t,$$

the equations for motion of an object fired vertically into the air. This again checks our analysis. (Suppose α is taken to be $-(\pi/2)$, what does this mean? Do the equations reduce to a sensible result?)

(2) What is the character of the general trajectory as exhibited in Eq. (4.10.8)? Is this still a parabola? It can be shown that $y = ax^2 + bx$ is the equation of a parabola with its axis parallel to the y-axis, but with its vertex displaced from the origin. Since Eq. (4.10.8) is of this form, it does represent a parabola located on the (x, y)-axes as shown in Fig. (4.11.1).

(3) Where is the vertex of the parabola located in the (x, y)-coordinates, and when is this position attained? We are asking for the values of t, x, and y when $v_y = 0$.

These values are to be obtained from Eqs. (4.10.5), (4.10.7), and (4.10.3). Verify the following conclusions:

At vertex:
$$t_{\text{vertex}} = \frac{v_0 \sin \alpha}{g}, \qquad (4.11.1)$$

$$h = y_{\text{vertex}} = \frac{v_0^2 \sin^2 \alpha}{2g}, \qquad (4.11.2)$$

$$x_{\text{vertex}} = \frac{v_0^2 \sin \alpha \cos \alpha}{g}$$

$$= \frac{v_0^2 \sin 2\alpha}{2g}, \qquad (4.11.3)$$

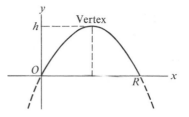

FIG. 4.11.1.   Graph of trajectory equation (4.10.8): parabola with axis parallel to y-axis and vertex displaced from the origin. Dotted curve to left of origin has no physical meaning in this context. Dotted curve to the right of point R would have meaning as continuation of trajectory if point 0 is above ground level.

the last equation making use of the trigonometric relation $\sin 2\alpha = 2 \sin \alpha \cos \alpha$.

Equation (4.11.2) gives the height above initial firing level reached by the projectile. How does this height change if the initial velocity is increased? If the angle α is decreased?

4.12 TARGETS AND RANGES

The experiment illustrated in Fig. 4.2.1 implies that a bullet, aimed at an object suspended at the same horizontal level, will strike the object if the latter is dropped at the instant the bullet is fired. What does our analysis predict about the same experiment performed with the gun aimed at a target not at the same horizontal level? Suppose the target is dropped from position (L, h) at the instant the gun is fired, as illustrated in Fig. 4.12.1. Let us solve for the vertical position y_L of the bullet and y'_L of the target after the time $t = L/v_{0x} \cos \alpha$ taken by the bullet to reach the horizontal location of the target.

From Eq. (4.10.8) the bullet is at:

$$y_L = - \frac{g}{2v_0^2 \cos^2 \alpha} L^2 + L \tan \alpha.$$

From the kinematic equation of vertical fall with $s_0 = h$, the target will, at the same instant, be at

$$y'_L = - \tfrac{1}{2} g t^2 + h$$

$$= - \frac{g}{2v_0^2 \cos^2 \alpha} L^2 + L \tan \alpha.$$

Thus $y_L = y'_L$; the bullet and target are at the same place at the same instant; the

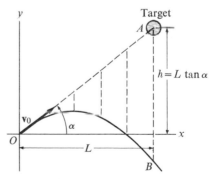

FIG. 4.12.1.   Gun at origin aimed at target A. Target falls at instant gun is fired. Projectile strikes target at B. Motion of projectile can be viewed as superposition of free fall from uniform rectilinear motion along line OA.

bullet still strikes the target! Depending on the size of the initial velocity v_0, the two objects may meet while the bullet is still rising (v_0 large) or, with v_0 small, the objects might meet at some point such as B in Fig. 4.12.1. If the ground is located at level $y = 0$, v_0 would have a critical value below which the bullet and target would reach the ground and not meet:

$$v_{0, \text{ crit}} = \sqrt{gL/\sin 2\alpha}.$$

PROBLEM 4.9.   Verify the preceding assertions by interpreting the appropriate equations.

Another interpretation of these results is the following: Motion along the parabolic trajectory (Fig. 4.12.1) can be thought of as a superposition of a uniform motion at velocity v_0 along straight line OA combined with free fall through various distances from this line, as shown by the dotted segments in the figure.

Two particularly interesting numbers describing the flight of the projectile are the time of flight and its horizontal range. Consider the case in which the projectile is fired over horizontal terrain so that it starts at level $y = 0$ and returns to level $y = 0$. The time of flight is then given by setting $y = 0$ in Eq. (4.10.6):

$$-\tfrac{1}{2}gt^2 + (v_0 \sin \alpha)t = 0.$$

This equation has two solutions: $t = 0$, which corresponds to the start of the motion at $(0, 0)$, and a second value of t, denoted by t_R, given by

$$t_R = \frac{2v_0 \sin \alpha}{g}, \tag{4.12.1}$$

which is the time of flight. The horizontal range is obtained by setting $y = 0$ in Eq. (4.10.8), giving

$$\frac{-g}{2v^2 \cos^2 \alpha} x^2 + \frac{\sin \alpha}{\cos \alpha} x = 0.$$

The solution $x = 0$ corresponds to the starting point. The other solution, denoted by R, is

$$R = \frac{2v_0^2}{g} \sin \alpha \cos \alpha = \frac{v_0^2}{g} \sin 2\alpha. \tag{4.12.2}$$

(See Fig. 4.11.1 for pictorial definition of R.)

Equation (4.12.2) informs us how the range of the projectile over horizontal terrain must depend on the magnitude and elevation of its initial velocity. Let us examine the dependence. If the initial speed v_0 (muzzle velocity) of the projectile is increased while keeping α constant, the range increases; this is no surprise, but it is not quite so obvious that the range must depend on the *square* of the muzzle velocity and must increase by a factor of four when the initial speed is doubled!

If v_0 is held constant while α is increased from low values, R increases, as we would expect. But when $\alpha = \pi/4$ or $45°$, 2α becomes $\pi/2$ and the sine function attains its largest value of $+1$. As α increases beyond this point, $\sin 2\alpha$ decreases. This means that the horizontal range R must have a maximum value (for a fixed muzzle velocity) at an initial velocity elevation of 45°!

In the *Two New Sciences*, Galileo is obviously delighted by this result, for he has Sagredo say:

> "The force of rigid demonstrations such as occur only in mathematics fills me with wonder and delight. From accounts given by gunners, I was already aware of the fact that in the use of cannons and mortars, the maximum range . . . is obtained when the elevation is 45° . . .; *but to understand why this happens far outweighs the mere information obtained by the testimony of others or even by repeated experiment.*" [Italics ours.]

And Salviati rejoins:

> "What you say is very true. The knowledge of a single fact acquired through discovery of its causes prepares the mind to understand and ascertain other facts without need of recourse to experiment, precisely as in the present case, where by argumentation alone the Author proves with certainty that the maximum range occurs when the elevation is 45°. He then demonstrates what has perhaps never been observed in experience, namely that of other shots, those which exceed and fall short of 45° by equal amounts have equal ranges. . . ."

PROBLEM 4.10.   From Eq. (4.12.2), prove the last assertion. [*Hint:* set $\alpha = 45° + \beta$, and interpret the results for cases where β has positive and negative values of equal magnitude.]

Galileo's attitude, as expressed in these quotations, is revealing of several facets of the scientific enterprise. First there is sheer delight in an elegant and simple mathematical result; there is again the emphasis on mathematization which we discussed in Chapter 2; then also the remark that one does not continue to appeal to experiment forever, but, after adequate validation of the basis of a theory, pursues its results and consequences with confidence. Finally there is the remark that we now "understand why this happens." This touches on the large philosophical question of the nature of scientific explanation, a question which recurs repeatedly in any study of the basis and significance of scientific knowledge.

To what extent has the theory "explained" or given us understanding of the previously observed fact that maximum range is attained at an angle of elevation of 45°? Certainly this is no longer an isolated, empirical fact about projectile motion; it is not just a coincidence unrelated to other factors. This prediction is a necessary consequence of: (1) the definitions of velocity and acceleration, (2) the fact that free fall is uniformly accelerated, (3) the fact that the two motions at right angles to each other are independent. It is *in terms of* these basic ideas, which are successfully used to predict many other details of the motion, that we "understand" the reason for the special property of an angle of elevation of 45° and see all the various other properties of the motion predicted and unified by one simple theory. But why free fall is uniformly accelerated, and why the velocity components are independent, are ideas which have no explanation in the present level of inquiry. They have been taken for granted, and, as a matter of fact, we have already indicated that they are not even absolutely correct. The understanding that we hold at this point is thus seen to be a relative understanding, far deeper than any view of the observed phenomena as unrelated, empirical facts, but far short of an understanding which also includes an explanation of the uniformity of the acceleration and independence of the velocity components.

The next level of inquiry is then addressed to the origin of the latter restrictions, and, if successful, understanding is deepened by explanation of these restrictions *in terms of* still more fundamental ideas. But this chain of inquiry never stops. Behind each level attained is a still deeper level, concerning which further questions are raised by inquiring minds.

4.13   QUESTIONS AND PROBLEMS

4.11. An object is projected horizontally, and its trajectory is shown to be a semi-parabola. How does the same trajectory appear to an observer in a set of axes (frame of reference) moving at the same horizontal velocity as that of the object? (See Fig. 4.2.2.)

4.12. A ball is thrown upward from a point in a moving railroad car. Where, relative to the point of origin in the car, does it fall if the car moves at uniform velocity? If the forward speed is increasing? If the forward speed is decreasing? If the car is going around a curve at uniform speed?

4.13. An experiment such as that in Fig. 4.2.1 is performed in an elevator. How will the trajectory appear to an observer in the elevator if the elevator is moving downward at uniform velocity? If the elevator is falling freely? What other questions can you invent about this physical situation?

4.14. Assess in your own words the role which you see mathematics playing in the structure of physical knowledge up to this point. Take into account ideas such as: definitions of concepts, graphical-algebraic representations, idealization, Galileo's admission that a projectile path is not really a parabola, the occasional emergence of physically meaningless results in formal

mathematical solutions, the prediction of effects and relations which were not anticipated intuitively. After experience with the ideas developed in this chapter, how would you describe the process of deriving a formula for a certain problem? Describe in your own words the strategy used in deriving Eqs. (4.10.8) and (4.12.2).

4.15. A long-range ballistic missile might have a range of over 5000 mi and speeds of many thousands of miles per hour. List carefully all the effects you can think of which would cause deviation from the theory of projectile motion put forth in this chapter.

4.16. In a frequently performed lecture demonstration experiment, a bullet is fired horizontally from a spring gun at another object suspended at the same level some distance away. The target is released by an electromagnet as the bullet leaves the muzzle of the gun.

(a) Suggest how an experiment of this kind might be set up. Is the target released at *exactly* the instant the bullet leaves the gun? How important is it that the target release occur simultaneously (suppose the target object is fairly large)? What requirement is imposed on simultaneity of release if both bullet and target are very small objects? Is it possible to attain exact simultaneity in this context? What does the term *mean*? How would you try to attain this goal if it were necessary to do so?

(b) A spring gun, firing wooden bullets, is set up 3 m above the floor. The target is initially at the same level, 10 m away. What range of muzzle velocities is required if the bullet is to strike the target somewhere above the floor but at least 1 m below the initial level from which the objects fall? In addition to solving the problem numerically, give a clear statement of the idealizations and assumption you invoke. (As a comparison, say something about how reliable your calculation would be if the target were a sheet of paper, held to the suspending magnet by a paper clip.) Sketch and label trajectories relevant to your numerical analysis.

4.17. Find the resultant of three displacements **A**, **B**, and **C**, given that $\mathbf{A} = [12, 6]$, $\mathbf{B} = [-3, 3]$, $\mathbf{C} - [\ 9, -1]$. Do this problem in two ways: (1) by a scaled diagram in which the vectors are drawn head to tail and the resultant is measured off; (2) by the arithmetical method of finding the components of the resultant vector and calculating its length. Compare the results. If you are slow and unskilled at these calculations, obtain necessary drill by making up additional problems of this type and working them out.

4.18. Resolve the vectors shown in Fig. 4.13.1 into components along the indicated axes graphically and arithmetically.

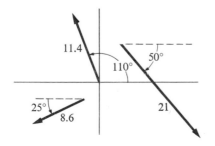

FIGURE 4.13.1

4.19. Suppose the vectors **A** and **B** in Problem 4.17 were velocities instead of displacements. Invent a physical situation in which two such velocities and their sum $\mathbf{A} + \mathbf{B}$ would have meaning and be of interest.

4.20. When we defined the components of a vector, it was specified that the axes to which the components are referred must be perpendicular to each other, but nothing was said about how these mutually perpendicular axes must themselves be chosen. Consider the two sets of axes x, y and x', y' shown in Fig. 4.13.2. Find the vector $\mathbf{A} - \mathbf{B}$ in two ways (by using the method of components with respect to each pair of axes). Are the results equivalent?

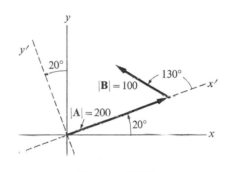

FIGURE 4.13.2

4.21. Making use of appropriate definitions, give a graphical demonstration and then a formal algebraic proof that $(\mathbf{A} - \mathbf{B}) + \mathbf{B} = \mathbf{A}$, where **A** and **B** are any vectors.

4.22. Suppose a man can throw a ball systematically with a speed of about 30 m/sec. He stands on a flatcar moving in a straight line at 20 m/sec and proceeds to throw balls in various directions. What will be the initial velocity, relative to a frame of reference on the ground, of (a) a ball thrown in a direction perpendicular to the tracks, (b) a ball thrown directly forward, and (c) directly backward? (Remember that velocity must be specified by direction as well as magnitude.) What arguments and evidence presented in this chapter are you using to justify

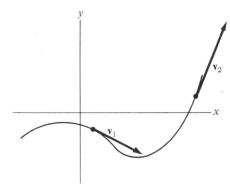

FIGURE 4.13.3

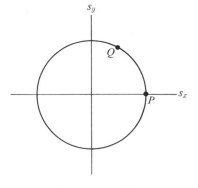

FIGURE 4.13.4

your calculations? In the light of warnings mentioned in Section 4.2, in what sense is your simple arithmetical treatment incorrect?

4.23. Assume a gun fires a projectile with a muzzle velocity of about 1000 ft/sec at an angle of elevation of 30°. Using ideas developed in Section 4.12, what numerical questions can you ask about characteristics of the trajectory and time intervals involved? Ask the questions and work out the answers. Include a calculation of resultant velocity at some point above the ground. What maximum range can be attained over level ground with this gun? What assumptions and restrictions are implicit in your solutions? In each of the quantities you have calculated above, how do you expect the actual value to differ from your idealized prediction; i.e., will the actual value be larger or smaller than predicted? Indicate your *algebraic* reasoning clearly in each case.

4.24. Figure 4.13.3 shows the trajectory of a motion (clearly *not* free fall) in an (x, y)-plane, and two instantaneous velocities v_1 and v_2 are indicated. (Note that the vectors are shown tangent to the trajectory.)

By means of a vector diagram, sketch the vector change in velocity $\Delta v \equiv v_2 - v_1$.

4.25. Consider circular motion of a particle in a counterclockwise direction. The trajectory is shown in Fig. 4.13.4. The particle moves along the circle from P to Q with uniform speed; i.e., the *magnitude* of its velocity vector is constant.

(a) Show the displacement vector associated with the displacement from P to Q.

(b) Draw velocity vectors at points P and Q.

(c) By means of a vector diagram, sketch the vector change in velocity Δv. In what sense is this motion accelerated? In what sense is it not accelerated?

SUPPLEMENTARY READING AND STUDY

A more elementary treatment of projectile motion:
  Physics, Physical Science Study Committee. Boston: D. C. Heath, 1960, Chapter 21

Other points of view; additional problems:
  Physics for the Inquiring Mind, E. M. Rogers. Princeton, N. J.: Princeton University Press, 1960, Chapter 2
  Physics for Students of Science and Engineering, R. Resnick and D. Halliday. New York: John Wiley & Sons, 1960, Chapter 4

Galileo's discussion of projectile motion:

Dialogue Concerning Two New Sciences, Fourth Day, Galileo Galilei.   Translated by H. Crew and A. de Salvio. New York: Dover Publications, 1952

Vectors and vector arithmetic:

Physics, Physical Science Study Committee, *op. cit.*, Chapter 6

Resnick and Halliday, *op. cit.*, Chapter 2

Calculus, Introduction, with Vectors and Analytic Geometry, Volume I, T. M. Apostol. New York: Blaisdell Publishing Co., 1961, Chapter 5

Particle Dynamics I: Force and Mass

5.1 INTRODUCTION

Deliberately restricting the scope of inquiry to exclude dynamics, Galileo formulated successful kinematical descriptions of free fall and projectile motion. In adopting this strategy, he was fully aware of the dynamical questions remaining to be asked and answered—questions concerning the causes of motion and regularities governing its changes. As we have seen, he had arrived at the conception of a law of inertia which, although incorrect on the scale of celestial phenomena, was utilized fruitfully and correctly for terrestrial motions. Galileo sensed that further progress in dynamics would come through careful experimental study of changes in motion occurring in collisions between particles, or in "percussion" as this phenomenon was commonly called.

This view was shared by others, and, throughout the middle part of the seventeenth century, considerable effort was devoted to the study of percussion. Descartes studied the problem and published as "laws of motion" a list of rules obeyed by colliding bodies. Many of his conclusions were later found to be incorrect. When, in 1668, the Royal Society invited definitive statements of the laws of motion and the "bringing into one view what those excellent men, Galileo, Descartes, Honoratus Fabri, Joachimus Jungius, Borelli, and others had invented," papers were submitted by John Wallis, Christopher Wren (the famous architect of St. Paul's Cathedral), and Christian Huygens. Each of these authors stipulated rules for calculating changes in motion of particles undergoing collision along the line of centers, given the masses and initial velocities of the particles. Wallis and Huygens, in particular, showed an awareness that "quantity of motion" (the product of mass and velocity, mv, which we now call *momentum*) had vector properties and was conserved in a collision.

Clearly, in that day, the phrase "laws of motion" implied an expression of the regularities to be observed in motions before and after action of bodies on each other; i.e., the problem of the action itself was avoided. In some ways this is a very powerful approach, as we shall see when we discuss the conservation laws in subsequent chapters, but it turned out that little progress was made toward a broad, general mastery of the physics of motion until the action (or "force") which changes motion was itself quantitatively defined and made usable in the analysis of physical problems.

It is interesting to note what may be a present-day parallel. In modern research on atomic nuclei and elementary particles, experimental knowledge is acquired by studies of "percussion": particles are accelerated to become projectiles which bombard other particles, all these events taking place on a scale of dimensions far smaller than we can ever discern by direct sense perceptions and through interactions very different from the direct material contact of ordinary experience. We observe with complex detection devices the changes that occur in the collisions: recoils, scattering at different angles, transformations of various kinds. We hope, from the regularities observed, to gain insight into the nature and structure of such particles and of the laws that govern their interaction with each other. At present much remains unknown or very dimly understood. Perhaps a new insight into how to conceive and define elementary particle interactions will one day cause the existing empirical knowledge to be seen as a unified whole, explainable and predictable in terms of a few intelligible and relatively simple ideas. In the seventeenth century, the insight that unified experimental knowledge of collisions and simultaneously made many kinds of motion predictable and understandable in relatively simple terms was provided by Isaac Newton.

Newton, who had been lecturing on mathematics and mechanics at Cambridge for some years, published his treatise, *Philosophiae Naturalis Principia Mathematica* (Mathematical Principles of Natural Philosophy), in 1687.

TABLE 5.1.1

DATES OF BIRTH AND DEATH, PLACES OF WORK AND RESIDENCE OF
SEVERAL INFLUENTIAL SCIENTIST-PHILOSOPHERS*
OF THE SEVENTEENTH CENTURY

Galileo Galilei	1564–1642	Pisa, Padua, Florence
Johannes Kepler	1571–1630	Prague, Linz
Rene Descartes	1596–1650	Paris, Amsterdam
Blaise Pascal	1623–1662	Paris
Robert Boyle	1627–1691	England
Christian Huygens	1629–1695	Holland
Robert Hooke	1635–1703	England
Isaac Newton	1642–1727	England: Cambridge, London
Gottfried Wilhelm Leibniz	1646–1716	Berlin

* A more detailed narrative concerning the discovery of the laws of planetary motion, the contributions of these natural philosophers, and the origin and influence of Newton's *Principia* will be found in Chapters 10–15.

In the *Principia*, he put forth what he himself regarded to be the "axioms on laws of motion," and these statements have a completely different cast from the collision rules of Descartes, Wallis, Wren, and Huygens. A dynamical concept of force is created and is associated quantitatively with action of bodies on each other.

To this day, Newton's laws form the basis of classical mechanics. Although found to be inadequate for description of atomic phenomena occurring at velocities which are an appreciable fraction of the velocity of light, they help us to describe and predict the motion of planets and satellites in the solar system, the patterns of motion in the atmosphere and the oceans, the propagation of sound and earthquake waves, the action of machinery, and the flight of aircraft.

5.2 THE LAW OF INERTIA

Among a list of definitions at the beginning of the *Principia* we find the following Definition IV:

> "An impressed force is an action exerted upon a body in order to change its state, either of rest, or of uniform motion in a right line."

Then as Law I of three laws of motion:

> "Every body continues in its state of rest, or of uniform motion in a right line, unless it is compelled to change that state by forces impressed upon it."

We have seen something of the history of this concept in Chapter 2; it was not new with Newton (although it is commonly referred to as Newton's First Law). In Newton's day and for some decades into the eighteenth century, the physics of motion continued to be taught from scholastic textbooks; pedantry is slow to change in any era. But by the latter part of the seventeenth century, Galileo's conception of inertia, refined and corrected, was accepted and taken for granted by most active, productive physical scientists. From our modern vantage point and familiarity with this mode of thought, we might even detect a trace of circularity in the combination of Definition IV and Law I, but Newton set the law of inertia at the head of the laws of motion and gave it the tone of a proclamation of emancipation from scholastic theory.

He saw uniform motion in a straight line as the natural state of material bodies. A body at rest relative to the earth is in uniform motion relative to a passing ship; in either case an action on our part or interaction with another body is necessary to change its state. Circular motion is not "natural," but can occur only if the body is deflected from a straight line by an external effect. Thus, in the absence of gravity, a projectile would fly off on a line tangent to the earth and would not circle the earth as Galileo had pictured. Among the actions which deflect bodies is "that force, whatever it is, by which the planets are continually drawn aside from the rectilinear motions, which they would otherwise pursue, and made to revolve in curvilinear orbits."

PROBLEM 5.1. A frictionless puck sliding on a level glass plate on a laboratory table certainly appears to move in a straight line at uniform velocity. Suppose the limited tabletop could be expanded into a level field of glass many miles in extent. Assuming friction to be still negligible, how would you expect the puck to behave on this field of glass? A quantitative, algebraic answer to this question is perfectly possible, but is well beyond the scope of the concepts so far developed in this text. Try to give a *qualitative* answer. Remember that the earth is rotating. You might simplify your thinking by transferring the field of glass to the North Pole and starting the puck sliding from the pole itself. Would the situation be any different if the experiment were performed at the South Pole? (A pat "answer" to this question is not expected.)

PROBLEM 5.2. In the light of the discussion developed in the preceding problem, how do you assess the validity of Newton's First Law when motion is viewed from a frame of reference fixed to the earth? What is a "straight line" in this context? What frame of reference is implied when we speak of the motion of planets around the sun and apply the First Law to the solar system?

5.3 OPERATIONAL DEFINITION OF A SCALE OF FORCE

Associated with the enunciation of the law of inertia is a qualitative conception of force—an action, impressed externally, changing the motion of a body. The next step is to refine the concept by quantitative definition. As in the case of acceleration, more than one approach is possible. Newton elected to associate force with total change of quantity of motion (momentum) imparted in a particular action. Our present conception of force is somewhat different from Newton's, and we shall carry out the discussion in modern terms.

We start by visualizing operations we could carry out with frictionless pucks on a level glass tabletop. Selecting a particular puck A which becomes a standard body in our experiments, we impart rectilinear accelerations by pulling it with a light spring, the extensions of which can be observed and marked (Fig. 5.3.1).

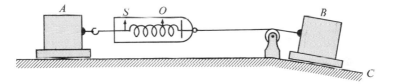

FIG. 5.3.1. Frictionless puck B on incline C imparts uniform rectilinear acceleration to puck A. Acceleration can be changed by increasing or decreasing slope of incline. Needle attached to end of spring is at position O when acceleration is zero and spring is relaxed. Spring is extended, and needle is at position such as S when acceleration is imparted.

We capitalize on our intuitive sense that different strengths of pull impart different accelerations to body A. With a particular action or pull we shall associate the numerical value of the acceleration it imparts, and construct what amounts to a force meter. Thus we might conduct the following experiments: Make a multiple-exposure photograph of accelerating puck A by flashing a light at successive uniform intervals of time. From the sequence of increasing displacements we can determine whether the acceleration is uniform and whether the extension of the spring is constant. All measurements of this type, whether made directly in the manner indicated schematically in Fig. 5.3.1 or accomplished in some indirect fashion, convincingly indicate that a constant spring extension is associated with a constant acceleration. Furthermore, we can satisfy ourselves that the effect is reproducible: the same spring extension imparts the same acceleration on different occasions* and in different directions (right or left, north or south). Given some confidence in the uniqueness and reproducibility of each experiment, we complete the scale of our force meter by labeling each needle position with the numerical value of acceleration imparted to body A. Thus the numbers 1, 2, 3, etc., would be placed at needle positions under which accelerations of 1, 2, 3 m/sec^2, respectively, are observed on the photographs. A similar method could be used to establish intermediate points; thus the number 1.50 would not necessarily be halfway between 1 and 2, but would be placed at the needle position associated with an observed acceleration of 1.50 m/sec^2; similarly for points such as 2.36, 3.82, etc. The force scale is calibrated without any assumptions whatsoever concerning uniformity or nonuniformity in the stretching of the spring.

We now have a tentative definition of force on a numerical scale; the force numbers, which we shall denote by the symbol F, have been made identical with the acceleration a particular action imparts to body A. Whether this arbitrary definition is fruitful and useful can be determined only by appeal to nature through further experiments.

5.4 APPLICATION OF FORCE SCALE TO OTHER BODIES

If we now replace body A by a different frictionless puck, denoted by D, we can impart acceleration to D in the manner of Fig. 5.3.1. In such experiments we find that a fixed scale reading, such as 3.00, is associated with a reproducible rectilinear acceleration of body D, but that the acceleration imparted is not in general 3.00 m/sec^2 as it was with body A; perhaps it is found to be 1.50 m/sec^2. What happens if we apply still other forces to body D? Do we obtain results systematically and simply related to the one already taken as an example? Table 5.4.1 illustrates results which might actually be obtained [column (3)] and contrasts them with imagined possibilities that are not realized in experiments [columns (4) and (5)]. (The simplest way for the reader to grasp the essential differences between the possibilities illustrated in Table 5.4.1 is to sketch rough graphs of F-versus-a for the data in columns (3), (4), and (5).)

Examining column (3), we see that it is possible to associate with body D a *single* number, 2, which will, in each case, multiply the acceleration and give the value of F imparting that acceleration; i.e., forces are directly proportional to the accelerations imparted to a body other than the one for which the force scale was arbitrarily defined, and the proportionality constant is clearly a unique value, or *property* associated with the new body.

---

* Of course we must be careful not to stretch the spring so greatly that the needle fails to return to zero position at zero acceleration, but this behavior can always be checked between experiments. The care we must exercise with our force meter is the same that we exercise with clocks and meter sticks in measuring time and length intervals; precise measurements are to be made under conditions of controlled temperature, freedom from shock, bending, and other extraneous effects. In principle, arriving at a knowledge of what effects are extraneous and how they must be controlled is a matter of experience and *successive approximation* in all techniques of measurement.

TABLE 5.4.1

ACCELERATIONS a IMPARTED TO BODY D BY
FORCES F DEFINED IN SECTION 5.3

(1) Applied force F (defined by acceleration imparted to A; units not named)	(2) Acceleration imparted to A, m/sec^2	(3) Observed acceleration imparted to D, m/sec^2	(4) (5) Imagined possibilities of acceleration of D (*not* realized experimentally), m/sec^2	
0.50	0.50	0.25	1.00	3.00
1.00	1.00	0.50	1.10	2.50
1.62	1.62	0.81	1.20	2.20
2.00	2.00	1.00	1.40	2.00
3.00	3.00	1.50	1.50	1.50
4.00	4.00	2.00	1.60	1.00

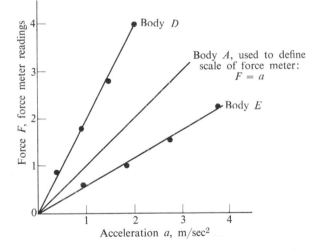

FIG. 5.4.1. F-versus-a graph for bodies A, D, and E. Body D has larger inertia than A (given force meter reading imparts smaller acceleration). Body E exhibits less inertia than body A.

If the experiment is performed with other bodies, we find the pattern repeated; each body has a unique number associated with it—large if the acceleration imparted by a given force is small, small if the acceleration is large. A graph of the results of several experiments would appear as illustrated in Fig. 5.4.1.

Once we have defined an arbitrary scale of force F in the manner specified in Section 5.3, it is found to be an *experimental, physical fact* that

$$F \propto a, \tag{5.4.1}$$

when forces, so defined, are applied to other bodies. If we denote the proportionality constant by m, we write

$$F = ma, \qquad\qquad (5.4.2)$$

where m is a property of the body being accelerated and is the slope of the corresponding line in Fig. 5.4.1. We call this property "mass." The existence of the single, unique number for a given body is *not* just a matter of definition, as was our scale of force; nor is it a matter of deduction from theoretical principles. It is an *experimental physical fact*—a "law of nature."

If m has a large value, we note that a large force imparts a small acceleration, and we say that the inertia or mass of the body is large in the sense that it is more difficult to accelerate such a body than one of lower mass. Our standard body A was, by definition, assigned the value $m = 1$. We might find another body of entirely different size, shape, color, and texture which also has the value $m = 1$; this body, despite all the differences in other properties, has one property completely in common with body A—mass, or inertia with respect to acceleration.

5.5   SUPERPOSITION OF MASSES AND FORCES

We seem to be on the verge of a significant physical generalization, but there remain important physical questions: If we combine two bodies for which we have determined separate values of m, what is the effective mass of the combination? If we make an additional force meter identical with the first and then, to a single body, apply two forces in the same direction, in opposite directions, at angles to each other, what acceleration is imparted to the body? What is the "net" or "effective" or "resultant" force? We are asking about the laws of superposition of mass and force, just as we had to ask about superposition of velocities in projectile motion. The answers to these questions might be *guessed:* that masses add arithmetically when bodies are combined; that equal forces in the same direction impart twice the acceleration imparted by one force; that equal forces in opposite directions subtract or cancel each other and impart zero acceleration; that forces at angles to each other add together with the same arithmetic obeyed by accelerations, and that forces therefore also behave as vector quantities.

Such guesses are continually being made in scientific research; they are frequently fruitful and rewarding and sometimes thoroughly misleading and confusing. In no case do the guesses, however reasonable, constitute proof of correctness of the idea. Our guesses concerning superposition of mass and force suggest physical experiments which might be performed to test the hypotheses; in suggesting tests and experiments, guesses can be very fruitful even if they turn out to be incorrect. But only the results of the suggested experiments justify final conclusions as to the validity of the guesswork.

To the experimental accuracy with which we are able, in ordinary mechanical situations, to measure accelerations, set up force meters, and determine masses, we find that our guesses about the arithmetical (scalar) superposition of masses and vector superposition of forces are correct, and any complete statement of the laws

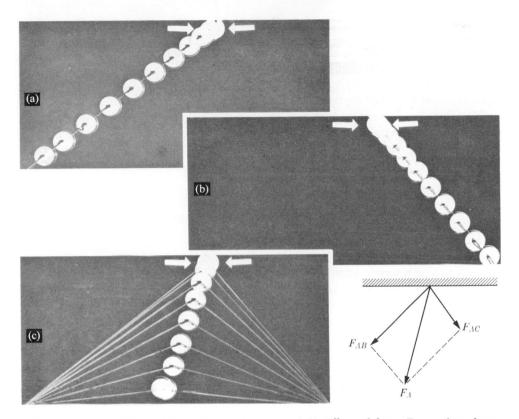

FIG. 5.5.1   (a) Effect of force F_{AB} acting alone.   (b) Effect of force F_{AC} acting alone. (c) Effect of simultaneous superposition of the two forces.   (Figure adapted from *Introduction to Mechanics, Matter, and Waves,* by Uno Ingard and William L. Kraushaar.   Addison-Wesley, 1960.)

of motion must include an enunciation of these physical facts.   Figure 5.5.1 consists of a set of flash photographs illustrating an experiment in the superposition of two forces that are not collinear.

5.6   THE SECOND LAW OF MOTION

The preceding sections outline a sequence of definition and experimental observation that reveals a high degree of order and simplicity in the physics of motion at ordinary, mechanical levels of experience.   Let us summarize the logical structure and physical information:

(1) The kinematic concept of acceleration is defined in terms of the primitive concepts of length and time, and is shown to obey vector arithmetic.   (See Chapters 1 and 4.)

(2) Force impressed on a particle is defined qualitatively as an action which imparts acceleration, and a numerical scale of force is defined by assigning to a par-

ticular force the numerical value of rectilinear acceleration it imparts to a standard particle.

(3) Forces so defined are shown by *experiment* to act independently of each other when more than one is impressed on the same body and to obey vector arithmetic when they are thus superposed. (We denote the final vector result of superposing several forces on a particle by $\mathbf{F}_{net}$.)

(4) Given the convention with respect to establishment of a scale of force, one can then find *experimentally* that with any individual particle one can associate a single number m such that

$$\mathbf{F}_{net} = m\mathbf{a} \qquad (5.6.1)$$

or, separating into components along Cartesian axes:

$$F_{x\,net} = ma_x, \qquad F_{y\,net} = ma_y. \qquad (5.6.2)$$

The quantity m is called the "mass of the particle."

(5) By further *experiment*, if particles are combined to form larger particles, mass is shown to be a simple additive property.

(6) Equation (5.6.1) is a statement of relationship at an instant of time; at any instant the acceleration is proportional to and in the same direction as the *net* applied force. The applied force may change in magnitude and direction from instant to instant, and the acceleration then changes with it. The direction of instantaneous force and acceleration may be very different from the direction of the instantaneous velocity. In order to evaluate the effect any force (uniform or varying) has on the motion of the body over an interval of time, it is necessary to carry out a "limit of the sum" calculation for that interval.

Equation (5.6.1) is usually referred to as the Second Law of Motion.* The apparent simplicity of the statement is deceptive: There are no adequate one-phrase definitions of force and mass. The operational story must be told in something like the summary statements given above. The Second Law contains within itself both definitional and experimental aspects, and these aspects must be carefully separated and identified. Furthermore, it should be noted that the concept of weight, or pull of the earth, has played no role whatsoever in our construction of the concepts of force and mass.

The student should not acquire the misconception that the Second Law was systematically "discovered" in the manner outlined above. Utilizing modern techniques, we could indeed carry out with very respectable precision the experiments described above, but such experiments were impossible in the seventeenth century. The law was guessed at by induction and gradually came to be universally accepted because it worked—its predictions turned out to be correct in every new situation to which it was applied. The discussion in this section is the very opposite of an historical treatment. It is an attempt to give a modern, retrospective view of the operational definition of concepts and of the content of the Second Law.

---

* In the *Principia*, the statement of Law II is quite different. Newton used the word force for a concept which we now call "impulse." This matter will be discussed further in Chapter 17.

Implicit in the Second Law are the ideas that velocity components at right angles to each other are independent (see discussion of projectile motion in Chapter 4), that m and **a** have unique values regardless of the velocity of the particle relative to us. In the realm of ordinary experience, no departure from this regularity was ever detected. It thus came as a profound shock when nineteenth-century science opened up new, subatomic levels of experience and discovered that nature was really not quite so accommodating. In electromagnetic phenomena, and in observation of atomic and subatomic particles moving at velocities of the order of magnitude of the velocity of light, values of m and **a** and the behavior of velocity components become functions of velocity relative to the frame of reference of the observer. Nature still reveals a systematic and intelligible order, but not the one extrapolated from experience with machines, vehicles, and projectiles. The "law of nature" expressed in (5.6.1) is, in more mature perspective, seen to be an approximation rather than an absolute, immutable law, fully adequate and immensely useful for description of our macroscopic, mechanical realm of experience, but nevertheless an approximation, and one which fails dramatically, in other realms.

5.7 THE METER-KILOGRAM-SECOND (MKS) SYSTEM OF UNITS

In setting up a force scale, we started by taking body A which served as a standard. As the concept of mass evolved, we realized that we were assigning a value $m = 1$ to the standard body and were comparing masses of other bodies with that of the standard. This means that our kinematic system of units, consisting only of meters and seconds, must be augmented by an additional unit—that of mass—when we incorporate dynamical concepts. The metric system of units was first devised and adopted in France in 1793. The standard of mass is a platinum cylinder kept at the International Bureau of Weights and Measures in Paris. Secondary standards, copies of the original cylinder, are available in various other national standard laboratories. This unit is called *one kilogram*. The system of units in which the meter, the kilogram, and the second are primary standards is called the mks system. In 1948 this system was adopted as the primary international standard by the General Conference on Weights and Measures.

If a force meter is made in the manner described in Section 5.3, using one kilogram as the standard body and measuring accelerations in m/sec^2, the resulting force units are called newtons; i.e., one newton (denoted by n) is that force which imparts an acceleration of 1 m/sec^2 to the 1-kg standard. For other combinations we would make use of the relation $F = ma$: a force of 6.0 n would impart to a 2.0-kg body an acceleration $a = 6.0/2.0 = 3.0$ m/sec^2.

The phrase "weight of a body" is a *name* for that force which the earth exerts on the body.* Thus, *by definition*, weight is a force and must be measured in newtons. Since the acceleration due to gravity varies slightly from place to place on the earth,

---

* If we imagine a body removed to the moon, to another planet, or to a star, we might also speak of its weight in the new environment. This weight would, in general, be numerically different from the weight on earth.

it is clear that the weight of a given body is not a constant property but is slightly different from one geographical location to another; the mass of the body, however, is *constant*. Taking acceleration due to gravity $g = 9.80$ m/sec^2, the weight of a 2.0-kg body is $2.0(9.80) = 19.6$ n. Expressing this idea in general terms: If W denotes the weight of a body of mass m, W is the force that imparts to the body an acceleration g. Substituting into Eq. (5.6.1), we obtain $W = mg$.

In the technical literature you will frequently encounter phrases or remarks about a "2-kg weight" or a "10-kg weight," etc. This is not an error but a shorthand. Weight is not being measured in kilograms; what is being referred to is the force with which the earth attracts a 2-kg or a 10-kg body. The phrase "10-kg weight" refers to an object on which the earth exerts a force of $10 \times 9.80 = 98.0$ n.

"Weight" and "mass" are entirely distinct concepts with very different operational definitions. In principle, we could unambiguously determine the mass of a body in empty space, far removed from any gravitational influence, under circumstances that make weight equal to zero. One of Newton's significant contributions was to make this conceptual distinction explicitly clear, even though the sharp tool of operational definition was not articulately and consciously put to use until the nineteenth century.

> PROBLEM 5.3. What is your own mass in kilograms? Your weight in newtons? Make up some additional problems of your own in which you estimate masses of familiar objects and calculate their weights as well as forces which impart other accelerations. (To establish a correspondence with units which may be more familiar to you: The earth exerts a pull of about 2.2 lb on a body with a mass of 1 kg.) If the standard body has a mass of 1.0 kg in Fig. 5.4.1, what are the masses of bodies D and E?

5.8   THE CENTIMETER-GRAM-SECOND (CGS) SYSTEM

A second widely used metric system is defined operationally in exactly the same manner as the mks system, except that acceleration is measured in cm/sec^2 and the unit of mass is taken to be the gram (one-thousandth of a kilogram). On the force meter, the needle position at which an acceleration of 2 cm/sec^2 is imparted to the 1-gm standard is labeled 2, and so forth. The units of force are called *dynes*, and 1 dyne is that force which imparts an acceleration of 1 cm/sec^2 to the 1-gm standard.

> PROBLEM 5.4. Which is a larger unit of force—dyne or newton? What is the weight, in dynes, of a body having a 1-gm mass? a 1-kg mass? From the respective definitions of units in the mks and cgs systems, calculate how many dynes correspond to one new-ton. Estimate the weight of a few (small) familiar objects in dynes [1 n is equivalent to 10^5 dynes].

5.9   THE ENGINEERING OR FOOT-POUND-SECOND (FPS) SYSTEM

In the engineering system, used in Britain and the United States, the weight of a certain standard platinum cylinder is taken to be the unit for force and is called one pound. (More precisely, 1 lb is defined as that force which imparts an acceleration of

32.1740 ft/sec^2* to the standard body.) Thus when the force meter is to be calibrated in the manner of Section 5.3, the needle position at which an acceleration of 32.2 ft/sec^2 is imparted to the cylinder is labeled 1.00; the force imparting 16.1 ft/sec^2 is labeled 0.50, the force imparting 64.4 ft/sec^2 is labeled 2.00, and so forth. Invoking the relation $F = ma$, we see that a number $m = 1/32.2$ is assigned to the standard cylinder on which the earth exerts a force defined as 1 lb. The unit mass, or a body for which $m = 1$, will be an object having 32.2 times the mass of the 1-lb cylinder. Such a body would, of course, weigh 32.2 lb; a force of 1 lb would impart to it an acceleration of 1 ft/sec^2. The unit of mass in this system is called a *slug*.

You will frequently read or hear references such as "a 50-lb mass." As in the reverse usage in the mks system, this does not mean that mass is measured in pounds. The reference is a shorthand for "the mass of a body which weighs 50 lbs"; this mass would be $50/32.2 = 1.55$ slugs.

PROBLEM 5.5. Describe in your own words the operational sequence of definitions in the fps system. Point out the similarities and differences between this system of definitions and the mks system. Calculate your own mass in slugs. Estimate the mass, in slugs, of a number of familiar objects.

PROBLEM 5.6. (a) Calculate the net force which would impart an acceleration of 3.5 ft/sec^2 to a body weighing 100 lb. (b) Calculate the mass and weight of a body to which a net force of 50 lb imparts an acceleration of 15 ft/sec^2. [*Answer:* (a) 11 lb; (b) 3.3 slugs, 107 lb.]

5.10   DIMENSIONS AND UNITS

It is frequently convenient to view length L, time T, and mass M as fundamental *dimensions* in terms of which the dimensions of other physical constructs can be expressed. Thus velocity has the general dimension L/T in all systems of units, and the particular units m/sec in the mks system. Acceleration has the dimensions L/T^2 while being expressed in the units ft/sec^2 in the fps system, etc.

By virtue of the Second Law, $F = ma$, force has the dimensions ML/T^2. From this point of view, one newton is the name for 1 kg·m/sec^2, and one pound is the name for 1 slug·ft/sec^2. Alternatively, we may regard one slug as the equivalent of 1 lb sec^2/ft.

In performing numerical calculations we must be sure that our use of dimensions and units is consistent. Multiplication of acceleration by a length cannot yield a displacement; the resulting quantity has the dimensions of velocity squared. Dividing force expressed in newtons by an acceleration expressed in cm/sec^2 will not give a value of mass in one of the regularly defined units.

Units and dimensions can be manipulated exactly like algebraic quantities in multiplication and division on either side of an equation. Utilization of this property to check the consistency of computational work is a quick and useful safeguard against many common numerical errors.

---

* This is, to a good approximation, the value of g at sea level and 45°N latitude.

TABLE 5.10.1

SUMMARY OF DEFINITIONS OF UNITS OF FORCE AND MASS

System of units	Acceleration	Mass	Force	Weight of unit of mass
mks	m/sec^2	Primary standard: 1 kilogram	Derived unit: 1 newton Imparts acceleration of 1 m/sec^2 to 1 kg	9.80 n
cgs	cm/sec^2	Primary standard: 1 gram	Derived unit: 1 dyne Imparts acceleration of 1 cm/sec^2 to 1 gm	980 dynes
fps	ft/sec^2	Derived unit: 1 slug Force of 1 lb imparts acceleration of 1 ft/sec^2	Primary standard: 1 pound Weight of standard body	32.2 lb

5.11 APPLICATIONS OF THE SECOND LAW

In applying mathematics to the description of rectilinear and projectile motion, we found that mathematical formalism operated in almost a machinelike fashion—a single, uniform procedure solved what appeared to be disparate cases of unidirectional motions, up-and-down motions, curvilinear projectile motions. This characteristic aspect of mathematical description of physical phenomena is, if anything, even more striking in the study of dynamics. A single, uniform procedure for analyzing the forces acting on a particle, together with application of the law $F_{net} = ma$, makes it possible to solve a huge array of problems.

In the statement of the Second Law, F_{net} refers to the net or resultant force impressed *externally* on a particular body. Forces which the body itself exerts on *other* objects are *not relevant*. The first step in our uniform procedure of analysis is to isolate the body in question; that is, we draw a picture of the body by itself, removed from contact or association with other objects, and sketch the external forces acting on it. We call this sketch a "free body diagram." Then, making use of the diagram, we substitute algebraic expressions into $F_{net} = ma$, solving for the quantity in which we are interested, be it an unknown force or an unknown acceleration.

Let us study a few simple physical situations, illustrating our systematic method as we go along.

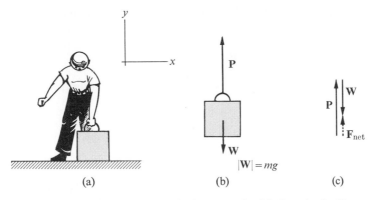

FIG. 5.11.1. (a) Vertical pull accelerates body upward. (b) Free body diagram showing external forces acting on body. (c) Vector diagram showing graphical determination of net force: $\mathbf{F}_{net} = \mathbf{P} - \mathbf{W}$.

CASE 1.   A body of mass m accelerates vertically under the influence of its own weight and an upward pull $\mathbf{P}$ exerted by us or by another object. Figure 5.11.1(b) shows the appropriate free body diagram. Two forces are acting on the block: $\mathbf{W}$, the weight, may be regarded as the resultant of all the parallel, downward forces that the earth exerts on smaller chunks of which we might visualize the block to be composed. We show $\mathbf{W}$ by means of an arrow passing through some central point where we might conceive the mass of the block to be concentrated. We show force $\mathbf{P}$ by another arrow placed along the line of action of our hand or of a string attached to the body. Our hand (or other object exerting this force) is not relevant and is not shown. If the block has sizable dimensions and we apply force $\mathbf{P}$ at one corner instead of along the center line, the block would tend to rotate as well as move vertically. In placing $\mathbf{P}$ and $\mathbf{W}$ along a common line of action we avoid the complication of rotational effects we are not yet prepared to analyze; it is in this sense that we are treating a finite object as a particle with only translational "degrees of freedom" of motion.

What questions might we now ask about the physical situation we have proposed? A reasonable program might be to investigate the vertical acceleration—what magnitude and direction does it have for different values of m and P? To accomplish this inquiry, we apply the Second Law.

Let us introduce x- and y-axes, orienting y in the vertical direction. In terms of components, the Second Law is written

$$F_{x\ net} = ma_x, \qquad F_{y\ net} = ma_y. \tag{5.11.1}$$

From the free body diagram we see that $F_{x\ net}$ and a_x are zero, and we are concerned only with the second equation. Taking the y-direction as positive upward, we have from inspection of the diagram that

$$F_{y\ net} = |\mathbf{P}| - |\mathbf{W}| = |\mathbf{P}| - mg. \tag{5.11.2}$$

This algebraic result is illustrated graphically by the vector diagram in Fig. 5.11.1. Substituting the expression for $F_{y \text{ net}}$ into the Second Law equation, we have

$$|\mathbf{P}| - mg = ma_y$$

and, solving for the quantity which is the subject of our inquiry,

$$a_y = \frac{|\mathbf{P}| - mg}{m}. \tag{5.11.3}$$

Equation (5.11.3) is the "solution" to the problem which we posed; let us extract, by verbal interpretation, all the information it contains:

(a) If $|\mathbf{P}| > mg$, a_y is positive, indicating an upward acceleration. Of course, it does not matter whether $\mathbf{P}$ is applied as a pull from above or as a push from below. To accelerate a body upward, the externally applied upward force must be *larger* than the weight of the body. Increasing m will decrease the acceleration if $\mathbf{P}$ remains fixed.

(b) If $|\mathbf{P}| = mg$, the acceleration is zero. This is the situation in which our pull is equal and opposite to the pull of gravity and the effects cancel. The body may be standing still (hanging from a spring balance, for example) or moving up or down at *uniform* velocity. In either case, the net force and acceleration are zero, and we speak of the system as being "in equilibrium."

(c) If $|\mathbf{P}| < mg$ in Eq. (5.11.3), a_y is negative, indicating a downward acceleration: If our upward pull is less than the weight, the body accelerates downward.

(d) If $\mathbf{P} = 0$, $a_y = -g$, and the body is in a state of free fall. If we reverse the indicated direction of $\mathbf{P}$ and push downward, we can extend the meaning of Eq. (5.11.3) and read out the additional interpretation that the downward acceleration would then have a magnitude larger than g.

PROBLEM 5.7.   Calculate the vertical force necessary to impart an upward acceleration of 32.2 ft/sec^2 to your own body. Calculate the upward force which would allow you to fall with a downward acceleration of 2.0 ft/sec^2.

CASE 2.   A box rests on a level floor; an upward force applied to the box is insufficient to impart vertical acceleration. The acceleration of the box is zero, but we are reluctant to believe that the force of gravity has disappeared or been turned off, simply because the box rests on the floor. Furthermore, if we get a toe or finger caught between the box and the floor, we are fully aware of a squeeze in that region. We thus infer the presence of a force acting on the box in a direction perpendicular or *normal* to the surface. (If the force had a component parallel to the surface, the box would be accelerated to the right or left, and this is clearly contrary to experience.) This is our justification for introducing the "normal force" $\mathbf{N}$ which is shown in Fig. 5.11.2.

The normal force is a "passive" force which adjusts itself to some value dictated by the law of motion. Such forces are always present when objects are pressed to-

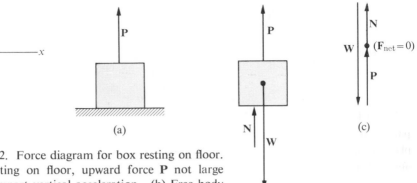

FIG. 5.11.2. Force diagram for box resting on floor. (a) Box resting on floor, upward force **P** not large enough to impart vertical acceleration. (b) Free body diagram. Floor exerts upward force **N** on box. (c) Vector diagram. Force **N** "adjusts itself" so that $\mathbf{F}_{net} = 0$.

gether by external actions. If we press a book against a wall, we infer, in the absence of acceleration, an equal and opposite normal force acting on the book.

The passive, normal force **N** does not arise without a physical effect in the wall or floor. A bedspring on which we place a box sags and deforms visibly before a large-enough upward force is exerted to balance the weight of the box. Similarly, although much less visibly, the floor, or the wall, is "dented" or deformed before the force **N** takes on an equilibrium value. We might think of **N** as arising from the tendency of the deformed body to "spring back" to its original shape.

Let us analyze how **N** adjusts itself in the case illustrated in Fig. 5.11.2. Taking positive direction upward:

$$F_{y\,net} = |\mathbf{P}| + |\mathbf{N}| - |\mathbf{W}|.$$

Since the acceleration is zero, $F_{y\,net} = ma_y = 0$, and therefore $|\mathbf{P}| + |\mathbf{N}| - |\mathbf{W}| = 0$, and

$$|\mathbf{N}| - |\mathbf{W}| - |\mathbf{P}| = mg - |\mathbf{P}|. \tag{5.11.4}$$

Interpreting Eq. (5.11.4): If $P = 0$, the normal force is equal to the weight of the body, as we should expect. If $|\mathbf{P}|$ is increased, $|\mathbf{N}|$ becomes smaller and equals zero when $|\mathbf{P}|$ is equal to the weight of the body. If $|\mathbf{P}|$ exceeds the weight of the body, **N** must be directed downward to keep the acceleration zero; i.e., the body must be glued or nailed down to the floor. (Redraw the free body and vector diagrams 5.11.2(b) and (c) for this case.) What are the direction and magnitude of **N** if **P** is applied downward instead of upward; i.e., if someone stands on the box? (Redraw the free body and vector diagrams for this case.)

CASE 3. A frictionless puck is being pulled along an inclined plane. The forces in this case are not collinear; we imagine them to pass through a common point and still treat the extended body as a particle, ignoring any effects that tend to tip or rotate it.

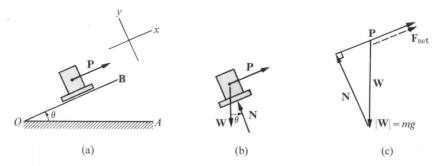

(a)   (b)   (c)

FIG. 5.11.3. (a) Frictionless puck of mass m accelerated along inclined plane by force $\mathbf{P}$ parallel to the plane. (b) Free body diagram showing forces acting on puck. Theorem in plane geometry: Two angles whose sides are mutually $\perp$ are equal. Since $\mathbf{W} \perp OA$ and $\mathbf{N} \perp OB$, the angle between $\mathbf{W}$ and $\mathbf{N}$ is equal to θ. (c) Vector diagram showing $\mathbf{F}_{net}$.

The free body diagram is shown in Fig. 5.11.3(b) and the associated vector diagram in Fig. 5.11.3(c). As in Case 2 above, the plane exerts a passive normal force on the puck. The questions which thrust themselves upon us are: To what value does the normal force $\mathbf{N}$ adjust itself in this case? What factors will determine the acceleration along the plane? Since we are planning to investigate quantities perpendicular to and parallel to the plane, respectively, it is clearly advisable to set up Cartesian axes in this orientation [as shown in Fig. 5.11.3(a)] rather than in the orientation used in the preceding examples. (Why?)

Since the component of $\mathbf{W}$ parallel to the plane is $mg \sin \theta$, we have for the net force in the x-direction:

$$F_{x\,net} = |\mathbf{P}| - mg \sin \theta$$

and, substituting into $F_{x\,net} = ma_x$,

$$|\mathbf{P}| - mg \sin \theta = ma_x,$$

$$a_x = \frac{|\mathbf{P}| - mg \sin \theta}{m}. \qquad (5.11.5)$$

Equation (5.11.5) indicates, for example, that the puck will be accelerated in a positive direction (up the plane) only if $|\mathbf{P}|$ is larger than $mg \sin \theta$.

In the y-direction the acceleration is zero, and we have:

$$F_{y\,net} = |\mathbf{N}| - mg \cos \theta = 0,$$

$$|\mathbf{N}| = mg \cos \theta. \qquad (5.11.6)$$

Interpreting the results, one should seek answers to the following questions: How must $|\mathbf{P}|$ be related to the weight of the body and the angle θ for the body to accelerate up the plane? Have zero acceleration? Accelerate down the plane? (Redraw the vector diagram 5.11.3(c) for the case in which $|\mathbf{P}|$ is small and the puck accelerates down the plane.) What happens when $\mathbf{P} = 0$? What happens to the normal force

N and the acceleration if the mass of the puck is increased? If the inclination θ is increased, all other quantities remaining fixed? All these questions can be answered by translating into words the arithmetical content of Eqs. (5.11.5) and (5.11.6). The interpretation is left as an exercise for the reader.

Note in retrospect the basic attitude taken in the Newtonian analysis of the dynamical problems we have been considering. Conditions of rest (or acceleration) are being "explained," while uniform motion is taken as the "natural" state. This conception is completely and fundamentally different from the Aristotelian-Scholastic one; the shift underlies the remark of Herbert Butterfield's with which we started Section 1.1.

FIGURE 5.11.4

PROBLEM 5.8. Using exactly the same procedure illustrated in the previous examples, analyze the dynamics of a frictionless puck being accelerated on a level surface by a force inclined as shown in Fig. 5.11.4. Draw both a free body diagram and a vector diagram. Interpret the results by analyzing how the normal force adjusts itself and how the acceleration depends on $|P|$ and on the inclination α of the force. The equations you write down will not be valid if $|P|$ exceeds a certain value. Interpret this statement. What will happen? At what value of $|P|$? What happens to $|N|$ and a_x if the *direction* of P is reversed? Select some reasonable values of m, $|P|$, and α in both the mks and fps systems, and calculate $|N|$ and a_x. (Pay attention to the resulting numbers in order to develop a physical sense for the magnitudes one might expect in acceleration of ordinary objects.)

PROBLEM 5.9. The formal technique of setting up and interpreting force diagrams illustrated in the preceding section will be basic to virtually all our work in the remainder of the text. There will be additional problems and exercises at the end of the next chapter, but students who still feel ill-at-ease with the analysis are urged to work additional problems at this point. One such problem would be to analyze the situation illustrated in Fig. 5.11.3 with force P inclined to the plane instead of parallel to it. Numerous additional exercises will be found in the texts cited in the supplementary reading list. In each instance, the student is urged to make a formal analysis and ask questions of the kind illustrated above, rather than just working through for a particular pat "answer" called for in a given problem.

PROBLEM 5.10. Define the following terms used in this chapter: percussion; calibrate (as in "calibrating the force meter"); induction (as in "reasoning by induction"); translational (as in "translational motion").

SUPPLEMENTARY READING AND STUDY

On a more elementary level:
  Physics, Physical Science Study Committee. Boston: D. C. Heath, 1960, Chapter 20

On a similar or somewhat more advanced level, with many additional problems:
  Physics for the Inquiring Mind, Eric M. Rogers. Princeton, N. J.: Princeton University Press, 1960, Chapter 7

Physics for Students of Science and Engineering, R. Resnick and D. Halliday. New York: John Wiley & Sons, 1960, Chapter 5

Introduction to Mechanics, Matter, and Waves, U. Ingard and W. L. Kraushaar. Reading, Mass.: Addison-Wesley, 1960, Chapters 2, 3

Original sources:

Philosophiae Naturalis Principia Mathematica, Isaac Newton. Translated by A. Motte, revised by F. Cajori. University of California Press, 1934, prefaces and pages 1–28. (Available in paperback.)

A Source Book in Physics, W. F. Magie. New York: McGraw-Hill, 1935, pages 30–46, excerpts from the *Principia*

Masterworks of Science, J. W. Knedler. New York: Doubleday, 1947, pages 171–189, excerpts from the *Principia*

Philosophical and epistemological discussions:

"On the Classical Laws of Motion," Leonard Eisenbud. *American Journal of Physics*, March 1958

Foundations of Physics, R. B. Lindsay and H. Margenau. New York: John Wiley & Sons, 1936, pages 85–92. (Also Dover paperback S377.)

Philosophy of Science, Philipp Frank. Englewood Cliffs, N. J.: Prentice Hall, 1957, Chapter 4

Historical evolution of concepts of force and mass:

Concepts of Force, Max Jammer. Cambridge, Mass.: Harvard University Press, 1957

Concepts of Mass, Max Jammer. Cambridge, Mass.: Harvard University Press, 1961

A History of Mechanics, René Dugas, translated by J. R. Maddox. New York: Central Book Co., 1955

CHAPTER 6

Particle Dynamics II: Particle Interactions

6.1 THE THIRD LAW OF MOTION

In Chapter 5 all our attention was focused on the behavior of a single body accelerating under the influence of external forces, and we made no inquiry concerning simultaneous effects on other objects. Yet, if we stop to visualize the circumstances under which objects are accelerated, we note that accelerations invariably involve a process of interaction. If we throw a stone or push a car, we feel ourselves recoil, which is a way of saying that we experience a force opposite to the one we exert. When two bodies collide, it is clear that each body experiences a force during the interaction, since each undergoes a change in velocity. When two electrically charged ping-pong balls, suspended on strings, are brought near each other, they *both* start swinging, indicating that *each* one experiences an external force. When wind blows against a wall, the direction of motion of the air is altered; the moving air is subjected to a force that changes its velocity, and at the same time a force is exerted on the wall.

Physical problems confront us with a wide array of such interactions. In order to apply the method of analysis developed in Chapter 5, it is necessary to isolate in succession each body of an interacting system. But in order to do so it is necessary to know something about how force behaves in the action of one body on another. Given the perception of some regularity in this behavior, one might begin to analyze the effect in Fig. 5.3.1 of body *B* on the string and of the string, in turn, on body *A*. Thus one might ultimately understand how the effect of gravity on body *B* results in an acceleration of body *A*, how this effect depends on the slope of incline *C*, and how the presence of body *A* influences the otherwise uninhibited motion of *B*. One might be able to follow dynamical effects through sequences of belts, links, pulleys and wheels in an engine. One might tackle the problems of the interaction of the earth and moon, of falling water driving a turbine, of propulsion of vehicles, of accelerations observed in electric and magnetic phenomena.

Newton discerned one possible way of grasping the regularity which nature exhibits when bodies interact dynamically; he enunciated it as Law III in the *Principia*. Translated into terms that we have defined, the Third Law states:

> "If one body exerts a force on a second, the second exerts an equal and opposite force on the first."

In the literature of physics, this was a new and original idea. All the other conceptions we have encountered had a prior history of development and discussion, but
historians can find no precedent for Law III in the writings of other investigators,
nor is there any explicit indication of it in any of Newton's own writings prior to the
Principia in 1687. It seems likely that Newton's perception of this law was at least in
part motivated by existing experimental knowledge that changes of quantity of
motion (momentum) were equal and opposite when bodies collided.   Obviously
aware of its novelty, Newton takes considerable pains to explain and justify Law III
in a scholium* which follows the statement of the laws:

> "If you press a stone with your finger, the finger is also pressed by the stone.
> If a horse draws a stone tied by a rope, the horse (if I may so say) will be equally
> drawn back towards the stone; for the distended rope, by the same endeavor to
> relax or unbend itself, will draw the horse as much towards the stone as it does
> the stone towards the horse. . . ."

Because his final objective was a model of the solar system† and a demonstration
of the universality of the inverse square law of gravitation, Newton was particularly
anxious to convince his readers of the applicability of the Third Law to "attractions,"
which in his vocabulary meant the influence on each other of separated objects (such
as magnets or electrically charged bodies):

> "In attractions, I briefly demonstrate the thing after this manner. Suppose
> an obstacle is interposed to hinder the meeting of any two bodies *A*, *B*, attracting
> one the other: then if either body, as *A*, is more attracted towards the other
> body *B*, than that other body *B* is towards the first body *A*, the obstacle will be
> more strongly urged by the pressure of body *A* than by the pressure of body *B*,
> and therefore will not remain in equilibrium: but the stronger pressure will pre-
> vail, and will make the system of the two bodies, together with the obstacle, to
> move directly towards the parts on which *B* lies; and in free spaces, to go for-
> wards in infinitum with a motion continually accelerated; which is absurd and
> contrary to the first law. . . . I made the experiment on the lodestone and iron.
> If these placed apart in proper vessels, are made to float by one another in stand-
> ing water, neither of them will propel the other; but, by being equally attracted,
> they will sustain each other's pressure, and rest at last in an equilibrium."

PROBLEM 6.1.   Analyze the preceding quotation. Newton adduces two different arguments to support his case; compare the premises and the logic of the two arguments.
    Make up some other physical illustrations of what might be expected to happen in
mechanical systems if the Third Law were not obeyed.

---

* A *scholium* is a commentary or set of explanatory remarks appended to enlarge and
amplify the main body of a text.
    † See Chapter 15 for a more detailed discussion.

The Third Law is deceptively simple in statement and exceedingly powerful in application. The best way to develop an understanding of its significance is to make use of it in constructing free body diagrams and in analyzing the dynamics of a few simple, idealized instances of motion of interacting bodies.

6.2 ILLUSTRATIONS APPLYING THE THIRD LAW

Example 1. Acceleration during act of leaping vertically upward.

The jumper flexes his legs and then extends them, impressing a downward force on the earth which, according to Law III, impresses an upward force back on him. This upward force we have labeled **N** in the free body diagram of the jumper, while marking his weight, the force exerted by the earth, **W**. Taking positive direction upward, and applying $F_{y\ net} = ma_y$, we have for Fig. 6.2.1(b):

$$|\mathbf{N}| - |\mathbf{W}| = ma_j, \tag{6.2.1}$$

where m is the mass and a_j the acceleration of the jumper. **N** and **W** are *not* equal and opposite forces and do *not* constitute a Third Law pair. Since the jumper accelerates upward, $|\mathbf{N}|$ must be greater than $|\mathbf{W}|$!

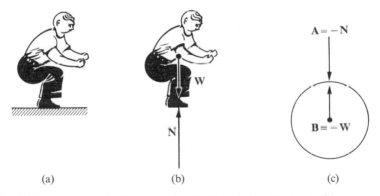

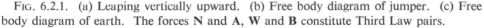

(a)   (b)   (c)

FIG. 6.2.1. (a) Leaping vertically upward. (b) Free body diagram of jumper. (c) Free body diagram of earth. The forces **N** and **A**, **W** and **B** constitute Third Law pairs.

To illustrate the significance of the Third Law, we must construct a free body diagram of the earth—the other object participating in this interaction [Fig. 6.2.1(c)]. Force **A** is the downward push exerted on the earth by the jumper as he kicks his feet. In accordance with the Third Law, this force is equal and opposite to the force **N** exerted by the earth on the jumper. Thus $|\mathbf{A}| = |\mathbf{N}|$ and $\mathbf{A} = -\mathbf{N}$, and so **A** and **N** constitute a Third Law pair. Note that these equal and opposite forces do not appear on the same force diagram; they appear on *different* diagrams as forces on different bodies.

The symbol **W** represents the gravitational force exerted on the jumper by the earth at all times, whether he is rising, falling, or standing still. According to the Third Law, he must always exert an equal and opposite gravitational force on the earth. We visualize this latter force as concentrated at the center of the earth and draw it as **B** in Fig. 6.2.1(c). Hence **W** and **B** constitute another Third Law pair with $\mathbf{B} = -\mathbf{W}$. Again, these equal and opposite forces appear on two *different* force diagrams.

Applying the Second Law to the force diagram of the earth,

$$|\mathbf{B}| - |\mathbf{A}| = |\mathbf{W}| - |\mathbf{N}| = Ma_e, \tag{6.2.2}$$

where M is the mass and a_e the acceleration of the earth. Equation (6.2.2) tells us that the earth recoils when we jump, just as a gun recoils when a projectile is fired or when motions of both bodies change in a two-body collision.

We do not sense the recoil of the earth (compare the magnitudes of a_j and a_e), but we have every reason to believe the analysis we have made. Our confidence comes from repeated experience of applying the laws of motion to cases in which the predictions can be verified by direct observation; the theory works, and our faith in it deepens as the range of phenomena the theory embraces successfully widens.

PROBLEM 6.2.   Consider the situation in which you sit on a box (your feet not touching the ground). Draw free body diagrams of yourself, the box, and the earth. Identify the Third Law pairs. Taking your own weight as given, solve for all other forces. Is the earth being accelerated under these circumstances? Why or why not?

PROBLEM 6.3.   Construct free body diagrams of the lodestone and iron on floats "at rest at last in an equilibrium" in Newton's experiment described in the quotation at the end of Section 6.1. Identify the Third Law pairs. (Do not ignore the vertical direction.)

PROBLEM 6.4.   A modern fable has it that the driver of a huge trailer van was seen leaning out of the cab and pounding the side of the van vigorously with a baseball bat. A passing driver, inquiring about this peculiar behavior, was told: "This is a seven-ton van. I am carrying ten tons of canaries and have to keep at least three tons of them flying." Discuss the physics of this tale. Make your analysis *very* technical but without trying to go into the complexities of the dynamics of flight. There are many ramifications you can invent: for example, suppose the floor of the van is made of heavy wire screen instead of being solid, etc.

Example 2. Transmission of force by ropes or strings.

Consider a situation in which a frictionless puck is accelerated horizontally by a pull applied to one end of a rope as shown in Fig. 6.2.2. Suppose the force $\mathbf{F}_1$ applied at the end of the rope is known. What force is applied to the puck at the other end? What are the forces on the rope itself? To investigate these questions, we draw free body diagrams of both the puck and the rope, as shown in Fig. 6.2.2(b) and (c). Here $\mathbf{F}_2$ is the force exerted by the block on the rope which is attached to it, and $\mathbf{F}_3$ is the equal and opposite force exerted by the rope on the block. These forces form a Third Law pair and appear on different force diagrams.

Applying the Second Law $F_{x \text{ net}} = ma_x$, taking positive direction to the right, we have for the rope:

$$|\mathbf{F}_1| - |\mathbf{F}_2| = m_r a_{rx}, \tag{6.2.3}$$

and for the puck:

$$|\mathbf{F}_3| = |\mathbf{F}_2| = m_p a_{px}. \tag{6.2.4}$$

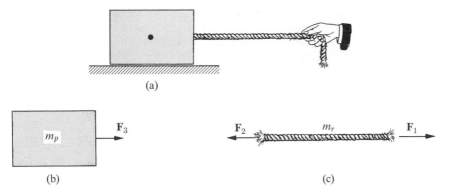

(a)

(b)   (c)

FIG. 6.2.2. Frictionless puck of mass m_p accelerated by pull on horizontal rope, mass m_r. Only horizontal forces are shown in the diagrams. The force $\mathbf{F}_3 = -\mathbf{F}_2$. These two forces constitute a Third Law pair.

Both the rope and the puck must have the same acceleration, otherwise the two would not stay together in their motion. Therefore

$$a_{px} = a_{rx} = a_x.$$

Let us solve for the acceleration a_x in terms of the known force $|\mathbf{F}_1|$. We should be able to judge whether the algebraic result makes sense, and we thus have a check on our handling of algebraic signs and manipulations. Adding Eqs. (6.2.3) and (6.2.4) eliminates $|\mathbf{F}_2|$, giving

$$|\mathbf{F}_1| = (m_p + m_r)a_x. \qquad (6.2.5)$$

This result does indeed make sense. It is exactly what we would have obtained had we treated the rope-puck combination as a single free body of total mass $m_p + m_r$. The resulting acceleration a_x is smaller than the acceleration which force $\mathbf{F}_1$ would have imparted if applied directly to the puck. This implies that $|\mathbf{F}_2| < |\mathbf{F}_1|$, and this is exactly what Eq. (6.2.3) tells us:

$$|\mathbf{F}_2| = |\mathbf{F}_1| - m_r a_x.$$

That is, $|\mathbf{F}_2|$ is smaller than $|\mathbf{F}_1|$ by the amount $m_r a_x$, which is the net force needed to impart acceleration a_x to the rope. If the rope or string has a very small mass, the difference between $|\mathbf{F}_1|$ and $|\mathbf{F}_2|$ may be negligible. How is "very small" to be defined in this context? This question is answered by comparing the magnitudes of the forces. Dividing Eq. (6.2.5) by (6.2.4) gives

$$\frac{|\mathbf{F}_1|}{|\mathbf{F}_2|} = \frac{m_p + m_r}{m_p} = 1 + \frac{m_r}{m_p}. \qquad (6.2.6)$$

If $m_r \ll m_p$, that is, if the mass of the rope is much smaller than the mass of the body to which it is attached, the forces at opposite ends of the rope are very nearly equal in magnitude. Under such circumstances we say that the mass of the string is negligible,*

---

* Many books use the term "massless string" in this context.

and we take the magnitude of the force to be essentially the same at either end without repeating each time the algebraic investigation which has just been carried out; i.e., we say that, to a good approximation, the string transmits the force undiminished. The fractional error made in this approximation is exactly the fraction m_r/m_p, as is apparent from Eq. (6.2.6).

If the body in Fig. 6.2.2 is fastened to the floor and $a_x = 0$, Eq. (6.2.3) indicates that $|\mathbf{F}_1| = |\mathbf{F}_2|$ regardless of the mass of rope. If $\mathbf{F}_1$ is a pull of 10 lb, $\mathbf{F}_2$ is an opposite pull of 10 lb. We call a stretching force of this kind a *tension* and define the numerical value of the tension to be 10 lb in the case illustrated. (If we replace the rope by a rod and push on the end of it with force $|\mathbf{F}_1|$, we speak of the rod as being subject to compression $|\mathbf{F}_1|$.)

When the body accelerates and m_r is not negligible, we say that the tension in the rope decreases continuously from its largest value $|\mathbf{F}_1|$ at the right-hand end to $|\mathbf{F}_2|$ at the left. If we keep increasing our pulling force until it exceeds the strength of the rope, and if the rope is uniformly strong throughout its length, it will break at the right-hand end, where the tension is largest.

FIG. 6.2.3.   Free body diagram of rope assuming shape of catenary under influence of gravity.

In analyzing the problem posed in Fig. 6.2.2, we ignored vertical forces in order to avoid a minor complication which should now be considered: The rope has weight. If the forces $\mathbf{F}_1$ and $\mathbf{F}_2$ are truly horizontal, what keeps the rope from accelerating downward? The answer, of course, is that $\mathbf{F}_1$ and $\mathbf{F}_2$ can never be truly horizontal. The rope assumes a symmetrical curved shape (called a *catenary*) under the influence of gravity, and the forces at the ends will be tangent to this curve, as shown in Fig. 6.2.3.

Applying the Second Law $F_{y\,\text{net}} = ma_y$ in the vertical direction and noting that $a_y = 0$, we see that

$$|\mathbf{F}_1| \sin \theta + |\mathbf{F}_2| \sin \theta - m_r g = 0$$

or, if the forces at the ends are nearly equal,

$$\sin \theta = \frac{m_r g}{2|\mathbf{F}_1|} . \tag{6.2.7}$$

If the weight of the rope is small and the applied force reasonably large, θ is a very small angle indeed, and our previous analysis is not significantly affected. But, *in principle*, Eq. (6.2.7) tells us that no force, *however large*, can stretch a rope to be perfectly horizontal.

PROBLEM 6.5.   Adopt some reasonable values for the weight of a rope and a thin string and for the forces to be applied. Calculate in each case the angle θ as defined in Fig. 6.2.3. Do not look up values of angles in the tables. Use the approximation that, for small angles, $\sin \theta$ is very nearly equal to θ itself, if θ is measured in radians. The best procedure in this case would be to do the whole calculation mentally with round numbers!

6.3   A PROBLEM OF CONCEPTUAL AND HISTORICAL INTEREST: ATWOOD'S MACHINE

In a *Treatise on the Rectilinear Motion and Rotation of Bodies*, published in 1784, George Atwood (fellow and tutor at Trinity College, Cambridge) describes a demonstration apparatus (Fig. 6.3.1) which he apparently devised during the 1770's for his lectures at Cambridge. "... *A* and *B* represent two weights affixed to the extremities of a very fine and flexible silk line; this line is stretched over a wheel ... moveable around a horizontal axis."

Atwood made m_A slightly greater than m_B by starting with identical metal bodies and loading A with a very small additional metal slug. The system then accelerates with a very small acceleration, and displacements and corresponding time intervals can be measured with ordinary instruments. Here is Galileo's "diluted" acceleration, now reappearing in an eighteenth-century experiment in dynamics. Atwood refers to Galileo and the inclined-plane experiments, but he makes it clear that he is interested in the dynamical problem of acceleration under constant force, and he claims far greater accuracy for his demonstration than is attainable in inclined-plane experiments.

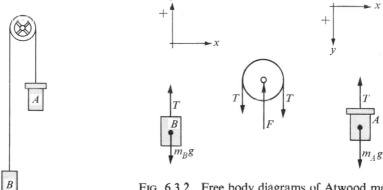

FIG. 6.3.2. Free body diagrams of Atwood machine components. Symbols denote magnitudes of respective forces.

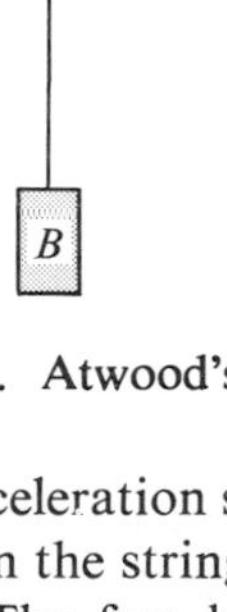

FIG. 6.3.1. Atwood's machine.

What acceleration should we expect for given values of m_A and m_B? What tension is present in the string? Let us analyze Atwood's machine by means of our standard method. The free body diagrams (based on ideas illustrated in Section 6.2) are shown in Fig. 6.3.2. Here we have abandoned the cumbersome vector notation and use a simplified system in which the symbols stand directly for the magnitudes of the forces. We have also made use of the results of Section 6.2 to assert that the fine silk line transmits the tension force undiminished from body A to body B, providing that the inertia of the string and rotating pulley system is negligible compared with the inertia of the accelerating bodies, and providing that frictional forces are negligible at the axle of the pulley. (In such experiments it is usually necessary to correct for the rotational inertia of the pulley, and Atwood was careful to do so. We shall discuss this part of the problem in a later chapter, and retain the simplifying assumption for the time being.)

Applying the Second Law to bodies A and B in Fig. 6.3.2 and taking the positive direction to be the direction of acceleration for the entire system (up for B and down for A) we obtain

$$m_A g - T = m_A a_A, \tag{6.3.1}$$

$$-m_B g + T = m_B a_B. \tag{6.3.2}$$

If the bodies are to remain a fixed distance apart, i.e., if the string is not to be continually stretching or contracting, then

$$a_A = a_B = a. \tag{6.3.3}$$

Adding Eqs. (6.3.1) and (6.3.2) so as to eliminate T, and making use of (6.3.3), we obtain

$$(m_A - m_B)g = (m_A + m_B)a$$

or

$$\frac{a}{g} = \frac{m_A - m_B}{m_A + m_B}. \tag{6.3.4}$$

The form of Eq. (6.3.4) has been selected deliberately in order to illustrate a mathematical point: Each side of the equation is *dimensionless:* on the left-hand side a is measured in g's, and this pure number is equal to another pure number expressed in terms of a ratio of masses on the right. Such dimensionless forms are frequently very useful in the analysis of physical problems: They lead to quicker insights into the significance of derived results; they allow simpler numerical estimates and calculations; they afford a check of the correctness of the derivation (if one side comes out dimensionless while the other does not, it is clear that a mistake has been made).

Substituting Eq. (6.3.4) back into either (6.3.1) or (6.3.2), we can solve for the tension in the string T (the steps are left to the reader):

$$T = \frac{2m_A m_B}{m_A + m_B} g. \tag{6.3.5}$$

PROBLEM 6.6.   Interpret the analysis of Atwood's machine. A suggested outline might go as follows:

(a) What does Eq. (6.3.4) tell us about the "diluted" acceleration? What ways do we have for making the acceleration small? Atwood performed the demonstration with different values of total mass and mass difference $m_A - m_B$, showing that the acceleration was uniform and that the value was in good agreement with that predicted by the equation. He also measured the negative acceleration observed if B were given an initial velocity downward. What do these demonstrations demonstrate? Plan a laboratory experiment of your own: Decide what numerical values of m_A and m_B you would select and what acceleration you would expect to observe.

(b) What does Eq. (6.3.4) say happens to the acceleration if m_B is made larger than m_A? What happens as either m_A or m_B is made very small?

(c) Without trying to analyze the effect of inertia of the pulley quantitatively, predict what effect it would have on the results of the experiment; i.e., would the observed acceleration be larger or smaller than the predicted one? What effect would air friction have if it were significant? (If the velocity is kept small, air friction turns out to be negligible.)

(d) Suppose we start by holding B so that the system is in static equilibrium. What is the tension in the string? [*Answer:* m_Ag.]

(e) Interpret Eq. (6.3.5). Show that when the system accelerates, the tension in the string is *less* than m_Ag and greater than m_Bg. Explain this result in a simple physical way.

(f) What happens between the instant we let B go (when the tension is still m_Ag) and the time Eq. (6.3.5) becomes valid? (Do not assume that there is a pat answer to this question. The phenomena involved are quite complex and cannot be analyzed mathematically with the concepts developed so far in this book. Try to give a qualitative account of what happens. Note that Eq. (6.3.3) is not valid during this interval.)

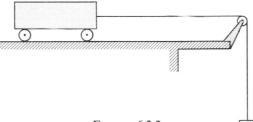

FIGURE 6.3.3

PROBLEM 6.7. Figure 6.3.3 suggests a physical situation in which a cart rolling on a table is accelerated by a weight rigged as shown. Analyze this problem in the same way we analyzed the Atwood machine and interpret the results in the manner suggested in Problem 6.4. Is the force acting on the cart equal to the weight hanging on the end of the string? Indicate clearly the assumptions and idealizations you make. How would the presence of friction affect your predictions; i.e., would the observed result be larger or smaller than predicted? Why? What acceleration would be imparted to a 5-lb cart by a 2-oz weight in the absence of friction? What is the tension in the string? Why is the tension *not* equal to 2 oz?

6.4 ANOTHER PROBLEM OF CONCEPTUAL AND HISTORICAL INTEREST: MACH'S "REACTION CAR" EXPERIMENT

Consider two bodies which are coupled by a compressed spring or which repel each other electrically or magnetically. At some instant the bodies are released; they fly apart, accelerating under the influence of the force they impart to each other. This is the most fundamental idealized two-particle interaction we can invent. Although in Fig. 6.4.1 the system is illustrated as consisting of frictionless cars on a table, we can equally well imagine the experiment being performed in empty space. Here the forces

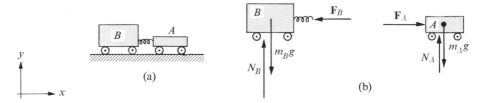

(a)

(b)

FIG. 6.4.1.   Reaction car experiment.   System assumed frictionless.   Italic symbols denote magnitudes of forces.

mg and N would be absent, and all that would be necessary is a frame of reference in which scales of length and time have been established so that events can be observed and accelerations determined.

Let us investigate how the accelerations, considered as unknown quantities, are related to the known masses of the bodies. We construct the free body diagrams shown in Fig. 6.4.1; the symbols on the diagrams refer to the magnitudes of the forces. Applying the Second Law $F_{x\ \text{net}} = ma_x$ with positive direction to the right, we have for body A

$$\mathbf{F}_A = m_A \mathbf{a}_A; \tag{6.4.1}$$

for body B

$$\mathbf{F}_B = m_B \mathbf{a}_B. \tag{6.4.2}$$

By the Third Law $\mathbf{F}_A = -\mathbf{F}_B$ or $|\mathbf{F}_A| = |\mathbf{F}_B|$.   Therefore

$$m_B a_B(t) = -m_A a_A(t). \tag{6.4.3}$$

As the bodies fly apart, the forces decrease and the accelerations change from instant to instant. The functional notation has been introduced into Eq. (6.4.3) to emphasize this fact. The behavior of the acceleration may be something of the kind indicated in Fig. 6.4.2.

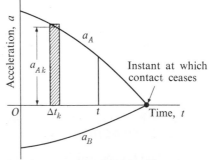

FIG. 6.4.2.   Acceleration-time graph for reaction cars pushed apart by compressed spring.   (What would be the form of the graph if the cars were not in mechanical contact, but repelled each other magnetically or electrically?)

Making use of ideas which were developed in Section 1.14 and Problem 1.14, we recognize the "area" between $t = 0$ and any instant $t = t$ under the a_A curve as the velocity $v_A(t)$ acquired by the body A at the given instant after having started from rest at $t = 0$. Similarly the area between the curve a_B and the t-axis is equal to $v_B(t)$.

Stating this in the symbols devised in Chapter 1, and making use of Eq. (6.4.3), we have

$$m_B \lim_{\substack{||\Delta||\to 0 \\ n\to\infty}} \sum_{k=1}^{n} a_{Bk}\,\Delta t_k = -m_A \lim_{\substack{||\Delta||\to 0 \\ n\to\infty}} \sum_{k=1}^{n} a_{Ak}\,\Delta t_k,$$

$$m_B v_B(t) = -m_A v_A(t), \tag{6.4.4}$$

where $v_B(0)$ and $v_A(0)$ are taken to be equal to zero. By an exactly similar argument, we would then say

$$m_B \lim_{\substack{||\Delta||\to 0 \\ n\to\infty}} \sum_{k=1}^{n} v_{Bk}\,\Delta t_k = -m_A \lim_{\substack{||\Delta||\to 0 \\ n\to\infty}} \sum_{k=1}^{n} v_{Ak}\,\Delta t_k,$$

$$m_B \,\Delta s_B = -m_A \,\Delta s_A, \tag{6.4.5}$$

where Δs_B and Δs_A denote displacements from initial position during the given time interval.

Combining the content of Eqs. (6.4.3), (6.4.4), and (6.4.5), we would say that at any instant t

$$\frac{a_B}{a_A} = \frac{v_B}{v_A} = \frac{\Delta s_B}{\Delta s_A} = -\frac{m_A}{m_B}, \tag{6.4.6}$$

if the bodies start from rest at $t = 0$.

PROBLEM 6.8.   (For students who have studied the mathematical concepts of derivatives and antiderivatives.)

An alternative way of deriving Eqs. (6.4.4) and (6.4.5) is to use the properties of anti-derivatives. Since $a \equiv dv/dt \equiv v'(t)$, Eq. (6.4.3) can be written $m_B v'_B(t) = -m_A v'_A(t)$. Taking antiderivatives, we would have $m_B v_B(t) = -m_A v_A(t) + C$.

(a) Show that, with the initial condition that carts start from rest at $t = 0$, C must be zero.

(b) Continue the argument in a similar way to derive Eq. (6.4.5).

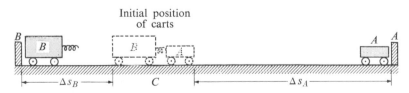

FIG. 6.4.3. Reaction car experiment in which positions of barricades B and A are adjusted by trial and error until carts, released from position C, strike barricades simultaneously. The ratio of displacements Δs is equal to the inverse ratio of the masses.

It is very easy to perform an experiment in which we measure the two displacements Δs_A and Δs_B. For example we can, by trial and error, adjust the positions of barricades A and B, as shown in Fig. 6.4.3, until the carts strike them simultaneously. The corresponding displacements Δs_B and Δs_A are indicated on the diagram.

What attitudes might we take toward such an experiment? If values of m_A and m_B have been previously established by the operational procedures (force meter experiments) described in Chapter 5, then experimental results which agree with Eq. (6.4.6) would be interpreted as a direct experimental confirmation of the Third Law. If, on the other hand, we accept the laws of motion on the basis of other evidence, we can use our measurements and Eq. (6.4.6) to compare masses m_A and m_B without prior knowledge of their values. If m_A is taken to be the standard kilogram, we can compare m_B (i.e., find m_B in kilograms) without making any force measurements whatsoever.

In 1883 the Austrian physicist Ernst Mach published a book (*Science of Mechanics*) in which he subjected the concepts and epistemology of Newtonian mechanics to a searching criticism. (In this work he came very close to some of the ideas which were later found to be at the root of the theory of relativity.) Mach pointed out that we might take it as a primary observation—a law of nature—that when two bodies interact only with each other they accelerate in opposite directions along a straight line and the ratio $|\mathbf{a}_B|/|\mathbf{a}_A|$ is a fixed reproducible number, depending only on the bodies themselves and not on the instant of measurement or the velocity or on the frame of reference (so long as the frame of reference is an "inertial" frame—one that is neither rotating nor accelerating in such a way as to cause an apparent departure from Newton's First Law).

Taking one body as a reference standard, this ratio can become the *definition* of mass. Thus it is possible to give an operational definition of mass without prior introduction of force as a primitive concept. In principle, the entire concept of force can be dispensed with, but this is not convenient, and force is reintroduced by defining it in terms of the function ma which has the same magnitude for both bodies in the interaction. Thus the force on body A is defined as the vector equal to $m_A\mathbf{a}_A$, and that on body B as the vector $m_B\mathbf{a}_B$. In this way, what we previously called the Second and Third Laws of Motion become incorporated into our physical statements through the definition of force. The final content of the theory is essentially the same; the method of solving actual physical problems remains identical; but in Mach's approach the sequence of definition and the language used to state the "law of nature" which is incorporated into the theory become quite different from those used in the modernized Newtonian approach outlined in Chapter 5. Many critics regard Mach's system as somewhat the more elegant and rigorous of the two, but there is no one system which is right in some absolute sense. A network of concepts and logical structure in science is validated, in the final analysis, by its internal consistency—by the fact that one can traverse the network along many paths and arrive at noncontradictory conclusions agreeing with observations of natural phenomena.

6.5 FRICTION

In all the illustrative problems considered up to this point, we have simplified matters by "thinking away" friction. In doing so we have already implicitly recognized friction as a force. Friction is our name for the "contrariness" in nature that resists and slows down the terrestrial motions most familiar to us. We say that bodies moving through air or liquids experience opposing forces of *fluid friction.* When one body rolls over another, the surfaces of the bodies are deformed at the line or point of contact. The rolling is always slightly uphill, and the resisting force is called *rolling friction* (Fig. 6.5.1). When surfaces tend to slip over each other, or when sliding actually occurs, the resisting force is called *surface friction* or *sliding friction.*

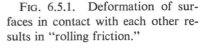

Fɪɢ. 6.5.1.   Deformation of surfaces in contact with each other results in "rolling friction."

No material surface is a perfect plane; even when it is very smooth, it has, on a microscopic scale, numerous irregularities (or "asperities," as they are referred to by researchers in the field). For many years it was widely assumed that the force of sliding friction was principally due to the surface roughness—to the interlocking of the asperities as they bumped and sheared each other during sliding. Some investigators, however, held to the hypothesis that the frictional force might be due to adhesion—molecular attraction between the materials where they come very close together at flattened asperities, as illustrated in Fig. 6.5.2.

A current expert in the field* remarks, "Modern work has definitely confirmed the adhesion hypothesis as against the roughness hypothesis because, among other reasons, very smooth surfaces almost invariably show as much (sometimes more) friction as do less smooth ones. However, in an attitude reminiscent of Aristotle's medieval disciples, most authors in mechanics still equate 'smooth' surfaces with frictionless surfaces."

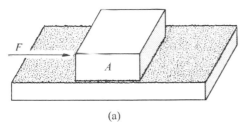

(a)

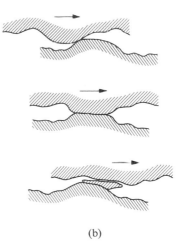

(b)

Fɪɢ. 6.5.2. (a) Force of sliding friction originates at contacts between the asperities of the two surfaces.   Films of "dirt" or extraneous material drastically alter the magnitude of frictional force. (b) Highly magnified sketch of the interaction between two protuberances. Wear particles, as shown in the lower figure, represent a relatively rare occurrence.   (After J. F. Archard, *Jour. Applied Phys.*, August, 1961.)

---

* E. Rabinowicz, Resource Letter F-1 on Friction, *American Journal of Physics*, December 1963.

Frictional forces have their origins in the very complex interplay of bulk and molecular properties of matter, and although the effects of these forces are among the commonest all-pervasive physical phenomena we encounter, they are perhaps among the least well understood. Very substantial effort in present-day research is being devoted to the development of better understanding of the detailed mechanisms of various types of friction.

Lack of complete mastery of the physics of friction, however, has not impeded the development of the rest of the science. Aristotelians and Scholastics never reached the point of idealizing or thinking away friction. This imaginative act on the part of Galileo and his successors in the seventeenth century led to the clarification of the kinematics of free fall and the elucidation of the laws of motion.

The next step beyond ignoring friction is to take it into account in approximate, empirical ways; simplifications which, in a sense, conceal our ignorance of the physics of the phenomenon but make it possible for us to include and estimate its effects, giving us insights and understanding which we would never attain if we waited for complete and accurate knowledge. In the following section we show how it is possible to "parameterize" friction in this fashion.

6.6   COEFFICIENT OF SURFACE FRICTION

If we apply a small horizontal force F to block A in Fig. 6.5.2, it does not accelerate as would a frictionless puck on a glass plate. We recognize the presence of an opposing force f and draw a free body diagram as shown in Fig. 6.6.1. Frictional force f is always found to act parallel to the surface in question and is a *passive* force, similar in this sense to the normal force N. If force F is gradually increased from zero, f increases, remaining equal and opposite to F, but this process has a limit. It is found that f has a maximum value which we shall denote by f_{max}. If F exceeds f_{max}, the body begins to slide, accelerated by the net force $F - f_{max}$. Once sliding begins, the frictional force actually decreases to a lower value. For this reason we speak of two types of surface friction: static and kinetic.

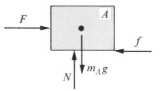

FIG. 6.6.1. Free body diagram of body on frictional surface (see Fig. 6.5.2a).

The following properties of f_{max} are established by experiment:

(1) f_{max} depends on the specific nature of the two surfaces in contact.

(2) f_{max} is proportional to the total normal force N with which one surface presses on the other and is approximately independent of the area exposed; i.e., in Figs. 6.5.2 and 6.6.1, f_{max} has roughly the same value regardless of whether block A is tall, with a small base area, or squat, with a very large base area, so long as N remains fixed. If N is increased by putting another block on top of A, f_{max} at the sliding surface increases.

TABLE 6.6.1

SOME AVERAGE VALUES OF COEFFICIENTS OF SURFACE FRICTION

Materials	Coefficient	
	Static friction, μ	Kinetic friction, μ_k
Steel on steel	0.70	0.50
Copper on steel	0.50	0.40
Copper on glass	0.70	0.50
Glass on glass	1.0	
Wood on wood	0.25 to 0.5	
Leather on metal	0.6	
Rubber on solids	1.0 to 4.0	
Metals on wood	0.4 to 0.6	
Lubricated metals	0.1 to 0.2	0.05 to 0.1

Since f_{max} is proportional to N, we write

$$f_{max} = \mu N, \tag{6.6.1}$$

where the proportionality constant μ is a property of the pair of surfaces in contact and is named "coefficient of static friction." (Prior to sliding, the frictional force f is *less* than μN; it has the value μN only when sliding is just about to begin.) Values of μ, experimentally determined for various pairs of surfaces, can be found tabulated in handbooks of engineering data (see Table 6.6.1). These values are to be regarded as useful approximations or guides to order of magnitude, and not as fixed, reproducible properties like density, or specific heat, or refractive index. For any given case, the actual value of μ depends on the roughness of the surfaces; the contamination from dirt, finger grease, or other films; atmospheric humidity; temperature; etc. (It should be noted that Eq. (6.6.1) is not a vector equation; f and N are not in the same direction; they are perpendicular to each other, and μ is only the proportionality constant between their scalar magnitudes.)

For description of sliding, we define a coefficient of kinetic friction, μ_k:

$$f_k = \mu_k N, \tag{6.6.2}$$

in which μ_k is always somewhat smaller than μ and, in general, has different values at different velocities of sliding. Since, over reasonable ranges of velocity, μ_k changes relatively little, it is frequently practical to make use of an average value for simplified calculations.

If a lubricating fluid is introduced between sliding surfaces, as is done in machines and mechanisms, frictional forces are markedly reduced, and are determined principally by properties of the fluid film which separates the moving surfaces. This is a reproducible situation, which has a reasonably sound theoretical foundation in the knowledge of the properties and dynamics of viscous fluids.

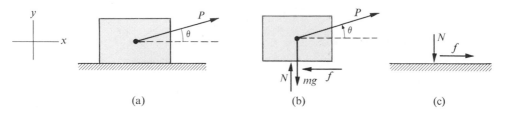

FIG. 6.7.1. Symbols denote magnitudes of forces. (a) Block of mass m pulled by force P. (b) Free body diagram of block. (c) Forces exerted on the floor by the block.

6.7 SOLUTION OF A PROBLEM INCLUDING SURFACE FRICTION

A block is pulled along a floor by an applied force P as shown in Fig. 6.7.1.

CASE 1.   Let us investigate the changes of the frictional force f with changes in magnitude and direction of P while the block is stationary. Applying the Second Law to the horizontal and vertical directions, we have

$$P \cos \theta - f = ma_x = 0,$$

$$N + P \sin \theta - mg = ma_y = 0.$$

Therefore

$$f = P \cos \theta, \tag{6.7.1}$$

$$N = mg - P \sin \theta. \tag{6.7.2}$$

These two equations tell us that if we start with $P = 0$ and increase the force gradually, the opposing frictional force adjusts itself accordingly and takes on values equal to $P \cos \theta$, keeping the horizontal forces balanced and the acceleration zero. At the same time the normal force N decreases because of the increasing upward component of P. If P becomes large enough for the static frictional force to approach its maximum value, with the block just about to slide, we have

$$f_{\max} = \mu N$$

and

$$f_{\max} = \mu(mg - P \sin \theta). \tag{6.7.3}$$

This equation tells us something we can understand intuitively, but which is not quickly anticipated by most people without the analysis: The maximum frictional force does not depend exclusively on the weight of the body. It also depends on the angle at which P is applied. Since P has an upward component, N is reduced, and this in turn reduces $f_{\max}$. (What would happen to $f_{\max}$ if the direction of P were reversed? Note that a new force diagram is necessary, since, in adjusting itself to external effects, the frictional force also changes direction.) If P becomes so large that its upward component exceeds the weight of the block, the body accelerates upward, and Eq. (6.7.2) is no longer valid.

CASE 2.   Let us investigate the factors affecting horizontal acceleration when $P \cos \theta$ exceeds f_{max}. We then have the horizontal and vertical equations of motion:

$$P \cos \theta - \mu_k N = ma_x, \tag{6.7.4}$$

$$N + P \sin \theta - mg = 0, \tag{6.7.5}$$

where $f = \mu_k N$ when sliding occurs. Since N adjusts itself under the influence of the applied force $\mathbf{P}$, let us take $\mathbf{P}$ as the known quantity and eliminate N from Eqs. (6.7.4) and (6.7.5), solving for a_x:

$$P \cos \theta - \mu_k(mg - P \sin \theta) = ma_x,$$

$$a_x = \frac{P}{m}(\cos \theta + \mu_k \sin \theta) - \mu_k g. \tag{6.7.6}$$

If the friction were zero, μ_k would be zero and Eq. (6.7.6) would reduce to $a_x = (P \cos \theta)/m$, which is exactly what we would expect for the frictionless case. This provides a partial, but not necessarily infallible, check of our analysis.

Suppose that in a particular case we hold the magnitude of the force $\mathbf{P}$ fixed but, starting at $\theta = 0$, calculate values of a_x as we increase the angle θ at which the force is applied. We find that the quantity $(\cos \theta + \mu_k \sin \theta)$ first increases, reaches a largest value, and then decreases as θ approaches $\pi/2$. (Verify this by calculating a few values for the case $\mu_k = 1$.) This means that, when friction is present, a maximum horizontal acceleration is imparted to the block, not when the pull is horizontal, but at some angle between 0 and $\pi/2$, depending on the coefficient of friction μ_k. What physical explanation would you advance for this phenomenon now that you know about it? (Is there an angle of maximum acceleration for a given value of P if the direction of $\mathbf{P}$ is reversed in Fig. 6.7.1?) How many of these insights would you have anticipated intuitively without being prompted by the mathematical analysis?

In many complex and important physical problems, systematic methods of mathematical analysis are essential for the attainment of correct insights and explanations. Intuition plays a vitally important role in original discovery, in the invention of interesting problems, and in the creation of fine experiments. But once the basic laws are established and are used to analyze involved situations, intuition can also be deceptive and misleading; in many cases it provides only an elusive *ex post facto* view. A research scientist must learn instinctively when to give free reign to his intuition and when to submit to the cold discipline of careful analysis.

PROBLEM 6.9.   "It is easier to pull a tennis court roller than to push one, but you do a better rolling job if you push." Either refute or justify this statement by making appropriate translation of the ideas developed in the preceding illustrative example. (Do not make your analysis exclusively verbal; draw appropriate free body diagrams, and present algebraic statements as the basis for your argument.)

PROBLEM 6.10.   Consider the physical situation suggested by Fig. 6.7.2: A block rests on an inclined plane; the mass and material of the block can be selected at will; the plane is pivoted at the foot, and the angle θ can be varied continuously from zero to inclinations which cause the block to slide down the plane.

(a) Draw a free body diagram of the block; in another diagram show the forces the block exerts on the plane.

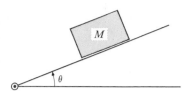

FIGURE 6.7.2

(b) Take as your problem an inquiry into how the frictional force changes as the plane is tilted, starting from $\theta = 0$. What parameters control the value of f up to the angle at which the block is on the verge of sliding and f approaches f_{max}?

(c) Denote by θ_{max} the angle at which sliding is about to begin, and show that $\tan \theta_{max} = \mu$. Interpret this result, paying particular attention to the surprising fact that neither m nor g are present in it. Why have these parameters disappeared? Would you have anticipated this result intuitively?

(d) This result suggests a laboratory method of determining coefficients of friction. What advantages would this method have over measurements based on pushing or pulling a block on a horizontal plane? Calculate the values of θ_{max} you would expect for a few combinations of surfaces.

(e) Obtain an algebraic expression for the acceleration of the block when θ exceeds θ_{max}. Assume you are preparing to make a laboratory measurement of such an acceleration. Select some reasonable numerical values of known quantities in such an experiment, and calculate the acceleration you would expect.

6.8   FLUID FRICTION

The study of fluid friction is a vast field of modern research. Its ramifications extend from molecular interactions which give fluids their viscosity to frictional effects that arise from the random motions, collisions, and interactions of macroscopic chunks of fluids in complex swirls and eddies of turbulent flow. Physical problems which motivate these studies range from the behavior of lubricating films, through the flow of liquids through pipes and channels in manufacturing processes, to the turbulent phenomena that regulate and influence the huge "engine" consisting of the atmosphere and the oceans.

We shall consider here only one minute aspect of the problem—resistance experienced by bodies moving through fluids. It was observed empirically, as far back as the seventeenth and eighteenth centuries, that very small particles (less than, say, 1 mm in diameter), moving slowly in liquids, experienced forces proportional to a linear dimension r and velocity v of the particles. This experimental observation can be described in the algebraic form

$$f = Krv. \tag{6.8.1}$$

The proportionality constant K depends on the shape of the particle and on the viscosity* of the fluid. During the nineteenth century the English mathematical physicist G. C. Stokes showed that Eq. (6.8.1), as applied to spherical particles,

---

* "Viscosity" is a technical term and denotes a property which is defined, measured, and tabulated for different fluids. Definitions and discussions of this property are to be found in somewhat more advanced textbooks.

could be derived from the equations of motion of viscous fluids, and it is hence known as Stokes' Law.

For larger particles moving relatively rapidly (raindrops falling in the atmosphere) Stokes' Law ceases to be a good approximation; the resisting force becomes more nearly proportional to the square of the velocity and more influenced by the density than the viscosity of the fluid.

Because the resisting force increases with velocity, a falling body experiences a *decreasing* acceleration. The velocity increases to a final constant value v_t when the weight of the body and the resisting frictional force become equal and opposite; v_t is called the "terminal velocity." If it were not for this frictional process, going out in a rainstorm could be a very painful experience; freely falling raindrops would attain velocities approaching that of sound, and would be more like bullets than like pattering drops of water.

PROBLEM 6.11.   Draw a free body diagram of a small spherical particle of radius r and density (mass per unit volume) ρ falling in a fluid under conditions such that Stokes's Law, Eq. (6.8.1), is valid.   Solve for the terminal velocity and interpret the result. Identify clearly any assumptions or idealizations which you make.   [*Answer:* $v_t = 4\pi r^2 \rho g / 3K$, providing the density ρ_0 of the surrounding or ambient fluid is very much smaller than ρ.]

6.9 A REMARK ABOUT PROBLEMS

What are the problems that one attacks through the concepts and mathematical machinery of Newtonian mechanics? Newton's attention centered on the "System of the World"—problems and theorems in which the paths of particles are conic sections, in which forces vary inversely as the square of distance of separation, and out of which one eventually constructs a model of the solar system that corresponds to observed facts and predicts unanticipated, but observable, phenomena. Daniel Bernoulli and Leonhard Euler in the eighteenth century were interested in terrestrial mechanics—the flow of fluids, rotation of bodies, and deformation of solids. The French mathematical physicists Lagrange and Laplace carried Newton's theory to a level of mathematical power and elegance in celestial mechanics and in the theory of the tides that Newton himself probably never foresaw.

Beside problems of this stature, the exercises which we call problems in a textbook seem to pale into insignificance. Nor are our textbook problems real problems of a practical, applied kind, such as those invented and formulated in daily activity by research physicists or engineers; they are simplified, idealized, abstracted ghosts of real problems—our carts and strings and frictionless pucks, our uniform forces and inclined planes. What is their justification? Do they bear any relevance to reality?

When one examines the achievements of science in giving us an understanding of our physical universe, he finds that very little of this achievement comes from the solution of real problems in complete detail. The actual situation is always too complex: complex in geometry, in mutual interactions, and in unascertainable frictional effects. Only the "unrealistic" abstraction turns out to be susceptible to mathematical analysis. Science is *not* "exact" in the popular sense of this term. Science has developed the capacity to isolate and define what is not known, what is being neglected. It has learned to identify its *inexactness*, the extent of error or the presence of idealizations, more clearly than most other disciplines. It is this capacity to define clearly what one knows and what one does not know that has been misinterpreted as "exactness."

A physicist wishing to study the dynamics of motion in the oceans or in the atmosphere does not start with a full-blown theory of the ocean itself. He studies flow of water in a rotating cylindrical tank; he invents simple problems which have no immediate relation to the formidably complicated parent one. Physicists studying atomic nuclei or the interior of solids operate in a similar way: They may start with an artificial problem of a group of particles arranged uniformly in a straight line. Artificial idealized abstractions frequently give unsuspected insights that are valid for more complicated cases and point the way to defining a next problem, which may bring the investigator a little closer to his goal. The good investigator is always keenly aware of the idealizations he has invoked, but this does not prevent him from continuing. Ability to invent ingenious approximations and idealizations and still retain the essential features of a physical problem is one of the distinctive characteristics of a fine researcher.

Problems, however simplified, are devices by means of which we can ask ourselves questions and penetrate to an understanding of physical phenomena as well as of the conceptual tools we have invented. With these overtones in mind, let us approach the problems that follow. Almost all these problems are open-ended; additional questions can be raised about them; new problems can be drawn from the ashes of the previous ones. Each suggestion can be the basis for a short and modest research which, although not at the exhilarating level of original work, is nevertheless not unlike the steps taken by an investigator in a new field.

6.10 PROBLEMS

6.12. Make a complete free body analysis of a tug-of-war contest. Draw force diagrams of the rope, of the opposing sides (treating them as particles), and of the earth. Identify clearly the forces that determine the horizontal acceleration of each body when one side is winning. What role does friction play? If the rope has negligible mass, compare the force the winning side exerts on the losing side with the force the losing side exerts on the winning side.

6.13. A car accelerates along a road and is subject to the influence of opposing frictional forces. Identify the origin and regions of action of some of the frictional forces. Draw force diagrams of the car and of the earth. Identify the force which imparts horizontal acceleration to the car.

6.14. A spring balance is calibrated to read 20 lb when a body weighing 20 lb is suspended from it, as shown in Fig. 6.10.1(a). Draw a "free body" force diagram of the spring balance. Suppose the spring balance measures the pull exerted in accelerating a 20-lb frictionless puck, as shown in (b). Draw a force diagram. What acceleration is imparted when the balance reads 20 lb? (Assume that the spring and pointer parts of the balance structure have negligible mass.) Suppose the spring balance is sus-

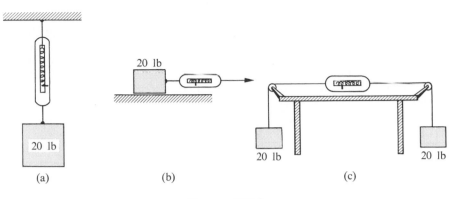

FIGURE 6.10.1

pended in the manner shown in (c). Draw a force diagram. What will be the reading on the balance? What will be the tensions in the strings, assuming them to have negligible mass? If you perform an acceleration experiment such as that illustrated in (b), and the spring-balance parts are not of negligible mass, what problems do you face in interpreting the results? Which end of the spring balance would you connect to the block? (Examine the construction of a spring balance before jumping to conclusions.)

6.15. (a) A bob of mass m (Fig. 6.10.2) is suspended on a string and is drawn away from the vertical by a horizontal force **P** (which may be exerted by a direct mechanical pull or by electric or magnetic effects). What value of P is required to hold the bob at an angle θ? What is the tension T in the string under these circumstances? Calculate the numerical values of P and T if the bob has a mass of 1.50 kg and θ is 38°. [*Answer:* $T = 18.7$ n, $P = 11.5$ n.]

(b) If the bob hangs from the roof of a car accelerating along a level road, it might also

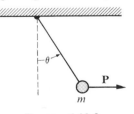

FIGURE 6.10.2

assume a position such as that shown in the figure (without our exerting a horizontal push or pull). If we observed such a situation, in which direction would we say the car was accelerating? Show that this device can be used as a very simple accelerometer (an instrument which measures acceleration), and that the acceleration of the car in g's is given directly by tan θ. Why is it not necessary to know the mass of the bob?

(c) If, in a completely closed laboratory room, we observed the bob hanging at an angle relative to the vertical, in what ways might we account for its behavior? If we had no way of seeing or observing anything whatsoever outside the room, how could we tell which interpretation is really true?

(d) Suppose our laboratory room were out in empty space where there is no downward reference direction. Would it be possible to use the bob-and-string system as an accelerometer? If so, how? If the room were accelerating uniformly, where would you find it most comfortable to "stand"?

6.16. Visualize yourself as standing in an elevator which can be accelerated up or down.

(a) Draw force diagrams of yourself and of the elevator.

(b) Investigate the values assumed by the normal force N which the elevator exerts on you by comparing N with your own weight: What is N when you are moving at uniform velocity? accelerating upward? accelerating downward? If you were standing on a platform scale, what would the scale read in each instance? What is N if the downward acceleration is equal to g, that is, if the elevator is falling freely? Is it possible, in principle, to accelerate downward with acceleration greater than g? What would have to be done to achieve this? Where would you be inclined to "stand" while accelerating downward with acceleration exceeding g?

(c) The sensation of having weight is a physical sensation which is intimately associated with our experience of the upward force N acting on us when we sit or stand or walk. In the elevator experience analyzed above, what sensation do we have as we accelerate up or down? Note carefully the origin of a sensation of decreased weight during the downward acceleration. Given this background, define the term "sensation of weightlessness." Under what circumstances might this sensation be experienced? (Do not confine yourself to the elevator problem, but use it as a point of departure.) When you experience a sensation of weightlessness, does your body necessarily have zero weight? What is the basis for all the talk one hears about weightlessness experienced by an astronaut? (See Problem 9.20 for a continuation of this discussion.)

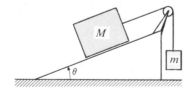

FIGURE 6.10.3

6.17. Investigate, more or less in the following outline, the problem suggested by Fig. 6.10.3, but do not hesitate to depart in other directions as well.

(a) If the plane is frictionless, what value of m is necessary to hold the large block M in equilibrium? Denote this value by m_0.

(b) If the coefficient of friction between the block and plane is μ, what are the smallest and largest values of m for which the block will not slide (either down or up the plane)? Denote these two values by m_1 and m_2, respectively.

(c) Suppose that, in a laboratory experiment, you determined m_1 and m_2 directly by trial and error. How would you estimate the value of m_0? From these data alone could you calculate μ, or would you need additional information?

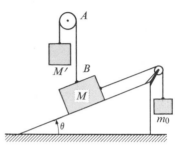

FIGURE 6.10.4

(d) Having estimated m_0, suppose you hang this mass on the string and rig up an additional mass and pulley as shown in Fig. 6.10.4. Predict the value of M' which will just barely lift the block off the plane. In what direction will the string AB orient itself under these equilibrium conditions? Try this system out in a laboratory experiment if the opportunity is available.

6.18. Design a laboratory experiment based on the situation proposed in Problem 6.7. Friction is not to be neglected; how would you determine the corrections which are necessary? [*Hint:* With a rolling cart the frictional forces are too small to be measured directly by a horizontal pull or by the method of Problem 6.10. Consider the possibility of studying the behavior of the cart as it coasts freely after a push. What other possibilities can you devise?] Decide what you would take as known and unknown quantities, and formulate the solution of the problem.

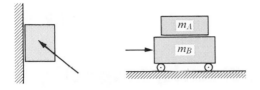

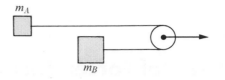

FIGURE 6.10.5   FIGURE 6.10.6

6.19. The sketches in Fig. 6.10.5 suggest problems to be investigated. What questions can you invent about them? (Assume friction to exist at surfaces which can slide over each other.)

6.20. Investigate the horizontal Atwood machine (Fig. 6.10.6) consisting of two frictionless pucks A and B on a glass plate. A constant force $\mathbf{F}$ is applied to the massless pulley, and the system is accelerated toward the right.

SUPPLEMENTARY READING AND STUDY

See references cited at end of Chapter 5.

Ernst Mach's critique of the Newtonian concepts is to be found in *The Science of Mechanics*. Chicago: Open Court Publishing Co., 1893

CHAPTER 7

Laws of Force: Elastic, Electric, Magnetic, and Gravitational

7.1 INTRODUCTION

In the great majority of interesting dynamical phenomena, forces acting on a particle vary with time and with the position of the particle. Consider a few illustrations: (1) A weight oscillates up and down on a stretched spring. The motion is rectilinear but certainly not uniformly accelerated. (We utilized the varying extension of a spring and reproducibility of its behavior in our operational definition of a force scale in Chapter 5.) Net force exerted in this case varies, and we expect a single numerical value of force to be associated with each position of the oscillating particle. (2) In the revolution of artificial satellites about the earth or of planets around the sun, the trajectory is, in general, elliptical or, in some instances, very nearly circular. The net force acting on the revolving particle varies with the position of the particle in its trajectory. (3) Electric forces of attraction or repulsion between charged particles depend on the separation of the particles, and the accelerations they impart to each other are therefore functions of position. (4) Electrically charged particles from outer space, arriving in the vicinity of the earth, are subject to magnetic effects which vary with position relative to the earth as well as with velocity of the particle.

In each one of these cases a particle moves, with continually varying acceleration, in a trajectory that is in some instances simple, in others geometrically quite complex. In each case the force acting on the particle depends not only on the relative positions of the interacting objects but on some intrinsic property of the objects themselves: strength of the spring, of gravitational and electrical properties of bodies, of magnetic effects in the vicinity of the earth.

The second law of motion, $\mathbf{F}_{net} = m\mathbf{a}$, relates only instantaneous values of force and acceleration; it does not directly inform us about a time history or trajectory of motion. But if we can establish a law of force, if we describe in a systematic way, as a function of time or of position, the net force acting on a particle, we also know its acceleration as a function of time or position. In the special case of uniform force and acceleration (as in free fall and projectile motion), we capitalized on such knowledge to generate complete descriptions of time history and trajectory. Supplemented by more powerful mathematical techniques, we might hope to attain equally detailed insights and equal power of prediction in the more complex phenomena just illustrated.

164

7.2 ELASTIC DEFORMATIONS; HOOKE'S LAW

In 1678 Robert Hooke wrote:

"The theory of springs, though attempted by divers eminent mathematicians of this age, has hitherto not been published by any. It is now about eighteen years since I first found it out, but designing to apply it to some particular use,* I omitted publication thereof . . .

"Take a quantity of even-drawn wire, either steel, iron, or brass, and coil it on an even cylinder into a helix of what length or number of turns you please, then turn the ends of the wire into loops, by one of which suspend this coil upon a nail, and the other sustain the weight you would have extend it, and hanging on several weights observe exactly to what length each of the weights do extend it beyond the length that its own weight doth stretch it to, and you shall find that if one ounce, or one pound, or one certain weight doth lengthen it one line, or one inch, or one certain length, then two ounces, two pounds, or two weights will extend it two lines, two inches or two lengths; and three ounces, pounds, or weights, three lines, inches or lengths; and so forwards. And this is the rule or law of nature, upon which all manner of restituent or springing motion doth proceed, whether it be of rarefaction, or extension, or condensation and compression." [See Fig. 7.2.1.]

Hooke goes on to describe similar experiments with angular displacements of a coil spring and with the stretching of wires. If we were to plot the results of experiments such as Hooke describes, we would obtain, for different springs, a graph like that in Fig. 7.2.2. Stating the law of force algebraically, we write

$$F = kx, \tag{7.2.1}$$

where F and x refer to magnitudes of force and extension. This equation is commonly called *Hooke's Law*. It asserts a linear relation between force and extension, in which the numerical value of k, the proportionality constant (or slope of the straight line in Fig. 7.2.2), is a property of the spring itself and is called the *force constant* of the spring.

Many elastic† deformations are quite well described by a linear relation, a Hooke's law, but there are many instances in which the situation is more complicated: Springs can be deliberately made nonuniform so as to exhibit a nonlinear force law. Objects, including ordinary springs, may exhibit a linear force law until they are

---

* Possibly in connection with his invention of the coil or hairspring used on the balance wheel of a watch.

† Elastic in this context does not mean "easily deformed"; it connotes the capacity of a system to return to its initial dimensions when the deforming force is removed, regardless of whether the deformation is large or extremely small; as, say, in the stretch of a steel bar under tension.

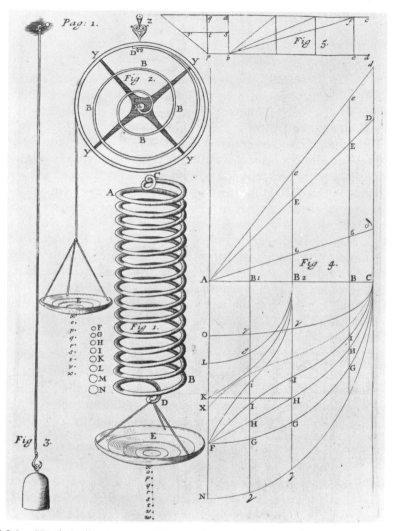

FIG. 7.2.1. Hooke's illustration of his spring experiment. (Photograph courtesy the Houghton Library, Harvard.)

loaded too heavily and stretched beyond their elastic limit; the plot of F versus x then ceases to be a straight line. Hooke claimed that air confined in a cylinder obeyed the linear relation (between force applied to a piston confining the air in the cylinder and the resulting displacement of the piston) for both rarefaction and compression; this is so nearly true for changes which are small compared with the total volume of gas that Hooke, working in a day when gas manipulation techniques were in their infancy, would have been hard pressed to observe a departure from linearity. His contemporary, Robert Boyle, showed in his famous experiments on the "spring of the air" that a better representation of gas behavior (at constant tem-

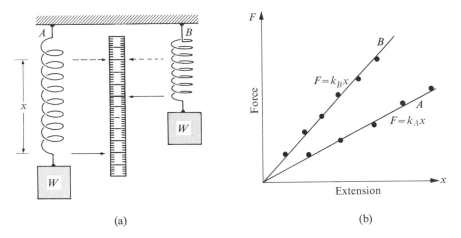

(a)   (b)

FIG. 7.2.2. Calibration of two springs; B stiffer than A. (a) Given weight W produces larger extension, x, of spring A than of stiffer spring B. When unloaded, the two springs have equal length, as indicated by dashed arrows.) (b) Plot of F versus x for springs A and B. Spring B has a larger force constant, k (slope of line); x is defined as extension relative to an equilibrium position of the spring.

perature) was given by the relation $p = K/V$, where p and V are the total pressure and volume of a gas, and K is a proportionality constant which has a fixed value at any one temperature. This is another illustration of a *nonlinear* force law.

PROBLEM 7.1.   We have so far studied three laws that are expressed in very similar algebraic form:

$$\mathbf{F}_{net} = m\mathbf{a}, \qquad f_{max} = \mu N, \qquad F = kx.$$

Contrast these three statements, articulating carefully the similarities and differences you can discern. Note, for example, that each one contains a proportionality constant that measures an intrinsic property of some object. What are the dimensions of the respective proportionality constants? In what sense is the word "law" applicable to each of these statements? In what sense are they "true"? In what sense not true? Suppose you were asked to list the three laws in some hierarchy or order of importance. In what order would you list them? Why?

PROBLEM 7.2.   Colliding elastic spheres undergo deformation, compressing each other during the interval of contact. Try to visualize the geometry of the deformation. Would you expect Hooke's Law to be valid in this case? Justify your answer.

PROBLEM 7.3.   A force of 5.25 lb stretches a certain spring balance 2.38 in. Calculate the force constant of the spring. Sketch the F versus x graph you would expect to obtain. [*Answer:* $k = 2.20$ lb/in.]

PROBLEM 7.4.   A helical spring is found to stretch 16.0 cm if a 1.30-kg mass is suspended from it. What acceleration would this spring impart to a 4.60-kg frictionless puck under a horizontal pull which extends the spring 12.0 cm? [*Answer:* 2.08 m/sec².]

7.3 ELECTRIC AND MAGNETIC FORCES*

From time immemorial men have been aware of the attraction of lodestone for iron and of the attraction of amber, after being rubbed, for light objects. Modern scientific inquiry into these phenomena began in the seventeenth century and had a great flowering in the eighteenth and nineteenth. A few farsighted individuals anticipated that along this road lay insights into the microscopic structure of matter itself, but it would have been difficult indeed to foresee that along the same road lay radio communication, the generation and transmission of power, the rise of a new industrial technology.

In following the evolution of the science of mechanics we were concerned with events and concepts close to direct sense perceptions. We can see motion of a stone; we have an intuitive sense of its acceleration; and, although we cannot see mass, we can feel the inertia of the stone as we throw it. Even so, it was not easy to construct an unambiguous and fruitful set of concepts with which to unravel and comprehend the hidden order in mechanical phenomena. Amber and lodestone confront us with an entirely new range of experience in which we become aware of a depth and complexity far beyond the level of mechanics. We observe bodies being accelerated, and we draw on mechanical concepts to say that "forces" are acting. But clearly these forces are very different from the pushes and pulls of a hand, or a rope, or a floor; they manifest themselves without mechanical contact between the interacting bodies and are affected by such actions as rubbing or pounding or handling. To distinguish these forces from others, we call them "electric" and "magnetic." Undeterred by the fact that these phenomena transcend our visual and tactual senses, we attempt to describe entities and events underlying and accounting for the observable phenomena. Such a structure is called a *model*. A model is an heuristic device—an aid to our imagination and understanding.

An evolving model frequently suggests experiments or tests that lead to corrections and modifications, or even abandonment, of the model itself. Such thinking is highly effective in other fields (history, sociology, economics) as well as in science. An able, original investigator makes powerful use of heuristic models, but he understands their artificial character, does not endow them with an aura of reality to which they are not entitled, and is not surprised when aspects of the invention turn out to be incorrect or when vivid details are found to be superfluous.

Let us try to divorce ourselves from prior knowledge of the vocabulary of electricity and magnetism and follow the development of concepts from the most fundamental evidence: What is it that we know? How do we know it? What is the model that we use? How real are the entities that transcend our senses and which we invent to help ourselves think?

In 1600 William Gilbert (1540–1603), physician to Queen Elizabeth, published a treatise entitled *De Magnete*. Here Gilbert put forth his realization that the earth itself is a magnet and interacts with compass needles and other magnets just as

---

* Much of the historical content of this and succeeding sections is based on Sir Edmund Whittaker's *History of the Theories of Aether and Electricity*. New York: Harper Torchbooks TB 531, 1960.

magnets interact with each other. He speculated that gravity and the motion of planets might be accounted for as magnetic phenomena; Kepler not long afterward engaged in similar speculations.

Gilbert clearly articulated the distinction between electric and magnetic phenomena: Inventing a very simple, sensitive detecting device (a small wooden needle balanced freely on a pivot, like a compass needle), he showed that many substances such as glass, sealing wax, sulfur, and gems could be "electrified," or made to behave like amber, and attract the wooden needle after being rubbed. He called attention to the fact that lodestone attracts only iron, whereas the electrified bodies can be shown to attract everything. The influence of lodestone on iron is not affected by immersing the objects in water, while under similar circumstances electrification disappears.

PROBLEM 7.5. Out of your own experience with magnets and frictional electricity, cite a few additional differences between magnetism and electrification. For example: include a statement (without using technical names) about the two-endedness of magnets, and the absence of a similar property in a rubbed comb or plastic rod. Describe experiments you have seen or could construct.

Believing that matter cannot act on other objects without direct contact, Gilbert propounded a model of electrification in which he visualized rubbed amber or glass as being surrounded by an invisible, imponderable effluvium which had been liberated from within the material by influence of friction. This effluvium extended to other bodies and drew them toward the electrified one. Gilbert's doctrine of the effluvium persisted well into the middle of the eighteenth century, at which time there evolved a vocabulary and point of view closer to those we hold today.

In our modern vocabulary, we say that bodies which exhibit electrical forces carry electrical charge, but this does not establish "charge" as a fluid, or a set of hooks, or a kind of paint; it does not tell us what charge is. Having names for entities such as "electrons" and "protons" doesn't help us either; we say that these entities carry electrical charge because, in the final analysis, we can trace our knowledge of them back to the operational circumstance that they would be attracted and repelled by rubbed amber or glass.

PROBLEM 7.6. Later seventeenth- and eighteenth-century investigators (probably influenced by Descartes, who promulgated an elaborate qualitative theory of interaction of bodies through vortices in the surrounding ether in order to account for gravitation and magnetism) visualized electric attraction as caused by vortices in the electric effluvium. A report of the French Academy in 1733 says: "Around an electrified body there is formed a vortex of exceedingly fine matter in a state of agitation, which urges towards the body such light substances as lie within its sphere of activity. The existence of this vortex is more than a mere conjecture; for when an electrified body is brought close to the face it causes a sensation like that of encountering a cobweb."

This sensation cannot be more vividly described. If you have never felt it, try the following on a dry day: Rub a shirt, blanket, or sweater of synthetic fabric against some other cloth and bring it near your face or arms. Using whatever knowledge you have acquired of electricity, how would you explain in modern vocabulary the origin of the sensation you experience? Is your explanation any better than the one quoted above? Why or why not? (What does "better" mean to you in this context?)

7.4   GRAY AND DESAGULIERS: ELECTRICAL CONDUCTION

Between 1729 and 1736 two English friends, Stephen Gray and Jean Desaguliers, reported the results of a series of experiments "showing that the Electrick Vertue of a Glass Tube may be conveyed to any other Bodies so as to give them the same Property of attracting and repelling light Bodies as the Tube does, when excited by rubbing; and that this attractive Vertue might be carried to Bodies that were many feet distant from the Tube."

They showed that a cork or other object as much as 800 or 900 feet away could be electrified by connecting it to the glass tube with materials such as metal wires or hempen string. They found that other materials, such as silk, would not convey the effect. As a matter of fact, they discovered in early, painstaking experiments that the distant object would not become electrified if the transmission line made contact with the earth, and they separated or insulated it from the earth by suspending it on silken threads. Gray had previously shown that solid or hollow objects of any given material behave the same way when electrified. From all these experiments it became clear that electrification is a surface effect; that the electric "virtue" or "fluid" would move freely along some materials (Desaguliers gave them the name of "non-electrics" or "conductors") from one body to another. The earth, the human body, metals, moisture are immediately recognized as conductors. Materials which do not conduct electricity come to be called nonconductors or insulators.

A metal rod or sphere when held in the hand and rubbed with fur shows no sign of electrification, but when mounted on a nonconductor, the metal is readily electrified. The electrical charge is no longer conducted away to be shared with the huge object which is the earth. When this was realized, it was found that practically any material can be electrified by friction.

Water is found to be a conductor. It renders insulators conducting when the surfaces are wet or moist. This makes understandable the rapid loss of charge by electrified bodies on humid days.

7.5   TWO KINDS OF ELECTRICAL CHARGE

During the same years that Gray and Desaguliers were developing the concept of conduction and classifying substances as conductors and nonconductors, Charles François du Fay (1698–1739), working in France, concentrated on another manifestation. Now, with the ease of hindsight, we consider it a bit strange that throughout the preceding centuries the electric force was considered essentially attractive. It must have been noticed that small particles, first attracted to a charged rod, are frequently strongly repelled after having come in direct contact with the rod or after the jumping of a spark on close approach. Gray, in 1729, casually mentions repulsion (in the remark quoted in the preceding section) but no one seems to have followed up the implications of the phenomenon until du Fay investigated it, with a preconceived model in mind, and made a profound discovery.

He observed that a scrap of gold leaf was always strongly repelled by an electrified glass tube with which it had made contact. He explained this by saying that the vortex of electric effluvium surrounding the glass tube first enveloped the gold leaf and impelled it toward the tube. On contact with the tube, the gold leaf acquired some "electric virtue" and its own vortex. The two vortices then repelled each other.

This model led du Fay to expect that the charged gold leaf would also be repelled by other electrified objects. "An examination of this matter," he wrote in 1733, "has led me to a discovery which I should never have foreseen, and of which I believe no one hitherto has had the least idea." He found that the charged gold leaf, repelled by the glass tube, was invariably *attracted* by excited "resinous" materials such as amber or sealing wax. He continued the experiments to show the inverse effect: that gold leaf repelled after contact with charged resinous materials was always attracted by excited "vitreous" materials such as glass or crystal. These facts obviously required modifications of the vortex model; the modifications were so artificial and cumbersome that the model was no longer useful as an aid to the imagination, and reference to it gradually disappeared from the literature.

We can repeat du Fay's experiments in an even more direct way: If we rub two glass rods with silk cloth (or plastic wrapping materials such as those available in grocery stores) and suspend one of them on a string, as shown in Fig. 7.5.1, we find that the

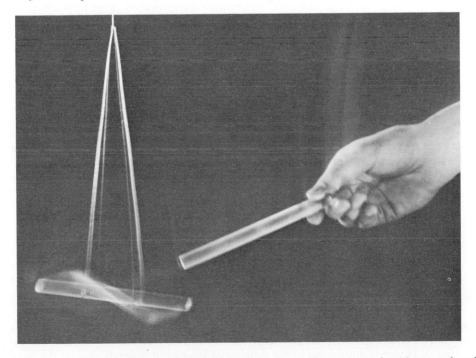

Fig. 7.5.1. Identical rods, rubbed with the same material, are always found to repel each other. (Courtesy Educational Services, Inc.)

rods always repel each other. Two hard rubber rods rubbed with fur are also found to repel; and, in general, repulsion is observed whenever identical materials are electrified in the same way. Since we are naturally inclined to say that identical objects, electrified in exactly the same way, carry like charges, we would summarize the experiments by saying that "bodies carrying like charges repel each other" or, more simply, "like charges repel." Note how the language has been constructed: "charge" is not an object, directly perceived, but is an attribute we have invented because there is something different about the rods before and after rubbing; we say that the charges are alike not because we perceive the charges as something identical in shape, color, hardness, texture, but because we have performed identical physical actions on materials that are alike in physical appearance and past history.

When we extend the observations, we find that the rubber and glass rods in the preceding experiments attract each other. A piece of amber and a lucite rod, both rubbed with wool, are found to repel the rubber rod as well as each other and to attract the glass rod. We are now led to say that rubber, amber, and lucite all carry like charges and that the charge carried by the glass is different. In additional experiments, we find that an electrified body, repelled by the rubber rod, is invariably attracted by the glass, and vice versa.* On the basis of this experience, we proclaim that there are two kinds of electrical charge, that like charges repel, and that unlike charges attract.

You can easily carry out experiments at home or in your room to help you remember the operations and the concepts. A charged toothbrush handle or comb can be suspended (as in Fig. 7.5.1) to act as a detector. A host of other articles are available: additional toothbrushes or combs, fountain pens, glass tumblers, leather, fabrics of all kinds, plastic wrapping films from laundry or grocery store. Be sure that everything is very dry and that, in holding an object, you are not draining away the charge through your own body.

PROBLEM 7.7. Describe an hypothetical experimental observation that would force you to say, "Here is a body which carries a third kind of electrical charge." Under these circumstances what would happen to statements based on use of the adjectives "like" and "unlike"? What is your view of the logical status of the statement, "There are only two kinds of electrical charge"? On what evidence is this assertion based? Has it been proved?

In papers published in 1733 and 1734, du Fay built up his evidence for the existence of two kinds of electricity, which he called "vitreous" (that on the glass rod rubbed with silk) and "resinous" (that on the rubber rod rubbed with fur). Benjamin Franklin (1709–90), working in America during the following decade, was initially unaware of

---

* To avoid repetition of cumbersome phrases, when we refer to electrified rubber and glass rods we shall mean rods that have been rubbed with fur and silk, respectively. Actually the kind of charge is not unique to the material of the rod; it depends also on the second material. For example: two rubber rods, one rubbed with fur and the other with plastic wrapping film, will *attract* each other, indicating *unlike* charges.

du Fay's discoveries and terminology. Favoring a model in which a single electrical fluid was transferred between bodies, he visualized electrified glass as having acquired an excess over a normal amount of electrical fluid, and he called this state "positive"; the object with which the glass was rubbed he visualized as having a deficiency of electric fluid, and called its state "negative." Franklin's terminology turned out to be more convenient than du Fay's and remains with us to the present day, although we now recognize two distinct kinds of charge and reject Franklin's model of a single electrical fluid.

PROBLEM 7.8. Magnets and the magnetic compass are familiar to most of us from childhood, and we are aware of statements about the poles of a magnet, like and unlike poles repelling and attracting, etc. We shall not, in the body of this text, take the space to develop the terminology of magnetism in the same detail as that of electricity, because the sequence is very similar. The student should be able to think through and clarify the vocabulary to himself with the help of the following outline of questions:

(a) How can we tell whether an iron bar is magnetized or unmagnetized? Cite several tests and experiments, describing what objects you would wish to have and what operations you would perform. Do not overlook the possibility of suspending the bar so that it can rotate freely, as in Fig. 7.5.1.

(b) What experience leads us to introduce the word pole, and talk about the two poles of a magnet?

(c) Given two identical bar magnets, a string, and no other equipment, by what operational procedure would you determine which poles are like and which are unlike? [*Hint:* Why are the poles of a magnet called north and south, respectively?] What experience leads us to say that like poles repel and unlike poles attract?

(d) What experience leads us to say that there are only two kinds of magnetic poles? What experience would controvert this?

(e) Having established our basic operations for identifying and naming the north and south ends of magnets and compass needles by reference to the earth, we can identify the polarity of any new magnet by testing it with one of the known ones. Suppose we now stand aside and view the earth as just another magnet which we are testing: Where is the north pole of the *magnet* that is the earth?

7.6 CONSERVATION OF CHARGE

With growing interest in electrical phenomena, hand-turned machines were devised for producing static, or frictional electrification. In 1745 a professor at the University of Leyden stumbled on the fact that a glass jar, coated on both the inside and outside with a metallic conductor (Fig. 7.6.1) could "accumulate" electric effects, as evidenced by the intensity of the shock or spark that could be drawn by touching the jar oneself or by touching it to other objects. Electric machines and Leyden phials quickly became

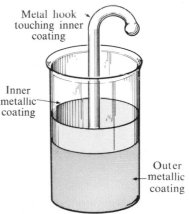

FIG. 7.6.1. Leyden phial.

standard equipment in research, and intensity of electrification was judged semi-quantitatively by the intensity of shocks and sparks. Using equipment of this kind, Franklin, in 1747, conducted a series of simple and ingenious experiments. Two phials were charged in the same way by simultaneously touching the hooks to the glass tube of the electric machine and the outer coatings to the earth. Franklin found that if the outer coatings were then connected to each other (by holding the jars with fingers on the outer coatings, his own body being the conductor), nothing happened when the hooks were brought together. However, when he held one bottle by the hook and the other by the coating and applied the coating of the first to the hook of the second, a spark occurred and both phials were completely discharged.

This experiment, together with variations of it, led Franklin to surmise that "electrical fluid" was merely shifted from one body to another in electrification and that the total quantity was always conserved. Franklin's evidence was crude and qualitative, but his intuition was sound. The conjecture influenced other investigators and proved to be very fruitful in subsequent research.

With the passage of time the hypothesis of conservation of electrical charge has been so strongly confirmed, in so wide a range of phenomena, that it has come to be viewed as one of the most fundamental of all natural laws.

7.7   MODEL OF ELECTRIFICATION

Let us review the model and language we have built up. We shall use the new vocabulary to make statements about electrification and to describe a few simple electrical phenomena:

Since all materials can be electrified but normally are "unexcited," we visualize all matter as containing both positive and negative electricity. In the normal state, the positive and negative charges, present in equal amounts, balance or neutralize each other. This can be thought of arithmetically as an adding of equal amounts of positive and negative charge to give zero, and illustrates the utility of the plus and minus nomenclature—otherwise "red" and "blue," "resinous" and "vitreous" would have been equally convenient names.

Electrification consists of leaving a body with an excess of either positive or negative charge. We then say that it carries a net charge. When we rub a glass rod with silk, it acquires a net positive charge; the silk simultaneously acquires an equal negative charge (or deficiency of positive charge).

If we touch a conductor, such as a metal-coated pithball, with the charged glass rod, the pithball exhibits a net charge which it acquires from contact with a small region of the nonconducting glass. The remaining charge on the nonconductor is unaffected.

The name "conductor" is selected because it implies the free motion of charge, the distinguishing characteristic of such material. Net charge distributes itself over a conductor until some sort of equilibrium is achieved; it cannot be retained on a limited portion of the object, as is perfectly possible on a nonconductor.

When a spark jumps through air between a charged rod to an uncharged pithball, the latter is found to have acquired a charge. The implication is that the air became conducting, and that the spark was somehow a mechanism for the transfer of charge from one body to the other. The electrical "breakdown" and jumping of sparks in all materials in the presence of intense electrification implies that electrical charges in matter can be separated by effects other than the rubbing of bodies against each other and that electrical forces must be intimately involved in the very structure of matter itself.

A sensitive detector of charge, called an electroscope, can be made as shown in Fig. 7.7.1. If a net charge is transferred to the electroscope by touching it with a charged glass rod, the positive charge so acquired spreads out over the conductor and causes the thin metal leaves to stand out at an angle, revealing the presence of a net charge. Touching the electroscope with the hand allows the charge to be conducted through the body to the earth, and the electroscope is said to be "discharged" through having been "grounded."

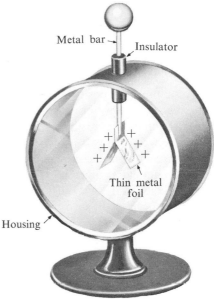

The behavior of the electroscope in the preceding example is identical whether one supposes that it is positive charge which is added or negative charge which is taken away. Without deeper knowledge concerning the role and disposition of electrical charge in the microscopic constitution of matter, it is impossible to tell whether one kind of charge, or the other, or both have been displaced in an electrical phenomenon. Ultimately we shall find that each of three possibilities is realized in different circumstances: negative charge is displaced in metallic conductors; both kinds of charge migrate in conducting

FIG. 7.7.1.   When the electroscope carries a net charge, the flexible metal leaves repel each other and stand out at an angle.   Deflection of the leaves varies with intensity of electrification.

liquids and gases, etc. After many vigorous polemics, eighteenth-century investigators gradually realized that no macroscopic experiments would ever resolve the question of which kind of charge was displaced, since any one of the three possible models serves equally well in accounting for observed effects. After this realization, polemics ceased, and effort was concentrated on exploiting the model in the design of more precise and demanding experiments. Usage drifted to the *convention* that positive charge is displaced. This convention is retained in most scientific literature to this day, and we shall adhere to it throughout this textbook whenever we describe macroscopic electrical phenomena.

PROBLEM 7.9.   When air and gases from the vicinity of a flame are passed into the housing of a charged electroscope, it is observed that the electroscope is rapidly discharged (almost as though it had been touched directly with one's hand). How might you account for this effect? Recognize at least two or three possibilities. Even in a very dry atmosphere, a charged electroscope does not retain its charge permanently; it is observed to discharge very slowly, and this effect is somewhat more pronounced at high altitudes than at low altitudes. What implications do you see in these observations? (Observations of essentially this kind played a fundamental role in the discovery of cosmic rays.)

7.8 INDUCED POLARIZATION

When a charged rubber rod is brought near an uncharged metal-coated pithball (Fig. 7.8.1), the ball is attracted toward the rod. This is an observed fact; does our model of electrical phenomena offer a reasonable explanation?

Assuming that positive charge is free to move in the normally neutral conducting coating, we readily visualize a displacement of the effective centers of positive and negative charge (as explained in the caption to Fig. 7.8.1), resulting in a net attractive force between the two objects. Here we are making a deduction from the fact that attractive or repulsive forces between charged bodies increase rapidly as the bodies are brought closer together. This effect is obvious on casual observation in your own experiments, and was well known long before Coulomb's quantitative experiments (Section 7.11) established the inverse-square law.

Suppose an electroscope is initially positively charged [Fig. 7.8.2(a)]. If a positively charged rod is brought near the electroscope (not touching and not close enough for a spark to jump), an induced polarization is superposed on the existing distribution of charge. More positive charge in the vicinity of the leaf causes the deflection of the leaf to increase [Fig. 7.8.2(b)]—an indication that a positively charged body is in the vicinity. In this way (providing the sign of the initial charge is known) the electroscope can be used to indicate the sign of electric charge on other objects.

The presence of a negatively charged body has the effect shown in Fig. 7.8.2(c), and the deflection of the leaf decreases. If the negative electrification of the rod is sufficiently high, the deflection of the leaf may first drop to zero as the rod approaches and then increase as strong induced polarization makes the vicinity of the leaf negatively charged [Fig. 7.8.2(d)]. Bringing one's hand or some other, large, uncharged body close to a charged electroscope causes a drop in the deflection of the leaf. How do you account for this effect?

PROBLEM 7.10. Describe the events illustrated in Figs. 7.8.1 and 7.8.2, assuming (a) a model in which only negative charge is displaced; (b) a model in which both positive and negative charge are free to move. What observable prediction does each model give? Is it possible, with these experiments, to determine which model is "correct"?

It is observed that nonconducting materials (bits of paper, very light pithballs) are attracted to the charged rod even in the absence of a conductive coating, albeit the attractive force is clearly much smaller. To explain this effect we invent a somewhat more elaborate model (Fig. 7.8.3). This model visualizes induced polarization of nonconducting or dielectric materials as a partial orientation of two-ended (positive-negative) dipoles within a structure that does not allow free displacement of electric charge.

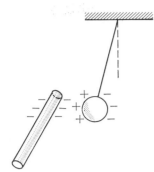

FIG. 7.8.1. Uncharged pithball is attracted to charged rod. Explanation: Some positive charge (assumed free to move in conducting coating of pithball) is attracted toward rod, leaving opposite side with excess of negative charge. Effective centers of positive and negative charge are displaced, with positive charge, on the average, closer to the rod. This results in net attractive force toward rod. Displacement of effective centers of positive and negative charge is called "induced polarization."

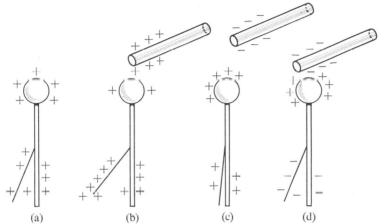

FIG. 7.8.2. Influence of charged bodies on the deflection of a charged electroscope.

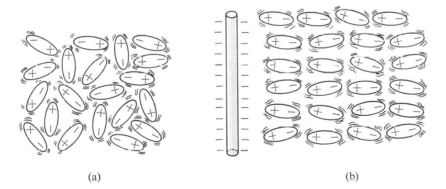

FIG. 7.8.3. Induced polarization of a dielectric (nonconductor) in presence of charged body. (a) Particles of unpolarized, nonconducting material are visualized as electric dipoles—minute rods with positive and negative ends. In normal state, dipoles jiggle in thermal motion and are randomly oriented so that the effect of one dipole is cancelled by that of its neighbors. (b) In presence of negatively charged rod, dipoles still jiggle in thermal motion, but, on the average, are twisted around with positive ends toward the rod. The effective centers of positive and negative charge are displaced, with the left side positively charged relative to the right.

PROBLEM 7.11.   An ordinary, unmagnetized iron bar will become magnetized, picking up nails and repelling a pole of a compass needle, when it is close to or in contact with a permanent magnet. This capacity of the bar disappears when the permanent magnet is removed. What analogies do you see between this behavior and the phenomena of electrical induction discussed in this section?

7.9 CHARGING CONDUCTORS BY INDUCTION

You can easily verify the following observation by carrying out some version of the experiment (Fig. 7.9.1).

If a conducting body, initially uncharged, is connected to the earth, and then disconnected, while a positively charged body is close by, the first body always acquires net *negative* charge. The connection to the earth can be established simply by touching the body *anywhere* on its surface. This phenomenon is called charging by induction. We can visualize a reasonable explanation in terms of the concept of induced polarization (Fig. 7.9.2). In connecting the ball with the earth, we make it possible for induced polarization to take place in the ball-earth system. If the connection to ground is severed before removal of the charged rod, the ball is left with a net opposite charge.

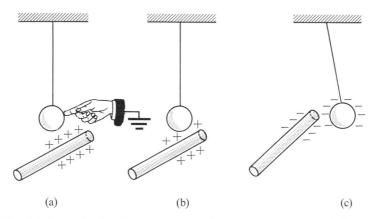

(a)   (b)   (c)

FIG. 7.9.1.   (a) A conducting ball is touched (i.e., connected to earth by a conducting path) while positively charged rod is close by. ($\pm$ is a widely used symbol for electrical connection to earth or "ground."   (b) The hand is removed while rod remains close by. (c) Positively charged rod is removed. Ball exhibits negative charge as evidenced by repulsion from negatively charged rod.

Once the phenomenon of charging by induction came to be understood in terms of a simple model, electrostatic machines were immediately improved.   By the 1760's, instead of simply relying on transfer of charge from a continuously rubbed body, elaborate machines were developed which took advantage of charging by induction. Such machines multiplied enormously the electrification attainable in Leyden jars, and made it possible to produce very intense sparks. Not only did research on electricity prosper, but electrical entertainment became a popular parlor game. Scientific

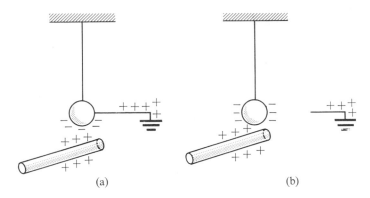

(a)   (b)

FIG. 7.9.2. Sequence of events in charging by induction. (a) Ball-earth system is subject to induced polarization, with region near positive rod becoming negatively charged as mobile positive charge is repelled to distant points. (b) Connection with earth is broken; ball is left with net negative charge.

apparatus houses (some catalogs still exist and make quaint reading) sold electrostatic machines with kits of accessories. Avant-garde hosts entertained their guests with unexpected electric shocks, dancing and whirling gadgets, and with electrified young ladies whose long hair would stand out radially from their heads.

It was during this period of enormous popular interest in electricity that Franklin performed his kite experiments to demonstrate that thunderstorm phenomena were essentially electrical and that lightning was a large-scale atmospheric manifestation of the sparks produced by electrostatic machines. This research and discovery caught the popular imagination and did much to propagate his fame and make him a celebrity.

Dramatic though some of the visual effects of electrostatic machines may be, the quantities of electricity and amounts of energy involved are very small. The invention of electrostatic induction machines had no technological consequences. When, approximately one hundred years later, Faraday discovered the phenomenon of *electromagnetic* induction—the possibility of generating large displacements of electricity during motion of conductors in a magnetic field—the inventions which followed included the dynamo, with all its impact on our industrial civilization.

PROBLEM 7.12. Suppose that you have at your disposal only a rubber rod which can be charged negatively. You wish to put a net positive charge on an electroscope. Describe how you might achieve this by charging the electroscope by induction (i.e., give a series of sketches indicating each successive action you would take and the charge distribution that would accompany each stage).

PROBLEM 7.13. Return to Section 7.6, where a brief description is given of how Franklin charged his Leyden phials by holding the hook to the glass tube of the electric machine and connecting the outer coating to the earth. Franklin learned by experience that if he did not make the latter step (temporarily connecting the outer coating to the earth) the phial would be only weakly charged. Explain these observations, using appropriate sketches of charge distribution.

7.10 INVERSE-SQUARE LAWS OF FORCE

With the publication of the *Principia* in 1687, Newton had shown* that the motions of planets around the sun (and of moons around their planets) could be quantitatively accounted for if one assumed a force, acting between the central and revolving body, varying inversely as the square of the distance of separation. As the eighteenth century progressed, continuing success in wide applications of the Newtonian theory won it an almost universal acceptance, and the inverse-square relationship, by gradual stages, acquired in the eyes of the scientific community its status as law rather than hypothesis.

In this climate, it is not surprising that many people, observing qualitatively the rapid decrease of electric and magnetic forces with increasing separation of interacting bodies, guessed that the variation might go as the inverse square of distance. With some notion as to what might be expected, it is possible to design improved experiments. During the second half of the eighteenth century skillful, ingenious work by a number of experimentalists was focused on verification of the electric and magnetic laws of force.

In 1750, John Michell (1724–93), a young Fellow at Queen's College, Cambridge, published observations showing that attraction and repulsion between magnetic poles varied inversely as the square of distance between them. Other scientists on the continent were asserting this law in the 1760's, and may have arrived at it independently of Michell's work. (The experiment with magnetic poles requires planning and theoretical analysis. Consider how you might set up such an experiment yourself. What apparatus would you use? All magnets are double-ended; it is impossible to obtain an isolated north or south pole. If you were trying to study the repulsion between two north poles what would you do about the fact that the south pole of each magnet was simultaneously *attracting* the north pole of the other? How would you measure the distance between the poles? Is this just the distance between the outside faces of the magnets, or might the "effective location" of a pole be some distance within the surface?†)

In 1766, Franklin noticed that cork balls seemed to be entirely unaffected when placed inside a strongly electrified metal cup, although they were attracted in the usual way when outside the container. He appealed to his friend Joseph Priestley (1733–1804), subsequently the discoverer of oxygen, to verify this observation. Priestley showed that when a hollow conductor is electrified, it carries no charge on the interior surface (except possibly in the immediate neighborhood of the opening) and that electrical forces inside the cavity were always zero. Publishing these results in 1767, he wrote: "May we not infer from this experiment that the attraction of electricity is subject to the same laws with that of gravitation and is therefore according to the squares of the distances; since it is easily demonstrated that were the earth

---

* A number of Newton's contemporaries, Robert Hooke in particular, had speculated on the possibility of an inverse-square law of gravitation, but had provided no quantitative application, test, or deduction from the hypothesis. See Chapter 15 for more detail.

† For a description of how an experiment might be performed, taking these factors into account, see the short article by R. A. Lufburrow, *Amer. Jour. Phys.* **31**, 60 (1963).

in the form of a shell, a body in the inside of it would not be attracted to one side more than another?"* Although not a convincing proof, this was indeed an acute and discerning speculation.

Summarizing the background developed in this section, we would say that by about 1770, eighteenth-century scientists were convinced that electric force between two electrified particles, magnetic force between two individual magnetic poles, and gravitational attraction between two gravitating particles were all subject to the same law of variation with respect to distance of separation, r:

$$F \propto \frac{1}{r^2}. \qquad (7.10.1)$$

It was recognized that this simple formula applied only to certain special cases: (1) To objects which could be treated as particles; i.e., objects whose dimensions were very small compared to the distance r. (2) To uniform spheres interacting gravitationally or electrically, in which case r represents the distance between the centers of the spheres; i.e., uniform spheres can be thought of as small particles located at the respective centers.

7.11 COULOMB'S LAW

It is immediately clear in observations of electrical phenomena that the same two particles can exert very different forces on each other at a given separation, depending on how they are electrified. To show directly or indirectly that in a certain instance the force varies inversely as the square of the separation renders only a partial description of the interaction. One is left with the additional question as to what intrinsic property, what state of the particles themselves, also affects the force. The clear differences among these states and properties are the manifestations that make it possible for us to distinguish operationally among electric, magnetic, and gravitational phenomena and create the vocabulary describing them. Is it possible to quantify these properties, give operational definitions which subject them to numerical measurement, enunciate laws of force that render a description more complete than the fragmentary $F \propto 1/r^2$?

Newton had achieved this for gravitation in 1687, and we shall discuss the gravitation law in the following section. For electricity the synthesis was achieved by Charles Augustin Coulomb (1736–1806) in a series of celebrated memoirs beginning in 1785. (See Fig. 7.11.1.) To study directly the small electrical forces between charged, conducting spheres, Coulomb invented a very sensitive instrument which we now call a "torsion balance" (Figs. 7.11.2 and 7.11.3). A balanced rod, carrying conducting sphere a at one end, is suspended on a nonconducting filament or fiber. The fiber

---

* This was a well-known theorem of gravitational theory and is valid only for an inverse-square law of force and for the interior of a uniform, spherical shell. See Chapter 23 and Appendix G for a more detailed discussion. The most accurate modern verification of the inverse-square law of electrical force is based on a precise and elegant repetition of Priestley's experiment.

Fɪɢ. 7.11.1. Charles Augustin de Coulomb (1736–1806).   French physicist.   After a
gravure. (Photograph courtesy The Bettmann Archive.)

twists if a force is exerted on a in a direction perpendicular to the rod, and acts as
a very sensitive spring, supplying a restoring force proportional to the angle of twist.
(This is, of course, a generalization or extension of Hooke's law.)

On inserting a charged sphere t through the opening m, charge was conveyed to a,
after which a was repelled and took up an equilibrium position at some distance from
t. The twist of the fiber at this initial position was measured, and then by turning
knob p from which the fiber was suspended, sphere a could be forced to come somewhat closer to t or allowed to recede farther away. From the changed distance r
between the spheres and the increased or de-
creased angle of twist of the fiber it was possible
to determine directly how the force F varied
with r. Coulomb showed that the force varied
as $1/r^2$ both for repulsion between like charges
and attraction between unlike.

Whereas Priestley's deduction from the absence of electrical force within a hollow container
was based on analogy with gravitation and was
beset with various complexities regarding the
uniformity or nonuniformity of electrification of
the outer surface, Coulomb's test was direct and

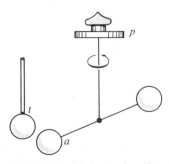

Fɪɢ. 7.11.2.   Schematic diagram
of Coulomb's torsion balance.

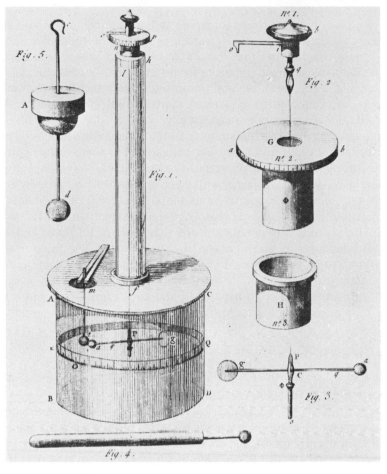

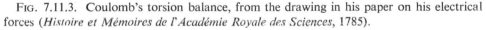

Fig. 7.11.3. Coulomb's torsion balance, from the drawing in his paper on his electrical forces (*Histoire et Mémoires de l'Académie Royale des Sciences*, 1785).

applied to interaction of both kinds of electricity. He provided convincing verification of what was up to then a good guess. It is highly likely, however, that his design of the experiment and his selection of spheres as the charged objects were guided at least in part by expectation of an inverse-square law. If the expectation had not been realized, he would probably have conducted searching and refined experiments to discover what might be wrong before abandoning the hypothesis and establishing the actual relationship.

Finally, Coulomb devised a way of justifying the assignment of numerical values to "quantity of electric charge." With spheres *a* and *t* both charged, the angle of twist of the fiber at equilibrium position was determined. Then an uncharged, conducting sphere of identical size was brought into contact with *a*. Under these circumstances Coulomb showed the force of interaction to be reduced to half its initial value, since half the initial angle of twist of the wire sufficed to keep the spheres the initial distance apart. If electrical charge is indeed conserved and measurable, one would argue from the symmetry of the situation that conducting spheres of equal size should share available charge equally, and that the charge carried by a was reduced to half its initial value in this experiment. Inference from symmetry is a powerful and frequently invoked mode of argument in physics. Its justification is that it *works;* natural laws appear to be associated with deep-seated mathematical symmetries, and we shall encounter additional examples in further study.

Again the symmetry of the situation suggests that sphere a has no special precedence over t, and that if a is left untouched but t is allowed to share charge with an equal sphere, the force of interaction will again be reduced to half its initial value. If both a and t were allowed to share charge with equal spheres, one would now anticipate a decrease in the force to one quarter of its initial value, and this is indeed the case.

Coulomb and others had already speculated that the electrostatic law may be in all respects analogous to that of gravitation, and that if one could devise an independent measure of the charges q_1 and q_2 carried by two particles, the force of interaction would be found to be proportional to the product q_1q_2. He even referred to q_1 and q_2 as the "electrical masses" of the particles. The experiments on sharing charge with equal spheres supported his hypothesis, and he put forth the formula which has ever since been referred to as Coulomb's Law:

$$F = k\frac{q_1q_2}{r^2},\qquad(7.11.1)$$

where k denotes a proportionality constant, and the force F is understood to act along the line connecting the two particles.

PROBLEM 7.14. Some physics laboratories have replicas of Coulomb's apparatus (Fig. 7.11.2) available for use, and you might wish to try your hand at these experiments. If you do, you will quickly come to appreciate how patient and skillful an experimenter Coulomb must have been. Even if you do not actually undertake the experiment, outline some of the problems you would face: How would you determine the total angle of twist of the fiber in any given equilibrium position? If, at equilibrium, the spheres a and t are fairly far apart, the force of interaction is not perpendicular to the rod on which a is mounted. Is this effect of any importance in the experiment? What difficulties would you expect from leakage of charge and what precautions would you take to minimize them? Why do you suppose the torsion balance is enclosed in a housing? Do you think it would be easier to work with repelling or attracting spheres? Why? What difficulty would you anticipate with the latter?

7.12   UNITS OF ELECTRICAL CHARGE

Having established a rational basis for the formula

$$F = k\frac{q_1q_2}{r^2}\qquad(7.12.1)$$

without defining units of measurement of q, it is now possible to turn around and use the formula as a basis for measuring charge by the observable effect it produces—the force of interaction between particles. Thus, in the cgs system of units, k was set equal to unity, and the unit (one statcoulomb) was defined as that charge, carried by identically charged spheres, when they attract or repel each other with a force of 1 dyne at a center-to-center separation of 1 cm.

An alternative approach is to define a unit of charge in some independent way, and then determine the value of k in Eq. (7.12.1); that is, k is the number which will multiply the independently measured combination $q_1 q_2 / r^2$ and give the magnitude of the observed electrostatic force under the given conditions. This procedure is adopted in the mks system, which we shall use throughout this text. The mks unit of charge (one coulomb) is defined not through electrostatic interactions but through the magnetic effects of electric currents. We shall defer consideration of the details of the definition for the time being, and accept the fact that, with this unit of charge, the proportionality constant k has the numerical value $8.99 \times 10^9 \, n \cdot m^2/coul^2$.* In mks units, Coulomb's Law becomes

$$F = 8.99 \times 10^9 \, \frac{q_1 q_2}{r^2}, \tag{7.12.2}$$

where F is in newtons, r in meters, and q_1 and q_2 in coulombs.

From the standpoint of electrostatics, one coulomb is a fantastically large amount of charge. If we conceive of two spheres one meter between centers, each carrying one coulomb of charge, the attractive or repulsive force between them would be 9×10^9 newtons. Since 1 lb is roughly 4.5 n, this means a force of 2×10^9 lb, or one million tons! The forces we actually observe in electrostatic experiments, such as those shown in lecture demonstrations, are more nearly of the order of magnitude 10^{-2} n at separations of several centimeters. If our major interest were in electrostatics, we would certainly use a smaller unit of charge (for example, the statcoulomb, 3.0×10^9 statcoul being equivalent to 1 coul), but our principal interest will actually be in the flow and displacement of electrical charge in conductors under the influence of batteries or generators. Here the quantities of charge displaced are enormously larger than the unbalanced charge observed in frictional electrification, and we have a hint of the dominant role of electricity in the structure of matter.

From time to time in the further progress of our study we shall have occasion to make very rough calculations, estimates of order of magnitude of some quantity, based on the most rudimentary data. These data may themselves be rough estimates or educated guesses drawn from memory, or visual impressions, or intuitions about what is "reasonable." Scientists and engineers frequently orient themselves toward a physical situation with such calculations, and on some occasions this becomes the starting point for research or discovery. For lack of a more definitive term, let us use the phrase "seat-of-the-pants" calculation. Try it for yourself in the following problem.

---

* This is the observed value for vacuum and is essentially undistinguishable in air. If the experiment were performed in a nonconducting medium such as oil or paraffin wax, however, the value of k would be found to be appreciably different from 8.99×10^9. Such effects are associated with polarization of the medium.

PROBLEM 7.15. You have seen lecture demonstrations or performed experiments yourself in which small objects— pithballs, pingpong balls, pieces of foil or paper—have responded to electrical forces. Perhaps you have seen a suspended pingpong ball take up an equilibrium position under the influence of another charged body (Fig. 7.12.1). Make reasonable estimates of relevant masses, forces, deflections, separations, etc., and carry out a seat-of-the-pants calculation of the order of magnitude of electrostatic charge on frictionally electrified objects. [*Answer:* anywhere in the range from 10^{-10} to 10^{-7} coul is reasonable.] Keep this order of magnitude in mind for future reference and comparison.

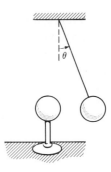

FIGURE 7.12.1

PROBLEM 7.16. It is an experimental fact that electrostatic forces between particles superpose vectorially just as do mechanical forces. As an exercise with this idea and with the arithmetic of Coulomb's Law, consider the situation sketched in Fig. 7.12.2. Particles A and B carry charges of $+1.8 \times 10^{-8}$ and -2.5×10^{-8} coul, respectively. Find the magnitude and direction of the resultant force on particle C, which carries a charge of $+1.0 \times 10^{-8}$ coul.

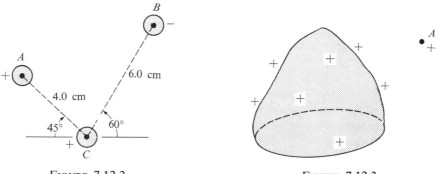

FIGURE 7.12.2   FIGURE 7.12.3

PROBLEM 7.17. A large object has an electric charge distributed over its surface. A charged particle A is located close by, as shown in Fig. 7.12.3. Suppose you were faced with the problem of calculating the force on A. What information would you require? How would you go about making the calculation? (You are not asked to make an actual calculation but to outline what you would do in principle.)

7.13 GRAVITATIONAL CHARGE

Because of an unfortunate choice of names, there has been much confusion about quantities appearing in the law of gravitation. We shall try to avoid this confusion by describing a thought experiment which has little to do with actual historical events and is based on what we already know to be true from indirect evidence. Suppose we construct a torsion balance similar to Coulomb's (Fig. 7.13.1), and bring a massive sphere C into the neighborhood of sphere A. The suspending fiber twists as A

is attracted toward C, and the attractive force at a
given separation can be measured. If C is removed and
a different sphere D is brought near A, we would in general observe a different force acting at the same separation
between centers. The bodies behave as though they
carried what we might call, for the sake of analogy, a
"gravitational charge." (When torsion balance experiments are performed to observe gravitational forces
it is necessary to be sure that the objects have not been
electrified by friction, because a minute electrical charge
can completely mask the gravitational effects. See Problem 7.19.) How can we obtain a quantitative measure of
the gravitational charge? This is a very different property from the electrical one. Nothing we do to sphere D,
short of cutting off pieces, changes its attraction for
A—least of all contact with an identical sphere, the trick

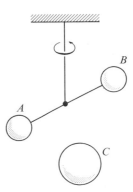

Fig. 7.13.1.   Torsion-
balance "thought experi-
ment" on gravitational
forces.

Coulomb used to show that the electrical force was
halved. The solution lies in an essentially empirical discovery: If it happens that
sphere D exerts on A exactly twice the force exerted by C, we find that if we place
D and C on frictionless pucks and determine their inertias in an acceleration experiment, the inertias (or inertial masses) are also exactly in the ratio of two to one.
This ratio is maintained regardless of the chemical composition or the kind of material; the gravitational forces exerted on A are always in exactly the same ratio as
the masses of the spheres.

This is a very remarkable result! On the face of things, there is no apparent reason
why "gravitational charge," the capacity to attract body A, should have anything
whatsoever to do with the resistance to acceleration by an applied force. Yet the
experimental results indicate that one is a direct measure of the other. For this
reason, the property we have called gravitational charge is usually called "gravitational mass," and here lies the source of verbal confusion. Gravitational and inertial
mass are entirely *different* properties *in principle*. It is a remarkable thing that one
turns out to be a measure of the other. (The scientific world took this to be little
more than an interesting coincidence until Einstein made it a cornerstone of the general
theory of relativity.)

Since the force at fixed separation doubles if we double the mass of either A or C,
and increases by a factor of six if we double one and triple the other, we are led to
write the law of force for gravitation:

$$F = G\frac{m_1 m_2}{r^2},\qquad\qquad(7.13.1)$$

where G is a proportionality constant and m_1 and m_2 are gravitational masses of the
interacting particles.

Newton, who did not have a sensitive torsion balance to play with, saw through
the riddle in a different way. He *interpreted* the apparent coincidence that all bodies,
regardless of their mass, have the same acceleration in free fall: Since the acceleration is the same in all cases, the *force* exerted by the earth must be proportional to

the inertial mass of the falling body. How he reasoned inductively beyond this is not at all clear. He did have the vision that gravitation is not just a property of the earth but is a universal force between all bodies. From this he might have taken the view that no object is privileged with respect to any other and that if the gravitational force were proportional to the mass of one of two interacting particles, by symmetry it should be proportional to the other as well.

For a hundred years after the publication of the *Principia*, Newton's law of gravitation had its triumphs in applications to celestial mechanics. The numerical value of the proportionality constant G remained undetermined, and a direct terrestrial test of the law of gravitation remained to be achieved. During the 1760's, John Michell invented a torsion balance (similar to that which Coulomb independently developed twenty years later for his electrical experiments) as part of a plan to determine the proportionality constant G in Eq. (7.13.1), and thereby to weigh the earth. (See Problem 7.18.)

Gravitational forces between objects of ordinary size are exceedingly small and are readily obscured by electric and magnetic effects. A sensitive torsion balance carrying fairly heavy lead spheres is all too readily set twisting by vibrations of walls or ceiling and by minute air currents. It will then keep oscillating back and forth slowly for hours, making measurements impossible until the spurious oscillation ceases. Successful and uncontaminated torsion-balance experiments on gravitational forces are rather difficult to make, and Michell's proposed experiment was not carried out successfully until his friend Henry Cavendish (1731–1810), one of the ablest experimentalists of the eighteenth century, finally produced definitive results in 1798. Cavendish determined the value of G by measuring the force between lead spheres of known mass. This universal constant has, of course, been more precisely established in the intervening years: In mks units,

$$G = 6.673 \times 10^{-11} n \cdot m^2 / kg^2.$$

PROBLEM 7.18.   It was indicated above that Michell and Cavendish had a more grandiose objective than just the determination of the numerical value of G; they sought to weigh the earth. (More precisely, we would say that they sought to determine the *mass* of the earth.) *Problem:* Complete this calculation, using the following outline (Fig. 7.13.2).

Consider F_1 to be the force exerted by the earth (near its surface) on a body of mass m_1. Then

$$F_1 = G \frac{m_1 m_E}{R_E^2},$$

where R_E is the radius of the earth (about 4000 mi), and we recognize F_1 as simply the weight of body m_1. Note that F_1/m_1 is the acceleration due to gravity, $g = 9.80 \text{ m/sec}^2$. Calculate m_E in kilograms and in tons.

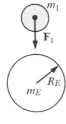

FIGURE 7.13.2

PROBLEM 7.19.   (a) Consider two brass spheres such as might typically be used in lecture demonstrations in electrostatics. The spheres might have masses of 100 gm. They might carry electrostatic charges of the order of 10^{-8} coul. Compare the magnitudes of the electric and gravitational forces acting between the spheres by calculating the ratio of the forces. To how many significant figures would we have to know the numerical values of k and q before it would be legitimate to introduce a correction for the gravitational effect? (See Fig. 7.13.3.)

(b) The hydrogen atom consists of a proton ($m = 1.67 \times 10^{-27}$ kg; $q = +1.60 \times 10^{-19}$ coul) and an electron ($m = 9.11 \times 10^{-31}$ kg; $q = -1.60 \times 10^{19}$ coul). The average separation between the particles is 0.53×10^{-8} cm. Calculate the ratio of electric to gravitational force between the particles and take note of the value. Gravitational forces will always be ignored relative to electric and magnetic forces in our discussions of atomic physics.

(For further discussion of this, see Section 35.4.)

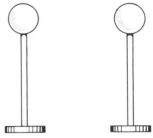

FIGURE 7.13.3

PROBLEM 7.20. The moon has 1/3.7 the diameter of the earth and 1/81 the mass. Argument: "Since gravitational force is proportional to the mass of an attracting body, acceleration due to gravity at the lunar surface should be 1/81 the acceleration at the earth's surface." The acceleration at the lunar surface is actually calculated to be $g/6$ rather than $g/81$; what is wrong with the argument given above?

7.14 INTERPLAY OF SCIENTIFIC IDEAS

The development of a model and discovery of the laws governing the behavior of frictional electricity extended from about 1730 to the end of the century, when the work of Galvani and Volta on current electricity gave the science a new direction and an even broader vista. In our present day, with thousands of scientists forming a new professional class, competitively attacking every new problem as soon as it is discerned, bringing to bear all the knowledge and experience of three hundred years of scientific thought, a sequence of the kind we have just studied would be enormously accelerated and telescoped in time. In the eighteenth century, we see it as though in slow motion, but the final mechanism is much the same.

Although our historical outline was of necessity abbreviated and contains many gaps, the student may still discern some of the factors which molded the advancing line of thought:

(1) Conceptual advances in the understanding of electricity, magnetism, and gravitation were not isolated, independent events. Knowledge of one field motivated preliminary ideas, reasoning by analogy, and design of experiments in another.

(2) Many discoveries stemmed from the communication of techniques, concepts, and experimental conclusions among scientists widely separated in national origin. Some discoveries were made independently and almost simultaneously simply because the time was ripe for the next advance. In other cases experimental techniques or ideas were rediscovered by an investigator unaware of the work of his predecessors.

(3) An elaborate vocabulary attended the heuristic models of electric and magnetic effects: effluvia, vortices, vitreous and resinous fluids, boreal and austral fluids (for the poles of magnets). Much of this vocabulary was associated with attempts to picture a mechanism by which electrically charged bodies (or magnetic poles) interacted with each other. As the futility of these models became apparent, the verbiage was gradually stripped off. Newton had treated the gravitation law as a mathematical formula, to be viewed with confidence because the deductions drawn from it agreed with observation. He eschewed attempts to describe a mechanism for gravitational attraction between bodies, and the result was a formal, mathematical treatment in which dynamical effects were associated with "action at a distance." Sir Edmund Whittaker writes, "When the law first stated by Priestley was at length decisively established by Coulomb, its simplicity and beauty gave rise to a general feeling of complete trust in it as the best available conception of electrostatic phenomena. The result was that attention was almost exclusively focused on action-at-a-distance theories, until the time, long afterwards, when Faraday led natural philosophers back to the right path." (Here Whittaker refers to the rise of field theory through the work of Faraday and Maxwell in the middle of the nineteenth century. We shall return to this theme in a later chapter. See Chapter 23.)

The reader has undoubtedly noticed the formal similarity of the laws of force between particles:

$$F_{grav} = G\frac{m_1 m_2}{r^2}, \qquad F_{el} = k\frac{q_1 q_2}{r^2}, \qquad F_{mag} \propto \frac{1}{r^2}.$$

(In the magnetic case it is possible to define a concept known as "pole strength," and couch the law in exactly the same form as the other two. We shall not devote time to this idea because it has not been very fruitful and is no longer widely used. A more fruitful approach to magnetism lies through the magnetic effects invariably associated with moving electrical charges.) Formal symmetry and similarity do not go unnoticed; they invite conjecture and a search for underlying explanation and unification. The greatest theoretical physicists (among them Einstein, Schrödinger, and Heisenberg) have devoted major effort to discovery of a unified field theory which might provide a common basis for understanding electricity, magnetism, and gravitation, and predicting the known similarities and differences. This achievement has so far eluded their grasp and remains a tantalizing goal for all who seek to find still deeper order and unity in nature.

SUPPLEMENTARY READING AND STUDY

Elementary introduction of electrical concepts:
   Physics, Physical Science Study Committee. Boston: D. C. Heath, 1960, Chapters 27, 28

More advanced treatment:
   Physics for Students of Science and Engineering, R. Resnick and D. Halliday. New York: John Wiley & Sons, 1960, Chapters 26, 27

For discussion of gravitational and inertial mass:
  Concepts of Mass, Max Jammer. Cambridge, Mass.: Harvard University Press, 1961

Early history of electrical concepts:
  A History of the Theories of Aether and Electricity, E. Whittaker. London: Thos. Nelson & Sons, 1951; also Harper Torchbook TB 531
  "Development of the Concept of Electrical Charge," D. Roller and D. H. D. Roller. In *Harvard Case Studies in Experimental Science*. Cambridge, Mass.: Harvard University Press, 1957

CHAPTER 8

Mathematics II: Derivatives and Antiderivatives*

8.1 INTRODUCTION

In preceding chapters, application of mathematics to the description of physical phenomena repeatedly led us to statements of functional relationship among physical variables. Position s and velocity v in uniformly accelerated rectilinear motion have been described as functions of time t. Trajectories of projectiles have been described by equations in which the vertical coordinate y is a function of the horizontal coordinate x. Using Newton's law of motion and an appropriate law of force, acceleration of a particle has been described as a function of position.

Such functional relationships motivate a number of mathematical questions: If we know position as a function of time; i.e., the function $s(t)$, is there a formal mathematical procedure by means of which we can discover the velocity function $v(t)$? Can the procedure be reversed? In Chapter 1 we dealt only with uniformly accelerated motion; what can be said about motions which are not uniformly accelerated? If we know the equation of a trajectory, is there an *algebraic* procedure for finding the direction of instantaneous velocity at any point, without recourse to the geometrical device of drawing a tangent to the curve and measuring its slope? When one knows the functional relation between acceleration and position, what can be derived concerning velocity and trajectory of the motion?

In the illustrations just cited, functional relationships have been established through the definition of physical concepts and the discovery of physical laws or principles; but the questions we have just raised about the functions themselves are essentially *mathematical* rather than physical. They are questions that would be equally meaningful in purely arithmetical language without physical names or interpretations for the variables.

---

*The concepts of derivative and antiderivative are used freely in discussions of physical problems from Chapter 9 on. It is recommended that Sections 8.1–8.6 be studied before proceeding to Chapter 9. Other sections of this chapter can be studied as the need arises in subsequent work.

In this chapter we shall explore some of the mathematical problems which have just been posed. The exploration generates new mathematical insights which will then be used to gain deeper penetration into physical problems. Such was the parallel course of mathematical and physical sciences in the seventeenth century. We deal here largely with concepts developed during this period, although we shall do so in a more modern language and from a more modern viewpoint. This mathematical science is called *calculus* or, in its broader ramifications, *analysis*.

8.2   THE DERIVATIVE OF A FUNCTION

In Section 1.8 and Fig. 1.8.2 we posed a question concerning a property of the function $s(t)$ and created the concept of instantaneous velocity defined by the calculation

$$\lim_{\Delta t \to 0} \frac{\Delta s}{\Delta t}.$$

Let us translate this calculation into the language and symbols of abstract mathematical functions.

Suppose there is given an arbitrary function $y = f(x)$, defined on a domain or interval of real numbers. At a particular value of x, denoted by x_0, the value of the function is denoted by $f(x_0)$. Let us denote another value of x, different from x_0, by $x_0 + h$; the corresponding value of the function is $f(x_0 + h)$. The number h may be positive or negative, but must be restricted to values which keep $x_0 + h$ within the domain of the function.

Consider now the number resulting from the calculation

$$\frac{f(x_0 + h) - f(x_0)}{h}. \qquad (8.2.1)$$

This quotient might be described as the average rate of change of $f(x)$ in the interval between x_0 and $x_0 + h$; it is an abstract analog of average velocity $\Delta s/\Delta t$. Geometrically interpreted in Fig. 8.2.1, this quotient represents the slope of the secant connecting points P and Q on the graph.*

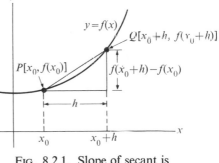

FIG. 8.2.1. Slope of secant is

$$PQ = \frac{f(x_0 + h) - f(x_0)}{h}.$$

---

* A frequently used alternative notation employs the symbol Δx in place of h. Quotient (8.2.1) is then written

$$\frac{f(x + \Delta x) - f(x)}{\Delta x}.$$

The numerator is sometimes denoted by $\Delta f(x)$ or by Δy if $y = f(x)$. The quotient may then be represented by the more compact notation $\Delta f(x)/\Delta x$ or $\Delta y/\Delta x$. The student should become conversant with all these notations. In certain contexts one is more convenient than another, and they will be used interchangeably.

Suppose, as originally suggested in the discussion of instantaneous velocity in Chapter 1, we bring Q closer and closer to P by assigning arbitrarily small values to h. We then ask whether the number denoted by

$$\lim_{h \to 0} \frac{f(x_0 + h) - f(x_0)}{h} \tag{8.2.2}$$

exists and how it might be evaluated algebraically if $f(x)$ is a known function. We of course recognize in expression (8.2.2) the abstract analog of instantaneous velocity, originally discussed in Section 1.8.

Let us take a particular function and try to evaluate the limit defined in (8.2.2). Consider the parabolic function $f(x) = kx^2$:

$$f(x_0) = kx_0^2,$$

$$f(x_0 + h) = k(x_0 + h)^2.$$

Substituting these expressions into (8.2.2):

$$\lim_{h \to 0} \frac{f(x_0 + h) - f(x_0)}{h} = \lim_{h \to 0} \frac{k(x_0 + h)^2 - kx_0^2}{h}$$

$$= \lim_{h \to 0} \frac{kx_0^2 + 2kx_0h + kh^2 - kx_0^2}{h}$$

$$= \lim_{h \to 0} \frac{2kx_0h + kh^2}{h}$$

$$= \lim_{h \to 0} (2kx_0 + kh) = 2kx_0. \tag{8.2.3}$$

PROBLEM 8.1. Show by means of an ϵ, δ proof (Section 3.13) that $2kx_0$ is indeed the

$$\lim_{h \to 0} (2kx_0 + kh).$$

Thus, when $f(x) = kx^2$, the number defined by expression (8.2.2) exists and is equal to $2kx_0$; it is $4k$ when $x_0 = 2$, $-2k$ when $x_0 = -1$, and so forth. In any particular instance the value of the limit depends on our choice of x_0, but in each instance x_0 is itself a fixed number. The limit is evaluated as h approaches zero and *not* as x approaches zero.

For a different function we would expect an algebraic result different from (8.2.3), and this is illustrated in Problems 8.2 and 8.3. In some cases, as at the origin in Fig. 3.11.1(b), the limit called for may not exist at a particular point; in other cases, such as Fig. 3.11.1(d), the limit may not exist at all, at any point. We shall examine this problem in greater detail in Section 8.4.

Expression (8.2.2) is a prescription for calculating a particular number which we now proceed to identify with a name and a symbol. This number is called the "value of the derivative of $f(x)$ with respect to x at $x = x_0$" and is denoted by the symbol $f'(x_0)$. (Read as "f prime of x zero".) Thus, if the limit exists,

$$f'(x_0) \equiv \lim_{h \to 0} \frac{f(x_0 + h) - f(x_0)}{h} ,$$

or, alternatively   (8.2.4)

$$f'(x_0) \equiv \lim_{x \to x_0} \frac{f(x) - f(x_0)}{x - x_0} .$$

In accordance with the concepts developed in Sections 3.12 and 3.13, "existence" of the limit means that for every $\epsilon > 0$ there exists a $\delta > 0$ such that

$$\left| \frac{f(x_0 + h) - f(x_0)}{h} \right| < \epsilon \qquad \text{for all} \quad 0 < |h| < \delta.$$

The symbol $|h|$ reminds us that this condition must be satisfied for both positive and negative values of h if we are to regard $f'(x_0)$ as existing.

FIG. 8.2.2. Tangent to curve $y = f(x)$ at point P is defined to be the straight line with slope $f'(x_0)$. Equation of the tangent line is

$$\frac{y - y_0}{x - x_0} = f'(x_0).$$

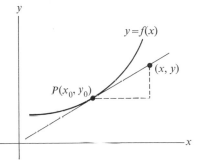

When the limit exists, as it does in the case illustrated by Eq. (8.2.3), $f'(x_0)$ is a uniquely specified number for each $x = x_0$; how might this number be interpreted? If we interpret definition (8.2.4) geometrically with the help of Fig. 8.2.1, the definition clearly refers to values assumed by the slope of secant PQ as point Q is brought closer and closer to point P. In geometry the straight line defined in this way is called the tangent to the curve. In calculus, however, we adopt a logical system in which geometrical concepts are defined in arithmetical terms rather than vice versa. Thus we use expression (8.2.4) to create an arithmetical definition of the concept of a tangent to a curve. The number $f'(x_0)$ is called the "slope of the curve at $x = x_0$." In consonance with our geometrical intuition, the straight-line tangent to the curve at $x - x_0$ is then *defined* to be the line represented by the equation

$$\frac{f(x) - f(x_0)}{x - x_0} = f'(x_0) \qquad \text{or} \qquad \frac{y - y_0}{x - x_0} = f'(x_0).$$

This equation is obtained by substituting into the point-slope form [Eq. (3.3.1) in Chapter 3] the coordinates of point $[x_0, f(x_0)]$ and the slope $f'(x_0)$. A graphical interpretation is illustrated in Fig. 8.2.2.

Example: To find the equation of the straight line tangent to the parabola $y = kx^2$ at $x = 4$.

Solution: In Eq. (8.2.3) it is shown that $f'(x_0) = 2kx_0$; therefore $f'(4) = 8k$, and $f(4) = 16k$. The equation of the tangent line is then

$$\frac{y - 16k}{x - 4} = 8k, \qquad y = 8kx - 16k.$$

PROBLEM 8.2.   Consider the function $f(x) = mx + b$. We recognize this as the equation of a straight line of constant slope m. In accordance with the preceding definitions and interpretations, we anticipate that $f'(x_0)$ must be constant and equal to m for all values of $x = x_0$. Verify this anticipation by carrying out the limit calculation defined by (8.2.4). Why is the result independent of b? Interpret this independence by graphical illustration.

PROBLEM 8.3.   Obtain expressions for $f'(x_0)$ for each of the following functions:

(a) $f(x) = x$,   (b) $f(x) = 2x^2 - 3x$,   (c) $f(x) = x^3$,

(d) $f(x) = ax^3$,   (e) $f(x) = 1/x = x^{-1}$.

[*Answer:* (a) 1; (b) $4x_0 - 3$; (c) $3x_0^2$; (d) $3ax_0^2$; (e) $-x_0^{-2}$.]

Comment on regularities which you discern in the results; i.e., what happens in the case of a sum or difference as in (b)? What is the connection between (c) and (d)? Is there a pattern which suggests the result one might expect for x^n? Does the limit exist in all cases? [Take particular note of the behavior at $x_0 = 0$ in example (e).] Find the value of the slope of the curve at $x_0 = 2$ in each case, and find the equation of the straight line tangent to the curve at that point. [*Answer:* (c) $y = 12x - 16$.]

If values of $f'(x_0)$ exist for every $x = x_0$ in a certain domain, we see that these values comprise the range of a new function. (Refer back at this point to Problem 3.7 and item 11 of Table 3.10.1.) This new function is derived from, and is a property of, the original function $f(x)$; it is called "the derivative of $f(x)$ with respect to x," and is denoted by a variety of symbols:

$$f'(x); \qquad \frac{df(x)}{dx}; \qquad \frac{d}{dx} f(x); \qquad \frac{df}{dx}; \qquad D_x f(x).$$

If we use $y = f(x)$, we would have corresponding symbols:

$$y'; \qquad \frac{dy}{dx}; \qquad D_x y.$$

Each of these symbols stands for the function

$$\lim_{h \to 0} \frac{f(x + h) - f(x)}{h}.$$

Thus we would write as a formal definition of the derivative of a function $y = f(x)$:

$$f'(x) \equiv \lim_{h \to 0} \frac{f(x + h) - f(x)}{h}. \tag{8.2.5}$$

Alternative notations for the same concept are:

$$\frac{dy}{dx} \equiv \lim_{h \to 0} \frac{f(x + h) - f(x)}{h}, \tag{8.2.6}$$

$$f'(x) \equiv \lim_{\Delta x \to 0} \frac{f(x + \Delta x) - f(x)}{\Delta x}, \tag{8.2.7}$$

$$\frac{df}{dx} \equiv \lim_{\Delta x \to 0} \frac{\Delta f(x)}{\Delta x}, \tag{8.2.8}$$

$$\frac{dy}{dx} \equiv \lim_{\Delta x \to 0} \frac{\Delta y}{\Delta x}. \tag{8.2.9}$$

The notation $f'(x)$ was introduced by Fermat, while the notation dy/dx was invented by the German philosopher-mathematician Leibniz.

Since the derivative of a function is itself a function, we might on occasion wish to evaluate the derivative of a derivative, and so on. In this context we speak of second or even higher derivatives. A second derivative is denoted by symbols such as

$$f''(x); \quad \frac{d}{dx}\left[\frac{df(x)}{dx}\right]; \quad \frac{d^2 f(x)}{dx^2}; \quad \frac{d}{dx}\left(\frac{dy}{dx}\right); \quad \frac{d^2 y}{dx^2},$$

etc. In kinematics we introduced the definitions

$$v \equiv \frac{ds}{dt}; \quad a \equiv \frac{dv}{dt}.$$

We would now write:

$$a = \frac{dv}{dt} = \frac{d}{dt}\left(\frac{ds}{dt}\right) = \frac{d^2 s}{dt^2}.$$

PROBLEM 8.4. Applying definition (8.2.5), find the derivatives of: (a) the constant function, $f(x) = a$; (b) $f(x) = \frac{1}{2}ax^2$; (c) $f(x) = \frac{1}{2}ax^2 + b$. [*Answer:* (a) 0; (b) ax; (c) ax.]

Take particular note of the fact that functions (b) and (c) have the same derivative, and comment on the following question: Given a particular function which we call $f'(x)$; is the function $f(x)$, of which f' is the derivative, uniquely determined by our knowledge of f' and the definition of derivative?

8.3 DERIVATIVES AND ANTIDERIVATIVES

The illustrative problem which leads to Eq. (8.2.3) shows that the function $2kx$ is the derivative of kx^2; in Problem 8.3 you showed that the function $3ax^2$ is the derivative of ax^3; and so forth. This nomenclature is reversed by introducing the term *antiderivative*. Thus the function kx^2 is said to be an antiderivative of $2kx$ with respect to x; ax^3 an antiderivative of $3ax^2$ with respect to x; $\frac{1}{2}ax^2 + b$ an antiderivative of ax, etc. In symbolic form, a function $F(x)$ is said to be an antiderivative of $f(x)$ if $F'(x) = f(x)$. Any statement about derivatives can be expressed as a statement about antiderivatives.

We use the indefinite article "an" in the above nomenclature because, as illustrated in Problem 8.4, both the functions $\frac{1}{2}ax^2$ and $\frac{1}{2}ax^2 + b$ have the same derivative. Thus a given derivative does not define one unique antiderivative function. It will be necessary to ascertain the extent to which antiderivatives of a given function can differ from each other, and it will be shown that functions with identical derivatives cannot be radically different mathematical forms, but must be expressions which differ from each other only by an additive constant term. In symbols this means that if the functions $F(x)$ and $G(x)$ are both antiderivatives of $f(x)$, then $G(x) - F(x) = C$, where C can be any arbitrary constant. Another way of stating the same idea is to say that if $F(x)$ is an antiderivative of $f(x)$, then the function $G(x) = F(x) + C$ is also an antiderivative of $f(x)$.

It is readily apparent, by substitution into the definition of derivative (8.2.5), that if $f(x)$ is the derivative of $F(x)$, it must also be the derivative of $F(x) + C$ because the constant subtracts out in the calculation. But it is by no means readily apparent that $F(x) + C$ is the most *general* antiderivative of $f(x)$ and that no other mathematical form can fulfill the necessary conditions. We shall examine this theorem in a somewhat more sophisticated way in Section 8.15, and, for the time being, accept it as a plausible assertion.

In order to establish the value of the constant C in any particular case, it is necessary to have one additional piece of information concerning the value of the antiderivative function at some particular value of x. Let us work through a specific illustration:

We are told that there exists a function $y = f(x)$ and that its derivative is given by

$$f'(x) = 3x, \tag{8.3.1}$$

or by the alternative form with identical meaning,

$$\frac{dy}{dx} = 3x. \tag{8.3.2}$$

Either one of these forms is said to represent a *differential equation*, and the implied problem is to solve for the original function y. In the light of the preceding discussion and the results obtained in Problem 8.4, the general antiderivative of $3x$ is

$$y = f(x) = \tfrac{3}{2}x^2 + C. \tag{8.3.3}$$

To determine a value for C we must know the value of $f(x)$ at some particular value of x; suppose it is given that $y = -1$ at $x = 0$; that is, $f(0) = -1$. This information is called a boundary condition or an initial condition. It follows by substitution into (8.3.3) that

$$-1 = \tfrac{3}{2}(0)^2 + C, \qquad C = -1.$$

Therefore, for the given boundary condition,

$$y = f(x) = \tfrac{3}{2}x^2 - 1.$$

If the boundary condition is $f(1) = \tfrac{5}{2}$, verify that $C = 1$, and that $y = \tfrac{3}{2}x^2 + 1$.

Being given Eq. (8.3.1) is equivalent to knowing the slope of $f(x)$ at every point. The preceding illustration shows that we can establish a single unique expression for $f(x)$ if we can find a particular antiderivative ($\frac{3}{2}x^2$ in the example), and then determine the appropriate additive constant from one given boundary condition such as $f(a) = b$.

Consider a second illustration, possessing a specific physical interpretation: A particle is accelerated at uniform acceleration denoted by a, and the velocity is known to be v_0 at $t = 0$. Translating this into mathematical notation, we write

$$v'(t) \equiv \frac{dv}{dt} = a, \tag{8.3.4}$$

where a is constant. Since a particular antiderivative, with respect to t, of the constant function a is at [see Problems 8.2 and 8.3(a)], we have

$$v(t) = at + C. \tag{8.3.5}$$

We are given that $v(0) = v_0$; substituting into (8.3.5), we obtain

$$v_0 = a \cdot 0 + C, \quad C = v_0.$$

Therefore

$$v(t) = at + v_0. \tag{8.3.6}$$

Compare this development with that of Section 1.11 and Fig. 1.11.1(b), which led to exactly the same result.

PROBLEM 8.5. Given the differential equation

$$f'(x) \equiv \frac{dy}{dx} = 4x - 3$$

and the boundary condition $y = 3$ when $x = 1$, find the function $f(x)$ which satisfies these conditions. [*Hint:* Make use of the result obtained in Problem 8.3(b) to establish a particular antiderivative. *Answer:* $y = 2x^2 - 3x + 4$.]

PROBLEM 8.6. Given the equation $v(t) = at + v_0$ for the velocity in a uniformly accelerated motion. (a) Rewrite this equation as a differential equation for the position function $s(t)$. (b) Establish the expression for $s(t)$, given the initial condition $s = s_0$ at $t = 0$. (Start by showing that $\frac{1}{2}at^2 + v_0t$ is a particular antiderivative and then apply the boundary condition.) Compare this treatment with the lengthy discussion leading to Eq. (1.11.5) in Section 1.11 and comment on the logical status of our analysis. Have we eliminated the necessity of the plausible but nonrigorous argument given in Section 1.11 concerning average velocity? Given the now directly derived expression for $s(t)$ and Eq. (8.3.6), introduce the definition of average velocity $\bar{v}$ and prove that for the interval between $t = 0$ and $t = t$:

$$\bar{v} \equiv \frac{\Delta s}{\Delta t} = \frac{v_0 + v}{2}.$$

It is now possible to secure a glimpse of what might be gained through systematic use of the concepts of derivative and antiderivative in problems we have already encountered. If we have the equation of a trajectory [as in Eqs. (4.3.5) or (4.9.8)], finding the derivative of the function establishes the slope of the curve at every point and therefore the direction of the instantaneous velocity, provided the derivative exists.*   Having defined instantaneous velocity as the derivative of $s(t)$, knowledge of position–time history as a differentiable *function* would allow us to determine the instantaneous velocity function. Thus from algebraic knowledge of an s-t history, we could obtain a complete algebraic description of instantaneous velocity without recourse to the geometrical device of drawing tangents to an s-t curve and measuring their slopes. Similarly, acceleration–time history could be deduced by finding the derivative of $v(t)$ whenever the latter is a known function. Since the position function $s(t)$ is an antiderivative of $v(t)$, knowledge of a velocity function should allow algebraic evaluation of the corresponding $s(t)$ by use of theorems concerning antiderivatives. In Chapter 1 we argued that area under a portion of v-t curve should equal the displacement occurring during the given time interval. This implies a connection between antiderivatives and the concept of area under a curve.

8.4 DIFFERENTIABILITY AND CONTINUITY

Theorem: If a function $f(x)$ is differentiable [i.e., if the derivative $f'(x_0)$ exists] at a point $x = x_0$, then $f(x)$ is also continuous at $x = x_0$.

To prove the theorem, we must show that $f(x_0)$ exists and that

$$\lim_{x \to x_0} f(x) = f(x_0),   \text{or alternatively,}   \lim_{x \to x_0} [f(x) - f(x_0)] = 0.$$

Proof: (1): The assumption that $f'(x_0)$ exists presupposes that $f(x_0)$ exists, since $f(x_0)$ occurs in the definition of the derivative.

(2) Examine the difference quantity $f(x) - f(x_0)$: Providing $x \neq x_0$, we have the identity

$$f(x) - f(x_0) = (x - x_0) \cdot \frac{f(x) - f(x_0)}{x - x_0} . \tag{8.4.1}$$

Taking limits of both sides and applying limit theorem (7) in Section 3.14:

$$\lim_{x \to x_0} [f(x) - f(x_0)] = \lim_{x \to x_0} (x - x_0) \cdot \lim_{x \to x_0} \frac{f(x) - f(x_0)}{x - x_0} = 0 \cdot f'(x_0).$$

Since we have assumed the existence of $f'(x_0)$, $\lim_{x \to x_0} [f(x) - f(x_0)] = 0$ and the theorem is proved.

---

 * If the derivative exists, the function is said to be "differentiable." A function may be differentiable in certain intervals of its domain and may not be differentiable at certain other points or intervals. Examples of such properties will be given in Section 8.4.

This theorem affords us a new way of proving that a particular function is continuous. If we establish the existence of a derivative at a certain point, we simultaneously establish the continuity of the function at that point.

Illustrating this idea in a physical context: If, in the motion of a particle, acceleration at any instant of time is known to be the derivative of a velocity function, the velocity function $v(t)$ must be continuous at that instant.

> **PROBLEM 8.7.** Make a similar statement about velocity and a corresponding position function $s(t)$.

The converse of the above theorem is not true, however. Continuity of a function does *not* assure the existence of a derivative. To prove such an assertion we need exhibit only one failure. Consider the absolute value function $f(x) = |x|$ illustrated in Fig. 3.11.1(b):

This function is continuous at $x = 0$ since $f(0) = 0$ and since $\lim_{x \to 0} |x| = 0$. If we attempt to form the derivative at $x = 0$, however, we obtain:

$$\lim_{h \to 0} \frac{f(0 + h) - f(0)}{h} = \lim_{h \to 0} \frac{|h| - 0}{h} = \lim_{h \to 0} \frac{|h|}{h}. \qquad (8.4.2)$$

For positive h, however small, expression (8.4.2) has a numerical value of $+1$, while for negative h, however small, it has the value -1. Therefore there exists no number A such that

$$\left| \frac{|h|}{h} - A \right| < \epsilon \qquad \text{for} \quad |h| < \delta,$$

and the limit being investigated does not exist at $x = 0$. Thus a function $f(x)$ may be continuous at a particular point $x = x_0$, but the derivative $f'(x_0)$ at that point may not exist. Geometrically interpreted, this corresponds to a case in which the graph of the function has a sharp corner, as illustrated in Fig. 3.11.1(b).

Other cases of non-differentiability are associated with discontinuities of a function; for illustrations see Figs. 1.8.3, 3.11.1(e), and 3.11.1(f).

> **PROBLEM 8.8.** Given the function $f(x) = |x| + |x - 2|$ defined on the interval $-1 \leq x \leq 3$. Sketch the function and investigate its continuity and differentiability at the points $x = 0, +1,$ and $+2$.

> **PROBLEM 8.9.** Given the acceleration function sketched in Fig. 8.4.1. Sketch at least two different velocity functions which might correspond to this acceleration function. [Sketch the $v(t)$ graphs on axes located vertically below the $a(t)$ graph, so that corresponding instants of time fall on the same vertical line.] Comment on the continuity and differentiability of $a(t)$ and $v(t)$. (The existence of more than one relevant velocity function is related to the discussion in Sections 8.3 and 8.15.)

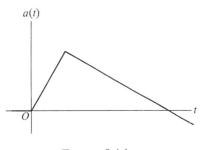

FIGURE 8.4.1

8.5 RULES AND THEOREMS FOR SOME ELEMENTARY CASES OF DIFFERENTIATION

The process of finding derivatives, called *differentiation*, can be systematized by establishing the derivatives of certain important elementary functions and by developing general theorems concerning the differentiation of sums, products, and other combinations of these functions. The resulting small body of rules makes it possible to differentiate a very large number of different functions without continual recourse to the basic definition of derivative. Let us summarize the derivatives and antiderivatives which follow easily from the examples worked out in Section 8.2 and from the results in Problems 8.3 and 8.4. (See Table 8.5.1.)

TABLE 8.5.1

TABLE OF DERIVATIVES AND ANTIDERIVATIVES OF A FEW SIMPLE FUNCTIONS

Function, $f(x)$	Derivative, $f'(x)$	Antiderivative, $F(x)$	
Constant: $f(x) = a$	$f'(x) = 0$	$F(x) = ax + C$	(1)
Linear: $f(x) = x$	$f'(x) = 1$	$F(x) = \frac{1}{2}x^2 + C$	(2)
$f(x) = ax$	$f'(x) = a$	$F(x) = \frac{1}{2}ax^2 + C$	(3)
Quadratic: $f(x) = x^2$	$f'(x) = 2x$	$F(x) = \frac{1}{3}x^3 + C$	(4)
Cubic: $f(x) = x^3$	$f'(x) = 3x^2$	—	(5)
Reciprocal: $f(x) = x^{-1}$	$f'(x) = -x^{-2}$	—	(6)
$f(x) = a\,g(x)$	$f'(x) = a\,g'(x)$	—	(7)

PROBLEM 8.10.   The last rule [item (7)] in Table 8.5.1 was not proved as a general theorem in Section 8.2, but is strongly implied by the special cases worked out in Problems 8.2, 8.3, and 8.4. Verbally interpreted, it means that a constant factor carries through a differentiation process and appears, unaltered, as a constant factor in the final result. Give a general proof of this theorem by substituting $f(x) = a\,g(x)$ into the definition of the derivative and showing that $f'(x) = a\,g'(x)$, providing $g'(x)$ exists. What is the point of this theorem; i.e., in what way does it enlarge the scope of Table 8.5.1?

Problems such as 8.3(b) and 8.6 have provided strong suggestions that the derivative of a sum or difference of two functions is equal to the sum or difference of the individual derivatives. Let us investigate this problem in completely general terms. Suppose that $f(x)$ is a sum of two functions:

$$y = f(x) = u(x) + v(x), \tag{8.5.1}$$

where $u(x)$ and $v(x)$ are both differentiable. Using definition (8.2.5), we have

$$f'(x) = \lim_{h \to 0} \left[\frac{u(x + h) + v(x + h) - u(x) - v(x)}{h} \right]. \tag{8.5.2}$$

By limit theorem (3) of Section 3.14,

$$f'(x) = \lim_{h \to 0} \frac{u(x+h) - u(x)}{h} + \lim_{h \to 0} \frac{v(x+h) - v(x)}{h}. \tag{8.5.3}$$

Therefore

$$f'(x) = u'(x) + v'(x) \tag{8.5.4}$$

or, in the Leibniz notation,

$$\frac{dy}{dx} = \frac{du}{dx} + \frac{dv}{dx}, \tag{8.5.4}$$

and it is proved that the derivative of a sum is equal to the sum of the individual derivatives, providing the derivatives exist. The equally simple parallel proof that if $f(x) = u(x) - v(x)$,

$$f'(x) = u'(x) - v'(x) \tag{8.5.5}$$

is left to the reader.

PROBLEM 8.11. Using theorems (8.5.4), (8.5.5), and items from Table 8.5.1, write down the derivatives of the following functions without going back to the fundamental definition of the derivative:

(a) $4ax^3 + 2bx + \dfrac{c}{x}$,   (b) $\dfrac{1}{4}t^2 - 3t + 5$,   (c) $1 - 2z^3 - \dfrac{3}{z}$.

PROBLEM 8.12. Write down antiderivatives for

(a) $3ax^2 - \dfrac{b}{x^2} + 2c$,   (b) $-\dfrac{3}{t^4} + 7t - 1$,   (c) $4z - 2z^2$.

8.6   THEOREMS FOR THE DIFFERENTIATION OF PRODUCTS AND QUOTIENTS

The simple results obtained in the preceding section could easily mislead us into supposing that the derivative of a product of two functions is equal to the product of the individual derivatives. That this is *not* the case is shown by the theorem obtained in the following analysis:

Given $y = f(x) = u(x) \cdot v(x)$, where $u(x)$ and $v(x)$ are assumed to be differentiable functions. Then

$$f'(x) = \lim_{h \to 0} \left[\frac{u(x+h) \cdot v(x+h) - u(x) \cdot v(x)}{h} \right].$$

This expression does not separate immediately in a simple way, and it is necessary to alter its form in order to make its properties more readily apparent. The strategy is to add and subtract the product $u(x+h) \cdot v(x)$ in the numerator:

$$f'(x) = \lim_{h \to 0} \left[\frac{u(x+h) \cdot v(x+h) - u(x) \cdot v(x) + u(x+h) \cdot v(x) - u(x+h) \cdot v(x)}{h} \right].$$

Coupling the first and fourth terms in the numerator in one expression, the second and third terms in another, and applying limit theorem (3) of Section 3.14:

$$f'(x) = \lim_{h \to 0} \left\{ u(x+h) \left[\frac{v(x+h) - v(x)}{h} \right] \right\} + \lim_{h \to 0} \left\{ \left[\frac{u(x+h) - u(x)}{h} \right] \cdot v(x) \right\}.$$

Since we have assumed $u(x)$ to be differentiable, it follows from the argument of Section 8.4 that $u(x)$ is continuous and that therefore $\lim_{h \to 0} u(x+h)$ exists and is equal to $u(x)$. The same can be said of $v(x)$. Therefore, applying limit theorem (7) of Section 3.14 to the above equation, we obtain

$$f'(x) = u(x) \cdot v'(x) + u'(x) \cdot v(x) \tag{8.6.1}$$

or, in the Leibniz notation,

$$\frac{dy}{dx} = u \frac{dv}{dx} + v \frac{du}{dx}. \tag{8.6.1}$$

(Note that we could have used the trick of adding and subtracting $u(x) \cdot v(x+h)$ in the numerator instead of $u(x+h) \cdot v(x)$, and would have obtained exactly the same final result.)

Example: Find the derivative of $f(x) = (4x^2 - 3)(x^3 + 1)$. We could, of course, multiply out the expression and differentiate it term by term as in the preceding section, but we would additionally have to establish the derivative of x^5. By utilizing (8.6.1), however, we have

$$f'(x) = (4x^2 - 3) \frac{d}{dx}(x^3 + 1) + (x^3 + 1) \frac{d}{dx}(4x^2 - 3),$$

and by the methods of the preceding section,

$$f'(x) = (4x^2 - 3)(3x^2) + (x^3 + 1)(8x).$$

Finally we obtain the theorem for differentiation of a quotient of two functions. Suppose that $y = f(x) = u(x)/v(x)$, where $u(x)$ and $v(x)$ are both differentiable. We shall show that

$$f'(x) = \frac{v(x) \cdot u'(x) - u(x) \cdot v'(x)}{[v(x)]^2}, \tag{8.6.2}$$

or

$$\frac{dy}{dx} = \frac{v \frac{du}{dx} - u \frac{dv}{dx}}{v^2}. \tag{8.6.2}$$

Proof:

$$f'(x) = \lim_{h \to 0} \frac{1}{h} \cdot \left[\frac{u(x+h)}{v(x+h)} - \frac{u(x)}{v(x)} \right]$$

$$= \lim_{h \to 0} \frac{1}{h} \cdot \left[\frac{u(x+h) \cdot v(x) - u(x) \cdot v(x+h)}{v(x)v(x+h)} \right].$$

If we add and subtract $u(x) \cdot v(x)$ in the numerator, we obtain

$$f'(x) = \lim_{h \to 0} \frac{1}{h} \cdot \left[\frac{u(x + h) \cdot v(x) - u(x) \cdot v(x) - u(x) \cdot v(x + h) + u(x) \cdot v(x)}{v(x) \cdot v(x + h)} \right]$$

$$= \lim_{h \to 0} \frac{v(x) \left[\dfrac{u(x + h) - u(x)}{h} \right] - u(x) \left[\dfrac{v(x + h) - v(x)}{h} \right]}{v(x) \cdot v(x + h)}.$$

Applying limit theorems from Section 3.14, we obtain Eq. (8.6.2), valid for all x for which $v(x) \neq 0$, and our theorem has been proved.

Example: To find the derivative of

$$f(x) = \frac{3x^2 - x + 1}{x - 5}.$$

From Theorem (8.6.2):

$$f(x) = \frac{(x - 5) \dfrac{d}{dx} (3x^2 - x + 1) - (3x^2 - x + 1) \dfrac{d}{dx} (x - 5)}{(x - 5)^2}$$

$$= \frac{(x - 5)(6x - 1) - (3x^2 - x + 1)(1)}{(x - 5)^2} = \frac{3x^2 - 30x + 4}{(x - 5)^2}.$$

PROBLEM 8.13.   Using the product or quotient theorems, find: (a) The derivative of

$$f(x) = \left(\frac{x}{2} - 1 \right) \left(\frac{1}{x} + \frac{x^2}{3} \right)$$

(b) The expression for the slope at any point on the curve

$$y = \frac{1}{z^2 + 1} \cdot \qquad \left[Answer: \frac{dy}{dz} = \frac{-2z}{(z^2 + 1)^2} \cdot \right]$$

(c) The velocity of a particle for which the position function is empirically established to be $s(t) = (3t + 2)/(t + 5)$ on the interval $0 \leq t \leq 10$, with s in meters and t in seconds. Suppose the domain of this function extended to negative values as far as $t = -10$; what problem arises in the evaluation of the derivative at $t = -5$? What comment would you make about the physical meaning and interpretation of the empirical function in this region?

8.7   THE DERIVATIVE OF x^n WHEN n IS A NATURAL NUMBER

In Table 8.5.1 we summarized the derivatives of x, x^2, and x^3. If, in an effort to guess the derivative of x^n, we examine these derivatives for indication of a pattern, we note that the derivative of x^n might in general be nx^{n-1}, at least when n is a natural number. This guess turns out to be correct not only for n as a natural number but for any real exponent r for which x^{r-1} is real and finite. (A case in which x^{r-1}

is not real is illustrated by $x^{1/2}$ for all $x < 0$; a case in which it is not finite is illustrated by x^{-1} at $x = 0$.) Although we shall not prove this theorem in its complete generality, we shall prove it for integer and rational exponents in this and following sections.

First let us show that the formula

$$\frac{d}{dx}(x^n) = nx^{n-1} \tag{8.7.1}$$

works for the particular case $n = 1$:

$$\frac{d}{dx}(x^1) = 1 \cdot x^{1-1} = 1 \cdot x^0 = 1 \cdot 1 = 1. \tag{8.7.2}$$

We have previously established that the derivative of x with respect to x itself is equal to 1, and it is apparent that the formula is valid for this case.

Now let us show that if we assume formula (8.7.1) to be valid for any particular natural number s, it must also be valid for the "successor" of s, the next natural number $s + 1$. We evaluate the derivative of x^{s+1}, treating it as the product of two functions $x \cdot x^s$, and making use of the product rule, Eq. (8.6.1):

$$\frac{d}{dx}[x \cdot x^s] = x\frac{d}{dx}(x^s) + x^s\frac{d}{dx}(x)$$

$$= x[sx^{s-1}] + x^s \cdot 1 = sx^s + x^s$$

$$= (s + 1)x^s. \tag{8.7.3}$$

Result (8.7.3) is exactly what we obtain if we substitute $s + 1$ for s directly in formula (8.7.1). Thus we have proved that, if the formula is valid for s, it must also be valid for $s + 1$. [At what step in derivation (8.7.3) did we introduce the assumption that the formula is valid for s?] Summarizing the analysis: We have shown that the formula is valid for $n = 1$, and we have also shown that if it is valid for *any* number n, it must also be valid for the next higher number $n + 1$. Therefore, being valid for $n = 1$, the formula must be valid for $n = 2$; being valid for $n = 2$, it must be valid for $n = 3$, etc. It is a fundamental postulate of the number system that this sequence includes *all* the natural numbers. (The form of proof we have just given is called a "proof by complete mathematical induction.")

A function $f(x)$ is called a *polynomial* if it is a sum of terms each of which is either a constant or the product of a constant and a positive integer power of x. [Examples: $f(x) = a + bx + cx^2$; $f(x) = \sqrt{3}x^5 - 3x^2$]. By application of rules (8.5.4), (8.7.1), and item (7) in Table 8.5.1, we can now evaluate directly the derivative of any polynomial. [For the two preceding examples: $f'(x) = b + 2cx$; $f'(x) = 5\sqrt{3}x^4 - 6x$].

A function $f(x)$ is called a *rational* function if it can be expressed as the quotient of two polynomials. Examples:

$$f(x) = \frac{2}{x^2 - 1}; \qquad f(x) = \frac{3x^4 + 2x}{x - 3}.$$

By application of the quotient rule (8.6.2) and theorem (8.7.1) we can readily evaluate the derivatives of rational functions. For the second of the two preceding examples,

$$f'(x) = \frac{(x - 3)(12x^3 + 2) - (3x^4 + 2x) \cdot 1}{(x - 3)^2} = \frac{9x^4 - 36x^3 - 6}{(x - 3)^2},$$

which is valid for all values of x except those which are roots of the denominator; i.e., those values of x which make the denominator equal to zero.

Thus, even though our rule for differentiating x^n is still restricted to positive integer values of n, we have enormously expanded our ability to find derivatives of new functions without repeatedly resorting to the original definition (8.2.5).

PROBLEM 8.14.   Find the derivatives of the following functions:

(a) $f(x) = x^7 - 2x^5 + 3;$ (b) $f(u) = \dfrac{1}{u^3 + 3};$

(c) $f(z) = \dfrac{5z + 4}{z^2 - 2z};$ (d) $f(s) = \dfrac{\frac{1}{2}s^2 + 3s}{s - 1}.$

$$\left[Answer: \text{ (d) } \frac{\frac{1}{2}s^2 - s - 3}{(s - 1)^2}. \right]$$

8.8 DERIVATIVE OF x^n WHEN n IS A NEGATIVE INTEGER

If we take n to be a negative integer, then $n = -|n|$, and $x^n = x^{-|n|} = 1/x^{|n|}$. This function can be differentiated as a quotient, using rule (8.6.2): Given $f(x) = 1/x^{|n|}$, defined for all $x \neq 0$, we can obtain

$$f'(x) = \frac{x^{|n|} \cdot 0 - 1 \cdot |n|x^{|n|-1}}{x^{2|n|}} = -|n|x^{-|n|-1}.$$

But since $n = -|n|$, the preceding equation becomes

$$f'(x) = nx^{n-1},$$

when n is a negative integer and $x \neq 0$. Thus rule (8.7.1), first stated in the preceding section, is seen to be valid for negative integers as well as for zero and positive integers, with the added qualification that the derivative does not exist at $x = 0$ if n is negative.

Examples:

$$\frac{d(kx^{-1})}{dx} = -kx^{-2}; \qquad \frac{d(x^{-3})}{dx} = -3x^{-4}.$$

PROBLEM 8.15.   Find the derivatives of the following functions:

(a) $f(x) = \dfrac{1}{3x^2};$ (b) $f(u) = 2u^{-5};$ (c) $f(x) = kx^{-a}.$

8.9 DERIVATIVE OF x^r WHEN r IS A RATIONAL NUMBER

Let r be a rational number defined by a ratio of positive integers m/n. Let us restrict x to the domain $x > 0$ so as to avoid the occurrence of imaginary values of the function; i.e., we keep the range of the function real.

In Section 8.11 we shall use a theorem developed in Section 8.10 to prove that

$$\frac{d}{dx}(x^{m/n}) = \frac{d}{dx}(x^r) = rx^{r-1} \qquad \text{for} \quad x > 0. \tag{8.9.1}$$

That is, rule (8.7.1) holds for all rational numbers. Here we shall simply assert this result and examine a few of its consequences. (We have restricted x to positive values to avoid difficulties associated with imaginary numbers and zero denominators.)

Functions of the form x^r are called *power functions*. We note in passing that the derivative of x^1 is a constant, the derivative of x^0 is zero, and the derivative of x^{-1} is $-x^{-2}$. We have no function in this group having the derivative x^{-1}, and therefore we as yet have no antiderivative for the function x^{-1}. An antiderivative of x^{-1} does indeed exist, but it is a very different type of function from a power function and will require separate study. This idea is underlined if we translate the differentiation theorem (8.9.1) into a statement about antiderivatives: given the function $f(x) = x^r$, the general antiderivative, $F(x)$, is given by

$$F(x) = \frac{1}{r+1}x^{r+1}, \tag{8.9.2}$$

valid for all r except $r = -1$, since in the latter case the denominator becomes zero.

Since we can now use rule (8.9.1) to evaluate the derivatives of power functions with rational exponents, it is possible to find the derivatives of radicals in a direct and simple way:

Example 1. $y = \sqrt{x} = x^{1/2}$ on the interval $0 \le x < \infty$,

$$\frac{dy}{dx} = \frac{1}{2}x^{(1/2)-1} = \frac{1}{2}x^{-1/2} = \frac{1}{2x^{1/2}} \qquad \text{valid for } 0 < x < \infty.$$

Example 2. $y = ax^{2/3}, \qquad \frac{dy}{dx} = \frac{2}{3}ax^{-1/3}.$

Example 3. $s = 2t^{-3/2}, \qquad \frac{ds}{dt} = -3t^{-5/2}.$

PROBLEM 8.16.   Find the derivatives of

$$\text{(a)} \ f(x) = ax^{3/2};$$

$$\text{(b)} \ f(z) = az^{5/4} + bz^{1/3};$$

$$\text{(c)} \ f(u) = \frac{5u^{-1/2}}{2u + 3}.$$

8.10   DERIVATIVES OF COMPOSITE FUNCTIONS: THE CHAIN RULE

In the theory of relativity, the concept of mass is redefined in such a way that the mass m of a particle moving relative to us at velocity v is given by

$$m = \frac{m_0}{\sqrt{1 - v^2/c^2}}, \tag{8.10.1}$$

where m_0 denotes the mass when the body is at rest relative to us, and c denotes the velocity of light; m_0 and c are both constants.

Suppose the velocity v is changing with time, and we wish to know the time rate of change of mass dm/dt. We then face the problem of finding the derivative of (8.10.1) with respect to t rather than v. The methods we have developed so far have all been concerned with finding derivatives with respect to the variable that appears explicitly in the formula of the function—in this case the derivative dm/dv. Evaluation of dm/dt presents a new problem.

The function illustrated in (8.10.1) is called a *composite function* or a "function of a function," since m is a function of v, and v is in turn a function of t. In functional notation we might write

$$m = f(v); \qquad v = g(t) \qquad \text{or} \qquad m(t) = f[g(t)].$$

An alternative functional notation rapidly gaining favor in mathematical literature is

$$m = f \circ g.$$

As a second illustration of a composite function, consider the case

$$y = (x^2 - 3x + 1)^{1/3}. \tag{8.10.2}$$

Suppose we wish to find dy/dx. Rule (8.9.1) tells us how to take derivatives of x^r, but in (8.10.2) we have not x itself but the quantity $(x^2 - 3x + 1)$ raised to a rational power. Having no convenient way of expressing (8.10.2) as a sum of terms such as x^r, we cannot find the derivative with the rules derived so far, even though x appears explicitly in the formula. Note that we can write (8.10.2) in the form

$$y = u^{1/3}, \qquad \text{where } u \equiv (x^2 - 3x + 1), \tag{8.10.3}$$

and in this manner view it as a composite function of the form $y = f(u); u = g(x)$ or $y(x) = f[g(x)]$. We know how to find dy/du; in this case it is $\frac{1}{3}u^{-2/3}$, but we do not know how to find dy/dx. Thus our two rather different illustrations are found to pose the same mathematical problem.

We shall prove the theorem that if $y(x) = f[g(x)]$, then

$$y'(x) = f'[g(x)]g'(x) \tag{8.10.4}$$

or, in the Leibniz notation with $u \equiv g(x)$,

$$\frac{dy}{dx} = \frac{dy}{du}\frac{du}{dx} \tag{8.10.4}$$

(providing the derivatives f' and g' exist). This theorem shows how to evaluate the derivative of a function of a function and is frequently called the *chain rule* of differentiation.

To develop a better sense of what the theorem means, we shall illustrate its use before giving the formal proof:

Example 1. Let us apply the theorem to Eq. (8.10.3):

$$f'[g(x)] = \frac{dy}{du} = \frac{1}{3} u^{-2/3} = \frac{1}{3} (x^2 - 3x + 1)^{-2/3}, \qquad g'(x) = \frac{du}{dx} = 2x - 3.$$

Therefore

$$y'(x) = \frac{dy}{dx} = \frac{1}{3} (x^2 - 3x + 1)^{-2/3}(2x - 3).$$

Example 2. $y = 3z^2 - \frac{1}{z}$, $\dfrac{dy}{dx} = \dfrac{dy}{dz} \dfrac{dz}{dx} = \left(6z + \dfrac{1}{z^2} \right) \dfrac{dz}{dx}.$

Example 3. Suppose the radius of a balloon or soap bubble varies with time, and we wish to know the rate at which the volume is changing. The volume of a sphere is given by $V = \frac{4}{3}\pi r^3$, and we have asserted that r is a function of time. Thus we have established a composite function

$$V = \frac{4}{3} \pi r^3; \qquad r = r(t), \tag{8.10.5}$$

and we seek an expression for dV/dt: Applying Theorem (8.10.4), we obtain

$$\frac{dV}{dt} = \frac{dV}{dr} \frac{dr}{dt},$$

$$\frac{dV}{dt} = 4\pi r^2 \frac{dr}{dt}. \tag{8.10.6}$$

In the absence of more detailed information concerning r as a function of t, we leave (8.10.6) as it stands. If we know an instantaneous rate of change of r, we can immediately calculate dV/dt. If we know a rate of change of volume, we can calculate the instantaneous rate dr/dt at any particular value of r, and so forth.

Restricted proof of the chain rule [Theorem (8.10.4)]:

Let y be a composite function $y = f[g(x)]$ or $y = f(u); u = g(x)$, and assume that both derivatives $f'[g(x)]$ and $g'(x)$ exist. Then, by the definition of a derivative,

$$y'(x) = \frac{dy}{dx} = \lim_{h \to 0} \frac{f[g(x + h)] - f[g(x)]}{h}$$

or, in a more compact notation,

$$y'(x) = \frac{dy}{dx} = \lim_{h \to 0} \frac{f(u + k) - f(u)}{h}, \tag{8.10.7}$$

where $k \equiv g(x + h) - g(x)$ and $u + k = g(x + h)$. The right-hand side of (8.10.7) resembles the difference quotient whose limit we call $f'(u)$, except that h appears in the denominator instead of k. If we multiply numerator and denominator by k, Eq. (8.10.7) takes the form

$$y'(x) = \frac{dy}{dx} = \lim_{h \to 0} \left[\frac{f(u + k) - f(u)}{k} \frac{k}{h} \right]$$

$$= \lim_{h \to 0} \frac{f[g(x + h)] - f[g(x)]}{g(x + h) - g(x)} \frac{g(x + h) - g(x)}{h} . \qquad (8.10.8)$$

This may seem like a perfectly reasonable operation, but since we are dividing by k as well as multiplying, we must examine the implications very carefully. The operation has meaning providing $k \neq 0$. The limit must be evaluated as $h \to 0$, and it is quite possible in principle for k to have values of zero for a succession of values of h, while h itself is not equal to zero. In such a case (8.10.8) would not be a valid equation. Let us exclude such cases and confine ourselves to a proof with an added restriction: Assume that $u = g(x)$ is a function such that there exists a neighborhood of $h = 0$ within which $k \neq 0$ except when $h = 0$.

Under this restriction (8.10.8) can be evaluated by application of limit theorem (7) in section (3.14), provided the respective limits exist. Thus we have the chain rule

or

$$y'(x) = f'(u)g'(x) = f'[g(x)]g'(x)$$
$$\left. \frac{dy}{dx} = \frac{dy}{du} \frac{du}{dx} , \right\} \qquad (8.10.4)$$

provided f and u are differentiable functions and provided $g(x + h) - g(x) \neq 0$ except when $h = 0$. (The latter restriction can be removed by a more general proof which we shall not take time to develop in this text. The functions that we shall have occasion to deal with by means of the chain rule will be ones that satisfy this condition. For a more rigorous treatment of this problem, the student should refer to a textbook on calculus.)

The chain rule is an illustration of a context in which the Leibniz notation is particularly simple and useful. The Leibniz form of (8.10.4) is strongly suggestive of physical interpretations: the rate of change of y with respect to x is viewed as the rate of change of y with respect to u multiplied by the rate of change of u with respect to x.

The theorem can obviously be extended through additional steps of composition of functions. Thus, if

$$y = y(u);$$

$$u = u(z);$$

$$z = z(x),$$

the chain rule takes the form

$$\frac{dy}{dx} = \frac{dy}{du} \frac{du}{dz} \frac{dz}{dx} . \qquad (8.10.9)$$

PROBLEM 8.17.   Find the derivatives with respect to x of

(a) $y = (1 - 3x^2)^6$;   (b) $y = \dfrac{5}{\sqrt{2 - x^3}}$ (What is the domain of this function?);

(c) $y = 2u^{+3/2}$.

(d) Assuming $x = x(t)$ in (a) and (b), write expressions for dy/dt.

$$\text{Answer: (b)}\quad \frac{dy}{dt} = \frac{15x^2}{2}(2 - x^3)^{-3/2}\frac{dx}{dt}.$$

(e) Find dm/dt in Eq. (8.10.1).

$$\text{Answer:}\quad \frac{dm}{dt} = \frac{m_0 v}{c^2}\left(1 - \frac{v^2}{c^2}\right)^{-3/2}\frac{dv}{dt}.$$

PROBLEM 8.18.   Suppose that in a rectilinear motion velocity v is regarded as a function of position s; s is regarded as a function of time t; and the derivatives of these functions are assumed to exist. Show that the chain rule then requires that acceleration

$$a \equiv \frac{dv}{dt} = v\frac{dv}{ds}$$

and that, as a consequence,

$$a = \frac{d}{ds}\left(\frac{v^2}{2}\right).$$

8.11   PROOF THAT RULE (8.9.1) HOLDS FOR RATIONAL r

Suppose that

$$y = x^r = x^{m/n}, \qquad x > 0, \tag{8.11.1}$$

where n is taken to be a positive integer and m is any integer, positive or negative. (Here x is restricted to positive values in order to avoid imaginary numbers and zero denominators.)

Since n is a positive integer, we can write Eq. (8.11.1) in the form

$$g(x) = y^n = x^m.$$

Taking derivatives and applying the chain rule, we obtain

$$\frac{dg}{dx} = \frac{dg}{dy}\frac{dy}{dx} = ny^{n-1}\frac{dy}{dx} = mx^{m-1}. \tag{8.11.2}$$

There is a weakness in this analysis; namely, that in applying the chain rule, we are assuming that the function x is differentiable; i.e., that dy/dx exists. But dy/dx is what we are trying to find, and assuming its existence a priori is not a completely rigorous procedure. The analysis can be justified, although we shall not undertake to do so here. The interested student can find the relevant discussion in a more advanced text.

Assuming the validity of this treatment, we solve (8.11.2) for dy/dx:

$$\frac{dy}{dx} = \frac{mx^{m-1}}{ny^{n-1}}, \qquad \text{where} \quad y = x^{m/n}.$$

Therefore

$$\frac{dy}{dx} = \frac{mx^{m-1}}{n(x^{m/n})^{n-1}} = \frac{mx^{m-1}}{nx^{m-m/n}} = \frac{m}{n}x^{m/n-1}, \tag{8.11.3}$$

completing the demonstration that the rule

$$\frac{d}{dx}(x^r) = rx^{r-1}, \qquad x > 0, \tag{8.11.4}$$

is valid for all rational numbers. The application of this rule has been illustrated in Section 8.9.

With some additional effort, combined with an extension of limit theorem (9), it would be possible to show that the same formula is valid for negative x in those cases where the integer n in $r = m/n$ is an odd number; i.e., those cases in which $x^{m/n}$ is a real number. With still more advanced methods it is also possible to extend the formula by showing it to be valid for *all* real values of the exponent, including the irrational numbers, but we shall not undertake to prove these extensions in this book.

8.12   DIFFERENTIALS: AN INTERPRETATION OF THE LEIBNIZ NOTATION

In Section 8.2 we gave a geometrical interpretation of $f'(x_0)$ as the slope of the tangent to the graph of the function at the point $P(x_0, y_0)$. Figure 8.12.1 presents a related interpretation of the ratio

$$\frac{f'(x)\,\Delta x}{\Delta x}.$$

The ratio itself is just $f'(x)$, the slope of the tangent to the curve at point $P(x, y)$. The numerator, however, can be interpreted as the directed distance BA and the denominator as the directed distance PB. The ratio of these two directed distances is also the slope of the tangent line.

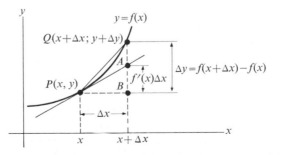

FIG. 8.12.1. Geometrical interpretation of the quantities Δy, Δx, and $f'(x)\,\Delta x$.

This interpretation suggests the following definitions:
(1) We associate the symbol dx with the quantity Δx; that is, $dx \equiv \Delta x$.
(2) Similarly, let us define a quantity dy by

$$dy \equiv f'(x)\Delta x = f'(x)\,dx. \tag{8.12.1}$$

These definitions endow the Leibniz notation, dy/dx for the derivative, with an interpretable significance as a ratio:

$$\frac{dy}{dx} = \frac{BA}{PB} = \frac{f'(x)\,\Delta x}{\Delta x} = \frac{f'(x)\,dx}{dx} = f'(x).$$

Up to this point we have refrained from interpreting the Leibniz notation and have utilized dy/dx as only a single, lumped symbol. Our new definitions allow us to exploit the notation in a number of useful ways outlined below.

The two quantities dy and dx are called "differentials of y and x," respectively. Note that, although dx is identified with Δx, dy and Δy represent very different quantities. While dy is associated with the directed distance BA (Fig. 8.12.1),

$$\Delta y \equiv f(x + \Delta x) - f(x)$$

is associated with BQ.

The utility of the new interpretation resides in the fact that if the increment Δx or dx is sufficiently small, the number $dy = f'(x)\,dx$ becomes a good approximation for Δy. This means that not only does $dy/\Delta y \to 1$ as $dx \to 0$ but that the difference $\Delta y - dy$ becomes very small relative to the "correct" value Δy; that is, $(\Delta y - dy)/\Delta y \to 0$ as $dx \to 0$. Let us prove these assertions, making use of the definitions of the quantities involved:

$$\lim_{\Delta x \to 0} \left(\frac{dy}{\Delta y}\right) = \lim_{\Delta x \to 0} \left[\frac{f'(x)\,\Delta x}{f(x + \Delta x) - f(x)}\right]$$

$$= \lim_{\Delta x \to 0} \left[\frac{f'(x)}{\dfrac{f(x + \Delta x) - f(x)}{\Delta x}}\right] = \frac{f'(x)}{f'(x)} = 1. \tag{8.12.2}$$

Also:

$$\lim_{\Delta x \to 0} \left(\frac{\Delta y - dy}{\Delta y}\right) = \lim_{\Delta x \to 0} \left(1 - \frac{dy}{\Delta y}\right) = 1 - \lim_{\Delta x \to 0} \left(\frac{dy}{\Delta y}\right) = 1 - 1 = 0. \tag{8.12.3}$$

[Identify the theorems which are employed in the steps of (8.12.2, 3).]

Example 1. When a short, intense electric spark releasing a quantity of energy E is fired between electrodes in water or oil, a gas bubble is formed which expands very rapidly to a maximum radius R and undergoes a sequence of oscillations. It is known that R is proportional to the cube root of E; that is, $R = KE^{1/3}$. How do small variations of E affect the maximum radius?

If we consider two values of energy release, E_2 and E_1, the difference between maximum radii R_2 and R_1 will be $\Delta R = R_2 - R_1 = K(E_2^{1/3} - E_1^{1/3})$. This is a cumbersome expression to deal with. Invoking the concept of the differential, however, we have

$$dR = R'(E) \, dE = \frac{K}{3} E^{-2/3} \, dE$$

and, dividing both sides by R, we obtain

$$\frac{dR}{R} = \frac{K}{3} \frac{E^{-2/3}}{R} \, dE = \frac{1}{3} \frac{dE}{E}.$$

The last equation tells us that for small variations, the fractional change in R is one-third the fractional change in E. Thus if the energy release changes by 6%, the maximum radius changes by 2%. Conversely, if an experiment is performed by high-speed photography in which R is measured on the film and the energy release E is calculated, a 1% error in the measurement of R will lead to a 3% error in the value of E. In general, the manipulation of differentials illustrated in this example frequently proves to be a powerful technique for estimating sizes of errors in calculations which are based on experimental measurements.

Example 2. There is a method of quickly estimating the square roots of numbers which differ somewhat from perfect squares; for instance, $\sqrt{150}$ which differs slightly from $\sqrt{144}$:

$$\text{If } y = x^{1/2}, \quad dy = \frac{1}{2} x^{-1/2} \, dx = \frac{dx}{2x^{1/2}} = \frac{dx}{2y}.$$

Therefore

$$(x + \Delta x)^{1/2} \approx y + dy = y + \frac{dx}{2y}.$$

(The symbol $\approx$ means "approximately equal to.") In the numerical example proposed above, we identify x with 144, Δx with 6, and y with 12:

$$\sqrt{150} = \sqrt{144 + 6} \approx 12 + \frac{6}{2(12)} = 12.25.$$

PROBLEM 8.19. Using the method of differentials, analyze how the fractional error in determining the volume of a sphere depends on the fractional error in measuring its diameter.

PROBLEM 8.20. Using a technique exactly parallel to that of Example 2 above, devise a method for estimating cube roots of numbers and use it to estimate the cube roots of 7, 9, and 30.

8.13 DERIVATIVES OF THE SINE AND COSINE FUNCTIONS

Given the function $f(\theta) = \sin \theta$. If we elect to form the expression for the derivative using the notation of definition (8.2.7), we have

$$f'(\theta) = \lim_{\Delta\theta \to 0} \frac{\sin (\theta + \Delta\theta) - \sin \theta}{\Delta\theta}. \tag{8.13.1}$$

The sine of a sum of two angles is given by a basic formula of trigonometry (see Appendix E),

$$\sin (\alpha + \beta) = \sin \alpha \cos \beta + \cos \alpha \sin \beta,$$

and Eq. (8.13.1) becomes

$$f'(\theta) = \lim_{\Delta\theta \to 0} \frac{\sin \theta \cos \Delta\theta + \cos \theta \sin \Delta\theta - \sin \theta}{\Delta\theta}$$

$$= \lim_{\Delta\theta \to 0} \left[\cos \theta \left(\frac{\sin \Delta\theta}{\Delta\theta} \right) - \sin \theta \left(\frac{1 - \cos \Delta\theta}{\Delta\theta} \right) \right]$$

and, by application of limit theorems in Section 3.14, we obtain

$$f'(\theta) = \cos \theta \lim_{\Delta\theta \to 0} \frac{\sin \Delta\theta}{\Delta\theta} - \sin \theta \lim_{\Delta\theta \to 0} \left(\frac{1 - \cos \Delta\theta}{\Delta\theta} \right). \tag{8.13.2}$$

Therefore, to obtain the derivative of the sine function, we must evaluate the two limits appearing in Eq. (8.13.2). Exactly the same limits arise in the expression for the derivative of the cosine, as shown in the following problem.

PROBLEM 8.21.   Given the trigonometric formula

$$\cos (\alpha + \beta) = \cos \alpha \cos \beta - \sin \alpha \sin \beta.$$

Following the notation and procedure used above in connection with the sine function, show that the derivative of $g(\theta) = \cos \theta$ is given by

$$g'(\theta) = -\cos \theta \lim_{\Delta\theta \to 0} \left(\frac{1 - \cos \Delta\theta}{\Delta\theta} \right) - \sin \theta \lim_{\Delta\theta \to 0} \frac{\sin \Delta\theta}{\Delta\theta}. \tag{8.13.3}$$

To evaluate the limits appearing in Eqs. (8.13.2) and (8.13.3), it is necessary to know something about the relations connecting the quantities $\sin \Delta\theta$, $1 - \cos \Delta\theta$, and $\Delta\theta$, and for this purpose it is necessary to go back to the fundamental definitions of the quantities themselves. We shall perform this investigation with the help of Fig. 8.13.1.*

Since we are interested in limits as $\Delta\theta \to 0$, we shall confine our investigation to small angles. Figure 8.13.1 shows a sector of a unit circle (radius = 1 unit) with $\Delta\theta < \pi/2$. The coordinates of point P are $(\cos \Delta\theta, \sin \Delta\theta)$; $\overline{PC}$ is perpendicular to $\overline{OP}$. The figure is constructed symmetrically about the x-axis; that is, triangles OPC and OQC are congruent.

---

* Although it is entirely possible to put the trigonometric ideas on a purely arithmetical foundation and to eliminate dependence on geometrical interpretations, an attempt to do so would take us beyond the level and scope of this text. We shall therefore frankly resort to the intuitive, geometrical development associated with Fig. 8.13.1, realizing that we are making a compromise and that more elegant methods, consistent with complete arithmetization of the calculus, do exist. Students interested in these logical issues should consult a more advanced text.

Although we have not established a rigorous arithmetical definition of the length of a curved line, we sense intuitively that the length of the straight line $\overline{QAP}$ is less than that of the arc $\overset{\frown}{QBP}$ and that therefore (taking half of each length) we have for positive $\Delta\theta$:

$$\overline{AP} < \overset{\frown}{BP}, \qquad \sin \Delta\theta < \Delta\theta,$$

$$\frac{\sin \Delta\theta}{\Delta\theta} < 1. \tag{8.13.4}$$

(Recall that the length of circular arc subtending an angle $\Delta\theta$ is equal to $R\Delta\theta$, provided that $\Delta\theta$ is measured in *radians*. In saying that $R = 1$ and $\overset{\frown}{BP} = \Delta\theta$ we are measuring $\Delta\theta$ in radians, and, accordingly, we must henceforth confine ourselves to radian measure.)

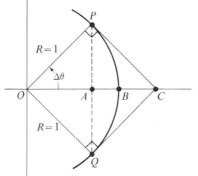

FIG. 8.13.1. Properties of angle $\Delta\theta$ when $0 < \Delta\theta < \pi/2$. Radius of circular arc $\overset{\frown}{PBQ} = 1$ unit; $\overline{AP} = \sin \Delta\theta$, $\overset{\frown}{BP} = \Delta\theta$, $\overline{CP} = \tan \Delta\theta$.

Inequality (8.13.4) is not altered if we change the sign of $\Delta\theta$; that is, if we consider $\angle COQ$ instead of $\angle COP$. Since $\sin(-\alpha) = -\sin \alpha$.

$$\frac{\sin(-\Delta\theta)}{-\Delta\theta} = \frac{-\sin \Delta\theta}{-\Delta\theta} = \frac{\sin \Delta\theta}{\Delta\theta}.$$

Therefore (8.13.4) is valid for $-\pi/2 < \Delta\theta < \pi/2$ or $0 < |\Delta\theta| < \pi/2$.

Returning to Fig. 8.13.1, we note that the length of arc $\overset{\frown}{QBP}$ must be less than $\overline{QC} + \overline{CP}$ and that therefore (taking half of each length) we have, for positive $\Delta\theta$:

$$\overset{\frown}{BP} < \overline{CP}, \qquad \Delta\theta < \tan \Delta\theta, \qquad \Delta\theta < \frac{\sin \Delta\theta}{\cos \Delta\theta}, \qquad \cos \Delta\theta < \frac{\sin \Delta\theta}{\Delta\theta}. \tag{8.13.5}$$

Since $\cos(-\Delta\theta) = \cos \Delta\theta$, inequality (8.13.5) is valid for negative as well as positive $\Delta\theta$; that is, for $-\pi/2 < \Delta\theta < \pi/2$ or $0 < |\Delta\theta| < \pi/2$.

From (8.13.4) and (8.13.5) we also have

$$\cos \Delta\theta < 1. \tag{8.13.6}$$

Inequalities (8.13.4), (8.13.5), and (8.13.6) yield the following group of consequences:
(1) From (8.13.4) we conclude that

$$|\sin \Delta\theta| < |\Delta\theta|.$$

Therefore $|\sin \Delta\theta| < \epsilon$ for all $\Delta\theta$ such that $0 < |\Delta\theta| < \delta$, where $\delta = \epsilon$. This indicates that we can make $\sin \Delta\theta$ arbitrarily close to 0 by making $\Delta\theta$ sufficiently small; that is,

$$\lim_{\Delta\theta \to 0} (\sin \Delta\theta) = 0.$$

Since we also have $\sin (0) = 0$, we conclude that the sine function is continuous at angle zero.

(2) We examine $(1 - \cos \Delta\theta)$ with a view toward evaluating

$$\lim_{\Delta\theta \to 0} \frac{1 - \cos \Delta\theta}{\Delta\theta}.$$

From (8.13.6) it follows that $(1 - \cos \Delta\theta) > 0$ and $|1 - \cos \Delta\theta| = 1 - \cos \Delta\theta$. Let us try to connect this quantity with $\sin \Delta\theta$:

$$|1 - \cos \Delta\theta| = (1 - \cos \Delta\theta) \frac{1 + \cos \Delta\theta}{1 + \cos \Delta\theta} = \frac{1 - \cos^2 \Delta\theta}{1 + \cos \Delta\theta} = \frac{\sin^2 \Delta\theta}{1 + \cos \Delta\theta}. \qquad (8.13.7)$$

From inequality (8.13.4) we can say that:

$$\sin^2 \Delta\theta < |\Delta\theta| \cdot |\Delta\theta| = (\Delta\theta)^2.$$

From Eq. (8.13.7) it then follows that

$$|1 - \cos \Delta\theta| < \frac{|\Delta\theta| \cdot |\Delta\theta|}{1 + \cos \Delta\theta} < |\Delta\theta| \cdot |\Delta\theta|. \qquad (8.13.8)$$

(The second part of the inequality follows from the fact that the denominator $1 + \cos \Delta\theta$ is always > 1, so long as we maintain our restriction that $|\Delta\theta| < \pi/2$.) From (8.13.8) we note that $|1 - \cos \Delta\theta| < \epsilon$ for all $\Delta\theta$ such that $0 < |\Delta\theta| < \delta$, where $\delta = \epsilon^{1/2}$. Therefore we conclude that

$$\lim_{\Delta\theta \to 0} (1 - \cos \Delta\theta) = 0; \qquad \lim_{\Delta\theta \to 0} (\cos \Delta\theta) = 1. \qquad (8.13.9)$$

Since we also know that $\cos (0) = 1$, we conclude that the cosine function is continuous at angle zero.

(3) From inequality (8.13.8) we have

$$\left| \frac{1 - \cos \Delta\theta}{\Delta\theta} \right| < |\Delta\theta|$$

and, again applying the definition of limit, we obtain

$$\lim_{\Delta\theta \to 0} \left(\frac{1 - \cos \Delta\theta}{\Delta\theta} \right) = 0. \qquad (8.13.10)$$

(4) From inequalities (8.13.5) and (8.13.6), we have

$$\left| 1 - \frac{\sin \Delta\theta}{\Delta\theta} \right| < |1 - \cos \Delta\theta|$$

and by inequality (8.13.8), it follows that

$$\left| 1 - \frac{\sin \Delta\theta}{\Delta\theta} \right| < |\Delta\theta| \cdot |\Delta\theta|.$$

Applying the definition of limit, we obtain

$$\lim_{\Delta\theta \to 0} \frac{\sin \Delta\theta}{\Delta\theta} = 1. \tag{8.13.11}$$

Equations (8.13.10) and (8.13.11) lead directly to the evaluation of (8.13.2) and (8.13.3). By direct substitution we obtain

$$\frac{d \sin \theta}{d\theta} = \cos \theta, \tag{8.13.12}$$

$$\frac{d \cos \theta}{d\theta} = -\sin \theta. \tag{8.13.13}$$

Example: To find $f'(x)$ when $f(x) = A \cos (kx)$. Using rule (7) in Table 8.5.1 and applying the chain rule with $\theta \equiv kx$, we have

$$\frac{df}{dx} = A \frac{d \cos \theta}{d\theta} \frac{d\theta}{dx} = -A (\sin \theta)k = -Ak \sin (kx).$$

Example: To find an antiderivative of $\cos (bx)$, where b is a constant. Taking $\theta = bx$, we have

$$\frac{d}{dx} [\sin (bx)] = \frac{d}{d\theta} (\sin \theta) \frac{d(bx)}{dx} = b \cdot \cos bx.$$

Since the derivative of $\sin (bx)$ is $b \cdot \cos (bx)$, we note that the derivative of $(1/b) \sin (bx)$ would be $\cos (bx)$. Thus $(1/b) \sin (bx)$ is the antiderivative we seek.

PROBLEM 8.22.   Equation (8.13.11) gives a limit which we shall have occasion to use repeatedly. Very simply interpreted, it says that, for small angles, the sine of the angle is very nearly equal to the angle itself when the latter is expressed in *radians*. Verify this fact directly from a table of sines by comparing the values of $\sin \theta$ and θ when θ is small. How large does θ have to be before $\sin \theta$ differs from it by more than 1%? more than 5%?

PROBLEM 8.23.   Applying quotient rule (8.6.2), show that

$$\frac{d \tan \theta}{d\theta} = \frac{1}{\cos^2 \theta}.$$

(Recall that $\tan \theta = \sin \theta/\cos \theta$.)

PROBLEM 8.24.   Find derivatives and antiderivatives of

(a) $f(t) = A \sin \omega t$, where A and ω are constants. [*Answer:* $f'(t) = A\omega \cos \omega t$.]
(b) $f(x) = a \sin (\omega x + b)$, where a, ω, and b are constants.
     [*Answer:* $F(x) = -(a/\omega) \cos (\omega x + b)$.]

PROBLEM 8.25.   Interpreted geometrically, Eq. (8.13.12) says that the slope at any point on a sine curve is equal to the value of the cosine function at the same θ.   Verify this interpretation intuitively by plotting sine and cosine curves on graph paper and sketching tangents to the sine curve at various points.   Give a similar interpretation of Eq. (8.13.13).

8.14   ASSERTION OF THE MEAN VALUE THEOREM

Consideration of Fig. 8.14.1 suggests the following geometrical regularity: If we draw a secant between two points P_0 and Q on a curve, and if the curve is of such a nature that it has a tangent everywhere between P_0 and Q, there is at least one tangent line which is parallel to secant $\overline{P_0 Q}$.   That this is not always the case is illustrated by Fig. 8.14.2(a), where the curve has an infinite discontinuity at $x = a$, and by Fig. 8.14.2(b), where the curve is continuous at $x = a$, but no tangent exists at this point. In both of these instances there exists no point between P_0 and Q at which the tangent to the curve is parallel to secant $\overline{P_0 Q}$.

Translating this idea into the language of analysis, we enunciate the following theorem:

If a function $y = f(x)$ is differentiable at every point on a certain interval, and if x_0 and $x_0 + h$ are two points within this interval, then there exists a number $\bar{x}$ between x_0 and $x_0 + h$ (more specifically $x_0 \leq \bar{x} \leq x_0 + h$) such that

$$\frac{f(x_0 + h) - f(x_0)}{h} = f'(\bar{x}).   \tag{8.14.1}$$

(If we interchange the positions x_0 and $x_0 + h$ in Fig. 8.14.1, making h negative instead of positive, we note that our assertion still seems to hold, providing the function has a derivative at every point in the interval.)

The theorem just asserted on the basis of the geometrical representations in Figs. 8.14.1 and 2 is called the *mean value theorem* or "theorem of the mean for

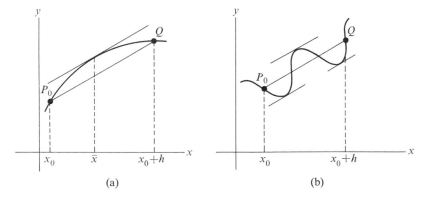

(a)   (b)

FIG. 8.14.1.   (a) Differentiable function.   At $\bar{x}$, located between P_0 and Q, the slope of the curve is equal to the slope of secant $P_0 Q$.   (b) Differentiable function.   At three distinct points located between P_0 and Q the slope of the curve equals the slope of secant $P_0 Q$.

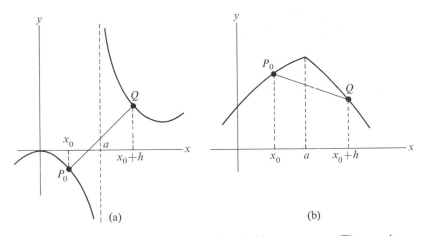

Fig. 8.14.2. Functions which are not differentiable at $x = a$. There exist no points located between P_0 and Q at which the slope of the curve equals the slope of secant P_0Q.

derivatives." It is one of the most fundamental theorems of analysis, and we shall have occasion to use it several times in future work. An arithmetical proof of this theorem is somewhat lengthy and will not be attempted in this text. Students should be aware that the geometrical interpretation given above helps make the theorem plausible but does not constitute an adequate proof from a mathematical standpoint. A formal proof will be found in virtually any modern textbook on calculus.

8.15 THE GENERAL ANTIDERIVATIVE OF f(x)

In Section 8.3 we argued that if $F(x)$ is an antiderivative of $f(x)$, then $F(x) + C$ is also an antiderivative of $f(x)$, but it was pointed out that this argument does not demonstrate that $F(x) + C$ is the *general* antiderivative—that no other function will satisfy the conditions.

It is possible to show that $F(x) + C$ is indeed the general antiderivative, and we shall carry out this proof as a demonstration of the use of the mean value theorem, asserted in the preceding section. The method of proof will be to assume that there exist two distinct antiderivatives of $f(x)$ denoted by $F(x)$ and $G(x)$, respectively, and to show that G and F can differ only by a constant term; i.e., that $G(x) - F(x) = C$.

Let us define a function $H(x)$, which is the difference between G and F, and ascertain its properties:

$$H(x) \equiv G(x) - F(x). \tag{8.15.1}$$

$H(x)$ must be a differentiable function, since $F(x)$ and $G(x)$ are differentiable by the initial hypothesis. Also

$$H'(x) = G'(x) - F'(x) = 0 \tag{8.15.2}$$

since, by definition, $G'(x)$ and $F'(x)$ are both equal to $f(x)$.

Let us suppose that Fig. 8.14.1(a) represents a graph of our newly defined function $H(x)$. Since $H(x)$ is differentiable within some interval, we can apply the mean value theorem for points P_0 and Q within this interval, writing

$$\frac{H(x_0 + h) - H(x_0)}{h} = H'(\bar{x}), \qquad H(x_0 + h) - H(x_0) = hH'(\bar{x}).$$

But since $H'(x)$ is zero *everywhere*

$$H(x_0 + h) - H(x_0) = 0 \qquad \text{or} \qquad H(x) - H(x_0) = 0$$

and

$$H(x) = H(x_0) = C, \text{ a constant.}$$

Thus it is a necessary consequence of the mean value theorem that if $H'(x)$ is everywhere zero on a certain interval, $H(x)$ itself must be a constant on that interval. Of course, this constant may be zero as a special case. Returning to definition (8.15.1) we see that this implies that two antiderivatives of the same function can differ only by a constant

$$G(x) - F(x) = C, \qquad G(x) = F(x) + C,$$

showing $F(x) + C$ to be the general antiderivative of $f(x)$.

8.16   PROBLEMS

8.26. Find the derivatives of the following functions:

(a) $f(x) = \dfrac{2x}{1 - x^2}$

(b) $f(x) = \dfrac{1 + x - x^2}{1 - x + x^2}$

(c) $f(u) = \dfrac{(3 + 2u^3)(2 - u)}{1 - 2u^2}$

(d) $f(z) = 1 + z + \dfrac{z^2}{2} + \dfrac{z^3}{3 \cdot 2}$

$$+ \dfrac{z^4}{4 \cdot 3 \cdot 2} + \dfrac{z^5}{5 \cdot 4 \cdot 3 \cdot 2}$$

$$+ \dfrac{z^6}{6 \cdot 5 \cdot 4 \cdot 3 \cdot 2}$$

Comment on the pattern that makes its appearance in (d). Although theorem (8.5.4) for the derivative of a sum is applicable only to sums containing a *finite* number of terms, speculate on the possible relationship between $f(z)$ and $f'(z)$ if the sum in (d) is

continued indefinitely. Guesses of this kind invite investigation of the properties, differentiability, etc., of infinite series—a branch of calculus we shall not have time to explore.

8.27. Given the parabola $y = ax^2$. Find the equation of the line tangent to the curve at $P_0(x_0, y_0)$. Show that this line intersects the x-axis at the point $(x_0/2, 0)$. Present this situation graphically on a set of xy-axes.

8.28. The trajectory of a projectile with initially horizontal velocity is given by Eq. (4.3.5):

$$y = \frac{-g}{2v_{0x}^2} x^2.$$

Find and interpret the expression for the direction of the instantaneous velocity vector at any point on the trajectory. Compare your analytic result with the graphical presentation in Fig. 4.8.2. [*Answer:* $dy/dx = -gx/v_{0x}^2$.]

8.29. Devise some problems of your own regarding the equations of tangents to specific curves, drawing on whatever experience you have had with analytic geometry up to this point.

8.30. For students familiar with the binomial theorem: From the definition of derivative we can formulate the following expression for the derivative of x^n:

$$\frac{d(x^n)}{dx} = \lim_{h \to 0} \frac{(x + h)^n - x^n}{h}.$$

Expand $(x + h)^n$ by the binomial theorem; evaluate the limit, and show that the final result is nx^{n-1}.

8.31. Suppose that $a = bt$ (m/sec^2) describes the acceleration in a nonuniformly accelerated rectilinear motion for the interval $0 < t < 20$ sec. Find expressions for $v(t)$ and $s(t)$, subject to the initial conditions $v = v_0$ and $s = s_0$ when $t = 0$.

$$\left[Answer: v(t) = \frac{bt^2}{2} + v_0; \right.$$

$$\left. s(t) = \frac{bt^3}{6} + v_0 t + s_0. \right]$$

8.32. Find antiderivatives for the following functions, making use of consequences of the chain rule when relevant:

(a) $f(t) = t^{-1/2} + t^{-1/3} + t^{-1/4}$

(b) $f(u) = \dfrac{1}{(u + 5)^2}$

[*Answer:* $F(u) = -1/(u + 5)$]

(c) $f(x) = 1 + x + \dfrac{x^2}{2} + \dfrac{x^3}{3 \cdot 2}$

$$+ \frac{x^4}{4 \cdot 3 \cdot 2} + \frac{x^5}{5 \cdot 4 \cdot 3 \cdot 2}$$

$$+ \frac{x^6}{6 \cdot 5 \cdot 4 \cdot 3 \cdot 2}$$

[Note the comment following Problem 8.26(d).]

(d) $f(z) = x(x^2 - 7)^{2/3}$

[*Answer:* $F(z) = \frac{3}{10}(x^2 - 7)^{5/3}$.]

SUPPLEMENTARY READING AND STUDY

(See references cited at end of Chapter 3.)

For additional elementary material on calculus:

Mathematics for the Millions, Lancelot Hogben. London: Allen & Unwin, 1936, Chapter 11. Also available in paperback reprint.

Mathematics in Western Culture, Morris Kline. New York: Oxford University Press, 1953, Chapter 15

What is Calculus About?, W. W. Sawyer. New York: Random House, 1961

For more advanced points of view:

Differential and Integral Calculus, R. Courant. New York: Interscience Publishers, Inc., 1937, Chapter 2

CHAPTER 9

Circular Motion of Particles

9.1 INTRODUCTION

Most of our attention up to this point has been focused on kinematics and dynamics of straight-line motion, and on the action of forces having unvarying direction in space. Even in the one curvilinear case, projectile motion, discussed in Chapter 4, we note the action of a vertical force, constant in both magnitude and direction, and we superpose the vertically accelerated rectilinear motion upon a horizontally uniform one. Such limitation in scope is part of the deliberate program of gradually building up concepts and insights by starting with the simplest physical abstractions, but the simplest cases are not necessarily the most prevalent or the most interesting. Among physical phenomena in the world around us, rectilinear motions are but a small minority, and we are confronted far more frequently with repetitive motions, having curved paths determined by forces of changing direction. Among such motions, the simplest variety is one we describe as circular—the motion of a bob on a string, of a rotating wheel, of a hand on a clock, of the earth on its axis, of electrically charged particles in a uniform magnetic field, and (to a first approximation) of planets around the sun. In this chapter we concern ourselves with certain aspects of the kinematics and dynamics of circular motion of particles.

9.2 POSITION COORDINATES AND THE CONCEPT OF ANGULAR VELOCITY

To describe the position of a particle in circular motion, we need a system of position coordinates. When we undertook to describe rectilinear motion in Chapter 1, we utilized coordinates of position along the number line as in Fig. 1.2.1; for two-dimensional motion of projectiles described in Chapter 4, we used Cartesian coordinates formed by two lines at right angles.

Suppose, however, that we wish to describe a circular motion in which *angular* displacements are equal in successive equal time intervals. (We call this uniform circular motion, and recognize the analogy to uniform rectilinear motion.) If we represent positions of a particle executing uniform circular motion by Cartesian coordinates x,y of Fig. 9.2.1(a), we find a relatively complex equation $(x^2 + y^2 = r^2)$ describing the trajectory of the particle, and we sense that x and y vary with time in a nonuniform way.   On the other hand, if we utilize the "plane polar" coordinates (r, θ) illustrated in Fig. 9.2.1(b), we find a very simple description of the trajectory, and, still more significantly, angular coordinates θ_2 and θ_1 are precisely the numbers we have in mind when we refer to angular displacement and to the uniformity of a circular motion.   We are thus strongly motivated to adopt the polar system.   Let us note its character: Angular positions are measured positively counterclockwise and negatively clockwise from reference line OA as in the usual trigonometric convention; we thus have position numbers θ, with significance and arithmetic properties completely analogous to rectilinear position numbers s in Chapter 1.   On the other hand, position numbers r on any radial line at angular position θ are laid off positively from center point O, and negative values of r have no geometrical significance and no physical interpretation.

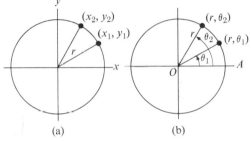

FIG. 9.2.1.   (a) Circular motion in Cartesian coordinates.   Locus described by $x^2 + y^2 = r^2$ (constant). (b) Circular motion in plane polar coordinates.   Locus described by $r =$ constant for all θ.

We can now go through exactly the same story originally developed in full detail in Chapter 1.   In observing changing position of a particle in a plane, we calculate numbers such as $\Delta r/\Delta t$ and $\Delta\theta/\Delta t$.   We recognize these as velocities; the condition for circular motion is that Δr, and therefore $\Delta r/\Delta t$, equal zero.   We are left with the concept $\Delta\theta/\Delta t$, which we call *average angular velocity*, and we recognize again all the possibilities of uniform, varying, and instantaneous velocity we discussed in the rectilinear case.   The quantity $\Delta\theta/\Delta t$ may be positive, negative, or zero, and these algebraic properties must be interpreted just as in the case of $\Delta s/\Delta t$ in Chapter 1. (A student who feels insecure with these ideas would do well to review Sections 1–10 of Chapter 1.)   A widely used symbol for angular velocity is the Greek letter ω (omega):

$$\text{Average angular velocity:} \qquad \bar{\omega} \equiv \frac{\Delta\theta}{\Delta t}, \qquad\qquad (9.2.1)$$

$$\text{Instantaneous angular velocity:} \qquad \omega \equiv \lim_{\Delta t \to 0} \frac{\Delta\theta}{\Delta t} = \frac{d\theta}{dt}. \qquad (9.2.2)$$

Thus, in circular motion, angular velocity is defined as the time derivative of the angular position function.   Conversely, the angular position function must be an antiderivative of the angular velocity function.   We shall usually express angular velocity in units of radians per unit time.

PROBLEMS 9.1.   A particle in uniform circular motion sweeps out 15 rad/sec (that is, $\omega = 15$ rad/sec).   Sketch a polar coordinate diagram showing a few positions of the particle at successive 0.1-sec intervals.   What would be the significance of $\omega = -15$

rad/sec? (Do not spend time on an accurately constructed plot. Make a freehand sketch, estimating sizes of relevant angles by eye.) Make up additional exercises of this type until you feel secure in your understanding of the meaning of uniform ω and your visualization of angles measured in radians.

PROBLEM 9.2.   In the light of definitions (9.2.1) and (9.2.2) and the concepts of recti-linear kinematics developed in Chapter 1, anticipate the definitions which will generate the concept of angular acceleration, conventionally denoted by the Greek letter α (alpha).

9.3 KINEMATICS OF UNIFORM CIRCULAR MOTION (ω = CONSTANT)

Consider a motion at uniform angular velocity:

$$\frac{d\theta}{dt} = \omega, \qquad \text{where } \omega \text{ is a constant.}$$

This is a simple differential equation, and we make reference at this point to the anti-derivative concepts developed in Section 8.3. Since ω is taken to be constant, its general antiderivative is $\omega t + C$, and

$$\theta = \omega t + C.$$

If the position number $\theta = \theta_0$ when $t = 0$, we have $C = \theta_0$, and

$$\theta = \omega t + \theta_0 \qquad \text{or} \qquad \theta - \theta_0 = \omega t. \tag{9.3.1}$$

Equation (9.3.1) is a kinematic equation, exactly analogous to (1.7.1). If θ is plotted against t with different values of ω, we have straight-line diagrams exactly analogous to Fig. 1.7.1, with similar interpretations of ω as the slope of the straight line, positive or negative depending on the direction of the circular motion.

It is frequently convenient to characterize or compare circular motions by means of numerical properties other than angular velocity ω. For example, one might utilize the time T needed to execute a complete revolution; i.e., a displacement $\theta - \theta_0 = 2\pi$ rad. Substituting these symbols into Eq. (9.3.1), we have

$$2\pi = \omega T, \qquad T = \frac{2\pi}{\omega} \text{ sec, or hr, etc.,/revolution.} \tag{9.3.2}$$

The time T is called the *period* of the motion.

An alternative way of describing the motion is to cite the number of revolutions n executed per unit time. From the definitions of the two quantities n and T, it is evident that

$$n = \frac{1}{T} = \frac{\omega}{2\pi}. \tag{9.3.3}$$

Another view would be to argue directly that if n represents the number of revolutions per second and there are 2π rad/rev, then $2\pi n$ rad/sec are swept out in the motion, and $\omega = 2\pi n$. The number of revolutions n is called the *frequency* of the motion.

PROBLEM 9.3.   What is the period of rotation of the earth on its axis? the period of its revolution around the sun? Calculate the frequency of each of these motions. Calculate the angular velocity of each of these motions. Do your numerical results represent instantaneous or average velocities? Explain and justify your answers carefully. [*Answer:* $\omega_{rot} = 7.27 \times 10^{-5}$ rad/sec.]

PROBLEM 9.4.   Given that a circular motion is uniform; that is, ω is a constant. What is the numerical value of $d\omega/dt$? Give an interpretation of this result using the vocabulary of derivatives, acceleration, etc. [*Answer:* $d\omega/dt = 0$.]

PROBLEM 9.5.   What are the period and angular velocity of a $33\frac{1}{3}$ rpm phonograph record? (The abbreviation rpm denotes revolutions per minute.) [*Answer:* $T = 1.80$ sec; $\omega = 3.48$ rad/sec.]

9.4   KINEMATICS OF UNIFORMLY ACCELERATED CIRCULAR MOTION

If the angular velocity of a rotating object is a function of time, we describe rate of change of angular velocity by the numbers

$$\bar{\alpha} \equiv \frac{\Delta\omega}{\Delta t}, \tag{9.4.1}$$

$$\alpha = \lim_{\Delta t \to 0} \frac{\Delta\omega}{dt} = \frac{d\omega}{dt}, \tag{9.4.2}$$

where α is called *angular acceleration*. These definitions are obviously modeled on our definitions of linear acceleration.

For the special case of motion at constant angular acceleration α, we have

$$\frac{d\omega}{dt} = \alpha, \qquad \text{where } \alpha \text{ is a constant.}$$

Then, exactly as in arriving at Eq. (9.3.1), we find that

$$\omega = \alpha t + \omega_0. \tag{9.4.3}$$

From definition (9.2.2):

$$\frac{d\theta}{dt} = \omega = \alpha t + \omega_0.$$

Finding the general antiderivative of $\alpha t + \omega_0$ and imposing the initial condition that $\theta = \theta_0$ when $t = 0$, we obtain

$$\theta = \tfrac{1}{2}\alpha t^2 + \omega_0 t + \theta_0. \tag{9.4.4}$$

Solving for t in (9.4.3) and substituting into (9.4.4), we obtain

$$\omega^2 - \omega_0^2 = 2\alpha(\theta - \theta_0). \tag{9.4.5}$$

Kinematic equations (9.4.3), (9.4.4), and (9.4.5) are easily recognized as exact counterparts of the rectilinear equations derived in Chapter 1. With methods of the calculus at our disposal, it has not been necessary to use the more lengthy algebraic-geometric derivation, and, in particular, it has not been necessary to engage in plausible, quali- tative arguments concerning $\bar{\omega}$ and its relation to ω_0 and ω at the beginning and end of a time interval.

This is a direct illustration of one way in which calculus is a more powerful mathe- matical tool than analytic geometry. Calculus allows us to deal with continuous change, to "capture the fleeting instant," and to obtain quantitative relationships that, in more complex cases, are completely beyond the scope of algebra and geometry.

9.5   NONRIGOROUS ARGUMENT CONCERNING THE RELATION BETWEEN INSTANTANEOUS ANGULAR AND LINEAR VELOCITIES

Consider the circular motion illustrated in Fig. 9.5.1. A particle is located at position 1 at instant t_1, and at position 2 at instant t_2, undergoing angular displace- ment $\Delta\theta$ in time interval Δt. What can we say about its instantaneous velocity at position 1? According to the scheme developed in dealing with trajectories (Chapter 4), the particle has an instantaneous velocity $\mathbf{v}_{t1}$, tangent to the circle at position 1. Let us denote the magnitude of the vector velocity $\mathbf{v}_{t1}$ by the symbol v_{t1} and the instantaneous angular velocity by ω_1.

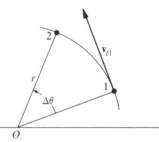

FIG. 9.5.1. Particle moves along circular trajectory from 1 to 2 in time interval Δt, undergoing angular displacement $\Delta\theta$. In- stantaneous linear velocity v_{t1} is tangent to circle at position 1.

We can interpret ω_1 as the number of radians which would be swept out in one second if the particle continued moving at this velocity. Therefore the length of arc swept out in one second would be $r\omega_1$. If, from position 1, the particle went into a purely rectilinear motion at uniform velocity, we might expect the magnitude of this velocity to be equal to the length of arc swept out in one second, and we make the plausible guess that $v_{t1} = r\omega_1$. In general, for any position in the circular motion, we would write

$$v_t = r\omega. \tag{9.5.1}$$

It is conventional to speak of $\mathbf{v}_t$ as the *tangential velocity*, since its instantaneous direc- tion is tangent to the trajectory. [The argument leading to Eq. (9.5.1) has been qual- itative and nonrigorous. After the student has become acquainted with the interpre- tation and utility of the relationship, we shall return to it and give a rigorous proof. See Section 9.6.]

In the light of Eq. (9.5.1) we see, for example, that although particles of a rotating wheel all have the same *angular* velocity, they possess tangential velocities which are *not* equal but which increase linearly with radial distances of the particle from the axis of rotation. Figure 9.5.2 illustrates the variation in tangential velocity of various points on the spokes of a rotating wheel.

If a wheel of outer radius R rolls on the ground (without slipping) at angular velocity ω about its center, a length of arc $R\omega$ is brought in contact with the ground in each succeeding second. Under these circumstances the wheel as a whole moves along the ground with a translational (linear) velocity $R\omega$. Thus, when rolling takes place without slipping, the translational velocity of a wheel is equal to the magnitude of the tangential velocity of a point on its periphery.

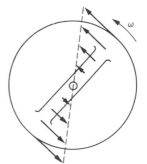

FIG. 9.5.2. Interpretation of Eq. (9.5.1.). Instantaneous velocity vectors for points along the spoke of a rotating wheel. Tangential velocity is greatest at periphery, zero at axis, and oppositely directed on either side of axis. Tips of arrows lie on a straight line.

If angular velocity varies with time, so does the tangential velocity, and we would write

$$v_t(t) = r\omega(t).$$

By an argument exactly parallel to that leading to Eq. (9.5.1), we might define a concept of *tangential acceleration*, a_t, and make plausible the relation

$$a_t = r\alpha, \qquad (9.5.2)$$

where α denotes angular acceleration, defined by $d\omega/dt$. (The student should test his understanding of the preceding discussion by stating the argument.)

PROBLEM 9.6. For about 15 sec starting at $t = 0$, a wheel has an angular velocity given by the equation $\omega(t) = 4.50 - 0.90\,t$ rad/sec.

(a) Describe what you would see the wheel doing if you watched it during the 15 sec for which the equation is valid.

(b) On the basis of your accumulating experience with kinematic equations, sketch (do not plot in detail) α versus t, ω versus t, and θ versus t graphs of the motion.

(c) Apply the formalism of the calculus directly to the above equation and obtain expressions for angular acceleration α and position θ as a function of t. Do these results agree with your sketches in part (b)? [*Answer:* $\alpha = -0.90$ rad/sec^2; $\theta - \theta_0 = 4.50t - 0.45t^2$.]

(d) Through what angle does the wheel turn from the instant $t = 0$ to the instant at which it reverses the direction of its rotation? [*Answer:* 11.3 rad.]

(e) If the wheel has a radius of 1.25 ft, find the instantaneous values of tangential velocity and acceleration of a point on the periphery at the instant $t = 2.20$ sec. [*Answer:* $v_t = 3.15$ ft/sec; $a_t = -1.12$ ft/sec^2.]

(f) If the wheel rolls on the ground without slipping, how far would it roll in the interval between $t = 0$ and $t = 4.30$ sec? [*Answer:* 13.8 ft.]

PROBLEM 9.7.   A bicycle wheel spinning on a shaft is being used for gyroscopic demonstrations. It is observed that its angular velocity decreases from 12.65 to 8.34 rad/sec in an interval of 15.8 sec. The decrease is presumably caused by air resistance and friction in the bearings.

(a) If you are to use the kinematic relations to make calculations and predictions about the behavior of the wheel in future cases of rotation, what idealizations, assumptions, and limitations are implied?

(b) In another experiment, the same wheel is given a spin such that its initial velocity is 10.0 rad/sec. Indicating your choice of positive direction, explaining all steps, and pointing out where and how you invoke the assumptions and idealizations listed in part (a), predict the total angle through which the wheel will rotate. What will be the angular position of a point on the wheel 50 sec after the wheel is spun? Interpret the results of your numerical calculations.

PROBLEM 9.8.   The mean radius of the earth is 3960 mi.

(a) Calculate the tangential velocity (associated with the earth's diurnal rotation) of a point on the equator. (Obtain the value in miles/hour and also in feet/second.)

(b) Calculate the tangential velocity of a point at 42° North latitude and the tangential velocity at the North Pole.

PROBLEM 9.9.   Calculate the frequency, angular velocity, and tangential velocity (feet/second and miles/hour) of an earth satellite having a 90-min period. Take the mean earth radius to be 3960 mi, the altitude of the satellite about 170 mi above the surface of the earth, and the orbit to be nearly circular. [*Answer:* $n = 0.67$ rev/hr; $\omega = 4.2$ rad/hr; $v_t = 17,000$ mi/hr.]

9.6 CALCULUS PROOF THAT $v_t = r\omega$

In the preceding section we gave a plausible argument that instantaneous linear velocity in circular motion should have the magnitude $r\omega$. With methods of the calculus at our disposal we can formulate a rigorous proof. Figure 9.6.1 illustrates a linear displacement ΔL occurring in a circular motion during a time interval Δt, ΔL has the Cartesian components

$$\Delta x = r[\cos (\theta + \Delta\theta) - \cos \theta], \tag{9.6.1}$$

$$\Delta y = r[\sin (\theta + \Delta\theta) - \sin \theta]. \tag{9.6.2}$$

Using our fundamental definition of components of velocity,

$$v_x = \frac{dx}{dt}, \qquad v_y = \frac{dy}{dt},$$

let us evaluate v_x and v_y for the uniform circular motion

$$v_x = \lim_{\Delta t \to 0} \frac{\Delta x}{\Delta t} = \lim_{\Delta t \to 0} \frac{r\,[\cos (\theta + \Delta\theta) - \cos \theta]}{\Delta t}. \tag{9.6.3}$$

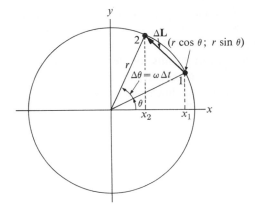

FIG. 9.6.1. Particle in uniform circular motion moves from position 1 to
position 2 in time interval Δt. Angular
displacement $\Delta\theta = \omega\Delta t$. Linear displacement indicated by vector $\Delta\mathbf{L}$.

Multiplying numerator and denominator of the last expression by ω and making use
of the fact that $\Delta\theta = \omega\Delta t$

$$v_x = \lim_{\Delta t \to 0} r\omega \frac{[\cos(\theta + \Delta\theta) - \cos\theta]}{\omega\Delta t} = r\omega \lim_{\Delta\theta \to 0} \frac{[\cos(\theta + \Delta\theta) - \cos\theta]}{\Delta\theta}. \tag{9.6.4}$$

But the limit sought in the last term of (9.6.4) is exactly what we mean by the derivative of $\cos\theta$ with respect to θ, and in Section 8.13 it is shown that

$$\frac{d\cos\theta}{d\theta} = -\sin\theta. \tag{9.6.5}$$

Therefore:

$$v_x = -r\omega\sin\theta = -\omega y, \tag{9.6.6}$$

where we have made use of the fact that at position 1, $y = r\sin\theta$. An exactly parallel
formulation leads to

$$v_y = r\omega\frac{d\sin\theta}{d\theta} = r\omega\cos\theta = \omega x. \tag{9.6.7}$$

The instantaneous linear velocity* at angular position θ is thus given by a vector

$$\mathbf{v} = [-r\omega\sin\theta; \; r\omega\cos\theta] = [-\omega y; \; \omega x]. \tag{9.6.8}$$

If we think of this vector as a straight line in the Cartesian plane of Fig. 9.6.1, the
slope of this line is given by the ratio of the components of the vector:

$$\frac{v_y}{v_x} = -\frac{\omega x}{\omega y} = -\frac{x}{y}. \tag{9.6.9}$$

---

* A somewhat more general proof can be given if ω is not considered uniform, but is
taken to be a continuous function of time. If the student has become familiar with the chain
rule of differentiation (Section 8.10), the preceding analysis can be replaced by $v_x = dx/dt = (dx/d\theta)(d\theta/dt)$. Since $x = r\cos\theta$, we obtain $v_x = -r\sin\theta \, (d\theta/dt) = -r\omega\sin\theta = -\omega y$, etc.

The slope of the *radial* line at position θ is, of course, $+y/x$. In Chapter 3, Problem 3.16, it is shown that two straight lines in the Cartesian plane are perpendicular to each other if the product of their slopes $m_1 m_2 = -1$. In the light of this theorem we see that instantaneous velocity $\mathbf{v}$ in circular motion must be perpendicular to the radius vector at the point in question and therefore tangent to the circle. This justifies our reintroducing the notation $\mathbf{v}_t$, characterizing the linear velocity as tangential.

The magnitude of the velocity is calculated from (9.6.8):

$$v_t^2 = \omega^2(x^2 + y^2) = \omega^2 r^2,$$

$$v_t = r\omega. \tag{9.6.10}$$

By using methods of the calculus and formal definitions of Cartesian components of velocity, we have eliminated ambiguous verbal arguments of the preceding section concerning lengths of arcs, etc., and given the results a rigorous basis.

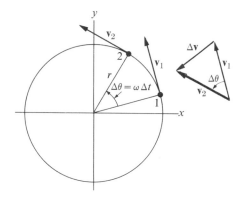

FIG. 9.7.1. The vectors $\mathbf{v}_1$ and $\mathbf{v}_2$ are instantaneous velocity vectors at position 1 and 2, respectively. Each has magnitude $r\omega$. Vector diagram shows change in velocity $\Delta\mathbf{v}$, where $\mathbf{v}_2 = \mathbf{v}_1 + \Delta\mathbf{v}$. (See Problems 4.24 and 4.25.)

9.7   LINEAR ACCELERATION IN UNIFORM CIRCULAR MOTION

Having demonstrated that instantaneous linear velocity in circular motion is always tangent to the circle, we are aware that the *direction* of this velocity must be continually changing even though its magnitude $r\omega$ remains constant when ω is uniform. Figure 9.7.1 is a vector diagram illustrating the vector change of velocity $\Delta\mathbf{v}$ occurring in the time interval Δt. We expect an acceleration to be associated with continually changing velocity, and with our knowledge of dynamics this should not be surprising. We are aware that we must pull on the string to keep a bob in circular motion; we know that we would have to keep nudging a frictionless puck on a glass plate toward a central point in order to make it move in a circular path rather than a straight line.

Let us evaluate the instantaneous components of acceleration, making use of the fundamental definitions

$$a_x = \frac{dv_x}{dt}, \qquad a_y = \frac{dv_y}{dt}, \tag{9.7.1}$$

and the results of Section 9.6, that

$$v_x = -\omega y, \qquad v_y = \omega x. \tag{9.7.2}$$

Taking derivatives of (9.7.2), with ω constant, we have

$$a_x = -\omega\frac{dy}{dt} = -\omega v_y = -\omega^2 x, \tag{9.7.3}$$

$$a_y = \omega\frac{dx}{dt} = \omega v_x = -\omega^2 y, \tag{9.7.4}$$

$$\mathbf{a} = [-\omega v_y; \omega v_x] = [-\omega^2 x; -\omega^2 y]. \tag{9.7.5}$$

Clearly the linear acceleration is not zero, even though ω is constant and the angular acceleration α is zero. What are the magnitude and direction of this acceleration?

The magnitude is given by

$$a^2 = \omega^4(x^2 + y^2) = \omega^4 r^2,$$

$$a = \omega^2 r. \tag{9.7.6}$$

The direction is determined by the slope of $\mathbf{a}$, given by:

$$\frac{a_y}{a_x} = \frac{-\omega^2 y}{-\omega^2 x} = \frac{y}{x}. \tag{9.7.7}$$

This shows the direction of $\mathbf{a}$ to be parallel to the radius vector at the instantaneous position, and (9.7.5) and Fig. 9.7.1 show that $\mathbf{a}$ is directed *toward* the *center* of the circle. The tangential acceleration is indeed zero, but the radially directed acceleration is not zero and has magnitude

$$a_r = r\omega^2 = \frac{v_t^2}{r} = v_t\omega. \tag{9.7.8}$$

This is called *centripetal acceleration*.

PROBLEM 9.10.   Show that the alternative expressions for a_r in Eq. (9.7.8) follow from the relation $v_t = r\omega$.

In a uniform circular motion the vector diagram for linear acceleration would be drawn as in Fig. 9.7.2. (Note use of a double arrowhead to distinguish acceleration from velocity.)

In a nonuniform circular motion with angular acceleration α, there exists a tangential component of acceleration $a_t = r\alpha$ [Eq. (9.5.2)], and the vector diagram for acceleration would be that shown in Fig. 9.7.3.

If we now review some of the physical situations we have considered, we note that in general, velocity and acceleration vector diagrams for a given motion differ from each other quite markedly. It is rarely the case that velocity and acceleration vectors are in the same direction. A few illustrative diagrams are collected in Fig. 9.7.4.

In circular motion a particle continually accelerates *toward* the center *without changing its distance from the center*. This is the essential significance of centripetal acceleration. We can readily conceive of motion in which r changes in magnitude;

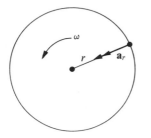

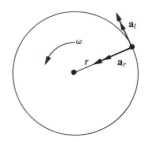

FIG. 9.7.2.   Circular motion at uniform angular velocity ω. Instantaneous acceleration vector $\mathbf{a}_r$ is directed radially inward. Hence $|\mathbf{a}_r| = r\omega^2$.

FIG. 9.7.3. Circular motion with positive angular acceleration α.   Total acceleration vector has tangential component $\mathbf{a}_t$ and radial component $\mathbf{a}_r$. Thus $|\mathbf{a}_t| = r\alpha$, $|\mathbf{a}_r| = r\omega^2$.

TYPE OF MOTION

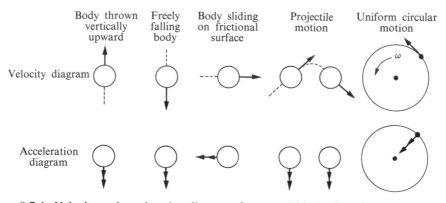

FIG. 9.7.4. Velocity and acceleration diagrams for several kinds of motion. Instantaneous velocity and acceleration vectors rarely have the same direction.

here the particle would have a radial component of velocity v_r as well as a tangential one. The motion would no longer be simply circular, and if v_r changes with time, the particle has a radial acceleration dv_r/dt over and above the centripetal acceleration $r\omega^2$.

PROBLEM 9.11.   A car moving at 40 mi/hr enters a circularly curved section of road, the curve radius being 1000 ft. Calculate the centripetal acceleration in feet/second^2. How does this acceleration compare in magnitude with g? Make up some additional problems of your own in which you consider a circular motion, select realistic values of v (or ω) and r, calculate centripetal acceleration, and compare the resulting acceleration with other magnitudes of acceleration with which you are becoming familiar. [*Answer:* 3.4 ft/sec^2; 0.105 g.]

PROBLEM 9.12.   Calculate the centripetal acceleration for each motion considered in Problems 9.8 and 9.9. Compare the centripetal acceleration of the satellite in Problem 9.9 with the value of g at the surface of the earth. In the light of your present knowledge, do you anticipate any connection between the values of g and the centripetal acceleration of the satellite? Explain your reasoning.

Since the results obtained in this and the preceding section mark a considerable extension of our concepts of velocity and acceleration, it is well to pause and take stock of what we have done. Treating motions at right angles to each other as independent, we have continued the program begun in the discussion of projectile motion and applied our basic definitions of rectilinear velocity and acceleration to a new curvilinear case. Whereas in projectile motion there existed a uniform acceleration along one Cartesian axis and the magnitude of the linear vector velocity changed continually, we now consider uniform circular motion in which the magnitude of linear vector velocity does not change at all. Here we discover that our basic definition of acceleration yields a value which is not zero. The calculated acceleration is constant in magnitude and appears in our calculation because the *direction* of the linear velocity is continually changing. This centripetal acceleration is not nearly so intuitively perceptible as the acceleration of free fall, but we have already alluded to our awareness of the fact that we must exert an external force on a whirling bob to keep it moving in a circular path, even when the angular velocity is uniform, and this sense of an exerted force and imparted acceleration is entirely consistent with the Newtonian dynamics developed in Chapter 5. In the next section we explore the application of Newton's laws to circular motion.

9.8   DYNAMICS OF CIRCULAR MOTION: ONE FORCE ACTING ON A REVOLVING PARTICLE

Let us imagine several situations in which a particle revolves in a circular motion at angular velocity ω around a fixed point, as illustrated in Fig. 9.8.1.

In each one of these cases the moving particle experiences an acceleration of magnitude $r\omega^2$, directed at every instant toward the center of the circle. In accordance with Newton's Second Law, we conclude that a force acts toward the center, and draw the force diagrams shown in Fig. 9.8.2.

Force **P** is to be determined by the Second Law relation:

$$\mathbf{F}_{net} = m\mathbf{a},$$

$$P = |\mathbf{P}| = mr\omega^2. \tag{9.8.1}$$

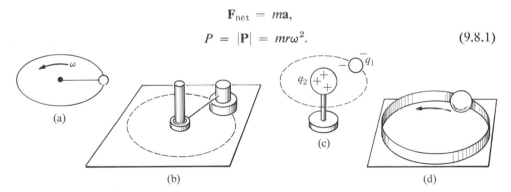

FIG. 9.8.1. Several idealized cases of circular motion. (a) Bob on string, revolving in horizontal plane. (b) Frictionless puck revolving in circular orbit on glass plate. (c) Negatively charged particle revolving around positively charged sphere in absence of gravitational forces. (d) Ball rolling inside circular hoop on frictionless table.

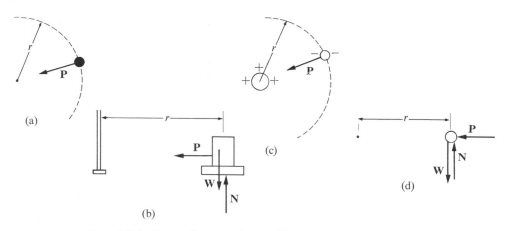

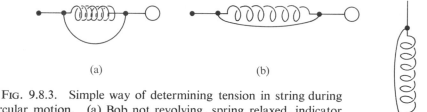

FIG. 9.8.2. Force diagrams for problems sketched in Fig. 9.8.1.

FIG. 9.8.3. Simple way of determining tension in string during circular motion. (a) Bob not revolving, spring relaxed, indicator string slack. (b) Bob revolving, spring extended, indicator string stretched taut. (c) Determine weight W necessary to produce same spring extension as occurred in step (b).

In Chapters 5 and 6 we applied the Newtonian laws to cases of rectilinear motion. Here we are extending their application to a curvilinear case and, in the process, are imposing a new test of the superposition principle. Equation (9.8.1) makes a prediction about a numerical relationship to be observed in uniform circular motion. In the light of our accumulating experience with the laws of motion, we fully expect this prediction to be verified, and many readers will probably have the opportunity to perform a laboratory experiment in this connection. Equation (9.8.1) is easily tested. The fact that it works,—that is, correctly predicts the numerical value of the centrally directed force acting on a revolving particle—helps establish the network of interlocking, internally consistent results that builds up our faith in the whole inductive generalization embodied in the dynamical laws.

To verify Eq. (9.8.1) in cases such as (a) and (b) of Fig. 9.8.1, it is necessary to determine the numerical values of m, r, and ω in a particular instance and to measure, independently, the tension in the string. The latter measurement may be achieved by inserting a small spring, as shown in Fig. 9.8.3, and finding what static force produces the same extension that is observed during rotation. [Describe how you would carry out the experiment, what calculations would be made, and what results would constitute verification of Eq. (9.8.1).] Equation (9.8.1) is found to be entirely correct. Let us interpret all its implications:

(1) It tells us that if a particle of mass m is to move in a circle of radius r at angular velocity ω, a force of magnitude $mr\omega^2$ is required just to keep the body in the fixed circle of radius r. A larger value of P, directed toward the center while ω remained fixed, would cause the body to move inward, and the trajectory would not be a circle of radius r. A value of P smaller than $mr\omega^2$ could not hold the body in a circle of radius r, and it would tend to accelerate outward, increasing its distance from the center. If at some instant the string were cut, making $P = 0$ [Figs. 9.8.1(a) and (b)] the particle could continue along a straight line tangent to the circle at the point where P became zero. (Visualize how its distance from the center would increase under such circumstances.)

(2) In cases (a), (b), and (d) of Fig. 9.8.1, the force P can adjust itself to changes in r or ω. If ω increases in (a) or (b), the tension P in the string increases, keeping $P = mr\omega^2$ up to the point at which the string finally breaks under a tension it can no longer sustain. The particle then flies off in a straight line. If ω increases in (d), the push of the hoop on the particle increases, also keeping $P = mr\omega^2$. In case (c), however, the force P cannot adjust itself. At any given radial distance r it has a fixed value and, according to Coulomb's law, is equal to $k(q_1q_2/r^2)$. We then have the equation

$$k\,\frac{q_1q_2}{r^2} - mr\omega^2. \tag{9.8.2}$$

Thus if q_1, q_2, and m are specified, circular motion at a particular radius r is possible at only *one* angular velocity $\omega = (kq_1q_2/mr^3)^{1/2}$. A larger angular velocity would be possible only at a smaller value of r, and vice versa.

It was on the basis of thinking of this kind that Newton postulated existence of an attractive force between the earth and the moon to keep the latter in its orbit, and then extended the conception to postulate a similar force between the planets and the sun He had the daring to suppose that all these forces were of the same kind—the kind that causes the apple to fall toward the earth—and was rewarded by the success and fruitfulness of his inductive guess. (See Chapter 15 for more detailed discussion.)

PROBLEM 9.13.   Draw force diagrams for the central sphere and the hoop in Figs. 9.8.1(c) and (d), respectively. Draw a free body diagram of the string in Figs. 9.8.1 (a) and (b).

PROBLEM 9.14.   A bob of mass 50 gm is whirled on a string in a horizontal circle of radius 80 cm at 1.2 rev/sec. Predict the tension in the string. [*Answer:* 2.3 n.] What would happen if the force on the bob were increased to 5 n without alteration in angular velocity? (Give a qualitative rather than a quantitative answer to the last question.) What would happen if ω decreased while the tension in the string remained 2.3 n?

9.9   DYNAMICS OF CIRCULAR MOTION:
TWO COLLINEAR* FORCES ACTING ON A REVOLVING PARTICLE

In Fig. 9.9.1 we suggest several physical situations in which two forces act simultaneously on a revolving particle. Verify the accompanying force diagrams.

* *Collinear* implies that the forces act along the same line.

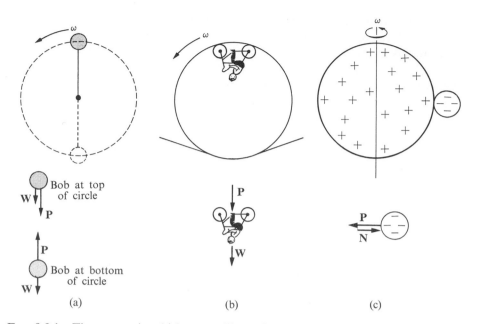

FIG. 9.9.1. Three cases in which two collinear forces act simultaneously on a revolving body. (a) Bob on string. Circle lies in vertical plane. (b) Loop-the-loop rider. (c) Negatively charged particle attracted to equator of rotating positively charged sphere. No gravitational forces. Sphere is a uniformly charged nonconductor.

Let us apply Newton's Second Law to the bob on the string and the loop-the-loop rider when each is at the top of a vertical circle. (We adopt a convention that positive direction is radially inward.)

$$\mathbf{F}_{net} = m\mathbf{a},$$

$$|\mathbf{P}| + mg = mr\omega^2,$$

$$|\mathbf{P}| = mr\omega^2 - mg. \tag{9.9.1}$$

The pull of the string or push of the track are forces which adjust themselves as ω changes. What interpretations are to be drawn from Eq. (9.9.1)? If ω and r are sufficiently large, $mr\omega^2 > mg$. Then an additional force, equal in magnitude to $mr\omega^2 - mg$, is needed to keep the particle in a circular path: the string pulls down on the bob and the track pushes down on the rider. As ω decreases, $|\mathbf{P}|$ decreases. If ω is sufficiently small it might be that $mr\omega^2 < mg$. Then the pull of gravity alone is a larger force than that necessary to keep the particle in a circular path: the bob and the rider fall near the top of the circular swing. The reader is urged to experiment with a bob on a string while following these interpretations in order to connect these purely analytical conclusions with tactile sensations and physical events. The following questions are left for the reader: What happens to the tension P in the string at the bottom of the vertical circle? How does the tension at the bottom compare with the tension at the top if we manage to keep ω constant?

Let us analyze the problem posed by Fig. 9.9.1(c):

$$\mathbf{F}_{net} = m\mathbf{a},$$

$$k\,\frac{q_1 q_2}{r^2} - |\mathbf{N}| = mr\omega^2,$$

$$|\mathbf{N}| = \frac{kq_1 q_2}{r^2} - mr\omega^2. \tag{9.9.2}$$

Equation (9.9.2) informs us that if the large sphere is not spinning ($\omega = 0$), the small particle is supported by a normal force $|\mathbf{N}| = kq_1 q_2/r^2$. As the large sphere begins to rotate, the force $\mathbf{N}$ adjusts itself, decreasing with increasing ω. In this fashion an increasingly larger portion of the constant electrical force $kq_1 q_2/r^2$ acts to impart the centripetal acceleration, and the negative particle presses more and more lightly against the sphere. When ω increases to the point that $kq_1 q_2/r^2$ is just equal to $mr\omega^2$, the particle is just being held in its circular orbit without pressing against the sphere at all. If ω is increased any further, the particle flies off.

PROBLEM 9.15.   A bob of mass 50 gm is whirled on a string in a vertical circle of radius 80 cm at 1.2 rev/sec. Predict the tension in the string at the top and bottom of the circle. Compare the results with that obtained in Problem 9.14, and comment on their significance. What would happen near the top of the circle if the angular velocity were decreased to about 0.5 rev/sec? (Present a numerical calculation to justify your conclusion in the last question.) In your own words describe the connection between the calculations you have made in this problem and the physical sensations you would experience at various points of a loop-the-loop ride in a roller coaster.

9.10 DYNAMICS OF CIRCULAR MOTION: FORCES NOT COLLINEAR

Suppose a car moves with linear velocity v along a circular curve, as sketched in Fig. 9.10.1(a). When the roadway itself is horizontal, neither mg nor $\mathbf{N}$ have horizontal components, and only the frictional force $\mathbf{F}_f$ is available to impart centripetal acceleration toward O:

$$F_f = \frac{mv^2}{r}. \tag{9.10.1}$$

As v becomes larger, the frictional force F_f must increase. If the limiting frictional force μN is exceeded, the car skids; i.e., tends to continue on a curve of larger radius than that of the road itself.

If the roadway is slightly banked at an angle θ, as shown in Fig. 9.10.1(b), both $\mathbf{N}$ and $\mathbf{F}_f$ have horizontal components directed toward the center O. This implies that less frictional force is required. Let us analyze the problem algebraically:

For the vertical (y) direction:

$$\mathbf{F}_{net\,y} = ma_y,$$

$$N \cos\theta - F_f \sin\theta - mg = 0. \tag{9.10.2}$$

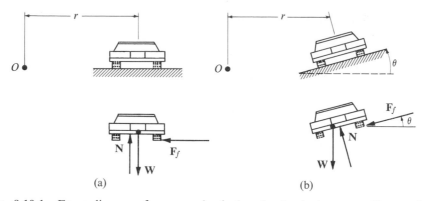

FIG. 9.10.1. Force diagrams for car on banked and unbanked curves. Center of curve at point O. (a) Car going around curve of radius r on unbanked roadway. (Velocity v is directed into plane of paper.) (b) Car going around curve of radius r on banked roadway.

For the horizontal (x) direction:

$$F_{\text{net } x} = ma_x,$$

$$N \sin \theta + F_f \cos \theta = m\frac{v^2}{r}. \qquad (9.10.3)$$

To see what happens to the frictional force, let us solve for F_f by eliminating N from Eqs. (9.10.2) and (9.10.3). The steps are left to the reader, the final result being

$$\frac{F_f}{\cos \theta} = \frac{mv^2}{r} - mg \tan \theta. \qquad (9.10.4)$$

Equation (9.10.4) supports our anticipation; for a given velocity and radius of curve, F_f decreases as the banking angle θ increases. How steeply should a road be banked? Argue that the optimum angle is determined by

$$\tan \theta = \frac{v^2}{rg}. \qquad (9.10.5)$$

For further guidance in interpretation of this analysis, see Problem 9.19 at the end of the chapter.

9.11   CENTRIPETAL FORCE

Throughout our investigation of circular motion, the frame of reference has been the earth. For motions of small geographical scale and of the range of velocities considered, Newton's laws hold very precisely, and the earth is, to a very good approximation, an inertial frame of reference. It is with respect to the earth or "laboratory" frame that we have derived $r\omega^2$ to be the centripetal acceleration of a particle in circular motion. In this frame of reference it is our experience that an action or force must be applied to impart the observed acceleration, and the generality of this experience is affirmed by our use of the word "laws" to describe Newton's three statements about dynamics. Recognizing that a net *external* force, acting toward the center, must be applied to keep a particle in circular motion relative to an inertial frame, we give this required net force the name *centripetal force*. In Fig. 9.8.2 the centripetal force is the applied effect denoted by P. In Fig. 9.9.1(b), the centripetal force is the *net* effect $P + mg$; in Fig. 9.9.1(c), it is $(kq_1q_2/r^2) - N$; in Fig. 9.10.1(b), it is $N \sin\theta + F_f \cos\theta$.

When circular motion is viewed from the inertial frame, this terminology describes the phenomenon completely: a net force, the resultant, perhaps, of several individual forces, acts to impart acceleration toward the center. This *net* force is called the centripetal force. *No other forces* act on the particle. In particular any use of the term "centrifugal force" is totally inappropriate when circular motion is described relative to an inertial frame.

The term "centrifugal force" is not without meaning, however, provided we describe the motion from an entirely different frame of reference. Suppose we imagine ourselves to be located on a large glass plate which is rotating relative to the earth; we lay off a set of axes on the plate and take this to be our frame of reference. If, sitting in the world of the glass plate, we now perform a few simple experiments with frictionless pucks, we quickly discover that Newton's laws do not hold in the same way as in the inertial frame.

A frictionless puck, when put down next to us on the plate, does not remain at rest but accelerates away from us. To keep the puck at rest with us, we must exert a force on it, keeping the force directed toward a fixed point on the glass plate. (We may or may not know this point to be the center of rotation of our glass-plate world relative to an inertial frame.) Thus, to keep the puck at rest, or in static equilibrium relative to us, we would have to exert a steady force on it, just as we exert such a force in holding an object up in the air. In the latter case we say that we exert a force equal and opposite to the pull of gravity.

If, in the glass-plate frame of reference, we wish to preserve the Newtonian laws—in particular the statement that a body remains at rest or moves at constant velocity in a straight line in the absence of a net external force—we must invent or imagine a new force which acts in a direction opposite to the one we must exert on the puck ourselves. We thus invent a force which allows us to draw a diagram such as that of Fig. 9.11.1.

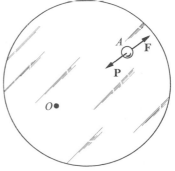

FIG. 9.11.1. Glass plate merry-go-round rotates about point O. If we live on the glass plate and use it as a frame of reference, we must always exert a force **P** on a frictionless puck to keep it at rest at position A. To preserve Newton's First Law, we invent a fictitious force **F**, which we say acts on the puck and accelerates it away from O in the absence of force **P**. The fictitious force **F** is called centrifugal force. It is a concept valid *only* in the rotating frame of reference.

Residing in the glass-plate world, and making all our measurements relative to this noninertial frame of reference, we find that the puck has zero acceleration relative to us only if we exert force **P**. To preserve the law that we observe zero acceleration only with zero net force, we invent force **F**, a fictitious force so far as any inertial frame would be concerned, and say that the body is in equilibrium because **P** and **F** are balanced; **F** is called the *centrifugal force*. It is a fictitious force which has meaning only if we are describing circular motion from the noninertial frame of the rotating body itself. We shall not attempt in this book to do dynamical calculations in non-inertial frames of reference, and therefore the term "centrifugal force" will never be relevant in our problems and calculations. But this is not meant to imply that the concept is a trivial one; centrifugal force and other fictitious forces, called Coriolis forces, must be invented to preserve applicability of the Newtonian laws in any rotating frame of reference. Meteorologists and oceanographers who wish to describe the dynamics of parcels of air and water relative to the earth itself rather than with respect to fixed stars must include these fictitious forces in their equations. So also must those who describe the motion of long-range missiles or the launching of satellites. Relevance or irrelevance of the concept of centrifugal force depends entirely on the frame of reference from which the motion is to be described.

9.12   REVOLUTION OF TWO ATTRACTING PARTICLES. CONCEPT OF CENTER OF MASS

Suppose we observe two gravitating spheres or two electrically charged particles (positive and negative, respectively) in space. We make our observations from an inertial frame of reference, say with respect to the fixed stars. If the particles are initially stationary, their interaction would cause them to accelerate toward each other, undergoing displacements in reciprocal proportion to their masses as in the Mach reaction-car experiment. If the particles are revolving around each other, however, at an appropriate angular velocity, the attractive interaction may be just enough to provide the required centripetal force, and, in empty space, this revolution could continue indefinitely.

Newton's Third Law requires that the force one particle exerts on the second be equal and opposite to the force the second exerts on the first. This requirement gives us the force diagram shown in Fig. 9.12.1.

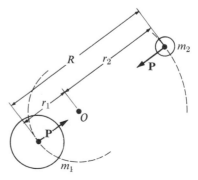

FIG. 9.12.1.   Two gravitating (or charged) spheres, attracting each other and rotating about point O.

Each particle is subjected to a force **P** which is equal to Gm_1m_2/R^2 in the gravitational case and to kq_1q_2/R^2 in the electrical. Let us assume that under these circumstances each particle moves in a circle* around a point O on the line of centers with angular velocity ω and with **P** as the requisite centripetal force.

With r_1 and r_2 the still unknown radii of the respective circles, we have:

Geometric condition: $\qquad\qquad r_1 + r_2 = R,$ $\qquad\qquad\qquad$ (9.12.1)

Dynamic condition: $\qquad m_1r_1\omega^2 = m_2r_2\omega^2 = P.$ $\qquad\qquad$ (9.12.2)

Equation (9.12.2) reduces to

$$m_1r_1 = m_2r_2,$$ $\qquad\qquad$ (9.12.3)

and solving for r_1 and r_2 from Eqs. (9.12.1) and (9.12.3), we obtain

$$r_1 = \frac{m_2}{m_1 + m_2} R,$$ $\qquad\qquad$ (9.12.4a)

$$r_2 = \frac{m_1}{m_1 + m_2} R.$$ $\qquad\qquad$ (9.12.4b)

Thus our solution for r_1 and r_2 locates point O, the existence of which we assumed to start with. Where is point O located? Equations (9.12.4) tell us the following:

(1) If $m_1 = m_2$, point O is located at the midpoint of the line of centers.

(2) If the masses are unequal, point O is closer to the body with the larger mass.

(3) If one body is very much more massive than the other, point O is located very close to the center of the massive body. Then the body of small mass simply seems to be revolving about its massive partner, but in reality the two bodies would always revolve about a common point O somewhere on the line of centers.

Point O, as defined by Eqs. (9.12.4), is called the *center of mass* of the system. It is found that revolution always takes place around the center of mass, even when the orbits are elliptical rather than circular.

Dynamical effects of motion around the common center of mass are found to be of profound importance in widely diverse circumstances. The influence of this rotation is of major significance in the semi-diurnal (twice a day) ebb and flow of the tide; it plays a role in the theory of the structure of atoms; and it helps determine the heat capacity of gaseous substances. Such revelations of order and unity in seemingly diverse and unrelated phenomena are among the striking features of a successful, convincing scientific theory.

PROBLEM 9.16.   Looking up relevant distances and masses, calculate the position of the center of mass of the earth-moon system; the earth-sun system; the hydrogen chloride molecule, which consists of one atom of hydrogen and one of chlorine. (See Appendixes B and D.)

---

* A rigorous analysis of possible motions of the two bodies is a rather complex mathematical problem. The basic solution was first given by Newton as part of his theory of universal gravitation and the structure of the solar system. In general, the motion can be shown to be elliptical; circular motion is a special case. We shall examine this plausible and important special case to obtain some feeling for the physics of the problem.

9.13   PROBLEMS

9.17. Construct a diagram similar to Fig. 9.7.1 except that $|v_2| > |v_1|$, implying a tangential as well as a centripetal acceleration. Carry out an analysis for acceleration components a_x and a_y essentially parallel to the analysis in Section 9.7, and show that at position 1 the instantaneous acceleration vector **a** has a radial component $-r\omega^2$ and a tangential component $r\alpha$. (This provides formal proof of the validity of Fig. 9.7.3.)

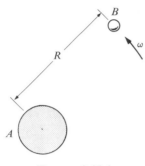

FIGURE 9.13.1

9.18. (a) Suppose sphere B in Fig. 9.13.1 rotates around a very much more massive sphere A, either under the influence of electrical attraction or under the influence of gravitational attraction. Using Coulomb's law and the gravitation law, and explaining all steps, find ω as a function of R for each case separately. [*Answer for the electrical case:* $\omega^2 = kq_A q_B/m_B R^3$.] Interpret the results by analyzing what the equations say about the angular velocity at various radii, and the effects of altering the electrical charges and masses of the respective bodies.

(b) State the definition of period of revolution T and derive the relation between T and R for both the electric and gravitational cases. Interpret the result. Suppose that a positively charged particle A has several negatively charged particles rotating around it, or that a planet, such as Jupiter, has a number of moons. What does the equation for T as a function of R predict about the relations among the periods of the charged particles or of the moons? Look up Kepler's Third Law elsewhere in the text and ascertain its relevance to this problem. (See Chapter 13.)

9.19. Using the analysis of Section 9.10 and Eq. (9.10.4) as a starting point, discuss the problem of banking a road. Include consideration of the following questions: Why is it desirable to bank a road at all? What variables does the optimum banking angle depend on? Can a given angle provide ideal banking for a wide range of velocities of the moving vehicle? How does the angle depend on the weight of the vehicle? Calculate the banking angle appropriate to the curve and vehicle velocity described in Problem 9.11.

9.20. Explaining steps and line of reasoning, and looking up any necessary numbers, calculate the tangential velocity which must be imparted to an artificial satellite to put it into a circular orbit at an altitude of 500 mi above the surface of the earth. (Do not neglect the fact that the gravitational force of the earth decreases with distance from the center.) Calculate the period of the satellite. Draw a free body diagram of an astronaut within the satellite. Account for his sensation of weightlessness, making specific reference to the results and discussion in Problem 6.16.

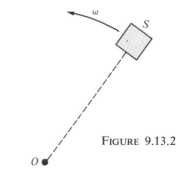

FIGURE 9.13.2

9.21. Imagine yourself to be in a laboratory room S which is located away from the earth in free space and is revolving around an axis somewhere outside the room, as indicated in Fig. 9.13.2. The room is completely closed and no views are to be had of outside bodies, but you have the usual appurtenances of a laboratory inside. Describe in your own words some of the physics you would observe in S. Where would you walk, i.e., which direction would be "down"? What would happen if you "dropped" an object or "threw it up in the air"? What would you mean by "weight of a body"? (What additional questions can you invent?)

9.22. In the problem posed by Fig. 9.9.1(c) and the discussion surrounding Eq. (9.9.2) it is shown that when the large sphere is spinning and carrying the small negatively charged particle with it, the net force (over and above the centripetal force) capable of accelerating the particle toward the sphere is smaller than kq_1q_2/r^2 by the amount $mr\omega^2$. In your imagination translate this problem into a discussion of the gravitational force acting on bodies on the rotating earth, and analyze the problem with attention to the following questions:

(a) Suppose we raise a body and let it fall toward the earth at the equator; compare the magnitude of the force which would impart this acceleration if the earth were not spinning with the magnitude when the earth is spinning. (Calculate the numerical value of the difference.) [*Answer:* Second force less than first by 0.35%.]

(b) Is there a similar effect for a body located at the North or South Pole? (Justify your reasoning and give a numerical answer.)

(c) How fast must the earth spin for a body at the equator to cease following the earth and be flung off into space?

The following are recommended as special problems for extra credit or more advanced work.

9.23. (Continuation of Problem 9.22.)
(a) Assume the earth to be perfectly spherical, and consider the problem of body A, with mass m_A, suspended by a string from a frame rigidly fixed to the earth

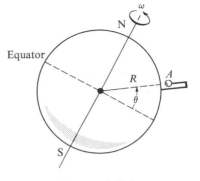

FIGURE 9.13.3

as shown in Fig. 9.13.3. If the earth were not rotating, we would expect the string to line up perfectly with a radial line to the earth's center. What happens on a rotating earth? (Draw a force diagram of body A.) Does the string point toward the center of the earth? If not, what angle does it form with the radial line at various latitudes θ? Calculate this angle for the latitude at which you happen to be located. Is there a latitude at which this angle has a greatest value?

(b) In the light of your analysis in part (a) and in Problem 9.22, discuss the following two questions: Precisely what is meant by the quantity g which we casually call the acceleration due to gravity? What do we mean when we say that the weight of a body is the "force exerted on it by the earth"? Are we talking about the total force?

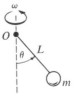

FIGURE 9.13.4

9.24. (Fig. 9.13.4). A bob of mass m hangs on a string or very thin (essentially massless) rod from a pivot at point O. The system is rotated around a vertical axis at angular velocity ω so that the bob describes a horizontal circle and swings outward to take up a position at some angle θ as shown. (This system is called a *conical pendulum*.) Draw a force diagram of the bob. Derive an expression for the functional dependence of θ on the angular velocity ω. Interpret the equation: How does θ depend on m and L as well as ω? Take note of the curious fact that θ remains zero at low values of ω until ω reaches a particular, critical magnitude! Select some reasonable numbers for m, L, and ω and calculate the corresponding angle θ. A balanced device of this kind, utilizing two bobs, with springs to provide restoring force, is called a *governor*. It is used to regulate (i.e., keep nearly constant) the speed of an engine. How might this be arranged?

9.25. When an artificial satellite is placed in orbit in the uppermost reaches of the earth's atmosphere, it experiences a small opposing force due to collision with gas molecules, dust particles, etc. This force is essentially a frictional one, similar in its overall effect to the forces which oppose motion and cause it to slow down in our everyday terrestrial experience. In the case of a satellite, however, the overall effect of the opposing force is to cause the satellite to spiral closer to the earth, finally expiring in flame on reaching denser regions of the atmosphere. As the radius of the satellite orbit decreases, the angular and tangential velocities *increase*. Increase of velocity under the influence of an opposing force is contrary to our intuitive experience, and apparently contrary to the laws of motion. How do you resolve this paradox?

9.26. In finding expressions for the tangential and centripetal components of acceleration in circular motion we dealt with a special case of the derivative of a vector quantity; we evaluated the derivative dv_t/dt. This restricted problem suggests the more general one: Given a vector quantity $\mathbf{A}$ without specific physical interpretation; $\mathbf{A}$ is a function of time t and changes in both magnitude and direction. Study the general character of the derivative $d\mathbf{A}/dt$. (Do not hesitate to investigate other textbooks in mathematics and physics in the process of this study.) As part of your study, try to show that, if the change of direction of $\mathbf{A}$ is described by an instantaneous angular velocity ω, there is always a component of $d\mathbf{A}/dt$ which is perpendicular to $\mathbf{A}$ and has magnitude $|\mathbf{A}|\,\omega$. Connect this generalization with the concept of centripetal acceleration developed in Section 9.7.

SUPPLEMENTARY READING AND STUDY

Noncalculus derivations of centripetal acceleration:

Physics, Physical Science Study Committee. Boston: D. C. Heath, 1960, Chapter 21

Physics for the Inquiring Mind, E. M. Rogers. Princeton, N. J.: Princeton University Press, 1960, Chapter 21

Physics for Students of Science and Engineering, R. Resnick and D. Halliday. New York: John Wiley & Sons, 1960, Chapter 4

Detailed treatment; many additional problems:

Mechanics, Heat, and Sound, 2nd ed., 7th printing, F. W. Sears. Reading, Mass.: Addison-Wesley, 1950, Chapter 10

Historical development of centripetal acceleration concepts:

Mechanics in the Seventeenth Century, René Dugas. New York: Central Book Co., 1958, Chapters 10 and 12

The Astronomy of Ancient Greece[*]

We can trace the beginning of our development in science to the imaginative minds of the great Greek thinkers. Although the use of optical instruments of precision was still 2000 years away, simple observation of the night sky had established, by about 400 B.C., enough data and interpretations concerning the motion of the stars to nourish several world-theories. The "fixed stars" and the Milky Way were commonly thought of as fixed with respect to one another on the surface of a very large sphere, within which was placed the rest of the universe (including the sun, the moon, the earth, and the five easily seen planets). One of the important questions of philosophy at the time was that of the motion of these bodies within the celestial sphere.

Modern scientists might approach such a problem by taking down as many and as accurate data on planetary paths as seem to be needed on the basis of some preliminary guesses or hypotheses, and then might set out to induce a model for the system and the general physical laws of motion for the celestial bodies. These general laws would then be accepted as valid if further observations, still more accurate and still more numerous data, were to bear out the predictions inherent in the laws. But this approach was not fully realized until after the Renaissance. The Greek philosopher, indeed, had invented another approach. On the basis of preliminary observations he formulated a scheme of planetary motion which did not so much need to be in accord with all subsequent observations but instead dovetailed with other, more strictly philosophical or theological problems. The followers of Pythagoras, for example, conceived that the relative sizes of the orbits of planets were proportional to the lengths of the successive strings on a harmoniously tuned stringed instrument. This was thought to assure a "harmony of the spheres," more satisfying and important to the general philosophical requirements of the Pythagoreans than would be the relatively narrower demands of quantitative predictability of physical events made by the modern astronomer. Or, to cite an example we have studied, one which involves an entirely different school in Greek science, Aristotle found in qualitative observa-

---

* Chapters 10–15, concerning the laws of planetary motion and universal gravitation, are by Gerald Holton, Professor of Physics, Harvard University. They are slightly revised versions of the corresponding chapters originally published in *Introduction to Concepts and Theories in Physical Science*, by Gerald Holton, Addison-Wesley Publishing Co., Reading, Mass., 1953. Reprinted by permission.

tions of the free fall of large and small bodies enough evidence to satisfactorily integrate these physical phenomena with his philosophically more wide-reaching, and therefore to him more satisfying, scheme of elements and of natural place.*

10.1 PLATO'S PROBLEM

Nothing is easier and more erroneous than to underestimate the point of view of the early Greeks. Not only did the mechanics of the Greeks "work" within the limits of current interest, but in some schools of thought it was also intellectually a majestic and deeply meaningful construct. Above all, it presents, as it were, the childhood of science, not to be judged in terms of the maturer point of view of contemporary knowledge. It may be true that eventually it outlived its usefulness, but it gave modern men the direction along which they could develop fruitfully. The influence of Greek thought is present in any contemporary activity, in science no less than in art or law, government or education.

Astronomy is a case in point. It is related that Plato (427–347 B.C.) set a problem for his students along these lines: The stars—eternal, divine, unchanging beings— move around the earth, as we can see, in that eminently perfect path, the circle. But a few "stars" appear to wander rather disturbingly across the sky, tracing perplexingly irregular figures in their yearly paths. These are the planets (from the Greek word for *wanderer*). Surely they too must *really* move in uniform, ordered circles, or rather, in their case, combinations of circles. Now, how can we account for the observations on planetary motion and "save the appearances"? Plato's important question may be paraphrased as follows: "Determine what *uniform* and *ordered* motions must be assumed for each of the planets to account for the apparent, more irregular movements." The very formulation of this historic problem strikingly summarizes for us the two main contributions of Greek philosophers to the topic of our discussion:

(a) Physical theory (e.g., the theory of planetary motions) is intelligible only in the context of a prior specific metaphysical theory (e.g., the theory that heavenly bodies must execute "perfect," circular motions).† This proved to be an unfruitful doctrine on which to base science. By the sixteenth and seventeenth centuries, after the great struggle to which we alluded in Chapter 2, it began to be abandoned in favor of the experimental sciences. Whitehead** makes the following brief analysis of this relatively recent separation of metaphysics from science:

"The reasons for its careful separation from scientific thought are purely practical; namely, because we can agree about science—after due debate—

---

* Review Sections 2.1–7 of this text. Benjamin Farrington's *Science in Antiquity*, Oxford (1936), is recommended as supplementary reading for these opening paragraphs. Also, consult Chapter 3 of *A Short History of Science and Scientific Thought*, by F. S. Taylor. New York: W. W. Norton, 1949.

† The term *metaphysics* is used in a specific sense: the discipline which studies principles of knowledge or of being in terms of intuitive, self-evident concepts, concepts of direct everyday experience, and analogies.

** A. N. Whitehead, *The Aims of Education*. New York: Macmillan, 1929.

whereas in respect to metaphysics debate has hitherto accentuated disagreement. These characteristics of science and metaphysics were unexpected in the early days of civilized thought. The Greeks thought that metaphysics was easier than physics, and tended to deduce scientific principles from *a priori* conceptions of the nature of things. They were restrained in this disastrous tendency by their vivid naturalism, their delight in first-hand perception. Medieval Europe shared the tendency without the restraint."

(b) Physical theory is built on observable and measurable phenomena (e.g., the apparent motion of the planets), concerns itself with uniformities of behavior underlying the apparent irregularities, and expresses itself in the language of number and geometry. This guiding idea, which Plato did not extend beyond astronomy and which was derived in part from the Pythagoreans, was a treasured hint which reappeared when Kepler and Galileo fashioned their experimental science. But Plato held that physical laws can be found from directly intuited principles, the aim being to explain specific phenomena in the context of a philosophic system. The truth of a principle was not measured, as it is today, by its usefulness in every conceivable known or predicted physical situation. Consider this sentence from Plato's *Phaedo*: "This was the method I adopted: I first assumed some principle, which I judged to be the strongest, and then I affirmed as true whatever seemed to agree with this, whether relating to the cause or to anything else; and that which disagreed I regarded as untrue."

Plato's specific astonomical question, which he did not seriously attempt to answer himself, became the prime concern of astonomers to the time of Galileo. Let us see how they tried to construct a system of the world in accordance with the postulate of "uniform and ordered motion," that is, a system which allows the celestial objects to move only in uniform (constant) circular motions or in combinations of several such motions.

10.2 THE ARISTOTELIAN SYSTEM

Obviously, the first guess to investigate in rationalizing the motion of celestial objects is the most simple geocentric* system, which places the earth at the center of the celestial sphere carrying the fixed stars. The observed daily motion of those fixed stars will result from our simple model at once if we require the large celestial sphere to rotate uniformly on a north-south axis once a day. We may then attempt to explain the apparent motion of the sun, the moon, and the five visible planets about the fixed earth by letting each be carried on a transparent sphere of its own, one within the other, all seven enclosed by the sphere of fixed stars, and the earth at the center of the whole scheme. But since those seven celestial bodies do not rise and set always at the same point of the horizon, since in fact the planets travel on most complicated paths against the fixed stars, sometimes even for a time reversing the direction of motion, we must give each of their spheres a whole set of simultaneous

---

* Earth-centered, from the Greek *gē*, earth.

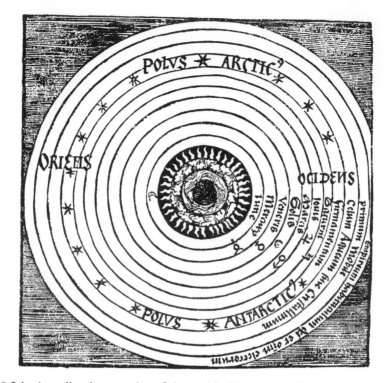

FIG. 10.2.1. A medieval conception of the world. The sphere of the moon (lune) separates the terrestrial region (composed of concentric shells of the four elements, Earth, Water, Air, and Fire) from the celestial region. Beyond the moon are the concentric spheres carrying Mercury, Venus, Sun, Mars, Jupiter, Saturn, and the fixed stars. (From a woodcut of 1508.)

rotations about different axes, each rotation of the proper speed and direction, each axis of the proper inclination, to duplicate the actually observed paths.

Here the mathematical genius of the Greek was indeed put to the test! The sun and the moon were relatively simple to discuss, but some of the planets offered much difficulty. Plato's pupil Eudoxus thought that 26 simultaneous uniform motions would do for all seven celestial bodies. In Aristotle's work are prescribed 29 additional uniform motions, partly to account for some of the most obvious discrepancies between Eudoxus' system and the observed paths.* Figure 10.2.1 represents in barest outline the most important features of a medieval Aristotelian scheme of the universe. Only the main spheres are indicated; the multitude of mutually supporting axes, etc., is not shown.

And yet, there remained easily observed features of the sky which were unexplained by Aristotle's system—notably the fact that the sun, the moon, Venus, Mars, and

---

* See *A Source Book in Greek Science*, by Morris R. Cohen and I. E. Drabkin (New York: McGraw-Hill, 1948) for most illuminating translations from the original sources.

Jupiter at times seemed nearer and at other times farther away from the earth. A set of uniform rotations of the celestial bodies on spheres *concentric* with the earth could never allow them to change their distance from the earth. Aristotle was aware of this, but discounted the importance of the simple, but eventually fatal, argument against the fundamental hypothesis of his system. He did not take the consequences which to us seem deceptively obvious, mainly because it was then, as it is now, incomparably easier to leave in doubt the testimony of a few contrary observations than to give up a whole world scheme which seemed conclusive and necessary from the point of view both of his philosophy and his mechanics. Of course, this does not mean that he proposed a theory he knew to be false. It must be emphasized that the original Aristotelian science was not simply bad modern science but an activity fundamentally different from it. Perhaps we may also see here an example of an important human trait which colors all scientific work and which even the greatest thinkers can never hope to overcome entirely—we all tend to deny the importance of facts or observations not in accord with our convictions and preconceptions, so that sometimes we ignore them altogether, even though, from another point of view, they stand before our very eyes. Moreover, even the most general and modern scientific theory does not hope or even seriously attempt to accommodate every single detail of every specific case. One is always forced to idealize the observations before attempting a match between "facts" and theory—not only because there are usually unavoidable experimental uncertainties in observation, but because conceptual schemes are consciously designed to apply to *selected* observations rather than to the totality of raw experience. As a consequence, the history of science is studded with cases in which it turned out too late that the neglected part of a phenomenon was actually its most significant aspect. But on the other hand, if we were to allow no tentative, half-true, or plainly wrong theories in science, we should probably never see a correct one evolving at all. Since the task cannot humanly be done in one jump, we must be satisfied with successive approximations.

10.3   THE HELIOCENTRIC* THEORY

Of course, the problem of planetary motion persisted. There were two different major types of attack after Aristotle—the heliocentric theory and the modified geocentric theory. Let us now discuss the first of these. Aristarchus of Samos (third century B.C.), perhaps influenced by the work of Heraclides of Pontus (fourth century B.C.), suggested that a simple world system would result if the sun were put at the center of the universe and if the moon, the earth, and the five then known planets revolved around the sun in orbits of different sizes and speeds. We do not know many details; his work on this subject is known to us only through references in other old writings. But evidently he assumed that the earth has a daily rotation on its north-south axis, as well as a yearly revolution in the orbit around the sun, and he placed the whole system in the sphere of fixed stars, which thereby could be considered at rest with respect to the center of the universe.

---

* From the Greek *helios*, sun.

This heliocentric hypothesis has one immediate advantage. It explains the bothersome observation that the planets are at times nearer to the earth and at other times farther away. But the ancient world saw three very serious flaws in Aristarchus' suggestion:

First, it did violence to philosophical doctrines (e.g., that the earth, by its very "immobility" and position is differentiated from the "celestial bodies," and that the natural "place" of the earth is the center of the universe). In fact, his contemporaries considered Aristarchus impious "for putting in motion the hearth of the Universe." Also, the new picture of the solar system contradicted common sense and everyday observation; the very words used in astronomy (sunrise, progression of planets, etc.) reflect the intuitive certainty that the earth must be at rest.

PROBLEM 10.1. List the "common-sense" observations concerning sun, stars, and planets from which the geocentric theory sprang, apparently so convincingly. Be careful not to *assume* the geocentric or any other theory in your description.

Second, Aristarchus does not seem to have fortified his system with detailed calculations and quantitative predictions of planetary paths, by our present standards an obvious condition for assuring recognition in the physical sciences. This work seems to have been purely qualitative, although in some other accomplishments he is said to have showed considerable mathematical powers.

Third, the Greek thinkers offered an ingenious bit of reasoning to refute Aristarchus. If the earth were to move around the sun, its large orbit would carry it sometimes near to a given fixed star on the celestial sphere, and sometimes farther away from it. Thus the angle at which we would have to look for this star would be different as seen from the various points in the earth's annual sweep. This phenomenon, called the annual *parallax* of the fixed stars, should occur on the basis of Aristarchus' heliocentric hypothesis, but it was not observed by the Greek astronomers.

In explanation we may say either (a) that the stellar parallax is so small as to be unobservable with the naked eye—which in turn requires the fixed stars to be unimaginably distant compared with the diameter of the yearly orbit of the earth, or (b) that Aristarchus was wrong and the earth does not move around within the celestial sphere. It seems natural that the ancients, predisposed to reject the heliocentric system, and also loath to consider an infinitely extensive universe, chose the second of these alternatives. The first, however, proved eventually to be the correct one. The parallax was indeed present, although so small that even telescopic measurements did not reveal it until 1838.

PROBLEM 10.2. The annual parallax of a given star may be crudely defined as half the angle between the two lines of sight drawn from the center of the earth to the star from opposite ends of a diameter across the earth's orbit. Since the Greeks could not detect the parallax, and since their accuracy of measurement was often only about $\frac{1}{2}°$, what must be the least distance from the earth's orbit to the nearest fixed star? (Express in astronomical units, or A.U., one A.U. being the sun's mean distance from us, or about 93×10^6 miles.) F. W. Bessel in 1838 first observed the annual parallax, which for the nearest bright star, α Centauri, is of the order of $\frac{3}{4}$ second of arc. What is its approximate distance from us? (Modern telescopes can measure parallaxes of about 0.01″, and therefore can directly determine distances of stars about 100 times as far away as α Centauri.)

The heliocentric theories of Aristarchus and others seem to have been so uninfluential in Greek thinking that we should ordinarily spend no time on them. But these speculations stimulated the crucial work of Copernicus eighteen centuries later. Fruitful ideas, it is evident, are not bound by time or space, and can never be evaluated with *final* certainty.

10.4 MODIFIED GEOCENTRIC THEORIES

We now turn to the other and more vigorous offshoot of the early astronomical schemes. To allow the planets to have variable distances from the earth while still keeping to the old belief of an immovable earth, the system of concentric spheres was modified in ingenious ways, principally by Hipparchus of Rhodes (second century B.C.) and the astronomer and geographer Claudius Ptolemy of Alexandria (second century A.D.).

(a) *Eccentric motion.* If the stationary earth were not exactly at the center of rotation of a uniformly moving celestial object, the latter would move along an *eccentric* path as seen from the earth, and vary in distance at different times. This scheme fits the apparent yearly motion of the sun fairly well, since it appears larger (and consequently nearer) at noon in our winter compared with our summer. Note that by admitting eccentric motions the astronomers really were dodging the old principle that required the planet motions to be circular around the center of the earth.

(b) *Epicyclic motion* Figure 10.4.1 represents an object P (such as the sun or a planet) having two simultaneous uniform rotary motions, one a rotation of P about a point D (in space) with radius PD, the other a rotation of the line OD about point O

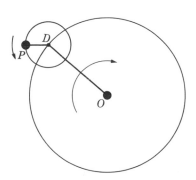

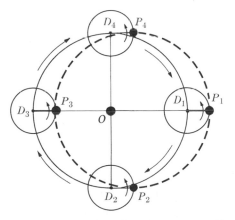

FIG. 10.4.1. An example of epicyclic motion of a planet P.

FIG. 10.4.2. Eccentric path represented by epicyclic motion.

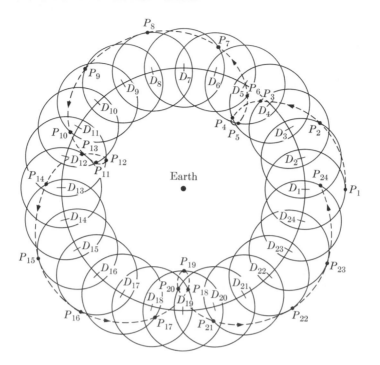

Fig. 10.4.3. Epicyclic motion of P, showing three temporary reversals of direction of P_4, P_{11}, and P_{18}. (Adapted from M. Cohen and I. Drabkin.)

(the position of the earth). The small circle is called an epicycle, the large circle the deferent. The two motions may have entirely independent speeds, directions, and radii. Figure 10.4.2 indicates the special case where the two combined motions yield an eccentric path (dashed line), and Fig. 10.4.3 shows, by the dashed line connecting 24 successive positions of P, the complicated motion resulting when P rotates about D several times while D moves once around O.

> PROBLEM 10.3.   What is the ratio of the speeds of revolution along the epicycle and the deferent in Fig. 10.4.3? What might be the path if the ratio were exactly 3:1?

This last type of motion does, in fact, exhibit most of the observed complications in the paths of planets as seen from the earth against the background of the fixed stars; note particularly the reversal in the direction of motion ("retrograde motion") at positions P_4, P_{11}, and P_{18}. Jupiter's path, one with 11 such loops, is covered in approximately 12 years per complete revolution around the earth.

By a proper choice of radii, speeds, and directions, an eccentric path can be traced just as well by an epicyclic motion. Ptolemy used one or the other, and sometimes mixtures of both types, depending on the problem. We must also note that the device of epicyclic motion suffers from the same philosophical difficulties as the eccentric.

The rotation of P about D is, if we wish to be strictly logical, just as much in conflict with old axioms as was the circular motion of P about a center other than the earth.

> **PROBLEM 10.4.** Construct as well as you can with compass and ruler the path of P (*similar* to Fig. 10.4.2), if P revolves around D twice while D goes around O once.

> **PROBLEM 10.5.** From observations we may form the following hypotheses. The sun moves around the earth from east to west once a day, just like the celestial sphere, but about four minutes per day less quickly. The sun also approaches the earth during our winter and recedes in summer, and in addition it slowly travels north of the equator in summer and south of the equator in winter. Suggest and draw the outlines of a qualitative geocentric model for these motions of the sun and celestial sphere about the earth, using some of the devices discussed.

Now we can summarize what has been retained from Plato and Aristotle, and what has been amended. Use is still made of *uniform and circular motions*, and of a *stationary earth*. Vanished is the scheme of spheres all concentric at the earth, and with it the need to have all rotations exactly earth-centered. This is even more strikingly evident when we discover that Ptolemy found it necessary to add still another device to the list in order to represent more faithfully some features of celestial motion. This device is the *equant*.

(c) *The equant.* Figure 10.4.4 shows an object P in cyclic motion around D, which in turn moves on a circle whose center is at O. The earth may be at O or, if this is a mixture of epicyclic and eccentric motion, the earth may be anywhere along the line AA', say at position E. So far the motion of D has been specified as uniform with respect to O, but to represent some planetary motion in Ptolemy's system it was necessary to let D revolve uniformly with respect to Q, the equant. That is, the angle DQA changes at a constant rate while D executes its circular sweep. Now D is no longer in strictly uniform circular motion, although its motion is still *uniform* (seen from Q) and *circular* (seen from O).

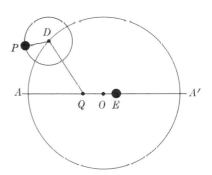

FIG. 10.4.4. Motion with respect to equant at Q.

Ptolemy's great work, known through Arab translations as the *Almagest*, built up a system of the world on the basis of these devices and the following preliminary assumptions:

> "(1) that the heaven is spherical in form and rotates as a sphere;
> (2) that the earth, too, viewed as a complete whole, is spherical in that form;
> (3) that it is situated in the middle of the whole heaven, like a center;
> (4) that by reason of its size and its distance from the sphere of fixed stars the earth bears to this sphere the relation of a point;
> (5) that the earth does not participate in any locomotion."

Implicit in his work is also the old, now somewhat distorted doctrine of uniform circular motions as the only behavior thinkable for celestial objects.

> PROBLEM 10.6.   What is the significance of the fourth point in Ptolemy's preliminary assumptions?

10.5   THE SUCCESS OF THE PTOLEMAIC SYSTEM

By adjusting the respective axes, directions of motions, rates and radii of rotations, number and size of epicycles, eccentrics, and equants, by fitting his devices to the observed paths in a cut-and-try fashion, by utilizing partial results of generations of previous astronomers—so did Ptolemy manage to assemble the apparatus which proved still useful to astronomers, navigators, and astrologers more than 14 centuries later. It was an answer to Plato's original question, and on the whole a magnificent piece of work. One pleasing feature was that centers of the epicycles of the moon, Mercury, and Venus fell on the same line between Earth and Sun (see Fig. 10.5.1).

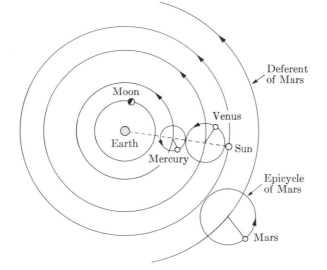

FIG. 10.5.1. Partial and schematic diagram of Ptolemaic system of planetary motion.

But the complexity and inaccuracy of detail in the whole scheme was considerable, and subsequent observations required amendment of some features of the model from time to time; e.g., the change of an assigned equant or the addition of another epicycle. By the time of Copernicus, this geocentric system required more than 70 simultaneous motions for the seven celestial bodies. But against this were five powerful reasons why the system was generally accepted wherever it became known:

(a) It gave an accurate enough description of what could be observed with the instruments of the times.

(b) It predicted the future paths of planets well enough for the purposes of the times, if only after cumbersome calculations; and when a serious discrepancy between predictions and observations occurred it could be resolved by tampering a little with the gears of the flexible apparatus. Today, even as at that time, the geocentric system is still preferred for calculations in navigation—and in astrology!

(c) It explains naturally why the fixed stars show no annual parallax.

(d) In most details it coincided with Greek philosophical and physical doctrine concerning the nature of the earth and the celestial bodies. Later, when reintroduced to Europe by the Arabs, the Ptolemaic system* was given theological significance by the scholastics. Furthermore, it was also in line with contemporary physics (e.g., projectile motion), based on the same philosophical doctrine of natural motion, natural place, and so forth. (See Chapter 2.)

(e) It had "common-sense appeal." It is almost unavoidable to hold the opinion that we actually can "see" the sun and stars moving around us, and it is comforting to think of ourselves on a stable, immovable earth.

But for all that, Ptolemy's theory was eventually displaced by a heliocentric one. Why did this happen? What were the most significant deficiencies in Ptolemy's picture? When is a scientific theory, from our present point of view, successful or unsuccessful? We shall want to answer these questions in detail after we have looked at an outline of the great rival scheme of planetary motion.

SUPPLEMENTARY READING AND STUDY

Cohen, M. R., and I. E. Drabkin, *A Source Book in Greek Science*. New York: McGraw-Hill, 1948. A wealth of source material and penetrating comments. See pages 90–143 for astronomy.

Farrington, B., *Science in Antiquity*. London: Oxford University Press, 1936, 1947, Home University Library.

Farrington, B., *Greek Science*. Pelican Books A142 and A192, 1944, 1949

Heath, Sir Thomas, *The Copernicus of Antiquity* (*Aristarchus of Samos*). London: Society for Promoting Christian Knowledge, 1920

Heath, Sir Thomas, *Greek Astronomy*. London: J. M. Dent, 1932

Singer, C., *A Short History of Science*. Oxford: Clarendon Press, 1941. Very useful.

Taylor, F. S., *A Short History of Science and of Scientific Thought*. New York: W. W. Norton, 1949, Chapter 3

Wightman, W. P. D., *The Growth of Scientific Ideas*. New Haven: Yale University Press, 1951, Chapters 1–4

---

* In connection with our study of the Ptolemaic system there is surely no more thrilling experience than to read that immortal excursion through the medieval universe, the *Paradiso* of Dante (for example, in the 1944 edition of the *Modern Library*).

CHAPTER 11

Copernicus' Heliocentric Theory

11.1 EUROPE REBORN

Our study takes us now to Renaissance Europe of the years around 1500 A.D. Astronomical theory had not progressed significantly since Ptolemy. St. Thomas Aquinas (1225–1274) had joined the Aristotelian ideas of celestial motions with Christian theology. The geocentric theory had received new meaning in terms of current philosophical doctrine; to question one was to attack the other, and so far there had appeared no one who thought it necessary or had the daring to battle seriously against such formidable allies.

But the "Dark Ages" were passing; the Renaissance movements spread out from Italy to sweep the Western world, and within a few generations there arose a new Ideal of Man, the confident individual full of curiosity and *joie de vivre*. (You may strikingly achieve a feeling for the changing atmosphere by comparing extremes, perhaps the paintings of a Hieronymus Bosch on the one hand with those of a Botticelli on the other.) In the topography of world history this great period of summing up old wisdom and of forming new attitudes is analogous to a watershed on which great rivers have their sources. It was the time in which there lived as contemporaries or within a generation of one another most of the men whose work heralded the new age: Gutenberg and da Vinci, Columbus and Vasco da Gama, Michelangelo and Dürer, Erasmus, Vesalius and Agricola, Luther and Henry VIII. One cannot help comparing this short time interval of decisive change with a similar break in the traditions of Western thought four hundred years later—a period which, between the publication of Darwin's *The Origin of Species* (1859) and the first large-scale release of atomic energy, bracketed such names as Mendel and Pasteur, Planck and Einstein, Rutherford and Bohr, and also such new forces as Marx and Lenin, Freud and Pareto, Picasso and Stravinsky, Shaw and Joyce.

11.2 THE COPERNICAN SYSTEM

When Nicolaus Copernicus (1473–1543) was a young student in Poland, the New World was discovered. During his exciting life he watched in his old world the gathering of great cultural changes. And on the very day he died he saw the first copy

FIG. 11.2.1. Nicolaus Copernicus (1473–1543). (From a woodcut of about 1590.)

of his great book, the *Revolutions*, which gave us a whole new universe.* The full title of Copernicus' main work, *Six Books Concerning the Revolutions of the Heavenly Spheres*,† startles us at the very outset with the implication of an Aristotelian notion of concentric spheres. He was indeed concerned with the old problem of Plato, the construction of a planetary system by combination of the fewest possible uniform circular motions. Fundamentally, Copernicus (see Fig. 11.2.1) was motivated to postulate his heliocentric system because it avoided two assumptions

---

* A highly readable and stimulating presentation is *Sun, Stand Thou Still; the Life and Work of Copernicus the Astronomer*. New York: Henry Schuman, Inc., 1947; also in paperbound pocket edition. The account reveals to us a most remarkable astronomer, mathematician, churchman, administrator, diplomat, physician, and able student of the classics and of economics—and yet a humble and compassionate man.

† Excerpts will be found in Knedler's and many other collections. The full dedication is printed as Appendix C in W. T. Sedgwick and H. W. Tyler's *A Short History of Science*. New York: Macmillan, 1929.

inherent in the geocentric theory as taught at the time, to which he took particular exception: (a) that the notion of the equant could be used freely, and (b) that the earth was to be considered at rest and at the center of the universe as a matter of dogma, which greatly complicated the description of celestial motions. But let us hear Copernicus' own arguments on these two points:

(a) ". . . the planetary theories of Ptolemy and most other astronomers, although consistent with the numerical data, seemed . . . to present no small difficulty. For these theories were not adequate unless certain equants were also conceived; it then appeared that a planet moved with uniform velocity neither on its deferent nor about the center of its epicycle. Hence a system of this sort seemed neither sufficiently absolute nor sufficiently pleasing to the mind.

"Having become aware of these defects, I often considered whether there could perhaps be found a more reasonable arrangement of circles, from which every apparent inequality would be derived and in which everything would move uniformly about its proper center, as the rule of absolute motion requires."

To Copernicus, any type of celestial motion other than uniform circular motion was "obviously" impossible: ". . . the intellect recoils with horror" from any other suggestion; ". . . it would be unworthy to suppose such a thing in a Creation constituted in the best possible way." These arguments are of the same type as those of his scholastic opponents, except that to them the immobility of the earth was equally "obvious."

Reading the classics, Copernicus found:

(b) ". . . according to Cicero, Nicetas had thought the earth moved, . . . according to Plutarch certain others [including Aristarchus] had held the same opinion . . . when from this, therefore, I had conceived its possibility, I myself also began to meditate upon the mobility of the earth. And although it seemed an absurd opinion, yet, because I knew that others before me had been granted the liberty of supposing whatever circles they chose in order to demonstrate the observations concerning the celestial bodies, I considered that I too might well be allowed to try whether sounder demonstrations of the revolutions of the heavenly orbs might be discovered by supposing some motion of the earth. . . . I found after much and long observation, that if the motions of the other planets were added to the motions [daily rotation, and yearly revolution about the sun] of the earth, . . . not only did the apparent behavior of the others follow from this, but the system so connects the orders and sizes of the planets and their orbits, and of the whole heaven, that no single feature can be altered without confusion among the other parts and in all the Universe. For this reason, therefore, . . . have I followed this system."

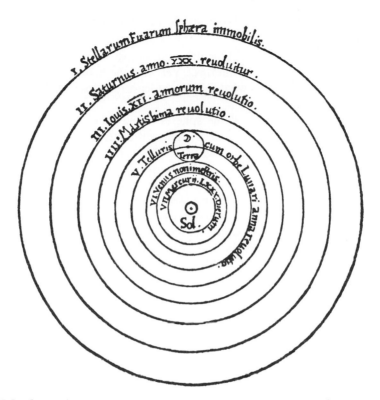

Fig. 11.2.2. Copernicus' diagram of his heliocentric system. (From his own work, 1543.)

Thus, in essence, Copernicus proposed a change of point of view for the representation of celestial motions along the lines of Aristarchus' heliocentric system. By highly gifted calculations, using some observations of his own, Copernicus then proved what Aristarchus had failed to do: that the motion of celestial objects as then known could indeed be represented by a combination of a few uniform circular motions in a sun-centered system. All planets, the earth included, could be imagined as moving on concentric spheres, with only relatively few and small epicycles and eccentrics still needed to account for the finer details of motion.* Moreover, the *same direction* of motion along almost all deferents and epicycles could be assumed, which had not been true for the geocentric model. But above all, the odious equant could be discarded. All motions were now truly circular and uniform with respect to their own centers. Plato's question was answered again, in an alternative way.

Copernicus' diagram (Fig. 11.2.2) shows the main concentric spheres carrying the planets around the sun. His accompanying text explains the outlines of the system

---

* The common center of the main spheres actually had to fall a little to one side of the unmoving sun, so that this system is not *quite* heliocentric, just as Ptolemy's earth-position did not coincide with the center of the sun's motion.

and, incidentally, gives us a magnificent insight into his deeper motivations:

> "The ideas here stated are difficult, even almost impossible, to accept; they are quite contrary to popular notions. Yet with the help of God, we will make everything as clear as day in what follows, at least for those who are not ignorant of mathematics. . . .
>
> "The first and highest of all the spheres is the sphere of the fixed stars. It encloses all the other spheres and is itself self-contained; it is immobile; it is certainly the portion of the universe with reference to which the movement and positions of all the other heavenly bodies must be considered. If some people are yet of the opinion that this sphere moves, we are of a contrary mind; and after deducing the motion of the earth, we shall show why we so conclude. Saturn, first of the planets, which accomplishes its revolution in thirty years, is nearest to the first sphere. Jupiter, making its revolution in twelve years, is next. Then comes Mars, revolving once in two years. The fourth place in the series is occupied by the sphere which contains the earth and the sphere of the moon, and which performs an annual revolution. The fifth place is that of Venus, revolving in nine months. Finally, the sixth place is occupied by Mercury, revolving in eighty days.
>
> "In the midst of all, the sun reposes, unmoving. Who, indeed, in this most beautiful temple would place the light-giver in any other part than that whence it can illumine all other parts? . . .
>
> "In this orderly arrangement there appears a wonderful symmetry in the universe and a precise relation between the motions and sizes of the orbs which is impossible to obtain in any other way."

11.3 BRACING THE SYSTEM

Knowing well that to many his work would seem absurd, "nay, almost contrary to ordinary human understanding," Copernicus attempted to fortify it against anticipated criticism in four ways.

(a) He tried to make plausible that his assumptions coincided with dogma at least as well as Ptolemy's. He had many passages (we have seen samples) on the deficiencies of the Ptolemaic system, on how harmonious and orderly his own seems, and on how pleasingly and evidently it reflects the mind of the Divine Architect. To Copernicus, as to all men of his period (and to many of our own), the observable world was but a symbol of the working of God's mind; to find symmetry and order in the apparent chaos of sense data was to him an act of reverence, a renewed proof of the Deity. He would have been horrified if he had known that his theory was ultimately responsible for the sharp clash, in Galileo's time, between science and dogma. Copernicus, we must not forget, was a highly placed and honored church dignitary. In matters of doctrine he might have regarded himself as a conservative who was objecting to current scholastic teaching only to the extent of wishing to make it more consistent with Aristotle's principles of mechanics. (Compare the forms of the systems in Figs. 10.2.1 and 11.2.2.)

(b) Copernicus prepared enough quantitative material to put his book mathematically on the same footing as Ptolemy's, that is, he calculated the relative radii and speeds of the elements in his system so that tables of planetary motion could be made. (Note how this compares with Aristarchus' more qualitative work.) The two theories were thus equally correct with respect to prediction of future planet positions within the then current error of observation of at least $\frac{1}{6}$ degree of arc. However, on looking at Copernicus' treatise, we must not expect to find a mathematical treatment of the type seen in modern texts. Remember that even our simplest trick of mathematical notation, $+$ and $-$ signs, did not come into use until after Copernicus' death.

(c) With considerable ingenuity and much success, Copernicus tried to answer several objections that were as certain to be raised against his heliocentric system as they had been, long ago, against Aristarchus'. To the argument that his earth, rotating so rapidly about its own axis, would surely burst like a flywheel driven too fast, he countered, "Why does the defender of the geocentric theory not fear the same fate for his rotating celestial sphere—so much faster because so much larger?" To the argument that birds in flight and the like should be left behind by the rapidly rotating and revolving earth,* he answered that the atmosphere is dragged along with the earth. As to the old question of the absence of parallax among the fixed stars, he could give only the same answer as Aristarchus (a good answer even though the Greeks did not accept it):

"... the dimensions of the world are so vast that though the distance from the sun to the earth appears very large compared with the size of the orbs of some planets, yet compared with the dimensions of the sphere of fixed stars, it is as nothing."

This distance to the fixed stars, he says elsewhere, is "so immense as to render imperceptible to us even their apparent annual motion. . . ."

He cites several other good arguments (and a few erroneous ones) to support his system, but these will sufficiently illustrate his point.

(d) To us the most impressive success of Copernicus is the reduction in the number of elements needed in his system (to about 34) and the consequent greater ease with which his apparatus can be used by the astronomer for the solution of practical problems. Science has learned to cherish these features: economy of concepts and assumptions, simplicity of formulation, applicability to a variety of problems. Copernicus knew well the advantage he held over the rival theory, and he hoped that he would be accepted on this basis, irrespective of current prejudices.

PROBLEM 11.1.   Make a list of assumptions underlying Copernicus' theory, analogous to the list for Ptolemy's (see Section 10.4).

---

* The orbital speed around the sun is about 70,000 mi/hr, and the speed of west-east rotation alone of a point on the equator is more than 1,000 mi/hr.

11.4   THE OPPOSITION TO COPERNICUS' THEORY

But Copernicus' hope was not quickly fulfilled. It took more than 100 years for the heliocentric system to be generally accepted by astronomers; in the meantime the theory and its few champions were faced with powerful opposition, some of it the very same which antagonists had used against the heliocentric ideas of the Greek philosophers.

(a) First came the argument from dogma concerning the immobility and central position of the earth. For all his efforts, Copernicus was in general unsuccessful in persuading his readers that the heliocentric system was at least as close as the geocentric one to the mind and intent of the Deity. All religious faiths in Europe, including the newly emerged Protestants, found enough Biblical quotations (e.g., Joshua 10:12–13) to assert that the Divine Architect had worked from a Ptolemaic blueprint.

> PROBLEM 11.2.   Read Joshua 10:12–13 and interpret the astronomical event referred to in terms of the two rival theories.

Martin Luther himself branded Copernicus a fool and heretic. The Papacy eventually put the *Revolutions* on the index of forbidden books as "false and altogether opposed to Holy Scriptures," withdrawing its approval of an earlier outline of Copernicus' work. Some Jewish communities forbade the teaching of the heliocentric theory. It was as if man's egocentric philosophy demanded the middle of the stage for his earth, the scene both of his daily life and prayer in a world created especially for his use, and of the drama of salvation with the expected eventual coming of the Saviour or Messiah.

Although it was allowed that for mathematical simplicity the Copernican scheme might indeed be useful, and although even St. Thomas Aquinas had grave misgivings about the Ptolemaic system because it did not stick to strictly uniform circular motions as interpreted by Aristotle, yet it seemed "philosophically false and absurd," dangerous, and fantastic to abandon the geocentric hypothesis. And in all truth, what other reaction could one have expected? We must try to appreciate the frame of reference of the time. In general, Europe then recognized as its two supreme sources of authority the Bible and Aristotle. Physical science as we now think of it was only gradually evolving; that was still the great period of learned and respected astrologers (like Nostradamus) and alchemists (like Paracelsus).

(b) A further explanation for the resistance which the Copernican theory had to overcome is to be sought in the damage the Copernican theory brought even to contemporary *physics*. This is well discussed by H. Butterfield:

> ". . . at least some of the economy of the Copernican system is rather an optical illusion of more recent centuries. We nowadays may say that it requires smaller effort to move the earth round upon its axis than to swing the whole universe in a twenty-four hour revolution about the earth; but in the Aristotelian physics it required something colossal to shift the heavy and sluggish earth, while all the

skies were made of a subtle substance that was supposed to have no weight, and they were comparatively easy to turn, since turning was concordant with their nature. Above all, if you grant Copernicus a certain advantage in respect of geometrical simplicity, the sacrifice that had to be made for the sake of this was nothing less than tremendous. You lost the whole cosmology associated with Aristotelianism—the whole intricately dovetailed system in which the nobility of the various elements and the hierarchical arrangement of these had been so beautifully interlocked. In fact, you had to throw overboard the very framework of existing science, and it was here that Copernicus clearly failed to discover a satisfactory alternative. He provided a neater geometry of the heavens, but it was one which made nonsense of the reasons and explanations that had previously been given to account for the movements in the sky."*

PROBLEM 11.3. Read Milton's *Paradise Lost*, Book VIII, lines 1–202, in which Adam and Raphael discuss the two systems from a classic point of view, which may well have mirrored the general opinion of educated Englishmen until the full impact of Newton's work was established.

(c) Third, argument arose from the oft-mentioned lack of observable parallax among fixed stars. Copernicus' only possible (and correct) reply was still unacceptable because it involved expanding the celestial sphere to practically an infinite distance away from the earth. This is to us no longer intellectually difficult, but it was a manifestly absurd notion at the time. Among many reasons for this, perhaps the intensely religious mind of the period could not be comfortable with a threatening Hell so close below the ground and a saving Heaven so infinitely far above. If we consider for a moment, it is evident that as a consequence of this attitude an actual observation of annual parallax at that time would not necessarily have settled the dispute in favor of Copernicus, for an obvious and simple Ptolemaic assumption of an additional yearly epicyclic motion superposed on the great daily rotation of the fixed stars would explain away such an observation in full accord with the geocentric system.

(d) A fourth important argument against the Copernican astronomy at the time was that apart from its powerful simplicity it offered to contemporary astronomers no other overruling *scientific* advantages over their geocentric astronomy; i.c., there was then no important observation which was explainable only by one and not by the other, no experiment to pit one against the other in a clear-cut decision. Copernicus introduced no fundamentally new experimental facts into his work, nor was the accuracy of his final predictions significantly better than previous estimates.

To us it is clear, although it did not enter the argument then, that the scientific content of both theories, the power of prediction of planetary motion, was about the same at that time. As Francis Bacon wrote in the early seventeenth century: "Now it is easy to see that both they who think the earth revolves and they who hold the

---

* H. Butterfield, *Origins of Modern Science*. London: G. Bell & Sons, 1950, page 27.

primum mobile and the old construction, are about equally and indifferently supported by the phenomena." In our modern terminology we would say (although this is not what Bacon had in mind) that the rival systems differed mainly in the choice of the coordinate system used to describe the observed movements. As measured with respect to the earth, the sun and stars *do* move, and the earth, of course, is at rest. On the other hand, measured with respect to the sun, the earth is not at rest. Any other system of reference, for instance one placing the moon at the origin of the coordinate system and referring all motions to that new center of the universe, is quite conceivable and equally "correct," although, of course, evidently most complex. The choice of a particular frame of reference should, as we now know, depend mainly on which will yield the simplest solution for a given problem. Therefore we cannot speak of such a choice as "true" or "false," but rather as convenient or inconvenient.

Consequently, every newly discovered peculiarity of planetary motion could have been accommodated in some geocentric representation as certainly as in a heliocentric one. In short, neither Aristarchus nor Copernicus could have hoped to convince people to whom the beauty of simplicity and ease of application of a theory were (understandably) less important than their own meaningful and by no means unworkable systems.

11.5 HISTORIC CONSEQUENCES

Eventually the vision of Copernicus did triumph; in a moment we shall follow the the work leading to the universal acceptance of the heliocentric theory, even though his specific *system* of uniform circular motions will have to be sacrificed along the way. We shall see that the real scientific significance and the reason for the ultimate glorification of Copernicus' work lie in a circumstance he would never have known or understood—in the fact that only a heliocentric formulation opens the way for an integration of the problem of planetary motion with the simple laws of "ordinary" (terrestrial) mechanics as developed during the following 150 years—a synthesis of two sciences, even of two methods, which was achieved through Newton's Theory of Universal Gravitation. Consequently, it became possible to explain, on the basis of the supposition that the earth turns and travels, such diverse phenomena as the diurnal and the annual apparent motion of the stars, the flattening of the earth, the behavior of cyclones, trade winds, and gyroscopes, and much else that could not be bound together into so *simple* a scheme in a geocentric physics.

But apart from this historic triumph, the memory of Copernicus is hallowed for two more reasons. First, he was one of those giants of the fifteenth and sixteenth centuries who challenged the contemporary world-picture and thereby gave life to that new and strange idea which later was to grow into science as we now know it. Secondly, his theory proved to be a main force in the gathering intellectual revolution which shook man out of his self-centered preoccupations. Out with the Ptolemaic system has to go also the self-confident certainty that a symbolic uniqueness about our position shows man is the sum and summit. If this certainty still exists, at least it cannot claim that science backs it up.

An important purpose of our story of planetary motion to this point has been preparation for the following digression before returning to our main topic. We may now ask briefly: By what standards shall we judge a scientific theory?

SUPPLEMENTARY READING AND STUDY

ARMITAGE, A., *Sun Stand Thou Still*. New York: Henry Schuman, 1947. Also published as *The World of Copernicus*, Mentor Book M65. The life and work of the great astronomer.

BOYNTON, H., *The Beginnings of Modern Science*. New York: Walter J. Black, 1948. Brief biographies and excerpts, *e.g.*, from Copernicus, pages 5–11.

BUTTERFIELD, H., *Origins of Modern Science*. London: G. Bell, 1949; Collier Books AS259V, 1962

KNICKERBOCKER, W. S. (ed.), *Classics of Modern Science*. New York: Alfred A. Knopf, 1927. Biographical notes and long excerpts. Chapter 2, excerpt from Copernicus. Also J. W. Knedler, *op. cit.*, pages 49–72. Also S. Commins and R. N. Linscott, *Man and the Universe: The Philosophers of Science*. New York: Random House, 1947, pages 43–69.

ROSEN, E., *Three Copernican Treatises*. New York: Columbia University Press, 1939. Includes translation of "Commentariolus," Copernicus' early work.

SEDGWICK, W. T., and H. W. TYLER, *Short History of Science*. New York: Macmillan, second edition, 1939. A useful book. See Appendix C in the 1929 edition for Copernicus' revealing dedication of his main work.

SHAPLEY, H., and H. E. HOWARTH, *Source Book in Astronomy*. New York: McGraw-Hill, 1929. Excerpts, *e.g.*, from Copernicus, pages 1–12.

CHAPTER 12

The Nature of Scientific Theory

As we now turn to the standards by which to judge scientific theories—and the rival planetary theories might serve as models—it is obvious that we cannot pretend to lay down criteria by which a working scientist should check his own progress during the construction of a theory. This cannot be done any more meaningfully than a scientific method can be constructed for his use. What we shall do here is something else; namely, to attempt a clarification of our thoughts on how we, as students of science and its development, may evaluate a particular theory, past or present.

12.1 THE PURPOSE OF THEORIES

We have argued that the task of science, as that of all thought, is to penetrate beyond the immediate and visible to the unseen, and thereby to place the visible into a new, larger context. For like a distant floating iceberg whose bulk is largely hidden under the sea, only the smallest part of reality impresses itself upon us directly. To help us grasp the whole picture is the supreme function of theory. On a simple level, a theory helps us to interpret the unknown in terms of the known. It is a conceptual scheme which we invent or postulate in order to explain to ourselves, and to others, observed phenomena and the relationships between them, thereby bringing together into one structure the concepts, laws, principles, hypotheses, and observations from often very widely different fields. These functions may equally well be claimed for the hypothesis itself. In truth, we need not lay down a precise dividing line, but might regard theory and hypothesis as differing in degree of generality. Therefore at one extreme we might find the *limited working hypothesis* by which we guide our way through a specific experiment, placing at the other end of the spectrum the *general theory*, which guides the design and interpretation of all experiments in that field of study.

Examples of general theories suggest themselves readily, even if we decide, perhaps rather arbitrarily, to use the word "theory" only for those few historic and general schemes of thought like the theories of planetary motion, of universal gravitation, of the nuclear atom, and the like. Galileo's theory of projectile motion welded together the laws of uniformly accelerated motion, including free fall and the principle of superposition of velocities, to produce one conceptual scheme, one over-all method of attacking, predicting, and interpreting every conceivable problem involving bodies moving under the influence of a constant force. Similarly, when Charles Darwin had pondered the results of such fields as paleontology and comparative anatomy, he could find an inspired connection in widely different types of observations, explaining previously separate truths in different disciplines as part of one grand scheme of thought, his theory of evolution.

> PROBLEM 12.1. Examine some one theory discussed in other courses with which you are thoroughly familiar—perhaps Gregor Mendel's theory of heredity, the Marxian theory of society, Sigmund Freud's theory of the unconscious, or a theory of "business cycles." Differentiate clearly in each case between the *data* available to the theorizer on one hand and the *hypotheses* used by him to explain the data on the other.

> PROBLEM 12.2. Do the same for Ptolemy's and Copernicus' theory of planetary motion.

If we inquire more deeply into the main purposes of theories, we find that there are, on the whole, three functions. Let us summarize them here briefly.

(1) A theory correlates many separate facts in a logical, easily grasped structure of thought. By correlating, by putting in juxtaposition and order previously unrelated observations, we can understand them; we always explain by pointing to a relationship. The Platonists explained the motion of planets by relating planets to certain "necessary" attributes of divine beings. Ptolemy and Copernicus explained it by relating the planetary paths to the mathematical combination of certain more or less simple geometrical figures. And not only will a fruitful theory explain the laws which it relates within its framework, it also will show where and why these laws may not hold precisely in practice; as, for example, Galileo's specific use of his theory of projectile motion to explain why projectiles are not expected actually to follow parabolas for very large paths. (See Section 4.4.)

It is a primitive fact about human beings that when they look at the moving parts of some intriguing new toy or gadget, they usually try to visualize a mechanical model of the hidden mechanism, to explain by one theoretical system the separate motions observed. This type of activity seems to be a necessity for the human mind. It is as if the intellect were restless until it were able to subordinate individual events to more inclusive schemes. It may be a matter of economy of thought, for a good theory allows us to grasp, remember, and deduce a large number of otherwise elusive facts. (Think of the wealth of facts summarized by the Copernican theory.)

And the simplest theory in physics is often based on a mechanical model. We recall Lord Kelvin's famous statement, "If I can make a mechanical model, then I can understand; if I cannot make one, I do not understand." This is, of course, not true for all scientists or all branches of science. Conceptual schemes can certainly not always be phrased in mechanical models, and furthermore there are several famous examples in the history of physics which prove that at times progress may be seriously delayed by a too-strong belief in a mechanical model. The last hundred years, particularly, have shown that such models, like all analogies, while often helpful as guides to the imagination, can cause it to fall into dangerous traps. For example, it undoubtedly was—and is—easier to think of light as a vibration moving through a material ether rather than as energy propagated through the void, and yet the ether picture carried with it some eventually inescapable fallacies. Similarly, we owe modern chemistry in large part to the simple, almost naïve pictorial representation which John Dalton used to order his thoughts about atoms and molecules but, again, a great deal of early trouble in his atomic theory could be traced to his too-concrete and prematurely complete mental picture, as we shall see in the section on the chemical atom.

In fact, it has sometimes been suggested that the science of the ancients, in relying frequently on analogies involving the behavior and drives of living beings, was *organismic*, whereas science from Newton on became *mechanistic*, to turn finally in our century more and more to abstract, *mathematical* sets of mental images. But neither is the mathematical type of model free from the dangers inherent in the mechanistic science. Yet our thoughts proceed, as it were, on crutches, and so depend on these schemes and pictures no matter how incomplete.

(2) Whether general or limited, theories and hypotheses are expected to suggest new relations, to start the imagination along hitherto unsuspected connecting paths between old and new facts. In this sense even the theories that were eventually abandoned or found altogether faulty, such as the Ptolemaic theory of planetary motion, the phlogiston theory of chemistry, or the caloric theory of heat, played a vital and positive role in the life of science, for they tended to propose problems, focus the attention, and integrate the effort of many scientists along the same lines rather than allowing it to be completely dispersed in random directions. Even a fallacious theory, if actively and widely pursued, can soon lead to the key observations needed for a better theory; for, as Francis Bacon remarked, truth arises more easily from error than from confusion.

PROBLEM 12.3.   The following table indicates the period of revolution about the sun (the so-called "sidereal period") of the planets in the Copernican system. Instead of Copernicus' values we shall list approximate modern results.

	Mercury	*Venus*	*Earth*	*Mars*	*Jupiter*	*Saturn*
Sidereal period (days)	88	225	$365\frac{1}{4}$	687	4330	10,760

(a) Examine these values and the order of spheres in the two systems (consult the diagrams) and then explain why Copernicus felt that there was exhibited order and harmony in his scheme, "a precise relation between the motion and sizes of the orbs." (b) If a new planet were discovered with a sidereal period of about 1830 days, what would the theory *suggest* about the limits of its orbit? If it should turn out that the actual orbit is larger than Jupiter's, is the whole theory wrong? Explain.

PROBLEM 12.4.   Compare the orbit of Venus in the two rival theories by referring to Figs. 10.5.1 and 11.2.2. If it were found that Venus was not self-luminous but obtained its light from the sun, what would these two theories suggest concerning the nature of the shadow on Venus that might be seen at different times through a telescope from the earth? [*Hint:* where would the sun have to be with respect to Venus and the earth when we see Venus fully illuminated? Make sketches of planetary position.]

(3) The foregoing paragraphs hint at a further purpose of theories: the prediction of specific new observable phenomena and the solution of practical problems. In Shakespeare's great tragedy, Hamlet's theory of his uncle's guilt yields him a prediction of how the suspect will react to the little play-within-the-play; conversely, the expected reaction proves Hamlet's theory to be very likely correct, and so gives him the desired solution to the problem of the old king's death. In astronomy and physics, where the problems and predictions needed are usually numerical ones, the theories are, as a rule, quantitative. The problems to be solved may be quite abstract (e.g., why the planets sometimes seem near, at other times far) or may be very practical ones. For example, just as some of the earliest speculations on celestial motions seem to have been prompted by the need to make calendars and to predict eclipses, so one of the problems Copernicus' theory helped to solve was the exact length of the year and of the lunar month, data needed for the revision of the calendar.

PROBLEM 12.5.   Read Copernicus' treatise in extensive extract (e.g., Knedler's book) and determine to what extent his work seems to exhibit these three purposes of theory.

12.2   CRITERIA FOR A GOOD THEORY IN PHYSICAL SCIENCE*

When we examine why scientists as a whole, in the historical development of science, have favored or rejected a given theory, we may discern a few criteria which seemed to have implicitly or unconsciously dominated the slowly evolving process of decision. (But by no means must we suppose that a theory is necessarily ever rejected solely because it fails to answer perfectly to one or another of the questions in the listing that follows.)

Three qualifications have already been cited. (1) A fruitful theory correlates many separate facts, particularly the important prior observations, in a logical, preferably easily grasped structure of thought. (2) In the course of continued use it suggests new relations and stimulates further research. (3) The theory permits us to deduce predictions that actually check with experience by test, and it is useful for solving long-standing puzzles and quantitative problems.

To illustrate: In Einstein's work on relativity, he first shows that those observations explained by contemporary physics are not in conflict with his brief set of assumptions, but that a large variety of facts from previously separate fields can all be deduced from these assumptions, thereby gathering them into one structure. Secondly, he demonstrates that a few hitherto unlooked-for effects should exist (such as the deflection of light beams passing near large masses) and he commands the experimental astrophysicists to search for these phenomena, for he knows and con-

---

* This material is based, in part, on unpublished lecture notes of Professor E. C. Kemble.

fesses that the theory depends on this verification. And lastly, not only does he use his theory to explain some old, previously unexplainable observations (e.g., the "erratic" component of the planetary motion of Mercury), but his work has also found amazingly useful applications in almost all branches of physics, from optics to nuclear physics.

The history of science has shown us that prosperous theories frequently have some of the following additional properties:

(4) When the smoke of initial battle has lifted, the successful theory often appears to have simple and few hypotheses—to the extent that the words "simple" and "few" have any meaning at all in science. The test of a theory comes through its use; hence the survival value of economy. A theory which needs a separate mechanism for each fact that it wishes to explain is nothing but an elaborate and sterile tautology.

(5) Ideally, the assumptions should be plausible—to contemporary scientists, of course—even if they are not immediately subject to test; and the whole tenor of the theory should not be in conflict with current ideas. Where this could not be arranged, the theory faced an often stormy and hostile reception and had to submit to long and careful scrutiny before its general acceptance. Therefore, it did not always grow as quickly and widely as one might have hoped. On the other hand, this cannot be helped, if nature disagrees with current common-sense preconceptions; in fact, precisely these preconceptions may block the road to the core of the difficult problems. As the work of Copernicus and Galileo has already shown us (a strange truth which will become even more evident in subsequent discussions), major advances in scientific theories often depend on the daring and persistence of one investigator who questions the obvious and stubbornly upholds the unbelievable.

This problem of the plausibility of new theories is difficult and fascinating. As Whitehead reminds us, all truly great ideas seemed somewhat absurd when first proposed. Perhaps we call them *great* ideas just because it takes an unusual mind to break through the pattern of contemporary thought and to discern the truth in implausible, "absurd" forms.

Why then do we not drop the tentative requirement of conformity? Why did almost all great innovators in science, from Copernicus to Einstein, initially meet with skepticism—or worse—from most of their colleagues? Is it just unreasoning conservatism on the part of the scientific fraternity? Not at all. In this little collection of cases, we are discussing only revolutionary theories, but we must not allow this to distort our perceptions: great revolutionary ideas arise only very rarely, compared with the large number of workable or even great ideas conceived within the *traditional* setting, so that the individual scientist is naturally predisposed to favor the traditional type of advance which he knows and believes in from personal experience. He, rather like Galileo's opponents, quite rightly must defend his fundamental concept of nature against large-scale destruction, particularly at the earlier stages, where the innovators cannot present very many results and confirmations of their new ideas. Indeed, sometimes the discoverers themselves are so strongly committed to the established ideas, so startled by the implications of their own work, that they predict the storm of condemnation or even simply fail to draw the final conclusions.

A beautiful and now famous instance of this sort appears in the original publication (1939) by Hahn and Strassmann, who are usually credited with the experimental discovery of nuclear fission. At that time it was still axiomatic in the thinking of all scientists that atomic nuclei are indivisible, that bombardment with small particles (e.g., neutrons) may at best change their internal atomic structure only superficially or slightly. But these two men, after firing neutrons into pure uranium, were left with material which by chemical test was proved to contain barium (Ba) and other elements whose atoms are about half as large as uranium atoms—"evidently" as we would say now, the result of splitting uranium atoms. But in an almost agonized expression of the labor pains attending the birth of all great recognitions, Hahn and Strassmann could not quite dare to accept the evidence of their own chemical experiments, and so they wrote: "As 'nuclear chemists,' in many ways closely associated with physics, we cannot yet bring ourselves to make this leap in contradiction to all previous lessons of nuclear physics. Perhaps, after all, our results have been rendered deceptive by some chain of strange accidents."*

Later, after having developed our view that science has its laws of evolution analogous to those governing the evolution of species, we shall appreciate more fully the significance of the bitter and long struggles that new theories may create within science. *The fitness of truths is most advantageously shaped and most convincingly demonstrated in vigorous contest.* The situation is, after all, not so very different in other fields. The predominant religious and social concepts of our time have not all developed quietly or been accepted spontaneously. If the physical sciences sometimes seem to have progressed so very much faster, if the recent struggles have been relatively short, we might, to a great extent, credit this to the emergence, from the seventeenth century onward, of a more or less tacit agreement among scientists about the standards by which to judge a new conceptual scheme—above all, of course, the pragmatic test of predictions.

Even so, scientists are, above all, human; a really new and startling idea may in retrospect clearly have fulfilled all these requirements without being widely accepted. Max Planck, with perhaps only a little too much bitterness about his own early struggles, says, "An important scientific innovation rarely makes its way by gradually winning over and converting its opponents: it rarely happens that Saul becomes Paul. What does happen is that its opponents gradually die out, and that the growing generation is familiarized with the ideas from the beginning."

(6) History points out another feature of successful theory: it is flexible enough to grow, and to undergo minor modifications where necessary. But if, after a full life, it eventually dies, it dies gracefully, leaving a minimum of wreckage—and a descendant.

---

* Contrast this caution and the willingness to be proved wrong by their fellow scientists, expressed in the previous quotation, with the sensational claims and impatient pomp of our modern pseudoscientific best-sellers, one of whose authors begins his treatise with the sentence that the work "is a milestone for Man comparable to his discovery of fire and superior to his invention of the wheel and arch . . . The hidden source of all psychosomatic ills and human aberration has been discovered, and skills have been developed for their invariable cure."

Let us consider these interesting points. In any field a prediction is no more than a guess unless it follows from some theory. And just as the meaning of a prediction depends on a theory, so does the validity of a theory depend on the correctness of the predictions. Like the very laws it correlates, a theory must be based on a finite, though perhaps small, number of observations; yet to be useful it may have to predict correctly a very large number of future observations. Think again of the Ptolemaic theory; it was built on many separate observations of planetary positions, but it yielded enough reasonably correct predictions to be still useful more than 1400 years later. Yet we see at once that physical theories are not likely to last forever. Sooner or later there will appear observations to contradict the predictions, probably in a region for which the conditions had to be extrapolated from the original range of the theory (e.g., the region of very small or very large quantities, or of much more precise measurements than served initially as a basis for the theory), or perhaps as a result of a general widening of the scientific horizon. With ingenuity one can usually find that the old theory can be modified to apply also to the new phenomena. Like an apple tree in an orchard, we keep a theory for the sake of its fruits; when the apple crop becomes poor, we then shall try to save the tree by judicious pruning and the like. In the endangered theory, perhaps a re-examination of some assumptions or concepts will save the scheme. But otherwise the only alternatives are to retain the old theory "as is" with the clear understanding of the restricted range to which it still applies, as before, and to develop a new structure to take care of the new range; or, if the flaws appeared within the proper jurisdiction of the old theory and the assumptions stand challenged beyond repair, to abandon it as soon as a new, better one can be contrived.

These three choices—expansion, restriction, or death—appear in the history of theories and of laws generally. We tend to remember and to honor most those schemes which indicated the solution in a crisis, or left some hint of a new start at their demise. In the words of Niels Bohr, "The utmost any theory can do [is] to be instrumental in suggesting and guiding new developments beyond its original scope."

But finally, lest our brief paragraphs on these criteria of good theories be mistaken for scientific dogma, we should echo the very humble opinion of Einstein on this same topic. He distinguishes between two main criteria, (a) the *external confirmation* of a theory, which informs us in experimental checks of the correctness of the theory, and (b) the *inner perfection* of a theory which judges its "logical simplicity" or "naturalness." He then qualifies these remarks as follows: "The meager precision of the assertions [(a) and (b) above] . . . I shall not attempt to excuse by lack of sufficient printing space at my disposal, but confess herewith that I am not, without more ado, and perhaps not at all, capable to replace these hints by more precise definitions."

12.3   QUESTIONS AND PROBLEMS

12.6. Investigate the death of a theory from another field with which you are very well acquainted (such as the phlogiston theory in chemistry or the theory of spontaneous generation in biology) in terms of our six criteria. What were the predictions which failed to come true, or the phenomena which contradicted the assumptions of the theory? Could it have been modified to serve for a time? Did a new theory rise directly from the old?

12.7. P. W. Bridgman writes in *Reflections of a Physicist* (Philosophical Library, New York, 1950, page 252) that in the current flux in ideologies, moral ideas, and other social concepts the intelligent scientist sees "... an exemplification of what his physical experience has taught him; namely, ideas are to be inspected and re-examined when the domain of application is extended beyond that in which they arose. In one very important respect he recognizes that the present epoch differs from former epochs in that the enormous increase in invention, bringing peoples nearer together and increasing their command over forces more advantageous to man, effectively provides just that extension in the domain of application of social concepts which he is prepared to expect would demand fundamental revision." Write a short essay on your opinion about this quotation, and also examine what other guiding ideas you think may be transferred to the field of social studies from the study of physical theories.

12.8. Was the geocentric theory as set forth by Ptolemy *false?* Was it *true?*

12.9. Discuss the relative advantages of the Ptolemaic and Copernican theories of celestial motion, comparing both theories according to each of the six criteria developed in the preceding section.

12.10. Do the same for the Aristotelian and Galilean theories of freely falling bodies (cf. Chapter 2).

SUPPLEMENTARY READING AND STUDY

ARONS, A., and BORK, A., *Science and Ideas* New York: Prentice Hall, 1964

BEVERIDGE, W. I. B., *The Art of Scientific Investigation.* New York: W. W. Norton, 1950

BRIDGMAN, P. W., *The Logic of Modern Physics.* New York: Macmillan, 1927. Chapters 1, 2, and the first part of 3

CAMPBELL, N. R., *Physics, The Elements.* Cambridge: Cambridge University Press, 1920

CONANT, J. B., *Science and Common Sense.* New Haven: Yale University Press, 1951; particularly Chapters 1–3

FEIGEL, H., and SELLARS, W. *Readings in Philosophical Analysis.* New York: Appleton-Century-Crofts, 1949; particularly pages 498–514

FRANK, P., *Modern Science and Its Philosophy.* Cambridge: Harvard University Press, 1949

JOHNSON, D., "Mysterious Craters of the Carolina Coast," *American Scientist*, January 1944; an exercise in "scientific methods"

MACH, E., *The Science of Mechanics*, original edition, 1883. LaSalle: The Open Court Publishing Co., 1942. A venerable classic which will still reward an interested reader. First parts of Chapters 1 and 2

MEES, C. E. K., *The Path of Science.* New York: John Wiley, 1946, Chapters 3 and 4

NASH, L. K., *The Nature of the Natural Sciences.* Boston: Little, Brown, 1963

NORTHROP, F. S. C., *Logic of the Sciences and the Humanities.* New York: Macmillan, 1947; particularly Chapters 1 and 2

POINCARÉ, H. *The Foundation of Science*, English translation. New York: Science Press, 1929; particularly Book I, Chapters 1 and 3 in "Science and Method"

RUSSELL, B., *Scientific Outlook*. New York: W. W. Norton, 1931, Chapters 2 and 3

SARTON, G., *The Study of the History of Science*. Cambridge: Harvard University Press, 1936; to page 52

SHAPLEY, H., *et al.*, *Readings in the Physical Sciences*. New York: Appleton-Century-Crofts, 1948, pages 401–423

WHITEHEAD, A. N., *Science and the Modern World*. New York: Macmillan, 1925; also Pelican *Mentor* Book M28

CHAPTER 13

Kepler's Laws

13.1 INTRODUCTION

The theory of planetary motion now develops with gathering momentum. We have reached the years around 1600 A.D. The Renaissance and Reformation are passing. Copernicus has been read by few and accepted by fewer astronomers. Through this silence we hear one striking voice sounding the first cries of a coming battle. The antiorthodox pantheist and evangelizing Copernican, Giordano Bruno, is traveling through Europe, announcing that the boundaries of the universe are infinitely far away and that our solar system is one of infinitely many. For his outspoken heresies he was tried by the Inquisition and was burned at the stake in 1600.

But the seeds of a new science are sprouting vigorously here and there. In England there is Francis Bacon (1561–1626) and William Gilbert (1540–1603); in Italy, Galileo (1564–1642). And at Copenhagen, Tycho Brahe (1546–1601), since the Greeks the first man to bring real improvements into astrometry, spends nearly a lifetime in patient observation and recording of planetary motion with unheard-of precision. His data are often accurate to less than half a minute of arc, more than twenty times better than those of Copernicus, even though the telescope has not yet been invented.

After Tycho's death, his German assistant Johannes Kepler (1571–1630) (see Fig. 13.1.1) continued the observations and above all the reductions of the voluminous data. Whereas Tycho had developed a geocentric system of his own,* which became widely accepted for a time, Kepler was a Copernican. The announced purpose of his work was the construction of better astronomical tables of planetary motion than were then available on the basis of the more dubious data of Copernicus' own period. But Kepler's motivation and main preoccupation was the perfection of the heliocentric theory, whose harmony and simplicity he contemplated "with incredible and ravishing delight." Particularly at the outset of his long labors he was strongly influenced by Pythagorean and neo-Platonic metaphysics. To him even more than to Copernicus, the clue to God's mind was geometric order and

---

* In Tycho's system (published in 1588), the moon, sun, and fixed stars revolved around a stationary earth, while all the five planets revolved around the sun. For a discussion of the role and influence of Tycho's ideas, see A. R. Hall, *The Scientific Revolution 1500–1800*, Boston: Beacon Press, BP29, 1956, page 65.

Fig. 13.1.1. Johannes Kepler (1571–1630).

numerical relation, expressed in the features of the simple heliocentric scheme. Among his earliest works we find, typically, an enthusiastic attempt to link the six known planets and their respective distances from the sun with the relationships between the five regular solids of geometry. The best one can say for this work was that it served to bring Kepler to the attention of Tycho and Galileo.

In attempting to fit the accurate new data on Mars' orbit to a Copernican system of simple uniform circular motion (*even* if equants were used), Kepler made a terrible discovery—he could not do it! After four years of calculations he still found that the new data placed the orbit just eight minutes of arc outside the scheme of Copernican devices. This is many minutes less than the error which Copernicus knew his own data to contain; therefore Copernicus would not have noticed this deficiency. But Kepler could trust Tycho's unfailing eye and superb instruments, and with an integrity that has become the characteristic attitude of scientists in the face of quantitative fact, he would not allow himself to hide this fatal difference behind some convenient assumptions. To Kepler, these eight minutes meant simply that the Copernican scheme of concentric spheres, epicycles, and eccentrics failed to explain the actual motion of Mars when the observations were made accurately enough.

One might feel tempted to return to the Ptolemaic scheme after all, and in fact it should be able to explain the motion of Mars, but only if we heap device on device. Thus in a sense both theories fail us; one is not quite accurate enough, and the other breaks under its own weight.

13.2 KEPLER'S FIRST LAW

Kepler must have been stunned, for after all he was a convinced Copernican. After years of continuous labor he at length discovered how the Copernican theory could be amended to make it applicable to both the old and the new observations— by dropping the one assumption which most bound it explicitly to the doctrines derived from ancient Greece. When he plotted the paths of planets on the basis of a heliocentric representation, and when instead of trying to interpret these paths as combinations of different motions he considered the shape of the orbits themselves, he found that they corresponded to a simple type of figure whose properties had been known to mathematicians since the second century B.C.—the ellipse. (See Section 3.7.) If, therefore, the ellipse is recognized as the natural path of celestial bodies, then we have a geometrically truly simple world-scheme. "Planets move in elliptical paths, with the sun at one focus of the ellipse." This may be our statement of Kepler's first of three great laws, the *Law of Elliptical Paths*. Note the similarity between this and Galileo's work on trajectories. We recall that Galileo explained how projectiles moved by pointing out that they all followed paths known to the mathematicians as parabolas. Kepler again matches a physical path against a mathematical curve, and so simultaneously describes and begins to explain planetary motion.

We have here an example of the enormous change in outlook in Europe that had begun more than two centuries before. More and more, events ceased to be regarded as *symbols* and were allowed to stand for themselves. Man ceased to be preoccupied with anthropomorphic riddles in an organismic world, and slowly became a factual observer and theorizer in a mechanistic world. Without this new attitude, there could have been no modern science, for if we are to start our science from experimental observables, we must have faith that we are dealing with the raw material of experience, not with symbols of complex mysteries. We must become enthusiastic about the observable world for its own sake, we must attain a tacit faith in the meaningfulness of nature and her direct accessibility to our understanding, before we can expect generations of scientists to devote themselves to the minute and often most tedious quantitative investigations of nature. In this sense Kepler's work heralds the change toward the modern scientific attitude—to regard a wide variety of phenomena as explained when they can all be described by one simple, preferably mathematical, pattern of behavior.

It seems at first astonishing that Kepler should be the one to follow this new road. He had begun his career as a symbol-seeking mystic, but now we may discern a reflection of the great change in his complex soul: he fashions his physical laws—

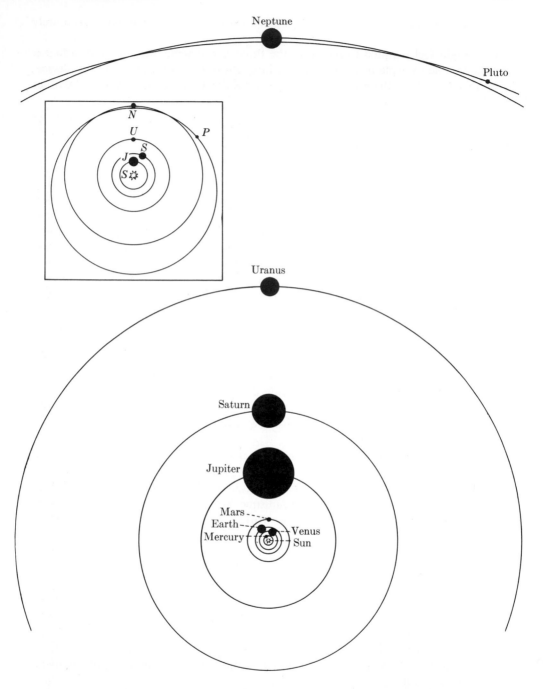

Fɪɢ. 13.2.1. Schematic outline of solar system, showing relative sizes ot the orbits and, to a different scale, the relative sizes of the planets. The insert traces Pluto's full orbit.

and looks for his symbolism afterwards. Philosophical speculation, still rather colorful, follows factual analysis, not the reverse; and to this day many scientists have found it quite possible to reconcile their physics and their personal philosophy on the basis of this sequence.

Kepler's first law, by amending the Copernican heliocentric theory, gives us a wonderfully simple mental picture of the solar system. Gone are all the epicycles and eccentrics; the orbits are clean and elliptical. Figure 13.2.1 shows a schematic representation of the present conception of the solar system—in essence Kepler's, but with the addition of the planets Uranus, Neptune, and Pluto, discovered much later. An attempt has been made to represent on the figure the relative sizes of the planets; the approximate relative sizes of the orbits, to a different scale, are indicated also, but since most of these ellipses are quite nearly circular, they are shown as circles where possible. All orbits are nearly in the same plane, except for the more pronounced tilt of Pluto's (which means that Neptune's and Pluto's paths do not cross at any point in space, although Fig. 13.2.1 may give that impression).*

After Kepler's initial joy over the discovery of the law of elliptical paths had subsided, he may have asked himself the obvious question, "Is it not rather mysterious that of all possible types of paths the planets all select just the ellipse?" We could understand Plato's predisposition for uniform circular motions, but we cannot readily comprehend nature's insistence on the ellipse! It is no longer a manmade mystery, but therefore all the darker. In fact, there was no rational answer until a reticent genius in England almost eighty years later showed the law of the ellipse to be one of the many surprising consequences of a much more far-reaching law of nature. We shall follow his reasoning in a few moments.

If for the present we accept Kepler's first law purely as a summary of observed facts—an "empirical" law—we note that by describing the paths as elliptical, the law gives us all the possible positions of a given planet—but it does not tell us *when* it will be at any of these positions; it talks about the shape of the orbit, not the changing speed along the orbit. This makes the law rather useless for an astronomer who wishes to know where he should expect to look for a planet at a given time. For an anxious moment it seems that Kepler has sacrificed the possibility of astronomical prediction for the sake of the simplicity of path. Less than nothing is gained, because the other theories gave at least the possibility of fairly good prediction of a planet's possible positions *and* of its time of appearance at each possible position.

13.3 KEPLER'S SECOND LAW

Kepler was perfectly aware that his first law alone was not enough to justify a jubilant overthrow of the apparatus of epicycles and eccentrics. He set out to discover a law which would relate the speed of a planet in any position of its orbit

---

* See F. L. Whipple's *Earth, Moon and Planets* (Philadelphia: Blakiston Co., 1941), for a readable account of the structure of the solar system. A brief summary is in Shapley, Wright, and Rapport, *Readings in the Physical Sciences* (New York: Appleton-Century-Crofts, 1948), pages 103–108.

with the speed in any other position. If such a relation could be found, the motion of any one planet would be specifiable by just a few separate figures: two data to specify the ellipse (e.g., the major and minor axes); one more to give the speed at a certain portion of the path, for instance when the planet is nearest the sun, "at the perihelion"; and a few additional data to place this ellipse at the correct tilt with respect to the others. Thus he could hope to summarize all features of planetary motion in a compact, elegant way.

But does the hoped-for relation between speed and path actually exist? There appears so far no necessary reason that it should. Kepler is said to have been in ecstasy when by sheer labor and ingenuity he finally read the needed second law out of his own voluminous data. Well he might have been; his whole labor would have been of little use without this additional discovery.

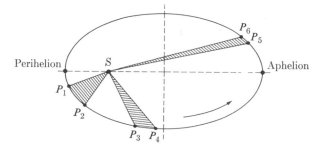

FIG. 13.3.1. Elliptical path of planets around sun S (at left focus), illustrating Kepler's second law (eccentricity much exaggerated).

Figure 13.3.1 indicates what he noticed. We are looking down on a greatly exaggerated representation of a planetary path around the sun S at one focus of the ellipse. The planet may be our earth; it is found to move from position P_1 to P_2 (say during a week in our winter). During an equal time interval in the spring the journey proceeds from P_3 to P_4, and from P_5 to P_6 in summer. The implication from the drawing is that the planet's speed along the orbit is greatest when nearest the sun, less when more distant. For the earth, the maximum orbital speed is 18.8 miles per second at perihelion, the minimum 18.2 miles per second at aphelion.

This gratifying regularity turns into a law by the deeper recognition that by measurement the area of the figure SP_1P_2 is the same as for SP_3P_4 and for SP_5P_6, etc. *During a given time interval a line from the planet to the sun sweeps out an equal area anywhere along its elliptical path.* This second law, or *Law of Equal Areas*, applies to all planets.*

If we once establish the elliptical orbit of the planet and the area swept out in a given interval of time (such as the area of sector SP_3P_4 in Fig. 13.3.1), we can proceed to mark off equal areas adjacent to each other and thereby determine the positions at which the planet would be located at successive equal intervals of time.

By taking relatively small intervals, we can establish quite precise values for the instantaneous velocity of the planet at each point on its ellipse, we can predict either

---

* Also to the moon in its path around the earth insofar as this is elliptical, and to all other satellites about their own planets.

how long it will take to reach a given spot or how far it will have gone in a given time interval. Thus Kepler's second law re-establishes the possibility of astronomical prediction, and in a simpler manner than through the multiplicity of geometric devices of the previous theories of planetary motion.

13.4　KEPLER'S THIRD LAW

Kepler's first and second laws were published together in 1609 in his *New Astronomy*. But he was still unsatisfied with one aspect of his achievement: it had not revealed any connection between the motions of the different planets. So far, each planet seemed to have its own elliptical orbit and speeds, but there appeared to be no over-all pattern for all planets. Nor was there any good reason why one should expect such a relationship. Kepler, however, was convinced that on investigating different possibilities he might hit on a simple rule linking the whole solar system.

This conviction, so strong that it seems to us like an obsession, was partly a remnant of his earlier numerological preoccupations. But it also indicates a deep undercurrent running through the whole history of science: the belief in the simplicity and uniformity of nature. It has always been a source of inspiration, helping scientists over the inevitable unforeseen obstacles, and sustaining their spirit during periods of long and fruitless labor. For Kepler it made bearable a life of heartbreaking personal misfortunes,* so that he could write triumphantly, on finally finding the great third law:

> "...after I had by unceasing toil through a long period of time, using the observations of Brahe, discovered the true distances of the orbits, at last, at last, the true relation ... overcame by storm the shadows of my mind, with such fullness of agreement between my seventeen years' labor on the observations of Brahe and this present study of mine that I at first believed that I was dreaming ..."

The law itself, in modern terminology, states that if T be the sidereal period of any chosen planet (i.e., the time for one complete orbital revolution about the sun), and $\overline{R}$ be the mean radius of the orbit of that planet,† then

$$T^2 = K(\overline{R})^3,$$

where K is a constant having the same value for *all* planets. But if $T^2/(\overline{R})^3$ is the same for all planets, we can calculate its numerical value for *one* planet (for the earth: $T_E = 1$ year, $\overline{R}_E \cong 9.3 \times 10^7$ miles), and thereafter we shall always be able to compute for any other planet its T if its $\overline{R}$ is given, and vice versa.

---

* Movingly described in Sir Oliver Lodge's *Pioneers of Science*. London: Macmillan, 1893; Dover Publications I 716, 1960.

† The value of $\overline{R}$ for an elliptical path is half the distance of a straight line from perihelion to aphelion (see Fig. 13.3.1); conveniently, most planetary paths are nearly enough circular so that $\overline{R}$ is then simply the radius of the circular orbit.

PROBLEM 13.1.   Using the third law and the data for T_E and $\overline{R}_E$ for the earth, compute values of $\overline{R}$ for a few other planets, taking the corresponding values of T from the quotation from Copernicus' *Revolutions* in Section 11.2.

Appropriately, Kepler's third law is often called the *Harmonic Law* because it establishes a beautifully simple relationship among the planets.   From this peak we may survey our progress so far.   Starting from the disconnected multitude of Ptolemaic gears we have reached a heliocentric formulation that views the solar system as a simple, logically connected unit.   Our mind's eye grasps the Keplerian universe at one glance, and recognizes the main motions as the expression of simple mathematical laws.

13.5   THE NEW CONCEPT OF PHYSICAL LAW

With Tycho's work, his own observations, and his powerful three laws, Kepler was able to construct the long-needed accurate tables of planetary motion which remained useful for a century.   We honor him for all these great accomplishments in astronomy (and these are only a few of the achievements of this prodigious man) but we must also not forget to single out two features of his work which had a profound effect on the development of all physical sciences.   One, which has been discussed, is the rather new attitude to *observed facts*.   We noted the change in Kepler's work from his earlier insistence on a geometric model and its form as the main tool of explanation, to the discussion of the movement itself and of the numerical relations underlying it.   The other is his successful attempt to formulate physical laws in mathematical form, in the language of geometry and algebra.   From then on, from the period of Kepler and Galileo, the *equation* develops naturally as the prototype of the laws in physical science.

In this sense, Kepler's science was truly modern; he more than anyone before him bowed to the relentless and supreme arbiter of physical theory, namely the evidence of *precise* and *quantitative* observation.   But in the Keplerian system the planets no longer are considered to move in their orbits because of their divine nature or the continual effort of angels, as in Scholastic teaching, nor because their spherical shapes themselves were self-evident explanation for their circular motion, as in Copernicus' thoughts, and so we are left without any physical agency to "explain" or give plausibility to the planetary motion so well described in these three laws. Kepler himself felt this need of backing up mathematical descriptions with physical mechanism.   While it was left to Newton to assign this task to gravitational forces, and thereby to tie Kepler's three laws together with the heliocentric conception and the laws of terrestrial mechanics in a monumental synthesis, Kepler entertained a then quite promising hypothesis: the recent work of Gilbert on magnetism had greatly intrigued him, and his rich imagination could picture magnetic forces emanating from the sun to "drive" the planets in their orbits.   (Newton later felt it necessary to prove in some detail that this hypothetical agency would not account for the quantitative observations.)

A final word about Kepler's place in present-day astronomy: Three centuries of telescopic observations have shown that Kepler's laws hold within well-understood and usually small deviations. The laws have also been found to have a much broader scope; for example, in atomic physics we shall use them to help us describe the paths of electrons around nuclei. Fruitful ideas, it is evident, are bound neither by time nor by space, nor yet by the artificial boundaries of academic fields.

13.6   QUESTIONS AND PROBLEMS

13.2. Evaluate, so far as you can, Kepler's contribution in terms of our criteria for a good theory.

13.3. Trace the changes and evolution of the Copernican heliocentric theory in the hands of Kepler, and then compare this with the development and expansion of some important theory from another field familiar to you (e.g., the Theory of Evolution, from its exposition in 1859 to the recent modifications of evolutionary genetics).

13.4. Does it seem possible that a revision of the geocentric theory can be made, doing away with equants, eccentric motions, etc., and instead describing the planetary paths *about the earth* directly by simple geometric figures? Is it likely that laws could be found for this simplified geocentric system which relate the paths, speeds, and periods of revolution of the different planets?

SUPPLEMENTARY READING AND STUDY

BAKER, R. H., *Astronomy*. Princeton, N.J.: Van Nostrand, 1930, and later editions; excellent introduction

BURTT, F. A , *The Metaphysical Foundations of Modern Science: A Historical and Critical Essay*. London: Routledge and Kegan Paul, 1924, and later; the Humanities Press, 1951; also Doubleday Anchor Book A41; Chapters 1 and 2

CASPAR, M., *Johannes Kepler*. Stuttgart: Kohlhammer, 1950

CROMBIE, A. C., *Medieval and Early Modern Science*. New York: Doubleday Anchor Book A167 a, b, 1959

DREYER, J. L. E., *History of the Planetary Systems from Thales to Kepler*. London: Cambridge University Press, 1906; republished as *A History of Astronomy from Thales to Kepler*. New York: Dover Publications, 1953, Chapters 15, 16

HOLTON, G., "Johannes Kepler's Universe: Its Physics and Metaphysics." *American Journal of Physics*, **24**, 1956, pages 340–351

Johannes Kepler, 1571–1630, edited by the History of Science Society. Baltimore: Williams and Wilkins, 1931

KEPLER, JOHANNES, "Epitome of Copernican Astronomy," Books 4 and 5, "Harmony of the World," Book 5, in *Great Books of the Western World*. Chicago: Encyclopedia Britannica, 1952, **16**

NEWMAN, J. R., *The World of Mathematics*. New York: Simon and Schuster, 1956, Volume I, pages 220–234

SHAPLEY, H., and H. E. HOWARTH. *A Source Book in Astronomy*. New York: McGraw-Hill, 1929, pages 13–19 and 29–40; excerpts from Brahe and Kepler

WHIPPLE, F. L., *Earth, Moon, and Planets*. Blakiston, 1941, and later printings

CHAPTER 14

Galileo's Contribution to Astronomy

"There are more things in heaven and earth, Horatio,
Than are dreamt of in your philosophy . . ."

Hamlet, Act I

One of the few friends and fellow-scientists with whom Kepler corresponded and exchanged news of the latest findings was Galileo Galilei. Although the Italian's *scientific* contribution to planetary theory is not so well developed as that of his friend across the Alps, he nevertheless was projected into history as a key figure in this subject. In a sense, Kepler and Galileo complemented each other in preparing the world for the eventual acceptance of the heliocentric theory—the one laying the scientific foundation with his astronomical work, the other fighting the dogmatic objections and, in his work on mechanics, helping to overturn the whole structure of scholastic physics with which the old cosmology was entwined.

For it was Galileo more than any other man who, as we have already seen, challenged the fruitfulness of the ancient interpretation of experience, and focused the attention of physical science on the productive concepts—time and distance, velocity and acceleration, force and matter—and not on qualities or essences, ultimate causes or harmonies, which were still the motivation of a Copernicus and at times the ecstasy of a Kepler. Galileo's insistence, so clearly expressed in his work on freely falling bodies, on fitting the concepts and conclusions to observable facts, on expressing his results in the concise language of mathematics, are now accepted as central achievements, re-enforcing the same traits then emerging from the work of Kepler. But perhaps the greatest difference between the work of Galileo and that of his scholastic contemporaries was his orientation, his viewpoint, the kind of question he considered important. To most of his opponents, Galileo's special problems were not general enough, since he excluded the orthodox philosophical problems. Then, too, his procedure for discovering truth seemed to them fantastic, his conclusions preposterous, haughty, often impious. There exists an almost perfectly parallel situation between these objections to Galileo's point of view and the outraged derision and even violence initially heaped on the discoverers of new ways of viewing the world in art, e.g., Manet and his impressionists.

FIG. 14.1.1. Galileo published the first results of his telescopic investigations in 1610 in a book titled *Sidereus Nuncius* (The Sidereal Messenger). The book captured the public imagination and was widely read and discussed. This copy of Galileo's drawing of the lunar surface as seen through the telescope is taken from the volume of the *Sidereus Nuncius* now in the DeGolyer Collection of the University of Oklahoma.

14.1 THE TELESCOPIC EVIDENCES

Like Kepler, Galileo was a Copernican in a Ptolemaic world. His specific contributions to the development of heliocentric theory are two: the construction in 1609 of a telescope for astronomical work, and the observations he made with its help. The same set of doctrines which then still generally upheld the geocentric system as the only possible choice also required that the celestial objects be "perfect" (spherical and unblemished), yet he could now plainly see spots on the sun and mountains on the moon (Fig. 14.1.1). Venus, sometimes fully illuminated by the sun and at other times not at all, was found to have moonlike phases. Saturn seemed to carry bulges around its equator. Most surprisingly, Jupiter showed him four (of its twelve now known) satellites or subplanets, adding in a catastrophic manner to the seven scholastically acceptable members of the planetary system, and offering to plain view a miniature solar system with an "obvious" center of rotation far from the earth (Fig. 14.1.2). The Milky Way* resolved into aggregates of individual

---

* Democritus (b. 460 B.C.), one of the originators of the atomistic view of matter, appears to have speculated quite successfully on the nature of the Milky Way and the appearance of the moon. See C. Bailey, *The Greek Atomists and Epicurus*. London: Oxford University Press, 1928, page 151.

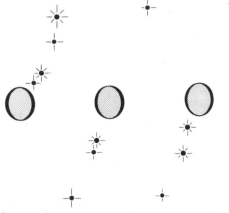

FIG. 14.1.2. Jupiter and its satellites, as they may appear through the telescope if observed a few days apart; drawn in the manner of Galileo's notebook. A few of the satellites can usually be seen through a good pair of binoculars.

stars. The stars themselves, now visible in much greater numbers, appeared still as pinpoints of light, thus aiding the Copernican argument that they are extremely distant.*

However, we must understand that these suggestive observations were to Galileo illustrations of a truth that seemed to him compelling even from a nonexperimental point of view. In his great work *The Dialogue on the Two Chief Systems of the World*, he stresses the one argument as much as the other. Observations alone, says Galileo, do not decide uniquely between a heliocentric and a geocentric hypothesis, "for the same phenomena would result from either hypothesis." This would be close to our modern view, but where we would make a choice between the two mainly on the basis of convenience in use, without regarding one as true and the other as false, Galileo understandably thinks of the earth's motion as "real," real just *because* it seems more reasonable and simplifies the picture. He then adduces several arguments, largely following Copernicus:

> "When we merely consider the immensity of the starry sphere in comparison with the smallness of the terrestrial ball ... and then think of the rapidity of the motion which completes a whole rotation in one day and night, I cannot persuade myself how anyone can hold it to be more reasonable and credible that it is the heavenly sphere which rotates, while the earth stands still."†

As a second point Galileo reminds his readers that in the geocentric model it is necessary to ascribe to the planets a motion opposite to that of the celestial sphere (why?), again an unreasonable, we might almost say unharmonious or unesthetic assumption. Third, Jupiter's four moons had shown him that there, too, existed

---

* Marjorie Nicolson gives an interesting discussion of the influence of the new knowledge on Milton's imagery in her paper on Milton and the telescope in *Science and Imagination*. Ithaca, N.Y.: Cornell University Press, 1956; also reprinted in *Science and Ideas*, edited by A. B. Arons and A. M. Bork. New York: Prentice-Hall, 1964.
† From the translation by Dannemann.

the rule that the larger the orbit of the rotating body as reckoned from the center of rotation, the longer the period of rotation (qualitatively, Kepler's third law). This Copernicus had pointed out long before for the case of the planets themselves, and it held true even in the Ptolemaic system—but with this disharmony: in the Ptolemaic system the characteristic periods of revolution around the earth increase from the short one ($27\frac{1}{3}$ days) for the moon, to the very large one (30 years) for Saturn—and then suddenly drop back to 24 hours for the celestial sphere. In the Copernican system, however, "the rapidity of the periods is very well preserved; from the slowest sphere of Saturn we come to the wholly motionless fixed stars. We also escape thereby a fourth difficulty . . . I mean the great unevenness in the movement of these very stars [on the Ptolemaic hypothesis], some of which would have to revolve with extraordinary rapidity in immense circles, while others moved very slowly in small circles, since some of them are at a greater, others at a less distance from the pole." Fifth, owing to the slightly changing tilt of the earth's axis, the apparent paths of the stars on the celestial sphere change slowly over the centuries, again an improbable or at any rate an unreasonable feature of a geocentric theory that claimed to be based on the immutable, ideal, eternal characteristics of the heavenly bodies. Next, Galileo found it impossible to conceive in what manner the stars could be fixed in the celestial sphere to allow them rapid rotation and even motion as a group (cf. last point), while also having them preserve their relative distances so perfectly. "It seems to me much easier and more convenient to make them motionless instead of moving" and to ascribe the apparent motions to that of one "small insignificant body in comparison with the whole universe," the earth itself. Lastly Galileo points out "I could also not explain why the earth, a freely poised body, balancing itself about its center [on the geocentric scheme] and surrounded on all sides by a fluid medium [postulated at the time to provide means for communicating the "force and power" needed to keep up the celestial motions] should not be affected by the universal rotation."

In the text, Galileo's hypothetical opponent answers to these points:

> "You support your arguments throughout, it seems to me, on the greater ease and simplicity with which the said effects are produced. You mean that as a cause [of the observed motion of planets and stars] the motion of the earth alone is just as satisfactory as the motion of all the rest of the universe with the exception of the earth; you hold the actual event to be much easier in the former case than in the latter."

These are meant to be accusing or scoffing remarks, as though, in modern terminology, one would say, "You are just a relativist, willing to throw to the winds, for the sake of convenience, all the sacred implications of our geocentric hypothesis." And, in fact, the fictional opponent then dismisses all of Galileo's arguments with this quite characteristic counter-argument:

> "For the ruler of the Universe, however, whose might is infinite, it is no less easy to move the universe than the earth or a straw balm."

Analyze carefully this part of Galileo's modern-sounding and conclusive reply (and incidentally notice the sly final phrases):

"What I said . . . does not refer to Him who causes the motion, but to that which is moved . . . . If we consider the moving bodies, we must unquestionably regard the motion of the earth as a *much simpler process* than that of the universe. If, furthermore, we direct our attention to *so many other simplifications* which may be reached *only* by this heliocentric theory, the daily movement of the earth must appear much more probable than the motion of the universe without the earth; for according to Aristotle's just axiom, 'It is vain to expend many means where a few are sufficient.' "

PROBLEM 14.1.   Examine each of Galileo's telescopic observations separately to determine whether it aided or disproved (a) the geocentric theory as an astronomical system, (b) the heliocentric theory as an astronomical system, (c) the philosophic doctrines behind the geocentric theory. In particular, note Galileo's observations for Venus, and refer to your answers to Problem 12.4. It should be clear that the Ptolemaic system, without some rearrangement, cannot account for all of Venus' moonlike phases. Propose a modification of the Ptolemaic system which would remove the difficulty while retaining the *geocentric* feature.

In his characteristic enthusiasm, Galileo thought that through his telescopic discoveries everyone would see, *as with his own eyes*, the absurdity of the assumptions which prevented a general acceptance of the Copernican system. But man can believe only what he is ready to believe. In their fight against the new Copernicans the scholastics were convinced that they were surely "sticking to facts," that the heliocentric theory was obviously false and in contradiction with both sense-observation and common sense, not to speak of the theological heresies implied in the heliocentric view. They had made Aristotelian science their exclusive tool for understanding facts, just as today most laymen make their understanding of physical theory depend on their ability to visualize it in terms of simple mechanical models obeying Newtonian laws. But at the root of the tragic position of the Aristotelians was, in part, the fact that an acceptance of the Copernican theory as even a *possible* theory would have had to be preceded by a most far-reaching re-examination and re-evaluation of their personal beliefs. It would have required them to do the humanly almost impossible, to discard their common-sense ideas, to seek new bases for their old moral and theological doctrines, and to learn their science anew (which was of course what Galileo himself did to an amazing degree, for which his contemporaries called him fool, or worse, and for which we call him genius). Being satisfied with their system, the Aristotelians were, of course, unaware that history would soon prove their point of view to be far less effective in man's quest to understand nature.

Galileo's concrete observations meant little to them. The Florentine astronomer Francesco Sizzi (1611) argued in this manner why there could not, *must* not be any satellites around Jupiter:

> "There are seven windows in the head, two nostrils, two ears, two eyes and a mouth; so in the heavens there are two favorable stars, two unpropitious, two luminaries, and Mercury alone undecided and indifferent. From which and many other similar phenomena of nature such as the seven metals, etc., which it were tedious to enumerate, we gather that the number of planets is necessarily seven ... Besides, the Jews and other ancient nations, as well as modern Europeans, have adopted the division of the week into seven days, and have named them from the seven planets: now if we increase the number of planets, this whole system falls to the ground. ... Moreover, the satellites are invisible to the naked eye and therefore can have no influence on the earth and therefore would be useless and therefore do not exist."

A year after his discoveries, Galileo had to write to Kepler:

> "You are the first and almost the only person who, after a cursory investigation, has given entire credit to my statements. ... What do you say of the leading philosophers here to whom I have offered a thousand times of my own accord to show my studies, but who, with the lazy obstinacy of a serpent who has eaten his fill, have never consented to look at the planets, or moon, or telescope?"

Before this anecdote is again forgotten, let us re-emphasize its salient point, so forcefully expressed by Lodge (*op. cit.*):

> "I know nothing of the views of any here present; but I have met educated persons who, while they might laugh at the men who refused to look through a telescope lest they should learn something they did not like, yet also themselves commit the very same folly. ... I am constrained to say this much: Take heed lest some prophet, after having excited your indignation at the follies and bigotry of a bygone generation, does not turn upon you with the sentence *'Thou art the man.'* "

14.2 SCIENCE AND FREEDOM

The tragedy that descended on Galileo is described in many places, and it is impossible to do justice to the whole story without referring to the details. Briefly, he was warned in 1616 by the Inquisition to cease teaching the Copernican theory, for it was now held "contrary to Holy Scripture." At the same time Copernicus'

book itself was placed on the Index Expurgatorius, and was suspended "until corrected." But Galileo could not suppress what he felt deeply to be the truth. Whereas
Copernicus had still invoked Aristotelian doctrine to make his theory plausible,
Galileo had reached the new point of view where he urged acceptance of the heliocentric system on its own merits of simplicity and usefulness, and apart from such
questions as those of faith and salvation. This was the great break.

In 1623, Cardinal Barberini, formerly his dear friend, was elevated to the Papal
throne, and Galileo seems to have considered it safe enough to write again on the
controversial topic. In 1632, after making some required changes, Galileo obtained
the Inquisitor's necessary consent to publish the work *Dialogue Concerning the Two
Chief Systems of the World* (from which the previous arguments for the Copernican
theory were drawn), setting forth most persuasively the Copernican view in a thinly
disguised discussion of the relative merits of the Ptolemaic and Copernican systems.
After publication it was realized that he may have tried to circumvent the warning
of 1616. Furthermore, Galileo's forthright and tactless behavior and the Inquisition's need to demonstrate its power over suspected heretics conspired to mark
him for punishment.

Among the many other factors in this complex story a prominent role is to be
assigned to Galileo's religious attitude—which he himself believed to be devoutly
faithful, but which had come under suspicion by the Inquisition. Galileo's letters
of 1613 and 1615 showed he held that God's mind contains all the natural laws,
and that the occasional glimpses of these laws which the human investigator may
laboriously achieve are proofs and direct revelations of the Deity quite as valid and
grandiose as those recorded in the Bible. "From the Divine Word, the Sacred Scripture and Nature did both alike proceed. . . . Nor does God less admirably discover
himself to us in Nature's actions than in the Scripture's sacred dictions." These
opinions—held, incidentally, by many present-day scientists—can, however, be taken
for symptoms of pantheism, one of the heresies for which Galileo's contemporary,
Giordano Bruno, had been burned at the stake in 1600. Nor did Galileo help his
case by such phrases as his quotation of Cardinal Baronius: "The Holy Spirit
intended to teach us in the Bible how to go to heaven, not how the heavens go."

The old, ailing man was called to Rome and confined for a few months. From
the partly still secret proceedings we gather that he was tried (in absentia), threatened
with torture, induced to making an elaborate formal renunciation of the Copernican
theory, and finally sentenced to perpetual confinement. None of his friends in Italy
dared to defend Galileo publicly. His book was placed on the Index (where it remained along with Copernicus' and one of Kepler's until 1835). In short, and this
is the only point of interest to us here, he was set up as a warning for all men that
the demand for spiritual obedience indisputably entails intellectual obedience also,
that there can be no free science where there is no free conscience. His famous
Abjuration, later ordered to be read from the pulpits throughout Italy and posted
as a warning, reveals an ominous modern sound.*

---

* The full condemnation and abjuration is printed as Appendix E in Sedgwick and Tyler,
op. cit., Chapter 11.

But without freedom, science cannot flourish for long. It is perhaps not simply a coincidence that after Galileo, Italy, the mother of outstanding men till then, produced for the next 200 years hardly a single great scientist, while elsewhere in Europe they arose in great numbers. To scientists today this famous facet in the story of planetary theories is not just an episode in passing. Not a few teachers and scientists in our time have had to face powerful enemies of open-minded inquiry and of free teaching, and again must stand up before those men who rightly fear the strength of unindoctrinated intellect.

Even Plato knew that an authoritarian state is threatened by intellectual nonconformists, and he recommended for them the now time-honored treatment: "reeducation," prison, or death. Within recent years Russian geneticists and astronomers were expected to reject well-established theories, not on grounds of persuasive new *scientific* evidence, but because of doctrinal conflicts. This same struggle explains the banishment from Nazi Germany's textbooks of the discussion of relativity theory because, by the obscure standards of racist metaphysics, Einstein's Jewish faith invalidated his work for Germans. This, too, was in part the meaning behind the "Monkey Trial" in Tennessee, where the teaching of Darwin's theory was to be suppressed for conflicting with certain types of Bible interpretations.

The warfare of authoritarianism against science, like the warfare of ignorance against knowledge, has not diminished since Galileo's days. Scientists take what comfort they can from the verdict of history, for less than 50 years later, Newton's great book, the *Principia*, had appeared, integrating the work of Copernicus, Kepler, and Galileo so brilliantly with the principles of mechanics that the long-delayed triumph of those pioneers of science was irrevocable, and more significant than they themselves might have hoped.

PROBLEM 14.2. In J. B. Conant's book, *On Understanding Science* (New Haven: Yale University Press, 1947) are summarized "Certain Principles of the Tactics and Strategy of Science" and "The Interaction of Science and Society." The following main points are made: (a) New concepts evolve from experiments or observations and are fruitful of new experiments and observations. (b) Significant observations are the result of "controlled" experiments or observations; the difficulties of experimentation must not be overlooked. (c) New techniques arise as a result of experimentation (and invention) and influence further experimentation. (d) An important aspect of scientific work is the interaction between science and society. Examine the development of planetary theory in terms of each of the four points (preferably after reading at least pages 101–109 in Conant's book).

SUPPLEMENTARY READING AND STUDY

BURTT, E. A., *The Metaphysical Foundations of Modern Physical Science: A Historical and Critical Essay.* London: Routledge and Kegan Paul, 1924, and later; the Humanities Press, 1951; also Doubleday Anchor Book A41, Chapter 3

BUTTERFIELD, H., *The Origins of Modern Science: 1300–1800.* London: G. Bell, 1949; New York: Macmillan, 1951; Collier Books AS 259V, 1962

CROMBIE, A. C., *Augustine to Galileo*. London: Falcon Press, 1952, Chapter 6, (1) and (2)

DE SANTILLANA, G., *The Age of Adventure: the Renaissance Philosophers*. Boston: Houghton Mifflin and Mentor Book MD184, New American Library, 1956. Discussion, with source materials, of the work of Copernicus, Kepler, Galileo, and Bruno.

DE SANTILLANA, G., *The Crime of Galileo*. Chicago: University of Chicago Press, 1955

DRAKE, S., *Discoveries and Opinions of Galileo*. New York: Doubleday, 1957; Anchor Book A94. Includes Galileo's *Starry Messenger* (1610) and *Letter to the Grand Duchess Christina* (1615).

GALILEO GALILEI, *Dialogue on the Great World Systems*, edited by G. de Santillana. Chicago: University of Chicago Press, 1953. In particular, read the historical introduction and the "Second day."

HALL, A. R., *The Scientific Revolution 1500–1800*. New York: Longmans, Green, 1954; Boston: Beacon Press, 1956, Chapter 6

KNICKERBOCKER, W. S., editor, *Classics of Modern Science*. New York: Knopf, 1927, Chapter 4; excerpt from Galileo

KOYRÉ, A., *From the Closed World to the Infinite Universe*. Baltimore: Johns Hopkins Press, 1957; Harper Torchbook TB31

MOULTON, F. R., and J. J. SCHIFFERES, *The Autobiography of Science*. New York: Doubleday, Doran, 1945, 1951. Brief condensations. See pages 63–77 (Galileo).

MUNITZ, M. K., editor, *Theories of the Universe*. Glencoe, Illinois: The Free Press, 1957, pages 174–201; discussion, with excerpts, of the work of Bruno, Galileo, and Kepler

SHAPLEY, H., and H. E. HOWARTH, *A Source Book in Astronomy*. New York: McGraw-Hill, 1929, pages 41–57; excerpts

TAYLOR, F. S., *Galileo and the Freedom of Thought*. New York: Franklin Watts, 1938; an appraisal of Galileo's work and tribulations

CHAPTER 15

Newton's Law of Universal Gravitation

15.1 SCIENCE IN THE SEVENTEENTH CENTURY

Between the time of Galileo's death and the publication of Isaac Newton's *Principia**
lie barely 44 years, yet an amazing change of the intellectual climate in science has
taken place during that time. On one side, the "New Philosophy" of experimental
science is becoming a respected and respectable tool in the hands of vigorous and
inventive investigators; and on the other, this new attitude is responsible for a gathering storm of inventions, discoveries, and theories. Even a very abbreviated list of
these, covering less than half of the seventeenth century and only the physical sciences,
will show the justification for the term "the century of genius": the work on vacuums
and pneumatics by Torricelli, Pascal, von Guericke, Boyle, and Mariotte; Wallis'
work in mathematics; Descartes' great studies on analytical geometry and on optics;
Huygens' work in astronomy and on centripetal force, his perfection of the pendulum
clock, and his book on light; the improvement of microscopes and the invention of
reflecting telescopes; Newton's work on optics, including the discovery of the solar
spectrum, and his invention of calculus simultaneously with Leibniz; the opening of
the famous Greenwich observatory; Roemer's measurement of the speed of light;
and Hooke's work, including that on elasticity.

The men of science are no longer isolated. Although we must not suppose that
suddenly *all* scientists are of a modern bent of mind, the adherents of the "New
Philosophy" are many and growing in numbers. They have formed several scientific
societies (Italy, England, France), of which the most famous is the Royal Society of
London (as of 1662). They meet and communicate with one another freely now, they
cooperate and debate, write copiously, and sometimes quarrel healthily. As a group,
they solicit support for their work, combat attacks by antagonists, and have a widely
read scientific journal. Science is clearly becoming well defined, strong, and international.

What is behind this sudden blossoming? Even a partial answer would lead us far
away from science itself, to an examination of the whole picture of quickening cultural,

---

* Full title: *Philosophiae Naturalis Principia Mathematica;* published in London, 1687.

political, and economic changes in the sixteenth and seventeenth centuries.*   One aspect is that both craftsmen and men of leisure and money begin to turn to science, the one group for improvement of methods and products, the other for a new and exciting hobby.   But availability of money and time, the need for science, and the presence of interest and organizations do not alone explain or sustain such a thriving enterprise.   Even more important ingredients are able men, well-formulated problems, and good mathematical and experimental tools.

Able scientists—these were indeed at hand.   Some, like Newton, were men in still primarily scholastic universities; others, like Newton's friends Edmond Halley and Christopher Wren, were initially gifted amateurs.

Well-formulated problems—these had recently become clear in the writings of Galileo.   It was he, above all, who had directed attention to the fruitful language of science, who had presented a new way of viewing the world of fact and experiment. His scorn of sterile introspection and blind subservience to ancient dogma echoed through all fields of science.†   Plato's old question, "By the assumption of what uniform and ordered motions can the apparent motions of the planets be accounted for?" had lost its meaning in the new science; the new preoccupation is illustrated by what may be called the two most critical problems in seventeenth-century science: "What forces act on the planets to explain their actually observed paths?" and "What accounts for the observed effects of terrestrial gravitation now that Aristotelian doctrines have failed us?"

Good mathematical and experimental tools were also being created.   With mathematics finding expression in physics, the two fields cross-fertilized and gave rich harvests.   The instrument maker and the scientist aided each other similarly.   But in trying to solve the riddle of the spectacular rise of science after Galileo, perhaps the most important factor is the realization that science has an explosive type of growth once the necessary conditions are given.   Around the time of Galileo the necessary conditions for growth were established: at last there were many men with similar attitudes working in the same fields; they could communicate more freely with one another and with the accumulated achievements of the past (partly through the relatively young art of printing); they had become impatient with qualitative reasoning and began to be more and more intrigued with the quantitative approach.   To use a modern analogy, the critical mass was reached, and the chain reaction could proceed.

This, from the point of science, was the new age in which Newton lived.   But a brief word of caution before we follow his work.   The history of ideas, in science as in any other field, is not just an account of visits with the most important names.   The work of each genius is made possible, is stabilized, is connected with the whole structure of science only through the labors of lesser-known men, just as a brick is surrounded by fortifying mortar.   A house is not just a heap of bricks—and science cannot be made by giants only.   As Lord Rutherford has said: "It is not in the nature of things for any one man to make a sudden violent discovery; science goes step by

---

* Some of these problems are skilfully analyzed in G. N. Clark, *Science and Social Welfare in the Age of Newton*.   London: Oxford University Press, 1937 and 1949.

† For a completely delightful example, read the first thirty or forty pages in the Everyman's Library edition of Robert Boyle's *Sceptical Chymist*, originally published in 1661.

step, and every man depends on the work of his predecessors. . . . Scientists are not dependent on the ideas of a single man, but on the combined wisdom of thousands of men." Therefore, properly, we should trace in each man's contribution the heritage of the past, the influence of his contemporaries, and the meaning for his successors. It would be exciting and rewarding, but here we can touch only on the barest outlines.

FIG. 15.2.1. Sir Isaac Newton (1642–1727).

15.2 A SHORT SKETCH OF NEWTON'S LIFE

Isaac Newton (Fig. 15.2.1) was born on Christmas day, 1642, in the small village of Woolsthorpe in Lincolnshire. He was a quiet farm boy who, like young Galileo, loved to build and tinker with mechanical gadgets and who seemed to have a secret liking for mathematics. Through the fortunate intervention of an uncle he was allowed to go to Trinity College of Cambridge University in 1661 (where he appears to have initially enrolled in the study of mathematics as applied to astrology!). He proved an eager and excellent student. By 1666, at twenty-four, he had quietly made spectacular discoveries in mathematics (binomial theorem, differential calculus), optics (theory of colors), and mechanics. Referring to this period, Newton once wrote:

"And the same year I began to think of gravity extending to the orb of the Moon, and . . . from Kepler's Rule [Third Law] . . . I deduced that the forces which keep the Planets in their orbs must [be] reciprocally as the squares of their distances from the centers about which they revolve: and thereby compared the force requisite to keep the Moon in her orb with the force of gravity at the surface of the earth, and found them to answer pretty nearly. All this was in the two plague years of 1665 and 1666, for in those days I was in the prime of my age for invention, and minded Mathematicks and Philosophy more than at any time since."

From his descriptions we may conclude that during those plague years, having left Cambridge for the time to study in isolation at his home in Woolsthorpe, he had developed a clear idea of the first two laws of motion and of the formula for centripetal acceleration, although he did not announce the latter until many years after Huygens' equivalent statement.*

After his return to Cambridge, he did such creditable work that he followed his teacher, Isaac Barrow, as professor of mathematics. He lectured, and contributed papers to the Royal Society, at first particularly on optics. His *Theory of Light and Colors*, when finally published, involved him in so long and bitter a controversy with rivals that the shy and introspective man even resolved not to publish anything else. As Bertrand Russell points out, "If he had encountered the sort of opposition with which Galileo had to contend, it is probable that he would never have published a line." Newton now concentrated most on an extension of his early efforts in celestial mechanics, the study of planetary motions as a problem of physics. In 1684 the devoted Halley came to ask his advice in a dispute with Wren and Robert Hooke as to the force which would have to act on a body executing motion along an ellipse in accord with Kepler's laws; Newton had some time ago found the rigorous solution to this problem ("and much other matter"). Halley persuaded his reluctant friend to publish the work, which touched on one of the most debated and intriguing questions of the time. In less than two years of incredible labors the *Principia* was ready for the printer; its publication in 1687 established Newton almost at once as one of the greatest thinkers in history.

A few years afterward, Newton, who had always been in delicate health, appears to have had what we would now call a nervous breakdown. On recovering, and for the next 35 years until his death in 1727, he made no major new discoveries, but rounded out earlier studies on heat and optics, and turned more and more to writing on theology. During those years he received honors in abundance. In 1699 he was appointed Master of the Mint, partly because of his great interest and competent knowledge in matters concerning the chemistry of metals, and he seems to have helped in reestablishing the debased currency of the country. In 1689 and 1701 he represented his university in Parliament. He was knighted in 1705. From 1703 to his death he was president of the Royal Society. He was buried in Westminster Abbey.

---

* This too must have been the time of the famous and disputed fall of the apple. One of the better authorities for this story is a biography of Newton written by his friend Stukeley in 1752, where we hear that on one occasion Stukeley was having tea with Newton in a garden under some apple trees, when Newton told him he realized "he was just in the same situation, as when formerly, the notion of gravitation came into his mind. It was occasion'd by the fall of an apple, as he sat in a contemplative mood . . ."

15.3 NEWTON'S *PRINCIPIA*

In the original preface to his work—probably the greatest single book in the history of science—we find a clear outline:

> "Since the ancients (as we are told by Pappus) esteemed the science of mechanics of greatest importance in the investigation of natural things, and the moderns, rejecting substantial forms and occult qualities, have endeavored to subject the phenomena of nature to the laws of mathematics, I have in this treatise cultivated mathematics as far as it related to philosophy [we would say 'physical science'] . . . for the whole burden of philosophy seems to me to consist in this— from the phenomena of motions to investigate [induce] the forces of nature, and then from these forces to demonstrate [deduce] the other phenomena, and to this end the general propositions of the first and second Books are directed. In the third Book I give an example of this in the explication of the System of the World; for by the propositions mathematically demonstrated in the former Books, in the third I derive from the celestial phenomena the forces of gravity with which bodies tend to the sun and the several planets. Then from the forces, by other propositions which are also mathematical, I deduce the motions of the planets, the comets, the moon, and the sea [tides] . . ."

The work begins with a set of definitions—mass, momentum, inertia, force, centripetal force. Then follows a section on *absolute* and *relative* space, time, and motion. To us it is of interest that Newton hardly anywhere made explicit use of the concept of *absolute* quantities, because, as he correctly states, "the parts of that immovable [absolute] space, in which those motions are performed, do by no means come under the observation of our senses."

Immediately thereafter we find the famous three Laws of Motion and the principles of composition of vectors (forces and velocities). At a later point follows an equally remarkable and important passage on "Rules of Reasoning in Philosophy." The four rules, reflecting the profound faith in the uniformity of all nature, are intended to guide scientists in making hypotheses, and in that function they are still up to date. The first has been called a *Principle of Parsimony*, the second and third, *Principles of Unity*. The fourth is a faith without which we could not use the processes of logic.

These four rules have been paraphrased as follows:

I. Nature is essentially simple, therefore we should not introduce more hypotheses than are sufficient and necessary for the explanation of observed facts. "Nature does nothing in vain, and more is in vain when less will serve." (This fundamental faith of all scientists is almost a paraphrase of Galileo's "Nature . . . does not that by many things, which may be done by few"—and he, in turn, perhaps with some irony, quoted the same opinion from Aristotle (see Section 14.1).

II. Hence, as far as possible, similar effects must be assigned to the same cause; e.g., "the descent of stones in Europe and in America; the reflection of light in the earth, and in the planets."

III. Properties common to all those bodies within reach of our experiments are to be assumed (even if only tentatively) as pertaining to all bodies in general; e.g., extension, mobility, inertia, the gravitational effect of the earth on the moon as well as on stone.

IV. Propositions in science obtained by wide induction are to be regarded as exactly or approximately true, until phenomena or experiments show that they may be corrected or are liable to exceptions.*

> PROBLEM 15.1.   Compare these four rules regarding scientific hypotheses with criteria for a good theory discussed in Section 12.2, (3) through (5).

> PROBLEM 15.2.   As a review of Newton's laws of motion, find what is *wrong* with the following argument. Imagine a stone of mass m_s falling toward the earth (mass m_e) with acceleration g. Evidently the force acting on the stone is the gravitational pull ($F_{grav} = m_s g$) which, by Newton's third law, also acts on the earth with equal magnitude but in the opposite direction. As seen from the falling stone, the earth approaches the stone also with acceleration g, and since the force on the earth is F_{grav}, we write $F_{grav} = m_e g$. Putting these equations together ($F_{grav} = m_s g$; $F_{grav} = m_e g$), we note that $m_s g = m_e g$ or $m_s = m_e$; i.e., *the stone must always have the same mass as the earth*. (Clue to answer: The equation $F = ma$ has attached to it a long "text" that, among other things, specifies a system of coordinates with respect to which the acceleration is to be measured.)

15.4 THE INVERSE-SQUARE LAW

The three main sections of the *Principia* contain an overwhelming wealth of mathematical and physical discoveries; included are the proofs leading to the law of universal gravitation, proofs so rigidly patterned† that it seems better to present here a development of this historic law in another plausible sequence. The arguments are sometimes rather subtle, and thus they afford a splendid illustration of the interplay between established laws, new hypotheses, experimental observations, and theoretical deductions in physical theory. The purpose of the following pages is to gain an understanding of the process, rather than to memorize the individual steps.

(a) Newton begins with the principal insight gained in the new philosophy: The planets and satellites are not in equilibrium. If they were, if no net force were acting on them, they would be moving in straight lines instead of elliptical paths, in accord with the first law of motion.

(b) Newton then proves that, regardless of the magnitude or nature of the effect, planetary motion must be taking place under the influence of a centrally directed force; i.e., a force directed toward a single, fixed point. This analysis begins in the manner illustrated in Sections 17.13 and 17.14. (The student should digress and study these two sections at this point; they are self-contained and can be studied apart from the

---

* Paraphrased after W. W. R. Ball, *Mathematical Gazette*, July 1914.

† It is not without interest to note that the *form* of the arguments in Newton is along the traditional deductive pattern of Euclid; as, for that matter, were the works of St. Thomas Aquinas and Spinoza.

rest of the material in Chapter 17). Thus Newton shows that a moving particle, subjected to a succession of discrete blows all directed toward a fixed point, will move in such a way that the radius vector between the fixed point and the particle will sweep out equal areas in equal times.

There is no reason why those time intervals should not be chosen as small as we please, so that in the limit as Δt approaches zero, the centrally directed force becomes a continuously acting centripetal force and the broken curve melts into a smooth one.

Then Newton proves the converse of this theorem, namely that if equal areas are swept out in equal time, the force acting on the particle must be a centrally directed force.

According to Kepler's empirical second law, it is known that planets do indeed sweep out equal areas in equal time, and Newton concludes that the force acting on each must be a continuous, centrally directed force. In the case of the ellipse, this center of force is one of the foci; for the circle, the center of the figure.

PROBLEM 15.3. Strictly speaking, we should also prove that blows *not* all directed to the same center O, but instead to any other points, will fail to yield an equal area law. Attempt such a proof.

(c) Now that we accept that the force must be centrally directed, a *centripetal force*, there appears the following crucial problem: "If a body revolves in an ellipse [including the special case of a circle], it is required to find the law of the centripetal force tending to the focus of the ellipse." Newton's mathematics proved for the first time that for paths along conic sections such as hyperbolas, parabolas, ellipses, and circles, the centripetal force at any instant must be proportional to the inverse square of the distance of the body to the focus. In short, any body obeying Kepler's first law of elliptical paths must be acted on by a force following the law $F = C/R^2$, where C is a constant for that body and R is measured from the center of the body to the center of forces, the focus of the ellipse.

The general proof of this theorem is beyond the scope of the present text. We shall present a different argument, however, one that is perhaps closer to Newton's very early line of reasoning mentioned in the quotation in Section 15.2. We shall show that if for a planet in a *circular* path the centripetal force *is* granted to be equal to $F = C/R^2$, there follows by derivation, without further assumptions, that the celestial body should also obey the law

$$T^2 = KR^3.$$

Conversely, since we can observe the latter to be actually true—it is Kepler's third law—we judge that the hypothesis $F = C/R^2$ is well founded for the case of planetary motion.

The derivation proceeds as follows. The centripetal force F_R (or now simply F), on the planet which, as assumed, is given by C/R^2, is also by Newton's second law equal to $m_p a_R$, where m_p is the mass of the planet and a_R is the centripetal acceleration.

For circular paths around the sun, as are actually followed by almost all planets with but little deviation,

$$a_R = \frac{v^2}{R},$$

v being the speed of the planet in its orbit. But

$$a_R = \frac{v^2}{R} = \frac{4\pi^2 R^2}{T^2 R} = \frac{4\pi^2 R}{T^2}, \qquad (15.4.1)$$

where T is the period of orbital revolution of the planet. It follows that

$$F = m_p a_R = m_p \frac{4\pi^2 R}{T^2}. \qquad (15.4.2)$$

Combining the last result with our assumed value for F, we have

$$\frac{C}{R^2} = m_p \frac{4\pi^2 R}{T^2},$$

or

$$T^2 = \left(m_p \frac{4\pi^2}{C} \right) R^3. \qquad (15.4.3)$$

Because m_p and C are constant, the term in parentheses in Eq. (15.4.3) is constant for a given planet, no matter what the size of its orbit. Therefore T^2 is proportional to R^3, as expected from Kepler's third law. By yielding that law, our assumption $F = C/R^2$ stands justified for the time being.

But we must recognize that this is only a tentative proof of the inverse-square law for the centripetal force. Kepler's law requires

$$\left(\frac{m_p 4\pi^2}{C} \right) = K,$$

where K is, for our solar system, the same constant for *all planets* in all their orbits around the sun. Not until we discover what C contains can we know whether the parenthesized term actually yields the same constant for all planets.

Let us note in passing that use has been made of Newton's second law of motion and of the equation for centripetal acceleration but that nothing has been said regarding the *nature* of the force acting on a planet.

Historically, Newton's demonstration that elliptical planetary paths imply an inverse-square law of the force came at a time when the idea of such a law was generally "in the air." Hooke had speculated regarding an inverse-square law of gravitational force and had engaged associates to attempt to observe whether the extension of a spring carrying a given chunk of material increased in a deep mine or decreased in a high building. (He reported being able to observe no significant effect.) Although Hooke was in secure command of the mathematics of his day, he did not compare with Newton as a creative mathematician, and he was not able to solve the problem of planetary motion.

15.5   NATURE OF THE CENTRIPETAL FORCE IN THE SOLAR SYSTEM

The *origin* of the centripetal force needed to keep the planets in their orbits has not been touched on so far. We recall that Kepler guessed that some driving magnetic force reached out from the sun to move the planets. He was wrong, but at least he was the first to regard the sun as the controlling mechanical agency behind planetary motion. Another picture had been given by the great French philosopher Descartes (1596–1650), who proposed that all space was filled with a subtle invisible fluid of contiguous material corpuscles; the planets of the solar system were supposed to be caught in a huge vortex-like motion of this fluid about the sun. This idea was attractive to the minds of the day, and consequently was widely accepted for a time, but Newton proved that this mechanism could not account for the quantitative observations on planetary motion as summarized, for example, in Kepler's laws. The problem remained.

At this point Newton proposed a dramatic solution: the centripetal force on the planets is nothing but a gravitational attraction of the sun, and the centripetal force on satellites revolving around planets is also completely given by the gravitational pull by the planets. (Less than a century before it would have been impious or "foolish" to suggest that terrestrial laws and forces regulated the whole universe, but now, after Kepler and Galileo had unified the physics of heaven and earth, it had become a natural thing to suspect.) If the earth attracts the moon with the same type of force with which it attracts a falling apple or a projectile, and if the sun attracts earth, moon, and all other celestial bodies with the same type of force, then there is no need for any additional cosmic force or prime mover, then gravity becomes a universal, unifying principle which, while in fundamental contradiction to the axioms of the Scholastics, would have gladdened the heart of Kepler.

But we must follow the argument. First paralleling young Newton's thoughts, let us see whether the centripetal force F needed to keep the moon in its (nearly enough) circular orbit about the earth *can* be identified with terrestrial gravity. The *direction* of F is by definition toward the center of the earth, and this checks with the direction of the force of gravity. But what about the *magnitude* of F? We apply the equation for centripetal force to this case, and find

$$F = m_m \frac{4\pi^2 R}{T^2}, \tag{15.5.1}$$

where m_m is the mass of the moon, R is now its distance from the center of rotation about the earth, and T its period of revolution.

Does this value for F actually coincide with the gravitational pull which the earth exerts on our satellite, as Newton proposed? That depends on the nature of the gravitational force. If gravity is propagated undiminished through all space, the weight of the moon will be simply $m_m \cdot g$, the same as a stone of the moon's mass when placed on giant scales somewhere on the surface of the earth. But not only does it seem unlikely that the gravitational acceleration stays the same no matter how far away from the earth we go, we also recall that in Section 15.4 we found evidence that the centripetal force (whatever its final nature) must fall off as the square of the increasing distance. If gravity is to account completely for the centripetal force, it too will have to follow an inverse-square law. Let us therefore assume that the weight of an object falls off according to such a law, and consider now whether the gravitational pull of the earth on the moon just equals the centripetal force in Eq. (15.5.1).

This is our argument: An object with the same mass as the moon, m_m, has the weight $m_m g$ when weighed at the surface of the earth, i.e., at a distance r (the radius of the earth) from the earth's center. That same object, when removed to a great distance R from the earth's center, will assume a smaller weight, which we shall call W_R, and which must fulfill the following proportion if the inverse-square law is to be obeyed:

$$\frac{m_m g}{W_R} = \frac{1/r^2}{1/R^2}, \quad \text{or} \quad W_R = m_m g \frac{r^2}{R^2}. \tag{15.5.2}$$

If the centripetal force F acting on the mass m_m rotating about the earth at distance R with a period T is really equivalent to the gravitational force W_R at that distance, the terms on the right-hand side of Eqs. (15.5.1) and (15.5.2) would also be equivalent:

$$\frac{m_m 4\pi^2 R}{T^2} = m_m g \frac{r^2}{R^2}, \quad \text{or} \quad T^2 = \frac{4\pi^2}{gr^2} R^3. \tag{15.5.3}$$

Conversely, if we substitute observed values of T, g, r, and R in Eq. (15.5.3) and find that the equation yields equal numbers on each side, then we are justified in regarding our hypotheses as valid; then the gravitational force *does* fall off as the square of the increasing distance, and *does* fully account for the needed centripetal force. [Incidentally, we note with satisfaction that Kepler's third law is implied in our result, Eq. (15.5.3).]

> PROBLEM 15.4. Substitute the needed values in consistent units and check to what extent Eq. (15.5.3) holds. The period T of the moon is about $27\frac{1}{3}$ days, $g = 32$ ft/sec^2, $r \cong 3960$ mi, $R \cong 60$ r.

This was the calculation which Newton, with contemporary data, found to "answer pretty nearly," probably within a few percent. The assumption of a strictly circular path and somewhat inaccurate values of r and g made it clear from the start that no *perfect* agreement could have been expected.

It has been a source of much speculation why Newton did not tell anyone of this remarkable result when he first conceived it, or for nearly 20 years thereafter. Apart from his reticence and his fear of litigations with jealous men, he seems to have been unable at the time to account clearly for one implied assumption in the argument, namely, that the earth's gravitational force acts as if originating at the very center of the globe, and that consequently the measurement of distances must be made, not to the globe's surface, but to its center. He understood this requirement later when writing the *Principia*, where he proved in general that two homogeneous spheres attract each other as though their masses were concentrated at the centers.

As a summary we may use Newton's own statement that "the moon gravitates toward the earth, and by the force of gravity is continually drawn off from a rectilinear motion, and retained in its orbit." Apart from the assumptions and approximations alluded to, we have made use of only the following new arguments: that the gravitational force falls off as the square of the distance, and that by Rules I and II of Section 15.3 we can identify terrestrial gravity with the centripetal force on the moon.

The previous paragraphs have not involved the forces between the sun and the planets, but we should again suspect that these ideas may be extended to the whole solar system. In Newton's words:

> "The force which retains the celestial bodies in their orbits has been hitherto called centripetal force; but it being now made plain that it can be no other than a gravitational force, we shall hereafter call it gravity. For the cause of that centripetal force which retains the moon in its orbit will extend itself to all planets, by Rules I, II, and IV."

But such rules are just guiding, not prescriptive ones. They suggest, but do not prove; this labor remains to be done.

15.6 CONNECTION BETWEEN MASS AND GRAVITATIONAL FORCE

The discussion in Sections 15.4 and 15.5 leaves us with the inductive inference that the gravitational force F_{grav} (or, more briefly, F_G) between *any* two spherically symmetric bodies is proportional to the inverse square of the distance between the two centers, everything else being kept constant:

$$F_G \propto \frac{1}{R^2}.$$

There remains the crucial question as to what besides the separation of the bodies—what property of the bodies themselves—helps determine the size of the gravitational force they exert on each other.

Let us consider two specific solid bodies, quite isolated from the rest of the universe, say a stone (m_1) and the earth (m_2) at a distance R between their centers. The pull of gravity, the weight of m_1 at the given distance R, is F_G. But by Newton's third law, the pull of the earth (m_2) on m_1 is just as large as the pull of m_1 on m_2; the weight of a stone F_G as measured by its attraction toward the earth *is equal* to the "weight of the earth" as measured by its attraction to the stone, strange though this may sound at first, *and either one may be called F_G* (Fig. 15.6.1).

However, we know by experiment that at a given locality the weight of the stone grows directly with the mass of the stone, or $F_G \propto m_1$. On the other hand, if the mass of the planet changed, we would expect that the weight of a given stone would change also (in fact, you would weigh much less on our little moon than on earth). In short, if experiments prove that $F_G \propto m_1$ at a constant distance R, then we would

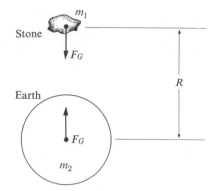

FIG. 15.6.1. The force of attraction exerted by the earth on a stone is equal in magnitude to the attraction exerted by the stone on the earth.

expect F_G to be proportional to m_2 also, since we have no reason to expect one of the two bodies to be "different" or "privileged" with respect to the other. (This inductive reasoning represents an appeal to symmetry, and our confidence in this mode of thought is repeatedly reinforced by the discovery of rules of symmetry in physical laws.)

From the proportionalities we have induced we obtain

$$F_G \propto \frac{m_1 m_2}{R^2}, \quad \text{or} \quad F_G = G\frac{m_1 m_2}{R^2}, \tag{15.6.1}$$

where R is the center distance between the two bodies (let us assume them to be homogeneous spheres) and G is a constant of proportionality. (At this point the student should reread Section 7.13, the discussion of the distinction between the concepts of gravitational and inertial mass.)

If we have confidence that Eq. (15.6.1) gives, in fact, the correct attraction which two bodies exert on each other, and if one were the sun (m_s), the other any planet (m_p), then the sun's pull would be

$$F_G = G\frac{m_p m_s}{R_{ps}^2}.$$

If the moon and the earth were taken separately, their mutual force would be

$$F_G = G\frac{m_m m_e}{R_{me}^2}.$$

15.7 THE LAW OF UNIVERSAL GRAVITATION

The preceding statements imply interpretation of Eq. (15.6.1) as a law of universal gravitation. If this interpretation is correct, this newly found law must certainly be compatible with all three of Kepler's laws. There is no trouble about the first two— elliptical orbits and the equal area relations must indeed result from this type of gravitational force, since it is centrally directed and is proportional to the inverse square of the distances in accordance with just those requirements, laid down in parts (b) and (c) of Section 15.4.

But what of Kepler's third law? We remember that our previous argument, center-ing on Eq. (15.4.3), was a little shaky. We had not really proved, with the force assumed there, that T^2/R^3 had to be a truly universal constant, with the same value for *all* planets in our universe. Now that we know more about the force acting in the solar system, we can try more rigorously to obtain such a result; for if we do *not* obtain it, gravity cannot be the sole force among the celestial bodies.

Let us test our law of universal gravitation against the nearly circular orbital motion of our own planet. The centripetal force that must exist on our mass m_p at distance R_{ps} from the sun is given by

$$\frac{m_p 4\pi^2 R_{ps}}{T^2}.$$

The gravitational force supposedly available is $Gm_p m_s/R_{ps}^2$. If the two coincide, if the gravitational force "supplies" and so "explains" the centripetal force, then

$$m_p \frac{4\pi^2 R_{ps}}{T^2} = G\frac{m_p m_s}{R_{ps}^2}, \quad \text{or} \quad T^2 = \left(\frac{4\pi^2}{Gm_s}\right) R_{ps}^3. \tag{15.7.1}$$

Now we really can see whether T^2/R_{ps}^3 is a constant for all planets, as required by Kepler's third law. The parentheses in Eq. (15.7.1), which is to be identified with that constant, contain only the constant of proportionality G, the mass of the sun, and a numerical factor; none of these is variable from planet to planet. Therefore T^2/R_{ps}^3 is truly constant, Kepler's law is fulfilled, and the assumption of universal gravitation is vindicated.

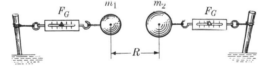

FIG. 15.7.1. $F_G = G(m_1 m_2/R^2)$.

But there remains yet another doubt. Is it proper to have assumed just now so glibly that G does in fact have the same value for all planets? (If it does not, the parenthesized term above is, after all, not constant for all bodies.) Here we turn to experiment. We can first measure G only for various materials on earth; using the equation

$$F_G = G\frac{m_1 m_2}{R^2},$$

we get

$$G = F_G \frac{R^2}{m_1 m_2}.$$

We may propose to measure F_G with spring balances, neglecting all other disturbing attractions except that between two known masses m_1 and m_2 at measured distance R from each other (see Fig. 15.7.1). It turns out that for any reasonably small masses in our laboratories, F_G is so exceedingly small that special techniques and precautions have to be adopted to measure any attraction between two such masses; for example, two 1-kg masses separated by 10 cm pull on each other with a force smaller than 10^{-8} newton. The most serious technical problems of measurement were solved by Henry Cavendish over 100 years after the publication of the *Principia*, and the best present value for G is about 6.67×10^{-11} n $\cdot$ m^2/kg^2 for all substances. (Cavendish's measurements were made with a delicate torsion balance.)

PROBLEM 15.5.   If a remeasurement of G were attempted with the arrangement shown in Fig. 15.7.1, and if the error inherent in our measuring devices is about 2×10^{-4} n, what is the smallest usable radius for each of two similar gold spheres which almost touch? (Density of gold = 19.3 gm/cm^3. This problem is fairly representative of what one has to go through before designing apparatus for experimentation.)

Cavendish's results, and all the more accurate ones since, have shown that G has indeed the same value, no matter what the composition of m_1 and m_2, even for meteorite material. Being disposed to apply terrestrial laws to celestial bodies, we extend our findings, and maintain that in the absence of evidence to the contrary all materials in the world, including sun, planets, and satellites, obey the same law of gravitation.

Although Newton knew in principle how to go about measuring G accurately, he lacked the precise instruments; nevertheless he devised an ingenious proof for the *constancy* of G, which is the main point at issue here. Consider a mass m_1 on the surface of our earth (of mass m_e), that is, at a distance r from the center of our globe. Its weight, which we called F_G, is of course also given by m_1g; therefore, by our new law,

$$m_1 g = G \frac{m_1 m_e}{r^2}, \quad \text{or} \quad G = \frac{r^2}{m_e} g. \tag{15.7.2}$$

At a given locality, r^2/m_e is, of course, a constant, regardless of its numerical value. If at that locality all substances show precisely the same value for g (the gravitational acceleration), then we have established that G, too, is constant, regardless of chemical composition, texture, shape, etc. This is just what Newton showed experimentally. His measurements of g were made not by just dropping small and large bodies, from which even Galileo had concluded that g cannot vary significantly, but by the much more accurate method of timing pendulums of equal lengths but of different materials. It was known by then that for a given length the period T of a simple pendulum is proportional only to $1/\sqrt{g}$. After exhaustive experiments, all pointing to the constancy of G, he could write: "This is the quality of all bodies within the reach of our experiments; and therefore (by Rule III) to be affirmed of all bodies whatsoever."

Thus G attains the status of the *universal* constant of gravitation (one of the very few truly universal constants in nature), and the proposed law of universal gravitation in Eq. (15.6.1) can be applied on a cosmic scale. And quite incidentally, Eq. (15.7.2) clears up a question on which both ancient Aristotelians and present-day students harbor strongest suspicions; namely, the reason why at a given locality the acceleration of gravity is constant for all bodies. The answer is that g depends only on G, m_e, and r^2, all constant at one locality.

15.8   CALCULATIONS BASED ON THE GRAVITATION LAW

Once a value for G is at hand, we may determine the mass of the earth [from Eq. (15.7.2)] and of the sun [from Eq. (15.7.1)].

Moreover, Eq. (15.7.1) should apply in the same form for a satellite moving around a planet of mass m_p, with a period T_{sat} and a radius (or a half major axis of the elliptical orbit) R_{p-sat}:

$$T_{sat}^2 = \frac{4\pi^2}{Gm_p} R_{p-sat}^3. \tag{15.8.1}$$

This yields the mass of any planet whose satellites we can observe.

PROBLEM 15.6.   Determine the mass of the earth and of the sun as indicated. [*Answer:* $m_{earth} = 5.98 \times 10^{24}$ kg, $m_{sun} = 333,000 \times m_{earth}$.]

PROBLEM 15.7.   The innermost of Saturn's nine satellites, Mimas, has a fairly circular orbit of 187,000 km radius and a period of revolution of about 23 hours. Find the mass of Saturn.

For the masses of the satellites themselves (including our own moon), and of the planets which boast of no moons (Mercury, Venus), no such simple calculations exist. There we may use the relatively minor and elaborate interactions between the celestial bodies, which we have conveniently neglected until now. Some of these are called *perturbations*, i.e., slight digressions from the regular path of a body because of the pull of other celestial objects.* Another detail which may be used to derive the relative mass of a satellite is the fact that Kepler's laws hold, strictly speaking, only if the center of mass of the system is considered to be at the focus of the ellipse. Furthermore, it is not the earth which moves in accordance with the first law in an elliptical orbit around the sun, but the center of mass of earth and moon together (a point about 1000 miles below the surface of the earth and on a line between the centers of those two spheres; see Section 9.12).

Except for such mass determinations (or for accurate astronomical and nautical tables), we usually forget about the complications. But one of the results obtained is that the moon's mass is about $\frac{1}{82}$ of the earth's, and that the sun's mass, determined in this indirect fashion, has the same value as followed from Eq. (15.7.1).

If follows also that, owing to perturbations, Kepler's laws cannot be expected to hold *exactly*. (In fact, astronomers before Newton had begun to worry more and more about these discrepancies, particularly for Saturn and for the moon.) Once more we find a set of laws breaking down when the precision of observations is increased beyond the original range. But this breakdown is not serious; it does not invalidate the overall outlines of the theory of planetary motion, particularly now that it is possible in principle to account in detail for each discrepancy by means of

---

* The pull of the planets on each other is small relative to the force exerted by the sun, but is large enough to produce observable effects on the planetary orbits.

the law of gravitation.* (For a table of data on the solar system, see Appendix B.)

PROBLEM 15.8.   With the data of Appendix B, compare the gravitational pulls of sun and earth on the moon. Why does the earth not lose the moon to the sun?

PROBLEM 15.9.   Describe, in quantitative detail, a possible method for obtaining the mass of our moon by sending to it an observable projectile which would be caught by the moon's gravitational pull and remain in an orbit around the moon as its satellite.

PROBLEM 15.10.   Compute the distance from the earth's center to an artificial satellite having a period of one day in its motion around the center of the earth. A satellite with this period could effectively stay always directly above one city on the equator. Why could it not be expected to stay directly above a city that is *not* on the equator?

PROBLEM 15.11.   Newton considered how one might launch a projectile "from the top of a high mountain" so that it does not fall to the earth (Fig. 15.8.1). He went on to "imagine bodies to be projected in the direction of lines parallel to the horizon from greater heights," that is, "1000 or more miles," which would "go on revolving through the heavens in those orbits just as the planets do in their orbits." What conditions must be fulfilled to produce such motions? (The response should contain numerical results.)

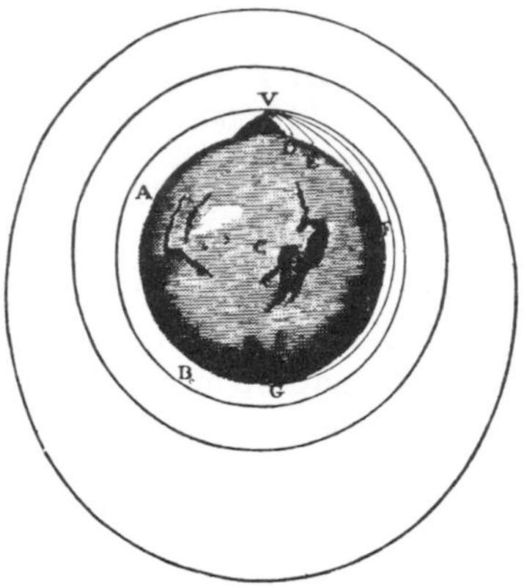

FIG. 15.8.1. Newton's presentation of the paths of projectiles launched horizontally from various heights above the earth's surface.

PROBLEM 15.12.   A planet of mass m_p and radius r_p has a moon of mass m_m and radius r_m. How far from the center of the planet is the point P where the gravitational pulls on an object due to m_p and m_m would balance? First derive the general formula; then find the numerical distance for the case of our earth and moon.

We have extended the law of universal gravitation in *one* direction—to all planets and satellites; it seems logical to extend it in the other direction—to all *parts* of every body. Newton writes in Book III of the *Principia:*

"Proposition VII. Theorem VII: That there is a power of gravity tending to all bodies, proportional to the several quantities of matter [i.e., the product of

---

* We are reminded of the 8 minutes of arc which Copernicus did not know of, and are tempted to marvel again how significant it is that these secondary effects were too small to appear earlier and confuse the original investigators. But in this case there seems to be an extra twist; if the perturbations were any larger, we might well not have a solar system to contemplate, because it would hardly be stable enough to last these billions of years without catastrophic collisions.

the masses] they contain. That all the planets mutually gravitate one towards another, we have proved before; . . . [we now introduce the idea that] the force of gravity towards any whole planet arises from, and is compounded of, the forces of gravity toward all its parts . . . If it be objected, that, according to this law, *all* bodies with us must mutually gravitate one toward another, whereas no such gravitation anywhere appears, I answer, that . . . the gravitation toward them must be far less than to fall under the observation of our senses."

With the aid of his own calculus Newton proceeds to show that if we assume the same universal law of gravitation for each smallest particle of a body (say of a sphere), we obtain in sum a resultant force of gravity for the whole body of such characteristics as are actually observable.

There offers itself now an overall view of the enormous range and sweep of the simple formula for the gravitational attraction of two bodies. *Postulating* the law just for each of the parts of a body, it gives us the attraction of the whole for some outside object. For the special case of the spherical celestial bodies, it provides a force necessary and sufficient for the description of all observed motions, for the derivation of all three laws of Kepler, and for the small, long-observed deviations therefrom. This was the vindication of Copernicus, Kepler, and Galileo—in the context of the greater, more far-reaching theory of universal gravitation. The whole structure is often referred to as the *Newtonian Synthesis*.

PROBLEM 15.13.   List the fundamental hypotheses of the theory of universal gravitation and the experimental consequences. Which hypothesis is not *directly* confirmable by experiment (although its consequences are)?

15.9 SOME INFLUENCES ON NEWTON'S WORK

What were the main intellectual tools, concepts, and attitudes with which Newton worked? If we wish to claim any insight into his time and his work we must at least summarize these facts now; most of them have already appeared scattered here and there through the discussion.

(a) Newton was not a "hard-boiled" scientist of the twentieth-century type, but was a child of his time. He was not free from all traces of what we regard as pseudo-sciences; apart from some early interest in astrology, he seems to have spent much time in his "elaboratory," cooking potions that to us would smell more of alchemy than of chemistry—although the aim there, as in all his activities, seems to have been the search for underlying general principles, not, of course, quick practical gains.* By our present standards we might also say that his belief in absolutes and his anthro-

---

* Sidelights on Newton's work as experimenter, chemist, theologian, and King's servant can be found in the collection of the History of Science Society, *Sir Isaac Newton (1727–1927)*. Baltimore: Williams & Wilkins Co., 1928.

pomorphic conception of a Creator carried very far into some of his scientific writings. But here we touch on the very secret of motivation for his scientific work; such a study, although fascinating in its own right, must to us remain a detail. First of all, we should consider the clear Galilean influence on Newton's formulation of the physical concepts of mass and the like. The decisive attitude throughout his work is that celestial phenomena are explainable by quantitative terrestrial laws; that these laws have legitimate general meaning and are not just mathematical conveniences covering unattainable "true" laws.

(b) To his fundamental faith in the proximity and accessibility of natural law, we must add a word about his methodology. His debt to the pioneers of the new experimental science is clear (for example, he made ingenious pieces of equipment and performed good experiments when the theory needed verification), but he also successfully combined this principally inductive approach with the deductive method then most prominently displayed in Descartes. With his mathematical powers enriching the experimental attitude, he set a clear, straight course for the methods of physical science.

(c) Not just his attitude toward concepts, but many of the concepts themselves came to him from Galileo and his followers: above all, force, acceleration, the addition of vector quantities, and the first law of motion. Newton also drew, of course, from Kepler; and through their books and reports to the Royal Society he kept in touch with the work of such contemporaries as Huygens and Hooke.

(d) Apart from his own experiments, he took his data from a great variety of sources; for example, Tycho Brahe was one of several astronomers, old and new, whose observations of the moon's motion he consulted. When he could not carry out his own measurements he knew whom to ask, and we find him corresponding widely with men like Flamsteed and Halley, both Royal Astronomers. There are evidences that he searched the literature very carefully when he was in need of exact data, for example, on the radius of the earth and the distance to the moon.

(e) Lastly, we must not fail to consider how fruitfully and exhaustively his own specific contributions were used repeatedly throughout his work. The laws of motion and the mathematical inventions appear again and again, at every turn in the development. But he was modest about this part of his achievement, and said once that if he had seen further than others *"it is by standing upon ye shoulders of Giants."*

15.10 SEVERAL DEDUCTIONS FROM THE GRAVITATION LAW

What amazed Newton's contemporaries and increases our own admiration for him was not only the range and genius of his work on mechanics, not only the originality and elegance of his proofs, but also the detail with which he developed each idea to its fullest fruition. It took almost a century for science to fully comprehend, verify, and round out his work, and at the end of a second century an important scientist and philosopher still had to confess: "Since his time no essentially new principle [in mechanics] has been stated. All that has been accomplished in mechanics since his day has been a deductive, formal, and mathematical development of mechanics on the basis of Newton's laws."

(a) An example of Newton's thorough mastery was his treatment of the moon's perturbations. The influence on its path of the gravitational forces from almost all other celestial bodies was considered, and the repeated use of the gravitational law yielded an astonishingly close approximation to every small complexity of motion. (A full list of influential factors in tabular form would now fill hundreds of pages.) For one minor variation of the path, however, Newton's published theoretical result was only half the observed value. He did not camouflage this defect, but clearly stated that his calculations gave the wrong figure. Consequently, a loud, long battle arose among some scientists, several of whom called for complete abandonment of the whole theory of gravitation on account of this discrepancy. Eventually the mathematician Clairaut noted a small error in the long calculations, clearing up the difficulty. Later still, some unpublished notes of Newton were found, showing that he, too, 50 years before Clairaut, had discovered and corrected his own mistake!

(b) Comets, whose dreaded appearance had been interpreted as sure signs of disaster throughout antiquity and the middle ages, were now shown to be nothing but passing clouds of material obeying the laws of gravitation, made visible by reflected light while near the sun. The great comet of 1682, whose path Edmond Halley watched carefully, indicated to him a period of recurrence of *approximately* every 75 years if the comet, although an eccentric member of the solar family, nevertheless were to obey the usual laws of mechanics, including Kepler's laws. Its return in 1756 and twice since, after covering a wide ellipse carrying it far beyond the last planet, were heralded as significant symbols of the triumph of Newtonian science. (See Fig. 15.10.1.)

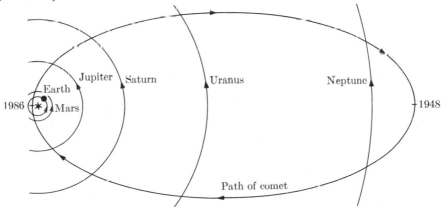

FIG. 15.10.1. Path of Halley's comet.

(c) Newton reasoned that the shape of planets and satellites might be explained as the result of the mutual gravity of the separate parts, which would pull a large quantity of initially fluid material (or a dust cloud) into a compact sphere. Further, although a motionless body might indeed form a perfect sphere, a planet rotating about an axis ought to assume the shape of an oblate spheroid, that is, it ought to bulge at the equator and be flatter at the poles. In fact, from the relative magnitude of the equa-

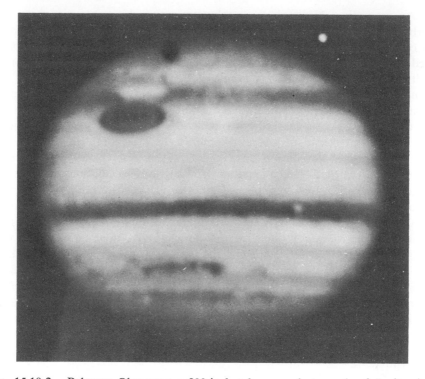

Fig. 15.10.2. Palomar Observatory 200-inch telescope photograph of Jupiter in blue light, showing oblateness of planet due to rotation about its axis. Note the large red spot in the upper left; also the satellite Ganymede (upper right) and shadow of Ganymede on surface of the planet. (Courtesy of Mt. Wilson and Palomar Observatories.)

torial bulge, say of Jupiter as seen through a good telescope (see Fig. 15.10.2), one may calculate the period of rotation about the axis (the length of a day on Jupiter).

For the earth, Newton predicted that the same effect would be found, and later, accurate measurements actually revealed the diameter of the earth from pole to pole to be less by 27 miles than across the equatorial plane. Consequently the gravitational force on an object at the pole is somewhat greater than at the equator, owing to the shorter distance from the center of gravity of the earth to the pole. This effect is relatively small, but another cause joins to diminish the acceleration of a freely falling body at the equator. At that region the surface velocity of a point on earth is about 1000 mi/hr, due to the rotation of the globe about its axis. Since the centripetal acceleration a_r is given by v^2/r, a_r for any object at the equator is about $\frac{1}{10}$ ft/sec^2 or 3 cm/sec^2, as we have calculated in Problem 9.22. This much acceleration is required just to keep the body from flying off along a tangent; consequently the acceleration of free fall (and therefore the apparent weight of the body) is proportionately less than it would be if our globe were not rotating. Measured values of the free-fall acceleration, all at sea level, range from about 9.83 m/sec^2 near the poles to 9.78 m/sec^2 near the equator with 9.80398 m/sec^2 the standard value for Cambridge,

Massachusetts. These observed values are, of course, the true acceleration due to gravity *minus* the centripetal acceleration at that latitude. But we shall be content with the convention that the letter g may stand for those *observed* values and yet be usually called "acceleration due to gravity."

In 1736 Louis XV sent the French mathematician-astronomer Pierre Louis de Maupertuis (1698–1759) on an expedition to Lapland to measure the length of a degree of the meridian. Maupertuis (together with Voltaire) was among those influential in developing understanding and appreciation of the Newtonian theory on the continent. In the course of his expedition, Maupertuis made accurate pendulum measurements of g, showing that its value increased with latitude in the manner predicted by the gravitational theory. This was probably one of the very earliest expeditions having geophysical research as its main objective. Maupertuis published his results in 1738 in a monograph titled "*Sur la figure de la terre.*"

> PROBLEM 15.14. Because of the bulging of the earth near the equator, the source of the Mississippi River, although high above sea level, is nearer to the center of the earth than is its mouth. How can the river flow "uphill"? [*Hint:* The word "uphill" needs contemplation.]
>
> PROBLEM 15.15. Review and solve Problems 9.22 and 9.23.

At present, the methods of measurement have been refined to such an extent that small local fluctuations in g can be detected and used to give clues of possible mineral deposits underground. But once one goes below the surface into a mine, g is found to change, becoming zero as the center of the earth is approached. The law of gravitation in its simple form holds only if the two bodies whose mutual attraction is to be measured are separated and not entwined or intergrown. Newton predicted this excellently, and a moment's thought will persuade us that at the center of the earth, at any rate, we could have no weight, because the forces of the earth's attraction from all sides would cancel. (See Section 24.3.)

15.11 QUALITATIVE EXPLANATION OF THE TIDES

The phenomenon of the tides, so important to navigators, tradesmen, and explorers through the ages, had remained a mystery despite the efforts of such men as Galileo,* but at least the main features, the semidiurnal high tide and the semimonthly spring tide (maximum high tide), were explained by Newton through application of the law of universal gravitation. He recognized that the moon (and to a lesser extent the other celestial bodies) would pull on the nearest part of the ocean, and so tend to "heap up" the waters. We do not want to take time for the many details involved, except to look at the conclusions. The bulge of water (which actually is raised at the

---

* See the Fourth Day of Galileo's *Dialogues Concerning the Two Chief World Systems* for his (incorrect) attempt to explain the phenomenon of the tides and for his use of this argument to support the thesis that the earth moves.

same time on *both* sides of the globe because of the revolution of the earth around the center of mass of the earth-moon system; see Section 9.12) does not stay directly under the moon but is displaced to a position a little ahead by the rotation of the earth. Thus a high tide at a point in the ocean is encountered some time after seeing the moon pass overhead, and again about 12 hours later (Fig. 15.11.1). The sun has a similar though smaller effect,* and since sun, moon, and earth are in line twice a month (at new and full moon), the two tidal forces coincide to produce semimonthly extremes of tide level. Between spring tides, sun and moon may partially cancel each other's effects (neap tides).

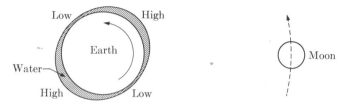

FIG. 15.11.1. Tides caused by the moon. The earth is to be imagined as rotating in this (much exaggerated) envelope of water. The high tide stays relatively fixed with respect to the moon.

The exact features of this complex phenomenon depend to a great extent on the topography of shoreline and ocean floor. Long series of actual observations help to predict individual features of the tides at each locality. In passing, we should notice that the "solid" earth has similarly explained tides, which must be allowed for in such exact experiments as refined astronomical observations, and that it is just such a tidal effect that offers one of the methods for the approximate calculation of the mass of the moon.

15.12   THE DISCOVERY OF NEW PLANETS

One of the most intriguing aspects of Newton's work still remains to be told: how, over 100 years after his death, Newton's law of universal gravitation helped to discover new planets. Lodge refers to it as follows:

> "The explanation by Newton of the observed facts of the motions of the moon, the way he accounted for precession and nutation and for the tides, the way in which Laplace [whose mathematical work extended Newton's calculations] explained every detail of the planetary motions—these achievements may seem to the professional astronomer equally, if not more, striking and wonderful; . . . But to predict in the solitude of the study, with no weapons other than pen, ink,

---

* The direct pull of the sun on the earth is about 175 times that of the moon, but tides are generated by the *difference* of pull on the waters on both sides of the globe; and that is larger for the moon. (Why?)

and paper, an unknown and enormously distant world, to calculate its orbit when as yet it had never been seen, and to be able to say to a practical astronomer, 'Point your telescope in such a direction at such a time, and you will see a new planet hitherto unknown to man'—this must always appeal to the imagination with dramatic intensity . . ."

One night in 1781 William Herschel of Bath, England, an extraordinarily energetic mixture of professional musician and gifted amateur astronomer, was searching the sky with his homemade, 10-foot telescope. For years he had patiently looked at and reexamined every corner of the heavens, finding new stars, nebulae, and comets, and he was becoming well known among astronomers. On that particular night he again found a celestial object, hitherto uncatalogued and of such "uncommon appearance" that he suspected it to be a new comet. Through the Royal Society the news spread. As observations continued night after night, it became evident that this was not a comet but a newly discovered planet, over 100 times larger than the earth and nearly twice as far from the sun as Saturn, until then the outermost member of the solar family. So *Uranus* was discovered—an unsuspected and sensational widening of the ancient horizon, a planet just barely visible to the naked eye, but previously mistaken for a star when occasionally observed.

By that time it was known how to compute the elliptic orbit of a planet from a few widely separated observations of its varying positions. Also, the expected small deviations from the true ellipse owing to the perturbing force of the other planets were accurately predictable on the basis of Newton's law of gravitation. Uranus' 84-year orbit was so mapped out for it by calculation, and all went well for many years. But by 1830 it became more and more evident that Uranus was misbehaving, and that the assumptions on which its schedule had been worked out were in need of revision.

Some thought that Newton's theory might not apply accurately, after all, over such immense distances, but they had nothing better to offer (and as has been well pointed out, theories are in general not overthrown by isolated contradictory facts but only by other, better theories). Others suggested that a hitherto unsuspected comet or a more distant planet might introduce additional perturbations into Uranus' path, but they, too, were merely guessing and made no concrete quantitative predictions.

But the idea of an undiscovered planet beyond Uranus intrigued John C. Adams, a young undergraduate at Cambridge University, and he undertook the immensely difficult mathematical task of locating the positions of this suspected perturbing body solely from the observed motions of Uranus, using throughout the law of gravitation in unmodified form. He had his mathematical result of the problem two years after graduation, and for the necessary confirmation wrote to the Royal Observatory at Greenwich, asking that their powerful telescope search for the hypothetical new planet at a predicted location beyond Uranus. Since Adams was an unknown young mathematician, however, he was not taken seriously enough to interrupt the current work there.

A few months later, another young man, Leverrier in France, published the result of similar, independent calculations, giving very nearly the same position for the suspected planet as had Adams. While finally some observations were slowly being undertaken in England to verify Adams' theoretical conclusions, Leverrier sent his own prediction to the head of the observatory at Berlin, who on the very evening of the letter's arrival himself searched for and recognized the planet at very nearly its predicted position. Thus *Neptune* was added to the solar system in 1846; and here was indeed a triumph of the law of universal gravitation!

Neptune, in turn, was closely watched. The orbital radius is about 30 times the earth's, and its period is therefore given by Kepler's law (correctly) as 164.8 years. But in time the perturbations of this planet and those of Uranus again became larger than was accountable in terms of known forces, and the hypothesis of still another planet was naturally made. An arduous 25-year-long search yielded the discovery of *Pluto* in 1930, announced on the double anniversary of Herschel's discovery of Uranus and of the birthday of Percival Lowell, whose calculations had led to the search and who had founded the observatory in Arizona at which the discovery was made. Another astronomer, W. H. Pickering, had made independent calculations and predictions of Pluto's position as far back as 1909, and had initiated a telescopic search for the planet at Mount Wilson Observatory in California. Nothing was found then, but after the discovery at the Lowell Observatory in 1930, the old Mount Wilson photographs were reexamined and showed that Pluto could have been found in 1919 if its image had not fallen directly on a small flaw in the photographic emulsion!

This story dramatizes the frequently forgotten possibility that for every overpublicized discovery which is made by "accident," without elaborate preparations, there may well be an equally important discovery which, also by accident, *failed* to be made despite careful research.

15.13   THE BODE-TITUS LAW

This chapter would be incomplete without a short discussion of the influence of a strange and simple empirical rule on the discovery of Neptune. This rule is known as "Bode's law" or the "Bode-Titus law" and was discovered by J. E. Bode (1747–1826), following a suggestion by his friend J. D. Titus.

At the start of his long search for regularity in the solar system, Kepler had discovered a crude relationship between the sizes of the various planetary orbits, but it was a rather fruitless jumble of numerological statements. The best that can be said of it was that its mathematical ingenuity first brought him to the attention of Brahe and Galileo. Later, the three Keplerian laws, unified by Newton's work, showed that there existed a simple universal relation between each planet's speed and orbit, but it left unanswered the question why a given planet did not move in some other possible orbit with a correspondingly different speed. Was there, for example, any specific reason why the earth could not pursue a course nearer to Mars', although necessarily with a relatively slower period of revolution? Nothing in Kepler's or Newton's work showed that the chosen orbit was in any way unique or necessary.

Since the whole effort of science is bent on finding simple regularities, it is no wonder that men continued to look for clues. Bode's law—obtained, no doubt, as Kepler's laws were obtained, by incessant mathematical play with the data to be explained—

established just such a clue, which, in the absence of physical reasons, must certainly look like a strange coincidence.

If we number the successively more distant planets from the sun with $n = 1$ (Mercury), 2 (Venus), 3 (Earth), . . . , then the radius of the orbit of any planet (in astronomical units) is given by the *empirical* formula

$$R = 0.3 \times 2^{(n-2)} + 0.4 \text{ (in A.U.)},$$

where 1 A.U. is the distance between earth and sun. But this formula works only if two exceptions are made. One is that a zero must be used instead of the factors $0.3 \times 2^{(n-2)}$ for the calculation of Mercury's orbital radius. Furthermore, although Mars can be assigned $n = 4$, Jupiter, the next planet, has to be assigned $n = 6$; Saturn, the next and outermost planet then known, has to have $n = 7$. The number $n = 5$ could not be given to any existing planet. This at once suggested to Bode that the disproportionately large space which actually extends between Mars and Jupiter harbored a yet unnoticed planet for which $n = 5$ and which, *according to this rule*, could be expected to have an orbital radius of 2.8 A.U. (Derive this predicted radius from the last formula.)

Here was a chance to confirm whether the rule was anything more than coincidence and fantasy! Bode was convinced that a search would reveal the suspected planet, and he wrote, in a manner which reminds us again of Copernicus' and Kepler's motivations, "From Mars outward there follows a space . . . in which, up to now, no planet has been seen. Can we believe that the Creator of the world has left this space empty? Certainly Not!"

At first no one discovered anything in that seemingly Godforsaken gap, and interest in the law must have lagged (one might say it did not fulfill the criterion of stimulation of further discoveries). But then, nine years after Bode's announcement, came Herschel's discovery of distant Uranus. With $n = 8$ as a logical number to assign, the law predicted an orbital radius of 19.6 A.U., only about 2% larger than the actual value derived by subsequent observation.

This agreement directed attention to the other predictions inherent in Bode's law, and the search for the "missing" planet was renewed with vigor. In time, the first result came, but, as so often in science, only as the by-product of research not directly concerned with this problem. In 1801, the Sicilian astronomer Piazzi, while compiling a new star catalogue, chanced on a new celestial object which was moving as rapidly as might a comet or a planet. In the exciting months that followed, astronomers and mathematicians co-operated to derive the orbit of the foundling, now christened *Ceres*. It was disappointingly puny—less than 500 miles in diameter—but the orbital radius came to 2.77 A.U., only about 1% less than Bode's law predicted for the missing planet in that region between Mars and Jupiter!

Even while Ceres was being hailed as the long-sought sister planet, another, smaller one was discovered with about the same orbit, and then others still, all smaller than Ceres. Today we know of almost 2000, some with very eccentric paths, but all evidently springing from one family with a common history—perhaps the fragments which were forming into one planet when its evolution was somehow interrupted, perhaps the shattered remnants of one larger planet in the predicted orbit. It is possible to speculate that there were two (or more) planets trying to establish orbits near each other, but that they eventually collided "because" Bode's law would "permit" only one orbit to be there. This line of reasoning would put Bode's law into a new light; we might be tempted to search later for other clues that the law expresses simply the series of dynamically possible, stable orbits for single planets.

The discovery of these *asteroids* or *planetoids* bore out Bode's law so strikingly that it was natural to apply it when the suspicion of a planet beyond Uranus first arose. The first available value for n being 9, the corresponding orbital radius would be

$$(0.3 \times 2^{(9-2)} + 0.4) \text{ A.U.},$$

that is, about 38.8 A.U. Adams and Leverrier based their calculations on the predictions of Bode's law to find the probable location, mass, and orbit of their hypothetical planet. When Neptune was afterward seen and its course plotted, the actual orbit was found to be 20% smaller than Bode's law had predicted—the first deficiency in the law, but by luck one not so serious as to invalidate the calculations that led to Neptune's discovery. Later, when Pluto was found, its actual orbital radius of 39.46 A.U. much more seriously contradicted the value of 77.2 A.U. which would follow from Bode's law; in fact, the Bode's law prediction for Neptune fits Pluto better! Therefore, either we must assign the law a more limited role than was initially hoped, or we search for a reason why it does not hold for the outermost planets, and for a modification to make it serviceable there also.

The latter alternative is the more fruitful of the two, but it must remain an unfulfilled wish until we can explain Bode's empirical, we might almost say numerological, law on some broader basis. Unless we know *why it holds* for Uranus, we cannot know *why it breaks down beyond Uranus.*

PROBLEM 15.16.   What can Bode's law predict concerning a hypothetical planet between the sun and Mercury? (On the basis of a somewhat doubtful single observation in 1859, it was once thought to exist and was given the name *Vulcan*, but has never been found since.) If suddenly an additional small planet were seen between Jupiter and Saturn, might Bode's law be recast in some other form to hold for all planets? Might there be a form of Bode's law for the Ptolemaic system? Is Bode's law true? Is it false?

PROBLEM 15.17.   Assume that in another planetary system than our own, the distance from the central star to each of the four inner planets is given by the following table:

Sequence number of planet (n):	1	2	3	4
Radius of orbit, in 10^6 miles (R):	3	5	9	17

Obtain from these data a "law," a formula that will relate R to n for each planet. At what distance do you expect the fifth planet to be?

15.14   TYPES OF PHYSICAL LAWS

This may be a good place to review very briefly the different types of laws which we have encountered here. At the first level of sophistication there is the type of law which we have just called *empirical* and which seems to summarize simply some fairly directly observed regularity, e.g., Bode's law, or Kepler's laws.* But as we have seen in our discussion of Kepler's work, even a regularity appearing rather obvious to us now may have been an insight which presupposed a difficult reorientation within science and which stimulated important further developments. At any rate, we must allow these rules a vital place in science.

Next in order, although any strict division is quite artificial, we may perhaps place those laws which represent an induction of one regulating principle from a variety of apparently very different phenomena. For example, Galileo's law of projectile motion and Newton's law $F = ma$ were perceptions not obvious from direct observation. In fact, in each case the formulation of the law had to be preceded by the definition of new concepts; in Galileo's case, acceleration and the independence of horizontal and vertical velocity components; in Newton's case, mass and to some extent force. Because these laws usually carry with them the definition of fundamentally important concepts involved therein, we might call them *definitional* laws (although that word has deceptive overtones). Examples of this type might include the conservation laws of energy and of momentum. (See Chapters 17, 18, 20.)

Thirdly, we turn to the remaining group, those laws which represent a general conclusion *derived from some postulate or theory*, whether new or old. For example, the lens laws which permit the design of optical instruments can be derived from a theory of the propagation of light. The law of pendulum motion can be deduced from the conceptual scheme of mechanics built around Newton's three laws of motion. And the law of universal gravitation certainly was not an empirical rule, nor did it serve to exhibit a new fundamental concept (all the factors in $F = (Gm_1m_2)/R^2$ were previously defined concepts, G being essentially a proportionality constant); instead, as we have seen, it was a generalization derived from the conceptual scheme featuring Kepler's rules, Newton's own laws of motion, and the hypothesis of mass attraction among the planets and the sun. This type of law, which we may perhaps name *derivative* (sometimes called *causal*), often seems the most satisfying of the three because, since it has been derived from some underlying theory, we are tempted to feel it is also somehow more fully "explained." Scientists therefore continually seek to reduce purely empirical laws to derivative ones, thereby giving the empirical law a measure of additional "meaning,"† while at the same time extending and fortifying the theory itself. There is a kind of symbiotic relationship here between law and theory. A theory becomes more and more respected and powerful the more phenomena can be derived from it, and the law describing these phenomena becomes more meaningful and useful if it can be made part of a theory. Thus, Newton's theory of universal gravitation gained greatly in stature because it enabled one to derive the laws governing the

---

* Also Boyle's law of gases, Hooke's law of elasticity, Snell's law of refraction, Balmer's formula in spectroscopy, Ohm's law of electricity, Gay-Lussac's law of combining gases, the law of definite proportions in chemistry, and the laws of intrusion in geology.

† This feeling appears somewhat fallacious if subjected to rigorous analysis. After all, the theory itself is acceptable only if its derived laws can be checked by experiments, and may in fact be incorrect *even if* the derived laws are correct (we shall see such an example when we come to deal with the theory of light). Nevertheless, great theories are relatively stable for long periods, and laws derived from them are as secure as we have any right to expect.

motion of the moon, which had been known by empirical rules since the days of the Babylonian observers. These rules in turn, now that they were "understandable" in terms of the theory, could be reformulated more accurately; in fact, the theory even enriched them, e.g., by calling attention to hitherto unnoticed peculiarities of the moon's motion. Another important example of this kind will be presented in the section on the nuclear atom; that theory has been so enormously important in modern science because it swallowed up whole textbooks full of isolated empirical and definitional laws from all branches of physics and chemistry, and reissued them as derivative laws springing from the unifying concept of the atom. (See Chapters 33 and 35.)

From this discussion we may perhaps draw some general conclusions valid beyond the physical sciences. Empirical rules may be valid enough in a limited field, but they do not contain enough information to warn the naïve user when some particular new case is really outside the field of applicability of the empirical rule. Not until the damage is done is it clear that the rule did not apply.

Most of our own everyday actions tend to be governed by this type of uncomprehended rule and plausible generalization. This is doubly unfortunate, as these rules, unlike those in science, are usually not even based on accurate clear-headed observation. While our life thereby may become simpler, it also is made more brutal and senseless, and we open ourselves up to an invasion of pseudoscience, superstition, and prejudice, even in matters subject to test and measurement. A concrete example may help to illustrate this point: A certain color tie, eye, or skin may indeed have characterized some past acquaintances whom I or my friends did not accept as intellectual equals, but in the absence of impartial proof that native intelligence depends on those colors (and particularly in the face of proof to the contrary) I shall have to revise my attitude toward these men, and instead of a generalized judgment on all as one group I must now be prepared to make individual judgment on each; perhaps I shall even be moved to investigate why my previous experiences with this group revealed that so many men had not been given an adequate education to develop their abundant natural talents.

To return to Bode's empirical rule, recent work has given hope that its features will be explained by (derived from) Newton's law of celestial mechanics. As hinted before, the mutual perturbations of planets over billions of years would leave only a few orbits as stable possibilities; and some cosmologists and astrophysicists at present seem to be near the inevitable proof that the celestial laws predict such stability for the orbits that are actually observed. But this is a most difficult mathematical problem which from time to time has challenged some of the greatest scientists during the past 100 years.

15.15   FURTHER CONSEQUENCES OF THE GRAVITATION LAW

Even in Newton's work we find further consequences of the law of universal gravitation. For example, he gave an accurate explanation for the long-standing mystery of the precession of the equinoxes, i.e., a very slow rotation of the earth's axis much like the wobbling motion of a rapidly spinning top. But now we turn to a more ambitious question. Do Newton's laws, so serviceable and fruitful within the solar system, continue to apply beyond, among the "fixed" stars?

To Copernicus or Galileo this question would have been meaningless, for it was not until Newton's time that relative motions were noticed in the celestial sphere (the discoverer was Halley). In fact, our whole solar system was found to move with respect to those distant stars. William Herschel, in 1803, also discovered that some star neighbors rotated about each other (double stars), and his son showed that their motions are compatible with the assumption of central forces between them, such as exist in the solar system.

This new picture of our living, moving universe, which the prophetic Giordano Bruno had sensed long ago, places the solar system in the uncrowded company of many billion other suns and their possible attendants (of which fewer than 6000 suns are visible without telescope). The whole cloud of stars forms our *galaxy*, a vaguely lentil-shaped region about 100,000 light years* across and about 1500 light years thick. Our planetary system, which is at a distance of about 30,000 light years from the galactic center (not even at the center of all solar systems!) is rather lost in this structure.

Such a picture evokes the thought that the mutual gravitational attraction of the stars should make the galaxy slowly gather up and coalesce into one solid mass at the center. Since this does not happen, motion of the stars being not all toward the center, there are then two explanations. Either the law of gravitation does not extend itself to the whole universe or, in analogy with the solar system itself, the whole galaxy is spinning around its axis, "distracting" the threatening gravitational attractions by making them do the chores of centripetal forces.

On examination, the second choice actually seems to hold.† Our own solar system revolves about the distant center of the galaxy at a speed of about 150 mi/sec. According to our present view, the edge of the whole galaxy, whose framework we see as the Milky Way,** completes one revolution in perhaps a quarter-billion years.

Now let us make a bold little computation. If Newton's laws hold, we should be able to compute the approximate mass of the whole galaxy from the rate of (circular) revolution of our own sun about the galactic center.

If we neglect that part of our galaxy lying in the shaded portion in Fig. 15.15.1, we may say that the centripetal force on our sun is the gravitational pull exerted on it by the mass of the galaxy (acting approximately as if that were all located at the center). Thus we expect that the following equation holds:

$$m_s \frac{4\pi^2 R_G}{T^2} = G \frac{m_s m_G}{R_G^2},$$

---

* One light year is the *distance* traveled by light in one year in vacuum, that is, 9.46×10^{12} km or 5.88×10^{12} mi.

† For a modern view of the structure of our galaxy and the universe beyond, see B. J. Bok and P. F. Bok, *The Milky Way*, Philadelphia: Blakiston Co., 1945; H. Shapley, *Galaxies*, Philadelphia: Blakiston Co., 1943; a short summary by Eddington is in Shapley, Wright, and Rapport, *Readings in Physical Sciences*, New York: Appleton, 1948, pages 122–128.

** Galaxy is derived from the Greek word *gala*, milk.

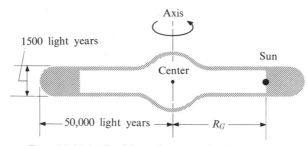

FIG. 15.15.1. Position of our sun in the galaxy.

where T stands for the period of revolution of the sun (about 2×10^8 years), m_G for the mass of the galaxy, m_s for the mass of the sun. The only unknown in this equation is m_G, and on solving for it, $m_G = 2 \times 10^{11}$ times the mass of the sun (check this).

But when we add up the mass of all the stars which our galaxy is likely to hold, even on the most generous estimate, we can account for less than half of those 200 billion units. Either our assumptions are wrong, or we can find some galactic mass other than that contained in the stars of our galaxy. The assumptions were, of course, rather crude, but short of abandoning the law of gravitation, no tinkering with those admittedly qualitative details will explain the calculated overabundance of mass. So we turn to the alternative—and certainly we *can* find evidences that our galaxy contains matter not congregated into suns and solar systems, namely, nebulae, interstellar dust, and most rarefied gases.

There are many such clues to the presence of this tenuous matter that would rescue the Newtonian laws, mainly its effect on starlight. But the density is inconceivably low, less than for the best vacuums in the laboratory, perhaps only a few atoms per cm^3. But this is spread over equally inconceivable distance, and an estimation of the total distributed material supplements the known star masses by about the missing amount. Thus our confidence in the law of gravitation rises to galactic proportions.

Beyond our world, starting at a distance of about thirty times our own galactic diameter, we find other galaxies scattered through space, as far as our biggest telescopes can reach. These island universes do not seem to differ greatly in size from ours and often appear like a spiral or pinwheel (see Fig. 15.15.2), probably the shape of our own galaxy also. (It is clear that if Kepler's third law holds for a whole galaxy, the outlying material will revolve more slowly than the masses near the center, hence the possibility of the spiral shape. On the other hand, if the whole system were to rotate like a solid disk, each part having the same period of revolution and angular velocity, then the centripetal force holding the system together could not obey an inverse-square law but would have to be linearly proportional to the distance from the center.)

Even as these distant galaxies seem to recede from us and from one another at the speed of 100 to 1000 mi/sec, they rotate at the same time at rates close to our own, hence may be assumed to contain about the same mass and to obey the same laws of mechanics. And with this extension of the law of gravitation to the expanding universe, "to all the distance of nature's infinitude," we find ourselves at the limit of

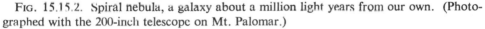

FIG. 15.15.2. Spiral nebula, a galaxy about a million light years from our own. (Photographed with the 200-inch telescope on Mt. Palomar.)

our imagination, and at the height of admiration for so universal a principle. There have been few products of human genius to match its ambitious promise and its exciting fulfillment.

15.16 "I FRAME NO HYPOTHESES"

The *theory* of gravitational forces, whose main hypothesis is the attraction of all particles of matter for one another, yields the derived *law* of universal gravitation, which in turn explains, as we have seen, Kepler's empirical laws and a wealth of other phenomena. Since one purpose of any theory is this type of explanation and summary, Newton's theory strikes us as eminently satisfactory. But there remained one feature which gravely bothered Newton's contemporaries and, indeed, students to our day. How could one account for gravity itself? What is it that causes the attraction of one body for another? Is there not some intervening medium which somehow transmits the pull in a mechanical fashion?

The very statement of these questions reflects how firmly the mind is committed to physical models and to mechanical explanations, and how unsatisfied a mathematical, abstract argument leaves our emotions initially. Rather than accept "action at a distance," i.e., the idea that bodies can exert forces on one another without the agency of a medium between them, most scientists preferred to think of all space as filled with some kind of omnipresent fluid, which, apart from being otherwise so tenuous by itself as to be undetectable by any experiment, still had to be strong and versatile enough to communicate all gravitational forces (and incidentally perhaps also serve to propagate light and electric and magnetic effects).

The search for some such medium was long and the arguments loud. At the end of Book III of the *Principia*, Newton put his often misinterpreted remarks:

> "But hitherto I have not been able to discover the cause of those properties of gravity from phenomena [observation and experimentation], and I frame no hypotheses . . . To us it is enough that gravity does really exist, and act according to the laws which we have explained, and abundantly serves to account for all the motions of the celestial bodies and of our sea."

This is a famous statement, an echo of Galileo's admonition in very similar circumstances (see Section 2.11). With the words, "I frame no hypotheses," Newton exempts himself from the obligation to account for the observed consequences of the gravitational theory by additional hypotheses (for example, of a mechanical ether) beyond those needed to derive the laws and observations. The mathematical law of gravity explains a wide range of observations; that is enough justification for accepting it. It is easily conceivable that one might eventually explain the law itself in terms of something still more fundamental, but that, Newton suggests, he is at the time unprepared to do. Nor does he feel that his theory suffers by this inability, for the purpose of scientific theory is not to find final causes and ultimate explanations, but to explain observables by observables and by mathematical argument; *that* he has done.*

On the other hand, his refusal, in the absence of experimental clues, to propose a mechanism by which the effect of gravity may pass from one body to another does not mean he will permit the opposite error, namely, dismissal of the question by the invention of some principle of gravity innate in matter, such as might well have satisfied a medieval scholar. This is brought out in a passage in the *Opticks*, in a discussion on the possible motion of the smallest particles of matter:

> ". . . And the Aristotelians gave the Name of occult Qualities not to manifest Qualities, but to such Qualities only as they supposed to lie hid in Bodies, and to be unknown causes of manifest Effects: Such as would be the Causes of Gravity, and of magnetick and electrick Attractions, and of Fermentations, if we should suppose that the forces or Actions arose from Qualities unknown to us and uncapable of being discovered and made manifest. Such occult Qualities put a stop to the Improvement of natural Philosophy, and therefore of late Years have been rejected. To tell us that every species of Thing is endow'd with an occult

---

* For a good discussion of Newton's much-debated statement, see F. Cajori's Appendix, Note 55, to his revision of the Motte 1729 translation of the *Principia;* also W. Dampier, *A History of Science*, New York: Macmillan, 1942 edition, pages 183–190.

specifick Quality, by which it acts and produces manifest Effects, is to tell us nothing: But to derive two or three general Principles of Motion from Phaenomena, and afterwards to tell us how the Properties and Actions of all corporeal Things follow from these Principles would be a very great step in Philosophy, though the Causes of those Principles were not yet discovered: And therefore I scruple not to propose the Principles of Motion above-mentioned, they being of very general Extent, and leave their Causes to be found out."

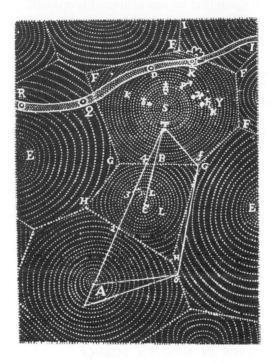

Fɪɢ. 15.16.1. A drawing by which Descartes illustrated his theory, in which all of space was presumed to be filled with matter. A comet, passing among the vortices, is briefly carried along by the general motion in the solar system around S.

Nevertheless, the question of how one body can be acted on by another across empty space has an obstinate appeal for our picture-seeking mind. Part of the great following of Descartes' vortex theory, the scheme generally accepted during most of Newton's life, was that it provided a plausible picture of a universe completely filled with a whirlpool of material corpuscles whose action on one another and on the planets was simple physical contact.* (See Fig. 15.16.1.) There we have an example of a plausible, easily grasped conceptual scheme which had the fault, fully appreciated by Newton but not by the majority of his contemporaries, of failing to agree quanti-

---

* See H. Butterfield's *Origins of Modern Science* for a brief but stimulating account of the long struggle between Newton's theory and Descartes'.

tatively with observations, specifically, of failing to allow the derivation of Kepler's laws. But by contrast with the most successful feature of Descartes' picture, its inherent appeal to the common sense of the muscles, Newton's lack of an intuitive "reason" for planetary motion stood out that much more glaringly. Newton had to spend much time in his later life to uphold his less intuitively appealing system against the Cartesians, and at the same time to refute insistent attempts within his own camp to introduce metaphysical implications into the law of universal gravitation. He declared again and again that he was neither able nor willing "to adjudge natural causes" of gravitation. This was all the more remarkable (and a large step toward the modern conception of what is required of physical theory) since Newton, who, we must remember, later regarded himself as much theologian as scientist, might have introduced an explicit theistic assumption at that point. As has been hinted before, the existence of a Creator is a persistent implicit hypothesis in his work, and at times it does come out into the open, rarely in the *Principia* but more often in his other writings. Thus he could say in the *Opticks* in explanation of the term "absolute space," "God moves the bodies within his boundless uniform sensorium." Privately, Newton, like his contemporaries, did in fact believe that some material agency would eventually be found to explain the action at a distance.

There are several strong hints in his writings that he entertained the idea of an all-pervading ether, e.g., *Opticks*, III, query 18, where he asks whether heat is not "conveyed through the *vacuum* by the vibration of a much subtler medium than air, which, after the air was drawn out [as by evacuating a vessel with a pump], remained in the *vacuum*"; this medium he imagined as "expanded through the heavens." At the time, this was a most reasonable speculation, proceeding as it did from some simple observations on the transmission of (radiant) heat to a thermometer suspended in an evacuated vessel. It is the more interesting that the tempting but vague picture was not permitted in the *Principia*.

15.17   NEWTON'S PLACE IN MODERN SCIENCE

So impressive were the victories of Newtonian mechanics in the early eighteenth century that, through the customary extrapolation from science to philosophy, there spread a mechanistic world view which asserted that man's confident intellect could eventually reduce *all* phenomena and problems to the level of mechanical interpretation. In economics, philosophy, religion, the "science of man"—everywhere the success of the work of Newton and the Newtonians was one of the strongest influences to encourage the rising "Age of Reason."*

One of the consequences of the mechanistic attitude, lingering on to the present day, was a widespread belief that with the knowledge of Newton's laws (and those of electrodynamics later) one could predict the whole future of the whole universe and each of its parts if only one were given the several positions, velocities, and accelera-

------

* A stimulating discussion of this important aspect of science will be found in J. H. Randall's *The Making of the Modern Mind*, Boston: Houghton Mifflin Co., 1940, Chapters 10–15.

tions of all particles at any one instant. It was a veiled way of saying that everything worth knowing was understandable in terms of physics, and that all of physics was essentially known. Today we honor Newtonian mechanics for less all-inclusive but more valid reasons. The factual content of the *Principia* historically formed the basis of most of our physics and technology, and the success of Newton's approach to his problems revealed the most fruitful method to guide the work of the subsequent two centuries in the physical sciences.

We also recognize now that despite its breathtaking scope of applicability, Newton's mechanics holds in its stated form only within a definable region of our science. For example, although the forces *within* each galaxy may be Newtonian, one can speculate that forces of repulsion instead of attraction operate between each galaxy and its neighbors (one interpretation of the greater speed with which more distant systems recede). And at the other end of the scale, among atoms and subatomic particles, an entirely non-Newtonian set of concepts has to be presented to account for the behavior of those small-scale worlds.

Even within the solar system, there are a few small residual discrepancies between predictions and facts. The most famous is the erroneous value of the position of closest approach to the sun by the planet Mercury; calculations and observations differ by some 43 seconds of arc per 100 years. A similar small failure of Newton's laws of motion and of gravitation exists for the path of a recurring comet that comes close to the sun and, to a progressively lesser degree, for the rest of the members of the solar system.

But these difficulties cannot be traced to a small inaccuracy of the law of gravitation (e.g., to a slight uncertainty of the exponent in the expression Gm_1m_2/R^2). On the contrary, as in the case of the failure of the Copernican system to account accurately for the detail and "fine structure" of planetary motion, we are here again confronted with the necessity of scrutinizing our assumptions. Out of this study has come the realization that no single revision can account for all these deviations from classical predictions, so that at present Newtonian science is joined at one end with relativity theory which, among many other achievements, covers phenomena involving bodies moving at high speeds and/or the close approach of large masses. At the other end Newtonian science borders on quantum mechanics, which gives us a physics of atoms and molecules. As for the middle ground, Newtonian mechanics still describes the world of ordinary experience and of "classical" physics as accurately and satisfyingly as it always has.

SUPPLEMENTARY READING AND STUDY

BLITZER, L., "Resource Letter SO–1 on Satellite Orbits." *Am. J. Phys.*, **31,** 233 (1963)

BOK, B. J., and P. F. BOK, *The Milky Way.* Cambridge, Mass.: Harvard University Press, 1957

BRINTON, C., *The Shaping of the Modern Mind.* Chs. 3 and 4. New York: New American Library, Mentor Book M98, 1953. Also Prentice-Hall Spectrum Book S63

BUTTERFIELD, H., *The Origins of Modern Science.* London: G. Bell, 1949; Macmillan, 1951; Collier Books Paperback AS259V, 1962

CASSIRER, E., *The Philosophy of Enlightenment.* Princeton, N. J.: Princeton University Press, 1951; Boston: Beacon Press, 1955

DIJKSTERHUIS, E. J., *The Mechanization of the World Picture.* Oxford: Clarendon Press, 1961

DUGAS, R., *Mechanics in the Seventeenth Century.* New York: Central Book Co., 1958

GILLISPIE, C. C., *The Edge of Objectivity.* Princeton, N. J.: Princeton University Press, 1960

HALL, A. R., *The Scientific Revolution: 1500–1800.* New York: Longmans, Green & Co., 1954; Boston: Beacon Press BP 29, 1956

GROSSER, M., *The Discovery of Neptune.* Cambridge, Mass.: Harvard University Press, 1962; the story of the work of Adams and Leverrier

KLINE, M., *Mathematics in Western Culture.* London: Oxford University Press, 1953

KOYRÉ, A., *From the Closed World to the Infinite Universe.* Baltimore: Johns Hopkins Press, 1957; New York: Harper Torchbook TB 31, 1958

MATHER, K. F., and S. L. MASON, *Source Book in Geology;* "The Cavendish Experiment." New York: McGraw-Hill, 1939, pages 103–107

MUNITZ, M. K., *Space, Time and Creation: Philosophical Aspects of Scientific Cosmology.* Glencoe, Ill: The Free Press, 1957

MUNITZ, M. K. (editor), *Theories of the Universe.* Glencoe, Ill.: The Free Press, 1957

RANDALL, J. H., *The Making of the Modern Mind.* Boston: Houghton Mifflin, 1926 and later editions

WIENER, P. P., and A. NOLAND (editors), *Roots of Scientific Thought; A Cultural Perspective.* New York: Basic Books, 1957; valuable historical essays on sixteenth- and seventeenth-century science

WOOLF, H., *The Transits of Venus; A Study of Eighteenth-Century Science.* Princeton, N. J.: Princeton University Press, 1959. Eighteenth-century expeditions and instances of international cooperation in which transits of the planet Venus across the face of the sun were observed from different places on the earth in order to measure the parallax of the planet and calculate the absolute value of the astonomical unit (the earth-sun distance).

CHAPTER 16

Mathematics III: Fundamental Theorem of Integral Calculus

16.1 INTRODUCTION

Starting with the kinematical discussion of displacement as area under a $v - t$ curve and as the limit of a sum (Sections 1.13 and 1.14), we have encountered several illustrations in which the concept of "limit of a sum" forces itself on our attention: adding up of velocity changes and of displacements in the reaction-car experiment (Section 6.4); adding up of forces between a large electrified (or gravitating) body and a particle in its vicinity (Section 7.10 and Problem 7.17). Wherever, in further study, we shall be concerned with properties distributed over space or changing with time, we shall be faced with the necessity of evaluating limits of sums: to find quantities of energy associated with electric, elastic, or gravitational effects; to find amounts of charge transported through an electrical circuit over an interval of time; to find the force exerted on a surface over which the pressure varies from point to point.

The results we have obtained in kinematics, relating displacements and velocities to acceleration and specified initial conditions by use of derivatives and antiderivatives (Sections 8.3 and 9.4), strongly suggest a connection between the concepts of "derivative" and "limit of a sum." Historians of mathematics usually date the discovery of the calculus from the period about 1655–1676 when Newton and Leibniz, working independently, arrived at a full appreciation of the importance of this connection and developed systematic algorithms* for exploiting it.

---

* An algorithm is a form or a notation for making a particular kind of calculation. For example, the particular form in which we carry out a long-division calculation in arithmetic is an algorithm for division of numbers. Leibniz' notation for derivatives provided an algorithm for systematizing calculations with derivatives and tabulating rules such as

$$\frac{d(uv)}{dx} = u\frac{dv}{dx} + v\frac{du}{dx},$$

applicable to combinations of many different functions. Newton used a different language and notation: he denoted the derivative of a function y by the symbol $\dot{y}$ and referred to derivatives and antiderivatives as "fluxions" and "fluents," respectively. These names are no longer used, but the dot symbol is still frequently used to denote derivatives, particularly with respect to time.

In this chapter we shall outline a plausible argument to show that the limit of a sum, determined by the properties of a particular function, is directly related to the anti-derivative of the function. (A rigorous mathematical proof of the theorem is beyond the scope of this text.)

16.2 EVALUATION OF AREA SUMS

Let us restate, in functional notation, concepts related to area under a curve as we developed them in Sections 1.13 and 1.14. Referring to Fig. 16.2.1, we have

$$A^{(s)} \equiv \sum_{k=1}^{n} f^{(s)}(x_k)\, \Delta x_k, \tag{16.2.1}$$

$$A^{(l)} \equiv \sum_{k=1}^{n} f^{(l)}(x_k)\, \Delta x_k. \tag{16.2.2}$$

It is our conjecture that, if $f(x)$ is an appropriately smooth curve, $A^{(s)}$ and $A^{(l)}$ assume values more and more nearly equal as the subintervals Δx_k are made smaller and more numerous, and that there exists a unique numerical value

$$A \equiv \lim_{\substack{\|\Delta\| \to 0 \\ n \to \infty}} \sum_{k=1}^{n} f(\bar{x}_k)\, \Delta x_k, \tag{16.2.3}$$

where $\bar{x}_k$ is some value of x within the kth interval.

To assure understanding of the notation and of the calculations that are implied, let us work out a complete numerical example. (The student will find that the most efficient way to absorb the significance of the illustration is to write out the details of the calculation for himself as he goes along, rather than just reading it passively.) Consider the function $f(x) = 2x^2$ on the closed interval $1 \le x \le 5$, as sketched in Fig. 16.2.2. To simplify the arithmetic we divide the interval uniformly with each

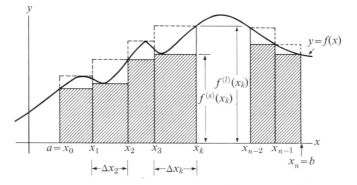

FIG. 16.2.1. $A^{(s)}$ denotes sum of areas of shaded rectangles, altitude of which is determined by smallest value of function, $f^{(s)}(x_k)$, in each subinterval. $A^{(l)}$ denotes sum of areas of rectangles, altitude of which is largest value of function, $f^{(l)}(x_k)$, in each subinterval.

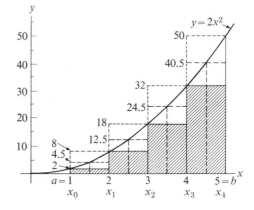

FIG. 16.2.2. Function $f(x) = 2x^2$ on interval $1 \leq x \leq 5$. Interval is divided uniformly into subintervals: $\Delta x_1 = \Delta x_2 = \cdots = 1$; $n = 4$. $A^{(s)} = $ sum of areas of shaded rectangles; $A^{(l)} = $ sum of areas of rectangles under dotted lines; $A^{(m)} = $ sum of areas of rectangles under dashed lines.

$\Delta x_k = 1$. Values of $f(x)$ at the ends and midpoint of each subinterval are calculated and shown on the graph.

In Table 16.2.1 we tabulate numbers for calculating three different areas: $A^{(s)}$, $A^{(l)}$, and an area $A^{(m)}$ of rectangles determined by the value of $f(x)$ at the midpoint of each subinterval. From the calculations shown in the table, we see that

$$\left.\begin{array}{rl} A^{(s)} &= 60, \\ A^{(l)} &= 108, \\ A^{(m)} &= 82.0. \end{array}\right\} \tag{16.2.4}$$

We would expect the last value to be closer to the area under the curve than either of the other two. Why?

PROBLEM 16.1. Divide the interval $1 \leq x \leq 5$ into eight uniform subintervals ($n = 8$) and construct a new table exactly like Table 16.2.1. Remember that the Δx_k's now equal $\frac{1}{2}$ rather than 1. Calculate the new values of $A^{(s)}$, $A^{(l)}$, and $A^{(m)}$ and compare them with those obtained above. What trend do you discern? Account for this trend by describing geometrical effects that take place in Fig. 16.2.2 when you take narrower subintervals.

TABLE 16.2.1

CALCULATION OF AREAS IN FIG. 16.2.2

Subinterval number, k	Length of subinterval, Δx_k	$f^{(s)}(x_k)\,\Delta x_k$	$f^{(l)}(x_k)\,\Delta x_k$	$f^{(m)}(x_k)\,\Delta x_k$
1	1	2	8	4.5
2	1	8	18	12.5
3	1	18	32	24.5
4	1	32	50	40.5
		60	108	82.0
		$A^{(s)} = \sum\limits_{k=1}^{4} f^{(s)}(x_k)\,\Delta x_k$	$A^{(l)} = \sum\limits_{k=1}^{4} f^{(l)}(x_k)\,\Delta x_k$	$A^{(m)} = \sum\limits_{k=1}^{4} f^{(m)}(x_k)\,\Delta x_k$

PROBLEM 16.2. Consider the straight line defined by $f(x) = 2x + 1$. Sketch the graph, and evaluate $A^{(l)}$, $A^{(s)}$, and $A^{(m)}$ for the interval $2 \leq x \leq 7$, establishing your own choice of subintervals Δx_k. $A^{(m)}$ is the exact value of the trapezoidal area. Why?

16.3 EVALUATION OF THE LIMIT OF A SUM

We now carry the calculation a step further and evaluate the number A (Definition 16.2.3) for the function $f(x) = 2x^2$ on the interval $1 \leq x \leq 5$. The notation is developed in Fig. 16.3.1.

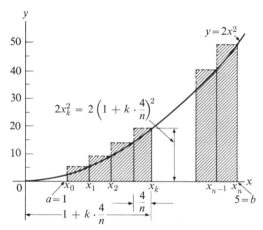

FIG. 16.3.1. Function $f(x) = 2x^2$ on interval $1 \leq x \leq 5$. Interval is divided into n equal subintervals. Each subinterval has length $\Delta x_k = (b - a)/n = 4/n$. The kth abscissa: $x_k = 1 + k \cdot (4/n)$.

If we calculate the area under the shaded rectangles, we have

$$A^{(l)} = \sum_{k=1}^{n} 2x_k^2 \, \Delta x_k = \sum_{k=1}^{n} 2 \left(1 + k \cdot \frac{4}{n}\right)^2 \left(\frac{4}{n}\right). \qquad (16.3.1)$$

Expanding the last term, we obtain

$$A^{(l)} = \sum_{k=1}^{n} 2 \left(1 + k \cdot \frac{8}{n} + k^2 \cdot \frac{16}{n^2}\right) \frac{4}{n},$$

$$= \sum_{k=1}^{n} \left(\frac{8}{n} + \frac{64}{n^2} k + \frac{128}{n^3} k^2\right). \qquad (16.3.2)$$

If we write out the summation indicated in (16.3.2), the first term, $8/n$, is repeated n times, once for each value of k; the second term has the constant factor $64/n^2$, and appears in the sum multiplied successively by $k = 1, 2, 3, \ldots$, etc. Thus (16.3.2) becomes

$$A^{(l)} = 8 + \frac{64}{n^2} \sum_{k=1}^{n} k + \frac{128}{n^3} \sum_{k=1}^{n} k^2. \qquad (16.3.3)$$

There exist well-known formulas for the two sums appearing in (16.3.3):

$$\sum_{k=1}^{n} k = (1 + 2 + 3 + \cdots + n - 1 + n) = \frac{n(n + 1)}{2}, \qquad (16.3.4)$$

$$\sum_{k=1}^{n} k^2 = [1 + 4 + 9 + \cdots + (n - 1)^2 + n^2] = \frac{2n^3 + 3n^2 + n}{6}. \qquad (16.3.5)$$

Therefore

$$A^{(l)} = 8 + \frac{64}{n^2}\left(\frac{n^2 + n}{2}\right) + \frac{128}{n^3}\left(\frac{2n^3 + 3n^2 + n}{6}\right)$$

$$= 8 + 32\left(1 + \frac{1}{n}\right) + \frac{64}{3}\left(2 + \frac{3}{n} + \frac{1}{n^2}\right). \qquad (16.3.6)$$

To evaluate A, the limit of the sum as the subintervals Δx_k are made narrower and their number n is increased, we seek

$$A = \lim_{n \to \infty} A^{(l)}.$$

Since the limits as $n \to \infty$ of $1/n$ and $1/n^2$ are equal to zero, we obtain from (16.3.6)

$$A = 8 + 32 + \tfrac{128}{3} = 82\tfrac{2}{3}. \qquad (16.3.7)$$

Exactly the same result is obtained if we set up an expression for $A^{(s)}$ and evaluate $\lim_{n \to \infty} A^{(s)}$. (Verify this assertion.) Compare the result $82\tfrac{2}{3}$ with the value of 82.0 for $A^{(m)}$ obtained in Table 16.2.1; taking narrower subintervals would, of course, have given a value of $A^{(m)}$ still closer to A. If an algebraic formula for $f(x)$ is not available, A cannot be evaluated by a limit calculation such as (16.3.7), and must be computed numerically from a graph or table of data, in the manner in which we computed $A^{(m)}$. By taking the Δx_k's sufficiently narrow, we can make this computation as precise as justified by the numerical accuracy with which the curve $f(x)$ is known, and the calculation can be readily programmed on a digital computer.

PROBLEM 16.3. Consider the straight line defined in Problem 16.2 by $f(x) = 2x + 1$. Evaluate the area for the interval $2 \le x \le 7$ by finding $\lim_{n \to \infty} A^{(l)}$ as in the preceding example. Compare the result with $A^{(m)}$ obtained in Problem 16.2.

PROBLEM 16.4. Consider the straight line defined by $f(x) = mx$ (Fig. 16.3.2). By means of a limit-of-a-sum calculation, evaluate the area between $x = a$ and a general abscissa location $x = x$. In order to check your result, note that the formula for area of a trapezoid gives

$$A = \frac{mx + ma}{2}(x - a) = \frac{m}{2}(x^2 - a^2).$$

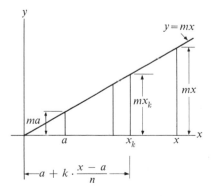

FIGURE 16.3.2

PROBLEM 16.5. Make up some additional problems of your own. For example: Investigate the area under a straight line of negative slope. Is the result different from that obtained in Problem 16.4? Investigate the "area" between a straight line and the x-axis when the ordinates of the straight line are negative; what algebraic sign is associated with the area in this case? Investigate the area under a simple cubic function. You will need the formula

$$\sum_{k=1}^{n} k^3 = \frac{n^2(n+1)^2}{4}.$$

What difficulties do you encounter if you attempt a limit-of-the-sum calculation with functions such as $x^{1/2}$ or x^{-2} or $\sin \theta$?

Although we have referred repeatedly to the concept of area in order to provide a simple, readily visualized interpretation of the calculation defined by

$$A \equiv \lim_{\substack{\|\Delta\| \to 0 \\ n \to \infty}} \sum_{k=1}^{n} f(\bar{x}_k)\,\Delta x_k, \qquad (16.3.8)$$

the calculation need have nothing to do with areas at all. Definition (16.3.8) refers to operations with numbers; no geometrical or physical interpretation of these numbers is a necessary part of the arithmetical concept. Conversely, in physical applications, we may accord the numbers an interpretation having nothing to do with geometrical areas: e.g., values of $f(x_k)$ might be interpreted as forces and Δx_k's as displacements in calculation of the physical quantity we shall call "work."

By arithmetical analysis, it is possible to give a rigorous proof of the following theorem.*

Theorem: If the function $f(x)$ is continuous in the closed interval $[a, b]$, then

$$A \equiv \lim_{\substack{\|\Delta\| \to 0 \\ n \to \infty}} \sum_{k=1}^{n} f(\bar{x}_k)\,\Delta x_k \qquad (16.3.8)$$

exists, and has a unique value independent of the choice of subintervals Δx_k (that is, the intervals may be nonuniform) and independent of the choice of the number $\bar{x}_k$ within the kth subinterval (that is, $f(\bar{x}_k)$ may be any value of the function which occurs within the kth subinterval).

By *limit* we mean (as in Section 3.11): For each ϵ, however small, there exists a positive number δ such that $|\sum_{k=1}^{n} f(\bar{x}_k)\,\Delta x_k - A| < \epsilon$, when all the Δx_k's are less than δ.

---

* The proof is beyond the scope of this text, and will not be given here. For a detailed discussion see (1) *Calculus*, Volume I, by Tom M. Apostol, New York: Blaisdell Publishing Co., 1961; (2) *University Calculus with Analytic Geometry*, by C. B. Morrey, Jr., Reading, Mass.. Addison-Wesley Publishing Co., 1962.

Under these circumstances, the function is said to be integrable over the interval $[a, b]$, and, in referring to the limit in (16.3.8) it is conventional to use another, somewhat less cumbersome, notation:

$$A \equiv \lim_{\substack{\|\Delta\| \to 0 \\ n \to \infty}} \sum_{k=1}^{n} f(\bar{x}_k) \, \Delta x_k \equiv \int_a^b f(x) \, dx. \tag{16.3.9}$$

(Read the last term as "integral from a to b of $f(x)$ with respect to x.") The integral sign $\int$ has evolved as a stylized version of the letter S for "Sum." The symbol dx can be given independent significance by extension of the concept of differential developed in Section 8.12, but we shall not undertake the extension at this point. For the time being we shall treat the integral notation as having meaning only as a whole, and regard it as a shorthand for the more cumbersome limit-of-the-sum expression. The process of evaluating an integral is called *integration*; the quantities a and b are called the lower and upper limits of integration, respectively. The word limit is used here in more or less its ordinary sense as a beginning or end point and not in the special mathematical sense of Sections 3.12 and 3.13.

16.4 AREAS AND ANTIDERIVATIVES

Consider the continuous function $f(x)$ shown in Fig. 16.4.1. Let $G(x)$ represent the area for the interval $[a, x]$. Then $G(x + h)$ denotes the area for the interval $[a, x + h]$, and the shaded area is equal to $G(x + h) - G(x)$. Here we invoke the ideas developed in Section 16.3 to support the assumption that area under the curve can itself be expressed as a function of x. (Recall the questions raised in Section 3.10 and Problem 3.7 regarding this point.)

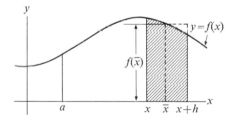

FIG. 16.4.1. $G(x)$ denotes area under curve for interval $[a, x]$. Area of rectangle $= h \cdot f(\bar{x}) = $ shaded area $= G(x + h) - G(x)$.

Let us select a value $\bar{x}$ between x and $x + h$ such that $f(\bar{x})$ is the altitude of a rectangle equal in area to the shaded area;* then

$$G(x + h) - G(x) = h \cdot f(\bar{x}). \tag{16.4.1}$$

---

* For a continuous function such as that shown in Fig. 16.4.1 it is intuitively reasonable that such a value of $f(x)$ exists in the interval. The Mean Value Theorem assures us that this is the case. For a more detailed discussion, with examples of circumstances under which the theorem is not valid, see Section 8.14.

Dividing Eq. (16.4.1) by h and taking limits as $h \to 0$:

$$\lim_{h \to 0} \frac{G(x + h) - G(x)}{h} = \lim_{h \to 0} f(\bar{x}). \qquad (16.4.2)$$

The left-hand side of (16.4.2) is simply $G'(x)$, the derivative of $G(x)$. The right-hand side is equal to $f(x)$, since $f(\bar{x})$ takes values close to $f(x)$ as $\bar{x} \to x$ and since we have asserted $f(x)$ to be continuous. Therefore (16.4.2) becomes

$$G'(x) = f(x). \qquad (16.4.3)$$

Translated into words, this says that $f(x)$ is the derivative of the area function or, conversely, that the area function is an antiderivative of $f(x)$. If we use the notation that $F(x) + C$ represents the general antiderivative of $f(x)$, then

$$G(x) = F(x) + C. \qquad (16.4.4)$$

Let us solve for C: We have the boundary condition that area is measured from the ordinate $x = a$; thus $G(a) = 0$, $G(a) = F(a) + C = 0$, $C = -F(a)$. Then

$$G(x) = F(x) - F(a). \qquad (16.4.5)$$

If we seek the area $G(b)$ for the interval $[a, b]$, Eq. (16.4.5) yields

$$G(b) = F(b) - F(a). \qquad (16.4.6)$$

That is, the area under $f(x)$ for the interval $[a, b]$ can be calculated as the difference between values of an antiderivative $F(x)$, evaluated at b and a, respectively.

16.5   FUNDAMENTAL THEOREM OF INTEGRAL CALCULUS

We now see that we have discovered two ways of calculating area under a curve continuous on the interval $[a, b]$: (1) as the limit of a sum, denoted by $\int_a^b f(x)\, dx$, and (2) as the difference between values of an antiderivative of $f(x)$. If the concepts used are not contradictory, we expect the two calculations to yield the same result; i.e., we expect that

$$\int_a^b f(x)\, dx = F(b) - F(a). \qquad (16.5.1)$$

(Rigorous proof of this assertion will not be given here but can be found in mathematics texts such as those cited in Section 16.3.)

To summarize: We assert the ideas encompassed by the name "Fundamental Theorem of the Integral Calculus":

Theorem: If $f(x)$ is a continuous function in the closed interval $[a, b]$, the limit of the sum denoted by $\int_a^b f(x)\, dx$ exists (independent of choice of subintervals Δx_k or of $\bar{x}_k$ within each subinterval) and is equal numerically to $F(b) - F(a)$, where $F(x)$ is any antiderivative of $f(x)$.

It is essentially for discovery and exploitation of this theorem that Newton and Leibniz are said to have created the calculus. Their discoveries were based on plausible, intuitive arguments of the kind we have invoked in this chapter; rigorous proofs were not achieved until long afterward.

Although our argument used the concept of area as an heuristic device, let us emphasize again that the Fundamental Theorem does not depend on this concept. It is a theorem about limits of sums and antiderivatives—concepts that have independent, purely arithmetical significance. Furthermore the theorem is valid regardless of whether $f(x)$ is positive or negative. The quantity $\int_a^b f(x)\,dx$ may be either positive or negative, and the algebraic sign must be interpreted in any given case in the light of the fundamental definitions of the calculations being made.

16.6 APPLICATIONS OF THE FUNDAMENTAL THEOREM

Let us work through several examples to illustrate how our new algorithm works:

Example 1. Given the constant function: $f(x) = 1$. Evaluate $\int_a^b f(x)\,dx$. [The answer is obvious from a glance at Fig. 16.6.1: The area we associate with the integral has the value $(b - a)$.] The formal procedure follows:

$$\int_a^b f(x)\,dx = \int_a^b 1 \cdot dx = x \Big|_a^b = (b - a). \qquad (16.6.1)$$

$$\underset{F(x)}{\uparrow} \qquad \underset{F(b)}{\uparrow} \quad \underset{F(a)}{\uparrow}$$

In the third term of (16.6.1) we have written x as an antiderivative, $F(x)$, of 1 and have introduced the symbol $\big|_a^b$ to indicate that we must evaluate it between the limits a and b. If we had taken $f(x) = k$ instead of 1, our final result would have been $k(b - a)$.

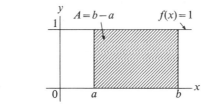

FIGURE 16.6.1

If the upper limit of integration is taken to be the general value x, we would have for $f(x) = k$:

$$\int_a^x k\,dx = kx \Big|_a^x = kx - ka = k(x - a). \qquad (16.6.2)$$

$$\underset{F(x)}{\uparrow} \quad \underset{F(x)}{\uparrow} \quad \underset{F(a)}{\uparrow}$$

Elaborate the following physical interpretations: (a) If k denotes a uniform acceleration and x is interpreted as time, the integral represents change in velocity over time interval $(x - a)$; (b) If k denotes uniform velocity, the integral represents a corresponding displacement.

Example 2.   Evaluate $\int_a^x f(x)\,dx$ when $f(x) = mx$. [This is Problem 16.4, and the answer previously obtained was $A = (m/2)(x^2 - a^2)$.]   The algorithm gives (see Fig. 16.6.2):

$$\int_a^x mx\,dx = \frac{mx^2}{2}\Big|_a^x = \frac{mx^2}{2} - \frac{ma^2}{2} = \frac{m}{2}(x^2 - a^2). \tag{16.6.3}$$

$$\uparrow \qquad\qquad \uparrow \qquad\quad \uparrow$$
$$F(x) \qquad\quad F(x) \qquad F(a)$$

Interpret this result if m is taken to be a uniform acceleration and mx a velocity increasing linearly with time.

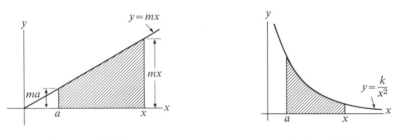

FIGURE 16.6.2   FIGURE 16.6.3

Example 3.   Evaluate $\int_a^x f(x)\,dx$ when $f(x) = k/x^2$.   (See Fig. 16.6.3.)   We have

$$\int_a^x \frac{k}{x^2}\,dx = -\frac{k}{x}\Big|_a^x = -\frac{k}{x} + \frac{k}{a} = k\left(\frac{1}{a} - \frac{1}{x}\right). \tag{16.6.4}$$

We can also evaluate this integral when the upper limit is infinite:

$$\int_a^\infty \frac{k}{x^2}\,dx = -\frac{k}{x}\Big|_a^\infty = 0 + \frac{k}{a}. \tag{16.6.5}$$

Interpret this last result as an area in the accompanying figure.   How can the sum be taken to infinity but the area remain finite?   What trouble would arise if we were to take $a = 0$ or some negative value?   What restriction in the statement of the Fundamental Theorem prepares us for this eventuality?   Does the symbol $\int_0^\infty (k/x^2)\,dx$ have meaning as a uniquely defined numerical value in the sense of the Fundamental Theorem?

Example 4.   A set of specific physical interpretations in rectilinear kinematics: Since acceleration $a \equiv dv/dt$;

$$\int_{t_1}^{t_2} a(t)\,dt = v(t_2) - v(t_1) = \Delta v, \tag{16.6.6}$$

where $v(t_2)$ corresponds to $F(t_2)$, an antiderivative of $a(t)$ evaluated at t_2, etc.   Since velocity $v \equiv ds/dt$,

$$\int_{t_1}^{t_2} v(t)\,dt = s(t_2) - s(t_1) = \Delta s. \tag{16.6.7}$$

PROBLEM 16.6. Evaluate the integrals of functions specified below and interpret each on a diagram.

(a) $f(x) = 2x + 1$ over the interval $[-1, 4]$. [*Answer:* 20.]
(b) $f(x) = 3x + 2$ over the intervals $[a, b]$ and $[0, 3]$. [*Answer:* $\frac{3}{2}(b^2 - a^2) + 2(b - a)$.]
(c) $f(x) = ax^2 + b$ over the interval $[-2, x]$. [*Answer:* $(a/3)(x^3 - 8) + b(x - 2)$.]

PROBLEM 16.7. Investigate

$$\int_a^x \frac{1}{x^{1/2}} dx.$$

What values of x must be avoided? What happens if you try to evaluate

$$\int_a^\infty \frac{1}{x^{1/2}} dx \qquad \text{for } 0 < a \le x?$$

How do you account for the fact that this result differs so markedly from that in Example 3, where a finite value was obtained for an infinite upper limit of integration?

PROBLEM 16.8. An angular acceleration $\alpha(t) = 2t - 3$ rad/sec^2 is imparted to a rotating wheel, starting from rest. Obtain expressions for the change in angular velocity and angular position occurring in the time interval $[t_1, t_2]$. Evaluate the changes numerically for the time interval $[0, 4]$. [*Answer:* $\Delta\omega = 4$ rad/sec; $\Delta\theta = -8/3$ rad.]

16.7 NOMENCLATURE AND DEFINITIONS

It is customary to call the limit of a sum denoted by $\int_a^b f(x)\,dx$ a *definite integral*, since it refers to a particular number evaluated by finding $F(b) - F(a)$. By analogy with this nomenclature, it is customary to denote the general antiderivative of $f(x)$ by the symbol

$$\int f(x)\,dx = F(x) + C, \tag{16.7.1}$$

referred to as an *indefinite integral*. This is the mathematical quantity that Newton called a "fluent."

In the case of the definite integral, we have not specified a meaning for the notation in cases where the "upper" limit $b \le a$. The following definitions are adopted:

If $b = a$:
$$\int_a^b f(x)\,dx \equiv 0. \tag{16.7.2}$$

If $b \ne a$:
$$\int_a^b f(x)\,dx \equiv -\int_b^a f(x)\,dx. \tag{16.7.3}$$

We are led to Definition (16.7.3) because the subintervals Δx_k become negative if $b < a$; this definition insures that $\int_a^b f(x)\,dx = F(b) - F(a)$, regardless of whether b is greater or less than a, since

$$-\int_b^a f(x)\,dx = -[F(a) - F(b)] = F(b) - F(a). \tag{16.7.4}$$

Definition (16.7.3) further establishes the convention that if $b < a$ while $f(x)$ is positive, the integral has a negative value; i.e., an integration toward the left along the axis is associated with an opposite algebraic sign from that of an integration toward the right.

A final remark concerning the meaning of "area": Although we used area of geometrical figures as a primitive, intuitive concept to help make plausible the assertion of the Fundamental Theorem, it has been indicated that the Fundamental Theorem can be proved rigorously from a purely arithmetical structure of postulates and deductions. Once this proof is given, we can reverse the sequence of views and regard the definite integral as being the arithmetical *definition* of area under a curve in circumstances where we wish to make a geometrical interpretation of the limit-of-the-sum calculation. The definition can readily be extended to apply to area included between two curves rather than one curve and the x-axis, and so forth.

16.8   AVERAGES

The shaded area, A, under the continuous curve in Fig. 16.8.1 is represented by the integral

$$A = \int_a^b f(x)\, dx. \qquad (16.8.1)$$

We can easily calculate the altitude, $\overline{f(x)}$, of a rectangle which has the same base, $b - a$, and equal area:

$$\overline{f(x)} = \frac{\int_a^b f(x)\, dx}{b - a}.\,^* \qquad (16.8.2)$$

The quantity $\overline{f(x)}$ is called the "average value of $f(x)$ in the interval $[a, b]$." Let us examine this concept for a number of different interpretations of x and $f(x)$.

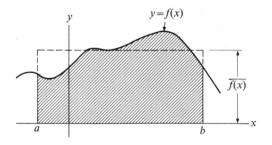

FIG. 16.8.1.   Shaded   area $A =$ $\int_a^b f(x)\, dx.$ Rectangle with same base $(b - a)$ and equal area has altitude:

$$\overline{f(x)} = \frac{A}{b - a} = \frac{\int_a^b f(x)\, dx}{b - a}.$$

---

* It is possible to prove a Theorem of the Mean for integrals (analogous to the Mean Value Theorem for derivatives (Section 8.14)) to the effect that if $f(x)$ is continuous on the closed interval $[a, b]$, there exists at least one value of $\bar{x}$ in the interval such that $\overline{f(x)} = f(\bar{x})$; that is, the function $f(x)$ takes on the value $\overline{f(x)}$ at least once within the interval $[a, b]$.

If we deal with velocity as a function of time, we have

$$\frac{\int_{t_1}^{t_2} v(t)\, dt}{t_2 - t_1} = \frac{\Delta s}{\Delta t} = \overline{v(t)}. \tag{16.8.3}$$

This is the arithmetical foundation of the concept of average velocity with which we started Chapter 1.

If $p(r)$ represents population density (number of residents per unit area) as a function of radial distance r from a metropolitan center, the average population density within a range R of the center is given by

$$\overline{p(r)} = \frac{\int_0^R p(r)\, dr}{R}. \tag{16.8.4}$$

The calculation in (16.8.3) is called a *time average* while that of (16.8.4) is called a *space average*.

In certain instances a quantity may be regarded as either a function of position or time; for example, the component of force accelerating a particle in the x-direction may vary in a complex way and may be expressed either as $F(x)$ or $F(t)$. We might then calculate two different averages, one over space, the other over time:

$$\overline{F(x)} = \frac{\int_{x_1}^{x_2} F(x)\, dx}{x_2 - x_1}, \tag{16.8.5}$$

$$\overline{F(t)} = \frac{\int_{t_1}^{t_2} F(t)\, dt}{t_2 - t_1}. \tag{16.8.6}$$

Except for the special case of a constant force, these two numbers are *not* equal to each other.

PROBLEM 16.9.   Interpret average acceleration $\overline{a(t)}$ [defined originally in Eq. (1.10.1)] in terms of an integral expression parallel to Eq. (16.8.3).

PROBLEM 16.10.   For the first 5 meters of depth, temperature $T(x)$ of the water in a lake is found to decrease with depth x according to the equation $T(x) = 20 - 0.60\, x^2$, where T is in °C and x is in meters.   Sketch the function and calculate the space average of temperature over the 5 meters for which the equation is valid. [*Answer:* $\overline{T(x)} = 15°C$.]

16.9 EARLY ORDEAL OF THE CALCULUS

Throughout the three editions of the *Principia*, the first of which was published in 1687, Newton never uses any of his algorithms of fluxions and fluents.   The proofs are carried out in the forms of Euclidean geometry, although, as we have seen in Chapter

15, it was necessary for him to introduce limit arguments in extending theorems to apply to cases of continuous, curvilinear motion. In numerous letters and manuscripts Newton claims that he discovered many of the theorems in the *Principia* by the method of analysis (calculus) and proved them by the method of synthesis (Euclidean geometry).

Historians differ as to why the *Principia* contains no calculus. Interpretations range from the assertion that Newton's claim is a subsequent distortion to the assertion that Newton, anticipating controversy concerning the notion of gravitation as an unexplained, occult interaction at a distance, wished to avoid additional controversy over a new and incompletely validated mathematical technique.

It is clear that Newton had reservations about the logical foundations of analysis. In his old age he several times cautioned his young friend Henry Pemberton, preparing the third edition of the *Principia*, to distrust the new mathematical techniques and to put his faith ultimately in the synthetic methods of the Greeks. Yet he was proud of his achievement, and in the early 1700's engaged in a violent polemic with Leibniz over priority for the discoveries.

In a scholium following the Lemmas* that open Book One of the *Principia*, referring to quantities such as those we have designated by Δv, Δt, and $\Delta v/\Delta t$, Newton writes: "Those ultimate ratios with which quantities vanish are not truly the ratios of ultimate quantities, but limits toward which the ratio of quantities decreasing without limit do always converge; and to which they approach nearer than by any given difference, but never go beyond, nor in effect attain to, till the quantities are diminished *in infinitum*."

Considering the date, this was a very creditable approach to the limit concept. Among Newton's predecessors (Fermat, Pascal, James Gregory, John Wallis, Isaac Barrow) and even in Leibniz, the idea was very much vaguer and less clearly articulated. However, even Newton himself did not stick to this definition, but resorted to locutions about "nascent" and "evanescent" quantities. Leibniz talked of dy and dx, of "infinitesimals of various orders" and "inassignables."

A host of pointed questions can be raised in this context: How close does a ratio approach its limit? What happens to the "error" of a sum as the subintervals in integration are made smaller? Is the calculus just an approximation in which certain unavoidable discrepancies are to be ignored simply because they are small?

The attack was taken up by many individuals, among them the philosopher Bishop George Berkeley. Berkeley was a lucid and critical thinker on matters of epistemology. He had previously criticized basic concepts of Newton's cosmology, and he took up a sophisticated discussion of the new mathematics in a tract called *The Analyst: Or a Discourse Addressed to an Infidel Mathematician* [referring to Newton's friend Halley]. *Wherein it is Examined Whether the Object, Principles, and Inferences of the Modern Analysis Are More Distinctly Conceived, or More Evidently Deduced than Religious Mysteries and Points of Faith.*

---

* These Lemmas are essentially a group of limit theorems, put down for subsequent use in extending Euclidean proofs to cases of continuous change.

Carl Boyer, a modern historian of the calculus,* writes: "Berkeley in this work did not deny the utility of the new devices nor the validity of the results obtained. He merely asserted, with some show of justice, that mathematicians had given no legitimate argument for their procedure, having used inductive instead of deductive reasoning."

The discussion continued throughout the eighteenth century, with, as in any period of controversy, numerous muddled and ingenuous contributions among the incisive ones. Morris Kline† summarizes the uneasiness of many eminent eighteenth-century mathematicians and mathematical physicists: ". . . Leonhard Euler and Joseph Louis LaGrange worked on the problem of clarifying the calculus, but without success. Both arrived at the conclusion that as it stood, the calculus was unsound, but that somehow errors were offsetting one another so that the results were correct. . . . Michel Rolle (1652–1719) . . . taught that the calculus was a collection of ingenious fallacies. Voltaire called the calculus 'the art of numbering and measuring exactly a Thing whose existence cannot be conceived.' . . . Jean d'Alembert (1717–83) felt obliged to advise his students that they should persist in their study of the calculus; faith would eventually come to them."

But concern about insecurity of the logical foundations did not prevent a prodigious flowering of mathematical physics. The Bernoullis and Euler advanced the theories of hydrodynamics, elasticity, and rotation of rigid bodies; Lagrange and Laplace brought the formulation of the theory of gravitation and its application to celestial mechanics and the tides to a level of quantitative precision that might have astounded Newton; Poisson applied calculus to the study of electric fields. Imaginative men did not hesitate to advance scientific inquiry, as Professor Bridgman puts it, by doing the utmost with their minds—no holds barred. Mathematics and physics intertwined in such a way during this period that progress in one was hardly distinguishable from progress in the other.

Tobias Dantzig,** one of the eminent teachers of the last generation, commented on the process: "By trying and erring, by groping and stumbling—so progressed our knowledge . . . man was guided in this progress not by logic but by intuition and the stored-up experience of his race. This applies to all things human, and I have made painstaking efforts to show that mathematics is no exception. . . . Distant outposts were acquired before the immediate territory had been explored. . . . It was the acknowledged right of logic to accept or reject new forms in whose birth it had no part. But the decisions of the judge were slow in coming . . . so while waiting for logic to sanctify their existence, [the new forms] throve and multiplied."

In 1812, a century and a half after the birth of the calculus, Cauchy evolved the definition of limit which we studied in Chapter 3—a definition that eschews locutions about "infinitesimals," "evanescence," or "approaching," but speaks directly of a

---

* *The History of the Calculus*, by Carl Boyer. New York: Dover Publications, 1959.

† *Mathematics: A Cultural Approach*, by Morris Kline. Reading, Mass.: Addison-Wesley, 1962.

** *Number, the Language of Science*, by Tobias Dantzig. New York: Doubleday Anchor Book A67, 1954.

single number that "exists." With this foundation, he gave the first mathematically satisfactory definitions of derivative and definite integral. In subsequent years there were built up and completed the rigorous proofs of the theorems we have asserted and tried to make plausible. The foundations of analysis are now secure, and their securing led to still additional mathematical insights and discoveries—to the entire complex of attitudes and points of view toward the nature of number and the structure of different branches of the science characterized as "modern mathematics."

16.10   PROBLEMS

16.11.   Find the area and average value of the ordinate of the parabola $y^2 = 4x$ on the interval [0, 5]. [*Answer:* Area $= \frac{20}{3}\sqrt{5}$; $\bar{y} = \frac{4}{3}\sqrt{5}$.]

16.12.   (a) Find the area and average value of the ordinate of $y = \sin\theta$ on the interval [0, π]. [*Answer:* Area $= 2$; $\bar{y} = 2/\pi$.]
(b) Find corresponding values for the function $y = \cos\theta$ on the same interval. [*Answer:* zero.]

SUPPLEMENTARY READING AND STUDY

See references cited at the end of Chapters 3 and 8.

For excerpts from Newton, Leibniz, and Berkeley:
A Source Book in Mathematics, Volume II, D. E. Smith. New York: Dover Publications, 1959 (Dover paperback S553)

History and evolution of the concepts:
The History of the Calculus and its Conceptual Development, C. B. Boyer. New York: Dover Publications, 1959 (Dover paperback S509)

Number, The Language of Science, T. Dantzig. New York: Doubleday Anchor Book A67, 1956

CHAPTER 17

Momentum

17.1 RECTILINEAR COLLISION OF TWO BODIES

What changes of motion take place when two particles, moving relative to each other along their line of centers on a level surface, collide? Simple experiments of this kind can be performed in a number of ways: Billiard balls, large glass marbles, or steel ball bearings can be rolled against each other—preferably along a groove or track to keep the relative motion along the line of centers. If you have access to small laboratory carts equipped with spring bumpers (or with magnets mounted so as to repel each other), you can perform similar experiments and alter the masses of the colliding bodies by loading or unloading the carts. Two collision experiments are illustrated schematically in Fig. 17.1.1.

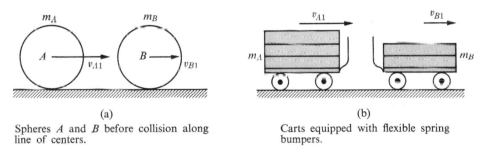

(a)
Spheres A and B before collision along line of centers.

(b)
Carts equipped with flexible spring bumpers.

Fig. 17.1.1. Rectilinear collisions. For collision to occur: $v_{A1} > v_{B1}$.

Following are a few regularities that can be very quickly discerned in collision experiments.

(1). With body B initially stationary ($v_{B1} = 0$) and body A moving to the right at velocity v_{A1}:

(a) If $m_A = m_B$, body A stops ($v_{A2} = 0$) and body B moves with velocity nearly equal to v_{A1}.

(b) If $m_A > m_B$, both bodies move to the right after collision, with B moving more rapidly than A.

(c) If $m_A < m_B$, body A bounces back while B moves to the right.

(d) If the bodies stick together on collision, the combination moves to the right with a speed smaller than v_{A1}.

(2). Bodies A and B initially moving toward each other with equal and opposite velocities:

(a) If $m_A = m_B$, the bodies bounce apart with equal and opposite velocities.
(b) If $m_A = m_B$ and the bodies stick together on collision, the final velocity is zero.

Try to secure the opportunity to perform a few qualitative experiments of this kind; actually seeing and observing the collisions will greatly improve your intuitive feeling for the phenomena being described. If possible, observe the gentle collision of carts with very flexible bumpers [flexible metal strips, fastened at only one end as in Fig. 17.1.1(b)]; here you will see the whole process take place as though in slow motion.

PROBLEM 17.1.   (a) Describe in as much detail as you can what happens to the colliding objects in Figs. 17.1.1(a) and (b) while they are in contact with each other. How does the force experienced by each body vary during the interval? Sketch a possible F-versus-t graph, using Fig. 6.4.2 as a model. What defines the interval of interaction in such collisions; i.e., when does the interaction begin and when does it end?

(b) Suppose that the carts in Fig. 17.1.1(b) are equipped with magnets mounted so as to repel each other (or that the carts carry like electrical charges). What would happen if you carried out some of the experiments described above? The carts need not touch each other; we still call this a collision. Sketch a possible F-versus-t graph. What is the interval of interaction?

(c) Suppose that the magnets are mounted so as to attract each other (or that the carts carry unlike charges). Describe some possible collisions, and sketch at least one F-versus-t graph. How would you rig an analogous mechanical experiment (with springs or rubber bands)?

(d) What influence do you ascribe to friction in these various experiments?

17.2 CLASSIFICATION OF COLLISIONS

Among the simple rectilinear collisions, we can empirically identify three different classes: (a) The colliding bodies stick together and move as a unit after collision. Such collisions are called "perfectly inelastic." (b) Bodies of equal mass, approaching each other with equal and opposite velocities, bounce apart with velocities reversed in direction but unchanged in magnitude (providing external frictional effects are negligible). A more general statement of this regularity, including cases of unequal mass and speed, is that the *relative* velocity with which the bodies approach each other is reversed in direction but is unchanged in magnitude after collision. This behavior is an *idealization*, approached by objects made of materials such as glass or steel, colliding in the absence of frictional forces. Such ideal collisions are called "perfectly elastic."   (c) In actual collisions, when the bodies bounce apart, the *relative* velocity between them after collision is reversed in direction but is smaller in magnitude than the relative velocity before collision. Such collision would be described as "partly elastic." The ratio of magnitudes of relative velocity after and before collision is frequently referred to as the "coefficient of restitution." If we denote by $v_{A1}, v_{B1}, v_{A2}, v_{B2}$, the velocities of bodies A and B before and after collision, respectively, an *elastic collision* is defined by

$$v_{B1} - v_{A1} = -(v_{B2} - v_{A2}), \qquad (17.2.1)$$

while the coefficient of restitution, c, a number less than unity, is defined by

$$c \equiv \frac{|v_{B2} - v_{A2}|}{|v_{B1} - v_{A1}|}. \qquad (17.2.2)$$

Collisions are rather complex events. Forces of interaction of the colliding bodies are certainly not constant; they vary in complicated ways. A variety of things can happen, depending on the masses and the different initial motions of the colliding bodies. Furthermore, collisions can occur at various angles (not along the line of centers), and might involve simultaneous interaction of more than two bodies.

Yet, if you reflect upon the simple, systematic effects observed in the special cases of collision described above, it is hard to escape the feeling that, regardless of the complexity of the detailed interaction, there exists a simple connection among the motions before and after collision. To establish this connection was the goal of pre-Newtonian physicists; they saw here the beginning of a science of dynamics. Galileo himself performed some experiments on the impact of falling water. His contemporary at the University of Prague, Marcus Marci (1595–1667) studied the collision of spheres. Descartes assembled a group of theorems about collisions which he called the Laws of Motion. Most of Descartes' theorems were incorrect. In 1668, Wallis, Wren, and Huygens (although they confused the concepts and identified mass with weight) put forth descriptions of rectilinear collisions that are essentially correct from a modern standpoint. (See Section 5.1.)

17.3 VIEWING COLLISIONS FROM DIFFERENT FRAMES OF REFERENCE

In building up his arguments concerning the superposition of velocities in projectile motion, Galileo repeatedly referred to observations one might make on a moving ship: An object dropped from the top of the mast would appear to fall in a straight line along the mast from the point of view of an observer on the ship; it would appear to move in a parabolic path from the point of view of an observer on the shore—the only difference residing in an addition or subtraction of the uniform horizontal velocity of the ship and *not* in an alteration of the physics of the phenomenon.

It is not surprising that seventeenth-century investigators of collisions immediately asked similar questions about the laws of impact. Is the dynamical phenomenon changed in any intrinsic way if a given experiment is performed on a moving ship? And experiments seem to have been performed to test the expectation that there would be no intrinsic change.

Huygens then proceeded to use the "thought experiment" on a moving ship from a most significant analytical point of view—a point of view that remained neglected until the end of the nineteenth century, when the crisis that resulted in the birth of the Theory of Relativity led to new appreciation of his insight. Let us paraphrase Huygens' treatment for a few very simple cases.

We start with the assertion that "equal, hard bodies" (meaning perfectly elastic bodies of equal mass), approaching each other with equal and opposite velocities, rebound with velocities unchanged in magnitude (Fig. 17.3.1). This is the only Law of Motion that Descartes stated correctly; it is consonant with our sense of symmetry (as with Coulomb's division of electrical charge by placing identical conducting spheres in contact) and thus offers itself as a particularly plausible initial postulate for a further line of deductions.

We next ask the question: What should we expect to happen if body B is stationary and body A, of equal mass, approaches with velocity v_{A1}? [Figure 17.3.2(a)]

In Fig. 17.3.2(b) we "transform" this collision by viewing it from a "ship" or frame of reference O' moving at velocity $v_0 = v_{A1}/2$ in the positive x-direction. In frame O', any velocity v' is related to a velocity v in frame O by the equation $v' = v - v_0$. Viewed from O', the collision becomes symmetrical; the bodies appear to approach

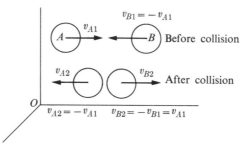

Fig. 17.3.1. Perfectly elastic collision of bodies of equal mass, approaching each other at equal and opposite velocities, as seen by observer in frame of reference O; v_{A1} is taken as positive. Other symbols stand for algebraic components, not magnitudes.

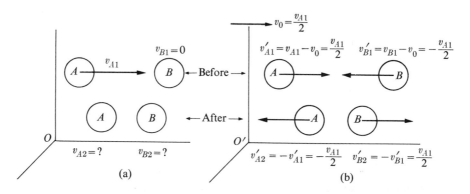

Fig. 17.3.2. (a) *Problem:* Body A moving at velocity v_{A1} collides with stationary body B of equal mass. What are the velocities v_{A2} and v_{B2} after collision? *Answer:* $v_{A2} = 0$; $v_{B2} = v_{A1}$. [See Eqs. (17.3.1).] (b) Collision in (a) viewed from frame of reference O', moving relative to frame O at velocity $v_0 = v_{A1}/2$. Bodies approach each other at equal and opposite velocities and rebound with velocities reversed. Velocity "transformation" relation: $v' = v - v_0$.

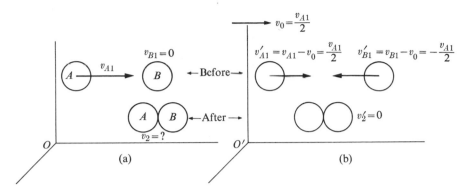

Fig. 17.3.3. (a) *Problem:* Body A moving at velocity v_{A1} collides with stationary body B of equal mass. Collision is perfectly inelastic; find v_2. *Answer:* $v_2 = v_{A1}/2$. [See Eq. (17.3.2).] (b) Collision in (a) viewed from frame of reference O', moving relative to frame O at velocity $v_0 = v_{A1}/2$. Bodies approach each other at equal and opposite velocities and stick together; $v_2' = 0$.

each other at equal and opposite velocities ($v_{A1}' = v_{A1}/2$; $v_{B1}' = -v_{A1}/2$) and must, according to the primary postulate, rebound with velocities reversed: $v_{A2}' = -v_{A1}/2$; $v_{B2}' = v_{A1}/2$. But then, transforming back to frame O:

$$\left. \begin{aligned} v_{A2} &= v_{A2}' + v_0 = -\frac{v_{A1}}{2} + \frac{v_{A1}}{2} = 0, \\ v_{B2} &= v_{B2}' + v_0 = \frac{v_{A1}}{2} + \frac{v_{A1}}{2} = v_{A1}. \end{aligned} \right\} \tag{17.3.1}$$

That is, body A will stop, and B will continue with velocity v_{A1}, and this result is readily confirmed experimentally. Starting with a postulate regarding the symmetrical case, we were able to deduce or predict what to expect in an unsymmetrical situation.

Let us apply Huygens' method to a perfectly inelastic collision (Fig. 17.3.3). In the symmetrical case, when bodies of equal mass and equal and opposite velocities collide and stick together, the final velocity is found to be zero. This becomes our first postulate for inelastic collisions. We proceed to deduce what to expect when A moves and B is stationary. From frame O', moving at $v_0 = v_{A1}/2$ to the right, the collision appears symmetrical, and $v_2' = 0$. Transforming back to frame O:

$$v_2 = v_2' + v_0 = 0 + \frac{v_{A1}}{2}. \tag{17.3.2}$$

That is, if body A with velocity v_{A1} collides inelastically with a stationary body of equal mass, the combination continues moving to the right with velocity $v_{A1}/2$.

PROBLEM 17.2. Apply Huygens' method to predicting what will happen in (a) perfectly elastic, (b) perfectly inelastic collisions of bodies of equal mass moving with initial velocities v_{A1} and v_{B1}, respectively (Fig. 17.3.4). [*Hint:* Let frame of reference O' move relative to O at velocity v_0 equal to the average of v_{A1} and v_{B1}.]

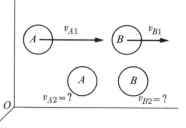

FIGURE 17.3.4

[*Answer:* (a) $v_{A2} = v_{B1}$; $v_{B2} = v_{A1}$. That is, bodies of equal mass exchange velocities in elastic collision; (b) $v_2 = (v_{A1} + v_{B1})/2$.]

PROBLEM 17.3.   Wallis and Huygens both asserted as one of the laws of impact that, in rectilinear collisions, the algebraic sum of "quantities of motion" (product of mass and velocity) before collision was equal to the algebraic sum of the new quantities after collision; i.e., that $m_A v_{A1} + m_B v_{B1} = m_A v_{A2} + m_B v_{B2}$. Construct a table illustrating that this theorem holds in each one of the special cases of Figs. 17.3.2(a) and (b), 17.3.3(a) and (b), and Problem 17.2.

PROBLEM 17.4.   Suppose we were to view the experiments discussed above from a frame of reference O' *accelerating* in the positive *x*-direction.   Would our method of analysis work?   What difficulties arise?

17.4   CONSERVATION OF MOMENTUM IN COLLISIONS

It is easily seen that, for the special cases dealt with above, the algebraic sum of the quantities $m_A v_{A1} + m_B v_{B1}$ before collision is equal to the sum $m_A v_{A2} + m_B v_{B2}$ after collision, regardless of the frame of reference from which the collision is viewed (see Problem 17.3).   One might reasonably make the inductive guess that the same restriction applies to collisions of bodies of unequal mass, and this is *experimentally confirmed*.   Many pre-Newtonian scientists were aware, as Huygens put it in 1668, that "the quantity of motion of two bodies may be either increased or diminished by their shock; but the same quantity, towards the same part, remains after subtracting the quantity of the contrary motion."   In modern terminology we say that the *mv*-product (called momentum) is "conserved" in a collision.

Of course, this relation holds only if the colliding bodies interact solely with each other and are not acted upon by external forces.   In the experiments we have been describing, friction would be an external force and would make the sum of *mv*-products after collision smaller than the sum before.   Performing the experiments on a sloping plane would introduce as an external force the component of gravitational pull along the plane.   Pushing or pulling the bodies would introduce an external force. If the bodies carried like electrical charges and repelled each other on close approach, the presence of a third charged object would introduce an external force acting on the colliding two.

We shall use the term "system" to describe two or more bodies that interact with each other to produce changes in motion.   When no *external* force is acting, we say that the system of interacting bodies is "closed." The assertion that momentum is conserved is found to be valid only for a closed system.

> PROBLEM 17.5.   Suppose we place a percussion cap on one body so that the cap goes off as the bodies collide, and the bodies rebound with larger velocities than they had before collision. Is this system "closed" in the sense of the definition given above? Is this collision "elastic" in the sense defined in Section 17.2?   Explain your answers in some detail. [*Answers:* Yes; no.]

17.5 A PRINCIPLE OF RELATIVITY

Let us return for a moment to the analytical technique used in Section 17.3— Huygens' method of viewing a given collision from different frames of reference. What assumptions have been made in adopting this view? If we examine our work carefully, we can identify three that are particularly significant:

(1) We assumed that a particular physical law was obeyed, regardless of our state of uniform motion in a straight line relative to the events being observed. Specifically, we assumed that in a perfectly elastic collision, bodies of equal mass, approaching each other with equal and opposite velocities, bounce apart with initial velocities reversed; that in a perfectly inelastic collision, they stop dead; and that these statements would be valid in any frame of reference moving at uniform velocity in a straight line.

(2) We assumed that velocities v' observed in frame O' are related to velocities v in frame O by the simple arithmetic of $v' = v - v_0$, where v_0 is the velocity of frame O' relative to frame O.

(3) We assumed that a given body has the same mass m whether viewed from frame O or frame O'.

Assumption (1) is an example of a principle of relativity. It asserts that a certain physical law or regularity (in this case a law of impact) remains "invariant" (unaltered) when viewed from a different inertial frame of reference. In the illustrations worked out in Section 17.3, it is readily apparent that numerical values of momentum for bodies in a given collision are quite different when viewed from O or from O'; momentum itself is *not* invariant to change of frame of reference. In each of the illustrations, however, total momentum before collision is equal to total momentum after, regardless of whether the event is viewed from O or O'; thus the *conservation* regularity *is* invariant to change of frame of reference, and appears to conform to the principle of relativity.

It has been indicated (Chapters 4 and 5) that assumptions (2) and (3) work extremely well under ordinary conditions but prove to be incorrect at velocities that are an appreciable fraction of the velocity of light.

Discussion of principles of relativity played a crucial role in physics toward the end of the nineteenth century. The problem was to identify precisely what laws, regularities, and properties *were* invariant to transformation from one inertial frame of reference to another. Electromagnetic phenomena did not seem to fit properly into the picture. Einstein showed that the difficulties and contradictions could be eliminated by giving a dominant role to the Principle of Relativity in an extended and generalized form and at the cost of abandoning the attractively simple arithmetic of assumptions (2) and (3). See Chapter 36 for a continuation of this story.

17.6 COLLISIONS AND $F_{net} = ma$

Newton's second and third laws, as we illustrated in Chapters 5 and 6, make it possible for us to analyze the motion of a system of bodies by isolating and dealing with one body at a time. Let us apply this technique to a two-body collision. (We have already set up the problem in dealing with the reaction-car experiment in Section 6.3, Fig. 6.3.4.) Consider one member of a colliding pair, such as body B in the illustrations of Section 17.3. A free body diagram is shown in Fig. 17.6.1.

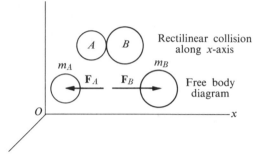

FIG. 17.6.1. Closed system: Rectilinear collision of bodies A and B. Force of interaction varies from instant to instant during interval of contact.

Applying Newton's second law to body B, we have

$$F_{x\,net} = ma_x, \qquad F_B(t) = m_B a_B(t), \qquad (17.6.1)$$

where the functional notation emphasizes the fact that force of interaction and resulting acceleration vary from instant to instant during the interval of collision. Figure 17.6.2 is a sketch of a possible F versus t history during such an interval. If we are interested in the overall effect of the collision on the motion of body B, we must know the cumulative effect of the force F_B. The force is, in general, not uniform; it varies in a complex way, and Eq. (17.6.1) tells us very little. The key to our problem resides in the word "cumulative"; by application of the Fundamental Theorem of Integral Calculus (Sections 16.5, 16.6) we are now able to evaluate just such cumulative effects.

Let us examine the physical significance of the shaded area A in Fig. 17.6.2. One way of representing this area is by the form:

$$A = \int_{t_1}^{t_2} F_B(t)\, dt. \qquad (17.6.2)$$

If we knew $F_B(t)$ as an empirical graph, we could evaluate A numerically as we did in Section 16.2. If we knew an algebraic formula for the function $F_B(t)$, and could find an antiderivative, we could evaluate A by application of the Fundamental Theorem.

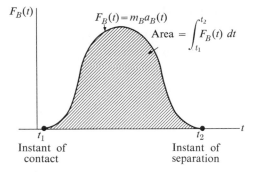

FIG. 17.6.2. Force-time history of body B during interval of contact with body A.

Since $F_B(t) = m_B a_B(t)$ instant by instant, we have an alternative way of calculating A:

$$A = \int_{t_1}^{t_2} m_B a_B(t)\, dt = m_B v_B(t)\Big|_{t_1}^{t_2} = m_B v_B(t_2) - m_B v_B(t_1)$$

$$= m_B v_{B2} - m_B v_{B1}, \tag{17.6.3}$$

where we have used the fact that $v(t)$ is an antiderivative of $a(t)$ in evaluating the integral. [In using the Fundamental Theorem in this way, what assumptions are we making about the continuity of function $a(t)$? Is this a reasonable assumption? Why?]

Combining Eqs. (17.6.2) and (17.6.3), we obtain a deceptively simple, but rather remarkable, result:

$$\int_{t_1}^{t_2} F_B(t)\, dt = m_B v_{B2} - m_B v_{B1} = \Delta(m_B v_B). \tag{17.6.4}$$

Equation (17.6.4) informs us that, no matter how complicated the variation of the net force, the area under the curve in Fig. 17.6.2 is always equal to the change in momentum of the body to which the net force is applied; i.e., the area can be expressed in terms of only the initial and final velocities, regardless of the complexity of the intermediate variation! The left-hand side of (17.6.4) represents one way of calculating a number, given a force-time history; the right-hand side represents an entirely different way of calculating a number. These two calculations must give the same number!

If, in a collision, we observe the change in momentum of body B and estimate the interval $t_2 - t_1$ during which the bodies were in contact, we can estimate the time average value $\overline{F_B(t)}$ of the force (see Section 16.8):

$$\overline{F_B(t)} \equiv \frac{\int_{t_1}^{t_2} F_B(t)\, dt}{t_2 - t_1} = \frac{\Delta(m_B v_B)}{\Delta t} \tag{17.6.5}$$

or

$$\overline{F_B} \cdot \Delta t = \Delta(m_B v_B); \tag{17.6.6}$$

$\overline{F_B}$ is that constant force which would produce the given momentum change in the same time interval as the actual, varying force.

17.7 IMPULSE AND MOMENTUM

We can readily generalize Eq. (17.6.4) to describe the effect of a net force $\mathbf{F}_{net}$ on a body of mass m. For motion in two dimensions:

$$\int_{t_1}^{t_2} F_{x\,net}(t)\,dt = \Delta(mv_x), \qquad (17.7.1)$$

$$\int_{t_1}^{t_2} F_{y\,net}(t)\,dt = \Delta(mv_y). \qquad (17.7.2)$$

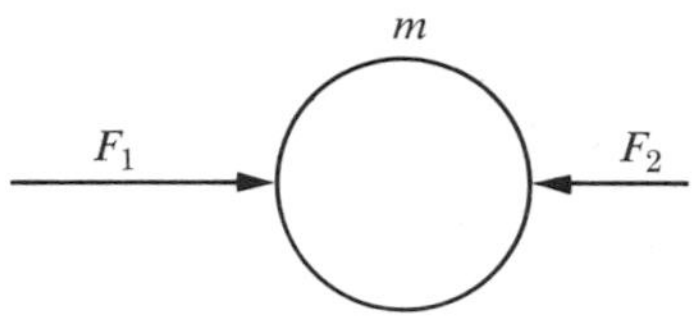

FIG. 17.7.1. Body of mass m acted on by collinear forces F_1 and F_2.

Since m is a scalar quantity, the momenta mv_x and mv_y must obey the same addition rules as velocity. Therefore mv_x and mv_y may be regarded as the x- and y-components of a total momentum vector $m\mathbf{v}$. Correspondingly, the integrals in Eqs. (17.7.1) and (17.7.2) must also be x- and y-components of a vector. Numbers calculated from such integrals are called "impulse." Thus

$$\int_{t_1}^{t_2} F_{x\,net}(t)\,dt$$

is called the "impulse imparted by the net force component, $F_{x\,net}$, during the time interval $t_2 - t_1$." Impulse is a vector quantity. We shall refer to Eqs. (17.7.1) and (17.7.2) as the Impulse-Momentum Theorem.

If a body is acted upon by several forces (Fig. 17.7.1), we use the following terminology:

$$\underbrace{\int_{t_1}^{t_2} F_{x\,net}(t)\,dt}_{} = \underbrace{\int_{t_1}^{t_2} F_1(t)\,dt}_{\substack{\text{Impulse imparted} \\ \text{by } F_1}} \; - \; \underbrace{\int_{t_1}^{t_2} F_2(t)\,dt}_{\substack{\text{Impulse imparted} \\ \text{by } F_2}} \; = \; \underbrace{mv_2 - mv_1}_{}. \quad (17.7.3)$$

Net impulse or impulse imparted by net force

= Change in momentum of body on which net force acts

Final momentum, mv_2

Initial momentum, mv_1

Change in momentum: $\Delta(mv) = mv_2 - mv_1$

(a)   (b)

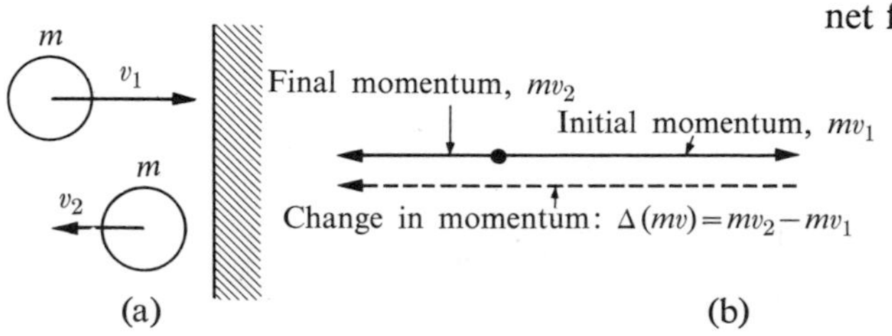

FIG. 17.7.2 (Example 1). (a) Ball approaches a fixed wall, at normal incidence, with velocity v_1 and rebounds with velocity v_2. (Collision is partly elastic.) (b) Vector diagram showing change of momentum of ball.

Example 1. A ball with mass $m = 100$ gm and horizontal velocity $v_1 = 3$ m/sec strikes a wall and rebounds with a smaller horizontal velocity $v_2 = -2$ m/sec. The interval of contact with the wall is of the order of 0.1 sec. Let us investigate the momentum change of the ball, the impulse imparted to it, and the average force acting during contact with the wall. The situation is sketched in Fig. 17.7.2 together with a vector diagram of the momentum change.

The change in momentum is

$$\Delta(mv) = mv_2 - mv_1 = (0.1)(-2) - (0.1)(3) = -0.5 \text{ kg·m/sec.}$$

That is, the change of momentum is directed toward the left. Since $\int_{t_1}^{t_2} F_{x \text{ net}}(t)\, dt = \Delta(mv_x)$, the net impulse imparted to the ball is -0.5 n/sec. (Note that 1 newton-second is identical with 1 kg·m/sec.) The average force acting on the ball during contact with the wall is estimated by:

$$\overline{F_B} = \frac{\Delta(mv)}{\Delta t} \sim \frac{-0.5}{0.1} \sim -5 \text{ n.}$$

By Newton's third law the average force acting on the wall $\overline{F_W} = +5$ n. The ball briefly experiences a force to the left; the wall briefly experiences a force to the right.

PROBLEM 17.6. Continue the analysis of Example 1 for the following cases:

(a) The ball makes an inelastic collision with the wall (that is, $v_2 = 0$, coefficient of restitution $= 0$). Draw the vector diagram for change of momentum, and calculate average force exerted on the wall, taking the interval of collision to be 0.1 sec, as before. How is this interval to be interpreted now that there is no rebound?

(b) The ball is incident to the wall at an angle of incidence θ_i (Fig. 17.7.3); $|v_1| = 3$ m/sec. Assume that the wall can exert a force only in a direction perpendicular to its plane; there can be no force component parallel to the wall. Apply both Eqs. (17.7.1) and (17.7.2). What must be the angle of rebound? Draw the vector diagram for change of momentum. Take $\theta_i = 38°$ and calculate the change in momentum and force exerted on the wall. Assume the coefficient of restitution to be the same as implied in Example 1. [*Answers:* $\theta_r = 49.5°$; $\Delta mv = -0.4$ kg·m/sec; $\overline{F_B} = -4$ n.]

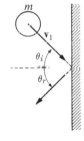

FIGURE 17.7.3

17.8 IMPULSE AND MOMENTUM IN A CLOSED SYSTEM

Let us return to the analysis of the rectilinear collision between bodies A and B (Fig. 17.6.1). Apply the Impulse-Momentum Theorem [Eq. (17.7.1)] to each body:

$$\int_{t_1}^{t_2} F_B(t)\, dt = m_B v_{B2} - m_B v_{B1}, \tag{17.8.1}$$

$$\int_{t_1}^{t_2} F_A(t)\, dt = m_A v_{A2} - m_A v_{A1}. \tag{17.8.2}$$

By Newton's third law, $F_A = -F_B$ instant by instant during the interaction, and the impulses imparted to bodies A and B are therefore equal and opposite. If we add Eqs. (17.8.1) and (17.8.2) we obtain

$$0 = m_B v_{B2} - m_B v_{B1} + m_A v_{A2} - m_A v_{A1},$$

which we can write in alternative forms:

$$\underbrace{m_A v_{A2} + m_B v_{B2}}_{\text{Total final momentum}} = \underbrace{m_A v_{A1} + m_B v_{B1}}_{\text{Total initial momentum}} \qquad (17.8.3)$$

$$\underbrace{m_A v_{A2} - m_A v_{A1}}_{\substack{\text{Change of momentum} \\ \text{of body } A}} = - \underbrace{(m_B v_{B2} - m_B v_{B1})}_{\substack{\text{Change of momentum} \\ \text{of body } B}} \qquad (17.8.4)$$

$$\underbrace{\Delta(m_A v_A) + \Delta(m_B v_B)}_{\text{Sum of all momentum changes}} = 0 \qquad (17.8.5)$$

These are all ways of saying that momentum is conserved in the collision of Fig. 17.6.1 *regardless of how the force of interaction varies during the collision;* we have an algebraic equation connecting initial and final conditions of motion without any reference whatsoever to intermediate stages.

We must not jump to the conclusion, however, that this constitutes a complete solution of the rectilinear collision problem. If we know the masses m_A and m_B and the initial velocities v_{A1} and v_{B1} and seek to predict the final motion, we are left with two unknowns, v_{A2} and v_{B2}. It is necessary to have additional information to determine each of these velocities.

If the collision is perfectly inelastic (the bodies stick together), we have the additional equation saying that both bodies have the same final velocity:

$$v_{B2} = v_{A2} = v_2.$$

Then, from Eq. (17.8.3):

$$v_2 = \frac{m_A v_{A1} + m_B v_{B1}}{m_A + m_B}. \qquad (17.8.6)$$

If the collision is perfectly elastic, we have the definition of such a collision [Section 17.2, Eq. (17.2.1)]:

$$v_{B2} - v_{A2} = - (v_{B1} - v_{A1}). \qquad (17.8.7)$$

This can be combined with (17.8.3) to obtain expressions for v_{B2} and v_{A2} in perfectly elastic rebound. (This problem will be discussed further in Problem 17.9 below, and in Chapter 18.)

If the collision is partly elastic, we have no additional *a priori* relation between v_{A2} and v_{B2} and must determine one of these velocities, or the coefficient of restitution [Eq. (17.2.2)], before being able to evaluate the other.

To simplify the discussion, we oriented our reference frame in Fig. 17.6.1 so that motion was along the x-axis. If we admit a component of motion in the y-direction also, Eq. (17.7.2) would give us another set of results exactly like (17.8.3) for the y-component of momentum. Thus each independent component of momentum is conserved in a closed system; i.e., the total momentum vector of the entire system remains constant.

To summarize the results of our various analyses:

By applying the second and third laws of motion to interaction of bodies, we find

(1) that the total momentum of a system of bodies can be changed by application of a net *external* force, imparting net impulse to the system as a whole.

(2) that the total momentum of a closed system of bodies, interacting only with each other, remains constant.

PROBLEM 17.7. Interpret Eq. (17.8.6) for the final velocity after inelastic collision. What happens if the bodies have equal mass? Does this agree with the analysis in Section 17.3? What happens if m_A is made very small relative to m_B? If m_B is very small relative to m_A? What happens when v_{B1} is small and negative? Large and negative?

The velocity of a bullet is sometimes determined by firing the bullet into a massive block suspended on wires and determining the velocity of the block immediately after impact. Interpret this experiment in the light of the discussion you have just given. Rewrite Eq. (17.8.6) to give an algebraic expression for the velocity of the bullet in terms of known quantities.

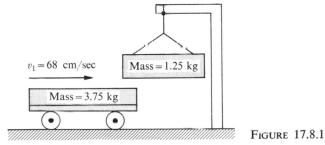

$v_1 = 68$ cm/sec   Mass $= 1.25$ kg

Mass $= 3.75$ kg

FIGURE 17.8.1

PROBLEM 17.8. A cart (mass $= 3.75$ kg) moves on a level table with a velocity of 68 cm/sec. The string suspending the brick (Fig. 17.8.1) is cut as the cart passes underneath. What will be the velocity of the combination after the brick lands on the cart? [*Answer:* 51 cm/sec.] (An experiment of this kind is very easy to set up in the laboratory.)

PROBLEM 17.9. Solve Eqs. (17.8.3) and (17.8.7) simultaneously, showing that for the perfectly elastic collision, conservation of momentum requires that

$$v_{A2} = \frac{m_A - m_B}{m_A + m_B} v_{A1} + \frac{2m_B}{m_A + m_B} v_{B1}, \qquad v_{B2} = \frac{2m_A}{m_A + m_B} v_{A1} - \frac{m_A - m_B}{m_A + m_B} v_{B1}.$$

Interpret the results for the case in which body B is initially at rest: Under what circumstances will body A bounce back? Under what circumstances will it continue in the initial direction? etc.

17.9 THE LAW OF CONSERVATION OF MOMENTUM

We have come to the assertion of conservation of momentum in rectilinear collisions by two routes: (1) induction from empirical study of collision experiments; (2) application of Newton's laws to interaction of particles in a closed system. As we accumulate experience with the solution of physical problems, we shall find that we can successfully apply the concept of "closed system," and the restriction that momentum be conserved, to phenomena far more complex and varied than the ones we have been studying in this chapter. So pervasive a regularity inevitably comes to be called a law, and we shall refer henceforth to the Law of Conservation of Momentum (abbreviated LCM for convenience).

What, then, is the logical status of the LCM among the regularities we observe in nature? In Section 17.8 we seem to have derived the LCM from the Newtonian Laws of Motion. Does this derivation imply that the Newtonian laws are more fundamental? Is the LCM simply a necessary consequence of these laws?

Consider the following physical problems that we did *not* attempt to pose in our first discussion of dynamics in Chapters 5 and 6:

(1) A raindrop falls through a region in which it continuously increases in size and mass because of condensation of surrounding water vapor.

(2) A rocket accelerates as it continuously ejects, at high relative velocity, part of its own mass in the form of burned fuel.

Nowhere in the operational sequence that led us to $F_{net} = ma$ did we envisage m to be itself a continuously variable quantity; we confined ourselves to situations in which m was found to be a fixed, intrinsic property of an unchanging particle. Is it possible to analyze dynamically the motions of the rocket and the raindrop? Yes, if we apply $F = ma$ particle by particle in the system and evaluate the limit of the sum of all the effects, but it usually turns out that problems of this kind are most effectively handled by using the idea of conservation of momentum.

Consider the following physical problems:

(1) Two bodies A and B are connected by a string in an Atwood machine and are prevented from accelerating because we restrain the system by hand. We suddenly let go, and the system accelerates after a change in tension propagates through the string. (See Problem 6.4f.)

(2) Two bodies collide in the manner illustrated in Fig. 17.9.1.

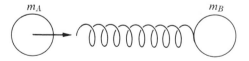

m_A m_B

FIG. 17.9.1. Body B is stationary. Body A "collides" with B by encountering and compressing the long flexible coil spring.

(3) A diaphragm clicks at one end of a room (making a sound). After a short interval the diaphragm of a microphone at the other end of the room is accelerated.

(4) Two charged particles separated by a distance r_1 in a vacuum (Fig. 17.9.2) repel each other with equal and opposite forces. Particle A is suddenly moved to a

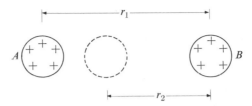

FIG. 17.9.2. Positively charged particles in a vacuum. Particle A is suddenly moved from position r_1 to position r_2.

new position r_2 where it experiences a new force, but a small time interval elapses before the force is observed to change at particle B.

In each of the preceding illustrations there is an interval of time during which interacting bodies do *not* exert equal and opposite forces on each other instant by instant during the interaction; we cannot apply the third law to these bodies during such intervals. In cases (1), (2), and (3) the bodies are separated by a material medium and we can trace the propagation of a disturbance or "wave" through the medium from one body to the other at finite velocity. We might visualize the Third Law as being applicable instant by instant to adjacent slices of the medium, pushing or pulling each other, but certainly not to the bodies at the extreme ends. In case (4) there appears to be no material medium, but nevertheless a disturbance is known to be propagated from one point to another at finite velocity (the velocity of light).

PROBLEM 17.10. What effect is transmitted to body B if the end of the flexible coil spring is sharply displaced back and forth in a transverse direction, as shown in Fig. 17.9.3?

FIGURE 17.9.3

In all these disparate cases, it turns out that we are forced to abandon the Third Law requirement that the separated bodies exert equal and opposite forces on each other instant by instant, but we can save the day by turning to the deeper regularity that momentum is conserved—and *transported* from one body to the other through the intervening medium.

Newtonian dynamics was an action-at-a-distance theory in the sense of the Third Law restriction—that forces between interacting particles be equal and opposite *instant by instant*. In abandoning this restriction and turning to conservation of momentum as the more fundamental law, we get our first glimpse of the motivations leading to the concept of "field" (electrical field in the case of Fig. 17.9.2): We visualize gravitating or charged bodies as modifying space in their vicinity to produce a "field." Changes and disturbances of a field are propagated at finite velocity, analogous to ripples on a water surface or a region of compression of the coil spring in Fig. 17.9.1. We shall elaborate on this point in subsequent chapters.

When we deal with particles moving at extremely high velocities (a substantial fraction of the velocity of light) we find it necessary to *redefine* the concept of inertial mass. Under these circumstances we find that the inertial mass of a given particle varies significantly as a function of its velocity relative to the observer, and again $F_{net} = ma$ fails us. Under these circumstances, we establish conservation of momentum as one of the regularities that is preserved (remains invariant) regardless of the frame of reference from which we observe a dynamical event. The law of conservation of momentum thus becomes one of the foundations of dynamics in the theory of relativity. (See Chapter 36.)

Through experience with problems of the kind we have illustrated in only a fragmentary way in this section, physicists have come to regard the law of conservation of momentum as being far more general and fundamental than the laws of motion we stated in Chapters 5 and 6. But $F_{net} = ma$ and the third law are nevertheless powerful and wonderfully useful tools within their broad range of applicability. As with most tools, literal and figurative alike, it is necessary to know when and under what circumstances it is *not* appropriate to use them.

17.10 FROM THE LAWS OF IMPACT TO DYNAMICS OF AN INDIVIDUAL BODY

It has been remarked previously (Chapters 5 and 6) that (a) the second law of motion as stated by Newton is a somewhat different idea from $F_{net} = ma$, which we have been referring to as the second law for convenience; (b) the third law seems to have no prior antecedents and is asserted for the first time in the *Principia*. In this and the following section we shall describe Newton's own version of the second law, and present some speculations as to how he might have been motivated to formulate the second and third laws as they appear and are utilized in the *Principia*.

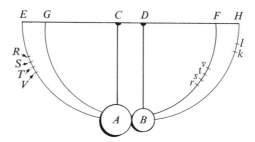

FIG. 17.10.1. Newton's diagram of his pendulum experiments.

Newton was well aware of the laws of impact and the regularity exhibited by the product mv, then called "quantity of motion." Not only does he refer to the systematization of the laws of impact by Wallis, Wren, and Huygens (see Section 5.1), but he also describes experiments of his own with colliding pendulums (Fig. 17.10.1) in which he carefully corrected for effects of air resistance and verified the laws with considerable precision. With this background, it seems natural for Newton to have accorded momentum a primary role in his formulation of dynamics. To trace a possible motivation for his form of articulation of the second and third laws of motion, let us note the context of his work.

There is a very clear-cut unity and focus in the *Principia*: The entire structure of reasoning and proof centers around elucidation of the "system of the world." When Newton discusses the motion of bodies, the trajectories are, for the most part, conic sections—not straight lines or other paths. When he explores the effect of forces, the force law receiving principal attention is that of inverse square—he does not spend time working out problems with constant forces as we did in Chapters 5 and 6, and he does not concern himself with simple collisions as we did earlier in this chapter; he takes these phenomena to be familiar and readily understood in relation to his new formulation.

In order to deal with motion of the planets, Newton must have been led to center his attention on the problem of analyzing the history of motion of a *single* body. He needed a way of describing a continuing dynamical effect on this single body rather than a statement about initial and final motions of two or more bodies after interaction. It seems quite possible that, motivated by this need, he discerned in the third law a way of getting from the impact and interaction of two bodies to the isolation of one of them. It is precisely for this purpose that we used the third law in our own elementary problems; it allowed us to isolate interacting bodies and study their motions separately. Newton did not use vocabulary such as "method of isolation" or "free body diagram," but he certainly handles problems from this point of view.

17.11 NEWTON'S SECOND LAW

If one accepts the third law concept of equal and opposite "action" of bodies on each other, together with the empirical fact that momentum is observed to be conserved in collisions, one is led to say that, during impact, the equal and opposite actions must impart equal and opposite changes of momentum to the interacting bodies. It is in this fashion that Newton may have been led to his statement of Law II (Newton uses the term "quantity of motion" rather than "momentum"):

"The change of motion is proportional to the motive force impressed; and is made in the direction of the right line in which that force is impressed."

and in an earlier Definition VIII:

"The motive quantity of a . . . force is the measure of the same, proportional to the motion which it generates in a given time."

Denoting Newton's "motive force" by the symbol **I**, and translating his verbal statements into symbols, we would write

$$\mathbf{I} \propto \Delta(mv) \qquad \text{or} \qquad \mathbf{I} = \Delta(mv), \qquad\qquad (17.11.1)$$

the latter form depending on appropriate choice of units.

If we go on to examine how Newton uses Law II in solving dynamical problems, we find that (as described in Section 17.14) he visualizes repeated sharp "blows" delivered to a body, causing abrupt changes in motion $\Delta(m\mathbf{v})$. In passing to the continuous case, he visualizes the blows coming closer and closer together, producing individually smaller $\Delta(m\mathbf{v})$'s, and invokes what amounts to a set of arithmetic–geometric limit theorems to evaluate the limit of his calculation.

In one of very few comments on a case of uniformly accelerated motion, Newton says,

> "When a body is falling, the uniform force of its gravity acting equally, impresses, in equal intervals of time, equal forces upon that body, and therefore generates a whole velocity proportional to the time."

From these illustrations and remarks it should be clear that, in using the terms "motive force" and "force," Newton was not referring to the concept we called force in Chapter 5. What he is actually referring to, as demonstrated by his own consistent use of the concept, is the quantity we called net impulse:

$$\mathbf{I}_{net} = \int_{t_1}^{t_2} \mathbf{F}_{net}(t)\, dt = \Delta(m\mathbf{v}). \tag{17.11.2}$$

Newton's "motive force" is an integrated quantity, a sharp blow, an accumulation over a short time interval $(t_2 - t_1)$; it is related to a total change of momentum $(\Delta m\mathbf{v})$; it is *not* viewed as a rate of change or as a derivative when used in dynamical problems. (Only in reference to statics, where time is no longer important, does Newton ignore the accumulation of motive force with passing time and use the word in the same sense in which we use it today.)

Newton's Law II is, in reality, the impulse-momentum relation of Section 17.7. Where do our modern version of the second law and concept of force originate? They seem to have been introduced during the eighteenth century by the mathematician MacLaurin and by the Bernoullis (Johann and Daniel) and Leonhard Euler. With rapid development of the calculus and with application of Newtonian dynamics to a multitude of problems on moving particles, fluids, rotating bodies, elastic deformations, it became more natural to begin the analysis of behavior of a continuously changing process by writing a differential equation. And $\mathbf{F}_{net} = m\mathbf{a}$ is really a system of differential equations:

$$F_{x\,net} = ma_x = m\frac{d^2x}{dt^2}, \qquad F_{y\,net} = ma_y = m\frac{d^2y}{dt^2}. \tag{17.11.3}$$

(For explanation of the second derivative notation, see Section 8.2.)

Jumping to the conclusion that, in using the word force, Newton must mean the same thing we mean today, many authors have interpreted Law II as an assertion that force is proportional to *rate of change* of momentum; i.e., that

$$\mathbf{F} = \frac{d}{dt}(m\mathbf{v}). \tag{17.11.4}$$

This form of the second law turns out to have a certain restricted applicability in ordinary Newtonian mechanics in situations in which the mass of a body varies in a particularly simple way (raindrops, sand pouring into moving freight car, etc.),* and it can also be retained in the theory of relativity, where mass becomes a function of velocity. Because of these possible extensions of the second law, some authors have ascribed to Newton a profundity of insight that has no historical basis. There is no evidence that he envisaged problems of varying mass, and his "motive force" is not proportional to a *rate of change* of quantity of motion.

It does not diminish Newton's stature to say that he did not have the added insight gratuitously attributed to him. The insight that he did have was profoundly original and extremely powerful. Its possible motivation from the laws of impact is far more intelligible in the context of Eq. (17.11.2) than in the misinterpreted context of (17.11.4). And for us, there is a lesson that is still worth repeating from time to time: The same word does not necessarily name the same idea for different people at different instants in time and space.

> PROBLEM 17.11.   Present an argument to the effect that it is not foolish for us to refer to (17.11.3) as Newton's Second Law of Motion even though Newton's own concept was embodied in Eq. (17.11.2).

17.12 CENTER OF MASS OF A SYSTEM OF PARTICLES

Consider a pair of particles m_1 and m_2 moving along the x-axis of coordinates (Fig. 17.12.1) with velocities v_1 and v_2. The total momentum of the system is

$$\mathbf{M} = m_1 v_1 + m_2 v_2. \tag{17.12.1}$$

If we think of $\mathbf{M}$ as being equal to the product $M\bar{v}$, where the total mass $M = m_1 + m_2$ and $\bar{v}$ is an appropriate average velocity:

$$M\bar{v} = m_1 v_1 + m_2 v_2,$$

$$\bar{v} = \frac{m_1 v_1 + m_2 v_2}{M} = \frac{m_1 v_1 + m_2 v_2}{m_1 + m_2}. \tag{17.12.2}$$

(The quantity $\bar{v}$ is called a "weighted" average, in this case weighted by the mass of the

FIG. 17.12.1. Particles of mass m_1 and m_2, instantaneously located at x_1 and x_2 and moving along x-axis with velocities v_1 and v_2. [*Note:* v_1 and v_2 denote algebraic components.]

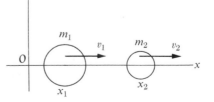

---

* Strictly speaking, this form of the second law is valid for only those special cases of open systems in which **v** is not only the instantaneous velocity of the accelerated object but is simultaneously the relative velocity of the added or subtracted mass.

particle with which each individual velocity is associated. Compare this calculation of an average in a discrete system with the calculation defined in Section 16.8.)

If we think of $\bar{v}$ as representing the velocity of some point with location $\bar{x}$ on the x-axis, we can write Eq. (17.12.2) in the form

$$\bar{v} \equiv \frac{d\bar{x}}{dt} = \frac{m_1 \dfrac{dx_1}{dt} + m_2 \dfrac{dx_2}{dt}}{m_1 + m_2} = \frac{d}{dt}\left(\frac{m_1x_1 + m_2x_2}{m_1 + m_2}\right). \tag{17.12.3}$$

The location

$$\bar{x} \equiv \frac{m_1x_1 + m_2x_2}{m_1 + m_2} \tag{17.12.4}$$

is called the center of mass of the system, and $\bar{v}$ is the velocity of the center of mass.

PROBLEM 17.12.   Establish the connection between this definition of center of mass and the one we encountered in Section 9.12. Show that Eqs. (9.12.4a) and (9.12.4b) are really identical in meaning with (17.12.4).

PROBLEM 17.13.   What would be the form of Eq. (17.12.4) if the system contained three bodies along the x-axis instead of two? n bodies?

PROBLEM 17.14.   Suppose the particles were distributed around the x-y plane. What would be the expressions for the coordinates $(\bar{x}, \bar{y})$ of the center of mass?

If forces act to accelerate the particles, their velocities and the velocity of the center of mass will change. Let us analyze the possibilities by examining the time derivative of $\bar{v}$; from Eq. (17.12.2), we have

$$M\frac{d\bar{v}}{dt} = m_1\frac{dv_1}{dt} + m_2\frac{dv_2}{dt} \tag{17.12.5}$$

and, since $F_{\text{net}} = m(dv/dt)$, we have

$$M\frac{d\bar{v}}{dt} = F_{1x} + F_{2x}, \tag{17.12.6}$$

where F_{1x} and F_{2x} are the net forces acting on particles 1 and 2 in the x-direction. If no net external force acts on the system as a whole, F_{1x} and F_{2x} are purely internal forces and must add up to zero in accordance with Newton's third law. Then

$$M\frac{d\bar{v}}{dt} = 0 \tag{17.12.7}$$

and, in the absence of a net external force, the center of mass of a system of particles remains stationary or moves in a straight line at uniform velocity regardless of how the individual particles collide or interact with each other.

If the net external force acting on the system is not zero, F_{1x} and F_{2x} will add up to some resultant value F_{ext}. In that case (17.12.6) becomes

$$M \frac{d\bar{v}}{dt} = F_{ext}. \qquad (17.12.8)$$

Translated into words, Eq. (17.12.8) says that a system of particles acted on by a net external force accelerates as though the particles were all concentrated at the center of mass and the net external force were applied at that point.

PROBLEM 17.15.   Sketch how the collisions of Figs. 17.3.1, 2(a) and 3(a) would appear to an observer who remained at the center of mass of the system throughout the history of each collision.

17.13 ANOTHER VIEW OF PARTICLE MOTION IN TWO DIMENSIONS

A particle of mass m moves with uniform velocity along a straight line AE (Fig. 17.13.1). Let us examine this motion with reference to an arbitrarily chosen origin O. Point O and line AE determine a plane in which this motion occurs. As the particle moves along AE, it undergoes displacements $AB = BC = CD \ldots$ in equal successive intervals of time. The radius vector from O to instantaneous positions of the particle changes continuously in magnitude and direction; we can think of this vector as successively sweeping out the triangular areas $OAB, OBC, OCD, \ldots$. It is immediately apparent that these successive areas are all equal to each other, since the triangles all have the same base $AB = BC, \ldots,$ and the same altitude denoted by $r_\perp$.

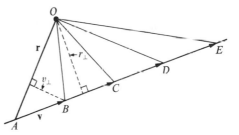

FIG. 17.13.1. Particle of mass m moves with uniform velocity along straight line AE. Points A, B, C, ... are positions occupied at equal successive intervals of time; $r_\perp$ is the perpendicular distance from origin O to line AE.

If we select the arbitrary interval of time to be the unit interval, then the triangles represent equal areas swept out by r in successive unit intervals of time. The area of any one triangle can be represented in two ways:

$$A = \frac{r_\perp v}{2} = \frac{r v_\perp}{2}, \qquad (17.13.1)$$

where $v =$ magnitude of uniform velocity of particle,
$r_\perp =$ defined in Fig. 17.13.1,
$r =$ instantaneous magnitude of $\mathbf{r}$ at beginning of a time interval,
$v_\perp =$ component of $\mathbf{v}$ perpendicular to $\mathbf{r}$.

The $r_\perp$ and v are fixed quantities, while r and $v_\perp$ vary continuously. Since the area A swept out in unit time is constant, Eq. (17.13.1) shows that the product $rv_\perp$ (or $mrv_\perp$) must be constant. For the special case in which reference point O lies on the line AE, $mrv_\perp = O$.

If $mrv_\perp$ had a fixed value only for uniform rectilinear motion, it would be of little interest; we shall show, however, in the next section, that it has a fixed value for a very important case of nonuniform motion—motion under the influence of a central force, a force always directed toward a fixed point O.

17.14 MOTION UNDER INFLUENCE OF A CENTRAL FORCE

Suppose a particle moving along line AB [Fig. 17.14.1(a)] receives, at position B, a sharp blow or impulse with duration Δt very much smaller than the time taken to travel distance AB. A sharp blow will cause an abrupt change in magnitude and direction of the velocity. Let us suppose that the blow at B is directed toward point O. The change of velocity must then be parallel to BO, and the new velocity, which we assume to be directed along BC', must lie in the plane already determined by line AB and point O; i.e., in the plane of the paper. A succession of subsequent blows, all directed toward O, will produce further changes in magnitude and direction of velocity, but always in the plane of the paper. Thus we prove, exactly as Newton did, that motion under the influence of centrally directed impulses must lie in a plane.

Let us return to the change produced at B.* Since the impulse at B is directed along BO, the component of velocity perpendicular to BO must remain unaltered. Letting AB represent the velocity at B, AM represent the component perpendicular to BO, construct $MN = AM$, and draw PN parallel to BO. The new velocity must have component MN perpendicular to BO, and the particle, headed in direction BC', must move to position C in the same time interval as that in which it previously moved from A to B. Thus, BC represents the new velocity after the blow at point O. Taking $BB' = AB$, we have $\mathbf{BB'} + \mathbf{B'C} = \mathbf{BC}$, and $\mathbf{B'C}$ represents the change of velocity imparted by the abrupt impulse delivered at B. Figure 17.14.1(b) repeats an exactly similar construction for the effect of a blow delivered at C, redirecting the velocity along CD'.

> PROBLEM 17.16.   Add to Fig. 17.14.1(b) by sketching the effect of an abrupt impulse at D directed along DO, redirecting the velocity to a point E along a new direction of your own choice. Add still another triangle for an equal interval of time assuming that no impulse is delivered at E.

> PROBLEM 17.17.   Construct a figure exactly like Fig. 17.14.1, except that impulses delivered at uniform intervals are directed *away* from point O instead of toward it.

In Fig. 17.14.1, triangles OAB and OBC have the same base OB and equal altitudes $AM = MN$; therefore their areas are equal. Triangles OBC and OCD have the same

---

* The reader will find the discussion of Fig. 17.14.1 much easier to follow and understand if he resketches the construction for himself, step by step, as he reads the text.

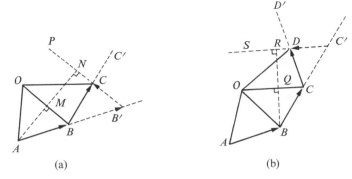

FIG. 17.14.1. (a) At position B particle receives sharp, impulsive blow directed toward O. Velocity of particle is abruptly changed and directed along BC'. Component of velocity perpendicular to BO remains unchanged. Therefore MN is constructed equal to AM and PN is drawn parallel to BO. Particle moves from B to C in same interval as that in which it moved from A to B. (b) At position C particle receives another sharp blow directed toward O. Velocity is changed and directed along CD'. RQ is constructed equal to QB, and SR is drawn parallel to CO. Particle moves from C to D in same time interval as that in which it moved from B to C.

base OC and equal altitudes $BQ = QR$; their areas are also equal—and so on, with additional centrally directed impulses delivered at uniform intervals of time. Thus the radius vector **r** from O to the instantaneous particle position sweeps out equal areas in equal times. In the *Principia*, Newton presents exactly this analysis and then argues that, as the time intervals between impulses are made shorter and shorter and the applied action becomes more and more nearly continuous, the path followed by the particle becomes more and more nearly a continuous curve. The limiting condition is that under influence of a continually acting (but possibly varying) force directed toward a single point O, a particle moves in a curved path. This path lies in a plane, and the radius vector **r** sweeps out equal areas in equal intervals of time. (Note that this is a generalization of Kepler's second law, discovered empirically for the elliptical orbits of the planets. See Chapter 15 for a description of Newton's use of these ideas in the *Principia*.)

17.15 ANGULAR MOMENTUM

Since the successive triangular areas in Fig. 17.14.1 are equal to each other, just as they were in Fig. 17.13.1, we see that, under the influence of centrally directed impulses, the former figure is a kind of "bending around" of the latter. The quantity $mv_\perp$ remains constant in both cases, and, by the limit argument outlined at the end of the last section, remains constant not only under a succession of discrete blows but also under the continuous action of a central force. The force on the particle may vary as the particle approaches or recedes from point O (as is the case in planetary motion), but the force on the particle, being always directed along the radial line to O, does not alter the numerical value of $mv_\perp$.

The quantity $mrv_\perp$ invites comparison with linear momentum because it contains the product mv, but it must not be confused with linear momentum; it is *dimensionally* a different quantity because of the factor r.   Linear momentum $m\mathbf{v}$ is defined with reference to a set of coordinate axes, relative to which we define velocity $\mathbf{v}$.   The quantity $mrv_\perp$ is called the angular momentum of a particle, and is defined with respect to a *particular point*, such as O in the preceding discussions.

In general, angular momentum $mrv_\perp$ of a particle may vary, depending on the forces to which the particle is subject. In the special case of motion under the influence of a *centrally* directed force (or under zero force), our analysis has led to the conclusion that angular momentum must be conserved. This suggests the conjecture that angular momentum of the particle can be altered only if the applied force has an instantaneous component $F_\perp$, perpendicular to the instantaneous radius vector $\mathbf{r}$.

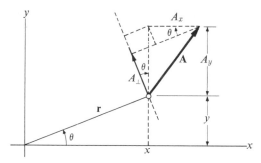

Fig. 17.15.1.   Vectors $\mathbf{A}$ and $\mathbf{r}$: $A_\perp = A_y \cos\theta - A_x \sin\theta = A_y \cdot (x/r) - A_x \cdot (y/r)$; $rA_\perp = xA_y - yA_x$.

We shall examine this problem further by constructing an analytical representation of angular momentum in a Cartesian system of coordinates. Figure 17.15.1 shows a general vector $\mathbf{A}$ with component $A_\perp$ in the direction perpendicular to radius vector $\mathbf{r}$. It is shown in the caption of the figure that

$$rA_\perp = xA_y - yA_x. \tag{17.15.1}$$

If we take $\mathbf{A}$ to correspond to velocity $\mathbf{v}$ and denote angular momentum by the conventional symbol L, we have, with the aid of (17.15.1):

$$L = mrv_\perp = m(xv_y - yv_x). \tag{17.15.2}$$

From this calculation in Cartesian coordinates, L will emerge with an algebraic sign: positive if the motion is counterclockwise and negative if clockwise, and we interpret the signs accordingly.

Since we have discovered that L is constant (that is, $dL/dt = 0$) under the influence of a central force, and since the derivative $d(mv)/dt$ emerged as an important quantity in our previous work, we have some motivation for examining the time derivative of L. Taking the time derivative of Eq. (17.15.2), treating m as constant and using the product theorem of differentiation [Eq. (8.6.1)]:

$$\frac{dL}{dt} = m\left[x\frac{dv_y}{dt} + v_y\frac{dx}{dt} - y\frac{dv_x}{dt} - v_x\frac{dy}{dt}\right]$$

with labels pointing to the terms: a_y, v_x, a_x, v_y

$$= m(xa_y - ya_x) = mra_\perp. \qquad (17.15.3)$$

Notice how obligingly the second and fourth terms subtract out!

For a case of two-dimensional motion in which the angular momentum L around a point O is constant ($dL/dt = 0$), we have from (17.15.3) that

$$(xa_y - ya_x) = 0, \qquad \frac{a_y}{a_x} = \frac{y}{x}. \qquad (17.15.4)$$

Since $y/x = \tan\theta$, is the slope of instantaneous radius vector $\mathbf{r}$ (Fig. 17.15.1), the instantaneous acceleration vector $\mathbf{a}$ must be parallel to $\mathbf{r}$, and the force applied to the particle must be parallel to $\mathbf{r}$ if angular momentum is to remain constant.

Thus we close our network of reasoning by tracing it along another route. In Section 17.14 we proved by *geometrical* reasoning that the quantity $mrv_\perp$ is conserved when motion occurs under the influence of a centrally directed force. In this section we proved by *analytical* reasoning that a quantity $L = m(xv_y - yv_x)$ is conserved if the force applied to the moving particle is centrally directed.

PROBLEM 17.18.   (a) Calculate the angular momentum of a particle (mass = 120 gm) revolving in a circle (radius = 85 cm) with an angular velocity of 11 rad/sec. [*Answer:* 0.95 kg·m²/sec.]

(b) Motion of planets and comets takes place under the influence of a central force. Halley's comet has a velocity of 33.5 mi/sec when it is closest to the sun (perihelion). The orbit, sketched in Fig. 17.15.2, is such that $OP = 5.45 \times 10^7$ mi; $OA = 3.29 \times 10^9$ mi. What velocity does the comet have when it is farthest from the sun (aphelion)? What can you say about velocities at intermediate positions?

FIGURE 17.15.2

17.16 TORQUE

It was conjectured in the preceding section that L can be changed only under the influence of a force with a component perpendicular to $\mathbf{r}$. Equation (17.15.3) helps us verify this conjecture:

$$\frac{dL}{dt} = x(ma_y) - y(ma_x) = r(ma_\perp). \qquad (17.15.3)$$

From the second law, $ma_y = F_{y\,\text{net}}$; $ma_x = F_{x\,\text{net}}$, and therefore:

$$\frac{dL}{dt} = xF_{y\,\text{net}} - yF_{x\,\text{net}} = rF_{\perp\,\text{net}}. \qquad (17.16.1)$$

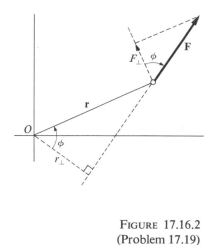

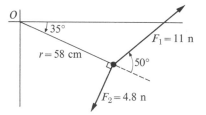

Fig. 17.16.1. Force **F** exerts counter-clockwise (positive) torque τ around point O; τ can be calculated in two ways: $\tau = rF_\perp = r(F \cos \phi)$, $\tau = r_\perp F = (r \cos \phi)F$.

FIGURE 17.16.2
(Problem 17.19)

[The last step follows from Eq. (17.15.1) and Fig. 17.15.1.] Thus dL/dt is not zero only when $F_{\perp \, net}$ is not zero.

Intuitively, or physically, the quantity $rF_\perp$ (Fig. 17.16.1), denoted by τ, gives us a measure of the twisting or turning effect an applied force exerts around point O. The turning effect is largest if the total force **F** is itself perpendicular to **r**; it is zero if the force is directed parallel to **r**. The quantity $rF_\perp$ is called the "torque" or "moment" exerted by the applied force.

Equation (17.16.1) tells us that angular momentum of a particle can be altered *only* if the net external torque is not zero. Several forces can be applied to a particle and the individual torques might add up to zero. In the two-dimensional case, torque can be thought of as acting counterclockwise or clockwise, causing L to increase or decrease with time; torques in these directions are associated with plus and minus signs, respectively.

The torque τ exerted by a force **F** can be calculated in two ways, as shown in Fig. 17.16.1. The distance $r_\perp$ is sometimes called the "radius arm" or "moment arm" of the force.

We thus have the statement

$$\tau_{net} = \frac{dL}{dt} = \frac{d}{dt}(mrv_\perp) \tag{17.16.2}$$

as the rotational analog of $\mathbf{F}_{net} = (d/dt)(mv)$. It must be noted that our treatment has been highly restricted: We have considered particles rather than extended bodies, and the motion has been confined to a plane containing the point O with respect to which angular momentum L is defined. (More complete discussions must be left to more advanced texts. It can be shown that, in three-dimensional problems, the quantities τ and L obey the same vector arithmetic as displacements, velocities, accelerations, and forces, providing the vectors τ and **L** are assigned directions perpendicular to the plane formed by r and $F_\perp$ in the case of torque and perpendicular to the plane formed by r and $v_\perp$ in the case of angular momentum.)

PROBLEM 17.19. Calculate the torque exerted on the particle (mass = 120 gm) shown in Fig. 17.16.2. [*Answer: τ = +2.1 m·n.*] If the particle has an instantaneous $v_\perp$ = 3.8 m/sec in the clockwise direction, calculate the instantaneous value of L. [*Answer: L = −0.26 kg·m²/sec.*] What is the rate of change of angular momentum at this instant? [*Answer: +2.1 kg·m²/sec.*]

17.17 CONSERVATION OF ANGULAR MOMENTUM IN A CLOSED SYSTEM

If two particles moving under the influence of a central force acting toward O collide (or interact with each other at a distance, as in Fig. 17.17.1), they will always exert equal and opposite torques on each other. Therefore, although they may alter each other's angular momentum, the changes are equal and opposite, and in a closed system of interacting particles, total angular momentum, L_{total}, must be conserved *as well as* total linear momentum, $(mv)_{\text{total}}$. This theorem can also be extended to three-dimensional problems, but the extension is beyond the scope of this text.

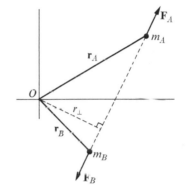

FIG. 17.17.1. Particles A and B interact by collision, or at a distance, as shown in the figure. $\mathbf{F}_A$ and $\mathbf{F}_B$, equal and opposite by Newton's third law, have the same moment arm $r_\perp$ about point O, and therefore exert equal and opposite torques on the particles; $\tau_A + \tau_B = 0$.

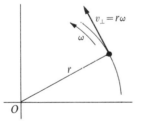

FIG. 17.18.1. Particle in circular motion at angular velocity ω around point O; $v_\perp$ is identical with tangential velocity $r\omega$; $L = mrv_\perp = mr^2\omega$.

17.18 THE SPECIAL CASE OF CIRCULAR MOTION

In the special case of circular motion at angular velocity ω about point O (Fig. 17.18.1), instantaneous angular momentum L is given by

$$L = mrv_\perp = mr^2\omega. \tag{17.18.1}$$

Suppose a frictionless puck is set into circular motion on a glass plate, as shown in Fig. 17.18.2. The motion is in a horizontal plane around the vertical tube AO. A string, attached to the puck at C, can be pulled up through the tube, drawing the puck radially inward toward O. Starting with the puck revolving around O at an initial radius r_1 and angular velocity ω_1, we draw it slowly toward O, so that the total

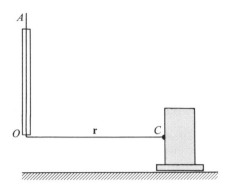

FIG. 17.18.2.   Frictionless puck on glass plate revolves in a horizontal plane about point O.   String AOC can be pulled up through tube AO, decreasing the magnitude of radius r.

velocity of the puck is very nearly equal to its tangential velocity.   (Then the force exerted by the string is very nearly perpendicular to the total vector velocity of the puck.)

PROBLEM 17.20.   Treating the puck as a particle, argue that, since $mr^2\omega$ must remain very nearly constant, the final angular velocity ω_2 at radius r_2 must be larger than ω_1. Obtain an algebraic expression for ω_2 in terms of ω_1, r_1, and r_2.   Assume some reasonable numbers and predict a final angular velocity to obtain a feeling for how large an effect this is.   What difficulty does this analysis encounter if the puck is pulled inward at a velocity comparable to its tangential velocity?   What insight does this analysis give you into the way a skater or an acrobat uses his arms to change the angular velocity of a spin?   In all these instances a body in circular motion experiences changing angular velocity; does that mean that a net torque must somehow be exerted?

17.19   PROBLEMS

17.21.   Describe in detail the sequence of momentum changes of yourself and the earth when you go through the action of jumping vertically upward and coming back down for an inelastic collision with the earth.   (Remember that, because of gravity, you are interacting with the earth even when you are not in contact with it.)

17.22.   Imagine yourself supplied with a cart that rolls with negligible frictional effects and is large enough for you to walk about on.   Denote your mass by m_s and that of the cart by m_c; adopt appropriate symbols for initial and final velocities.   Make *algebraic* analyses of the following situations:

(a)   Suppose that initially you are standing at one end of the cart and that all velocities

are zero.   You walk to the other end of the cart and stop.   Describe in detail what happens.   What is your final displacement relative to the cart?   Relative to the ground? What is the displacement of the center of mass of the system?   What is the sequence of momentum changes?   (In your analysis, consider various possible ratios of m_s/m_c such as $m_s/m_c < 1$, $m_s/m_c = 1$, $m_s/m_c > 1$.

(b)   Suppose you run toward the stationary cart and jump on with velocity v_{s1}.   You then walk to the other end of the cart and jump off with a velocity greater than v_{s1}.

Analyze and describe the sequence of momentum changes.   What is the final condition?   Has momentum been added to the system by your jumping off with a higher velocity than that with which you jumped on?

(c) Invent some other possible experiments and predict the results.

17.23. A sailboat is stalled on a lake for lack of wind. The skipper's only piece of auxiliary equipment is a large fan which he has set up so as to blow air at the sail, with the sail let out to a position at right angles to the axis of the boat. Will this technique get the boat home? (Do not be satisfied with a pat answer. Analyze the problem by visualizing the history of a small parcel of air of mass m. What happens at the fan to the parcel of air? What happens to the boat? Suppose the parcel of air could be "bounced" off the sail like the ball in Problem 17.6? What is a more likely behavior of the air as it strikes the sail? What momentum changes are involved? In the final analysis, what would be the most effective way of utilizing the fan?)

17.24. Describe, in terms of momentum changes, the mechanism of propulsion of a propeller-driven boat and of a rocket. Point out carefully the similarities and the essential differences between the two cases.

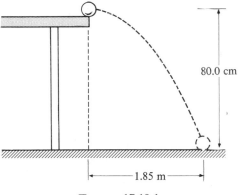

FIGURE 17.19.1

17.25. In a laboratory experiment a marble (mass = 15.0 gm), struck near the edge of the table, flies off with horizontal velocity v_1 and lands on the floor at the position shown in Fig. 17.19.1.

(a) Calculate the initial momentum of the marble and the momentum at the instant it strikes the floor.

(b) Draw a vector diagram showing the change of momentum of the marble, and calculate the numerical magnitude.

(c) What impulse is delivered to the marble during its flight? (Evaluate the impulse in two different ways and make sure they check.) [*Answer:* $mv_1 = 0.0687$ kg·m/sec; $\Delta mv = 0.0594$ kg·m/sec.]

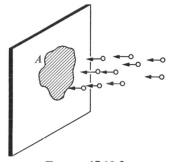

FIGURE 17.19.2

17.26. A stream of particles, each with mass m and velocity v, strikes a wall at normal incidence (Fig. 17.19.2). If n particles strike the wall in each second, obtain an algebraic expression for the average force exerted on the wall if the collision is (a) perfectly inelastic [*Answer:* nmv], (b) perfectly elastic [*Answer:* $2nmv$].

If all the particles strike the wall within an area A, what is the average pressure exerted on this area? If mass = 2 gm, $v = 8.0$ m/sec and $n = 50$ particles/sec, calculate numerical values of force exerted on the wall. What would happen to the force if the angle of incidence were changed?

17.27. In his *Astronomia Nova*, of 1609, seventy-eight years before Newton's *Principia*, Kepler made what has become a famous and often-quoted remark: "If two stones were placed in any part of the world, near each other and yet beyond the sphere of influence of a third related body, the two stones, like two magnetic bodies, would come together at some intermediate place, each approaching the other through a distance in proportion to the mass of the other." Kepler's word for mass was the Latin *moles* —a term denoting bulk of matter in some vague sense. Clearly defined conceptions of inertial and gravitational mass were still far in the future. Yet Kepler must be given credit for a profound insight. Comment on the statement quoted above: In modern terms, what are all the dynamical implications of Kepler's statement? Is the prediction consistent with our present knowledge? What name have we given the "intermediate place" to which Kepler refers? What relation do you see between this problem and the reaction car experiment discussed in Section 6.4?

17.28. Refer back to Problem 9.18, in which you were asked to find ω as a function of R for cases in which a small particle B revolves in a circular orbit around the center of a massive sphere A, under the influence of either electrical or gravitational attraction. For each of these cases derive the relation between angular momentum L of particle B and the orbital radius R. Interpret the results: What is the difference between this physical situation and that in Problem 17.20; that is, why is L a function of R in this case and independent of R in Problem 17.20? What kind of action is necessary to change the radius of a particle orbit in the electrical or gravitational case; i.e., is a radial push or pull sufficient, or is a torque also required? [*Answer:* Electrical case: $L = (kq_A q_B m_B R)^{1/2}$; gravitational case: $L = (Gm_A m_B^2 R)^{1/2}$.]

17.29. A time-varying force, described by the function $F_B(t) = 45(2t - t^2)$, acts on body B during the interval $0 \le t \le 2$, where F is in newtons and t in seconds. Sketch the F-versus-t history. Evaluate the impulse delivered to the body by F_B and calculate the average value of the force. If F_B were the net force exerted, and B had a mass of 2.8 kg, calculate the velocity change imparted to B. [*Answer:* $I = 60$ n/sec; $\overline{F}_B = 30$ n; $\Delta v = 21$ m/sec.]

PROBLEMS FOR MORE ADVANCED WORK

17.30. Consider the angular momentum of a particle in circular motion: $L = mr^2\omega$. Investigate the nature of dL/dt if r is constant; what can you say about the relation between torque and angular acceleration in this case? Investigate dL/dt for the case in which r varies (the particle in circular motion has a component of radial velocity $v_r = dr/dt$) while ω is constant. Interpret the result in terms of torque necessary under such circumstances. Investigate dL/dt for the case in which both r and ω vary; solve for the connection between angular acceleration and v_r when the external torque is zero. Relate this last result to the analysis in Problem 17.20.

17.31. A rocket is propelled by continuously ejecting some of its own mass (in the form of burned fuel) at very high velocity v_0 relative to itself. We observe the motion of the rocket from frame of reference O in the absence of gravity or other external force (Fig. 17.19.3). At instant t the rocket has momentum $m_r v_r$, where m_r and v_r are instantaneous values of rocket mass and velocity. Suppose the rocket ejects fuel at the rate dm_f/dt. In a short time interval Δt, the rocket ejects a parcel of fuel of mass $(dm_f/dt)\Delta t$, moving relative to our frame of reference with velocity $v_0 + v_r$. Note that v_0 may be either positive or negative and that the rocket may be either speeding up or slowing down; note also that $dm_f/dt = -dm_r/dt$ (conservation of mass). Equate the total momentum of the system at the beginning and end of the interval Δt, and show that

$$\frac{dv_r}{dt} = -\frac{v_0}{m_r}\frac{dm_f}{dt}.$$

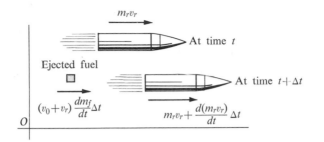

FIGURE 17.19.3

The quantity $v_0 \, (dm_f/dt)$ can be regarded as a force. (Why?) It is called the *thrust* of the rocket motor.

If m_f is the initial mass of the fuel, and M is the mass of the rest of the rocket, show that, in the absence of external forces, the change in velocity resulting from expenditure of all the fuel is given by

$$\Delta v_r = -v_0 \ln \left(1 + \frac{m_f}{M} \right),$$

where the symbol "ln" denotes the natural logarithm. Interpret this result. A reasonable value of v_0 is 6000 ft/sec. Calculate the velocity change that would be imparted to a rocket of total initial mass of 50,000 lb, of which 45,000 lb is fuel. If the thrust of the motor is 100,000 lb about how long is the period of action of the motor? [*Answer:* $\Delta v_r = 9400$ mi/hr; $\Delta t = 84$ sec.]

SUPPLEMENTARY READING AND STUDY

Non-calculus treatment of linear momentum concepts; many additional problems:
    Physics, Physical Science Study Committee. Boston: D. C. Heath, 1960, Chapter 23

Thorough development of linear momentum and force concepts, using calculus; challenging problems:
    Introduction to Mechanics, Matter, and Waves, U. Ingard, W. L. Kraushaar. Reading, Mass.: Addison-Wesley, 1960, Chapters 3, 4

Angular momentum:
    Advanced Topics Program, PSSC Course in Physics. Watertown, Mass.: Educational Services, Inc., 1962, Chapter A-1
    Ingard and Kraushaar, *op. cit.*, Chapter 9
    Basic Concepts in Physics, C. W. Sherwin. New York: Holt, Rinehart and Winston, 1961, Chapter 3

Historical discussions and excerpts:
    A Source Book in Physics, W. F. Magie. New York: McGraw-Hill, 1935, Chapter 2
    A History of Mechanics, R. Dugas. New York: Central Book Co., 1955, Chapters 4, 5
    The Mechanization of the World Picture, E. J. Dijksterhuis. Oxford: Oxford University Press, 1961, pages 373–380, 410–412

CHAPTER 18

Energy

18.1 INTRODUCTION

In summarizing his rules of impact for the Royal Society in 1668 (see Section 5.1), Huygens included the following statement:

> "The sum of the products arising from multiplying the mass of each hard (elastic) body into the square of its velocity, is the same both before and after the stroke."

Leibniz encountered the same quantity, mv^2, in other lines of investigation and, in 1695, gave it the name *vis viva* or "living force." Huygens' statement is a recognition of conservation of *vis viva* in certain ideal collisions. Thus, for a two-body collision, we would have the two equations:

$$m_A \mathbf{v}_{A1} + m_B \mathbf{v}_{B1} = m_A \mathbf{v}_{A2} + m_B \mathbf{v}_{B2}, \tag{18.1.1}$$

$$m_A v_{A1}^2 + m_B v_{B1}^2 = m_A v_{A2}^2 + m_B v_{B2}^2. \tag{18.1.2}$$

These are entirely independent relations; (18.1.2) cannot be derived from (18.1.1). The first is a *vector* equation; the second is a relation among scalar quantities. The first is always true, in all collisions both elastic and inelastic; the second is an approximation, very nearly correct for bodies that collide with coefficient of restitution [Eq. (17.2.2)] close to unity, but not at all applicable to inelastic collisions.

For a perfectly inelastic collision, $\mathbf{v}_{B2} = \mathbf{v}_{A2} = \mathbf{v}_2$ (that is, the bodies stick together and move with a common velocity), and we are left with just one unknown in Eq. (18.1.1); if we know the initial conditions, the final one is determined. If the bodies bounce apart, however, we have two unknown quantities, $\mathbf{v}_{B2}$ and $\mathbf{v}_{A2}$. Since repetition of a particular experiment yields fixed reproducible values of both $\mathbf{v}_{B2}$ and $\mathbf{v}_{A2}$, it is clear that some additional condition, besides (18.1.1), must govern the collision phenomenon. In the limit of elastic behavior, the added condition seems to be (18.1.2).

Is this condition related to the laws of motion, as we found (18.1.1) to be? What is the physical significance of *vis viva*? How is it connected with the concept of elasticity? Study of these questions leads us to a conservation law that, to the best of our present knowledge, seems to embrace *all* natural phenomena.

In Section 17.6, we established a connection among the laws of motion and conservation of momentum by starting with $\mathbf{F}_{\text{net}} = m\mathbf{a}$, calculating the integral of force with respect to time, and showing that this integral (net impulse) was equal to the change of momentum imparted to the body. In the following section we begin a parallel investigation by studying the variation of force and acceleration as functions of position, x, instead of time, t. This investigation will lead us back to Huygens' empirical discovery concerning *vis viva*.

18.2 HORIZONTAL DISPLACEMENT UNDER CONSTANT FORCES

Consider a case in which two horizontal forces act on a cart during horizontal displacement (Fig. 18.2.1). Taking positive direction to the right, and using the free body diagram and $F_{x\,\text{net}} = ma_x$, we have:

$$P - f = ma_x, \tag{18.2.1}$$

where symbols P and f denote the absolute values of **P** and **f** respectively.

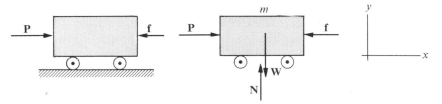

FIG. 18.2.1. Horizontal displacement of cart under influence of forces **P** and **f**.

What can we say about change in motion for various *displacements*, Δx, of the cart? If the applied forces are equal and opposite, the velocity does not change at all. If the forces are constant but unequal, a uniform acceleration is imparted, and velocity, acceleration, and displacement are connected by the kinematic relation

$$v_x^2 - v_{0x}^2 = 2a_x\,\Delta x. \tag{18.2.2}$$

If we eliminate a_x from (18.2.1) and (18.2.2), we have a relation among force, displacement, and velocity change:

$$P - f = \frac{m(v_x^2 - v_{0x}^2)}{2\,\Delta x}. \tag{18.2.3}$$

Multiplying both sides by Δx, we obtain

$$(P - f)\,\Delta x = \tfrac{1}{2}mv_x^2 - \tfrac{1}{2}mv_{0x}^2 = \Delta(\tfrac{1}{2}mv_x^2).^* \tag{18.2.4}$$

_____

* Compare the general form of this equation with the impulse-momentum relation that would be obtained if we used the kinematic relation $v_x - v_{0x} = a_x\,\Delta t$ instead of (18.2.2). We would then obtain, on eliminating a_x: $(P - f)\,\Delta t = \Delta(mv)$. Recall that, even when acceleration is not uniform, this theorem is valid in the general form

$$\int_{t_1}^{t_2} F_{\text{net}}(t)\,dt = \Delta(mv).$$

This parallelism later motivates us to examine $\int_{x_1}^{x_2} F_{\text{net}}(x)\,dx$.

The last step was not a matter of caprice; it has a very explicit motivation. Note what has been achieved in Eq. (18.2.4). On the right-hand side we now only have terms which are intrinsically *properties* of the body and its instantaneous motion; on the left-hand side we have combined the numbers which have to do with the *action* applied externally—the force and associated displacement. (Such a separation of characteristic quantities is *not* effected in Eq. (18.2.3).)

Let us now make a careful interpretation of Eq. (18.2.4), translating into words the ideas that it implies:

(a) First examine and interpret the algebraic signs. What is the significance of plus and minus signs on the right-hand side, in the term $\Delta(\frac{1}{2}mv^2)$? The instantaneous quantity $\frac{1}{2}mv^2$ is intrinsically positive regardless of the sign of v_x; therefore $\frac{1}{2}mv_x^2$ does not have vector properties. Furthermore $\Delta(\frac{1}{2}mv_x^2)$ is positive if the final value of $\frac{1}{2}mv_x^2$ is greater than the initial, and negative in the opposite case; that is, the sign of $\Delta(\frac{1}{2}mv_x^2)$ simply tells us whether $\frac{1}{2}mv_x^2$ increases or decreases in size during the action, and no longer has anything to do with directions in *space*. We describe this by saying that $\frac{1}{2}mv_x^2$ and $\Delta(\frac{1}{2}mv_x^2)$ are *scalar* rather than vector quantities.

(b) On the left-hand side of Eq. (18.2.4), we have the product of two vectors which are parallel to each other, $(P - f)$ and Δx. How must we interpret the algebraic sign of this combination? If both the net force and displacement are positive, $\Delta(\frac{1}{2}mv_x^2)$ is positive, and the body's $\frac{1}{2}mv_x^2$ has been increased; similarly if the net force and the displacement are both negative. If the net force and the displacement are oppositely directed, $\Delta(\frac{1}{2}mv_x^2)$ is negative, and the body's $\frac{1}{2}mv_x^2$ is decreased. Thus the product $(P - f)\,\Delta x$ is also a scalar quantity (as it obviously must be in order to equal a scalar), and its algebraic sign tells us whether the $\frac{1}{2}mv_x^2$ property of the body is increased or decreased during the displacement Δx. It is increased if $(P - f)$ and Δx are in the same direction (positive or negative), and is decreased if they are oppositely directed.

(c) Suppose $f = 0$ in Eq. (18.2.4). Then

$$P\,\Delta x = \Delta(\tfrac{1}{2}mv_x^2). \tag{18.2.5}$$

Interpretation: If there is no force opposing $\mathbf{P}$, and if $\mathbf{P}$ and $\Delta\mathbf{x}$ are in the same direction, the $\frac{1}{2}mv_x^2$ property of the body is increased during the displacement, and the increase is equal to $P\,\Delta x$. This is by no means a trivial statement; it says that we have two entirely different ways of calculating the same number. If we know P and Δx, we can predict the change in $\frac{1}{2}mv_x^2$ of the body. If we know from direct observation a change in $\frac{1}{2}mv_x^2$, we can calculate what force would have imparted this change in any particular displacement. Furthermore, Eq. (18.2.5) implies that although a given action P will impart very different velocities to bodies of different mass, it will always impart exactly the same change in the quantity $\frac{1}{2}mv_x^2$ to *any* body.

(d) If $P = 0$, and the body is initially moving toward the right with velocity v_{0x}, we have from Eq. (18.2.4):

$$-f\,\Delta x = \tfrac{1}{2}mv_x^2 - \tfrac{1}{2}mv_{0x}^2. \tag{18.2.6}$$

Since Δx will be positive (body assumed moving to the right), and f is taken as acting to the left, the body will experience a decrease in $\frac{1}{2}mv_x^2$; that is, $\frac{1}{2}mv_x^2 < \frac{1}{2}mv_{0x}^2$. This would be the physical situation for example if $\mathbf{f}$ were a frictional force, and the body were sliding to the right after an initial push. If $\mathbf{f}$ is a frictional force, it acts only while the body slides, and Eq. (18.2.6) would be applicable only up to the instant and position at which $v_x = 0$.

(e) Let us rewrite Eq. (18.2.4) in still another way:

$$P \, \Delta x = f \, \Delta x + \Delta(\tfrac{1}{2}mv_x^2). \tag{18.2.7}$$

Many ways of talking about the behavior of these numbers could conceivably be developed, but one particular language has evolved and taken root. If we think of $P \, \Delta x$ as an action imparted by us in a case where $f = 0$, it is easy to convey the content of Eqs. (18.2.5) and (18.2.7) verbally by saying "our action $P \, \Delta x$ has been 'preserved' or 'transformed' into a change in $\tfrac{1}{2}mv_x^2$ of the body."

If $f \neq 0$, we translate Eq. (18.2.7) with the statement "part of our action $P \, \Delta x$ is transformed into a change in $\tfrac{1}{2}mv_x^2$ of the body and the remainder is 'used up' against the opposing action $f \, \Delta x$."

If the body initially has a velocity v_{0x} toward the right, it is capable of exerting an action in that direction; e.g., striking a nail and displacing it into a wall. In such a case $\tfrac{1}{2}mv_x^2$ decreases to zero, being "used up" against the opposing action $f \, \Delta x$.

Thus we begin to talk about these numbers as though some sort of entity were involved because our structure of language, visualization, and description seems to impel us to do so. Nevertheless we must discipline ourselves to remember that we are dealing with a construct and not an entity.

(f) Suppose that in Fig. 18.2.1 the force $\mathbf{P}$ were oriented at an angle θ to the horizontal, while $\mathbf{f}$ retained the indicated direction. Equation (18.2.7) would then become

$$(P \cos \theta) \, \Delta x = f \, \Delta x + \Delta(\tfrac{1}{2}mv_x^2). \tag{18.2.8}$$

Note that now the relevant action which is "preserved" or "transformed" is no longer $P \, \Delta x$ but is $(P \cos \theta) \, \Delta x$; that is, the numerical value describing what is preserved or transformed must be calculated by taking the *component* of force in the direction of the displacement and not the force itself.

PROBLEM 18.1. Consider the situation described by Eq. (18.2.6): A body moves with initial velocity v_{0x} at $t = t_0$ and is acted upon by an opposing force $\mathbf{f}$. If $\mathbf{f}$ is a frictional force, how far will the body slide before coming to a stop? [*Answer:* $\Delta x = \tfrac{1}{2}mv_{0x}^2/f$.] How is this algebraic result related to the one obtainable directly from the kinematic equation (18.2.2)? Suppose that instead of being a passive frictional force, $\mathbf{f}$ is a continuing active push exerted by you; the motion would not cease at the instant v became zero. Describe the motion and show that Eq. (18.2.6) says the same thing in algebraic terms.

18.3 VERTICAL DISPLACEMENT UNDER CONSTANT FORCES

If a body is displaced vertically up or down under the influence of a constant force (Fig. 18.3.1), we have, by a series of steps identical with those leading to Eq. (18.2.4):

$$P - m_A g = m_A a_y = \frac{m_A(v_y^2 - v_{0y}^2)}{2 \, \Delta y}, \tag{18.3.1}$$

$$P \, \Delta y = m_A g \, \Delta y + \Delta(\tfrac{1}{2}m_A v_y^2). \tag{18.3.2}$$

Suppose we lift the body slowly through a displacement Δy, exerting a force P very nearly equal in magnitude to mg and producing a negligible change in $\frac{1}{2}m_A v_y^2$. In Eq. (18.3.2) our action is represented by the number $P\,\Delta y = m_A g\,\Delta y$, and the body now occupies a higher level than it did before. In allowing the body to return to its original level, we can let it fall freely ($P = 0$), in which case

$$(\tfrac{1}{2}m_A v_y^2) = -m_A g\,\Delta y. \tag{18.3.3}$$

Since Δy is now negative, the quantity $\frac{1}{2}mv_y^2$ increases by the amount $|m_A g\,\Delta y| = |P\,\Delta y|$; that is, by precisely the amount associated with our lifting the body originally.

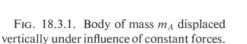

FIG. 18.3.1. Body of mass m_A displaced vertically under influence of constant forces.

On the other hand we might elect to allow the body to return to its original level without appreciable change in $\frac{1}{2}m_A v_y^2$. We can arrange this by running a string over a (frictionless) pulley and hanging an object B of equal weight at the other end. As A comes down slowly, B is raised to the position initially occupied by A. Thus the original quantity $P\,\Delta y = m_A g\,\Delta y$ still remains available—either to appear as $\frac{1}{2}mv_y^2$ of a moving body or to raise another equal body to the same height.

Suppose we throw the body vertically upward, so that it has the property of $\frac{1}{2}m_A v_{0y}^2$ when it leaves our hand at the reference level. The body rises until $\frac{1}{2}m_A v_y^2 = 0$; at that instant [from Eq. (18.3.2)]:

$$0 = m_A g\,\Delta y + (0 - \tfrac{1}{2}mv_{0y}^2),$$
$$m_A g\,\Delta y = \tfrac{1}{2}m_A v_{0y}^2. \tag{18.3.4}$$

The body rises vertically a distance Δy such that $m_A g\,\Delta y$ is just equal to the initial value $\frac{1}{2}m_A v_{0y}^2$. If it is allowed to fall freely back to its initial level, Δy returns to zero, and the original $\frac{1}{2}m_A v_{0y}^2$ is restored. Alternatively, by a string-and-pulley arrangement, body A can be lowered while raising body B; Δy for body A has been restored to zero, but the Δy has been transferred to body B, which can raise other bodies or can fall freely, recovering the value $\frac{1}{2}m_A v_{0y}^2$ originally imparted to body A when it was thrown upward.

If a ball bearing, dropped from a height Δy above a level steel block, experiences a perfectly elastic collision, bouncing upward with $|v_y|$ unchanged, the process of "converting" $mg\,\Delta y$ to $\frac{1}{2}mv_y^2$ and back again could go on indefinitely, without diminution of either of these numbers.

If, however, the bounce is only partially elastic or friction acts on the moving body, its $\frac{1}{2}mv_y^2$ seems to "leak" away. If the body strikes the ground without bouncing at all (perfectly inelastic collision), its $\frac{1}{2}mv_y^2$ seems to disappear abruptly, and cannot be restored without our lifting or projecting it once more.

PROBLEM 18.2. In your own words analyze some other physical situations in terms of the arithmetic of Eq. (18.3.2):

(a) Suppose that at an initial level y_0 you start pushing the body upward with force P larger than mg. This is continued up to level y_1, where the body leaves your hand with velocity v_1 and rises to a highest point y_2, from which it falls back to y_0.

(b) Analyze a case in which motion occurs with $P < mg$.

PROBLEM 18.3. Show that Eq. (18.3.3) can be rewritten in the form:

$$\tfrac{1}{2}m_A v_y^2 + mgy = \tfrac{1}{2}m_A v_{0y}^2 + mgy_0. \tag{18.3.5}$$

Using this form of the equation, analyze some cases of rising and falling motion (with $P = 0$).

18.4 DISPLACEMENTS UNDER VARYING FORCES

A discerning reader might offer the objection that the analyses carried out in the preceding sections have really told us nothing that we did not already know directly from the kinematic relations for uniformly accelerated motion and Newton's Second Law; he might point out that we simply rearranged an algebraic combination of these equations and developed a jargon about the results. And his objection would be entirely valid if that were as far as the investigation could be carried.

The analyses in Sections 18.2 and 18.3, however, are illustrative of a deep and general relationship that turns out to be valid whether or not the forces are constant—a relationship that is ultimately found to embrace all physical phenomena and to include electrical, chemical, and thermal effects as well as mechanical ones.

How can we analyze the problems suggested in Figs. 18.2.1 and 18.3.1 if the force $\mathbf{P}$, and therefore acceleration $\mathbf{a}$, are not constant, and Eq. (18.2.2) is inapplicable? The form of Eqs. (18.2.4) and (18.3.2) offers us a hint: The products $(P - f)\,\Delta x$ and $(P - mg)\,\Delta y$ can be interpreted as areas on a force-displacement diagram. Figure 18.4.1 shows such an interpretation of both sides of Eq. (18.2.4).

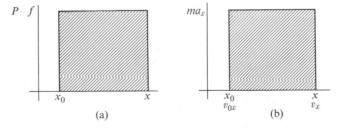

FIG. 18.4.1. Equation (18.2.4) interpreted in terms of areas on $(P - f)$-versus-x and ma_x-versus-x diagrams: $(P - f)\,\Delta x = ma_x\,\Delta x = \Delta(\tfrac{1}{2}mv_x^2)$.

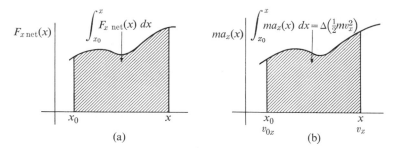

FIG. 18.4.2. Graphical interpretation of Eq. (18.4.6). Note that the area in (b) depends only on initial and final values of velocity and not on the intermediate history of the motion.

We have identified areas with integrals, and we recognize the area in Fig. 18.4.1(a) as

$$\int_{x_0}^{x} F_{net}(x)\, dx = \int_{x_0}^{x} (P - f)\, dx = (P - f)x \Big|_{x_0}^{x} = (P - f)(x - x_0)$$

$$= (P - f)\, \Delta x. \tag{18.4.1}$$

Could it be that the area under the ma-versus-x curve ($\int_{x_0}^{x} ma_x(x)\, dx$) always equals $\Delta(\frac{1}{2}mv_x^2)$ regardless of whether F_{net} is constant or varies in a complex way? This question leads us to investigate the integrals which follow from:

$$F_{x\,net} = ma_x,$$

namely

$$\int_{x_0}^{x} F_{x\,net}(x)\, dx = \int_{x_0}^{x} ma_x(x)\, dx. \tag{18.4.2}$$

To evaluate the integral on the right-hand side of (18.4.2), we need an antiderivative of acceleration a with respect to displacement x. Velocity v is an antiderivative of a with respect to t, and does not satisfy the requirement. Here we can bring to bear the function-of-a-function or chain rule analysis of Section 8.10, Eq. (8.10.4); treating v as a function of x and x as a function of t (see Problem 8.18):

$$a \equiv \frac{dv}{dt} = \frac{dv}{dx}\frac{dx}{dt} = v\frac{dv}{dx}. \tag{18.4.3}$$

(What mathematical conditions must be satisfied to validate use of the chain rule? Are these reasonable assumptions to make concerning the physical quantities v and x?) Applying the chain rule again, we have

$$\frac{d}{dx}\left(\frac{v^2}{2}\right) = \frac{d}{dv}\left(\frac{v^2}{2}\right)\frac{dv}{dx} = v\frac{dv}{dx} = a. \tag{18.4.4}$$

Therefore the quantity $v^2/2$ is an antiderivative of a with respect to x, and we can write:

$$\int_{x_0}^{x} ma_x(x)\, dx = m\left(\frac{v_x^2}{2}\right)\Big|_{x_0}^{x} = \tfrac{1}{2}mv_x^2 - \tfrac{1}{2}mv_{0x}^2 = \Delta(\tfrac{1}{2}mv_x^2). \qquad (18.4.5)$$

This is a remarkable result: the area under the ma_x-versus-x curve is always equal to $\Delta(\tfrac{1}{2}mv_x^2)$, regardless of how a_x varies during the interval. We have completely freed ourselves of the restriction imposed in the previous analyses. Equation (18.4.2) becomes

$$\int_{x_0}^{x} F_{x\,net}(x)\, dx = \tfrac{1}{2}mv_x^2 - \tfrac{1}{2}mv_{0x}^2 = \Delta(\tfrac{1}{2}mv_x^2). \qquad (18.4.6)$$

This theorem is interpreted graphically in Fig. 18.4.2.

PROBLEM 18.4.   (a) Apply Theorem (18.4.6) to the constant-force problems suggested by Figs. 18.2.1 and 18.3.1: Evaluate the integral on the left-hand side, and show that Eqs. (18.2.7) and (18.3.2) follow directly.

(b) Suppose that P, f, and mg are not constant. Write down relations corresponding to (18.2.7) and (18.3.2) in which the integrals are left unevaluated; i.e., in forms such as $\int_{x_0}^{x} P(x)\, dx$, etc.

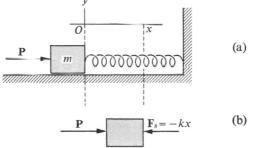

FIG. 18.5.1.   (a) Frictionless puck displaced to the right by force **P** against opposing force exerted by spring. (b) Free body diagram of displaced puck. Displacement x measured from relaxed position of spring.

18.5   DISPLACEMENT AGAINST THE RESTORING FORCE OF A SPRING

If we displace a body against the opposing force of a compressed spring (Fig. 18.5.1), we encounter a problem, similar in many ways to that of displacing a body vertically against the opposing pull of gravity, but here the opposing force increases with increasing displacement in accordance with Hooke's law. Evaluating the integral in (18.4.6), we have (with P and F_s denoting magnitudes of the indicated forces):

$$\int_{0}^{x} F_{net}(x)\, dx = \int_{0}^{x} (P - F_s)\, dx$$

$$= \int_{0}^{x} P\, dx - \int_{0}^{x} kx\, dx = \int_{0}^{x} P\, dx - \frac{kx^2}{2}. \qquad (18.5.1)$$

Then, making use of Eq. (18.4.6), we obtain

$$\int_0^x P \, dx = \frac{kx^2}{2} + \Delta(\tfrac{1}{2}mv^2)$$

or

$$\int_{x_0}^x P \, dx = \frac{kx^2}{2} - \frac{kx_0^2}{2} + \Delta(\tfrac{1}{2}mv^2). \tag{18.5.2}$$

If the body is released with an initial velocity of zero from an initial position x_0 and allowed to move freely ($P = 0$), Eq. (18.5.2) becomes

$$0 = \frac{kx^2}{2} - \frac{kx_0^2}{2} + (\tfrac{1}{2}mv^2 - 0),$$

$$0 = \frac{kx_0^2}{2} - \frac{kx^2}{2} + (0 - \tfrac{1}{2}mv^2),$$

$$\frac{kx_0^2}{2} = \frac{kx^2}{2} + \tfrac{1}{2}mv^2, \tag{18.5.3}$$

where x is any position occupied after the body is released, and v is the velocity at that position.

PROBLEM 18.5.   Interpret Eqs. (18.5.2) and (18.5.3) by analyzing various physical situations in terms of the arithmetic of these equations, just as we did with the gravitational problem in Section 18.3.   Show that exactly similar conservation relationships obtain.   There are, however, important differences in the character of the motion that can take place: If we drop a body vertically through a displacement Δy, it acquires a quantity of $\tfrac{1}{2}mv^2$ equal to $mg\,\Delta y$ and will continue dropping and acquiring additional $\tfrac{1}{2}mv^2$ if the fall is not interrupted.   If in the case of the spring, however, we release the body from a position $+x_0$ (Fig. 18.5.1), it will move toward the left and, on returning to $x = 0$, it will have acquired a quantity of $\tfrac{1}{2}mv^2$ equal to $kx_0^2/2$.   It will then continue moving to the left, but the acceleration will be directed toward the right because of the stretching of the spring.   In the case of free fall, there was no such reversal of the direction of acceleration.   Argue from the equations that the body will move to position $-x_0$, at which point the direction of motion will again be reversed.   In the absence of friction, this oscillation would continue indefinitely (as in the case of the bounding steel ball in Section 18.3).   The motion is "symmetrical" around $x = 0$; what mathematical characteristic of Eq. (18.5.3) accounts for this symmetry?   Solve Eq. (18.5.3) for v, and interpret the result.

18.6   DISPLACEMENT AGAINST AN INVERSE-SQUARE-LAW FORCE

A particle carrying positive charge q_1 occupies a fixed position (Fig. 18.6.1), while a particle of mass m and negative charge q_2 is displaced along a radial line under the action of force **P**.   Friction is assumed negligible, and the electrical force F_E is given

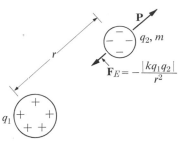

FIG. 18.6.1.   Particle of mass m and charge q_2 is displaced radially against electrical force $\mathbf{F}_E$.

by Coulomb's Law. Evaluating the integral in theorem (18.4.6):

$$\int_{r_0}^{r} F_{\text{net}}(r)\, dr = \int_{r_0}^{r} P\, dr - \int_{r_0}^{r} \frac{|kq_1q_2|}{r^2}\, dr = \int_{r_0}^{r} P\, dr - |kq_1q_2| \left[-\frac{1}{r}\right]_{r_0}^{r}$$

$$= \int_{r_0}^{r} P\, dr + |kq_1q_2| \left(\frac{1}{r} - \frac{1}{r_0}\right).$$

Then

$$\int_{r_0}^{r} P\, dr = -|kq_1q_2| \left(\frac{1}{r} - \frac{1}{r_0}\right) + (\tfrac{1}{2}mv^2 - \tfrac{1}{2}mv_0^2) \tag{18.6.1}$$

and, for cases in which $P = 0$,

$$\tfrac{1}{2}mv_0^2 - \frac{|kq_1q_2|}{r_0} = \tfrac{1}{2}mv^2 \qquad \frac{|kq_1q_2|}{r}$$

or

$$\Delta(\tfrac{1}{2}mv^2) = |kq_1q_2| \left(\frac{1}{r} - \frac{1}{r_0}\right). \tag{18.6.2}$$

PROBLEM 18.6.   Interpret Eqs. (18.6.1) and (18.6.2) in the manner illustrated in preceding sections. Compare this problem with those analyzed in Sections 18.3 and 18.6. What troubles arise if r or r_0 is taken to be zero?

Example. An outwardly directed radial velocity v_0 is imparted to the negatively charged particle (Fig. 18.6.1) at radial position r_0. For relatively small values of v_0, the particle moves out some distance along the radial line and then "falls" back toward q_1. What is the smallest value of v_0 for which the particle will recede indefinitely far from q_1 (that is, will not fall back)?

Translation of the problem into symbols: Find the particular value of initial velocity $v_0 = v_e$ such that the final velocity $v \to 0$ as $r \to \infty$. Solving for $1/r$ in Eq. (18.6.2), we obtain

$$\frac{1}{r} = \frac{\tfrac{1}{2}mv^2 - \tfrac{1}{2}mv_0^2}{|kq_1q_2|} + \frac{1}{r_0},$$

$$\lim_{v \to 0} \frac{1}{r} = \frac{-\tfrac{1}{2}mv_0^2}{|kq_1q_2|} + \frac{1}{r_0}.$$

Therefore the limit of $1/r$ as $v \to 0$ exists, and for $1/r = 0$ we obtain

$$\dot{v}_e = \sqrt{2|kq_1q_2|/mr_0}.$$

This velocity is called the "velocity of escape"; of course, any velocity greater than v_e will also result in "escape" of the particle. (We shall return to examples of this kind in later discussions of atomic physics. For the relevance of this concept to satellite and space-probe problems, see Problem 18.8.)

PROBLEM 18.7.   Consider a particle of mass m undergoing radial displacements in the neighborhood of the earth. m_E and r_E denote the mass and radius of the earth, respectively. This problem is obviously completely analogous to that posed in Fig. 18.6.1. Neglecting friction, show that

$$\int_{r_0}^{r} P\, dr = -Gmm_E \left(\frac{1}{r} - \frac{1}{r_0} \right) + \Delta(\tfrac{1}{2}mv^2), \tag{18.6.3}$$

$$\tfrac{1}{2}mv_0^2 - \frac{Gmm_E}{r_0} = \tfrac{1}{2}mv^2 - \frac{Gmm_E}{r}, \tag{18.6.4}$$

and interpret the results.

Show that acceleration due to gravity at the surface of the earth $g = Gm_E/r_E^2$, and that Eq. (18.6.3) reduces to Eq. (18.3.2) if P is constant and the displacement $r - r_0$ is small relative to the distance from the center of the earth.

PROBLEM 18.8.   Using results obtained in Problem 18.7, show that the velocity of escape v_E of a particle from the surface of the earth is given by

$$v_E = \sqrt{2gr_E}. \tag{18.6.5}$$

Calculate the escape velocity. [Answer: $v_E = 7.0$ mi/sec $= 25,000$ mi/hr.] Interpret the result: Why is it independent of the mass of the particle? What influence would air friction have; i.e., in which direction would it be necessary to correct the idealized estimate? How do you account for the fact that escape velocity is finite; i.e., why is it not necessary to impart an infinite velocity in order to make the particle recede to an infinite distance? (Interpret this in terms of area under the F_G-versus-r diagram and refer to Example 3 and Problem 16.7 in Section 16.6.) Compare the numerical value of the estimated escape velocity v_E with the numerical value of orbital velocity v_t in the vicinity of the earth (refer to Problem 9.20). What relevance does the estimate of v_E have to the problem of projecting space vehicles to other planets or into orbit around the sun?

18.7 SUMMARY OF ANALYSES BASED ON THEOREM (18.4.6)

In Table 18.7.1 we summarize the results of analyses made in the preceding sections. Interpretation of these analyses revealed a restricted kind of conservation. In idealized cases, characterized by absence of friction or inelastic collisions, our action [represented by integrals $\int_{s_0}^{s} P(s)\, ds$] is "preserved." In the absence of an opposing force, the preservation takes the form of an exactly equal increase in $\tfrac{1}{2}mv^2$ of the dis-

TABLE 18.7.1

SUMMARY OF ANALYSES BASED ON THEOREM

$$\int_{s_0}^{s} F_{net}(s) \, ds = \Delta(\tfrac{1}{2}mv^2)$$

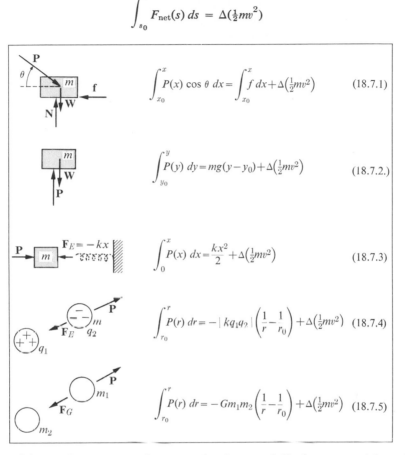

$$\int_{x_0}^{x} P(x) \cos \theta \, dx = \int_{x_0}^{x} f \, dx + \Delta(\tfrac{1}{2}mv^2) \qquad (18.7.1)$$

$$\int_{y_0}^{y} P(y) \, dy = mg(y - y_0) + \Delta(\tfrac{1}{2}mv^2) \qquad (18.7.2.)$$

$$\int_{0}^{x} P(x) \, dx = \frac{kx^2}{2} + \Delta(\tfrac{1}{2}mv^2) \qquad (18.7.3)$$

$$\int_{r_0}^{r} P(r) \, dr = -|kq_1q_2| \left(\frac{1}{r} - \frac{1}{r_0}\right) + \Delta(\tfrac{1}{2}mv^2) \quad (18.7.4)$$

$$\int_{r_0}^{r} P(r) \, dr = -Gm_1m_2 \left(\frac{1}{r} - \frac{1}{r_0}\right) + \Delta(\tfrac{1}{2}mv^2) \quad (18.7.5)$$

placed particle. In the presence of an opposing force and displacement with negligible increase of $\tfrac{1}{2}mv^2$, our action is preserved in the sense of being associated with numerically equal values such as

$$\int_{y_0}^{y} mg \, dy, \qquad \int_{x_0}^{x} kx \, dx, \qquad \int_{r_0}^{r} \frac{|kq_1q_2|}{r} \, dr.$$

Here the original action is "stored" by virtue of the changed position of the particle; it can be transformed back into an equal amount of $\tfrac{1}{2}mv^2$ by removing force **P** and letting the particle "fall" freely to its original position, or it can be harnessed to produce the displacement of another particle.

When we push against a frictional force, however [Eq. (18.7.1)], the quantity $\int_{x_0}^{x} f \, dx$ is "lost." From its new position the particle will not spontaneously accelerate back to its initial position; the quantity $\int_{x_0}^{x} f \, dx$ is not recoverable as additional $\tfrac{1}{2}mv^2$.

In all these cases, our statements apply to numbers calculated in tightly prescribed fashion—in accordance with Theorem (18.4.6).   Forces, velocities, accelerations, arbitrarily invented combinations such as F/v, mv/a, etc., are *not* conserved in dynamical processes.   Conservation is a relatively rare property.

Seventeenth- and eighteenth-century scientists were aware of the partial conservation on the part of numbers calculated as in Table 18.7.1. Leibniz gave a clear analysis and discussion of what amounted to Eq. (18.7.2). But full awareness of the general conservation law operating in nature did not come until the nineteenth century, when, through the contributions of Rumford, Mayer, Joule, and Helmholtz, it was realized that the action exerted against friction did not really "disappear," but that a given numerical value of $\int f \, dx$ always resulted in the generation of a fixed amount of heat (as measured by temperature changes produced in standard amounts of water), and that twice the value of $\int f \, dx$ resulted in exactly twice as much heat, etc. Up to that time, heat had been thought of as an intangible fluid entity, obeying its own private conservation law.   With growing understanding of the atomic-molecular structure of matter, it came to be realized that the entire picture fell beautifully and simply into place if "heat" were taken to be associated with increase or decrease in $\frac{1}{2}mv^2$ of the random, chaotic motion of the molecules themselves. This wide-reaching generalization will be discussed in a following chapter.

18.8 WORK AND ENERGY

At this point it becomes appropriate to say something about terminology. We have deliberately refrained from naming the new concepts in order to focus attention on numerical relationships and operational descriptions.   The names we select are metaphors borrowed from everyday speech: "force," "work," "energy." Our modes of thought are intimately affected, and sometimes even determined, by the structure of our language and vocabulary. Borrowing metaphors from ordinary speech has more than once involved science in a morass of misunderstanding and confusion from which it was extricated only by an act of genius. (We have already seen something of the character of this verbal problem in connection with our study of motion.)

Late seventeenth and early eighteenth century scientific literature contains polemics concerning the proper definition of force. Huygens and Newton held that force was properly measured in terms of change of quantity of motion (mv). Leibniz argued that force was more properly connected with *vis viva* (mv^2). Much confusion stems from the fact that participants in the argument were using the same name for different operational concepts.   Until the middle of the nineteenth century, considerable confusion prevailed because of the indiscriminate, interchangeable use of the terms force and energy.

In our modern terminology the issue is clarified by reserving the word force for the concept we defined operationally in Chapter 5. The name energy is introduced to describe the numbers we have been dealing with in this chapter. Numbers calculated from integrals of force with respect to displacement, $\int_{s_1}^{s_2} P(s) \, ds$, we call "work done by the force P in the displacement from s_1 to s_2," and we speak of work as a form of energy.

In the more general situation [Eq. (18.7.1)], where P might act at an angle θ to the displacement, we have seen that the quantity conserved is *not* $\int_{s_1}^{s_2} P(s)\, ds$, but is rather

$$\int_{s_1}^{s_2} P(s) \cos \theta \, ds. \tag{18.8.1}$$

Thus, in order to take advantage of the conservation idea, it is necessary to define work by integrals like (18.8.1); that is, we must not use the magnitude of the force itself in the arithmetical calculation, but its component in the direction of displacement. In the first line of Table 18.7.1, the forces **W** and **N** are said to do zero work, since they have zero components in the direction of displacement. Such forces are sometimes referred to as *zero work forces*.

We may push on an unyielding wall for a long time and become very tired from doing so, but, in the sense of our physical definition, we have done zero work. As a scientific concept, work is not necessarily a measure of our own exhaustion—an illustration of the fact that our metaphors do not transform literally and, unless clearly separated from the original context, can easily introduce elements of confusion into our thought.

Work integrals emerge with algebraic signs: *positive* if force and displacement were in the *same* direction; *negative* if they were in *opposite* directions. In the former case (positive), we speak of the "work done *by* the force"; in the latter case (negative), we speak of the "work done *against* the force."

The quantity $\frac{1}{2}mv^2$ is called *kinetic energy*. The relation

$$\int_{s_0}^{s} F_{\text{net}}(s)\, ds = \Delta(\tfrac{1}{2}mv^2) \tag{18.8.2}$$

is called the Work–Kinetic Energy Theorem. Translating it into words, we say that "all the work done by a *net* force is transformed into kinetic energy (KE) of the moving body." With reference to Eq. (18.7.1), we say that "part of the work done by force **P** is converted into KE, while part of it is dissipated in doing work against friction."

"Energy" is not a substance, fluid, paint, or fuel which is smeared on bodies and rubbed off from one to another. We use this term to denote a construct—numbers, calculated in a certain prescribed way, that are found *by theory and experiment* to preserve a remarkably simple relationship in very diverse physical phenomena.

18.9 POTENTIAL ENERGY

In the problems summarized in Table 18.7.1, we noted that work done against elastic, electrical, and gravitational forces can be "stored" by virtue of changes of position within the system of interacting bodies. If a body has initial velocity v_0 directed oppositely to an elastic, electric, or gravitational force, its KE decreases from $\frac{1}{2}mv_0^2$ to zero as the body "rises," but this energy is also "stored," since it is recoverable either as KE in "falling" back to the initial position or in the "elevation" of still another body through a string-and-pulley arrangement.

Energy stored in this fashion and convertible to other forms is called the *potential energy* (PE) of the system. In Table 18.7.1, changes in PE are associated with integrals such as

$$\int_{y_0}^{y} mg\, dy = mg(y - y_0), \qquad \int_{x_0}^{x} kx\, dx = \frac{kx^2}{2} - \frac{kx_0^2}{2}.$$

We speak, then, of different forms of potential energy: gravitational, elastic, electrical, and so forth.

Forces that permit storage of potential energy are called conservative forces, whereas friction is referred to as a dissipative force. An amount of work done against a dissipative force is not destroyed; it results in the production of a fixed amount of heat, but clearly the energy is not stored and recoverable in the same sense as the work done in compressing a spring or raising a weight.

Kinetic energy is determined by the mass and velocity of the moving particle. Therefore it is, in a significant sense, a property of the particle itself, a description of its state or condition. Potential energy, on the other hand, is generally associated with interactions of a *system* of particles and is not a property intrinsic to any one member of the system.

Having adopted this language, we wish to say that the PE of a system *increases* [Δ(PE) is positive] when a weight is raised or a spring is compressed, and that it *decreases* [Δ(PE) is negative] when a weight is lowered or the spring is allowed to relax. Thus we want Δ(PE) to be positive when work is done *against* a conservative force, and negative when work is done *by* a conservative force. This requirement leads us to the following general definition: If F_c is the component of a conservative force along the direction defined by s:

$$\Delta(\text{PE}) \equiv -\int_{s_1}^{s_2} F_c\, ds. \tag{18.9.1}$$

The vector symbol F_c in this case refers to plus or minus values of the component, depending on whether it is oriented in the positive or negative s-direction.

PROBLEM 18.9.   Show that definition (18.9.1) gives a positive value of Δ(PE) whenever the displacement is in a direction opposite to F_c. Describe several physical cases to which this formulation corresponds. Show that definition (18.9.1) gives a negative value of Δ(PE) whenever the displacement is in the same direction as F_c; describe several corresponding physical changes.

Example 1.   Describe in the vocabulary of energy transformations the sequence of events that takes place when a stone is thrown vertically upward.

"In throwing the stone we perform a certain amount of work. Part of this work is transformed into kinetic energy of the stone, and the rest into potential energy at the elevation at which the stone leaves our hand. After the stone leaves our hand and continues to rise, the KE we imparted to it is converted into PE. At the apex of its flight, all the work we did in throwing it has been stored as PE, of the earth-stone system (except for a small amount dissipated against air friction). As the stone falls, the PE is converted into KE until, on returning to the ground, all the work we performed originally is present in the form of KE of the stone. If the stone strikes the ground in perfectly inelastic collision, all the KE is transformed into heat, raising the temperature of the stone, the ground, and the surrounding air."

Example 2. Calculate the change in PE associated with pushing a body of mass m up the frictionless inclined plane shown in Fig. 18.9.1.

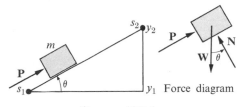

FIGURE 18.9.1

If we take the positive direction of s to be up the plane, the component of conservative gravitational force $\mathbf{F}_c$ along the plane is given by

$$\mathbf{F}_c = -mg \sin \theta. \tag{18.9.2}$$

Then, from definition (18.9.1):

$$\Delta(\text{PE}) = -\int_{s_1}^{s_2} (-mg \sin \theta)\, ds = mg \sin \theta (s_2 - s_1). \tag{18.9.3}$$

(This is also the work we would perform if we pushed the body up the plane with negligible change of KE. The force exerted by us in these circumstances would have magnitude $P = mg \sin \theta$, as is apparent from the force diagram in Fig. 18.9.1.)

Note, however, that

$$y_2 - y_1 = (s_2 - s_1) \sin \theta \tag{18.9.4}$$

and, on substitution for $(s_2 - s_1) \sin \theta$, Eq. (18.9.3) becomes

$$\Delta(\text{PE}) = mg(y_2 - y_1) = mg\, \Delta y. \tag{18.9.5}$$

But this is the change in PE associated with raising the body vertically from y_1 to y_2. It seems that $\Delta(\text{PE})$ depends only on the difference in level through which the body is raised, and not on the length of the sloping path from s_1 to s_2!

This result is susceptible to generalization: Suppose a body is transported from position 1 to 2 in a vertical plane along a complicated curved path, as shown in Fig. 18.9.2. We can imagine cutting up the curve into a sequence of short inclined planes, each one as in Fig. 18.9.1, and evaluating $\Delta(\text{PE})$ as the limit of the sum of quantities of work done along each plane as the number of subdivisions increases without limit. We shall not carry out the formal analysis, but we would certainly expect the final result to be $mg\, \Delta y$.

This same idea can be extended to *any* conservative force: the change in PE between two points depends only on the location of the points, and is completely independent of the path followed from one point to the other.

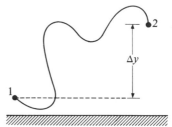

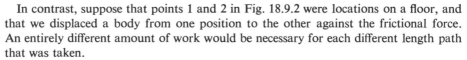

FIG. 18.9.2.   Body transported from position 1 to position 2 in a vertical plane.

In contrast, suppose that points 1 and 2 in Fig. 18.9.2 were locations on a floor, and that we displaced a body from one position to the other against the frictional force. An entirely different amount of work would be necessary for each different length path that was taken.

This distinction is sometimes made the *definition* of the difference between conservative and dissipative forces, a conservative force being one for which $\int_{s_1}^{s_2} \mathbf{F}_c \, ds$ is independent of the path followed between s_1 and s_2.

PROBLEM 18.10.   Describe the following events or phenomena in the vocabulary of energy transformations: (a) A cart is given a push up an inclined plane; it rolls some distance up the plane and then rolls back (do not ignore friction).   (b) A pendulum swings back and forth.   (c) A body hanging at the end of a coil spring oscillates up and down around the equilibrium position.   (d) A positively charged particle is projected directly toward another positively charged particle which is fixed in position.   (e) The problem of escape velocity, analyzed in Section 18.6 and Problem 18.8.

PROBLEM 18.11.   A particle carrying positive charge q_B is moved from position 1 to position 2 (Fig. 18.9.3).   Evaluate $\Delta(\text{PE})$ along paths $1a2$ and $1b2$, and show that identical results are obtained: $\Delta(\text{PE}) = kq_A q_B[(1/r_2) - (1/r_1)]$.   Show that the algebraic sign of the result is consistent with the requirement that PE increase when work is stored during the displacement.

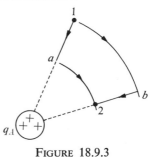

FIGURE 18.9.3

18.10 UNITS AND DIMENSIONS

Quantities of work and potential energy are calculated from products of force and displacement, the dimensions of which we denote by F and L, respectively.   Thus the dimensions of work are $F \times L$, and the units would be newton·meters in the mks system and foot·pounds in the engineering system.

Kinetic energy, defined by $\frac{1}{2}mv^2$, has the dimensions ML^2/T^2, where M, L, and T denote dimensions of mass, length, and time, respectively.   Work, PE, and KE are all quantities that, in accordance with our algebraic derivations, are to be combined with each other by addition and subtraction.   For this operation to make sense, the dimensions of work and KE must be identical.   We can readily verify this identity by noting that force F has the same dimensions as mass $\times$ acceleration or ML/T^2. Hence $F \times L$ has dimensions of ML^2/T^2, identical with those of KE.

TABLE 18.10.1

ENERGY UNITS

System	Work and PE, $F \times L$ units	KE, ML^2/T^2 units	Name of energy unit
mks	newton·meter	$\dfrac{\text{kilogram(meter)}^2}{(\text{second})^2}$	joule
Engineering	foot·pound	$\dfrac{\text{slugs(feet)}^2}{(\text{second})^2}$	foot·pound
cgs	dyne·centimeter	$\dfrac{\text{gram(centimeter)}^2}{(\text{second})^2}$	erg

Table 18.10.1 summarizes energy units and names that are utilized in the various systems.

18.11   REFERENCE LEVEL FOR ENERGY CALCULATIONS

All the equations we have derived are statements of relationship among energy *changes*. These energy changes are associated with alteration of the condition or "state" of a system, as defined by changes in motion and position of bodies. We have no way of defining reference levels for energy that are zero in some absolute sense; we can designate any arbitrarily chosen state as corresponding to a zero level and calculate increases or decreases or energy relative to this reference state.

For example, we can designate the potential energy of a body as zero at an elevation y_0. Then, at any elevation above y_0, we would say that the instantaneous value of PE is positive, while at any level below y_0, we would say that the PE is negative. This does not assign absolute values to PE; we are really talking about changes relative to the reference level at y_0.

In the case of electrically or gravitationally attracting particles, we dealt with PE changes of the system as we moved one particle around to various radial distances from the other. (See Table 18.7.1.) It is frequently convenient to take the zero level of PE as that of infinite separation of the particles. We would then denote the PE at some finite radius r as

$$- \frac{|kq_1q_2|}{r} \qquad \text{or} \qquad - \frac{Gm_1m_2}{r}$$

in the electrical and gravitational cases, respectively. This does not mean that PE is negative in an absolute sense, but that PE decreases in transferring one particle from a very remote position to radial distance r from the second one, just as it would in lowering a body from a zero reference level at the ceiling of a room.

Systems such as those described in Table 18.7.1 are said to be isolated when no external work is supplied to the system; i.e., external force $\mathbf{P} = 0$. For an isolated system in the absence of dissipative forces, we can summarize the results in Table 18.7.1 by saying that

$$\Delta(PE) + \Delta(KE) = 0. \tag{18.11.1}$$

Alternatively, we can write

$$PE + KE = H, \tag{18.11.2}$$

where H represents a "total energy," being the sum of potential and kinetic energies (relative to arbitrarily chosen levels) at some particular condition of the system, and PE and KE denote instantaneous values of these energies at any other instant or point in the process. Note that Eq. (8.11.2) is simply a generalized statement corresponding to Eqs. (18.3.5), (18.5.3), (18.6.2), and (18.6.4). In many of the specific interpretations and descriptions you have been given in preceding problems, the ideas that are generalized in Eqs. (18.11.1) and (18.11.2) have been invoked, perhaps without the reader's being explicitly conscious of the general statement.

18.12 PERFECTLY INELASTIC COLLISIONS

Our circuitous track now brings us back to the questions that, in Section 18.1, motivated our investigation: what does *vis viva, mv^2*, have to do with elastic and inelastic collisions? We sense that we are confronted with a distinction between dissipative and conservative effects; let us examine the problem in these terms.

Consider first the collision we called "perfectly inelastic." The bodies collide and stick together; clearly some of the kinetic energy, converted into work done in compressing and deforming the bodies, is not returned into the form of KE, as in the relaxation of an elastic spring. This conclusion is amply confirmed by the fact that colliding bodies are observed to warm up in inelastic collisions. It is easy to calculate the amount of KE dissipated: Consider a perfectly inelastic, rectilinear collision between a stationary body of mass m_B and a body of mass m_A with initial velocity v_{A1}. From Eq. (17.8.6), we have

$$v_2 = \frac{m_A}{m_A + m_B} \cdot v_{A1}, \tag{18.12.1}$$

where v_2 is the velocity of the combination $(m_A + m_B)$ after collision. Then

$$\Delta(KE) = \tfrac{1}{2}(m_A + m_B)v_2^2 - \tfrac{1}{2}m_A v_{A1}^2 \tag{18.12.2}$$

and, by making use of (18.12.1), we obtain

$$\Delta(KE) = -\left(\frac{m_B}{m_A + m_B}\right) \cdot \tfrac{1}{2}m_A v_{A1}^2 \tag{18.12.3}$$

or

$$\frac{\Delta(KE)}{KE \text{ initial}} = -\frac{m_B}{m_A + m_B}. \tag{18.12.4}$$

PROBLEM 18.12. Fill in the algebraic steps between (18.12.2) and (18.12.3). Interpret Eq. (18.12.4): What is the meaning of the minus sign? How much KE is dissipated if the bodies have equal mass? Note that almost *all* the KE is dissipated if m_A is very much smaller than m_B. Note also that momentum is conserved *regardless* of dissipation of KE.

18.13   ELASTIC COLLISIONS

If the bodies do not stick together on collision it is necessary to visualize the character of the interaction. In collisions between particles carrying like electrical charges or between repelling magnets (where the objects approach each other and fly apart without mechanical contact), the initial KE of the moving particles is stored as PE as they approach each other, and then, in the absence of friction, is completely returned to KE as the bodies fly apart. Thus, as far as initial and final conditions are concerned, KE is completely conserved in such collisions; and we would write

$$\tfrac{1}{2}m_A v_{A1}^2 + \tfrac{1}{2}m_B v_{B1}^2 = \tfrac{1}{2}m_A v_{A2}^2 + \tfrac{1}{2}m_B v_{B2}^2. \tag{18.13.1}$$

Very nearly the same thing happens when hard bodies such as billiard balls or steel balls collide: initial KE is stored as PE of deformation of the bodies, and is restored to KE as they fly apart. No mechanical collision conserves KE perfectly; some small amount is always dissipated. This does not make Eq. (18.13.1) a useless artifact, however. Even when KE is not perfectly conserved, we can use (18.13.1) to set certain bounds on the final velocities and give us important insights into the observed results.

Equation (18.13.1) is, of course, identical with (18.1.2); conservation of *vis viva* corresponds to conservation of KE. For a rectilinear, two-body collision, with conservative forces of interaction, we now have the two simultaneous equations: (18.13.1) for conservation of KE and, for conservation of momentum:

$$m_A v_{A1} + m_B v_{B1} = m_A v_{A2} + m_B v_{B2}. \tag{18.13.2}$$

Let us rewrite these equations as follows:

KE equation: $\qquad m_A(v_{A1}^2 - v_{A2}^2) = m_B(v_{B2}^2 - v_{B1}^2),$

$$m_A(v_{A1} - v_{A2})(v_{A1} + v_{A2}) = m_B(v_{B2} - v_{B1})(v_{B2} + v_{B1}). \tag{18.13.3}$$

Momentum equation: $m_A(v_{A1} - v_{A2}) = m_B(v_{B2} - v_{B1}). \tag{18.13.4}$

Dividing (18.13.3) by (18.13.4), we obtain

$$v_{A1} + v_{A2} = v_{B2} + v_{B1} \qquad \text{or} \qquad v_{B1} - v_{A1} = -(v_{B2} - v_{A2}). \tag{18.13.5}$$

Equation (18.3.5) is identical with Eq. (17.2.1). It says that if KE is conserved, the bodies fly apart with the same relative velocity with which they approached each other, but the direction of the relative velocity is reversed. This was our original definition of the perfectly elastic collision; we now see that this definition is equivalent to the requirement that KE be conserved. The latter requirement is now usually regarded as the primary definition of perfectly elastic collisions.

PROBLEM 18.13. Review and reinterpret Problem 17.9. It deals with the solution for v_{A2} and v_{B2} in terms of v_{A1} and v_{B1} in the perfectly elastic collision. Consider the case in which $v_{B1} = 0$: how do velocities v_{A2} and v_{B2} behave as: (a) m_A becomes much larger than m_B; (b) m_A becomes much smaller than m_B; (c) $m_A = m_B$? KE is conserved but it is *redistributed* in the system; investigate what happens to the KE of m_A under such various circumstances. Note that m_A always loses some KE in elastic collision with a stationary body.

18.14   PROBLEMS*

18.14. A cart *weighing* 90.0 n is initially at rest on a horizontal plane at the instant t_1 (Fig. 18.14.1). A constant external force **P** is applied as shown; **f** denotes the opposing frictional force acting on the body. Coefficient of friction $\mu = 0.080$. The force **P** acts during a time interval between the instants t_1 and t_2 and accelerates the body from position s_1 to s_2. Then **P** is abruptly removed, and the body coasts to a stop at instant t_3 and position s_3.

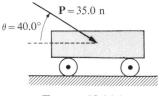

$P = 35.0$ n

$\theta = 40.0°$

FIGURE 18.14.1

(a) Draw the body by itself showing all the forces acting on it. Stating what principle applies, make use of it to calculate the acceleration imparted to the body up to time t_2.

(b) Describe in terms of energy (work delivered and dissipated, kinetic energy acquired and dissipated) all that happens to this system in the time interval between t_1 and t_3.

(c) Give the definitions of work and impulse both as limits of sums and in the shorthand integral notation.

(d) Using the above integrals and the rules of the calculus, obtain *algebraic* expressions (i.e., in symbols only) for (1) the net impulse delivered to the body in the horizontal direction; (2) the work delivered to the body by the force **P** in accelerating the body from s_1 to s_2; (3) the work done against **f** in the same displacement. The algebraic expressions should be in the notation indicated on the diagram and in the introductory paragraph. Steps must be briefly explained. [*Answer:* (2) $\int_{s_1}^{s_2} P \cos \theta \, ds = P \cos \theta \, (s_2 - s_1)$.]

(e) Suppose the time interval $(t_2 - t_1)$ is 3.00 sec. Calculate the numerical value of the net impulse delivered to the body in this interval. What momentum change is imparted to the cart? [*Answer:* 50.7 n·sec.]

(f) Suppose the displacement $(s_2 - s_1)$ is 8.23 m. Calculate the numerical values of the quantities of work called for in questions (d2) and (d3). What is the kinetic energy of the body at position s_2? Justify your answer briefly. [*Answer:* KE = 139 joules.]

(g) Given that the kinetic energy of the cart at position s_2 is 139 joules. Using *only* the energy ideas described in question (b) (not invoking acceleration or deceleration), calculate the distance $(s_3 - s_2)$ which the body will coast before coming to a stop. Make your *reasoning* clear. Note that the magnitude of **f** changes after **P** is removed. [*Answer:* $s_3 - s_2 = 19.3$ m.]

---

* Problems 9.18, 17.28, 18.18, and 18.20 are designed as preparation for study of the Bohr-Rutherford atomic model in Chapter 35.

(h) Do the time interval $(t_2 - t_1) =$ 3.00 sec and the displacement $(s_2 - s_1) =$ 8.23 m correspond to the same or to different experiments? Make your reasoning clear.

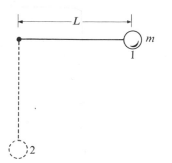

FIGURE 18.14.2

18.15. A simple pendulum consists of a particle of mass m on a string of length $L = 85$ cm (Fig. 18.14.2). The bob is released from rest at position 1. Estimate the velocity it acquires on dropping to position 2. What idealizations do you make in your analysis? Show that when the bob passes through position 2 the tension in the string will be three times the weight of the bob.

18.16. A common method of determining the velocity of a bullet is to use the system known as a "ballistic pendulum," shown in Fig. 18.14.3. The bullet is fired into a massive block, suspended by wires, and the height Δy through which the block rises after impact is measured. Suppose you wish to set up an experiment in which you will use bullets known to have a mass of about 10 gm and

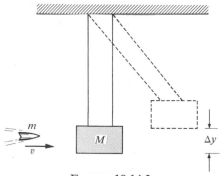

FIGURE 18.14.3

a velocity of the order of 800 m/sec. Design the rest of your experiment; i.e., what mass M would you elect to use in the pendulum block, and what rise Δy would you expect? Describe the sequence of events in this experiment in the vocabulary of momentum and energy concepts. Is the KE of the bullet conserved? Calculate the KE of the bullet before impact and the KE of the combination after impact, and compare the numerical values.

18.17. In Example 2 of Section 18.9 it is shown that, in the absence of friction, the work done in pushing a body up an inclined plane is exactly equal to the work that would be done in raising the body vertically through the same height. Suppose that these quantities of work were not equal; describe a machine that you might devise to take advantage of the inequality. Do you believe in the possibility of such a machine? What insights does this analysis give you into the law of nature that we are exploring, and into some of the ways in which this law might be stated?

18.18. Consider the situation discussed in Section 9.8 and Fig. (9.8.2) where a negatively charged particle revolves in a stable circular orbit around a stationary positively charged particle. If we measure PE from a zero level at infinite separation, show that at radius r:

$$\text{PE} = -\frac{kq_1q_2}{r}, \quad (18.14.1)$$

$$\text{KE} = \tfrac{1}{2}mv^2 = \frac{kq_1q_2}{2r}, \quad (18.14.2)$$

Total energy $E(r)$ at radius $r = -\dfrac{kq_1q_2}{2r}.$

$$(18.14.3)$$

Interpret the final result: Show that the energy difference between two orbits r_1 and r_2 is given by

$$E(r_2) - E(r_1) = \frac{kq_1q_2}{2}\left(\frac{1}{r_1} - \frac{1}{r_2}\right).$$

$$(18.14.4)$$

What must happen to the energy of the system if the particle is transferred from a smaller to a larger orbit? If it is transferred from a larger to a smaller orbit? Write down and interpret the parallel equations for the gravitational case. What happens to an earth satellite as it experiences collisions with the sparse population of molecules and dust particles along its orbit?

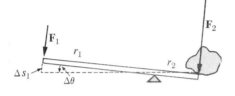

FIGURE 18.14.4

18.19. A lever is used to pry up a stone, as shown in Fig. 18.14.4. Draw a free body diagram of the lever, assuming that the forces which are being exerted are perpendicular to the lever and that the weight of the lever is negligible. Suppose that under the action of F_1 the lever is displaced through the small angle $\Delta\theta$, F_1 undergoing displacement along the arc Δs_1. Acceleration and kinetic energy changes are negligible; i.e., the effects of F_1 and F_2 are essentially balanced, as in the slow compression of a spring or elevation of a body. Argue that, in the absence of dissipative effects, conservation of energy requires that the algebraic sum of quantities of work done by F_1 and F_2 must be zero. Write this as an algebraic equation. Note that $\Delta s_1 = r_1 \Delta\theta$ and that a similar relation holds for Δs_2. Show that

$$F_1 r_1 = F_2 r_2. \qquad (18.14.5)$$

Interpret this result in terms of the concept of torque developed in Section 17.16. How would you reformulate the problem if F_1 and F_2 were not perpendicular to the lever? (The principle of conservation of work,

applied in the analysis of this problem, was known and used as early as Hellenistic times, and was well known in European science. It provided a standard way of analyzing the action of simple machines. The extension of the principle to include mechanical kinetic and potential energy came at the end of the seventeenth century.)

18.20. (a) A ball weighing 0.25 lb is thrown vertically into the air and attains a height of 100 ft. Estimate the initial KE of the ball. [*Answer:* 25 ft·lb.]

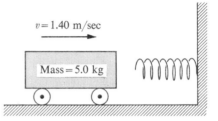

FIGURE 18.14.5

(b) A cart with mass $m = 5.0$ kg and a velocity of 1.40 m/sec strikes a spring, as shown in Fig. 18.14.5. (It has been previously established that a weight of 10 n stretches the spring by 2.0 cm.) How much will the spring be compressed before the block comes to a stop? [*Answer:* 14 cm.]

FIGURE 18.14.6

(c) Particle B in Fig. 18.14.6 is fixed in position. Pith ball A (mass = 0.10 gm) approaches along the line of centers from very far away with an initial velocity of 3.0 m/sec. Each particle carries an electric charge of 4.0×10^{-8} coul. Estimate the distance of closest approach of A to B. [*Answer:* 3.2 cm.]

SPECIAL PROBLEMS FOR MORE ADVANCED WORK

18.21. Consider the problem discussed in Section 17.18 (Fig. 17.18.2 and Problem 17.20). (a) From the analysis carried out in Problem 17.20, write an algebraic expression for the change in KE of the puck when it is pulled in from radius r_1 to r_2.

(b) Set up an expression for the force that must be exerted on the puck to pull it in slowly as described in the problem, and evaluate the work done by this force in pulling the puck in from r_1 to r_2. Verify that this quantity of work is exactly equal to the change in KE evaluated in part (a).

18.22. A frequently used graphical representation is an "energy diagram," the coordinates of which are energy and position. Figure 18.14.7 shows such a diagram for the case of a body of weight mg at various vertical positions y. The equation of the PE line is mgy. If the body is released at elevation y,

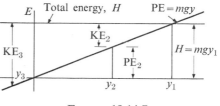

FIGURE 18.14.7

it has total energy $H = mgy_1$. As it falls, H remains constant, PE decreases, KE increases. All this is represented on the diagram. Construct and analyze energy diagrams for (a) the case of a body oscillating back and forth on a spring (as in Fig. 18.5.1), (b) a negatively charged particle in the neighborhood of a stationary positively charged one, (c) a body oscillating up and down on a spring, i.e., spring force and gravitational force act simultaneously.

SUPPLEMENTARY READING AND STUDY

For development of the energy concepts from different points of view:

Physics, Physical Science Study Committee. Boston: D. C, Heath, 1960, Chapters 24, 25

Physics for the Inquiring Mind, Eric M. Rogers. Princeton, N. J.: Princeton University Press, 1960, Chapter 26

Foundations of Modern Physical Science, G. Holton and D. H. D. Roller. Reading, Mass.: Addison-Wesley, 1958, Chapter 18

Introduction to Mechanics, Matter, and Waves, U. Ingard and W. L. Kraushaar. Reading, Mass.: Addison-Wesley, 1960, Chapters 6, 7

For an historical discussion of the origin of work and energy concepts:

Historical Roots of the Principle of Conservation of Energy, E. N. Hiebert. Madison: State Historical Society of Wisconsin, 1962

CHAPTER 19

Temperature and Heat

19.1 INTRODUCTION

We remarked several times in the preceding chapter that work done against dissipative forces was not "destroyed," but had the effect of producing a definite amount of heat. Historically, this insight was not quickly won; it was attained only after extensive exploration of what proved to be a temporarily very useful, but nevertheless erroneous, theory—the caloric theory of heat.

The fundamental laws governing transformation of energy were discovered and mathematically formulated toward the middle of the nineteenth century. This new branch of physics came to be called *thermodynamics*. As the Newtonian system unified through one simple set of principles the dynamics of celestial and terrestrial phenomena, so the science of thermodynamics unified certain aspects of mechanical, electrical, chemical, thermal, and magnetic processes.

This synthesis is in many ways as dramatic and as far-reaching in its impact on human thought as the Newtonian; its study begins with the study of heat.

19.2 THERMOMETERS

As our intuitive perceptions of length, time, force, and inertia lead us to construction of the concepts of mechanics, so do our intuitive perceptions of hot and cold lead us into the development of a science of heat. Historically, this science made very little progress until the invention of sensitive and accurate thermometers made it possible to perform reproducible experiments with bodies undergoing changes in temperature.

All thermometry is based on observing changes in some "thermometric" property of a material substance as it becomes hotter or colder. Familiar alcohol and mercury thermometers utilize the expansion and contraction of a liquid under constant pressure. The constant-volume gas thermometer utilizes increase and decrease in pressure of a gas held rigidly at constant volume. Other thermometers are based on changes of electrical resistance of a metal (e.g., platinum); changes of electrical potential differences at the contact between two different metals (thermocouple); changes in the spectrum of light emitted by a glowing substance; and so forth.

Galileo invented and used a crude "thermoscope" around 1600 while he was still at Padua. It consisted of a glass bulb containing air and having a long stem which extended downward into a vessel of water. As the bulb became hotter or colder the air inside expanded or contracted and the water level rose or fell in the stem. This device was, of course, sensitive to atmospheric pressure variations as well as heating and cooling.

Various improved thermoscopes were made by subsequent investigators. Sensitivity to pressure variations was eliminated by the use of liquids completely sealed in complicated glass bulbs and tubes. Toward the end of the seventeenth century, the practice was introduced of calibrating thermometer scales by marking fixed points (such as melting of snow and melting of butter) and dividing the scale into some arbitrarily chosen number of uniform intervals. Newton performed experiments with such a device.

Between the years 1714 and 1717, D. G. Fahrenheit (1686–1736) constructed reliable alcohol and mercury thermometers, using simple, cylindrical glass tubes and bulbs, and proposed what we now know as the Fahrenheit scale. During the period 1710–1743, there also evolved the Celsius (centigrade) temperature scale.*

19.3 THERMAL EQUILIBRIUM

With the development of reliable thermometers, calibrated in a reproducible manner, it became possible to perform quantitative experiments on heating and cooling of different substances. During the same years that "electricians," as they called themselves, were clarifying the nature of electrification and electric charge, other investigators were applying the new thermometric tools. Among these, Joseph Black (1728–1799) played a particularly important role, refining and sharpening the concepts of heat and temperature through researches performed in the years between 1759 and 1762. Black was a Scottish physician who at various times was professor of medicine and chemistry at the Universities of Glasgow and Edinburgh.

Generalizing one class of observations, Black wrote:

"By the use of thermometers we have learned that, if we take . . . different kinds of matter—such as metal, stones, salts, wood, cork, feathers, wool, water and a variety of other fluids—although they be all at first of different temperatures, and if we put them together in a room without a fire and into which the sun does not shine, the heat will be communicated from the hotter of these bodies to the colder, during some hours perhaps, or the course of a day, at the end of which time, if we apply a thermometer to them all in succession, it will give precisely the same reading. The heat therefore distributes itself upon this occasion until

---

* Readers unfamiliar with the definitions of these temperature scales will find them defined in many introductory physics or chemistry texts or in technical handbooks. The Celsius scale is named for a Swedish astronomer Anders Celsius who was among those proposing and utilizing a centesimal scale during the 1740's. Actually, Celsius' original scale was inverted relative to the modern scale, in that he assigned the number 0 to the steam point and 100 to the ice point.

none of these bodies has a greater demand or attraction for heat than every other .... The heat is thus brought into a state of equilibrium. ... We must therefore adopt, as one of the most general laws of heat, the principle that all bodies communicating freely with one another and exposed to no inequality of external action, acquire the same temperature, as indicated by a thermometer."

Familiar though this idea may be to us now, we must remember that it is far from obvious. Stone, metal, wood or cloth *feel* entirely different to the touch when they are at exactly the same temperature.   Black's generalization could only come from quantitative observation and deliberately constructed experiments.

Prior to Black's time, the words heat and temperature were used more or less interchangeably; Fahrenheit speaks of "degrees of heat" when reporting temperature measurements.   Black made the significant conceptual refinement of distinguishing between these terms. "Temperature" henceforth refers to the number observed on a thermometer scale; "heat" becomes a construct, a name for something exchanged between bodies while changing temperature and coming to equilibrium. Equilibrium is recognized operationally as the circumstance under which bodies have ceased changing their physical state or condition.

Black's generalization concerning thermal equilibrium incorporates an idea that is stated more analytically in modern treatises under the name of the Zeroth Law of Thermodynamics: If body A is in thermal equilibrium with B, and B is in equilibrium with C, then A and C are also in thermal equilibrium.

It is a well-known fact that the temperature of bodies can be changed by mechanisms other than bringing objects of different temperatures near together. Temperatures of bodies, particularly volumes of gas, can be increased or decreased by compressing or expanding them quickly. The temperature of electrical conductors can be increased by passing electric current through them. Such processes are called *adiabatic*; in neither case does contact with a hotter or colder body play a significant role. Clearly our definition of the phrase "transfer of heat" requires further sharpening and clarification in operational terms. In modern terminology, we say that heat is transferred between two systems when they come to thermal equilibrium without doing work on each other. Such qualifications on terminology do not appear explicitly in the writings of early investigators, although the general idea is, of course, implied. (Clear operational definition is the mark of a mature science. The treatment given here is too abbreviated to be definitive. We shall point out some of the important conceptual and verbal problems; for more detailed and rigorous discussion, the reader should consult one of the more advanced references on heat and thermodynamics cited at the end of this chapter.)

19.4 QUANTITY OF HEAT

Work by a number of Black's predecessors, coupled with careful experiments and lucid interpretation by Black himself, provided the logical basis for talking about "quantity of heat": When equal volumes or masses of water, initially at different temperatures, were mixed, it was observed that the final equilibrium temperature of the mixture was always exactly halfway between the two initial temperatures (providing precautions were taken to isolate the system thermally; i.e., reduce the tendency to come to equilibrium with the surrounding air or other objects). The results of this experiment may be described algebraically by saying that, in coming to equilibrium, the temperature changes Δt of the hot and cold masses of water are equal and opposite:

$$\Delta t_h = -\Delta t_c. \tag{19.4.1}$$

When different masses of water were mixed, it was observed that the temperature changes were inversely proportional to the respective masses:

$$\frac{\Delta t_h}{\Delta t_c} = -\frac{m_c}{m_h},$$

that is, the lesser mass undergoes a proportionately larger temperature change, so that the products $m\,\Delta t$ remain equal in magnitude:

$$m_h\,\Delta t_h = -m_c\,\Delta t_c. \tag{19.4.2}$$

Since the numerical quantities in (19.4.2) are fixed and reproducible in any given situation, it becomes inviting to think of them as measuring something exchanged between the two masses of water—something lost by one and gained in equal amount by the other. From such observations stem our locutions about "exchange of quantities of heat," and the product $m\,\Delta t$ is taken as a measure of such quantity when different samples of the same substance are mixed or brought into contact with each other at different temperatures.

The experimental technique of observing temperature changes when mixing or contact is brought about in a thermally insulated system is often called the *method of mixtures*. A container in which the experiment is performed is called a *calorimeter* and the process of measurement is called *calorimetry*.

19.5 SPECIFIC HEAT OR HEAT CAPACITY

In further experimental observations, Black showed that Eq. (19.4.2) was valid only when the same substances are mixed, and that it clearly fails to predict temperature changes for mixtures of mercury and water or for other combinations of different substances. He also showed that using volumes instead of masses in Eq. (19.4.2), a formulation claimed to be correct by some of his contemporaries, was equally wrong.

Black's experiments led him to the conclusion that each substance could be reproducibly and systematically compared with some standard (say water) in its capacity to absorb heat and change temperature. For example, in the method of mixtures, it is found that 100 gm of mercury behave like 3.3 gm of water, signifying that water has a much larger capacity for heat, in that a given quantity of heat produces in 3.3 gm of water the same temperature change it produces in a much larger mass (100 gm) of mercury.

Finding this property to be measurable and reproducible, Black was led to describe it by means of a proportionality constant applied to the $m \, \Delta t$ product. Thus Eq. (19.4.2) would be modified to read

$$c_A m_A \, \Delta t_A = -m_w \, \Delta t_w, \tag{19.5.1}$$

where $m_w \, \Delta t_w$ would be described as the amount of heat gained or lost by a quantity of water in a mixture experiment, while $c_A m_A \, \Delta t_A$ would be described as the heat lost or gained by another substance A. If the substance A is water, $c_A = 1$. If A is some other substance, $c_A m_A$ may be interpreted as the equivalent amount of water; e.g., in the case of mercury, for which numerical values were cited above, $c_A = 0.033$ and, with 100 gm mercury, $c_A m_A = 3.3$ gm water equivalent.

It remains to define units in which heat is measured. The product $m_w \, \Delta t_w = 1$ if m_w and Δt_w are both unity. The following names are now given to quantities of heat that change the temperature of a unit mass of water by one degree on some temperature scale:

Calorie: Amount of heat that elevates the temperature of 1 gm water by 1 degree Celsius.

Kilocalorie: Amount of heat that elevates the temperature of 1 kg water by 1 degree Celsius.

Btu: Amount of heat that elevates the temperature of 1 lb water by 1 degree Fahrenheit.

(The symbol Btu denotes British thermal unit.)

Since the product $c_A m_A \, \Delta t_A$ denotes a quantity of heat, c_A must have the dimensions of quantity of heat per unit mass per unit change in temperature; for example, $c_A = 0.033$ cal/gm·C° for mercury. This number differs for different materials, and, in each case, is a unique, reproducible property. Following Black, this property is called *specific heat* or *heat capacity*.

PROBLEM 19.1.   Using Eq. (19.5.1) as a basis, describe how you would perform experiments to compile a table of specific heats, c_A, for various substances. Give specific details of apparatus you would require, how you would establish initial temperatures of samples, etc. Take into account the fact that the calorimeter cup or container in which the experiment is performed must participate in the temperature change taking place within it, even if the cup itself is well insulated from its surroundings. (Black was the first experimenter to take this fact carefully into account. His predecessors failed to do so.) Note that if two substances, A and B, exchange heat with the water, Eq. (19.5.1) can be generalized to:

$$c_A m_A \, \Delta t_A + c_B m_B \, \Delta t_B + m_w \, \Delta t_w = 0. \tag{19.5.2}$$

Describe carefully the precautions you would take to minimize systematic errors. What are the possible sources of these errors? How would they affect your results; i.e., would your calculated values tend to be higher or lower than the true ones? (After working out your own methods and procedures, see Problem 19.2. It may supply you with a few useful hints.)

Table 19.7.1 lists the specific heats of a number of substances. Once such a table is available, we can predict results in experiments that do not involve water. Equations (19.5.1) and (19.5.2) can be generalized to the form:

$$c_A m_A \Delta t_A + c_B m_B \Delta t_B + c_C m_C \Delta t_C + \cdots = 0, \qquad (19.5.3)$$

applicable to temperature changes taking place in a system that is insulated from its surroundings. Note that each of the quantities in (19.5.3) may be positive or negative depending on the algebraic sign of Δt; interpret the meaning of the algebraic sign as it applies to quantities of heat. Experience with the concepts and calculations we have just described leads us to say that "heat is conserved when heat exchanges take place within a thermally isolated system." But this statement, by itself, does not provide or even imply a specific model or theory as to the *nature* of heat.

> PROBLEM 19.2. A very simple calorimetry experiment is conducted in the following way: The brass calorimeter cup has a mass of 54 gm and contains 118 gm of water. The cup is insulated to some extent by being placed within another can, so that the cup is surrounded by still air, the temperature of which is about 20°C. A sample of metal, having a mass of 152 gm, is heated to 99.0°C in boiling water, quickly dried off, and placed in the calorimeter cup which is initially at 15.0°C. The final equilibrium temperature is found to be 24.7°C. Find the specific heat of the sample. [*Answer:* 0.107 cal/gm·C°.] According to Table 19.7.1, what material might this be? Note that this experiment was designed so that the initial temperature in the calorimeter cup was about 5° below the ambient (surrounding) temperature, and the final temperature was about 5° above ambient temperature. This is arranged deliberately after an initial crude run to discover an approximate value of c. What is the point of this design of the experiment?

19.6   REFINEMENT OF THE SPECIFIC HEAT CONCEPT

As we have seen in previous examples, the initial definition of a concept frequently points the way to further investigation and experiment. Insights gained in these experiments lead to refinement and redefinition of the original concept. Through a sequence of successive approximations, we fashion more general and rigorous descriptions of nature.

In the years following Black's introduction of the specific heat concept, more accurate observations showed that the value of c for any particular substance is different, depending on the physical circumstances under which heat is transferred. In particular, gases show a substantially smaller value of c if the heating or cooling occurs at constant volume, in a rigid container, than if it occurs in a cylinder in which a moving piston keeps the gas at constant pressure. If heating is carried out under conditions of arbitrarily changing pressure and volume, c is found to be different for each different "path" or sequence of states. Hence it is apparent that specific heat becomes a uniquely definable property only if the path of the heating process is uniquely specified.

The method of mixtures is usually used under conditions of constant atmospheric pressure, and the specific heat so determined is denoted by the symbol c_p, "specific heat at constant pressure." The specific heats discussed in Section 19.5 should all have a p-subscript on this account. Another readily definable path is the constant-volume process; specific heats so determined are labeled c_v. It is extremely difficult to confine liquids and solids so rigidly that heating can take place at constant volume; furthermore, c_p and c_v for liquids and solids differ only very slightly (for water the difference is of the order of 0.5%), and the difference is frequently neglected in making calculations. Gases, however, can be readily contained at constant volume, and the difference between c_p and c_v is large, of the order of 30 or 40%. Air, for example, has $c_p = 0.241$ and $c_v = 0.172$ cal/gm·C°, respectively. This difference will be referred to again in the following chapter; it provided an important clue to the connection between work and heat and thus provided a link in the chain of evidence that led to the generalization of the principle of conservation of energy.

A second refinement induced by accurate experiments came with the realization that specific heat is not constant even when the path is specified: it was discovered that c_p varies with the temperature. If water is assigned a value of $c_p = 1.000$ cal/gm·C° in the range between 14.5° and 15.5°C, it is found that $c_p = 0.998$ near 30°C and 1.005 near 90°C. The variation is small at ordinary temperatures, but nevertheless significant and observable. If the variation had been large, initial evolution of the heat concepts would probably have been slower and more difficult.

Recognizing c_p to be a function of temperature, we can refine the concept so as to interpret $c_p(t)$ as a quantity similar to an instantaneous velocity—an instantaneous rate at which heat must be supplied per gram per Celsius degree. A quantity of heat Q transferred between temperatures t_1 and t_2 must be calculated as the limit of a sum, just as we calculate displacements from instantaneous velocities:

$$Q = \int_{t_1}^{t_2} m_A c_{pA}(t)\, dt. \tag{19.6.1}$$

PROBLEM 19.3.   Explain (19.6.1) in your own words, and interpret it as an area on a diagram. Explain in more detail the analogy between this calculation and the calculation of displacement, Δs, given the velocity function $v(t)$. Interpret the algebraic sign associated with Q.

19.7   PHASE CHANGES AND LATENT HEATS

When ice melts, or a molten metal crystallizes into its solid state, or a liquid is vaporized, we speak of these phenomena as *changes of phase*. It was clear to early investigators that phase changes had something to do with thermal effects, but prior to the development of a clear distinction between the concepts of heat and temperature, it would have been virtually impossible to recognize the essential feature that distinguishes change of phase from ordinary heating or cooling.

Black was the first to provide a correct description:

> "Melting had been universally considered as produced by the addition of a very small quantity of heat to a solid body, once it has been warmed up to its melting point; and the return of the liquid to the solid state, as depending on a very small

diminution of its quantity of heat. . . . It was believed that this small addition of heat during melting was needed to produce a small rise in temperature as indicated by a thermometer. . . .

"The opinion I formed . . . is as follows. When ice or any other solid substance is melted . . . a large quantity of heat enters into it . . . without making it apparently warmer, when tried by [a thermometer]. . . . I affirm that this large addition of heat is the principal and most immediate cause of the liquefaction induced."

Black goes on to marshal his evidence; first from the length of time it takes ice and snow to melt:

"And if the common opinion had been well founded—if the complete change of ice and snow into water required only the addition of a very small quantity of heat—the mass, though of a considerable size, ought to be all melted within a very few minutes or seconds by the heat incessantly communicated from the surrounding air. Were this really the case, the consequences of it would be dreadful . . . for even as things are at present, the melting of large amounts of snow and ice occasions violent torrents and great inundations in the cold countries. . . . But were the ice and snow to melt suddenly, as they would if the former opinion of the action of heat . . . were well founded, the torrents and inundations would be incomparably more irresistible and dreadful. . . . This sudden liquefaction does not actually happen. The masses of ice and snow require a long time to melt. . . ."

Black describes a variety of experiments designed to prove his contention, among them a demonstration that the temperature of ice exposed in a warm room does not change, while the temperature of an equal amount of cold water rises significantly. He argues that both the ice and water must be absorbing heat from the air at about the same rate.

He then presents the results of a quantitative calorimetric experiment:*

The calorimeter consisted of a glass cup with a mass of 32 gm, containing 467 gm of water, initially at 88°C. Black took a piece of ice at 0°C, wiped it dry, weighed it quickly (404 gm) and placed it in the calorimeter, observing the equilibrium temperature to come to 12°C. The amounts of water and ice are not very different from each other, and, in the absence of phase change, one would have expected a final temperature near 40°C. The observed final temperature was very much lower, providing quantitative evidence for Black's hypothesis that a large quantity of heat must be transferred in order to melt ice at 0°C. Black assumed that heat was conserved in this process just as in the case not involving phase change. Let us carry out his calculation in our modern formalism, denoting by L_f the heat required to melt one gram of ice.

---

* Since Black reports his data in unfamiliar apothecaries' units, we have converted them into metric units and expressed the temperature in degrees Celsius.

TABLE 19.7.1

SPECIFIC HEATS AND LATENT HEATS OF VARIOUS SUBSTANCES

Substance	Constant-pressure specific heat, c_p (near room temp.), cal/gm·C°	Melting point, °C	Latent heat of fusion, L_f, cal/gm	Latent heat of vaporization, L_v (at normal boiling point), cal/gm	Normal boiling point, °C
Air	0.241				
Alcohol (ethyl)	0.456	−117.3	24.9	204	78.5
Aluminum	0.214	660	94		1800
Brass	0.092	940			
Bronze	0.087	1050			
Copper	0.093	1083	42		2300
Glass	0.20				
Gold	0.0312	1063	15.9		2600
Iron	0.107	1535			3000
Lead	0.0306	327	5.47		1620
Mercury	0.0332	−39	2.82	70.6	357
Silver	0.0558	960	26.0		1950
Sodium chloride	0.210	801	124		1450
Tin	0.0542	232	13.8		2260
Water	1.000	0	79.7	539	100
Ice	0.49	0			
Wood	0.42				

(Black used a value of 0.5 cal/gm·C° for the specific heat of glass.) Then:

$$467(1.00)(12 - 88) + 32(0.5)(12 - 88) + 404(12 - 0) + 404L_f = 0. \qquad (19.7.1)$$

| Heat gained by warm water | Heat gained by calorimeter cup | Heat gained by water from melted ice | Heat required to melt ice |

Solving for L_f, we obtain $L_f = 79$ cal/gm for ice at 0°C.

Black showed that this was a reproducible property, and introduced the name *latent heat*. Reasoning by analogy, he was sure that a latent heat was also associated with vaporization and demonstrated this to be the case. ($L_v = 539$ cal/gm for water at 100°C.) Black ultimately measured latent heats of fusion and vaporization of other substances, demonstrating the broad significance of the concept. (Table 19.7.1 lists latent heats of some familar materials.)

While Black was conducting these researches, among his students and assistants was a young man by the name of James Watt (1736–1819). Robinson, Black's biographer, writes that "[Watt] chanced to have in his hand, for repairs, a model of Newcomen's steam engine, belonging to the natural philosophy class, and was delighted with the opportunity which this small machine gave him for trying experiments connected with the theory of ebullition (boiling) which he had just learned from

Dr. Black." Subsequently, Watt's improvements of Newcomen's engine were to play an important role in the advent of the industrial revolution.

Further investigation of the phenomenon of phase change shows that melting points and boiling points change with the total pressure exerted on the system, and that latent heats are also altered under these circumstances. The freezing point of water is lowered by an increase in the pressure; the freezing point of many other substances is increased. The effect is small for the solid-liquid transitions, since solids and liquids are relatively incompressible, but the effect is very marked for the liquid-vapor transition, because of the presence of a gas phase.

PROBLEM 19.4. A calorimeter consisting of a glass vessel (mass = 125 gm) contains 1075 gm of water at 10°C and is surrounded by air at about 20°C. Steam at 100°C is bubbled slowly into the water until the temperature of the system rises to 30°C. The calorimeter is then weighed, and the mass is found to have increased by 36 gm. Evaluate the latent heat of condensation of the steam, setting up the problem in the form used in Eq. (19.7.1) and identifying each term by a verbal description.

19.8 THEORIES OF HEAT

In the *Novum Organum*, Francis Bacon wrote, "Calor est motus expansivus, cohibitus, et nitens per partes minores." Robert Boyle suggested that the "Nature of Heat [consists in] a various, vehement, and intestine commotion of the Parts among themselves." Robert Hooke affirmed that "Heat is a property of a body arising from the motion or agitation of its parts." Newton in Query 5 at the end of the *Opticks* asks, "Do not Bodies and Light act mutually upon one another; that is to say, Bodies upon Light in emitting, reflecting, refracting and inflecting it, and Light upon Bodies for heating them, and putting their parts into a vibrating motion wherein heat consists?"

Many seventeenth-century thinkers held a corpuscular view of the structure of matter, and at least some of these, as indicated by the quotations, had established in their minds a clear association between heat and motion of the constituent particles. No one was successful, however, in developing or implementing this idea in such a way as to make fruitful predictions or design convincing experiments.

The eighteenth century saw a proliferation of theories based on imponderable fluids. The principle of inflammability, called "phlogiston," was viewed as a fluid gained and lost by bodies during combustion and other chemical reactions. Electric and magnetic effects were described in terms of fluids and effluvia (see Chapter 7). In the interaction of these various views, the general climate of thought and vocabulary was one that encouraged a view of heat as still another imponderable fluid, and this view was, of course, strongly reinforced by the clear-cut demonstration of conservation of heat in calorimetric experiments. It is not surprising, therefore, that the speculations and conjectures of seventeenth-century physicists were put aside; Black, Lavoisier, and others rejected them explicitly. Lavoisier, whose own investigations ultimately demolished the phlogiston theory, gave the fluid principle of heat the name caloric (from the latin word *calor*), and the Caloric Theory was launched on a long and fruitful history, carrying well into the nineteenth century, when it gave way to the Principle of Conservation of Energy.

The caloric fluid was postulated to have the following properties: (1) it is a material substance that can neither be created nor destroyed; (2) the fluid is elastic, and the particles repel each other but are attracted by the particles of other substances, the magnitude of the attraction being different for different materials; (3) caloric can be either "sensible" or "latent"; in the former case it diffuses rapidly among the attracting particles and surrounds each with an "atmosphere" of the fluid; in the latter case caloric fluid combines with the attracting particles in a manner similar to that of chemical combinations.

This model provided very plausible explanations of a number of familiar phenomena (besides the conservation of heat in calorimetric experiments). Entrance of caloric fluid among the particles of a substance would cause the latter to tend to spread farther apart, increasing the pressure on the walls as a gas is heated in a rigid container or causing the expansion of liquids and solids. The particles of ordinary substance were assumed to attract each other gravitationally. Since the particles must be close together, and attract each other with strong forces, in liquids and solids, the caloric fluid would have less effect in causing expansion of liquids and solids than it would have on gases. The marked rise in temperature which occurs when a gas is rapidly compressed or a material is rubbed or hammered was accounted for as a squeezing out of caloric fluid from the spaces it occupied among the ordinary particles.

These are, of course, essentially qualitative applications of the caloric model. In the hands of Laplace and other mathematically oriented physicists, the theory yielded interesting quantitative predictions and relations that we shall not have time or space to outline. The point to be made is that the caloric model came to be widely accepted toward the end of the eighteenth century, because of its attractive simplicity and many successful applications. It yielded plausible explanations and useful results where other models had failed to do so.

19.9   THE ATTACK ON THE CALORIC THEORY

Despite the wide acceptance of the caloric theory, a small number of investigators were dissatisfied with the hypothesis of a material fluid having so many specially tailored properties. Exemplifying this school of thought was a versatile and brilliant man by the name of Benjamin Thompson (1753–1814). Thompson was born in Woburn, Massachusetts, lived for a time in Concord, New Hampshire (then called Rumford), left America because of royalist sympathies during the Revolution, and made a brilliant career in England and on the Continent as an administrator and natural philosopher. For a time he held (simultaneously) the posts of Minister of War, Minister of Police, Major General, Chamberlain of the Court, and State Councillor under the Elector of Bavaria. When the Elector made Thompson a Count of the Holy Roman Empire, he assumed the name of Count Rumford and was henceforth referred to by that title.

Rumford was intensely interested in thermal phenomena. In the course of his investigations, he invented stoves, an improved fireplace chimney, steam-heating systems, lamps, and coffee-makers. He was the first to appreciate the importance of the phenomenon of convection (the circulation of fluids arising from density differences due to heating and cooling) in the transfer of heat, and he conducted a number of crucial experiments relevant to the caloric theory.

A long-standing dispute centered around whether the caloric fluid, as a material substance, had weight. Some investigators claimed that bodies gained weight when heated. Other experiments purported to show that water gained weight as it froze, and it was even suggested that caloric fluid had a negative weight. Rumford had a distaste for *ad hoc* inventions of this kind and, having access to a very fine balance at the court of the Elector, he set out in 1787 to repeat the weighing experiments. He took great care to avoid spurious effects due to air currents, changes in temperature of the balance arms, etc., and, in describing the results of his investigations some years later, concluded that heating and cooling of a substance had no detectable effect on its weight. This clearly supported his doubts concerning the material nature of the caloric fluid.

Rumford then turned his attention to the heat produced by friction, and one of his experiments has become particularly famous. He reported it in 1798 to the Royal Society:

> "Being engaged lately in superintending the boring of cannon in the workshops of the military arsenal at Munich, I was struck by the very considerable degree of heat that a brass gun acquires in a short time in being bored, and with the still higher temperature (much higher than that of boiling water) of the metallic chips separated from it by the borer."

This was hardly a newly discovered phenomenon, but Rumford sensed that here was an avenue to "farther insight into the hidden nature of heat." He showed that the small chips had the same specific heat as the bulk metal and that one could not argue that caloric fluid was set free during the boring because the chips had a smaller heat capacity. He further showed that just as much heating took place when a blunt boring tool was used and almost no metal was cut.

Rumford regarded as most significant the "remarkable circumstance that the source of heat generated by friction in these experiments appeared to be evidently *inexhaustible*. It is hardly necessary to add that anything which any insulated body or system of bodies can continue to furnish *without limitation* cannot possibly be a *material substance*; and it appears to me to be extremely difficult, if not quite impossible, to form any distinct idea of anything capable of being excited and communicated in the manner in which heat was excited and communicated in these experiments, except it be MOTION."

But Rumford remained puzzled by the origin of the motion: "I am very far from pretending to know how or by what means or mechanical contrivance that particular kind of motion in bodies which has been supposed to constitute Heat is excited, continued and propagated. . . . But, although the mechanism of heat should, in fact, be one of those mysteries of nature which are beyond the reach of human intelligence, this ought by no means to discourage or even lessen our ardour . . . to investigate the laws of its operation." Not having a theory with which to connect the generation of heat with any other factors in his experiments, Rumford was not motivated to make quantitative measurements of the relation between heat and work. He did, however, study the transfer of heat through a vacuum, the behavior of water as it expanded at temperatures below 4°C, and the behavior of mixtures of different liquids, all as part of a systematic attack against the caloric theory.

During the early 1800's, Humphry Davy, a protege of Rumford's at the Royal Institution and later to become one of the most eminent chemists of his time, continued Rumford's line of attack.

Rumford, Davy, and their followers did not overthrow the caloric theory. A useful and fruitful theory is not abandoned as soon as it fails to fit one or two stubborn facts. The theory can be modified and adjusted, even though it might creak a bit in the process. Such was the response of scientists who continued to use the caloric theory toward the end of the eighteenth century. Rumford was not ignored. Laplace and Lavoisier in their *Memoir on Heat* of 1786 considered the rival hypotheses of heat as motion and heat as caloric fluid and said:

"We will not decide at all between the two foregoing hypotheses. Several phenomena seem favorable to the one, such as the heat produced by the friction of two solid bodies, for example; but there are others which are explained more simply by the other—perhaps they both hold at the same time. . . . In general, one can change the first hypothesis into the second by changing the words 'free caloric,' 'combined caloric,' and 'caloric released' into '*vis viva*,' 'loss of *vis viva*,' and 'increase of *vis viva*.'"

While there was nothing more convincing to replace it, the caloric model continued to be used. Accurate measurement of quantities of heat and analysis of calorimetric experiments did not, in the final analysis, depend on a "correct" model—all that was needed was a good heuristic one. The caloric theory served the purpose admirably, but it is unlikely that many of its users were as sophisticated as Laplace and Lavoisier and sensed its heuristic character; many investigators probably believed in a literal caloric fluid.

Years later it came to be realized that some of the correct results that seemed to stem from the caloric theory did not depend at all on the specific model being used, but followed from such aspects as the mathematical definition of quantity of heat Q in terms of specific heats c_p and c_v. In this sense it made no difference what heuristic device was used to interpret the physical significance of Q or to visualize the nature of heat. Other models, which preserve the same definitions, yield the same mathematical consequences. As we shall see, the caloric theory was eventually supplanted by an entirely different picture—one that explains and organizes a far wider range of phenomena, and in which heat is recognized as a form of energy rather than as a material fluid. This theory preserves exactly the same mathematical definition of Q and predicts the same relations that were supposedly derived from the caloric model.

Models of physical processes have played a vital role in the evolution of scientific thought. Some ideas are advanced, found to be seriously wanting at an early stage of investigation, and are abandoned and forgotten. In many cases, however, models that were only later found to be erroneous or of very limited range of applicability have proved to be exceedingly fruitful in the early stages of a new scientific synthesis. They have served as heuristic devices, aiding imagination and reasoning by facilitating analysis of specific problems, helping predict results to be expected in new situations, suggesting new investigations, and suggesting new tests of the model itself. When such models and theories yield to modification and refinement, or even when they are overthrown, to be replaced by entirely new views, they leave us an important legacy: the deeper insights, the more widely applicable theories won by initial reliance on the less adequate, or even erroneous, model. In its day, the caloric theory played a very helpful role; it should not be surprising that it was not easily overthrown.

19.10 THE QUANTITATIVE RELATION BETWEEN WORK AND HEAT

The attack begun by Rumford was carried to its completion in the 1830's and 1840's in the groping that took place for a synthesis among interlocking phenomena in mechanics, heat, electricity, and chemistry. The unifying principle turned out to be that of energy. Prominent in the evidence that led to the abandonment of the caloric theory were the quantitative experiments of James Prescott Joule.*

James Prescott Joule (1818–1889) was a well-to-do Manchester brewer who devoted himself to science from an early age. Joule was profoundly attracted to experimental science, and he had a vision of a grander conservation law than that of caloric fluid.

Europe in the 1830's was in the full flood of the technological revolution. Industry depended on the steam engine for mechanical power generated by heat supplied in burning fuel. Faraday had discovered electromagnetic induction, and primitive electric generators were being used in experiments of all kinds. In this atmosphere, Joule conceived the idea (simultaneously held by other investigators) of a possible quantitative connection between work and heat. Such a connection is not obvious; people as able as Rumford and Davy failed to close the gap. Furthermore, if a systematic, quantitative connection between heat and mechanical action exists, one can conceive of any number of possible functional relationships. Joule, with a large supply of the gifted scientist's sixth sense, hit upon what turned out to be the right combination.

In 1840 he reported some experiments on the production of heat by electric current, and in 1843 he presented quantitative results. Using falling weights to turn a magneto-electric machine (generator), he immersed in water the conductor through which the electric current flowed and measured the heat so generated. Comparing the heat evolved with the work (in excess of friction) needed to turn the generator, he reported 13 measurements with an average result that 838 ft·lb of work was accompanied by the heating of 1 lb of water through 1°F; that is, that 1 Btu $\backsimeq$ 838 ft·lb.

---

* Generally pronounced to rhyme with *pool*. His picture appears on page 428.

Later the same year he reported on additional experiments:

"My apparatus consisted of a piston perforated by a number of small holes, working in a cylindrical glass jar containing about 7 lb of water. I thus obtained one degree of heat per lb of water from a mechanical force capable of raising about 770 lb to the height of one foot, a result which will be allowed to be very strongly confirmatory of our previous deductions. I shall lose no time in repeating and extending these experiments, being satisfied that the grand agents of nature are, by the Creator's fiat, *indestructible*; and that wherever mechanical force is expended (work is dissipated), an exact equivalent of heat is *always* obtained."

In 1845 Joule reported experiments on the temperature drop observed in rapidly expanding air, and showed that 1 Btu of heat was equivalent to 795 ft·lb of work. He then initiated a long series of increasingly accurate experiments on the production of heat in water by frictional effects:

"The apparatus . . . consisted of a brass paddle wheel working horizontally in a can of water. Motion could be communicated to this paddle by means of [falling] weights. . . . The paddle moved with great resistance in the can of water, so that the weights (each of four pounds) descended at the slow rate of about one foot per second. The height of the pulleys from the ground was twelve yards, and consequently, when the weights had descended . . . , they had to be wound up again to renew the motion of the paddle. After this operation had been repeated sixteen times, the increase of the temperature of the water was ascertained. . . .

"The equivalents I have already obtained are: 1st, 823 lb derived from magneto-electrical experiments; 2nd, 795 lb deduced from the cold produced by rarefaction of air; and 3rd, 774 lb from experiments on the motion of water through narrow tubes. This last class of experiments being similar to that of the paddle wheel, we may take 832 lb as the equivalent derived from the friction of water."

Joule continued his experiments, improving the accuracy and working with different materials, both solid and liquid. In 1850 he published an extensive summary of results with a final statement:

"The quantity of heat produced by the friction of bodies, whether solid or liquid, is always proportional to the quantity of [work] expended. The quantity of heat capable of increasing the temperature of a pound of water . . . by 1°F requires for its evolution the expenditure of mechanical [work] represented by the fall of 772 lb through the space of one foot."

Thus Joule explained the source of heating in Rumford's experiments. Recognition of heat as another form of energy means that Joule's number (usually called the "mechanical equivalent of heat") is simply a conversion factor between different units of measurement. The statement that 1 Btu is equivalent to 772 ft·lb is analogous to the statement that 1 inch is equivalent to 2.54 cm. This conversion factor is usually denoted by J, in honor of Joule, and the currently accepted values are

$$1 \text{ Btu} \simeq 778.26 \text{ ft·lb}, \qquad 1 \text{ calorie} \simeq 4.186 \text{ joules.}$$

Joule's experiments, together with the work and thought of some of his contemporaries (to be discussed in the following chapter), led to the formulation of the general principle of conservation of energy. This prodigiously fertile synthesis of mechanics and theory of heat invited a return to the earlier view of heat as being associated with the motion (kinetic energy) of constituent particles. But the development of the science of energy did not require a clear and adequate theory of the structure of matter; it was not necessary to define precisely what was moving and how. The essence of the theory lay in mathematical relationships among observable, macroscopic properties of matter without relying on elucidation of the microscopic phenomena. This is not to say that a microscopic model was uninteresting or undesirable; such a theory came later, and deepened still further our insights and understanding. We shall encounter an analogous situation when we see how Young and Fresnel evolved a highly successful wave theory of light without having any clear idea of what was "waving," and how Maxwell ultimately provided a detailed explanation in terms of electrical and magnetic fields.

19.11 PROBLEMS

19.5. State the definitions of the Celsius and Fahrenheit temperature scales, and, from these definitions, derive an algebraic relation for converting a Fahrenheit reading to Celsius and vice versa.

19.6. How much heat must be supplied to convert one kilogram of ice at $-10°C$ to steam at $100°C$ by heating at constant atmospheric pressure? [*Answer:* 719.2 kcal.]

19.7. 500 gm of copper at 95°C are placed in a glass calorimeter containing 320 gm of water at 10°C. The calorimeter cup weighs 130 gm. Predict the final temperature, indicating what idealizations and assumptions are being made. If the ambient temperature is 25°C, what would you expect to observe in the actual experiment; i.e., is your prediction likely to be too low or too high?

19.8. On the basis of information contained in Table 19.7.1, design an experiment for the verification of the figure given for the latent heat of vaporization of mercury, assuming that you would have access to a mercury-distillation apparatus, delivering mercury vapor at the normal boiling point. Decide on quantities of material that you might use and on initial temperature conditions. Estimate the final temperature you would expect. Assume the ambient temperature to be 20°C.

19.9. How much frictional work must be supplied in order to boil away 1500 gm of water initially at 20°C? What assumptions are implied in your calculation?

19.10. Estimate the lower limit of velocity that a lead bullet must have in order to become melted when stopped in an inelastic collision with a rigid wall. Assume the initial temperature to be some ordinary atmospheric value. What idealizations are implied in your calculations? Why is your answer a lower limit? Why is no specification made of the mass of the bullet? Actually, the temperature of the bullet before striking the wall is likely to be considerably higher than the atmospheric temperature. Why? What influence does this have on your estimate? [*Answer:* of the order of 350 m/sec.]

19.11. In his 1845 paper in the *Philosophical Magazine*, Joule wrote: "Any of your readers who are so fortunate as to reside amid the romantic scenery of Wales or Scotland could, I doubt not, confirm my experiments by trying the temperature of the water at the top and at the bottom of a cascade. If my views be correct . . . the temperature of a [falls] would be raised about one-fifth of a degree by [a drop] of 160 ft."

Verify this estimate, using the presently accepted conversion factor. Joule's "I doubt not" was probably a bit hasty. Such an observation would be likely to be seriously confused by a number of extraneous factors; identify a few of these.

SUPPLEMENTARY READING AND STUDY

Physics for Students of Science and Engineering, R. Resnick and D. Halliday. New York: John Wiley & Sons, 1960, Chapters 21, 22

Source Book in Physics, W. F. Magie. New York: McGraw-Hill, 1935, pages 125–211

Harvard Case Histories in Experimental Science, Volume I, Case 3. Cambridge, Mass.: Harvard University Press, 1957

Count Rumford: Physicist Extraordinary, S. C. Brown. Garden City, N. Y.: Doubleday, 1962, Science Study Series, S 28

Heat and Thermodynamics, M. Zemansky. New York: McGraw-Hill, 1957, Chapter 1

CHAPTER 20

Conservation of Mass and Conservation of Energy

20.1 INTRODUCTION

Around the middle of the first century B.C., the Roman poet Lucretius wrote in *De Rerum Natura*:

> "[superstition] cannot be dispelled by the sunbeams, the shining shafts of day, but only by an understanding of the outward forms and inner workings of nature. In developing this theme, our starting point will be this principle: *Nothing can be created by divine power out of nothing*. . . . If things were made out of nothing, any species could spring from any source and nothing would require seed. Men could arise from the sea and scaly fish from the earth, and birds could be hatched out of the sky. . . . The second great principle is this: *Nature resolves everything into its component atoms and never reduces anything to nothing*. If anything were perishable in all its parts, anything might perish all of a sudden and vanish from sight. . . ."

The theme of conservation of some entity in natural phenomena—a theme frequently adopted on *a priori*, metaphysical premises—sounds and resounds in writings of natural philosophers. To Descartes it was inconceivable that absolute numerical value of quantity of motion could fail to be preserved, and he deduced erroneous conclusions from this erroneous premise.

Leibniz convinced himself on metaphysical grounds that *vis viva* and "force" (work) must be conserved, and he attained an insight into the restricted principle of conservation of mechanical energy. Huygens asserted a principle of impossibility of perpetual motion in articulating his conviction that one cannot extract something from nothing in the harnessing of natural phenomena.

During the second half of the eighteenth and first half of the nineteenth centuries, these vague intuitions—based on a sense of orderly connection between initial and final conditions in processes of physical change—came to be expressed as scientific laws or principles. These principles, which grasp some characteristic permanence in what would otherwise be a chaotic flux of events, are among the most powerful generalizations available to science. Not only do they unify ranges of phenomena that would otherwise constitute entirely separate compartments of scientific knowledge, they provide the very basis of what we refer to as "understanding" and "explanation" in scientific thought. One of these principles, the law of conservation of momentum, we have already discussed in Chapter 17; we now examine the laws of conservation of mass and of energy.

20.2   THE CONCEPT OF MATTER

In describing physical phenomena, we have frequently referred to "matter" or "material substance." We all use these terms quite casually in much of our discourse, and, within a certain restricted range of experience, we understand each other. The reference is to tangible objects, discernible to the senses as having extension in space, an incapacity to occupy the same position simultaneously with other such objects, offering resistance to acceleration, and sometimes having the property of impenetrability.

But what are the *intrinsic* properties of matter? What do a ball of wool and a lump of lead have in common? In particular, what might we mean by *quantity* of matter? Aristotle defined intrinsic properties as ones that "allow of neither intensification nor remission," and this idea carries through the history of western philosophy, being repeated, for example, by Newton in essentially the same words. Properties—such as shape, texture, color, odor—that did not seem intrinsic to materials were referred to as "accidental properties" or "accidents."

From early times there prevailed an intuitive association of matter with weight. Lucretius avers, "If there is as much matter in a ball of wool as in one of lead, it is natural that it should weigh as heavily, since it is a function of matter to press everything downwards. . . ."

In medieval times discussion of this conceptual problem was motivated by theological interest in the sacrament of the Eucharist—the transubstantiation, in the ritual of the mass, of the bread and wine into the body and blood of Christ. What was the character of this miracle; was matter transformed, leaving accidents of texture and color unaffected?* The words "massa" and "moles" were used to denote lumps or quantities of material; Kepler used the latter term (see Problem 17.27) in his reference to the interaction of objects removed from the influence of the earth. Descartes, Wallis, Huygens, and other seventeenth-century thinkers, like Lucretius, associated weight with quantity of matter.

Newton, building on an intuitive, operationally undefined notion of density, gives as Definition I in the *Principia*: "The quantity of matter is the measure of the same, arising from its density and bulk conjointly. . . . It is this quantity that we mean hereafter everywhere under the name of body or mass." Thus Newton defined mass as

---

* Readers interested in this episode of interaction between theology and natural philosophy will find an illuminating discussion in Jammer's book, cited in the reading list at the end of this chapter.

the product of density and volume. Since density, in modern terms, is defined as mass per unit volume, many authors accuse Newton of having fallen into an obvious circularity. It is very unlikely that Newton was so naive; he seems rather to have been building on density as a primitive concept.

Newton went on to make a clear conceptual distinction between mass and weight. Then, in careful experiments, measuring the periods of pendulums having identical geometrical design but bobs of entirely different materials, he confirmed the hypothesis that inertial and gravitational mass could be measured by the same number, regardless of the chemical nature and appearance of a particular body. (See Section 15.7.)

In Chapters 5, 6, and 7 we developed a modern, operational view of the Newtonian concept of inertial mass, and we avoided making any explicit connection between this operationally defined dynamical property and quantity of matter. Eighteenth and nineteenth-century scientists did make this connection, however, and statements and "definitions" of mass as quantity of matter persist in some textbooks to this day. Ernst Mach in the *Science of Mechanics* (1883) severely criticized this notion:

"... we do not find the expression 'quantity of matter' adapted to explain and elucidate the concept of mass, since that expression itself is not possessed of the requisite clarity. And this is so, even if we go back, as many authors have done, to an enumeration of the hypothetical atoms. ... The moment we suppose that we are dealing with chemically different materials, the assumption that there is still something that is measurable by the same standard ... needs to be justified.

"When two bodies perfectly equal in all respects are placed opposite each other, we expect, in accordance with the principle of symmetry, that they will produce in each other in the direction of their line of junction equal and opposite accelerations. But if these bodies exhibit any difference, however slight, of form, of chemical constitution, or are in any other respects different, the principle of symmetry forsakes us, *unless we assume or know beforehand* that sameness of form or of chemical constitution are not determining factors."

Mach then goes on to propose the definition of mass that we discussed in connection with the reaction-car experiment [Section 6.4, Eq. (6.4.6)] and follows with the remark: "In our concept of mass no theory is involved; 'quantity of matter' is wholly unnecessary in it. ..."

With the advent of the Theory of Relativity (see Chapter 36) at the beginning of this century, it became apparent that inertial mass of a body varies with its velocity relative to the frame of reference of a particular observer. It was demonstrated that such changes of inertial mass were directly related to changes in the kinetic energy of the moving body, and furthermore it proved necessary to associate inertial mass with intangible, intuitively unfamiliar electromagnetic effects and energies. In still more recent work, in elementary particle physics, it has been necessary to associate inertial mass with entities (particles called *neutrinos*) that possess kinetic energy and angular momentum but exhibit zero electrical charge and probably have zero "rest mass;" i.e., zero inertial mass when they have zero velocity relative to us.

What then shall we mean by the term matter?

Where eighteenth- and nineteenth-century science seemed to grasp a simple and reassuring identity of mass and matter, twentieth-century science again confronts matter as an elusive concept, lacking sharp and unequivocal definition.

20.3 LAVOISIER AND THE LAW OF CONSERVATION OF MASS

Profound alterations in the appearance and character of material substances were long known in processes such as combustion, refining of ores, and actions of acids on metals or other materials. Changes of this kind are called "chemical." We now recognize that chemical processes involve not only readily apparent changes in the appearance, properties, and masses of liquids and solids, but are also frequently accompanied by the evolution or absorption of gases. Furthermore, we recognize differences between gases—differences residing in properties such as density, toxicity, and chemical effect on other materials.

These realizations, although commonplaces to us by virtue of a long-established vocabulary of description, were not easily or rapidly won by seventeenth- and eighteenth-century investigators. Many techniques had to be developed and much observational experience accumulated before it was realized that all gases were not air (even though they might be colorless and tasteless) and could be distinguished from each other by properties such as the ability to support or stifle combustion, produce toxic effects on living organisms, or react differently with a variety of other substances. The famous instance of the discovery of oxygen by Scheele, Priestly, and Lavoisier was really not so much a sharply delimited discovery as a slowly won awareness of the significance of experimentally observable differences between this gas and air.*

The second half of the eighteenth century saw the development of gravimetric (accurate weighing) techniques, and improved methods of containing and handling gases. With the development of such techniques, there followed quantitative observations of changing weights of different materials participating in chemical changes. Joseph Black, whose studies of heat we discussed in Chapter 19, performed gravimetric experiments in which he accounted for the weights of all materials in certain chemical reactions, but the total import of these experiments was apparently not clear to Black himself or to his contemporaries. Clarification of the fundamental principles involved came through the work of Antoine Laurent Lavoisier (1743–1794) and his attack on the then-prevalent theory of chemical change.

At the middle of the eighteenth century, the most widely held theory of chemical change assumed the existence of an imponderable fluid called "phlogiston," which was taken to be the principle of flame or fire. When ores heated with charcoal formed metals, it was assumed that phlogiston from the charcoal combined with the ore as a

---

* For an historical analysis of this episode, see Chapter 6 of *The Edge of Objectivity*, by C. C. Gillispie, Princeton University Press, 1960. For a discussion of this event in the context of emergence of scientific discoveries, see Chapter 6 of *The Structure of Scientific Revolutions*, by T. S. Kuhn, University of Chicago Press, 1962.

"metallizing principle." When charcoal burned in air, its phlogiston escaped and combined with the air. Burning ceased in an enclosed space when the air was fully combined or saturated with phlogiston.

Lavoisier undertook the careful gravimetric study of chemical changes in "closed systems"—closed in the sense that no material was allowed to enter the "system" or to escape during the observations. He showed that metals such as mercury, when heated gently in the presence of air, form "ores" that weigh more than the original metal; he further showed that some of the air is used up in the process. When the "ore" was heated at a higher temperature, Lavoisier showed that it could be decomposed to restore the original metal and the original amount of air. He recognized that air consisted of two different gases, and demonstrated that one of these (oxygen, previously described by Priestley as "dephlogisticated air") combined with substances, or was restored on decomposition, in the reactions he was studying. These discoveries made the phlogiston theory untenable, and it was rapidly abandoned during the 1780's, following publication of Lavoisier's research.

Lavoisier's careful gravimetric experiments (some of which were performed during the same years that Rumford utilized his sensitive balance to test whether objects changed weight on heating or cooling) led not only to an understanding of the nature of combustion and to the downfall of the phlogiston theory* but also to a clear enunciation of the principle of conservation of mass. Summarizing, in his textbook of 1789, the results of numerous painstaking experiments, Lavoisier observed:

> "We must lay it down as an incontestable axiom, that in all operations of art and nature, nothing is created; an equal quantity of matter exists both before and after the experiment . . . and nothing takes place beyond changes and modifications of these elements. Upon this principle the whole art of performing chemical experiments depends."

Proof of the conservation of mass in closed systems probably did much to reinforce the identification of mass with quantity of matter in the minds of eighteenth- and nineteenth-century scientists. We shall avoid this identification, and shall always refer to "conservation of mass," leaving the word "matter" without operational definition.

Some marginalia concerning Lavoisier: Although he categorically rejected one fluid theory (that of phlogiston), he continued to use another—the caloric theory of heat. With some stated qualifications (see the quotation in Section 19.9), he continued to utilize the latter in his explanation of thermal phenomena, and apparently found its plausibility and usefulness persuasive, as did most of his other contemporaries, with the notable exception of Count Rumford.

Chemical experimentation was an avocation with Lavoisier. Professionally, he had established himself in a good living as a tax collector under the government of Louis XVI. This occupation was not calculated to make him *persona grata* to the revolution-

---

* For a detailed description of the overthrow of the phlogiston theory, see *Harvard Case Histories in Experimental Science*, Case 2, Harvard University Press, 1957.

ary regime, and he was executed at the height of the terror in 1794. Lavoisier's widow was subsequently courted by Rumford, and their turbulent marriage became a subject of gossip in Parisian society of 1805–07.

20.4 MAYER'S STATEMENT OF THE PRINCIPLE OF CONSERVATION OF ENERGY

Chapters 18 and 19 provided some fragmentary glimpses of the evolution of the energy concepts. First came the recognition of the restricted principle of conservation of mechanical energy; then the growing recognition of a quantitative connection between mechanical energy and heat. Generalization and extension of the conservation principle during the 1840's finally led to the abandonment of the caloric theory.

FIG. 20.4.1. Julius Robert Mayer (1814–1878).

The first published enunciation of the principle of conservation of energy appeared in a highly speculative, almost metaphysical, paper in Justus Liebig's *Annalen der Chemie und Pharmacie* in 1842. The author was a young German physician, Julius Robert Mayer (1814–1878), and the paper, titled "Remarks on the Forces* of Inorganic Nature," appeared in the chemical journal after having been rejected by a prominent physical publication on the grounds that it contained too many unsupported generalizations.

---

* Mayer uses the German word *Kraft* (force) for ideas we now denote by the word *energy*.

At the beginning, Mayer puts forth his basic assumptions and point of view:

"Forces [energies] are causes: accordingly, we may in relation to them make full application of the principle—*causa aequat effectum*. If the cause *c* has the effect *e*, then *c* = *e*; if, in its turn, *e* is the cause of a second effect *f*, we have *e* = *f*, and so on. . . . In a chain of causes and effects a term or a part of a term can never, as plainly appears from the nature of an equation, become equal to nothing. This first property of all causes we call their *indestructibility*. If the given cause *c* has produced an effect *e* equal to itself, it has in that very act ceased to be: *c* has become *e*. . . . This capability of assuming various forms is the second essential property of all causes. Taking both properties together, we may say, causes are quantitatively indestructible and qualitatively convertible objects.

"Two classes of causes occur in nature, which, so far as experience goes, never pass one into another. The first class consists of such causes as possess the properties of weight and impenetrability; these are kinds of matter: the other class is made up of causes which are wanting in the properties just mentioned, namely forces [energies]. . . . Forces are therefore indestructible, convertible, imponderable objects."

Such metaphysical jargon and dubious logic were hardly likely to command much respect in the scientific community. Furthermore, the question of convertibility and indestructibility of energy depends on experimental proof as well as on appropriate definition of energy concepts, rather than on an *a priori* identification of energy with an ill-defined and logically shaky notion of cause and effect. Yet Mayer goes on to reveal significant insights; after referring to conservation of energy in frictionless mechanics, he asks:

"In numberless cases we see motion cease without having caused another motion or the lifting of a weight; but a force (energy) once in existence cannot be annihilated, it can only change its form: and the question therefore arises, What other forms is force, which we have become acquainted with as falling force (PE) and motion (KE), capable of assuming?"

After referring to experiments on generation of heat by friction, he says:

"Without the recognition of a causal connection between motion and heat, it is just as difficult to explain the production of heat as it is to give any account of the motion that disappears. . . . We prefer the assumption that heat proceeds from motion, to the assumption of a cause without effect and of an effect without a cause—just as the chemist, instead of allowing oxygen and hydrogen to disappear without further investigation and water to be produced in some inexplicable manner, establishes a connection between oxygen and hydrogen on the one hand and water on the other. . . . If falling force (PE) and motion (KE) are equivalent to heat, heat must also naturally be equivalent to motion and falling force."

Encouraged by the analogy to conservation of mass as exhibited in chemistry, and having a vision of still another conservation of imponderable effects, he extends his thesis:

"In watermills . . . the fall of the water gives rise to motion which afterwards disappears again, calling forth unceasingly a great quantity of heat; and inversely, the steam engine serves to decompose heat again into motion or the raising of weights. [In a locomotive engine with its train] the heat applied under the boiler passes off as motion, and this is deposited again as heat at the axles of the wheels."

Finally Mayer does not avoid the crucial scientific question:

"How great is the quantity of heat which corresponds to a given quantity of motion (KE) or falling force (PE)? For instance, we must ascertain how high a given weight requires to be raised above the ground in order that its falling force may be equivalent to the raising of the temperature of an equal weight of water from 0°C to 1°C."

20.5 MAYER'S ESTIMATE OF THE MECHANICAL EQUIVALENT OF HEAT

Mayer was not an experimentalist like Joule, and he did not undertake a program for determining this quantity, but with keen insight he pointed to one of the few bits of experimental information then available: he gave an interpretation of the difference between the constant-pressure and constant-volume heat capacities of gases. (See Section 19.6, where it is stated that for air $c_p = 0.241$ and $c_v = 0.172$ cal/gm·C°.)

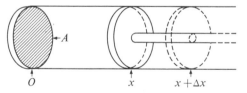

FIG. 20.5.1. Cylinder with cross-sectional area A. Piston may be rigidly fixed in position or may be displaced inward or outward.

Transcribed into modern terminology and using modern numbers, Mayer's analysis runs as follows: Consider a quantity of air confined in a cylinder with a movable piston (Fig. 20.5.1). If the piston is fixed in position, 0.172 cal of heat must be supplied for each gram of air contained in the cylinder to elevate the temperature 1°C; in the process the pressure in the cylinder increases. If the piston is not rigidly fixed, but is initially in equilibrium with a pressure of one atmosphere (1.013×10^5 n/m²) both inside and outside the cylinder, the piston will move outward, while the gas expands on heating and the pressure remains constant. Under these conditions a larger amount of heat than before, 0.241 cal, must be supplied for each gram of air to increase in temperature by 1°C. Mayer's interpretation was that this process must be analogous to that which took place when steam expanded in an engine; the excess heat over 0.172 cal/gm must be converted into work necessary to push the piston outward against the pressure of the atmosphere.

Let us formulate an expression for this amount of work: Suppose that the piston in Fig. 20.5.1 is displaced, as the gas expands under constant pressure p, from position x to $x + \Delta x$. Since pressure is defined as force per unit area, the total force exerted on the piston must be pA, and the work W done by the gas in the expansion must be

$$W = pA \, \Delta x. \tag{20.5.1}$$

But $A \, \Delta x$ is simply the volume change ΔV of the gas, and we can write

$$W = p \, \Delta V. \tag{20.5.2}$$

PROBLEM 20.1.   Argue that in the general case, where pressure might vary from position to position, the work done by the gas would be given by

$$W = \int_{V_1}^{V_2} p \, dV. \tag{20.5.3}$$

Interpret this as an area under a curve.

To compare the excess heat supplied with the work done, it is necessary to know ΔV. Thus, one must establish experimentally the volume change experienced by one gram of air when the temperature changes by 1°C while the pressure remains constant at one atmosphere. This number is determined to be 2.83 cm^3/gm·C° or 2.83 × 10^{-6} m^3/gm·C°. Now it is possible to compare the quantities of heat and work:

The work done by one gram of gas expanding at a constant pressure of one atmosphere is given by

$$W = p \, \Delta V,$$
$$= 1.013 \, (10^5) \, \text{n/m}^2 \times 2.83 \times 10^{-6} \, \text{m}^3/\text{gm·C}°$$
$$= 0.286 \, \text{joule/gm·C}°.$$

The heat in excess of that required at constant volume is

$$0.241 - 0.172 = 0.069 \, \text{cal/gm·C}°$$

(valid to only two significant figures). Therefore 0.069 calories of heat should be equivalent to 0.29 joules of work or

$$1 \, \text{cal} \approx 4.2 \, \text{joules},$$

a result which is clearly in accord with the values cited in Section 19.10.

The numerical values of c_p, c_v, and volume changes available to Mayer in 1842 were less accurate than the ones we have used in this calculation, but his result was correct in principle, and was in essential agreement with the values subsequently published by Joule.

One very significant tacit assumption is contained in Mayer's interpretation of the gas expansion: namely, that *all* the excess heat supplied is converted into work done by the expanding gas and that no potential energy is stored or released within the gas itself by virtue of the separation of its constituent particles. This turns out to be a very good approximation for ordinary gases at moderate pressures, but it is only an approximation and not a fundamental, necessary mode of behavior. In real gases the molecules attract each other with relatively weak forces, and small amounts of potential energy are stored as the average spacing of molecules increases during expansion of the gas.

Fig. 20.6.1. James Prescott Joule (1818–1889).

20.6   JOULE'S ENUNCIATION OF THE PRINCIPLE OF CONSERVATION OF ENERGY

Joule's initial work and thinking was done without awareness of Mayer's publication of 1842. His first quantitative results on the equivalence of work and heat were published in 1843, and were followed over subsequent years by the many additional measurements described in Section 19.10. Not only did Joule marshal this extensive array of experimental evidence, but, with his friend William Thomson, he conducted a careful investigation of the behavior of gases to determine the extent to which potential energy might be stored or released during expansion, putting the analysis first made by Mayer to a more critical test.

In a popular lecture delivered in Manchester in 1847, Joule sounded the knell of the caloric theory:

"The most prevalent opinion until of late, has been that [heat] is a *substance* possessing, like all other matter, impenetrability and extension. We have however shown that heat can be converted into living force (KE) and into attraction through space (PE). It is perfectly clear, therefore, that unless matter can be converted into attraction through space, which is too absurd an idea to be entertained for a moment, the hypothesis of heat being a substance must fall to the ground. Heat must therefore consist of either living force or of attraction through space. . . . I am inclined to believe that both of these hypotheses will be found to hold good—that . . . sensible heat will be found to consist in the living force of the particles of the bodies in which it is induced; whilst in other [instances], particularly in the case of latent heat, the phenomena are produced by the separation of particle from particle, so as to cause them to attract one another through a greater space."

Joule's sense of exhilaration in the perception of a far-reaching conservation law is evident in the following poetic remarks from the same lecture:

"The motion of the air which we call 'wind' arises chiefly from the intense heat of the torrid zone compared with the temperature of the temperate and frigid zones. Here we have an instance of heat being converted into the living force of currents of air. These currents of air, in their progress across the sea, lift up its waves and propel the ships; whilst in passing across the land they shake the trees and disturb every blade of grass. The waves by their violent motion, the ships by their passage through a resisting medium, and the trees by the rubbing of their branches together and the friction of their leaves against themselves and the air, each and all of them generate heat equivalent to the diminution of the living force of the air which they occasion. The heat thus restored may again contribute to raise fresh currents of air; and thus the phenomena may be repeated in endless succession and variety."

"When we consider our own frames, 'fearfully and wonderfully made,' we observe in the motion of our limbs a continual conversion of heat into living force, which may be either converted back again into heat or employed in producing an attraction through space, as when a man ascends a mountain. Indeed the phenomena of nature, whether mechanical, chemical or vital, consist almost entirely in a continual conversion of attraction through space, living force, and heat into one another. Thus it is that order is maintained in the universe—nothing is deranged, nothing ever lost, but the entire machinery, complicated as it is, works smoothly and harmoniously. And though, as in the awful vision of Ezekiel, 'wheel may be in middle of wheel,' and every thing may appear complicated and involved in the apparent confusion and intricacy of an almost endless variety of causes, effects, conversions, and arrangements, yet is the most perfect regularity preserved. . . ."

20.7   LOGICAL STATUS OF THE CONSERVATION LAWS

With slowly growing acceptance of the principle enunciated by Mayer and Joule, the concept was extended quantitatively to include other mechanical phenomena, such as wave propagation and the flow of fluids. The young German physicist Helmholtz (1821–1894) published a paper in 1847 in which he gave a quantitative treatment of the energetics of certain simple electric, magnetic, and chemical phenomena. Conservation of energy played an important role in the development of an understanding of light and electromagnetism; it is one of the fundamental pillars of the Theory of Relativity.

When, during the 1930's, phenomena observed in certain types of radioactive decay (beta emission) seemed to violate the laws of conservation of energy and momentum, it was postulated that a virtually unobservable particle, called the neutrino, was emitted and that this elusive entity accounted for the missing linear momentum, angular momentum, and energy. Later this same entity proved useful in explaining other nuclear phenomena, and considerable faith was built up in the construct because of its wide usefulness and its serviceability in preserving the conservation laws. It was predicted that neutrinos should occasionally interact with atoms among which they passed, but such interactions were estimated to be exceedingly infrequent. It was not until 1952 that experimental techniques, sufficiently sophisticated to detect such rare events, were developed. The search proved successful, and the predicted events were observed.

As a result of such experiences, built up over a period of over 120 years, scientists have developed a profound faith in the fundamental validity of the conservation laws as expressions of order in nature. It is therefore desirable to scrutinize a little more deeply the logical status of these assertions. Are the conservation laws essentially convenient definitions or conventions, as Poincaré implies in some of his discussions?*

If the conservation law for energy appears to fail, will we be always able to rehabilitate it by inventing a new particle or a new form of energy?

Professor Eric Rogers illustrates some of the points at issue in the following dialogue in which "You" and "Faustus" debate a theory of the origin of frictional forces.†

You. I don't believe in demons.

Faustus. I do.

You. Anyway, I don't see how demons can make friction.

Faustus. They just stand in front of things and push to stop them from moving.

You. I can't see any demons even on the roughest table.

Faustus. They are too small, also transparent.

Y. But there is more friction on rough surfaces.

F. More demons.

Y. Oil helps.

F. Oil drowns demons.

---

* See Chapters 6 and 7 of *Science and Hypothesis*, by Henri Poincaré. New York: Dover Publications, 1952.

† *Physics for the Inquiring Mind*, Eric Rogers. Princeton University Press, 1960.

Y. If I polish the table, there is less friction and the ball rolls farther.

F. You are wiping the demons off; there are fewer to push.

Y. A heavier ball experiences more friction.

F. More demons push it; and it crushes their bones more.

Y. If I put a rough brick on a table, I can push against friction with more and more force, up to a limit, and the block stays still, with friction just balancing my push.

F. Of course, the demons push just hard enough to stop you from moving the brick; but there is a limit to their strength, beyond which they collaspse.

Y. But when I push hard enough and get the brick moving there is friction that drags the brick as it moves along.

F. Yes, once they have collapsed the demons are crushed by the brick. It is their crackling bones that oppose the sliding.

Y. I cannot feel them.

F. Rub your finger along the table.

Y. Friction follows definite laws. For example, experiment shows that a brick sliding along the table is dragged by friction with a force independent of velocity.

F. Of course, same number of demons to crush, however fast you run over them.

Y. If I slide a brick along the table again and again, the friction is the same each time. Demons would be crushed in the first trip.

F. Yes, but they multiply incredibly fast.

Y. There are other laws of friction: for example, the drag is proportional to the pressure holding the surfaces together.

F. The demons live in the pores of the surface: more pressure makes more of them rush out to push and be crushed. . . .

If matters are kept on this plane, and no connection is made to other physical phenomena, knowledge, or properties, the term "friction" is nothing more than a name synonymous with the behavior of Faustus' conspirational society of demons. Faustus' explanations are completely *ad hoc*—they are expressly concocted to cover each particular point; there is no way of refuting them. If we invoke some new observation or experiment in an attempt to test a particular statement and show it to be false, Faustus will invent an appropriate demonic activity to cover the new case. Such a model or hypothesis is said to be "unfalsifiable," meaning that it is, in principle, impossible to refute it by appeal to experience. In a sense, it is as unfalsifiable as the simpler statement, "A particle will move or not move when an electrically charged body is brought near to it."

If we repeatedly extend the conservation laws to incorporate newly discovered phenomena, it is legitimate to ask whether "momentum" and "energy" are names for demons. Are the conservation laws *ad hoc*, unfalsifiable statements, adopted by convention and used because of their simplicity and convenience?

Karl Popper,* the logician and philosopher of science, argues that scientific hypotheses can never be conclusively verified because it is impossible to test them on each of

---

* *The Logic of Scientific Discovery*, Karl Popper. New York: Basic Books, Inc., 1959.

the infinity of particular cases to which they might apply, but he points out that scientific hypotheses might at least be distinguished from mathematical or even metaphysical systems by the criterion of falsifiability—it should be possible, in principle, to refute or prove them false by appeal to experience: "... what characterizes the empirical method is its manner of exposing to falsification, in every conceivable way, the system to be tested. Its aim is not to save the lives of untenable systems but, on the contrary, to select the one which is by comparison the fittest, by exposing them all to the fiercest struggle for survival."

And Professor Bridgman argues that the conservation laws are indeed falsifiable in this sense; that they are far from being tautologies or pure conventions:

"A remark of Poincaré is often quoted to the effect that if we ever found the conservation law for energy appearing to fail we would recover it by inventing a new form of energy. This it seems to me is a misleadingly partial characterization of the situation. If in any specific situation the law apparently failed, we would doubtless first try to maintain the law by inventing a new form of energy, but when we had invented it we would demand that it be a function [of numbers, or parameters, that describe the state of the system] and that the law would continue to hold for all the infinite variety of combinations into which the new parameters might be made to enter. Whether conservation would continue to hold under such extended conditions, could be determined only by experiment. The energy concept is very far from being merely a convention."*

Our experience to date with the laws of conservation of momentum, energy, and mass does indeed satisfy Bridgman's criterion. It is the wide-flung network of successfully achieved experimental and theoretical connections, interlinkages, cross-checks—the entire fabric of which can be tested for internal consistency—that encourages us to believe that the Newtonian Synthesis and the conservation principles are something more than definitions or demonologies.

20.8   THE SECOND LAW OF THERMODYNAMICS

We shall start this discussion by describing a number of apparently unconnected physical situations; they illustrate an idea that will be developed in subsequent comments:

(1) If we bring together two bodies initially at different temperatures and allow them to exchange heat, they are always observed to tend toward thermal equilibrium; the warmer one decreases and the colder increases in temperature; heat gained by one body is equal to that lost by the other. As far as conservation of energy is concerned, it would be perfectly possible for the hotter body to gain a given amount of heat from the colder one with a corresponding increase in the temperature difference, but this is never observed to happen spontaneously. If we wish to cool the colder body and

---

* *The Nature of Thermodynamics*, P. W. Bridgman. Harvard University Press, 1941.

transfer heat to the warmer one, we can do so only by supplying additional energy in the form of work and paying the necessary cost: this is precisely what we do when we freeze ice cubes in a refrigerator.

(2) If we subject ice to pressure, the ice tends to turn into liquid water. Subjecting cold water to pressure does not tend to convert it into ice. Again there is a particular direction to the spontaneous change that occurs. The reverse change would not violate any conservation laws, but it does not occur.

(3) Hydrogen and oxygen combine rapidly and violently to form liquid water and liberate heat. Fortunately, water does not absorb heat from its surroundings and separate itself into hydrogen and oxygen, even though energy conservation would not be violated. We can effect the decomposition of water by supplying work in the form of electrical energy in the process of electrolysis, but this decomposition is certainly not spontaneous. Similarly, we can reverse the chemical reaction taking place in an electric battery by recharging the battery, but the original reaction in the battery takes place spontaneously, while the reverse reaction only takes place at our expense.

(4) When a body slides on a rough surface under the influence of friction, the kinetic energy of the body is dissipated and converted into heat. Although energy conservation would not be violated, we never observe a body to extract heat from its surroundings, convert it into kinetic energy, and start sliding along the surface.

(5) A major portion of our industrial technology and virtually all of our transportation devices depend on the operation of "heat engines." Fuel is burned to supply heat at high temperature, usually to an expanding gas as the "working substance." The working substance goes through a regular and repeated cycle of changes, and work is delivered to the machinery of a plant or in the form of motion of a vehicle. Why must we go to the expense of securing and burning fuel? In the air around us, in the earth under our feet, in the waters of the ocean is an endless supply of heat. All we need to do is draw on this supply and convert it into work. Yet it is our unalterable experience that this easy road to utilization of energy is impossible; that to obtain work from heat we must supply the heat initially at a temperature higher than that of the surroundings—as a matter of fact, the higher the better. It is a further facet of this experience that all of a given quantity of heat can never be converted into work in an engine which operates in a continuous cycle; some of the initial heat supply must always be thrown away to the surroundings by the engine exhaust.

(6) An alternative way of contrasting the illustrations (4) and (5) is to say that a given quantity of work (or kinetic energy) can easily be converted entirely into heat, but it is impossible, by means of an engine operating in a continuous cycle, to convert a given amount of heat entirely into work, even though energy conservation would not be violated.

It is not at all obvious that the preceding physical illustrations have very much in common with each other. Yet they all illustrate a very fundamental fact: The law of conservation of energy tells us nothing about the *direction* in which processes will occur spontaneously. Clearly an additional principle or principles are operative in natural phenomena.

One of the most spectacular triumphs of scientific theory is the analysis that identifies the additional principle and gives it a mathematical formulation. This theory starts with an acceptance of the proposition that heat can never flow spontaneously from a body of lower to a body of higher temperature and ultimately shows that all of the different illustrations given above are manifestations of a common underlying regularity. They are all governed by the same fundamental law, usually referred to as the second law of thermodynamics.

Not only does mathematical formulation of the second law provide equations which predict all the equilibrium trends described in the preceding illustrations, it also embodies a fundamental definition of an absolute temperature scale. Temperature can be defined entirely in terms of quantities of energy exchanged between bodies, without any reference whatsoever to the expansion-contraction, electrical resistance, or other properties of any particular substance.

A discussion of this formulation is beyond the scope of this text; for further details an interested reader should consult references cited at the end of the chapter.

In subsequent chapters, when we study some of the consequences of the kinetic theory and the corpuscular structure of matter, we shall see that the systematic, spontaneous directions of change in the processes described above can be associated with the statistical behavior of huge populations of atoms or molecules. The inexorable direction of spontaneous change is toward equilibrium—toward a uniform condition of distribution of energy, toward a condition in which further spontaneous change is no longer possible. Without a continuing supply of energy from the high-temperature, atomic fuel-burning source that is the sun, the earth would long since have become a dead world, with all processes stopped, and all matter in a uniform state of thermal equilibrium.

20.9 PERPETUAL MOTION AND THE LAWS OF THERMODYNAMICS

The term "engine," when used in a technical context, usually refers to a device that exchanges heat and work with its surroundings and repetitively goes through the same sequence or cycle of states or events—no permanent changes occur within the engine, since it always returns to the same starting conditions. Suppose that in every cycle a device of this kind were to absorb a certain amount of heat Q and deliver a different amount of work W; that is, suppose $Q \neq W$. If W were greater than Q, we could convert part of this work into an amount of heat Q, return this amount of heat to the engine, and use the rest of the work to run a vehicle or a machine in a factory, and all this time there would be no permanent change of any kind within the engine itself. We would thus have an endless supply of work coming out of a finite system, without any cost associated with a supply of fuel; energy, under these circumstances, would be created out of nothing, and we recognize this as a violation of the conservation principle.

A similar violation would occur if Q were greater than W: an endless supply of energy would be disappearing into a finite system without altering the system in any permanent way. Also we might reverse the sequence of the process in the engine, putting a net amount of work in, while taking a larger amount of heat out. This would also violate the conservation principle; we would achieve an endless supply of energy (say for heating a house), without any further expenditure for fuel.

A device operating in the manner just described, supplying endless quantities of energy without producing any permanent changes within itself, is called a "perpetual-motion device of the first kind." We have a deeply ingrained sense that such a process is impossible and that in any full cycle of operation of an engine we must have $Q = W$ or $Q - W = 0$. Thus, another way of approaching the law of conservation of energy is through acceptance of what is called a "postulate of impotence"—an assertion of the impossibility of some event or process. In this case we assert, as a fundamental law of nature, the impossibility of a perpetual-motion device of the first kind.

This negative statement can be shown to be logically equivalent to the positive assertion that energy must be conserved, and that $Q - W = 0$ in any full cycle of a repetitive process. For any arbitrary change of state of a system (not a complete cycle) from condition 1 to condition 2, we might denote by Q_{12} and W_{12} the heat absorbed and work delivered, respectively. It can be shown mathematically (for details see a more advanced text) that if $Q - W = 0$ for a complete cycle, it is necessary that $Q_{12} - W_{12}$ between any two specified states of the system must be a fixed number regardless of the sequence or method of changing the system from state 1 to state 2. Therefore the difference $Q_{12} - W_{12}$ is spoken of as the "change of *internal energy*" of the system, and is usually denoted by the symbol ΔU. The algebraic statement

$$\Delta U = Q_{12} - W_{12} \tag{20.9.1}$$

asserts the existence of a *property* of a system; the internal energy U, which changes whenever the state of the system changes; $\Delta U = 0$ if the system is carried through a cycle and returns to its initial conditions. Equation (20.9.1) is a mathematical formulation of the principle of conservation of energy and of the denial of the possibility of perpetual motion of the first kind. Called the First Law of Thermodynamics, it is the tool that Helmholtz used in his famous paper of 1847 in which he extended the energy concept to electric, magnetic, and chemical phenomena.

Returning to illustration (5) of Section 20.8, we note the description of another very attractive invention. If, without violating conservation of energy, we could construct an engine that, operating in a cycle, would take heat from the atmosphere or the ocean and convert this heat entirely into work, we would still be able to secure a supply of usable energy without the cost of providing fuel. Again we sense that nature does not allow us this easy access to utilization of energy, even though we do not violate the conservation law; the engine we have visualized is called a "perpetual-motion device of the second kind." The Second Law of Thermodynamics can be stated as a second postulate of impotence—an assertion of the impossibility of producing perpetual motion of the second kind. This impossibility is intimately associated with the fact that heat cannot flow spontaneously from bodies of lower to bodies of higher temperature.

We could, of course, operate a cyclic engine which used the surrounding atmosphere as a source of heat, if we had available a region of substantially *lower* temperature to which we could reject part of the initial quantity of heat after having converted the remainder into work. Such a device would not violate either of the laws restricting the conversion of energy, but a lower-temperature region is not available to us, and, without it, utilization of heat from the surroundings is precluded.

It is sometimes remarked with tongue in cheek that the First and Second Laws of Thermodynamics imply that not only is it impossible to win the game in which we engage with nature, it is also impossible to break even!

20.10 ACCEPTANCE OF THE LAWS OF THERMODYNAMICS

Although in the 1830's and 1840's many scientists were groping, from various directions, toward the synthesis of the energy concepts embodied in the First and Second Laws of Thermodynamics, there was no conceptual crisis attendant upon this development. The caloric theory was useful and remained plausible in many respects, despite the attacks by Rumford and Davy. Under these circumstances, the new views were slow in meeting acceptance.

In 1824 a young French engineer, Sadi Carnot (1796–1832), published a work entitled "Reflections on the Motive Power of Heat." In this treatise Carnot gave a statement of the Second Law in essentially the same terms we used at the end of Section 20.9. He also pointed the way toward the definition of a temperature scale in terms of quantities of heat absorbed and rejected by ideal engines. His investigation was motivated by a desire to improve the performance of steam engines and to learn to what extent consumption of fuel could be minimized while a maximum amount of work could be produced. There was little mathematical formalism in Carnot's treatise, and he made use of the caloric theory, assuming, for example, that all of the input heat was eventually rejected to the condensers, not recognizing that some of it was converted into mechanical work done by the engine.

The views of Carnot, Mayer, and Joule met with little response from the scientific community. As late as 1847, when Joule presented a paper at the Oxford meeting of the British Association for the Advancement of Science, he was asked by the chairman to confine himself to a short description because his previous communications had evoked relatively little interest. Later, in describing this session, Joule wrote:

> "This I endeavored to do, and discussion not being invited, the communication would have passed without comment if a young man had not risen . . . and by his intelligent observations created a lively interest in the new theory. The young man was William Thomson."

William Thomson (1824–1907), later Lord Kelvin, was destined to become one of England's most distinguished scientists. That meeting with Joule marked the beginning of a long and lasting friendship and collaboration. Kelvin had already been deeply impressed with Carnot's ideas and was working toward a clear formulation of the absolute temperature scale. He perceived that Joule's conception was different from Carnot's, defining still another regularity in nature, and he became one of the most vigorous proponents of the new theory.

Describing the Oxford meeting from his own point of view 35 years later (1882), Kelvin wrote,

"Joule's paper at the Oxford meeting made a great sensation. Faraday was there and was much struck with it, but did not enter fully into the new views. It was many years after that before any of the scientific chiefs began to give their adhesion . . . [some] were for many years quite incredulous as to Joule's results because they all depended on fractions of a degree of temperature—sometimes very small fractions. His boldness in making such large conclusions from such very small observational effects is almost as noteworthy and admirable as his skill in extracting accuracy from them."

It has been remarked that a new theory rarely converts or changes the views of an older generation; opposition dies out, and the new generation advances the new views. So it was with the energy concepts, first articulated in 1842 and 1843. With the young Helmholtz' great paper of 1847 on the First Law, and with the work on the Second Law of Kelvin in England and of Clapeyron and Clausius (1850) on the continent, came the mathematical formulations that clarified many confused and interlocking threads and made the two separate energy laws applicable to a vast range of physical–chemical phenomena.

After that the ideas were accorded increasingly rapid acceptance, and both Mayer and Joule were duly honored for their contributions. Sadly enough, they and their respective supporters subsequently engaged in controversy over priority for the discovery. An ironical footnote to this controversy is added by the results of a more recent examination of Carnot's private papers and notebooks. Although, in his treatise of 1824, Carnot used the caloric theory and did not recognize that some heat was converted into work in the operation of the steam engine, his unpublished notebooks show that, prior to his untimely death in 1832, he was essentially in full command of the conservation principle and of the relation between heat and work. In this sense, Carnot holds priority over both Mayer and Joule.

SUPPLEMENTARY READING AND STUDY

On concepts of matter and mass:

The Science of Mechanics, Ernst Mach. Chicago: Open Court Publishing Co., 1893, page 216 ff

Concepts of Mass, M. Jammer. Cambridge, Mass.: Harvard University Press, 1961, Chapters 4–8

On Lavoisier and the overthrow of the phlogiston theory:

Harvard Case Histories in Experimental Science, Case 2: The Overthrow of the Phlogiston Theory. Cambridge, Mass.: Harvard University Press, 1957

The Edge of Objectivity, C. C. Gillispie. Princeton, N. J.: Princeton University Press, 1960, Chapter 6

Thermodynamics:

A Source Book in Physics, W. F. Magie. New York: McGraw-Hill, 1935, pages 196–247

The Edge of Objectivity, *op. cit.*, Chapter 10

Time and Thermodynamics, A. R. Ubbelohde. New York: Oxford University Press, 1947

Physics for Students of Science and Engineering, R. Resnick, D. Halliday. New York: John Wiley & Sons, 1960, Chapters 22, 25

Heat and Thermodynamics, M. Zemansky. New York: McGraw-Hill, 1957

CHAPTER 21

Rotation of Rigid Bodies

21.1 INTRODUCTION

In studying the dynamics of rotation, we have, up to this point, restricted ourselves to relatively simple problems by dealing only with the behavior of individual particles. Wherever physical inquiry leads us, however, we encounter problems involving rotation of extended objects or groups of particles: Practically every piece of machinery contains rotating parts that receive energy through application of torque. Gyroscopes have come to play an indispensable role in the construction of accurate navigational compasses. The earth itself is deformed from spherical shape because of rotation about its axis. Motion of the atmosphere and pulsating oscillations of the terrestrial globe produce minute variations in the earth's angular velocity that are detectable as variations in the length of day. Cosmologists who attempt to theorize concerning the formation of the solar system must consider the angular momentum, not of just a single particle, but of the system as a whole; an acceptable theory must account for the fact that all the planetary orbits lie in very nearly the same plane and for the fact that the planets move in the same direction in their orbits around the sun. At an opposite extreme of physical phenomena, when we undertake to interpret the heating of gases in atomic-molecular theory, we find it necessary to visualize molecules as extended objects with kinetic energy of rotation as well as translation in order to account for their observed heat capacities.

These are some of the problems that have motivated the study of rotation. As usual, we make our entry into the new area not by grasping at the very difficult "real" problems but by formulating more tractable, albeit somewhat artificial, problems capable of leading us step by step to the more subtle insights. To begin an inquiry into the rotational dynamics of extended objects, let us visualize the consequences of experiments illustrated in Figs. 21.1.1 and 21.1.2.

When equal forces, but unequal torques, are applied to identical wheels, it is observed that a larger angular acceleration is imparted to the wheel experiencing the larger torque (Fig. 21.1.1); that is, the same force does not necessarily impart the same rotational acceleration to identical bodies. If equal torques are applied to wheels of identical mass but with different distributions of this mass around the axis of rotation, it is observed that a larger angular acceleration is imparted to that wheel whose mass is, on the average, closer to the axis (Fig. 21.1.2); that is, the effective

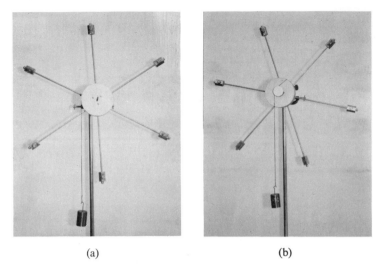

(a)   (b)

Fig. 21.1.1. Two identical wheels consist of spokes fixed in a central hub that rotates on high-quality bearings. Each spoke carries a movable bob that can be set at different radial positions, thus changing the mass distribution around the axis of rotation. With the bobs in outer positions on both wheels, strings are wrapped around the larger drum in (a) and the smaller drum in (b), and equal weights are suspended from the two strings; i.e., a larger torque is applied to wheel (a) than to wheel (b). It is observed that wheel (a) acquires a much larger angular acceleration than wheel (b) when the weights are allowed to fall. [Note that if equal weights are suspended from each string, the tensions in the two strings are *not* exactly equal, since the weights will have somewhat different linear accelerations of descent, a. The difference between the tensions is small if a/g is small; i.e., if a is a small fraction of the acceleration due to gravity. See examples and problems in Chapter 6.]

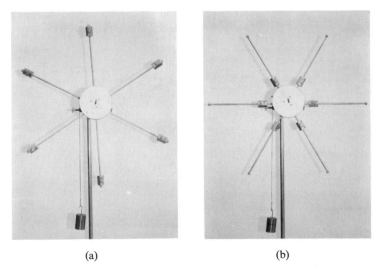

(a)   (b)

Fig. 21.1.2. Bobs on the spokes of wheel (b) are moved in toward the axle. Nearly equal torques are applied to both wheels. It is observed that wheel (b) accelerates much more rapidly than wheel (a).

rotational inertias of the two wheels are very different even though their inertial masses are identical.

Qualitatively, we might have anticipated these results from the analysis of particle motion made in Sections 17.13–17.18, but we now confront quantitative problems precipitated by the fact that the particle concept has been carried as far as it will go. We cannot treat an extended rotating body as a single particle to which $\mathbf{F}_{net} = m\mathbf{a}$ is directly applicable; we must recognize it as a collection of interacting particles and must try to find whether there still exist simple dynamical descriptions of the behavior of the object as a whole. What is the relation between applied torque and its resulting effects? What is the appropriate way of describing the rotational inertia of an extended body?

These are the problems we shall explore in this chapter, but, as usual, we must start with particularly simple abstractions, and it is important to understand how special are the cases we select. Imagine a fairly general case of three-dimensional motion of an extended object: Suppose you take an irregularly shaped stick, whirl it around over your head, and throw it. The stick flies through the air with a complex motion, tumbling and turning. Our previous analyses apply to only one point in this system— the center of mass. This point pursues a parabolic path—the trajectory of a projectile under the influence of uniform, vertical gravitational force. We can visualize the tumbling and turning of the stick as additional rotations around the center of mass, but this is, nevertheless, a very complex motion. The situation is even more complicated if we apply a concentrated force at some arbitrary point on the moving object; this action would keep changing the translational motion and the rotational motion and would keep accelerating the displacement of the axis around which the rotation occurs. If the body were deformable or were a loose aggregation of interacting particles, the motion would be still more complex.

In contrast, we can now appreciate how highly simplified a case of rotation is exemplified in Figs. 21.1.1 and 21.1.2:

(a) The rotating body has a simple, regular shape.

(b) The motion is essentially two-dimensional. (We shall think of all particles of the wheel as lying in a plane and rotating in that plane around the axis at the center.)

(c) The body is rigid; i.e., it does not deform or change shape during the rotation, and each particle travels in a circular path.

(d) The axis around which the rotation occurs occupies a fixed position in our frame of reference; i.e., we restrict ourselves to a pure rotation and do not consider simultaneously the translational motion of the body as a whole.

21.2   ANGULAR MOMENTUM OF AN EXTENDED TWO-DIMENSIONAL BODY

Suppose we have a group of N independent particles moving in a plane. If m_k is the mass of the kth particle, r_k its radial distance from some arbitrarily chosen point O, and $v_{\perp k}$ its velocity component perpendicular to r_k, the angular momentum L_k of this particle about O would be given by

$$L_k = m_k r_k v_{\perp k}. \tag{21.2.1}$$

In the light of the experience we have accumulated with superposition of physical effects, we might expect the total angular momentum L of the entire group of particles about O to be given by*

$$L = \sum_{k=1}^{N} L_k = \sum_{k=1}^{N} (m_k r_k v_{\perp k}). \tag{21.2.2}$$

If the N particles occupy perfectly fixed positions relative to each other and the configuration remains unaltered as the group moves relative to our coordinate system under the influence of external forces, we say that the particles form a *rigid body*. In a rigid body rotating about point O, each particle must have the same angular velocity ω about point O; otherwise the configuration would be changing, and the body would not be rigid. For each particle in the rigid body, we have

$$v_{\perp k} = r_k \omega, \tag{21.2.3}$$

and the total angular momentum, if all the particles lie in the same plane, is given by

$$L = \sum_{k=1}^{N} (m_k r_k^2 \omega). \tag{21.2.4}$$

Since ω is a constant factor in this sum, we can write

$$L = \omega \sum_{k=1}^{N} (m_k r_k^2). \tag{21.2.5}$$

We could apply (21.2.5) to describe the angular momentum of the wheels in Figs. 21.1.1 and 21.1.2: ω would be the instantaneous angular velocity of each particle in the rigid group making up the wheel. The quantity $\sum_{k=1}^{N} (m_k r_k^2)$ has nothing to do with the motion as such, but is an intrinsic property of the rigid body; its magnitude depends on the mass of the body and on how this mass is distributed around point O. It is conventional to introduce the notation

$$I \equiv \sum_{k=1}^{N} (m_k r_k^2). \tag{21.2.6}$$

Then 21.2.5 becomes

$$L = I\omega. \tag{21.2.7}$$

The property I is called *moment of inertia*. We shall say more about methods of calculating I in a subsequent section. At this point, let us develop a feeling for how I is calculated and how it varies in very simple configurations.

---

* Note that this simple arithmetical superposition is valid only if the particles move in the *same plane* about O. If they move in different planes, the superposition is more complicated: It can be shown that each L_k may be treated as a vector perpendicular to the plane of the rotation of the particle in question, and the L_k's must then be combined by *vector* addition rather than by the simple arithmetic of (21.2.2).

PROBLEM 21.1.   Consider three particles, mounted on rigid rods and distributed about point O, as shown in Fig. 21.2.1.   Estimate the moment of inertia of this configuration, neglecting the masses of the rods. [*Answer:* $I = 0.062$ kg·m^2.]

What would happen to I if the angles between the rods were changed but the lengths of the rods remained unaltered? Which wheel in Fig. 21.1.2 has the larger moment of inertia? Why?

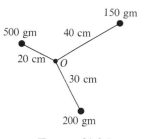

FIGURE 21.2.1

21.3   NET TORQUE APPLIED TO TWO-DIMENSIONAL RIGID BODY ROTATING AROUND A FIXED AXIS

Suppose we apply an external force **F** at a point or particle on a rigid body, as suggested in Fig. 21.3.1. If the axis of the wheel were not fixed, the entire object would rotate and translate in some complex manner. If the axis remains fixed, we realize that the mounting that holds the wheel must be exerting forces on the axle, and these forces prevent the displacement of the axis of rotation or any change in its direction in space. Under these circumstances **F** is not the only external force acting on the wheel, but it is the only external force exerting a torque around the axis, and the magnitude of this torque is given by $rF_\perp$. In the experiments visualized in Figs. 21.1.1 and 21.1.2, it is just such a net external torque that imparts angular acceleration to the wheels. We could apply additional forces at various points, and the net external torque applied to the wheel would be given by the algebraic sum of the individual torques, taken positive counterclockwise and negative clockwise, respectively.

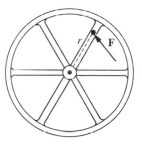

FIG. 21.3.1.   External force **F** applied to point on wheel.

Let us examine what happens within the wheel, particle by particle. External forces are applied only at one, or at most several, points, and only the particles at these points experience an external torque. All the particles constituting the wheel, however, experience internal forces of interaction with other particles; it is through this system of interactions that the rigid configuration is preserved. All internal interactions involve equal and opposite forces along the line of interaction (and therefore equal and opposite torques, as demonstrated in Section 17.17). For each positive torque on one particle there is an equal and opposite torque on another particle, and when we add up all the effects algebraically, particle by particle, the internal torques must add up to zero. We are left only with the net external torque acting on the body. In symbols, we would write

$$\sum_{k=1}^{N} \tau_{\text{net } k} = \tau_{\text{net, external}}. \tag{21.3.1}$$

Can we relate the net external torque acting on a rigid body to the acceleration imparted to the body? In Section 17.16, Eq. (17.16.2), we showed that for any individual kth particle,

$$\tau_{\text{net } k} = \frac{dL_k}{dt} = \frac{d}{dt}(m_k r_k v_{\perp k}). \tag{21.3.2}$$

Since in Fig. 21.3.1, all the particles making up the rigid body rotate in the same plane about the same point O, we can apply Eq. (21.3.1) to this body, particle by particle, and add up the effects. With τ_{net} denoting the total external torque around point O:

$$\tau_{\text{net}} = \sum_{k=1}^{N} \tau_{\text{net } k} = \frac{d}{dt}\sum_{k=1}^{N}(m_k r_k^2 \omega) = \frac{d}{dt}\omega\sum_{k=1}^{N}(m_k r_k^2). \tag{21.3.3}$$

Since I is constant for a rigid body, Eq. (21.3.3) reduces to

$$\tau_{\text{net}} = I\frac{d\omega}{dt} = I\alpha, \tag{21.3.4}$$

where α denotes the angular acceleration of the rigid body.

Let us interpret Eq. (21.3.4). It is, for example, applicable to the situation depicted in Fig. 21.1.1, and it accounts for the results that were described: Equal forces applied to identical wheels will not produce equal angular accelerations unless the torques imparted by the forces are equal; the larger torque will impart the larger angular acceleration.

In Figs. 21.1.2 (a) and (b), we described a situation in which equal torques are applied to wheels having different moments of inertia. Since the masses were asserted to be equal, it is clear that $I(b) < I(a)$. Equation (21.3.4) predicts that (b) will then experience the higher angular acceleration.

Thus, in those cases where it is applicable, the equation $\tau_{\text{net}} = I\alpha$ is the rotational analog of $\mathbf{F}_{\text{net}} = ma$: Net torque around the axis of rotation corresponds to net force in the linear case, and moment of inertia is the rotational equivalent of mass.

Although our derivation of the equation was restricted to a body with particles confined to a single plane, it turns out that this restriction can be relaxed. The equation applies equally well to a body (such as a cylinder) which is extended in the direction parallel to the axis of rotation—providing the axis is fixed in space and providing that I is calculated in such a way that r_k is the perpendicular distance of the kth particle from the axis of rotation rather than the radial distance from a point O. (A proof of this assertion will not be given here; it can be found in more advanced texts.)

PROBLEM 21.2. Suppose a force of 12 n is applied at a point halfway out along the 40-cm rod in Fig. 21.2.1 and at an angle of 30° to the rod. What angular acceleration would be imparted to the body? [*Answer:* $\alpha = 19$ rad/sec^2.]

21.4   CALCULATION OF MOMENTS OF INERTIA OF EXTENDED BODIES

We now examine a little more closely just what is involved in calculating moments of inertia of extended bodies such as bars, wheels, discs, etc. Having the definition

$$I \equiv \sum_{k=1}^{N} m_k r_k^2, \tag{21.4.1}$$

the reader has probably already surmised that we shall be confronted with a limit-of-the-sum calculation or integration. Let us trace the formulation of the problem.

Example 1. Consider a thin bar, of length L_x, uniform density ρ, and uniform circular or rectangular cross-sectional area A, rotating about an axis through its center (Fig. 21.4.1). Imagine dividing the bar up into N small chunks. The kth chunk is shown in the figure; the volume of this chunk is $A \, \Delta x_k$, and its mass is $\rho A \, \Delta x_k$.

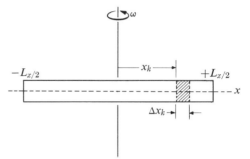

FIG. 21.4.1. Bar of uniform cross section A and length L_x rotating about axis through its center.

The moment of inertia of this chunk around the axis of rotation is approximately $\rho A x_k^2 \, \Delta x_k$. We characterize this as an approximation because the chunk itself is an extended object and not a particle. To obtain the moment of inertia of the bar we must calculate the limit of the sum as the chunks are made indefinitely small:

$$I = \lim_{\substack{\|\Delta\| \to 0 \\ N \to \infty}} \sum_{k=1}^{N} \rho A x_k^2 \, \Delta x_k. \tag{21.4.2}$$

In the light of the discussion of integration in Chapter 16, we recognize (21.4.2) as the following integral:

$$I = \int_{-L_x/2}^{+L_x/2} \rho A x^2 \, dx = \rho A \left. \frac{x^3}{3} \right|_{-L_x/2}^{+L_x/2} = \frac{\rho A}{3} \left[\frac{L_x^3}{8} - \left(-\frac{L_x^3}{8} \right) \right] = \frac{\rho A L_x^3}{12}. \tag{21.4.3}$$

Since the total mass M of the bar is equal to $\rho A L_x$, we can write

$$I = \tfrac{1}{12} M L_x^2 \tag{21.4.4}$$

for the moment of inertia of a uniform bar about an axis through its center.

PROBLEM 21.3. Reformulate the preceding example for the case in which the axis is taken at one end of the bar instead of through the center. Show that for this axis $I = \tfrac{1}{3} M L_x^2$. Give a physical explanation of the difference between the two results.

Example 2. Consider a thin hoop of radius r and of uniform cross section A and density ρ (Fig. 21.4.2). If we divide the hoop into N chunks, each subtending an angle $\Delta\theta_k$, the length of the kth chunk is $r\,\Delta\theta_k$ and the mass is $\rho Ar\,\Delta\theta_k$. Since each chunk is located at the same radial distance from the center at O, the moment of inertia of the hoop about an axis through O perpendicular to the plane of the hoop is given, approximately, by

$$I = \lim_{\|\Delta\|\to 0} \sum_{k=1}^{N} \rho Ar^3 \,\Delta\theta_k = \int_0^{2\pi} \rho Ar^3 \,d\theta = \rho Ar^3 \theta \Big|_0^{2\pi} = 2\pi\rho Ar^3.$$

Since the total mass M of the hoop is $2\pi r\rho A$, then

$$I = Mr^2. \tag{21.4.5}$$

In this calculation we have neglected the fact that the hoop has extension in the radial direction, and we have treated each chunk as though all of it were concentrated at a radial distance r from the axis; i.e., a "thin" hoop is one for which the width is much smaller than the radius. Subject to this approximation, Eq. (21.4.5) informs us that the moment of inertia of a thin hoop is very nearly equal to the moment of inertia of a single particle of mass M concentrated at a distance r from the axis of rotation.

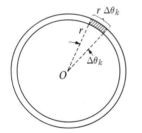

Fig. 21.4.2. Thin hoop of radius r.

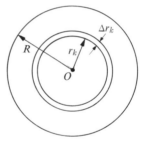

Fig. 21.4.3. Uniform disc of density ρ, radius R, and thickness t (perpendicular to plane of disc.) Axis of rotation is perpendicular to the disc at O.

Example 3. Consider a uniform disc (or cylinder) of density ρ, thickness t, and outer radius R (Fig. 21.4.3). The total mass $M = \pi R^2 t\rho$. We take the axis of rotation perpendicular to the disc at O, and imagine dividing the disc into N thin hoops each of radial width Δr_k. The mass of such a hoop is $2\pi\rho t r_k\,\Delta r_k$ and, using Eq. (21.4.5), its moment of inertia about the axis is $2\pi\rho t r_k^3\,\Delta r_k$. The total moment of inertia of the disc is then

$$I = \lim_{\|\Delta\|\to 0} \sum_{k=1}^{N} 2\pi\rho t r_k^3 \,\Delta r_k = \int_0^R 2\pi\rho t r^3 \,dr = 2\pi\rho t \frac{r^4}{4}\Big|_0^R$$

$$= \frac{\pi\rho t R^4}{2} = \tfrac{1}{2}MR^2. \tag{21.4.6}$$

By similar procedures, we can calculate the moments of inertia of other objects. For example, we can calculate the moment of inertia of a sphere around one of its

TABLE 21.4.1

MOMENTS OF INERTIA OF VARIOUS BODIES

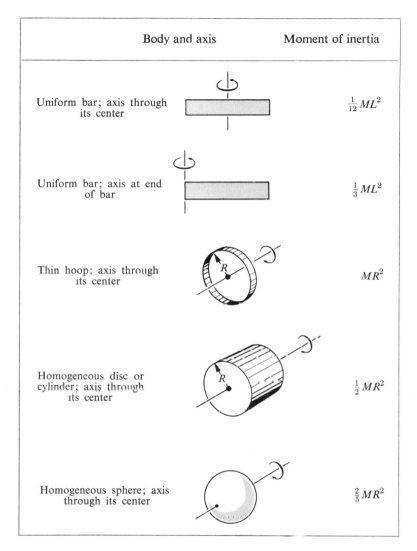

Body and axis	Moment of inertia
Uniform bar; axis through its center	$\frac{1}{12}ML^2$
Uniform bar; axis at end of bar	$\frac{1}{3}ML^2$
Thin hoop; axis through its center	MR^2
Homogeneous disc or cylinder; axis through its center	$\frac{1}{2}MR^2$
Homogeneous sphere; axis through its center	$\frac{2}{5}MR^2$

diameters by visualizing the sphere as being sliced into parallel discs by planes perpendicular to the axis in question. (See Problem 21.23 at the end of this chapter.) In cases of complex or irregular bodies, even if we could not evaluate our integral algebraically, we could still calculate the moment of inertia numerically, just as we would calculate the area under an irregular curve numerically if we could not describe the curve by means of a function with a known antiderivative.

In Table 21.4.1 we summarize the moments of inertia of a few objects of simple shape.

Problem 21.4.   An aluminum wheel (Fig. 21.4.4) has a density of 2.7 gm/cm³. The rim has inner and outer radii of 10.0 and 11.4 cm, respectively, and a thickness of 1.0 cm. The spokes have a cross-sectional area of 0.5 cm². Using formulas obtained in the preceding examples, estimate the moment of inertia of the wheel around the axis through its center. [*Answer:* 3.2×10^4 gm·cm² or 3.2×10^{-3} kg·m².]

Figure 21.4.4

21.5   WORK DONE BY A TORQUE IN ANGULAR DISPLACEMENT

If we accelerate the rotation of a rigid body around a fixed axis by application of a net external torque, it is clear that we are doing work on the body and imparting to its particles a kinetic energy of circular motion around the axis of rotation. We should be able to analyze this process in terms of the energy concepts developed in preceding chapters and make sure that this analysis is consistent with the dynamical equation $\tau_{net} = I\alpha$ developed in Section 21.3. In order to pursue this cross-check in our network of concepts and reasoning, let us first establish an algebraic expression for work done by a torque.

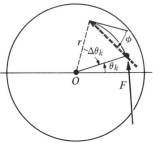

Fig. 21.5.1.   Disc free to rotate about axis at O. Force F acts at point on the disc during small angular displacement $\Delta\theta_k$. Length of arc through which F is displaced $= r\,\Delta\theta_k$. Torque exerted by F: $\tau(\theta_k) = Fr \cos \phi$.

In Fig. 21.5.1 a force F is shown acting at a point on a rigid body when the body is at a particular angular position θ_k. At this instantaneous position the torque exerted by F around the axis at O is $\tau(\theta_k) = Fr \cos \phi$. For a small angular displacement $\Delta\theta_k$, we have the following relations:

(1) Linear displacement through which the force acts is equal to the arc length $r\,\Delta\theta_k$.
(2) Component of force F in direction of displacement $= F \cos \phi$
(3) Work done by force F during displacement $= Fr \cos \phi\,\Delta\theta_k = \tau(\theta_k)\,\Delta\theta_k$.

If the body is displaced from angular position θ_1 to θ_2, we divide the total displacement into N parts, and the total work done during the entire displacement is given by

$$W = \lim_{\|\Delta\|\to 0} \sum_{k=1}^{N} \tau(\theta_k)\,\Delta\theta_k = \int_{\theta_1}^{\theta_2} \tau(\theta)\,d\theta. \qquad (21.5.1)$$

Thus work done by a force in rotational displacement around a fixed axis is equal to the integral (with respect to angular displacement) of the torque exerted by this force. This result can be generalized for the case in which many forces are applied to the rotating body simultaneously; the superposed torques can be replaced by one equivalent torque, and the work done is still represented by Eq. (21.5.1).

In the special case of a constant torque, Eq. (21.5.1) reduces to

$$W = \tau(\theta_2 - \theta_1) = \tau \, \Delta\theta. \tag{21.5.2}$$

(The angular displacement must be expressed in radians when computations are made. Why?) Equations (21.5.1) and (21.5.2) are obviously the rotational counterparts of the corresponding expressions applicable in linear displacements: $\int_{s_1}^{s_2} F(s) \, ds$ and $F \, \Delta s$.

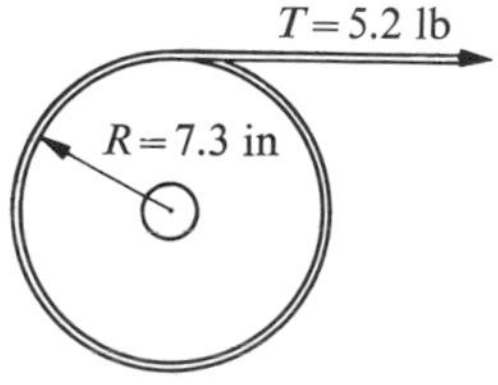

PROBLEM 21.5. A constant torque is exerted on the wheel in Fig. 21.5.2 by means of a constant force $T = 5.2$ lb pulling on a string wrapped around the rim of the wheel. Calculate the work done during an angular displacement of 150°. [*Answer:* 3.8 ft·lb.] Show that this is equal to the work done in the simultaneous linear displacement of the force T.

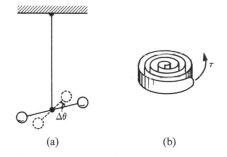

$T = 5.2$ lb

$R = 7.3$ in

FIGURE 21.5.2

In the same paper in which Robert Hooke described the force law for elastic stretching of a helical spring (see Section 7.2), he also described the force law associated with elastic twisting of a stretched wire and of a coil spring such as that used in a watch [Figs. 21.5.3(a) and (b)]. To translate his description into modern terminology: Hooke showed experimentally that the angular displacement from the relaxed position was proportional to the applied torque;

$$\tau(\theta) = \kappa\theta \tag{21.5.3}$$

in direct correspondence with the linear force law $F(x) = kx$ (discussed in Section 7.2). All the restrictions that apply to the case of linear displacement also apply to the torsional one: the wire and the spring must not be twisted beyond their elastic limit; properties will vary somewhat with temperature; etc.

FIG. 21.5.3. Hooke's law for twisting of a stretched wire or a coil spring: $\tau(\theta) = \kappa\theta$, where θ denotes angular displacement from relaxed position.

$\Delta\theta$

(a)   (b)

PROBLEM 21.6. What are the dimensions of the torsional spring constant κ? What would you expect to be the relative magnitudes of κ for a fairly thick rod and thin wire? Why were thin wire suspensions used by Cavendish and Coulomb in their torsion balance measurements of gravitational and electrical forces? In the light of the concepts now developed, describe the principle of the torsion balance.

PROBLEM 21.7.   Show that the work done in twisting a wire from the relaxed position through an angular displacement is given by

$$W = \tfrac{1}{2}\kappa\theta^2. \tag{21.5.4}$$

Compare this with the corresponding expression for stretching or compressing a helical spring. What happens to the work done in twisting the wire?

21.6   KINETIC ENERGY OF ROTATION AROUND A FIXED AXIS

When a rigid body rotates around a fixed axis (Fig. 21.6.1) at angular velocity ω, each of the N particles into which we might imagine the body to be subdivided moves in a circle. The particle m_k at radial position r_k has a tangential linear velocity $r_k\omega$, and therefore a linear kinetic energy $\tfrac{1}{2}m_k r_k^2 \omega^2$. The total KE of the body as a whole would then be given by

$$\text{KE} = \sum_{k=1}^{N} \left(\tfrac{1}{2}m_k r_k^2 \omega^2\right). \tag{21.6.1}$$

Since the constant factors $\tfrac{1}{2}$ and ω^2 appear in each term of the summation, we can factor them out and write

$$\text{KE} = \tfrac{1}{2}\omega^2 \sum_{k=1}^{N} m_k r_k^2.$$

Recognizing the summation as the moment of inertia I, we have

$$\text{KE} = \tfrac{1}{2}I\omega^2, \tag{21.6.2}$$

an expression for the total kinetic energy of rotation of a rigid body around the fixed axis for which I is the moment of inertia.

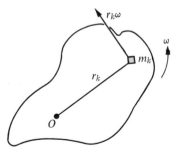

FIG. 21.6.1. Rigid body rotating around axis through O at angular velocity ω. Tangential velocity of particle m_k is equal to $r_k\omega$.

We can now combine our calculations of work and kinetic energy: If a net torque τ_{net} is applied to a rigid body rotating around a fixed axis, the principle of conservation of energy requires that the work done by the net torque equal the change of kinetic energy of the body:

$$\int_{\theta_1}^{\theta_2} \tau_{\text{net}}(\theta)\, d\theta = \tfrac{1}{2}I\omega_2^2 - \tfrac{1}{2}I\omega_1^2 = \Delta(\tfrac{1}{2}I\omega^2). \tag{21.6.3}$$

This corresponds to the Work-Kinetic Energy Theorem [Eq. (18.8.2)] for translational displacements; again, as in our discussion of angular momentum, I plays the same role in the rotational case as m does in the translational, and ω takes the place of v.

In deriving (21.6.3), we started with ideas originally developed in connection with rectilinear displacements and translated them to the rotational case. If our lines of reasoning have been internally consistent (free from contradictions), Eq. (21.6.3) and the dynamical relation $\tau_{\text{net}} = I\alpha$ [Eq. (21.3.4)] must be consistent with each other. Any contradiction between these two equations would be a warning signal. It is readily apparent, however, that the two equations are consistent, since (21.6.3) can be derived directly from $\tau_{\text{net}} = I\alpha$ by a series of steps with which we are already familiar.

PROBLEM 21.8.   In Chapter 18, we started with $F_{\text{net}}(s) = ma(s)$, and, carrying out an integration with respect to position s, showed that

$$\int_{s_1}^{s_2} F_{\text{net}}(s)\, ds = \Delta(\tfrac{1}{2}mv^2).$$

Following exactly the same sequence of steps, start with $\tau_{\text{net}}(\theta) = I\alpha(\theta)$, and derive Eq. (21.6.3).

PROBLEM 21.9.   In the language of energy transformations, describe what happens when: (a) You spin a wheel by imparting a sharp twist around the axis. It then slows to a stop because of friction at the bearings. (b) You displace the bar of a torsion balance (Fig. 21.5.3a) and then let it go. The bar rotates back and forth and the oscillation gradually dies down.

21.7   EXAMPLES OF DYNAMICS OF ROTATION AROUND A FIXED AXIS

Example 1.   In analyzing the Atwood's machine in Section 6.3, we remarked that a complete solution of the problem must include the effect of rotational inertia of the pulley. Since the pulley in Atwood's machine rotates around a fixed axis, completing the analysis is a simple and straightforward application of the new relations we have developed. In Fig. 21.7.1 we show the free body diagrams for Atwood's machine, and in the notation adopted for tension in the string, we take into account the fact that

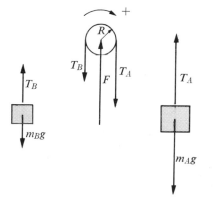

FIG. 21.7.1.   Free body diagrams for Atwood's machine. The diagrams originally sketched in Fig. 6.3.2 are corrected to take into account the effect of the rotational inertia of the pulley.

$T_A \neq T_B$ because of the rotational inertia of the pulley around its axis. Taking the positive direction as indicated in the figure, and applying $F_{\text{net}} = ma$ to bodies A and B, we have

$$m_A g - T_A = m_A a_A, \tag{21.7.1}$$

$$T_B - m_B g = m_B a_B. \tag{21.7.2}$$

Applying the dynamical relation $\tau_{\text{net}} = I\alpha$ to the pulley, we have

$$T_A R - T_B R = I\alpha, \tag{21.7.3}$$

where I denotes the moment of inertia of the pulley around the fixed axis of rotation. (We have neglected any opposing torque due to friction at the axle of the pulley.) Finally, if the string moves over the pulley without slipping or stretching, the tangential acceleration $R\alpha$ of a point on the pulley must be equal to the linear accelerations of bodies A and B, and we have the relation among the accelerations:

$$a_A = a_B = R\alpha = a, \tag{21.7.4}$$

where a will be used to denote any one of the three equal quantities. We can now rewrite the preceding equations in the following form:

$$m_A g - T_A = m_A a, \tag{21.7.5}$$

$$T_B - m_B g = m_B a, \tag{21.7.6}$$

$$T_A - T_B = \frac{I}{R^2} a. \tag{21.7.7}$$

We can eliminate T_A and T_B simply by adding the three equations:

$$m_A g - m_B g = \left(m_A + m_B + \frac{I}{R^2} \right) a,$$

$$\frac{a}{g} = \frac{m_A - m_B}{m_A + m_B + I/R^2} = \frac{m_A - m_B}{m_A + m_B} \cdot \left[\frac{1}{1 + I/(m_A + m_B)R^2} \right]. \tag{21.7.8}$$

When we neglected the inertia of the pulley, we obtained [Eq. (6.3.4)]:

$$\frac{a}{g} = \frac{m_A - m_B}{m_A + m_B}. \tag{21.7.9}$$

As we should have been able to guess intuitively, our previously predicted value of a/g was a bit too high because the rotational inertia of the pulley must be included in the total inertia of the accelerating system. From Eq. (21.7.8), we see that we must lower our original prediction by dividing it by $1 + I/(m_A + m_B)R^2$; that is, in neglecting the inertia of the pulley, we introduce the fractional error $I/(m_A + m_B)R^2$. (Atwood himself was careful to make the necessary correction in performing his demonstration experiments.)

PROBLEM 21.10.   If you have performed a laboratory experiment with an Atwood machine, estimate the moment of inertia of the pulley that you used and estimate the error introduced into the predicted acceleration when the inertia of the pulley is neglected. If we were to take into account the effect of an opposing frictional torque at the axle of

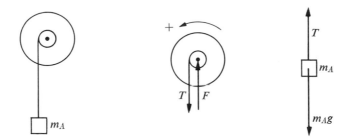

FIG. 21.7.2. String is wrapped around axle of wheel. Body of mass m_A is suspended from the string.

the pulley, where would this term appear in our equations? Would the predicted acceleration be increased or decreased?

Example 2.   Consider the problem illustrated in Fig. 21.7.2, where a body of mass m_A is suspended from a string wrapped around the axle (radius r) of a wheel with moment of inertia I. The wheel accelerates as the body falls. Taking the positive direction as indicated, and neglecting frictional effects, we have the relations:

$$m_A g - T = m_A a_A, \qquad Tr = I\alpha, \qquad a_A = r\alpha = a.$$

Solving for acceleration and tension in the string, we obtain

$$\frac{a}{g} = \frac{1}{1 + I/m_A r^2}, \tag{21.7.10}$$

$$\frac{T}{m_A g} = \frac{1}{(m_A r^2/I) + 1}. \tag{21.7.11}$$

PROBLEM 21.11.   Fill in the algebraic steps leading to Eqs. (21.7.10) and (21.7.11). Interpret these results. Do they make sense for the case in which I is very large? very small? What do the results reduce to if the wheel is a solid cylinder with the string wrapped around its periphery?

Another approach to the same problem can be made through the energy relation. Suppose the body of mass m_A is released from rest and drops through a vertical height Δh. The potential energy of the system decreases by $m_A g \, \Delta h$, and, if frictional effects are neglected, this energy must appear as kinetic energy of both the wheel and the falling body. If ω and v represent, respectively, the angular velocity of the wheel and the linear velocity of the body A attained after starting from rest, the algebraic formulation of our verbal statement of conservation of energy is:

$$m_A g \, \Delta h = \tfrac{1}{2} m_A v^2 + \tfrac{1}{2} I \omega^2, \tag{21.7.12}$$

with the auxiliary relation

$$v = r\omega, \tag{21.7.13}$$

since the tangential velocity of a point on the axle must equal the linear velocity of A if the string is neither stretching nor contracting.

PROBLEM 21.12.   Combining Eqs. (21.7.12) and (21.7.13), show that

$$v^2 = \frac{2m_A g r^2}{m_A r^2 + I} \Delta h = \frac{2g}{1 + I/m_A r^2} \Delta h. \qquad (21.7.14)$$

Comparing this result with the kinematic relation $v^2 - v_0{}^2 = 2a(s - s_0)$, show that the acceleration implied in Eq. (21.7.14) is in complete agreement with the result obtained in (21.7.10). What is the point of this demonstration?

Example 3.   Static equilibrium. Figure 21.7.3 shows a top view of a rigid body pivoted on a vertical axis through point O. Forces $\mathbf{F}_1$, $\mathbf{F}_2$, and $\mathbf{F}_3$ act in a horizontal plane. Taking the positive direction of torque as indicated in the figure, we note that forces $\mathbf{F}_1$ and $\mathbf{F}_2$ exert positive torques of magnitude $F_1 r_1 \cos \phi_1$ and $F_2 r_2 \cos \phi_2$, respectively, while $\mathbf{F}_3$ exerts a negative torque of magnitude $F_3 r_3 \cos \phi_3$. Substituting into the dynamical relation $\tau_{\text{net}} = I\alpha$, we have

$$F_1 r_1 \cos \phi_1 + F_2 r_2 \cos \phi_2 - F_3 r_3 \cos \phi_3 = I\alpha. \qquad (21.7.15)$$

If the torques are balanced so as to impart zero angular acceleration around O, we have $\tau_{\text{net}} = 0$, and

$$F_1 r_1 \cos \phi_1 + F_2 r_2 \cos \phi_2 - F_3 r_3 \cos \phi_3 = 0. \qquad (21.7.16)$$

Such a balance of torques would correspond to a condition of zero rotation of the rigid body around the axis at O, or to rotation at uniform angular velocity.

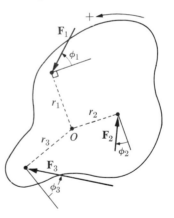

FIG. 21.7.3.   Top view of rigid body pivoted on vertical axis through point O. Forces $\mathbf{F}_1$, $\mathbf{F}_2$, $\mathbf{F}_3$ exert torques around this axis.

Note that, since the axis O is fixed, the pivot must exert a force on the rigid body. This fourth force has not been shown in Fig. 21.7.3, since it exerts zero torque about O, but if it were not present, the body would move off in a complicated pattern of translational and rotational motions *not* described by either Eq. (21.7.15) or (21.7.16).

PROBLEM 21.13.   Sketch a vector polygon of the four forces acting on the rigid body in Fig. 21.7.3 to indicate how you would determine graphically the magnitude and direction of the force exerted by the pivot. Note that this force is the one that prevents the combination of $\mathbf{F}_1$, $\mathbf{F}_2$, and $\mathbf{F}_3$ from imparting *translational* motion to the body.

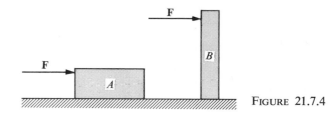

FIGURE 21.7.4

In the light of this analysis, we can now state the full set of requirements determining static equilibrium with respect to motion of an extended body in two dimensions: Not only must the net external torque be zero about any axis around which the body might be pivoted, but the x- and y-components of the external forces must also be balanced. Stated algebraically, the conditions for static equilibrium in two dimensions are:

$$\tau_{\text{net}} = 0, \qquad F_{x\,\text{net}} = 0, \qquad F_{y\,\text{net}} = 0. \tag{21.7.17}$$

PROBLEM 21.14. In numerous dynamical problems we have, for simplicity, treated extended bodies as though they were point masses (or particles of negligible size), and we considered only the translational motion that might occur. We might guess that we could use this method reasonably successfully in describing the pushing of box A over a frictional surface (Fig. 21.7.4), but our intuition warns us that we are probably over-extending the simplification if we try to apply it in case B. Why? Analyze the problem in terms of the concepts developed in this section, visualizing the weight of an object as being represented by a single force acting at the center of mass. Draw appropriate force diagrams and compare relevant torques.

21.8 ANALOGIES BETWEEN THE TRANSLATIONAL AND ROTATIONAL EQUATIONS

It must already be clear that there exists a close, formal analogy between the dynamical equations of translational motion and those for rotation of a rigid body around a fixed axis. This analogy is dramatized by the summary in Table 21.8.1.

TABLE 21.8.1

TRANSLATIONAL AND ROTATIONAL EQUATIONS OF MOTION

Translation of a body of mass m	Rotation of a rigid body of moment of inertia I around a fixed axis
$F_{\text{net}} = ma$	$\tau_{\text{net}} = I\alpha$
$\displaystyle\int_{t_1}^{t_2} F_{\text{net}}(t)\,dt = \Delta(mv)$	$\displaystyle\int_{t_1}^{t_2} \tau_{\text{net}}(t)\,dt = \Delta(I\omega)$
$\displaystyle\int_{s_1}^{s_2} F_{\text{net}}(s)\,ds = \Delta(\tfrac{1}{2}mv^2)$	$\displaystyle\int_{\theta_1}^{\theta_2} \tau_{\text{net}}(\theta)\,d\theta = \Delta(\tfrac{1}{2}I\omega^2)$

The only equation in this group that we have not yet discussed is the second one in the rotational column. It is left to the reader to show that this equation follows immediately when we integrate $\tau_{\text{net}} = I\alpha$ with respect to time; it has exactly the same implications for rotational motion that the impulse-momentum theorem has for translational motion. The number $\int_{t_1}^{t_2} \tau_{\text{net}}(t)\, dt$ is called "angular (or rotational) impulse."

21.9 ROTATION AND TRANSLATION IN TWO DIMENSIONS

Consider the events that occur when we allow a cylinder to roll down an inclined plane. The cylinder as a whole acquires translational velocity, and at the same time it acquires an angular velocity about its own axis. If we attempt to describe the energy transformations that occur, we note that in the descent of the cylinder, potential energy has been converted into kinetic energy but that the kinetic energy is distributed among two modes of motion—translational and rotational. If, on the other hand, we allow a frictionless puck to slide down the same plane, the potential energy is converted into translational kinetic energy only. Experimental observation reveals that the sliding puck will always beat the rolling cylinder in a race down the plane. (If you have the opportunity, you will find it interesting to perform some simple exploratory experiments with objects rolling down an inclined plane. You will find, for example, that different-sized homogeneous spheres will stay quite close together if released simultaneously on a smooth plane; so will different-sized cylinders. But a sphere will always show a somewhat larger acceleration than a cylinder. This observation might have proved quite disturbing to Galileo had it occurred to him to try such an experiment.)

Can we extend our previous descriptions of motion to apply to this new combination of translation and rotation? It turns out that the description is very simple if we separate the motion into two parts: motion of the center of mass of the body relative to our frame of reference and motion of the body relative to its own center of mass. To formulate the problem algebraically, let us return to the concept of center of mass, discussed in Section 17.12.

Suppose that a system consists of two particles of mass m_1 and m_2 with velocity components in the xy-plane, as shown in Fig. 21.9.1. The center of mass of the pair of particles has a velocity $\mathbf{v}$ with components $(\bar{v}_x, \bar{v}_y)$, and we have, from Eq. (17.12.2:)

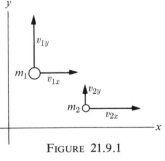

FIGURE 21.9.1

$$\bar{v}_x = \frac{m_1 v_{1x} + m_2 v_{2x}}{m_1 + m_2}, \qquad (21.9.1)$$

$$\bar{v}_y = \frac{m_1 v_{1y} + m_2 v_{2y}}{m_1 + m_2}. \qquad (21.9.2)$$

The velocity $\mathbf{v}_1'$ of body m_1 relative to the center of mass of the system would be given by the vector $\mathbf{v}_1' = \mathbf{v}_1 - \mathbf{v}$, and the x-component of this relative velocity would be given by $v_{1x}' = v_{1x} - \bar{v}_x$. Similarly, $v_{2x}' = v_{2x} - \bar{v}_x$. Let us calculate the kinetic energies associated with the relative velocity components v'_{1x} and v'_{2x}:

$$\tfrac{1}{2}m_1 v'^2_{1x} = \tfrac{1}{2}m_1(v_{1x} - \bar{v}_x)^2 = \tfrac{1}{2}m_1 v^2_{1x} - m_1 v_{1x}\bar{v}_x + \tfrac{1}{2}m_1\bar{v}^2_x,$$

$$\tfrac{1}{2}m_2 v'^2_{2x} = \tfrac{1}{2}m_2(v_{2x} - \bar{v}_x)^2 = \tfrac{1}{2}m_2 v^2_{2x} - m_2 v_{2x}\bar{v}_x + \tfrac{1}{2}m_2\bar{v}^2_x.$$

Adding these two equations, we obtain

$$\tfrac{1}{2}m_1 v'^2_{1x} + \tfrac{1}{2}m_2 v'^2_{2x} = \tfrac{1}{2}m_1 v^2_{1x} + \tfrac{1}{2}m_x v^2_{2x}$$
$$- (m_1 v_{1x} + m_2 v_{2x})\bar{v}_x + \tfrac{1}{2}(m_1 + m_2)\bar{v}^2_x. \quad (21.9.3)$$

From Eq. (21.9.1) we have $(m_1 v_{1x} + m_2 v_{2x}) = (m_1 + m_2)\bar{v}_x$, and therefore the last two terms of Eq. (21.9.3) reduce to $-\tfrac{1}{2}(m_1 + m_2)\bar{v}^2_x$. We can rearrange (21.9.3) to give

$$\tfrac{1}{2}m_1 v^2_{1x} + \tfrac{1}{2}m_2 v^2_{2x} = \tfrac{1}{2}m_1 v'^2_{1x} + \tfrac{1}{2}m_2 v'^2_{2x} + \tfrac{1}{2}(m_1 + m_2)\bar{v}^2_x. \quad (21.9.4)$$

A similar calculation for the y-component of relative velocity would give an exactly similar equation.

Since $v^2_1 = v^2_{1x} + v^2_{1y}$; $v^2_2 = v^2_{2x} + v^2_{2y}$; $\bar{v}^2 = \bar{v}^2_x + \bar{v}^2_y$, we can add the x- and y-equations and obtain

$$\tfrac{1}{2}m_1 v^2_1 + \tfrac{1}{2}m_2 v^2_2 = \tfrac{1}{2}m_1 v'^2_1 + \tfrac{1}{2}m_2 v'^2_2 + \tfrac{1}{2}(m_1 + m_2)\bar{v}^2. \quad (21.9.5)$$

Translated into words, this equation says

Total kinetic energy of motion in xy-plane: KE$_{total}$		Kinetic energy of motion relative to center of mass: KE$'$		Kinetic energy associated with total mass of system moving at center of mass velocity: KE$_{CM}$
	$-$		$+$	

Now suppose that particles m_1 and m_2 are formed into a rigid body through being connected by a rigid rod of negligible mass; their motions become restricted so that distances from the center of mass cannot change. The velocities v' then become tangential velocities of rotation about the center of mass, and KE$'$ is the kinetic energy of rotation about the center of mass. We would obtain an exactly similar result for a rigid body consisting of many particles, and we therefore generalize Eq. (21.9.5) to state that the total kinetic energy of a rigid body moving in a plane can be calculated by adding the kinetic energy of rotation around the center of mass and the translational kinetic energy of the entire body at center-of-mass velocity:

$$KE_{total} = \tfrac{1}{2}I_0\omega^2 + \tfrac{1}{2}M\bar{v}^2, \quad (21.9.6)$$

where I_0 and ω represent moment of inertia and angular velocity around the center of mass, and M represents the total mass of the body.

Later on, when we construct a molecular model of the behavior of gases, we shall visualize a huge population of molecules in which the individual members move randomly, colliding with each other and with the walls of the container, continually exchanging translational and rotational energies, and acquiring larger amounts of such energy as the container is heated. First, however, let us return to the problem posed at the beginning of this section.

21.10 ROLLING ON AN INCLINED PLANE

We can now use a simple energy analysis to study the rolling of objects down an inclined plane. Suppose a body of mass M and radius R rolls down the plane (Fig. 21.10.1) with negligible dissipation of mechanical energy. In descending a height Δh, the decrease in potential energy would be $Mg\,\Delta h$, and all of this would appear as kinetic energy. If the body is released from rest, and $\bar{v}$ denotes the instantaneous translational velocity after a descent Δh, Eq. (21.9.6) requires that:

$$Mg\,\Delta h = \tfrac{1}{2}I_0\omega^2 + \tfrac{1}{2}M\bar{v}^2. \tag{21.10.1}$$

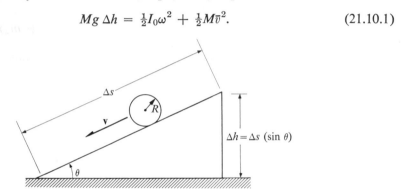

FIG. 21.10.1. Body of radius R rolling down inclined plane.

If a body rolls on a surface without appreciable slipping, there must be a direct relationship between $\bar{v}$ and ω: In an interval Δt the center of mass is displaced a distance $\bar{v}\,\Delta t$ and, in the absence of slipping, the body must have rotated through an angle such that this same length of arc ($\bar{v}\,\Delta t$) is laid off along the surface. If the body rotates at angular velocity ω, the length of arc must equal $R\omega\,\Delta t$, and we have the relation

$$\bar{v}\,\Delta t = R\omega\,\Delta t, \qquad \omega = \bar{v}/R, \tag{21.10.2}$$

when rolling takes place without slipping.

Equation (21.10.1) then becomes

$$Mg\,\Delta h = \tfrac{1}{2}I_0\frac{\bar{v}^2}{R^2} + \tfrac{1}{2}M\bar{v}^2 = \left(\frac{I_0}{R^2} + M\right)\frac{\bar{v}^2}{2},$$

$$\bar{v}^2 = \frac{2g\,\Delta h}{1 + (I_0/MR^2)}. \tag{21.10.3}$$

In the light of the results tabulated in Table 21.4.1, let us take $I_0 = kMR^2$, where k

is a number depending on the geometrical form of the rolling object. Equation (21.10.3) then becomes:

$$\bar{v}^2 = \frac{2g\,\Delta h}{1+k} = \frac{2g\sin\theta\,\Delta s}{1+k}, \tag{21.10.4}$$

where $\bar{v}$ represents the translational velocity acquired by the rolling body after starting from rest and descending through a height Δh. Since this is a case of uniform acceleration through a displacement Δs along the plane, we can compare (21.10.4) with the kinematic relation $v^2 = 2a\,\Delta s$, and we recognize the translational acceleration a to be given by:

$$a = \frac{g\sin\theta}{1+k}. \tag{21.10.5}$$

Let us interpret these results:

(a) For a frictionless puck *sliding* down the plane without rotation, the velocity acquired would have been $2g\,\Delta h$, the same as that acquired in free fall through the elevation Δh. This is represented in Eq. (21.10.4) by the case $k = 0$ (no rotational contribution, effectively zero moment of inertia). For a rolling body k is not zero, and the translational velocity is decreased, some of the kinetic energy going into rotation.

(b) Equation (21.10.4) predicts that all homogeneous cylinders will roll together down the inclined plane because both M and R have cancelled out of the equation; only k remains, and it is equal to $\frac{1}{2}$ for all homogeneous cylinders regardless of total mass and outer radius. Thus all homogeneous cylinders will roll down an inclined plane with translational acceleration

$$a = \tfrac{2}{3}g\sin\theta. \tag{21.10.6}$$

(c) For homogeneous spheres $k = \frac{2}{5}$, which is slightly less than $\frac{1}{2}$. Therefore the translational acceleration will be slightly *greater* than that of a cylinder, and a homogeneous sphere of any size will always beat a homogeneous cylinder in rolling down a plane.

PROBLEM 21.15.   (a) How will a thin hoop behave in comparison with a cylinder in rolling down an inclined plane? Obtain expressions corresponding to (21.10.6) for the translational accelerations of a hoop and a sphere. How would the behavior of a homogeneous wooden cylinder be altered if it were covered with an outer rim of lead? Suppose we were able to conduct experiments in which the object continued to roll without slipping, even at large inclinations of the plane. What value of acceleration would be approached by various bodies as the plane approached vertical orientation, $\theta = 90°$? Why would the acceleration *not* be that of free fall?

(b) Galileo used spheres in his inclined-plane experiments and was apparently unaware that other shapes would exhibit a different acceleration. Speculate on how empirical discovery of this effect might have influenced his interpretation of the experiments.

21.11 PROBLEMS

21.16. The dumbbell in Fig. 21.11.1 consists of 150-gm bobs fastened to 20-cm-long rods, pivoted around a fixed axis at O. The mass of each rod is 100 gm. The spheres have radii of 2.0 cm, and the rods have radii of 0.50 cm.

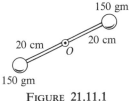

FIGURE 21.11.1

(a) Estimate the moment of inertia of the system about axis O, perpendicular to the rod. [*Answer:* $I = 0.015$ kg·m².] Estimate the moment of inertia around a longitudinal axis coinciding with the axes of the cylindrical rods. [*Answer:* $I = 0.00005$ kg·m².]

(b) If an external torque of .032 m·n is applied to the dumbbell about the axis at O, and the opposing frictional torque at the pivot is 0.02 m·n, predict the angular acceleration of the system. [*Answer:* 20 rad/sec².]

(c) At a certain instant the angular velocity of the dumbbell is 12 rad/sec. Calculate the instantaneous values of angular momentum and kinetic energy. What net angular impulse would have imparted this angular velocity if the body started from rest? [*Answer:* 0.18 kg·m²/sec; 1.1 joules; 0.18 m·n/sec.]

(d) At the instant that $\omega = 12$ radians/sec the external torque is removed. How long will the dumbbell rotate, and through what angular displacement, before the frictional torque brings it to a stop? [*Answer:* 9.0 sec; 54 rad or 8.8 rev.]

21.17. A pendulum bob of mass m is suspended on a very light string of length L. When the bob is displaced in a positive direction from equilibrium position, as shown in Fig. 21.11.2, the weight of the bob exerts a negatively directed torque around point O. Analyze this problem in terms of

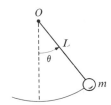

FIGURE 21.11.2

the concepts developed in this chapter, and show that the angular acceleration of the bob at position θ will be given by

$$\alpha = -\frac{g}{L} \sin \theta. \qquad (21.11.1)$$

Interpret the result: What is the significance of the minus sign? Why is the angular acceleration independent of the mass of the bob? What is the character of the motion predicted by Eq. (21.11.1)?

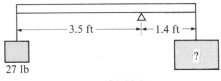

FIGURE 21.11.3

21.18. A uniform bar weighing 16 lb is pivoted as shown in Fig. 21.11.3. A body weighing 27 lb is suspended at the left-hand end of the bar. (a) What weight suspended at the right-hand end will cause the bar to balance? (b) What total force will be exerted on the bar at the pivot? Explain in your own words the connection between this problem and Problem 18.19. [*Answer:* (a) 80 lb; (b) 123 lb.]

21.19. A cylindrical yo-yo consists of two discs fastened to a short bar of radius r. A string is wrapped around the bar, as shown in Fig. 21.11.4. The end of the string is

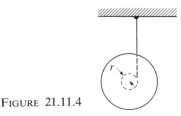

FIGURE 21.11.4

fastened to a rigid support, and the yo-yo is allowed to fall. Adopt suitable symbols and analyze the problem in the light of concepts developed in this chapter.

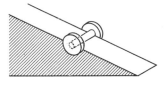

FIGURE 21.11.5

21.20. In demonstrations of uniform acceleration under the influence of gravity it is possible to "dilute" the acceleration far more than Galileo did on his inclined plane by using the device shown in Fig. 21.11.5. The construction is similar to the yo-yo except that the discs are more massive and the rod connecting them is longer. When the device rolls down an inclined track, it accelerates very much more slowly than a rolling uniform cylinder or sphere. Explain this behavior, using language and concepts developed in this chapter. Predict what happens when the object leaves the track and rolls on the horizontal table.

21.21 Suppose that you are standing at the outer edge of a circular platform which is free to rotate about a vertical axis at its center. The mass of the platform is 200 kg and the radius is 2.3 m. Initially the system is at rest, and you start walking along the periphery at a velocity of 1.8 m/sec relative to the earth. Stating all your assumptions and idealizations, predict the behavior of the platform (giving a numerical result). How long will it take you to return to the point on the platform from which you started? What will happen when you stop walking?

21.22. Consider designing a rotational analog of the ballistic pendulum (Problem 18.16) in the following way. A massive cylinder of mass M and radius R is pivoted on its axis and restrained in its rotation by a

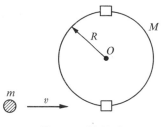

FIGURE 21.11.6

stiff coil spring with torsional spring constant κ (Fig. 21.11.6). A bullet of mass m and velocity v is fired into a block at the periphery of the wheel. The wheel rotates and is caught by a ratchet at maximum deflection so that the total angular displacement $\Delta\theta$ can be measured. Explaining steps, idealizations, and assumptions, derive an expression for the velocity of the bullet in terms of known and measured quantities. Describe how you might determine the spring constant κ.

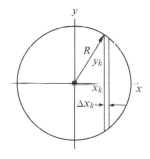

FIGURE 21.11.7

21.23. Imagine slicing a sphere into parallel discs perpendicular to one of the diameters. Calculate the moment of inertia of the sphere ($I = 2/5\ MR^2$) by evaluating the limit of the sum of the moments of inertia of the parallel discs. In Fig. 21.11.7 the discs are taken perpendicular to the x-axis.

The radius of the kth disc:

$$y_k = \sqrt{R^2 - x_k^2}.$$

SUPPLEMENTARY READING AND STUDY

Angular Momentum and Its Conservation, Advanced Topics Program extending the PSSC course in Physics. Watertown, Mass.: Educational Services, Inc., 1962, Chapter A-1

Physics for Students of Science and Engineering, R. Resnick and D. Halliday. New York: John Wiley & Sons, 1960, Chapter 12

Introduction to Mechanics, Matter, and Waves, U. Ingard and W. L. Kraushaar. Reading, Mass.: Addison-Wesley, 1960, Chapter 12

Mechanics, Heat, and Sound, second edition (Principles of Physics Series), F. W. Sears. Reading, Mass.: Addison-Wesley, 1950, Chapters 11, 12

CHAPTER 22

Waves

22.1 INTRODUCTION

When we drop a stone into a quiet pond or sharply displace the end of a rope or long helical spring (Fig. 22.1.1), we produce motions that are transmitted from one point to another in the water or on the rope, eventually affecting regions very remote from the location of the initial disturbance.

In such instances, water is not displaced bodily to outer reaches of the pond from the point at which the stone fell; coils of the helical spring in Fig. 22.1.1 are not displaced from one end to the other with the disturbance that moves along the spring. What we see are motions that are communicated from one layer of the medium to the next, and our eye observes the propagation of a "pulse"—a shape or a disturbance. This shape moves along the medium with a finite velocity, and, in the illustrations cited above, it is apparent that two very different velocities can be distinguished. One velocity is that of the pulse as a whole; we call this *propagation velocity*. The other

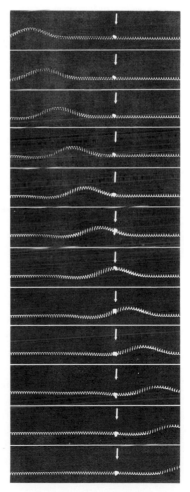

FIG. 22.1.1. Successive photographs showing propagation of pulse on a rope or helical spring. Initial disturbance is produced by imparting a sharp transverse (back and forth or up and down) deflection of the end of the spring. Note that motion of particle on spring is *up and down* while pulse shape moves from left to right. (From *Physics*. Boston: D. C. Heath, 1960.)

velocity is that of the particles of the medium; this is referred to as *particle velocity*. The particles of water and of rope move up and down or back and forth in a direction *perpendicular* to that in which the pulse moves, and within the region of the moving pulse, some layers of particles are moving up while others are moving down.

The propagation of a pulse or disturbance in a medium represents a new kind of motion, distinctly different from the bodily displacement of particles or rigid bodies that we have studied up to this point. We call this phenomenon wave motion or wave propagation.

Our concern in this chapter will be to build on everyday experience and simple laboratory observations in an effort to develop some feeling for the nature of wave motion, and for the way in which waves behave when they arrive at boundaries or interact with each other. Our approach will be essentially kinematic and phenomenological: we shall describe the essential properties and characteristics of wave behavior without carrying out a mathematical analysis of dynamical effects and relationships. It is perfectly possible to apply Newtonian mechanics to wave motion and to predict the effects of forces and accelerations, but an analysis at this level will be left for more advanced courses and texts.

It is characteristic of the pattern of scientific thought that insights and conceptions which are developed or clarified at some simple, easily approachable level of perception frequently serve as models or analogies for explanation of phenomena at more complex, more remote levels. In the physical situation we have been describing, both particle and wave motion are directly perceptible to the senses of sight and touch. Although we can neither see nor feel mechanical effects in the air when we experience phenomena of sound, we soon become aware that sounds always originate with some kind of motion. Sounds are heard at a distance from the source when a blow is struck, when an explosion occurs, when a string or other object vibrates sufficiently rapidly. We quickly seize upon the plausible analogy, comparing the invisible spreading of an acoustic disturbance in the air with the spread of other waves we know from visual experience. At one point in the First Day of the *Two New Sciences*, Salviati illustrates this mode of thought and connects an action producing sound with that simultaneously producing ripples on a water surface:

> "That undulations of the medium are widely dispersed about a sounding body is evinced by the fact that a glass of water may be made to emit a tone merely by the friction of the fingertip upon the rim of the glass; [and in the] water is produced a series of regular waves. The same phenomenon is observed to better advantage by fixing the base of the goblet upon the bottom of a rather large vessel of water filled nearly to the edge of the goblet; for if, as before, we sound the glass by friction of the finger, we shall see ripples spreading with utmost regularity to large distances. . . . I have often remarked, in thus sounding a rather large glass nearly full of water, that at first the waves are spaced with uniformity, and when, as sometimes happens, the tone of the glass jumps an octave higher, I have noted that at this moment each of the aforesaid waves divides into two; a phenomenon which shows clearly that the ratio involved in the octave is two."

In the historical development of wave concepts, the qualitative insights came long before the dynamical, mathematical theory of acoustic waves provided quantitative theoretical validation. After the middle of the seventeenth century, scientific investigation moved rapidly to new ranges of physical phenomena: inquiry was directed toward the nature of light and heat, the nature of electricity and magnetism, the structure of matter. To help visualize, explain, and explore these subtle, nonmechanical levels of experience, scientists made use of models and analogies based on familiar mechanical phenomena of particle behavior on the one hand, and of wave motion on the other. Such models have had a profound influence on the evolution of modern physical concepts, and we shall encounter several illustrations of this interaction in subsequent chapters.

22.2 TYPES OF WAVES

Pulses on a string and ripples on a water surface exemplify a class of waves described as *transverse*, in the sense that the direction of particle motion is perpendicular, or transverse, to the direction of propagation of the wave form. Transverse waves, when excited within the body of a solid medium such as the earth or a steel beam, are called *shear waves*.

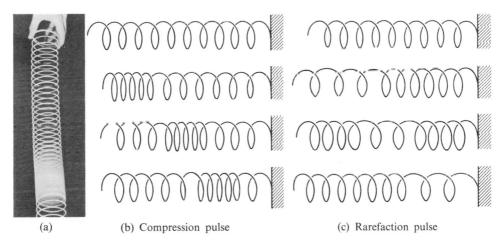

| (a) | (b) Compression pulse | (c) Rarefaction pulse |

FIG. 22.2.1. Propagation of compression and rarefaction pulses among the loops of a helical spring. A region of increased or decreased "density" of coils is produced by a longitudinal deflection parallel to the direction of propagation of the disturbance. A wave of this type is called *longitudinal*. Sound waves in air or water are also longitudinal waves of compression and rarefaction. (Photo (a) Courtesy Educational Services, Inc.)

In contrast, consider the wave illustrated in Fig. 22.2.1, in which pulses of compression or rarefaction are propagated among the loops of a helical spring. The particle velocity of the individual loops is parallel to the direction of propagation, and this type of wave is characterized as longitudinal. Sound waves in air or water are longitudinal waves of compression and rarefaction, completely analogous to the waves illustrated in Fig. 22.2.1. Only longitudinal waves can propagate within the body of a fluid medium; shear waves cannot propagate because a fluid cannot transmit appreciable transverse stress from one layer to the next.

FIGURE 22.2.2

PROBLEM 22.1. Visualize air contained in a tube and represent by means of dots the particles of air distributed uniformly throughout the tube (Fig. 22.2.2). Suppose that the piston is moved abruptly toward the right and then toward the left. Sketch, in the manner of Fig. 22.2.1(b) and (c), the propagation down the tube of pulses of compression and rarefaction.

FIGURE 22.2.3

$$\xrightarrow{\text{P}} \quad \begin{array}{c} A \qquad\qquad\qquad\qquad\qquad B \end{array}$$

PROBLEM 22.2.   A long solid rod is lying at rest on a table (Fig. 22.2.3). Suppose you apply a push P at end A hard enough to displace the rod. Does end B move to the right at the instant you touch A? Describe what happens in this case. In what ways is it similar to the situation in Figs. 22.2.1 and 22.2.2? In what ways different?

Consider the suspension illustrated in Fig. 22.2.4. Weighted rods are attached to a wire or flexible metal tape and suspended as shown. Suppose that the bottom dumbbell is quickly rotated through an angular displacement in the horizontal plane. The twist is communicated to the next rod and the next, and a disturbance, called a *torsional wave*, is propagated up the suspension. In the system of Fig. 22.2.4 the disturbance travels relatively slowly and can be followed by eye. If we twist the end of an iron bar or the crankshaft of an engine, the resulting torsion wave travels very rapidly and involves very small angular displacements; we cannot see it visually, but we could detect its effects with sufficiently sensitive, rapidly responding electrical instruments.

In some cases a given disturbance may entail several different types of waves simultaneously. For example, earthquakes involve a complicated superposition of both longitudinal and shear waves, together with other types that are confined to surfaces of discontinuity such as the surface of the earth itself or to layers within the earth. Each type of wave travels at its own characteristic velocity, with the longitudinal waves (designated as "P" waves by seismologists) arriving first at a point of observation and the shear ("S" waves) arriving afterward.

The velocity of waves of various kinds depends, in general, on properties of the medium and on the size or amplitude of the disturbance in the wave itself. Very large deflections on a string or very large pressure pulses in the air (explosion waves or sonic booms from aircraft) propagate more rapidly than very small disturbances. Small disturbances propagate with a velocity that depends only on properties of the medium. The velocity of such a wave on a stretched string is given by $V = \sqrt{T/\mu}$, where T is the tension in the string and μ is the mass per unit length. In the language of physics, *sound* is defined as referring to small-amplitude waves, and the velocity of sound in a fluid is given by $V = \sqrt{(dp/d\rho)}_{\text{adiabatic}}$, where the derivative describes the rate of change of pressure with density under conditions such that there is no time for appreciable heat flow from compressed to rarefied regions in the wave. Two very restricted derivations of these relationships are illustrated in Appendix F.

It is frequently convenient to represent a wave form by means of a picture or graph. We can readily imagine taking a photograph of a wave on a string or on a water surface and plotting a scaled version of such a photograph on a set of coordinates in which the ordinate represents the transverse displacements and the abscissa represents corresponding horizontal positions. This would be an instantaneous picture of the wave in a quite literal sense, as in Fig. 22.1.1. For the torsional wave of Fig. 22.2.4 we might plot *angular* displacement as a function of vertical

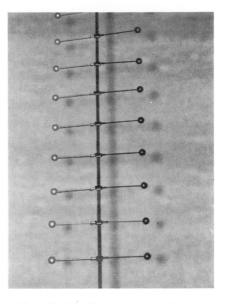

FIG. 22.2.4. Torsional wave is propagated up the suspension if bottom dumbbell is rotated through an angular displacement in horizontal plane.

position. This would no longer be a photographic likeness of the wave form but would convey the basic idea on a two-dimensional graph.

For the wave on the helical spring (Fig. 22.2.1) we might plot instantaneous longitudinal displacements from equilibrium position of points on the spring and obtain a diagram such as Fig. 22.2.5, where the crest represents a region of compression or bunching of the coils, and the trough a region of rarefaction. To delineate a sound wave we might plot instantaneous pressures as a function of horizontal position and obtain a diagram very similar to Fig. 22.2.5, with essentially similar implications of compression and rarefaction. These last representations are certainly not photographic likenesses, but they nevertheless convey simple and readily interpretable information about the "shapes" of the wave forms.

Another graphical representation of a wave disturbance can be given by plotting a graph of displacements or pressure variations, etc., at a *fixed* point in the medium

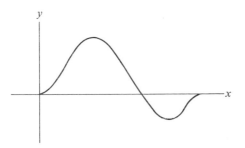

FIG. 22.2.5. Hypothetical graph that might represent longitudinal displacements versus normal horizontal position, x, of coils of a helical spring, or of pressure versus horizontal position in a sound wave.

as a function of time. In this text, we shall make little use of this representation, but both forms are widely used in the literature and are, of course, closely related mathematically. Each has its own advantages in the appropriate context.

22.3 WAVELENGTH AND FREQUENCY OF PERIODIC WAVE TRAINS

Wave disturbances can assume an infinite variety of forms. Several principal types, together with the vocabulary used to describe them, are illustrated in Fig. 22.3.1. Regular periodic wave trains, such as those in Figs. 22.3.1(c) and (d), are excited by sources having a regular, oscillatory motion of some definite frequency —a vibrating string or tuning fork, a vibrating rod producing ripples at a water surface. If the source makes ν (Greek letter "nu") complete oscillations in one second, it must emit ν complete waves. If we take up a point of observation in the medium, we observe ν crests or ν complete waves pass by in each second. We therefore associate a definite frequency ν with any periodic wave train, and we recognize this frequency to be identical with that of the source. The period T (the duration of the complete cycle of the wave) is given by $T = 1/\nu$.

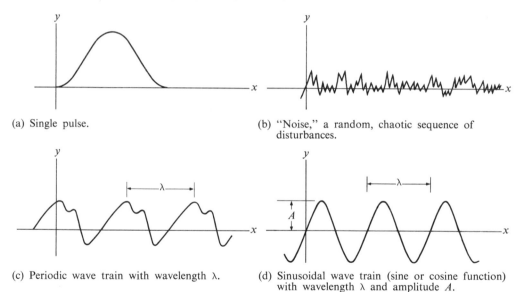

(a) Single pulse.

(b) "Noise," a random, chaotic sequence of disturbances.

(c) Periodic wave train with wavelength λ.

(d) Sinusoidal wave train (sine or cosine function) with wavelength λ and amplitude A.

FIG. 22.3.1. Illustrations of several different types of wave.

We have an intuitive sense that for any particular kind of wave, a low frequency should be associated with a long wavelength and a high frequency with a short wavelength. Let us explore the arithmetical relationship. A periodic wave train of frequency ν (Fig. 22.3.2) is moving at propagation velocity V. If we watch a crest that passes point of observation A at $t = 0$, one second later the crest will have advanced to position B a distance V away from A. The space AB will contain ν wavelengths. Therefore the individual wavelength λ must be given by

$$\lambda = \frac{V}{\nu} = VT. \tag{22.3.1}$$

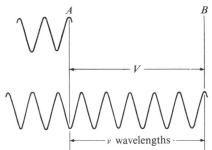

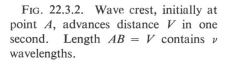

FIG. 22.3.2. Wave crest, initially at point A, advances distance V in one second. Length $AB = V$ contains ν wavelengths.

PROBLEM 22.3. Interpret Eq. (22.3.1):   A vibrating source in a ripple tank oscillates at 3.6 cycles/sec, and the ripples in the given depth of water propagate at 4.8 cm/sec. Calculate the wavelength of the ripples. The musical note middle C has a frequency of about 260 cycles/sec, and the velocity of sound in air is about 1100 ft/sec. Calculate the wavelength of this sound wave. Suppose a 260-cycle/sec sound wave is excited in water, will the wavelength be larger, smaller, or equal to the wavelength in air? On what do you base your answer?

22.4 RELATIVE PHASES OF SINUSOIDAL WAVE TRAINS

The wave forms produced by a tuning fork vibrating in air or by a bar vibrating in a ripple tank are very nearly sinusoidal; i.e., we can to a very good approximation represent the experimentally observed wave forms by a sine or cosine function.

Figure 22.4.1 illustrates how this curve fitting is achieved. We are given a sinusoidal wave form of amplitude A and wavelength $\lambda = 8$ ft. We can choose the origin of coordinates anywhere we please, and we have elected to place it at point 0. This immediately suggests that the curve is to be represented by a sine function since

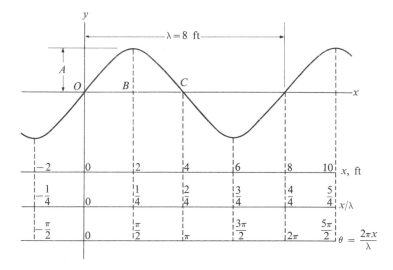

FIG. 22.4.1. Sinusoidal wave form; origin of coordinates taken at point of zero deflection, with deflections increasing toward the right. Equation of curve: $y = A \sin (2\pi x/\lambda)$.

$\sin \theta = 0$ when $\theta = 0$ and increases as θ increases. (See Fig. E.2.2 in Appendix E.) The maximum value of the sine function is unity, and the maximum deflection in the wave form is A; our first impulse might then be to represent the given curve by the equation $y = A \sin x$. A few simple checks show that this equation has absurd implications. At $x = 4$ ft the deflection in Fig. 22.4.1 is zero, but the equation would read $y = A \sin 4$, which is not zero. If we measured the horizontal distance in meters instead of feet, $x = 1.22$ m, and the deflection at the same position would be given by $y = A \sin 1.22$, which is not equal to $A \sin 4$. Depending on the units in which we elect to measure horizontal distance x, we can get any number we please.

The inconsistency, of course, lies in the fact that sine and cosine functions were defined with pure numbers as their domain; geometrically, these pure numbers can be interpreted as angles. Horizontal distance x, however, is a dimensional quantity expressed in arbitrary units. If we attempt to relate $\sin x$ to the given wave form, we shall simply get a meaningless jumble. In order to obtain $y = 0$ at $x = 4$, it is necessary to associate a pure number, or angle, θ with $x = 4$ such that the sine of this value of θ is zero. Similarly we must associate another value of θ with $x = 6$ such that the sine of this value is -1, etc.

Fig. 22.4.1 shows how this association can be achieved. First we describe horizontal positions in terms of numbers of wavelengths x/λ, as shown in the second row of numbers along the abscissa. Then we note that a whole wavelength $(x/\lambda = 1)$ corresponds to $\theta = (2\pi) \cdot 1$, and that the angle corresponding to one quarter wavelength must be

$$\theta = 2\pi \cdot \tfrac{1}{4} = \pi/2,$$

and that, in general, for x/λ wavelengths $\theta = 2\pi(x/\lambda)$. Therefore the equation describing the sinusoid having the origin located as shown in Fig. 22.4.1 is

$$y = A \sin \frac{2\pi x}{\lambda}. \qquad (22.4.1)$$

PROBLEM 22.4. Suppose that the origin in Fig. 22.4.1 were located at point B; show that the curve would then be represented by $y = A \cos 2\pi x/\lambda$. If the origin were at point C, show that the equation would be $y = -A \sin 2\pi x/\lambda$.

PROBLEM 22.5. A wave on a string is known to be represented by the equation $y = 0.25 \sin (2.36x)$, where deflection and horizontal distances are measured in feet. What are the amplitude and wavelength of this wave? [Answer: $A = 0.25$ ft, $\lambda = 2.66$ ft.]

Figure 22.4.2 illustrates several sinusoidal wave trains, of identical amplitude and wavelength, shifted relative to each other along the x-axis. We speak of these waves as "differing in phase" or as being "shifted in phase" relative to each other, and the phase difference is measured quantitatively by the *angle* of shift or by the number of wavelengths. There are, of course, many different phase shifts that would reproduce the patterns illustrated in Fig. 22.4.2. For example, the out-of-phase pattern of (c) relative to (a) can be re-established by any angular shift, either right or left,

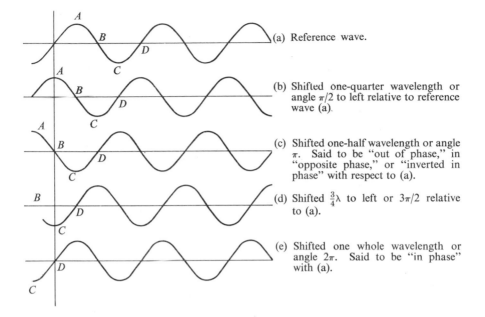

(a) Reference wave.

(b) Shifted one-quarter wavelength or angle $\pi/2$ to left relative to reference wave (a).

(c) Shifted one-half wavelength or angle π. Said to be "out of phase," in "opposite phase," or "inverted in phase" with respect to (a).

(d) Shifted $\frac{3}{4}\lambda$ to left or $3\pi/2$ relative to (a).

(e) Shifted one whole wavelength or angle 2π. Said to be "in phase" with (a).

FIG. 22.4.2. Sinusoidal waves of a given wavelength in various different phases relative to each other.

of an odd multiple of π or an odd number of half-wavelengths. Similarly, the in-phase pattern of (e) and (a) can be re-established by any angular shift of 2π or by an integral number of whole wavelengths. We shall be particularly concerned with these two special cases when we deal with superposition and interference of sinusoidal wave trains in Sections 22.14–17.

22.5   WAVES IN TWO DIMENSIONS

One of the most distinctive aspects of a wave disturbance is the manner in which it spreads out in either two or three dimensions from a source. If we touch a quiet water surface with a pencil point or our fingertip, we see a circular wave pulse spread out from the origin of the disturbance. By vibrating the pencil point up and down we can send out a continuous train of waves, successive crests and troughs forming concentric circles around the source. In an exactly analogous manner, a vibrating tuning fork sends out a continuous train of sound waves. At distances large relative to the size of the fork itself, the fork appears to be a point source, with successive regions of compression and rarefaction forming concentric spherical shells around it.

A specific vocabulary is developed for the description of waves propagating in two or three dimensions. A region of constant phase (a crest, a trough, a locus of zero deflection, or a locus of any arbitrarily chosen deflection from $-A$ to $+A$) is called a *wave front*. Lines drawn in such a way as to be everywhere normal to the wave fronts they cross are called *rays*. For ripples from a point source on a water

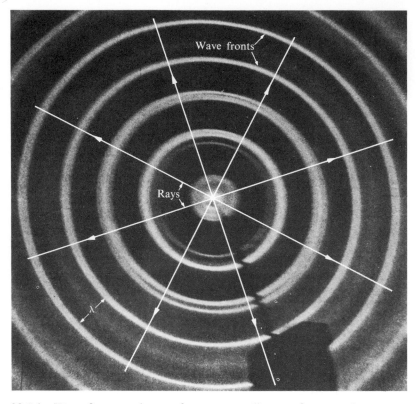

FIG. 22.5.1. Wave fronts and rays of waves spreading out from a point source. (From *Physics*. Boston: D. C. Heath, 1960.)

surface, wave fronts form concentric circles, as illustrated in Fig. 22.5.1, and rays are radial lines originating at the point source. Figure 22.5.1 would serve equally well as an illustration of wave fronts and rays lying in a plane cross section of a spherical sound wave emitted by a vibrating tuning fork.

Waves may also be generated by the motion of an extended source. If we vibrate a long bar up and down at a water surface, it will generate a wave having the same phase along its entire length. At distances relatively close to the bar, the successive wave fronts have the form of parallel straight lines. Such waves are called "plane" or "straight" waves; their rays are also parallel to each other and do not diverge as do the rays of circular waves. Figure 22.5.2

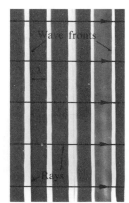

FIG. 22.5.2. Straight waves emitted by bar vibrating in ripple tank. Both the wave fronts and the rays are straight lines. (From *Physics*. Boston: D. C. Heath, 1960.)

illustrates this case, and could equally well apply to a plane cross section taken through a sound wave emitted by a large diaphragm vibrating, as a whole, back and forth along the x-axis. At distances very large relative to the size of the bar or diaphragm, the wave fronts would appear to be circles of very large radius centered at the source. On the other hand, small sections of circular wave fronts of very large radius, far from the source, appear to be very nearly plane and are frequently treated to a very good approximation as plane waves with essentially parallel rays. The basic simplicity of the plane and circular waves resides, in part, in the fact that the rays are straight lines in both cases.

22.6 DIFFRACTION

Figure 22.6.1 illustrates three characteristic patterns formed when a plane wave encounters an obstacle pierced by a single opening. Waves continue to propagate through the opening, but the wave pattern on the other side is determined by the relation between the wavelength λ of the wave and the width D of the opening. Such bending and modification of a wave front on passing through an opening is called *diffraction*. Diffraction effects are small when λ is much smaller than D (Fig. 22.6.1c) and become increasingly pronounced as λ becomes of the order of magnitude of D or larger. The pattern illustrated in Fig. 22.6.1(b) is called a single-slit diffraction pattern, and will be discussed in more detail in Section 22.17. When λ is larger than the opening (Fig. 22.6.1a) the slit becomes, to a good approximation, a point source of circular waves.

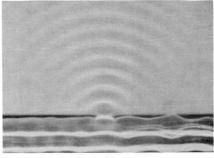

(a)

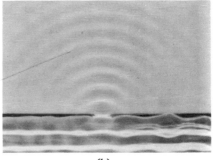

(b)

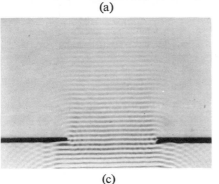

(c)

FIG. 22.6.1. Plane waves incident on slits of various widths, D. (From *Physics*. Boston: D. C. Heath, 1960.) (a) $\lambda \sim D$. Slit approximates point source of circular waves. (b) $\lambda \sim 0.7D$. Emerging waves form single-slit interference pattern. (c) $\lambda \ll D$. Waves exhibit some diffraction at edges, but remain straight in central portion.

If a wide "beam" of particles, all traveling parallel to each other, were to arrive at a barrier, as in Fig. 22.6.1, a narrower parallel beam, of width D, would continue on the other side, with perhaps a few particles deflected (or scattered) out of their original path by the edges of the slit. A wave with $\lambda/D \ll 1$ behaves in a somewhat analogous fashion, but the pronounced diffraction effects of Fig. 22.6.1(a) and (b) are uniquely characteristic of wave behavior and markedly different from the behavior of a beam of particles. We shall subsequently see this distinction used repeatedly to characterize wave disturbances versus particle motion under circumstances in which it is otherwise not at all obvious what sort of phenomenon one is dealing with.

22.7 REFRACTION

In many circumstances the velocity of wave propagation may vary from point to point in a medium. The velocity of ripples decreases with decreasing depth of water; if a ripple tank has a sloping bottom, the propagation velocity becomes a function of position in the tank. Sound velocity in air or water increases with increasing temperature; if the temperature varies in the horizontal and vertical directions, as it does in both the atmosphere and the ocean, sound velocity becomes a function of position in the medium.

When a quantity varies in space, it is said to have a "space gradient." The gradient in a particular direction x is measured by the derivative or space rate of change

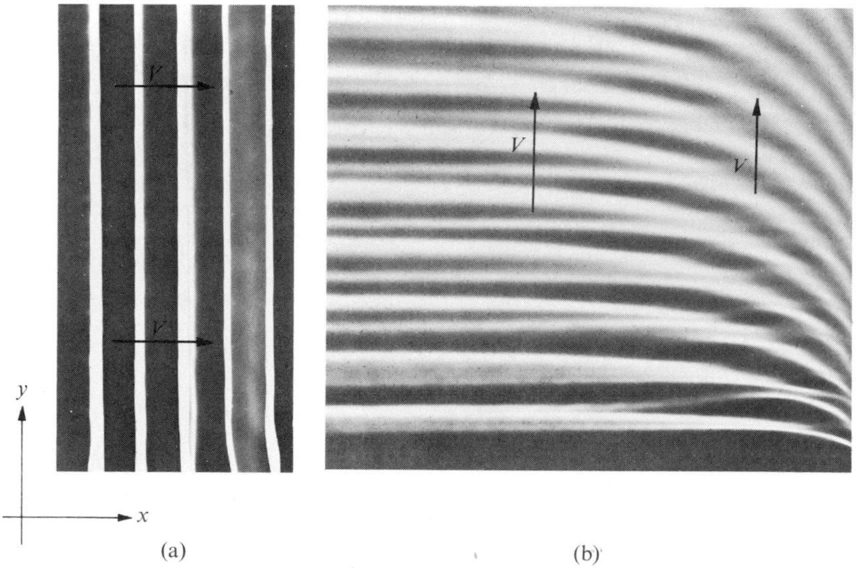

(a)   (b)

FIG. 22.7.1. Waves propagating over sloping bottom. Water becomes shallower from left to right: dV/dx negative. Waves propagate in directions shown by arrows. (Photograph from *Physics*. Boston: D. C. Heath, 1960.)

of the quantity in that direction. For example, a temperature gradient in the x-direction at any particular point is measured by the derivative dT/dx. Similarly, a gradient in propagation velocity is measured by dV/dx. Figure 22.7.1 illustrates the behavior of ripples propagating over a sloping bottom. The water becomes shallower in the positive x-direction, and therefore the gradient dV/dx in propagation velocity is negative.

Any local portion of a wave front propagates forward at the local propagation velocity. In Fig. 22.7.1(a) the ripples move into water of decreasing depth, with wave fronts aligned parallel to loci of constant propagation velocity. Moving into regions of lower velocity, the fronts remain parallel to each other but the wave length ($\lambda = V/\nu$) decreases, since the frequency is fixed, having been established by the driving source.

In Fig. 22.7.1(b) the wave fronts are not parallel to regions of constant propagation velocity. As a result the left-hand portions of the ripples, in deeper water, move faster than the right-hand portions. The wave fronts tend to bend around as shown in the figure; the rays are no longer straight lines emanating from the source, but curve toward the region of lower propagation velocity.

The phenomenon of distortion of wave fronts and bending of rays under the influence of gradients in the propagation velocity is called refraction. Refraction occurs not only under the conditions illustrated in Fig. 22.7.1(b) but also when a wave propagates through an interface between two uniform regions having sharply different propagation velocities: when a sound wave in air encounters a water surface or when ripples in a water layer of uniform depth encounters a "shelf" at which the depth changes to another uniform value. In these instances the propagation velocity gradient is zero in each region, but refraction occurs sharply at the boundary, where there is an abrupt change in the propagation velocity. This case is easy to study mathematically, and will be analyzed in Section 22.11.

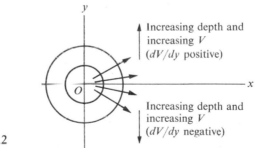

FIGURE 22.7.2

PROBLEM 22.6. Consider a ripple-tank situation with velocity gradients as indicated in Fig. 22.7.2. The bottom slopes away very gradually on either side of the x-axis, so that the axis is a line of minimum (not zero) depth and of minimum propagation velocity. The velocity V increases with distance from the x-axis in both the $+y$ and $-y$ directions. A point source of ripples is located at O. Make a rough qualitative sketch of what will happen to the several rays indicated in the figure as the waves propagate away from O. What happens to a ray if it crosses the x-axis?

22.8 MOVING SOURCE

Figure 22.8.1 illustrates the changes of wavelength that arise when a point source of ripples moves over a water surface with a velocity v_s lower than the propagation velocity V in the medium.

Let us calculate wavelengths along the axis of motion of the source. Taking v_s positive when it is in the same direction as V and negative when its direction is opposite to V, making use of the derivation suggested in Fig. 22.3.2, we find that the wavelength of ripples in the medium is given by

$$\lambda = \frac{V - v_s}{\nu_s}. \tag{22.8.1}$$

From a frame of reference stationary relative to the water surface, we observe ripples of wavelength λ to have an apparent frequency ν_{app} given by

$$\nu_{\text{app}} = \frac{V}{\lambda}. \tag{22.8.2}$$

Eliminating λ from (22.8.1) and (22.8.2), we can write

$$\nu_{\text{app}} = \frac{V}{V - v_s} \nu_s = \frac{1}{1 - (v_s/V)} \nu_s. \tag{22.8.3}$$

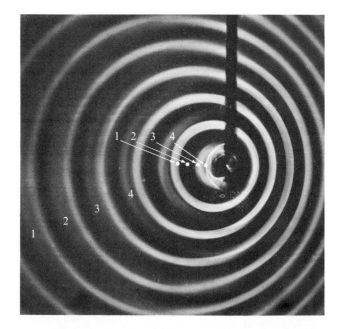

FIG. 22.8.1. Point source of fixed frequency ν_s moves toward the right at uniform velocity v_s, emitting crest 1 from position 1, crest 2 from position 2, etc.; v_s is smaller than propagation velocity V. Wavelength ahead of moving source is shorter, and wavelength behind is greater, than undisturbed wavelength from stationary source. (Courtesy Educational Services, Inc.)

Note that Eqs. (22.8.1) and (22.8.3) apply only along the line of motion of the source and do *not* tell us about values of λ and ν_{app} at positions away from the line of motion. A complete analysis of Fig. 22.8.1 is perfectly possible but will not be undertaken here.

> PROBLEM 22.7.   How might a figure such as 22.8.1 be constructed with compass and ruler; i.e., what must the relation be between the unperturbed wavelength and the spacing of positions 1, 2, etc.? Construct such a figure for yourself. Justify Eq. (22.8.1) by using an argument such as that presented in Fig. 22.3.2 (or by using any other explanation you feel is clear and logical). Verify that Eq. (22.8.1) makes sense physically by testing its agreement with the facts exhibited in Fig. 22.8.1. What happens as $v_s \rightarrow V$?

> PROBLEM 22.8.   We cannot see the wavelengths of sound waves, but our ears discriminate their apparent *frequency* through our sense of pitch: a note or tone of higher frequency has a higher pitch than one of lower frequency. Interpret Eq. (22.8.3) by deducing its predictions concerning the relative pitch we would expect to hear if we listened to a stationary tuning fork and then caused the fork to move toward us or recede from us at velocity v_s. Do the predictions make physical sense? What happens as $v_s \rightarrow V$?

If we ourselves, as observers, adopt a frame of reference that moves at velocity v_0 relative to the medium in which the waves propagate, the waves appear to go more slowly if we move in the same direction as the waves and pass us more rapidly if we move in the opposite direction. This also affects the apparent frequency ν_{app} that we would detect, even when the source itself is stationary relative to the medium; i.e., when $v_s = 0$. An analysis of this case is left for Problem 22.27 at the end of the chapter.

The phenomenon in which wavelengths and apparent frequencies are altered by motion of source and observer relative to the medium is called the *Doppler effect*. (Doppler was an Austrian scientist who, in 1842, worked out the theory for sound waves, and then called attention to the relevance of this phenomenon to investigation of the nature and behavior of light. A test of the theory was carried out in Holland in 1845, with trumpeters riding a railroad flat car and musically trained observers estimating, by ear, the apparent change in pitch. The two groups then exchanged positions.)

22.9   BOW WAVES

Our analysis in Section 22.8 was carefully restricted to the case $v_s < V$. It is perfectly possible, however, for the source velocity to exceed the propagation velocity. This happens when a speedboat runs through the water, when we move a pencil point rapidly along the surface in a ripple tank, when a bullet or airplane exceeds the speed of sound. Under such circumstances, the wave cannot get out ahead of the source; the source is continually at the very leading edge of the disturbance and generates a characteristic pattern called a *bow wave* (Fig. 22.9.1).

Bow waves formed by the boat and bullet are actually quite complicated phenomena. The disturbance in each case is intense and the amplitude quite high. In the case of the bullet or supersonic* plane, the wave produced by supersonic motion is called a *shock wave*. The velocity of propagation of high-amplitude waves depends not only on the medium but also on the instantaneous amplitude of the wave itself; shock wave velocity, for example, decreases with decreasing amplitude, approaching the local velocity of sound as the amplitude becomes very small. Some of the complex features and curvature apparent in Figs. 22.9.1(a) and (b) are associated with the effects of large wave amplitude.

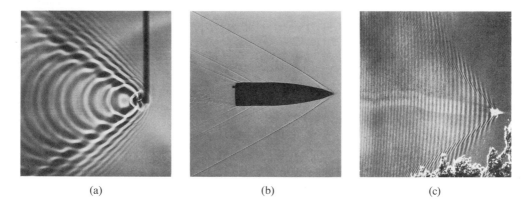

(a)   (b)   (c)

FIG. 22.9.1.   Bow waves generated in various circumstances.   (a) Vibrating source moving through ripple tank with velocity of source v_s greater than ripple propagation velocity V. (Courtesy Educational Services, Inc.) (b) Projectile moving through air.   (Courtesy U. S. Naval Ordnance Laboratory.) (c) Speedboat.

If we idealize the problem, however, and confine ourselves to waves of small amplitude, the bow wave takes the form of two plane wave fronts. We can construct the basic pattern by drawing circles representing wave crests emitted at regular intervals by a vibrating source, as shown in Fig. 22.9.2. If the source does not vibrate, but emits a single disturbance because of its continuous motion, we see just the bow wave with relatively little disturbance in the wake.

From Fig. 22.9.2 it is easy to deduce the dependence of the bow wave angle α on the velocities v_s and V. During the time interval Δt, the source moves from 0 to B, a distance $v_s \Delta t$. During the same interval, the first wave crest, emitted at 0, moves a distance $OA = V \Delta t$. Then

$$\sin \alpha = \frac{V \Delta t}{v_s \Delta t} = \frac{V}{v_s}. \qquad (22.9.1)$$

We shall find this result to be very useful in analyzing the reflection and refraction of wave trains at sharp interfaces.

___

* The term "supersonic" refers to velocities exceeding that of sound.

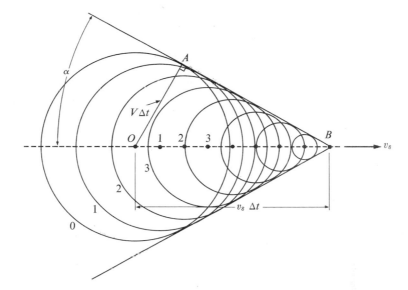

Fig. 22.9.2. Successive crests emitted by vibrating source moving at velocity v_s, greater than wave propagation velocity V. Crest 0 was emitted when source was at position O, crest 1 from position 1, etc. "Envelope," or line tangent to the various crests, forms the bow wave.

Problem 22.9. Suppose that a glass plate with a straight edge is placed on the bottom of a ripple tank so that the water depth changes abruptly from a thin layer over the plate to the original depth in the tank. A pencil point is now run along the water surface at the interface where the depth changes; i.e., immediately above, and parallel to, the edge of the plate. Using a compass, construct a bow wave that might result, taking into account the fact that the velocity of ripples is lower in the shallower layer of water.

Problem 22.10. Using a compass, construct the figure intermediate to 22.8.1 and 22.9.2; that is, the figure for which $V = v_s$. What is the character of the bow wave in this case? What would be the form of the bow wave if v_s were only slightly greater than V? (Construct a figure.) In the light of the two figures you have constructed, interpret the relevance and applicability of Eq. (22.9.1) to cases in which $v_s \rightarrow V$.

22.10 REFLECTION AND TRANSMISSION AT SHARP INTERFACES

When one end of a helical spring is rigidly fastened to a support, a moving wave pulse, arriving at this end, cannot produce the sequence of up and down motions imparted to particles elsewhere on the spring. This situation is always accompanied by the effects illustrated in Fig. 22.10.1. The arriving, or "incident," pulse is bounced back from the fixed end as a similar pulse, inverted in phase and traveling in the opposite direction. The bouncing back of an incident wave is called *reflection*.

It is observed that some reflection invariably occurs whenever there is a change in the medium through which the wave propagates. Figure 22.10.2 illustrates reflections that occur when wave pulses encounter a juncture between a light and heavy

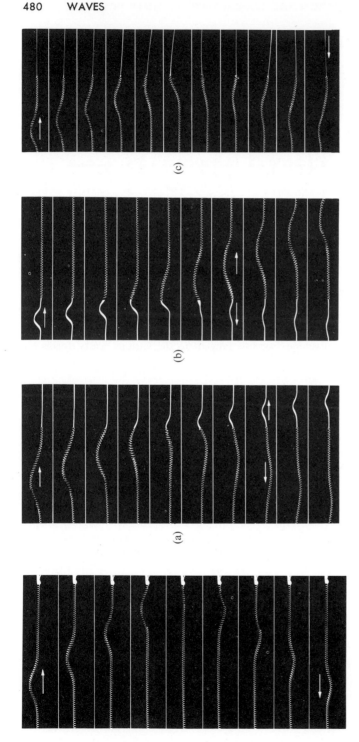

FIG. 22.10.1. Pulse traveling from left to right, reflected at rigidly fixed end of string. Sequence shows shape of string at successive uniform intervals of time. Note that reflected pulse is upside down or inverted in phase relative to incident pulse. (From *Physics*. Boston: D. C. Heath, 1960.)

FIG. 22.10.2. Reflection and transmission of pulses at junction of light and heavy strings. (a) Pulse traveling from left to right on light string is partly reflected and partly transmitted at junction with heavier string. Transmitted pulse has same phase as incident pulse, but reflected pulse is inverted. (b) Pulse traveling from left to right on heavy string is partly reflected and partly transmitted at junction with lighter string. Reflected pulse is not inverted in phase relative to incident pulse. (c) Pulse on string is essentially completely reflected without phase inversion at junction with very light thread. (Photographs from *Physics*. Boston: D. C. Heath, 1960.)

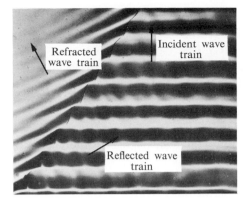

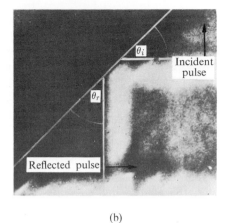

(a)   (b)

FIG. 22.10.3. (a) Simultaneous reflection and refraction of straight ripples at a line of abrupt change in depth in the ripple tank. (b) Reflection of straight pulse at rigid wall in ripple tank. (From *Physics*. Boston: D. C. Heath, 1960.)

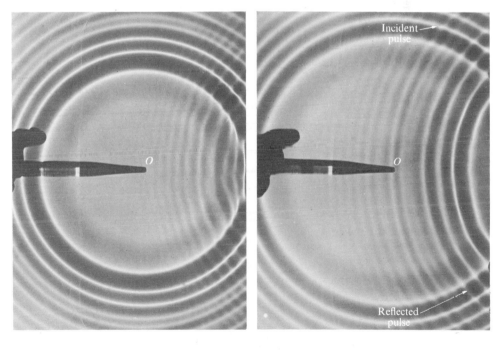

(a)   (b)

FIG. 22.10.4. Circular pulse reflected from straight barrier in a ripple tank. In (a), pulse is arriving at the wall; in (b), a short time interval later, pulse has propagated to larger radius, and part of it has been reflected. Reflected pulse is a circle with center at a point that is a mirror image of source point on opposite side of wall. (Photographs from *Physics*. Boston: D. C. Heath, 1960.)

spring. Notice that, in general, some disturbance is always transmitted through such a boundary, and some is reflected. Situations in which an end of the spring is rigidly fixed (Fig. 22.10.1) or almost completely free (spring tied to a very light thread as in Fig. 22.10.2c) represent extreme cases in which the medium of propagation is abruptly terminated, and a wave cannot be transmitted through the boundary.

Figures 22.10.1 and 22.10.2 illustrate wave reflection and transmission in one dimension. In two- and three-dimensional situations, water ripples and sound waves also undergo reflection and transmission at any region of change in the character of the medium. Sound waves are reflected from cliffs or walls (echos) and from water surfaces. Sound waves traveling in a tube are reflected on arrival at the open end, the open end representing a change in the medium because the air outside is not confined by walls as it is within the tube. While sound waves are reflected at a boundary, some sound is also transmitted *through* the interface, as we recognize on hearing the muffled sound of voices through the wall of a room.

In a similar fashion, ripples on a water surface undergo reflection at boundaries of various kinds—from a wall or from a region of abrupt change in the depth of water. Figures 22.10.3 and 22.10.4 illustrate the reflection of wave pulses from a straight barrier in a ripple tank. If the interface consists of an abrupt change in depth rather than a rigid barrier, a wave is also transmitted into the region on the other side of the interface (Figure 22.10.3a). The transmitted wave is also referred to as a refracted wave. It can be regarded as a propagation of the incident disturbance into the medium, the refraction taking place abruptly at the interface.

22.11   THE LAWS OF REFLECTION AND TRANSMISSION

Figure 22.11.1 is a line drawing of the wave fronts and rays for a situation similar to that shown in Fig. 22.10.3(a), and serves to define the terminology we shall use in this context. If $\theta_i = 0$, the incident ray is normal to the interface and the wave is said to be at normal incidence. If $\theta_i = 90°$, the wave is said to be at grazing incidence. A photograph taken a short time later would show the entire pattern displaced to the right a distance $v_s \Delta t$.

In experiments such as those illustrated in Fig. 22.10.3, we always note that θ_r seems to be very nearly equal to θ_i. Furthermore θ_t is observed to be greater or less than θ_i, depending on whether V_t is greater or less than V_i. If θ_i is increased, the other two angles are increased. It is inviting to try to construct a theory of wave behavior that would account for these qualitative observations and that would predict quantitative relations as well. We shall construct such a theory by showing that we can visualize the reflected and transmitted wave fronts as bow waves originating with the motion of point O' along the interface.

As the incident wave moves forward at velocity V_i, its point of contact (O' in Fig. 22.11.1) with the interface moves toward the right at a velocity we shall denote by v_s. Thus, after a time interval Δt, the incident wave front will have propagated a distance $V_i \Delta t$ and will be in the location shown by dotted lines in Fig. 22.11.1.

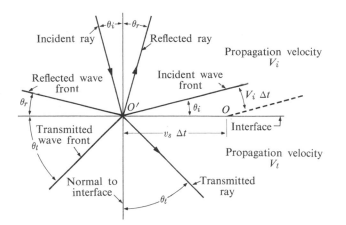

FIG. 22.11.1. Terminology used in describing reflection and transmission at an interface. Arrows on rays indicate direction of propagation of respective waves. The angle θ_i = angle of incidence, θ_r = angle of reflection, and θ_t = angle of transmission or refraction.

Point O' will have moved to position O, a distance $v_s \, \Delta t$. Therefore

$$\sin \theta_i = \frac{V_i \, \Delta t}{v_s \, \Delta t},$$

$$v_s = \frac{V_i}{\sin \theta_i}. \tag{22.11.1}$$

Let us interpret this result: (1) At grazing incidence: $\sin \theta_i = 1$, since $\theta_i = 90°$. Then $v_s = V_i$ and the point of contact moves with the propagation velocity of the wave.

(2) As θ_i is made less than $90°$, $\sin \theta_i$ decreases, and $v_s > V_i$. Thus, in general, the point of contact moves along the interface at a velocity higher than that of the wave propagation. We showed in Section 22.9 that a disturbance moving at $v_s > V$ will generate bow waves. This suggests that we might regard the reflected and transmitted wave fronts as bow waves generated by the contact point as it moves along the interface.

PROBLEM 22.11. Verify that Eq. (22.11.1) implies that $v_s \to \infty$ as $\theta_i \to 0$. Interpret this result by describing the behavior of the point of contact as the wave approaches normal incidence. Do you find anything particularly unpalatable about the possibility of an infinite velocity in this context?

Figure 22.11.2 shows the pattern of incident, reflected, and transmitted wave fronts at two successive instants of time. Treating OA and OB as bow waves, we have,

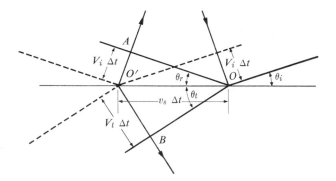

FIG. 22.11.2. Point of contact of incident wave front moves along interface from O' to O with velocity $v_s = V_i/\sin\theta_i$, generating the reflected and incident wave fronts as bow waves.

in accordance with Eq. (22.9.1):

$$\sin\theta_r = \frac{V_i}{v_s}, \tag{22.11.2}$$

$$\sin\theta_t = \frac{V_t}{v_s}. \tag{22.11.3}$$

Using Eq. (22.11.1) to eliminate v_s from (22.11.2), we obtain

$$\sin\theta_r = \frac{V_i}{V_i}\sin\theta_i = \sin\theta_i,$$

$$\theta_r = \theta_i. \tag{22.11.4}$$

Equation (22.11.4) is called the law of reflection, and, translated into words, informs us that the angle of incidence must equal the angle of reflection. Such reflection from a smooth surface is frequently referred to as *specular*.

Eliminating v_s from Eq. (22.11.3), we obtain

$$\sin\theta_t = \frac{V_t}{V_i}\sin\theta_i, \tag{22.11.5}$$

$$\frac{\sin\theta_t}{\sin\theta_i} = \frac{V_t}{V_i}. \tag{22.11.6}$$

Equation (22.11.6) is called the law of refraction.

PROBLEM 22.12. Interpret Eq. (22.11.6). How is θ_t related to θ_i when $V_t > V_i$? when $V_t < V_i$? Sketch the orientation of wave fronts and rays for each case. If, in a transmitted wave, you observe the ray to have been bent *away* from the normal, on which side of the interface will you find the higher propagation velocity? Compare your sketches and analysis with Fig. 22.10.3(a).

PROBLEM 22.13. Suppose it is given that $V_t/V_i = 0.5$. Sketch the position of the refracted ray and wave front as the incident wave approaches grazing incidence. Suppose that $V_t/V_i = 2$. Sketch the position of the refracted ray and wave front as θ_i approaches 30°. What happens if θ_i exceeds 30°? Plot a graph of θ_t-versus-θ_i for each of these two cases. Compare and interpret the graphs.

It is sometimes convenient to describe propagation velocities not in units of feet/sec or meters/sec but in terms of some standard reference velocity V_0. For example, in the case of sound in air, V_0 might be taken to be the velocity at 0°C: 1087 ft/sec. A standard convention is adopted in which the dimensionless ratios $n_i \equiv V_0/V_i$ and $n_t \equiv V_0/V_t$ are used to describe the two media forming the interface. With this definition, the law of refraction takes the form

$$\frac{\sin \theta_t}{\sin \theta_i} = \frac{V_t}{V_i} = \frac{V_t/V_0}{V_i/V_0} = \frac{n_i}{n_t}. \tag{22.11.7}$$

The quantities n_t and n_i are called indices of refraction of the respective media. The medium of higher index of refraction exhibits lower propagation velocity.

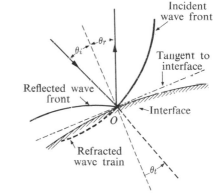

FIG. 22.11.3. Reflection and refraction of a curved wave front at a curved interface ($V_t < V_i$). Equations (22.11.4) and (22.11.6) apply to rays shown in the diagram.

In Figs. 22.11.1 and 2 we seem to have been dealing exclusively with plane wave fronts incident at plane interfaces, and this might make it appear that the laws of reflection and refraction we have derived are not general but are restricted to these special cases. Our results, however, are *not* restricted in this way. We can generalize our argument by imagining Figs. 22.11.1 and 2 to be enormously magnified pictures of the geometrical situation immediately in the neighborhood of the contact point at the interface. The straight lines indicating the interface and wave fronts are then simply the lines tangent to an interface and wave fronts that are actually curved. A larger view of the situation may be something like that shown in Fig. 22.11.3, while Fig. 22.11.2 may be regarded as a greatly expanded sketch of the geometry in a small region about point O. Equations (22.11.4) and (22.11.6) are valid for this case instant by instant, but since the incident wave and the interface are both curved, θ_i and the other angles change continuously as the wave moves along the interface. Furthermore, because of the curvature, it is usually more convenient to describe angles in terms of the various rays and the normal to the interface rather than in terms of the tangents to the curved wave fronts.

Reflection and refraction can also take place at a rough, broken, or corrugated surface. Roughness must be measured in relation to the wavelength of the incident wave. A smooth surface is one in which the dimensions of the surface irregularities are much smaller than the wavelength; here the reflection and refraction take place as predicted in this section, and the resulting waves are said to be *coherent*.

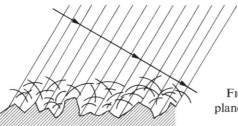

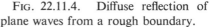

FIG. 22.11.4.   Diffuse reflection of plane waves from a rough boundary.

If the dimensions of the irregularities, however, are of the same order of magnitude as the wavelength, locally reflected and refracted wavelets do not overlap in a regular way to produce a bow wave, but propagate out in random phase relative to each other, as indicated in Fig. 22.11.4. Such reflected waves are said to be *incoherent*, *diffusely reflected*, or *scattered*.

22.12   CRITICAL ANGLE FOR TOTAL REFLECTION

Let us return to the law of refraction in the form

$$\sin \theta_t = \frac{V_t}{V_i} \sin \theta_i, \tag{22.12.1}$$

and examine the behavior of θ_t with increasing θ_i when a wave is refracted into a medium of higher propagation velocity; i.e., for the case $V_t/V_i > 1$.

When $\theta_i = 0$, θ_t is also zero, indicating that a normally incident wave is transmitted without refraction. As θ_i increases, θ_t also increases, but $\theta_t > \theta_i$, since $V_t/V_i > 1$. This means that the refracted ray must be bent *away* from the normal. As long as θ_i is small enough, the product $(V_t/V_i) \sin \theta_i$ is less than 1, and θ_t is less than 90°. When θ_i increases to a value such that $\sin \theta_i$ is greater than V_i/V_t, however, Eq. 22.12.1 assigns $\sin \theta_t$ a value greater than 1, but the sine function is so defined that its magnitude never exceeds 1 for any angle whatsoever, and we have apparently exceeded the applicability of our equation. What has gone wrong?

Let us return to the largest value of θ_i that yields a meaningful result: this is the value θ_{ic} such that

$$\sin \theta_{ic} = \frac{V_i}{V_t}. \tag{22.12.2}$$

For this particular value of θ_i, we find that $\theta_t = 90°$, and the transmitted ray is parallel

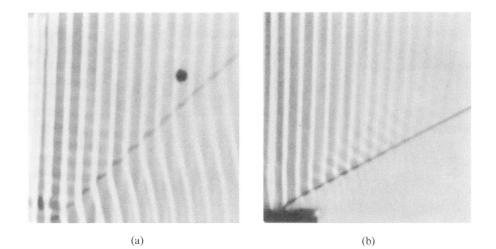

(a)   (b)

FIG. 22.12.1. Reflection of ripples at an abrupt increase of depth in the ripple tank. (a) $\theta_i < \theta_{ic}$; refracted and reflected waves are both present. (b) θ_i close to θ_{ic}; refracted wave has almost disappeared. Incident and reflected waves are visible. (From the film, "Barrier penetration—Bragg reflection—Doppler effect," produced by Educational Services, Inc.)

to the interface. It is perfectly possible, however, to increase θ_i beyond the value θ_{ic}; in order to find out what happens under these circumstances, it is necessary to appeal to experiment or to a more complete dynamical analysis of the wave behavior. In either case, we find that for angles of incidence greater than θ_{ic}, there ceases to be any transmission of disturbance into the second medium, and the incident wave is said to be totally reflected at the interface. The angle θ_{ic} is called the *critical angle for total reflection*. Figure 22.12.1 illustrates the total reflection of ripples when $\theta_i > \theta_{ic}$ at a region of abrupt increase in the depth of water.

Refraction as well as total reflection of explosion pulses and earthquake waves from layers of different propagation velocity within the earth's crust and the ocean bottom play a dominant role in certain areas of geophysical research. Layers and geological structures, inaccessible to direct sampling and determination of physical structure or chemical composition, can be characterized by propagation velocities inferred from travel times of reflected and refracted waves. Much geological oil-prospecting depends on such analyses, and our model of the structure of the interior of the earth is based largely on inferences drawn from seismic (earthquake) wave observations.

PROBLEM 22.14. What is the critical angle for total reflection of a sound wave (in air) from a water surface? Take the velocity of sound to be about 1100 ft/sec in air and 4900 ft/sec in water. What is the critical angle at a sand bottom in which the sound velocity is about 1.25 times that in the water above? Sketch several diagrams of incident, reflected, and transmitted rays at different angles of incidence for each of these two cases.

22.13 SUPERPOSITION

A dramatic aspect of wave behavior is exhibited in the manner in which wave pulses, traveling in different directions, can literally pass through each other without any appreciable effect on their form and propagation. The deflections at any given location add algebraically from instant to instant, and the pulses continue propagating as though each were present alone. This phenomenon is illustrated for pulses on a spring in Fig. 22.13.1 and 22.13.2, and constitutes another example of the broad concept of superposition referred to in a variety of different contexts in earlier chapters. It is apparent that the waves illustrated obey a simple superposition principle. The superposition of trains of water ripples is illustrated in Figs. 22.10.3 and 22.10.4.

Since we are able to discern different sounds simultaneously, we infer that sound waves also superpose, traveling through each other without alteration.

Our descriptions of the formation of bow waves and of coherent and diffuse reflection have already utilized the superposition concepts implicitly. In the following sections we shall pursue additional consequences of this aspect of wave behavior.

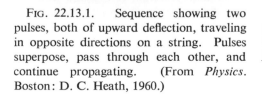

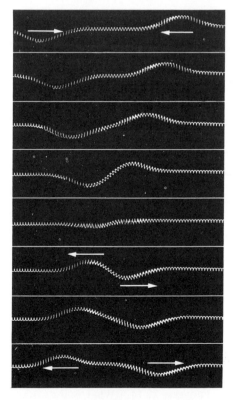

FIG. 22.13.1.   Sequence showing two pulses, both of upward deflection, traveling in opposite directions on a string. Pulses superpose, pass through each other, and continue propagating.   (From *Physics*. Boston: D. C. Heath, 1960.)

FIG. 22.13.2.   Sequence showing superposition of two pulses of opposite deflection traveling in opposite directions.   (From *Physics*. Boston: D. C. Heath, 1960.)

(a) Rack consists of metal bars that are free to slide up and down. Their tops are cut to form a sinusoidal wave form. Wooden template, cut to the same wave form, can be "superposed," lifting the bars from below. In this picture wave trains are in phase with each other.

(b) Constructive interference. Wave trains are superposed crest to crest and trough to trough. Resultant wave form has twice the amplitude of the individual wave trains.

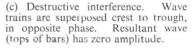

(c) Destructive interference. Wave trains are superposed crest to trough, in opposite phase. Resultant wave (tops of bars) has zero amplitude.

(d) Wave forms with same amplitude but slightly different wavelength. If they are out of phase at one point, they will be in phase at another.

(e) Superposition of wave forms in (d) leads to succession of regions of destructive and constructive interference. This phenomenon is called "beating" or "beats."

FIGURE 22.14.1

22.14 INTERFERENCE

If we contrive to make two periodic trains of the same wave form and wave-length overlap while traveling in very nearly the same direction, we can anticipate two extremes that might occur in the superposition (Fig. 22.14.1). This special case of superposition is referred to as *interference*, and the examples illustrated in Figs. 22.14.1(b) and (c) are called constructive and destructive, respectively.

Figure 22.14.2 shows patterns observed when circular ripples originate from two point sources, oscillating in phase with each other, and placed fairly close together in the ripple tank. The geometry of the pattern changes as either the wavelength or the distance between the sources is changed. On examining the photographs, we

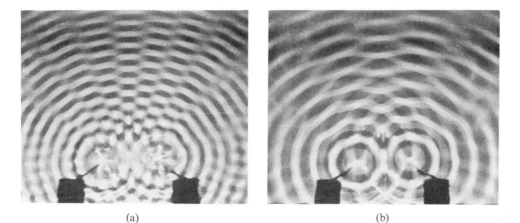

(a)   (b)

FIG. 22.14.2. Ripple-tank photographs showing interference pattern formed by super-position of circular waves from two point sources. Spacing between sources is identical in (a) and (b), but wavelength is larger in (b). (From *Physics*. Boston: D. C. Heath, 1960.)

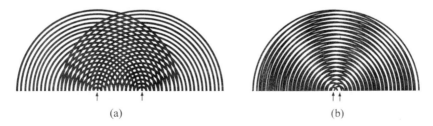

(a)   (b)

FIG. 22.14.3. Lines represent crests; spaces between them represent troughs. When source spacing d is much larger than the wavelength λ, waves crisscross each other as in (a) without forming a pronounced pattern. When d is only slightly larger than λ, the waves intersect at a more oblique angle, and a pattern is formed as in (b). The dark loci are regions where crests cross troughs and simulate nodal lines of destructive interference. Light regions are loci where crests cross crests and troughs cross troughs, simulating constructive interference.

can readily identify lines (called nodal* lines) along which the resultant wave amplitude appears to be zero. Here the waves from the two sources overlap systematically crest to trough and interfere destructively, as illustrated in Fig. 22.14.1(c). In the sectors between the nodal lines, we can identify constructive interference as the waves superpose crest to crest and trough to trough.

The reader will find it very illuminating to produce diagrams such as those in Fig. 22.14.3 by drawing circles with a compass carrying a very blunt pencil, making a wide line. Taking a fixed wavelength as shown in the figure and changing the spacing between the sources, he can develop a feeling for how the pattern of dark loci, simulating destructive interference, fans *out* as the spacing d between the sources is made smaller and more nearly equal to λ, and how it contracts into the crisscross pattern of Fig. 22.14.3(a) as d is made much larger than λ. Fig. 22.14.4 shows a greatly expanded drawing of the region near the two sources in Fig. 22.14.3(b).

Examining Fig. 22.14.4, we note that the principal axis is itself a locus of constructive interference. Everywhere along it the waves from the two sources arrive in phase,

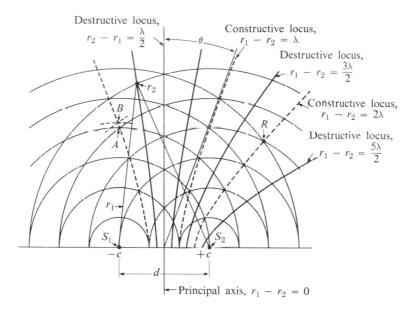

Fig. 22.14.4. Greatly expanded drawing of region near sources in Fig. 22.14.3(b). Loci of constructive and destructive interference are hyperbolas with foci at S_1 and S_2. At relatively large distances from the origin the hyperbolas are indistinguishably close to their asymptotes, and appear to be straight lines radiating from the origin at angles θ to the principal axis. The loci are fixed in space even though the waves are continually moving. As the crests which intersect at point A both move outward to the dotted positions, their intersection moves to B along the fixed locus of constructive interference.

---

* The term "node" refers to a point or region of permanently zero deflection or disturbance.

having traveled equal distances $r_1 = r_2$. The first locus of destructive interference to the right of the axis is one along which the waves are everywhere exactly out of phase; the wave from S_1 has traveled a distance r_1 which exceeds r_2 by exactly one-half wavelength; i.e., the locus is defined by the relation $r_1 - r_2 = \lambda/2$. The other loci are defined in a similar way; for example, point R is in a region of constructive interference because the seventh crest from S_1 superposes on the fifth crest from S_2, the phase lag being exactly two wavelengths; that is, $r_1 - r_2 = 2\lambda$.

It has been implied in the preceding discussion that we are concerned with interference patterns formed by waves from two separate vibrating sources. We could, of course, produce an exactly equivalent situation by allowing a plane wave train to impinge on a barrier with two small openings or slits a distance d apart. If the openings themselves are narrower than the wavelength, they act as point sources (Fig. 22.6.1a), diffracting the incident wave and emitting circular wavelets exactly in phase with each other. The resulting interference pattern is precisely like that of two separate vibrating sources.

PROBLEM 22.15.   Using a compass, construct figures similar to Figs. 22.14.3 and 4, and locate the loci of constructive and destructive interference. Explain in your own words the definitions of several of these loci by accounting for the phase difference between the two waves in each case.

22.15   ELEMENTARY ANALYSIS OF THE TWO-SOURCE INTERFERENCE PATTERN

Examination of Figs. 22.14.2, 3, and 4 reveals that the loci of constructive and destructive interference are curved lines (in the next section we shall show that these curves are hyperbolas), but that the curvature is pronounced only in the immediate neighborhood of the sources. At distances of the order of two or three times the source spacing d, the loci are indistinguishable from straight lines radiating from an origin located at the midpoint between the sources. This property suggests a very simple way of obtaining an algebraic description of the angles θ (Fig. 22.14.4) between various particular loci and the principal axis.

In Fig. 22.15.1 and its accompanying caption, it is shown that for points relatively far out along the first nodal line the inclinations of radii r_1 and r_2 toward each other can be neglected; the radii can be treated as though they were essentially parallel to each other. On this basis a simple relation among θ, λ, and d can be inferred from the small right triangle $A'S_2S_1$ in Fig. 22.15.1(b). It is immediately apparent that

$$\sin \theta_1 = \frac{\lambda}{2d}, \tag{22.15.1}$$

where θ_1 denotes the angular position of the first nodal line on either side of the principal axis. Other nodal lines will occur at larger angles, for which the distance S_1A' in Fig. 22.15.1(b) is equal to three half-wavelengths, five half-wavelengths, etc.

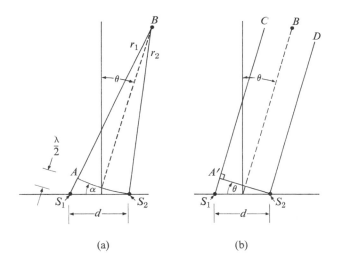

(a)   (b)

FIG. 22.15.1. (a) Point B lies relatively far out on the first nodal line, the locus $r_1 -$ $r_2 = \lambda/2$. With B as a center, we draw arc S_2A. The length S_1A is then equal to $\lambda/2$ and, since S_2A is very nearly a straight line, we can think of α as an angle whose sine is $\lambda/2d$. (b) Point B lies on first nodal line, but instead of radii r_1 and r_2, we draw lines S_1C and S_2D parallel to the nodal line. Line S_2A' is then drawn perpendicular to S_1C. Angle $A'S_2S_1$ is then equal to θ. When point B is relatively far from the origin, triangle AS_2S_1 in (a) is very nearly identical with triangle $A'S_2S_1$ in (b). S_1A' is then very nearly equal to $\lambda/2$ and θ is very nearly equal to α. Thus $\sin \theta = \lambda/2d$, to an extremely close approximation.

Expressing this result more compactly, we note that nodal lines occur at those angles θ_n for which:

$$\sin \theta_n = (2n - 1)\frac{\lambda}{2d}, \qquad n = 1, 2, 3, 4, \dots, \tag{22.15.2}$$

$(2n - 1)$ being an expression that gives us the successive odd numbers when we substitute integer values for n.

In an exactly similar fashion, we note that constructive interference will occur along lines oriented in such a way that the path difference S_1A' in Fig. 22.15.1(b) will be equal to one, two, three, or any other whole number of wavelengths. Thus we conclude that loci of constructive interference will lie at angles θ_n for which:

$$\sin \theta_n = n\frac{\lambda}{d}, \qquad n = 1, 2, 3, 4, \dots. \tag{22.15.3}$$

Thus, if we know λ and d, we can immediately predict the angular positions of the various constructive and destructive loci. If we do not know λ but determine the source spacing and measure, say θ_2, the angular position of the second nodal line, we can compute the wavelength of the wave train.

PROBLEM 22.16. Interpret Eqs. (22.15.2 and 3), and connect them explicitly with various loci in Figs. 22.14.2, 3, and 4. Note that for any particular source spacing d and wavelength λ, the number n ceases to have physical significance after exceeding a certain value. Why? For any given pattern, how do you determine the highest meaningful value of n? What is this value in Fig. 22.14.4? What happens when λ becomes larger than d? Larger than $2d$? (Note that if $\lambda \gg 2d$, the two sources cannot be distinguished from a single source emitting circular waves into the medium.)

PROBLEM 22.17. In a ripple-tank experiment with a spacing of 3.0 cm between the sources, a point on the first nodal line is found to be located as shown in Fig. 22.15.2. Compute the wavelength of the ripples. [*Answer:* $\lambda = 1.2$ cm.]

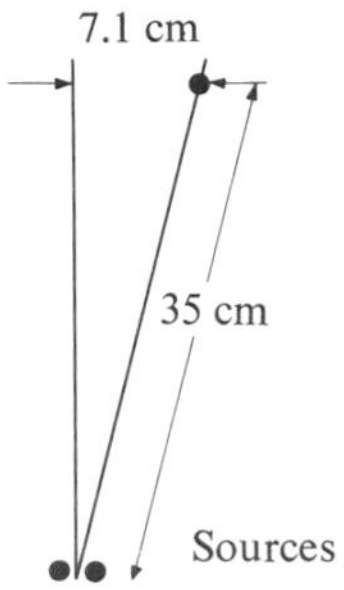

7.1 cm

35 cm

Sources

FIGURE 22.15.2

PROBLEM 22.18. Suppose that Fig. 22.14.4 represents a ripple-tank experiment in which $d = 6.0$ cm and $\lambda = 2.0$ cm. Suppose further that you cannot see the pattern directly for lack of projection of a shadow pattern, but that you are equipped with a small probe that is sensitive to wave amplitude. You start at a point on the y-axis at a large radius R from the source and move the probe around the circular arc of radius R. Predict what the probe will indicate, giving numerical values of angles at which you expect a maximum or a minimum response. [*Answer:* minima at $\theta = 9.6°$, $30°$, $56°$; maxima at $\theta = 19°$, $43°$.]

PROBLEM 22.19. Suppose that you were to perform an experiment exactly like that in Problem 22.18, except that the sources are two tuning forks having a frequency of 440 cycles/sec, placed 7.0 ft apart and vibrating exactly in phase with each other. This time the sensitive "probe" is your own ear as you walk around the arc of a circle at radius R from the source. Describe what you would hear, giving numerical values of appropriate angles. (Take the velocity of sound to be 1100 ft/sec.)

PROBLEM 22.20. Suppose that the two point sources vibrate unreliably, randomly shifting their phase relative to each other. What would happen; would you expect to observe an interference pattern? Suppose that in Fig. 22.14.4 the vibration is steady but the phase relation between the sources is changed, so that S_2 emits a trough at precisely the moment S_1 emits a crest (i.e., the phase lag would be equivalent to $\lambda/2$). What would happen to the interference pattern?

22.16 RIGOROUS ANALYSIS OF TWO-SOURCE INTERFERENCE PATTERN

We shall now show that a rigorous analysis of the two-source pattern gives the same results as those obtained in the preceding section.

Section 3.8 discusses the equation of a curve defined to be the locus of points $P(x, y)$ such that the absolute value of the difference between distances to two foci F_1 and F_2 has a fixed value $2a$, smaller than the distance F_1F_2 which is denoted by

2c. This curve is called an hyperbola, and its equation is shown to be

$$\frac{x^2}{a^2} - \frac{y^2}{c^2 - a^2} = 1. \tag{22.16.1}$$

From the definitions of the loci of constructive and destructive interference in Fig. 22.14.4, we note that these loci must be hyperbolas with the source spacing d corresponding to the quantity $2c$, and with the respective phase lags of $\lambda/2$, λ, $\frac{3}{2}\lambda$, 2λ, etc., corresponding in each individual case to the quantity $2a$. The hyperbola of Eq. (22.16.1) has branches symmetrically situated about the y-axis, and the observed wave interference pattern has precisely this symmetry.

The hyperbolic character of the nodal lines can be discerned in Fig. 22.14.2 and is very apparent when one looks obliquely at the water surface of a ripple tank in which a two-source interference pattern is being formed.

PROBLEM 22.21. Derive Eq. (22.16.1) and convert it into an equation of the first (off-axis) locus of constructive interference in terms of d and λ.

$$\left[Answer: \frac{4x^2}{\lambda^2} - \frac{4y^2}{d^2 - \lambda^2} = 1. \right]$$

In Section 3.8 it was shown that the asymptotes of an hyperbola are described by the equations

$$y = \pm \frac{\sqrt{c^2 - a^2}}{a} x \tag{22.16.2}$$

or

$$\sin \theta = \frac{2a}{2c}, \tag{22.16.3}$$

where θ denotes the angle between the asymptote and the y-axis.

At relatively large distances from the origin the hyperbola becomes very nearly a straight line, virtually indistinguishable from its asymptote, and we can therefore represent the loci of constructive and destructive interference in our two-source pattern by means of Eqs. (22.16.2) and (22.16.3). In our present formulation d corresponds to $2c$, and the path difference $\lambda/2$, λ, $3\lambda/2$, etc., for any particular locus corresponds to $2a$.

On substituting into Eq. (22.16.3), we obtain for $2a$ equal to an odd number of half-wavelengths (destructive interference):

$$\sin \theta_n = (2n - 1)\frac{\lambda}{2d}, \qquad n = 1, 2, 3, 4, \ldots, \tag{22.16.4}$$

and for $2a$ equal to an integral number of whole wavelengths (constructive interference):

$$\sin \theta_n = n\frac{\lambda}{d}, \qquad n = 0, 1, 2, 3, 4, \ldots, \tag{22.16.5}$$

exactly as in the preceding section. The case $n = 0$ in (22.16.5) corresponds to the principal axis.

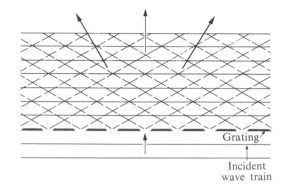

FIG. 22.17.1. Plane wave train in ripple tank incident on a plane grating. Arrows show directions of propagation of three emerging wave trains.

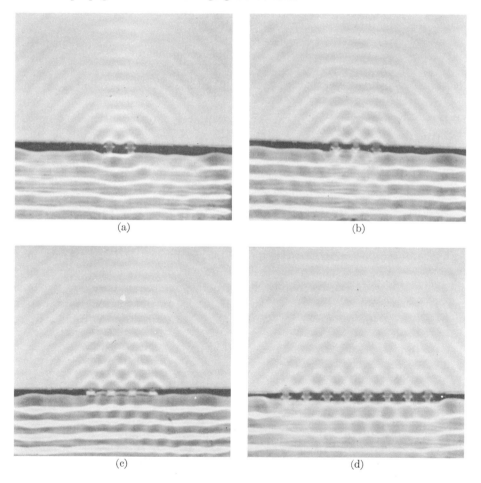

(a)   (b)

(c)   (d)

FIG. 22.17.2. Ripple-tank photographs showing alteration of transmitted wave pattern as more openings are added to an array so as to form a "grating." (From the film, "Interference and Diffraction," produced by Educational Services, Inc.)

22.17 PLANE WAVE TRANSMITTED THROUGH A GRATING

An important modification of the interference pattern is produced when, instead of just two sources, we have a large array of sources, uniformly spaced along a straight line, and all emitting circular waves in the same phase. This condition can be achieved in the ripple tank by allowing a plane wave train to impinge on a grating—a barrier pierced by narrow slits uniformly spaced a distance d apart. The slit opening D is smaller than λ. The slits diffract the incident wave and act as coherent point sources. A sketch of what is observed in such a situation is shown in Fig. 22.17.1. Emerging from the grating are several *plane* wave trains having different directions of propagation relative to the principal axis!

The ripple-tank photographs in Fig. 22.17.2 show how this pattern is built up, as more and more openings are added to the array.

We can help ourselves understand Figs. 22.17.1 and 2 by once more constructing wavelets with a compass. Such a construction is illustrated in Fig. 22.17.3. (The reader will find it easier to follow the discussion if he constructs a diagram such as 22.17.3 for himself.) In this construction we find that wavelets overlap so as to reconstitute plane wave fronts (as in the illustration of the bow wave in Fig. 22.9.2), the fronts being pointed up more clearly if we draw tangents to them, as we have at

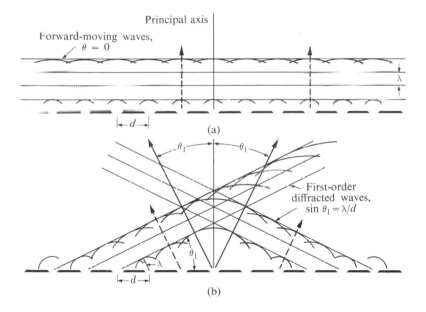

Fig. 22.17.3. Plane waves diffracted through openings in a uniformly spaced grating. In the forward direction ($\theta = 0$) wavelets superpose after equal distances of travel to form forward-moving plane waves as in (a). In the direction θ_1, wavelets with path differences of one whole wavelength between successive openings superpose to form a bow wave traveling at an angle θ_1 relative to the principal axis. Another wave is to be expected at a larger angle θ_2, such that path differences between waves from successive openings are two whole wavelengths, etc.

several locations in Fig. 22.17.3. One reconstituted wave front (Figure 22.17.3a) travels in the original direction along the principal axis; the inclination of its ray relative to the axis is zero. Additional plane wave fronts are formed propagating in the particular direction θ_1 (Fig. 22.17.3b) indicated by the respective rays, but there are *no* organized wave fronts traveling in any direction between 0 and θ_1.

It is evident from Fig. 22.17.3(b) that

$$\sin \theta_1 = \frac{\lambda}{d}$$

and that, in general, plane wave fronts would be formed moving in directions defined by

$$\sin \theta_n = \frac{n\lambda}{d}, \qquad \text{where } n = 0, 1, 2, 3 \ldots, \qquad (22.17.1)$$

the pattern being symmetrical on either side of the principal axis. The case $n = 0$ represents the wave traveling parallel to the principal axis, while the two waves on either side of the axis with $n = 1$ and angle θ_1 are called the first-order waves; the ones for $n = 2$, the second order-waves, etc. Second-order waves will not exist if $(2\lambda/d) > 1$. As d is made larger or λ smaller, θ_1 decreases, and more orders of waves appear in the pattern. A grating used in this fashion is called a *diffraction grating;* the wavelets diffracted through the small openings are responsible for the resulting interference pattern.

Contrast the effect of the grating with the two-source pattern exhibited in the figures of Section 22.14. If you walk around the periphery of a two-source pattern at a large distance from the source, you would observe fairly sharp regions of destructive interference at certain particular angles. Between these angles you would observe broad regions in which the waves do not cancel each other but vary in amplitude from zero at one nodal line, through a maximum of constructive interference, to zero at the next nodal line. In these regions the wave fronts are curved, and rays exist for all angles between those of the two nodal lines that bound the region. If you walk around a circle at a large distance R from the grating, however, you would observe a plane wave arriving along the principal axis and additional plane waves at the sharply defined directions θ_1 and θ_2, but you would observe no waves having rays at intermediate angles. The effect of the grating as opposed to the double source is to produce a tremendous sharpening of the directions of constructive interference and to extinguish the waves in the intermediate directions.

PROBLEM 22.22. Interpret Eq. 22.17.1. Describe how you might utilize a diffraction-grating experiment to determine the wavelength of an unknown wave. Answer the questions raised in Problem 22.18, supposing that you use a grating with a slit spacing of 6.0 cm instead of a double source.

22.18 SINGLE-SLIT DIFFRACTION PATTERN

We return now to the sequence of ripple experiments illustrated in Fig. 22.6.1. Experience with the double-source and diffraction-grating patterns has taught us that interference effects can be expected to be most pronounced when the wave-

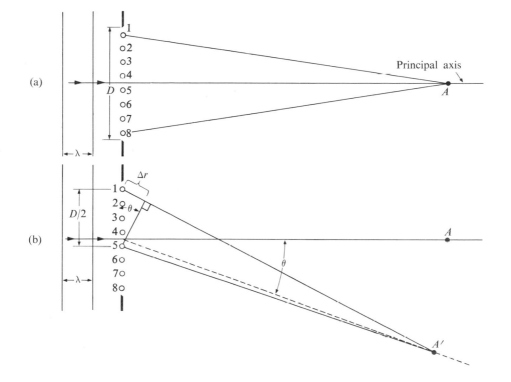

FIG. 22.18.1. (a) Along the principal axis at points such as A: For every fictitious source point above the axis, there is a symmetrically placed source point at the slit below the axis (1 and 8, 2 and 7, etc.). Waves arriving at A from these pairs of points travel the same distance and interfere constructively. Therefore the net effect is to produce constructive interference everywhere along the principal axis. (b) As the point of observation is moved away from the axis along the arc from A to A', path lengths from the fictitious source points change, and wavelets arrive at A' more and more out of phase with each other. At some angle θ_1, Δr will become equal to $\lambda/2$, and waves from sources 1 and 5 will cancel each other. The other pairs (2 and 6, 3 and 7, etc.) will cancel at the same time. There will be a nodal line at angular position θ_1, given by $\sin \theta_1 = (\lambda/2)/(D/2) = \lambda/D$.

length λ is somewhat less than that of a source spacing d. In Fig. 22.6.1(b) we have a definite interference pattern when the slit opening D is itself somewhat larger than λ. This pattern is apparently completely fanned out in (a), where $\lambda \sim D$, and the opening behaves more like a point source. The pattern is apparently compressed into a forward-propagating beam of waves when $\lambda \ll D$, as in Fig. 22.6.1(c).

These observations motivate an attempt to interpret the pattern in Fig. 22.6.1(b) by visualizing an array of point sources lined up along the slit opening D, and emitting waves in phase with each other, as sketched in Fig. 22.18.1.

Figure 22.18.1(a) indicates that we would expect constructive interference all along the principal axis. Figure 22.18.1(b) indicates that we would expect the wave amplitude to decrease as we move to angular positions θ away from the principal axis, and that we would expect nodal lines on either side of the axis at angular positions given by

$$\sin \theta_n = (2n - 1)\frac{\lambda}{D}, \qquad \text{where } n = 1, 2, 3 \ldots. \qquad (22.18.1)$$

Similarly, we would expect lines of greatest amplitude at angles given by

$$\sin \theta_n = 2n\frac{\lambda}{D}, \qquad \text{where } n = 0, 1, 2, \ldots. \qquad (22.18.2)$$

PROBLEM 22.23.   Extend the explanation given in the caption of Fig. 22.18.1(b) so as to derive and justify Eqs. (22.18.1) and (22.18.2). Interpret these equations. At what value of n for a given λ/D do they cease to have physical meaning? What approximations are implicit in the treatment? (Compare with the discussion associated with Fig. 22.15.1.) Make several sketches which are similar to 22.18.1(b), but which show how the path lengths differ and sources pair up along the next outlying regions of constructive and destructive interference.

22.19   DISPERSION

Figure 22.19.1 shows the refraction of two sets of ripples of different wavelength at an abrupt change in depth in a ripple tank. In Fig. 22.19.1(a), a low-frequency wave is refracted. Since the refracted ray is bent *toward* the normal to the interface and since the wavelength is shorter after refraction than before, we conclude that

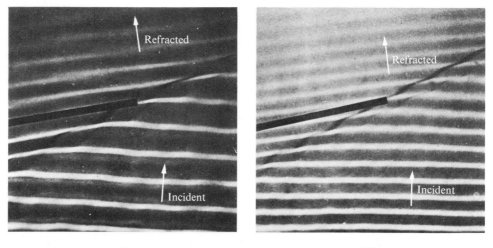

(a)   (b)

FIG. 22.19.1.   Dispersion: Waves of two different wavelengths refracted at an abrupt change of depth in ripple tank. Position of black marker was not changed when wavelength was shortened. Experiment shows that wave velocity in this case is a function of wavelength as well as depth of water. (From *Physics*. Boston: D. C. Heath, 1960.)

$V_i > V_t$. (Why?) A black marker is lined up with the refracted wave fronts to mark their orientation. The ripple frequency is then increased (wavelength decreased), producing the situation shown in Fig. 22.19.1(b). We note that the refracted wave fronts are no longer parallel to the black marker. The angle of refraction, θ_t, is slightly *larger* in case (b) than in case (a). From the law of refraction, Eq. (22.11.6), we have

$$\frac{\sin \theta_t}{\sin \theta_i} = \frac{V_t}{V_i}. \tag{22.19.1}$$

Since θ_i is the same for both cases in Fig. 22.19.1, we conclude that

$$\left(\frac{V_t}{V_i}\right)_{\text{case (b)}} > \left(\frac{V_t}{V_i}\right)_{\text{case (a)}}.$$

Since the medium remained completely unchanged in this experiment and only the frequency was altered, we are forced to conclude that ripple velocity depends not only on the depth of water but also on the frequency (or wavelength) of the ripples. Careful velocity measurements would fully confirm this conclusion; ripple velocity is actually a fairly complicated function of both wavelength and water depth (as well as of the surface tension of the liquid).

The phenomenon of variation of wave propagation velocity with wave frequency is called *dispersion*, and a medium which exhibits this property is characterized as a *dispersive medium*. Not all media exhibit dispersive effects. Small-amplitude waves on a stretched spring all have very nearly the same velocity over a wide range of frequencies. Air shows extremely little dispersion of sound waves over the wide range of audible frequencies. Long water waves (i.e., those whose wavelengths λ are much greater than the depth of water D in which they move) all have the same velocity $V = \sqrt{gD}$, independent of the wave frequency (g denotes acceleration due to gravity).

We can always recognize the presence of dispersion, either by direct evidence of variation of velocity with wavelength or indirectly by observation of different refraction of different wavelengths at an interface, as in Fig. 22.19.1.

22.20   ENERGY AND MOMENTUM IN WAVE PROPAGATION

The laws of conservation of energy and momentum are found to apply to wave propagation fully as rigorously as they apply to the simpler particle motions and displacements discussed in earlier chapters. Detailed mathematical calculations substantiating this assertion can be carried out in straightforward fashion, but are beyond the scope of this text. We can, however, readily draw some useful qualitative insights from our direct experience with wave phenomena.

To keep generating a bow wave from a moving object or to keep generating a continuous periodic wave train from a vibrating source, it is obvious that we must maintain a continuous supply of energy in the form of work done on the source. If we fail to do so, the source "runs down": the moving boat coasts to a stop; the wave rippler stops moving up and down; the tuning fork stops vibrating.   This running down and coming to a stop, however, is very different from frictional sliding of a block on a table.   In the latter case the kinetic energy of the block is totally converted into heat, raising the temperature of the block and its surroundings. In the former case, the running down is accompanied by extremely little temperature rise; instead, a disturbance propagates to regions remote from the source and is capable of accelerating objects, and causing displacements against resisting forces, at these remote points.

In other words, both momentum and energy are lost by the source, but the energy is not immediately dissipated as heat.   Nor are the momentum and energy imparted to the medium in such a way that it moves as a unit, like a rigid body.   Momentum and energy are *propagated through* the medium from layer to layer and region to region by the wave disturbance at its own finite velocity V.

Any small region of a wave disturbance possesses momentum given by the product of the mass of the region m and the local transverse or longitudinal particle velocity v; similarly, the region possesses kinetic energy $\frac{1}{2}mv^2$.   The system as a whole also possesses potential energy by virtue of the position of the region in question.   In a water wave, potential energy is associated with the upward or downward displacement of particles of water against the restoring gravitational force.   In a transversely vibrating string, potential energy is associated in an exactly similar way with displacements against the restoring effect of the tension in the string.   In longitudinal waves, as in a helical spring or sound in air, potential energy is associated with the compressions and rarefactions of the medium.

Thus the work that we do to keep the source emitting waves is propagated as both kinetic and potential energy to distant points, and, after a time lag determined by the wave propagation velocity, is capable of exerting forces and doing work on other objects at these remote positions.   But the force exerted on the medium by the vibrating source is not immediately transmitted to the distant object whose motion is being excited; Newton's third law, as we made use of it in Chapter 6, does *not* apply to a simple pair of forces between the source and the distant object.   The two bodies do not act on each other directly at a distance.   Rather, we can only think of adjacent particles of the medium exerting equal and opposite forces on each other; for the system as a whole we must think of the relation between initial and final conditions: we must think of energy and momentum as being conserved in the propagation of a disturbance through the medium (or "field") between the source and the receiver of the effects.   (At this point the reader might find it useful to reread Section 17.9, in which these ideas were first discussed in a preliminary way.)

A moment's thought will now convince us that transfer of momentum and energy by wave propagation is one of the most common and all-pervasive physical effects that we encounter: If we push a solid object by applying a force to one side, it does not accelerate instantaneously as a whole; the force we exert causes a compression wave that propagates at the velocity of sound through the solid, transmitting the disturbance to the other side of the object in an extremely short, but nevertheless finite, time interval.   (See Problem 22.2.)   In an elastic collision of hard bodies, there is no such thing as perfect rigidity; the interval of interaction between the bodies is finite and is accompanied by deformation and by the complicated bouncing back and forth of compressions and rarefactions within the colliding bodies.

> PROBLEM 22.24. Think of some other everyday experiences in which forces act to accelerate systems of various kinds, and analyze the situation qualitatively by describing the wave propagations that must occur. Describe what happens in Atwood's machine between the instant of its release and the time at which the acceleration settles down to the value predicted in Eq. (6.3.4).

The emission of waves, energy, and momentum by a source is frequently referred to as *radiation*. A radiating source runs down unless energy is supplied to it. The radiated energy is transmitted to distant points. Energy propagated through any region is related to the local wave amplitude, but the relation is not immediately obvious; calculation shows that, in general, the rate at which energy flows past a point of observation in the medium is proportional to the *square* of the amplitude at that point. As a wave recedes from its source, the amplitude decreases, principally because the energy in a given layer is spread out over an ever-increasing surface. A very small portion of the decrease, however, results from frictional dissipation within the medium as the wave moves along. Gradually, the radiated energy is converted into heat, warming up the medium through which the disturbance passes. Sometimes, as with water waves, the dissipative process may be enhanced at a boundary where waves splash and tumble at a beach or wall instead of being completely reflected.

The concept of radiation will be found to play a very significant role in our subsequent discussions of the nature of light and of the structure of matter.

22.21 PROBLEMS

22.25. Suppose you are given the equation

$$y = A \sin\left(\frac{2\pi x}{\lambda} - \phi_0\right)$$

as representing the graph of a sinusoidal wave train, where ϕ_0 is a constant that can be chosen at will. Interpret this equation and the role played by ϕ_0. [*Hint:* examine what happens to the graph if you take the special cases $\phi_0 = 0, \pi/2, 2\pi$, and then infer the general property.]

22.26. Figure 22.21.1 is a graph of the manner in which sound velocity varies with depth in some regions of the ocean: It is fairly uniform in a relatively shallow stirred layer near the surface. It then decreases with increasing depth and decreasing temperature, reaching a minimum value at roughly 4000 feet. At greater depths the temperature decreases only very slightly,

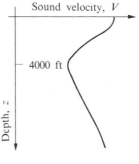

FIGURE 22.21.1

but sound velocity continues to increase with increasing pressure of the great height of the water column.

Sketch the behavior of several rays emitted from a sound source at a depth of 4000 ft. Note the basic similarity of this situation to that suggested in Problem 22.6. A small explosive charge, dropped from the surface and set to go off at about 4000 ft, can be detected by underwater hydrophones at distances of as much as 3000 mi, but charges set off at appreciably shallower or deeper positions cannot be heard over nearly so great a distance. Why? (This basic phenomenon was predicted theoretically by oceanographers during World War II, and was utilized as a rescue device under the name of "Sofar." Lifeboats were equipped with Sofar charges, and their location at sea, at distances of thousands of miles, could be triangulated by receiving stations on the coast.)

22.27. A source, stationary relative to a medium, vibrates with frequency ν_s and emits waves of length λ. We, as observers, move with velocity v_0 relative to the medium. Argue that the apparent wave frequency we observe is given by

$$\nu_{\text{app}} = \frac{V - v_0}{\lambda} = \frac{V - v_0}{V}\nu_s. \qquad (22.21.1)$$

Interpret this result. What would happen to the apparent pitch of a sound as we move toward or away from the source? Comparing Eqs. (22.8.3) and (22.21.1), note the surprising fact that the two situations are *not* exactly symmetrical. If a given source moves toward us at velocity v_s, the apparent frequency is *not* the same as that observed when we move toward the source with the same velocity. (In each case the apparent frequency increases but not by the same amount.) Try to account for this asymmetry. Would you have predicted it without the mathematical analysis?

A tuning fork sounds the note middle C at 256 cycles/sec. Calculate the apparent frequency that you would hear on moving toward or away from it at various velocities. How fast would you have to move to have this sound like the note A at 440 cycles/sec? (Express the result in miles/hour, and comment on the feasibility of producing this large an effect.)

22.28. A water ripple is incident at 37° to an interface at which the ratio of indices of refraction is 1.35. Calculate the angle of refraction for both possible directions of crossing the interface and sketch the incident, reflected, and refracted rays and wave fronts. [*Answer:* $\theta_t = 26.5°$ or $54.3°$, depending on which medium carries the incident wave.]

22.29. Suppose that two identical sinusoidal wave trains are traveling in exactly opposite directions. Sketch the waves in several successive phases relative to each other and plot the superposition pattern. Note that the resultant pattern changes with time but does not move along the direction of propagation of the component waves. (This resultant pattern is called a standing wave. Standing wave patterns play an essential role in the description of the vibration of strings and air columns in musical instruments. More detailed discussions of this phenomenon will be found in the reading references at the end of the chapter.)

22.30. Figure 22.21.2 shows an interference pattern observed when a point source of ripples is placed close to a reflect-

Fig. 22.21.2. (From *Physics*. Boston: D. C. Heath, 1960.)

ing barrier. (This phenomenon is usually referred to as the "Lloyd mirror" effect.) Discuss, analyze, and explain Fig. 22.21.2, deriving and interpreting *algebraic expressions* for the location of nodal lines and constructive maxima. What would happen if the source were moved closer to the barrier? Farther away?

22.31. Consider the following fantasy: We are operating a vehicle in the dark depths of the ocean, far from both surface and bottom. Our only device for detecting motion relative to the water is the acoustic apparatus shown in Fig. 22.21.3. The apparatus consists of a right-angle frame with arms of equal length L. A sound pulse emitted at O spreads out in all directions, and a small portion of the wave is reflected back to O from the reflectors R_y and R_x that are positioned at the ends of the arms.

Suppose that we are moving through the water in the x-direction at uniform velocity u.

(a) At $t = 0$ a wave pulse is emitted from O. It spreads at velocity of sound V_0, is reflected from R_y when the latter is at position A, and the reflected signal arrives back at the origin after a time interval Δt_y. The origin is by this time in position O_1, having moved a distance $u\,\Delta t_y$. A ray of the wave front follows path OAO_1 through the medium. Show that the time interval Δt_y is given by

$$\Delta t_y = \frac{2L}{V_0}\,\frac{1}{\sqrt{1 - (u^2/V_0^2)}}\cdot \qquad (22.21.2)$$

(b) The same pulse, emitted at $t = 0$, will also be reflected from R_x. This reflection

will return to O after a time interval Δt_x. Show that Δt_x and Δt_y are *not* equal: obtain the relation

$$\Delta t_x = \frac{2L}{V_0}\,\frac{1}{1 - (u^2/V_0^2)}\cdot \qquad (22.21.3)$$

Which reflection is the first to return to the origin?

(c) Suppose we have a device sufficiently refined to measure Δt_y and Δt_x very precisely; can we use this acoustic apparatus to tell us whether or not we are moving relative to the water? How? Suppose we are not necessarily moving in the x-direction indicated in the figure, but can rotate the frame so that the arm OR_x points in any direction we please. Can we determine the direction of the line along which we are moving? How? Can we determine in which direction we are moving along this line? Can we make any meaningful observations of this kind if $u > V_0$? What results would we have to obtain to justify the conclusion that we are not moving relative to the water? [*Note:* The situation assumed in this problem as an exercise is not quite as fantastic as may appear. We find ourselves in an analogous situation when we try to ascertain our motion relative to an hypothetical "medium," in which we might conceive light to be propagated. Extremely sensitive experiments of precisely the kind analyzed in this problem have failed to detect such motion. These concepts and results play a fundamental role in generation of the Theory of Relativity, and we shall return to this discussion in Chapter 36.]

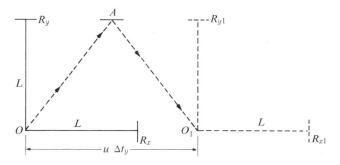

FIGURE 22.21.3

SUPPLEMENTARY READING AND STUDY

Physics, Physical Science Study Committee. Boston: D. C. Heath, 1960, Chapters 16, 17, 18

Physics for the Inquiring Mind, E. M. Rogers. Princeton, N.J.: Princeton University Press, 1960, Chapter 10

Physics for Students of Science and Engineering, R. Resnick and D. Halliday. New York: John Wiley & Sons, 1960, Chapters 19, 20

CHAPTER 23

Electric and Magnetic Fields I:
Qualitative Concepts

23.1 INTRODUCTION

Seventeenth-century European thought was characterized by vigorous rejection of scholastic and medieval attitudes. Teleological explanations and attribution of occult properties to physical systems were discredited, discarded, and replaced by the successful mathematization of natural philosophy. The Newtonian synthesis emerged as a prototype which other fields of thought would strive to emulate. Historians and philosophers frequently refer to the seventeenth century as the Age of Reason.

Correspondingly, the eighteenth century is frequently described as the Age of Enlightenment. This was a period of consolidation of the intellectual victories won in the preceding century. In science, paralleling the extremely rapid development of differential and integral calculus and the solution of differential equations, came an intense exploitation of Newtonian mechanics. Leonhard Euler (1707–83), a German who spent many years in St. Petersburg, advanced the mechanics of fluids and of rigid body rotation. [He seems to have been the first to have explicitly written and used Newton's second law in the form $F_{x\,\text{net}} = m(d^2x/dt^2)$.] Joseph Louis Lagrange (1736–1813) and Pierre Simon de Laplace (1747–1827) developed still more powerful mathematical generalizations of the Newtonian laws. Lagrange introduced functions of coordinates and velocity whose relationship to potential and kinetic energy and to the conservation laws was only to be fully appreciated two generations later. Laplace, in two great treatises, *Mécanique Céleste* and *Exposition du Système du Monde*, applied the new mathematical methods to advance and refine Newton's system of the world. He proposed a cosmological theory for the formation of the solar system from a primordial nebula. He provided powerful analytical methods for treating the interactions and perturbations of gravitating bodies and thus opened a new level of precision in the interpretation and prediction of astronomical data. Where Newton had been able to advance only a qualitative explanation of the tides, Laplace presented a sophisticated mathematical theory, revealing many hitherto unfathomed variations and details—including a class of tidal motions related to the combined effects of the rotation and the spherical shape of the earth, effects that meteorologists and oceanographers have come to understand more fully only in recent years.

While the seventeenth-century revolution was thus being consolidated, the great popularizers of the Age of Enlightenment—men like Voltaire, Diderot, and Condorcet —were making the results and insights available to educated readers beyond the immediate circle of savants and academicians, and their writings reached the consciousness of literate people in many lands. But at this point also began the present divergence between the streams of scientific and literary–philosophical thought. The prodigiously rapid and complicated mathematization of physical science placed firsthand contact with its methods and insights beyond the range of those lacking advanced mathematical training. The day of the gifted amateur, as exemplified by Benjamin Franklin, was virtually over.

"Explanation of natural phenomena" came to mean explanation in terms of Newtonian mechanics. It was assumed that the physical behavior of electricity, light, and matter would eventually be encompassed in this scheme, and, with sufficient diligence and objectivity, questions of philosophy and problems of human society were expected to yield to parallel methods of inquiry and analysis.

Laplace, even more vividly than Newton, had a grandiose vision of a universe operating like a clockwork, without external tinkering or adjustment. His differential equations indicated that knowledge of a set of initial conditions (positions and velocities of all particles at a given instant of time) led to prescription of the entire history of motion both past and future. When Napoleon asked what place Laplace had for God in the *Mécanique Céleste*, it is said that Laplace answered, "I have no need of that hypothesis."

Concerning this era, Isaiah Berlin, the English historian, remarks, "The eighteenth century is perhaps the last period in the history of Western Europe when human omniscience was thought to be an attainable goal."

The beginning of the nineteenth century saw the highest peak attained by "mechanistic" philosophy—an outlook in which the universe was likened to a vast, complex mechanism, knowable in its entirety if one could simply encompass sufficient detail, and operating in all respects and for all time in accordance with Newtonian laws of motion.

After discoveries concerning the nature of light and the structure of matter, made later in the nineteenth and early twentieth centuries, this philosophical position became untenable. Penetration to knowledge of the nature of light and the structure of matter came through the study of electricity and magnetism. We pick up, therefore, the discussion of electric and magnetic phenomena that we temporarily put aside after our brief study of the laws of force in Chapter 7.

23.2 A "NEW ELECTRICITY": GALVANI AND VOLTA

About 1791 Luigi Galvani (1737–98), an Italian anatomist at Bologna, reported a series of experiments he had been conducting since 1780 when an assistant had accidently observed that a frog's legs were violently contracted if a metal scalpel were touched to a certain leg nerve during dissection. In subsequent experiments Galvani showed that the contractions occurred when the operator made contact with a nerve by means of an electrical conductor and if the frog's legs were connected

by means of an electrical conductor to ground. In other experiments he showed
that contractions were produced if the frog were placed on an iron plate and if a
brass hook, making contact with a nerve, were simultaneously pressed against the
iron; in general, the effects being most pronounced if two dissimilar metals were
used. With nonconductors, the effects did not occur.

In view of the shocklike aspect of the muscular contractions and the necessity of
using electrical conductors, Galvani associated the phenomenon with electricity.
(This is not so remote an inference as might at first appear. At that time the sensation
of shock and muscular contraction were, aside from electroscope deflection and passing of sparks, one of the principal ways of identifying the presence of electric charge.
Cavendish made surprisingly accurate measurements of the relative conducting power
of various materials by comparing the physiological shock sensations he experienced
on taking a discharge from a Leyden jar through the conductor. It was also well
known that a few sea creatures such as the gymnotus (a species of electric eel) and
the torpedo fish (electric ray) were able to convey a shock similar to that obtained
from a Leyden jar, and they were described as sources of "animal electricity.")
At this point Galvani seems to have abandoned his careful physical investigations
and to have gone off in the direction of somewhat premature physiological speculations concerning the origin of a special animal electricity in the brain and its distribution through the nerves* to activate the muscles. Beyond this he sought to find
how one might exploit the new knowledge of animal electricity in the cure of disease.

On publication of Galvani's work, a more physical thread of investigation was
re-instituted by Alessandro Volta (1745–1827) of Pavia. Volta's interest in electricity had led him to develop delicate and highly sensitive electrometers (electroscopes
provided with a scale for measuring deflection of the movable element). With these
instruments he failed to find any electric charge stored in the animal tissues and
ascertained that the muscular contractions depended entirely on the presence of a
bimetallic junction (direct contact between two different metals) connected externally by the frog's leg or body.

In 1792 Volta referred to the effects as those of a "very feeble artificial electricity"
and wrote,

> "I am persuaded that the electric fluid is never excited and moved by the proper
> action of the organs, or by any vital force, or extended to be brought from one
> part of the animal to another, but that it is determined and constrained by
> virtue of an impulse which it receives in the place where the metals join."

Thus Volta, eschewing vague, unphysical notions of "vital force," based the design
of his investigation and experiments on the working hypothesis that he was dealing
with the same phenomenon observed with electrostatic machines and Leyden jars,
even though this was far from conclusively demonstrated at that time.

---

* Physiologists now understand nerve action to be essentially electrochemical in nature,
but in a rather different way from Galvani's vague hypotheses.

23.3 THE VOLTAIC PILE

By 1795 Volta convinced himself that a continuous flow of electricity took place whenever two different metals were in contact with each other and with a moist conductor. In 1796 he showed that if two metal plates were simply held in contact with each other (by insulating handles) and then pulled apart, each one carried an equal and opposite charge, as evidenced by the deflection of a very delicate electrometer. And in a famous letter to the Royal Society, dated March 20, 1800, Volta described the discovery of a new technique for greatly multiplying the effect:

"Yes! the apparatus of which I speak, and which will undoubtedly astonish you, is only an assemblage of a number of good conductors of different sorts arranged in a particular way. Thirty, forty, sixty pieces or more of copper, or better of silver, each in contact with a piece of tin, or what is much better, of zinc and an equal number of layers of water or some other liquid which is a better conductor than pure water . . . or pieces of cardboard or of leather, well soaked with these liquids; when such moistened layers are placed between each couple (or combination of two metal plates, laid one on the other), such an alternative series of these three kinds of conductors, always in the same order, makes up the new device. This instrument imitates the effects of Leyden jars . . . by giving the same disturbances as they. In truth the effects are much inferior to those of highly charged jars in the force and noise of their explosions, in the sparks, and in the distance through which the charge can pass, and are equal in effect only to a jar very feebly charged, but a jar nevertheless of an enormous capacity, and which further infinitely surpasses the power of electrical jars in that it does not need, as they do, to be charged in advance by means of an outside source; and in that it can give the disturbance every time that it is properly touched, no matter how often."

Thus Volta emphasized the identity of effects produced by his pile with those produced by "common" electricity. Not only did he demonstrate shocks and sparks and the necessity of providing a continuous, electrically conducting path from one side of the pile to the other (just as such a path was necessary from one side of the jar to the other), but he also showed that the sensitive electrometer could be charged positively at one end of the pile and negatively at the other. In particular, Volta emphasized the *continuity* of the process, but not having an instrument for the direct detection of continuous flow of electrical charge, he had to adduce as evidence his own physiological sensations in grasping the terminals and allowing the conduction to take place through his own body.

The voltaic pile, which we now recognize under the name of "electric battery," produced an immediate sensation and revived the lagging research in electricity. Within a short time, scientific apparatus houses were offering Volta's piles as regular items of equipment for research and demonstration.

Very shortly after receipt of Volta's letter in London, Nicholson and Carlisle, having constructed a pile in accordance with Volta's instructions, followed up the chance observation of evolution of gas at the terminals of the pile where the connecting wires had been wet with water to provide a better electrical connection. They led conductors from the ends of the pile into a vessel of water, acidified to render it a better conductor, and detected hydrogen being evolved at one conductor and oxygen at the other. (The steady evolution of gas at the conductors further dramatized the fact that a continuous process was taking place in the system when electrical connection was made between the terminals of the pile, and this was further reinforced by the observation of continuous heating of the connecting wires, soon noted by many investigators.) Nicholson and Carlisle thus discovered the phenomenon of electrolysis of water into its component gases. Humphry Davy, in his chemical researches at the Royal Institution, seized upon this device for decomposing other materials, and discovered the metals sodium and potassium by electrolyzing their molten salts. Gradually it came to be realized that chemical effects taking place outside the pile always occurred at the expense of simultaneous chemical change within the pile itself. Although a good theoretical model was still far in the future, it was clear that the electrical effects associated with Volta's pile had a deep underlying relation to what was then called chemical affinity—the tendency of certain substances to enter into chemical combination with each other—and motivation was provided for further research on the role of electricity in the structure of matter.

Thus physical research in electricity came to be joined to the science of chemistry; we shall return to these questions in subsequent chapters. But now we shall turn to pursue other physical aspects of Volta's discovery.

23.4 ELECTRICITY IN MOTION*

The electrical phenomena we studied in Chapter 7 are referred to as static because we dealt with fixed quantities of electrical charge residing in various objects, and with the steady forces that then obtained. We considered conduction and "leakage" only as disturbing factors, although we recognized that charge could move from one object to another until some sort of equilibrium was attained, or until positive and negative charges neutralized each other. When motion of charge occurred, it did so with extreme rapidity, and we did not investigate the possibility of slowing down the process. Let us now visualize the following situation: Fig. 23.4.1 shows two metal plates separated by two or three centimeters of air. [A device in which conducting plates or foils are separated by an insulator (air, oil, wax, etc.) is called a *capacitor*.] A small pith ball with a conducting coating is suspended between the plates on a light thread. Suppose we charge one plate by rubbing it with plastic film, cloth, or fur, and then charge the second plate by induction, by touching it, or by connecting and disconnecting it from ground. If we have previously connected an electroscope to the plates, as shown in the figure, the electroscope will show a

---

* To illustrate the relationship between static electricity as we described it in Chapter 7 and the dynamic effects of a voltaic pile, we shall describe several "thought experiments." These experiments are quite readily carried out in the laboratory, and students may be interested in performing them, to obtain a better feeling for the phenomena involved.

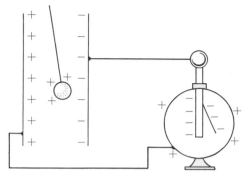

FIG. 23.4.1. Charged capacitor and electroscope. Pith ball is suspended so that it
can swing back and forth between the
plates; as it swings, the capacitor and
electroscope are discharged.

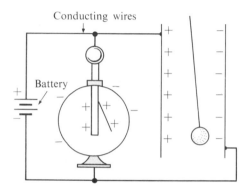

FIG. 23.4.2.   Capacitor plates connected to electric battery of several hundred volts. Pith ball continues to swing
back and forth; electroscope shows no decrease in charge.

deflection. (The deflection is enhanced by taking advantage of the induction afforded
when the case is connected to one plate and the knob to the other.) If the pith ball
is now brought into contact with the right-hand plate, it acquires a positive charge.
Being repelled from the positive plate and attracted to the negative, it is accelerated,
acquires kinetic energy, and strikes the left-hand plate, converting the kinetic energy
into heat. On contact with the negative plate, the positively charged pith ball neutral-
izes some of the negative charge on the plate and is itself recharged negatively. It
then swings back to the left and repeats the process. We thus have a little "motor,"
with the pith ball swinging regularly back and forth. With each swing, the electroscope deflection decreases slightly, and the device gradually runs down, just as the
spring-wound motor in a child's toy does. Eventually the plates are discharged
(or their charge becomes so weak that the electrical force exerted on the pith ball
is no longer great enough to swing it to one plate or the other against the restoring
gravitational force). We could, of course, have produced the same end result extremely rapidly simply by connecting the two plates with a wire, but the pith ball
slows down the process and dramatizes the significance of "charge in motion."
As we watch the pith ball swinging back and forth, charge is continually being transported past our point of observation—positive charge from the left to right and
negative from right to left. The net effect is to discharge the plates; i.e., the same
net effect that might have been produced by displacement of only positive charge
in one direction or only negative charge in the other. With the swinging pith ball,
we can see what is happening; with the connecting wire, we cannot discern the
mechanism of transport, but we recognize the basic similarity and continue to use
our previous convention, thinking of positive charge being displaced.

If we now connect a battery (three or four B batteries of 90 volts each in series may be necessary) to the plates, as in Fig. 23.4.2, a sensitive electroscope will again show charge, and the pith ball will continue swinging back and forth between the plates indefinitely without discharging the electroscope. We infer that the battery keeps replenishing charge on the plates as the pith ball transfers it. The swinging pith ball completes an electric "circuit." The electroscope does not discharge even when the circuit is completed by connecting the plates with a conductor such as a moist string (or a high-resistance wire), and under these circumstances we infer that charge must be moving continuously from one plate to the other. The plates and electroscope are discharged by the moist string only if we disconnect one side of the battery.

Combined with the continuous effects of heating and electrolysis cited previously, this evidence strongly supports the view that Volta's pile is a device in which electricity is not in "equilibrium;" it tends to flow continuously from one side to the other so long as a conducting path or some other kind of charge-transfer mechanism is provided.

Experiments such as those described above lead us to speak of "circuits" and of the flow of steady "electric currents." They exhibit a clear relation between static phenomena associated with frictional electricity and the apparently very different context represented by the voltaic pile, and it becomes reasonable to think of electric current in terms of coulombs/second of charge transported past a point in an electric circuit. The mechanism of conduction of electricity, however, is far from resolved by the concepts we have developed so far, and this is not to be likened to the swinging pith ball. The conduction mechanism is very different in different physical situations and with different materials; indeed, the mechanism is intimately connected with the microscopic electrical structure of matter. Research on the latter has fed back deeper knowledge and understanding of electricity, and vice versa. We shall return to these considerations later, but in the meantime, here is a very pertinent cautionary remark made by Faraday at a time when the vocabulary of electrical science had developed to the point outlined in the preceding sections:

"Whether there are two fluids or one, or any fluid of electricity, or such a thing as may rightly be called a current, I do not know; still there are well-established electric conditions and effects which the words 'static,' 'dynamic,' and 'current' are generally employed to express; and with this reservation they express them as well as any other."

PROBLEM 23.1.   When the terminals of a battery are connected by wires to each other or to opposite sides of a cell in which electrolysis takes place, careful measurements show that there is no detectable local accumulation of charge *anywhere* in the circuit. Suppose there *were* a continuing accumulation of charge at a particular point; how might it manifest itself? What do you infer from the fact that such accumulation is not observed? Note that local accumulations of charge *do* arise when a battery is connected to a capacitor, and the "circuit" is not "completed."

PROBLEM 23.2. On the basis of your present knowledge, describe in the vocabulary of energy and energy transformations all stages of the behavior of the pith ball swinging between charged capacitor plates. (Do not neglect potential energy, changes in which were not dwelt on in the brief description given in connection with Fig. 23.4.1.)

23.5 MAGNETIC EFFECT OF AN ELECTRIC CURRENT

Deliberate search for a connection between electricity and magnetism dates from at least as early as the eighteenth century. Franklin tried to magnetize a needle by electrical discharge. Sir Edmund Whittaker in his *History of the Theories of Aether and Electricity* reports that "In 1774 the Electoral Academy of Bavaria proposed the question, 'Is there a real and physical analogy between electric and magnetic forces?' as the subject of a prize." In 1805 two French investigators attempted to determine whether a freely suspended voltaic pile orients itself in any fixed direction relative to the earth; in 1807, Hans Christian Oersted (1777–1851), professor of natural philosophy at the University of Copenhagen, announced his intention of investigating the effects of electricity on the magnetic compass needle. Oersted's intention did not bear fruit for some time, but in July 1820 he published a pamphlet describing the results of experiments that "were set on foot in the classes for electricity, galvanism, and magnetism, which were held by me in the winter just past."

In these experiments Oersted showed that a magnetic compass needle was subjected to a systematic pattern of forces in the presence of a wire closing a voltaic circuit and carrying an electric current. The compass needle behavior is illustrated in Fig. 23.5.1.

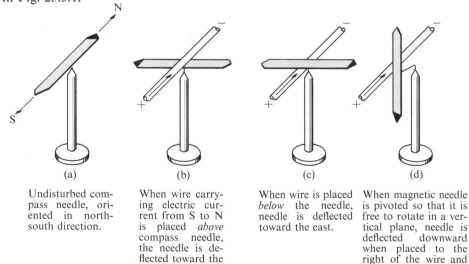

(a)	(b)	(c)	(d)
Undisturbed compass needle, oriented in north-south direction.	When wire carrying electric current from S to N is placed *above* compass needle, the needle is deflected toward the west.	When wire is placed *below* the needle, needle is deflected toward the east.	When magnetic needle is pivoted so that it is free to rotate in a vertical plane, needle is deflected downward when placed to the right of the wire and upward when placed to the left.

FIG. 23.5.1. Oersted's experiment. (We adopt the widely used convention that electric current flows from the positive to the negative terminal in a wire connecting the terminals of a voltaic pile.) The directions of deflection of the compass needle are all reversed if the direction of current is reversed.

Following Oersted's discovery, it was immediately surmised that the magnetic effect of the current should induce magnetism in pieces of iron just as is done by an ordinary magnet, and this was quickly verified. Since the magnetism thus induced in small iron filings causes the filings to line up in the direction of external magnetic force like an array of tiny compass needles, a sprinkling of iron filings is frequently used to map out the direction of magnetic force throughout a given region. Figure 23.9.2 illustrates the pattern formed by iron filings around a current-carrying conductor, and shows that the magnetic force at any point is directed along the tangent to a circle centered at the wire. Oersted deduced the tangential or "circular" pattern directly from the behavior of the compass needle, before the effect was visually revealed with iron filings.

A mnemonic (memory-aiding) device for recalling the relation between direction of current and direction of force on a N magnetic pole is suggested in Fig. 23.5.2. For the sake of simplicity, we shall talk about the force on a N magnetic pole, but it is well to remember that there is simultaneously an oppositely directed force acting on the S pole. The direction of force on a N magnetic pole at any given point is called the "direction of the magnetic field" at that point.

Direction of
current

FIG. 23.5.2. Right-hand rule I. Mnemonic device for recalling direction of force on N magnetic pole of compass needle in neighborhood of current-carrying wire: With the right hand, point thumb in direction of conventional (positive) current; curl of fingers around wire shows direction of circular pattern of force on a N magnetic pole.

By observing the magnitude of deflection of the compass needle from its normal N–S orientation, Oersted had access to a rough measure of the intensity of the effect. (The influence of the earth's magnetism on the compass needle provides the restoring force with which the influence of the conductor is being compared.) To obtain appreciable deflections it was necessary to use currents "able to make a metallic wire red hot." The compass needle deflections were smaller with batteries having a smaller number of plates (lower current), and decreased with increasing distance from the wire. No needle deflection from normal N–S orientation occurs, and no iron-filing pattern tends to form, when the circuit is broken.

PROBLEM 23.3. Among a variety of observations, Oersted reports the following: (a) "The kind of metal [forming the conductor] does not alter the effects, except, perhaps, as regards their intensity. We have employed with equal success wires of platinum, gold, silver, copper, iron, bands of lead and tin, and a mass of mercury."   (b) The effects on the needle remain virtually unaffected when rock, wood, glass are placed between the wire and the needle, and "the effects already mentioned are not changed if the magnetic needle is shut up in a copper box filled with water." (c) "Needles [of copper, glass, and resin], suspended like the magnetic needle, are not moved by the effect of the current-carrying wire."

What do you think is the point of these experiments? What do they demonstrate, and what inferences do you draw from them? Suppose the effect being observed were electrostatic rather than magnetic, what would happen in the case of the needle in the copper box filled with water? Actually, the interposition of various materials *does* alter the force exerted on the compass needle, but so slightly that devices very much more sensitive than Oersted's are required to observe the effect. How does this knowledge influence your conclusions?

One of the many questions prompted by Oersted's discovery is: What would happen if an electrically charged object is moved at different velocities? Is this analogous to an electric current in a wire, and are similar magnetic effects produced? Most physicists were fully convinced that the answer would be affirmative. Faraday asserted in 1838: "If a ball be electrified positively in the middle of a room and be then moved in any direction, effects will be produced as if a current in the same direction had existed." Maxwell also agreed that a moving electrified body must be equivalent to an electric current. Such effects, however, are very weak because electrostatic charges are extremely small (see Section 7.12), and a direct experimental test was not achieved until 1875, when H. A. Rowland* showed the presence of the expected magnetic effects in the neighborhood of a rapidly rotating, electrostatically charged disc.

Oersted's pamphlet of 1820 made an immediate sensation throughout Europe, promoted a host of additional questions, and stimulated a flurry of investigation, particularly in France where there was currently great interest in electric and magnetic phenomena. Such episodes recur from time to time in the history of science. Usually they are characterized by an experimental or theoretical discovery for which the scientific community is well prepared conceptually. No revolution is involved, no sharp break in which old models and deeply entrenched modes of thought must be discarded in favor of new and unfamiliar conceptual patterns. Under these circumstances, the discovery, surprising and unexpected though it might sometimes be, is quickly assimilated and appreciated; further consequences are readily pursued; and there is no prolonged period of gradual acceptance, residual doubt, and conservative opposition such as characterized the Copernican and Newtonian revolutions or the acceptance of the conservation law propounded by Mayer and Joule. The announcement of the discovery of the fission of the uranium atom in January 1939, for example, created a sensation and a flurry of investigation not unlike that which occurred after the publication of Oersted's pamphlet.

---

* Rowland, a young American physicist, performed the experiment in Helmholtz's laboratory in Berlin. He was spending a year in Europe prior to assuming the professorship of physics at the newly founded Johns Hopkins University.

23.6 FORCE BETWEEN MAGNETS AND CURRENT-CARRYING CONDUCTORS

We have dealt with a number of different cases in which bodies exert forces on each other: impact, gravitational attraction, attraction or repulsion of electrically charged bodies, attraction or repulsion of magnets for each other, and attraction of a magnet for a piece of iron. In each instance we have taken for granted the fact that two interacting bodies exert forces on each other along a line connecting the bodies. Oersted's experiment confronts us with a clear departure from this pattern. When a current flows through a wire, a small compass needle or iron filing is subjected to a force which is not directed toward the wire itself but instead is *perpendicular* to the radial line from the wire. This circumstance plays a significant role in motivating the development of the "field" concept, and we shall return to it later.

Following up the influence of the wire on the compass needle, Oersted himself was among the first to point out that: "As a body cannot put another in motion without being moved in its turn, when it possesses the requisite mobility, it is easy to foresee that the current-carrying wire must be moved by the magnet." This is, of course, a reference to Newton's third law, the implication being that, when one reverses the roles of the objects in Oersted's experiment, an easily moved current-carrying wire should exhibit the action of a force when placed in the neighborhood of a rigidly fixed magnet.

Oersted, Faraday, and others quickly verified this prediction and determined the direction of the force in arrangements having simple geometry. Since the force

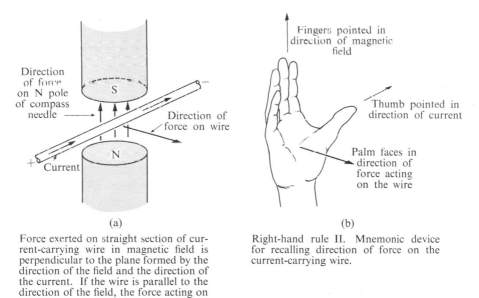

Direction
of force
on N pole
of compass
needle

Direction of
force on wire

Current

(a)

Force exerted on straight section of current-carrying wire in magnetic field is perpendicular to the plane formed by the direction of the field and the direction of the current. If the wire is parallel to the direction of the field, the force acting on it is found to be zero.

Fingers pointed in direction of magnetic field

Thumb pointed in direction of current

Palm faces in direction of force acting on the wire

(b)

Right-hand rule II. Mnemonic device for recalling direction of force on the current-carrying wire.

FIG. 23.6.1. Force on current-carrying wire placed between the poles of a fixed magnet. If either the direction of the field or the direction of the current is reversed, it is observed that the direction of the force is reversed.

does not act along the line connecting the magnetic pole and the wire, it is not immediately obvious what the direction of force on the wire must be; it is necessary to make observations, and Fig. 23.6.1 shows the facts that are established experimentally. A straight section of wire experiences a force perpendicular to the plane defined by a line showing the direction of conventional current and a line showing the direction of the magnetic field.

It is observed that the force acting on a section of current-carrying wire is *zero* if the section of wire is oriented *parallel* to the magnetic field and has a *maximum* value if the wire is *perpendicular* to the direction of the magnetic field.

PROBLEM 23.4.   Sketch several situations in which the orientations of current and magnetic field directions are different from the orientation shown in Fig. 23.6.1(a), and use right-hand rule II of Fig. 23.6.1(b) to predict the direction of force on the wire.

23.7   FORCE BETWEEN CURRENT-CARRYING CONDUCTORS

Another consequence of Oersted's discovery is the expectation that two current-carrying conductors might exert forces on each other, since the magnetic effect produced by one could interact with the current of the other, and vice versa. It should be noted, however, that this argument is not a proof and requires experimental verification. As was pointed out by Arago, one of the French academicians, a magnet exerts a force on each of two unmagnetized pieces of iron, but the pieces of iron, when separated from the magnet, exert no force on each other. The situation with current-carrying conductors could conceivably be analogous; namely, that the presence of a magnet is essential, and that without the magnet, the current-carrying conductors are magnetically as neutral as the pieces of iron.

Within a week after receipt of the news of Oersted's discovery in France, André Marie Ampère (1775–1836) reported to the French Academy:

"[I arranged] in parallel directions two straight parts of two conducting wires joining the ends of two voltaic piles. One wire was fixed and the other, suspended on points and made very sensitive to motion by a counterweight, could swing toward or away from the first wire while remaining parallel with it. [Rather than light, flexible wires, Ampère used a heavy conductor that could be bent so as to hold a suitable form. A schematic diagram of his apparatus is shown in Fig. 23.7.1.] I then observed that when I passed a current of electricity in both of these wires at once, they attracted each other when the currents [Ampère was using the already well established positive-current convention] were in the same direction and repelled when they were in opposite directions."

The following critical question might immediately be asked about this phenomenon: You are connecting wires to an electrical device—the electric battery. How do you know that the force between the wires is essentially magnetic? How do you know it

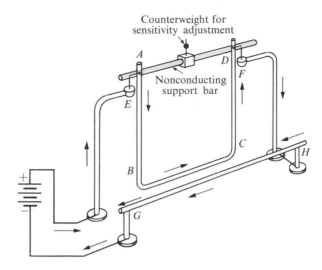

FIG. 23.7.1. Schematic diagram of Ampère's apparatus. Conducting wire frame *ABCD* rests on metal points immersed in small cups of mercury (*E* and *F*), and is free to swing back and forth in pendulum-like motion. Sensitivity is adjusted by raising or lowering counterweight. When current flows in direction indicated by arrows, stationary conductor *GH* repels conductor *BC* and frame swings away from *GH*. Angle of deflection of frame from initial vertical position is a measure of the repulsive force.

is not simply an electrostatic force arising from electrical charges acquired by the conducting wires?

Ampère anticipated this question, and his paper carries his answer:

"These attractions and repulsions between electric currents differ fundamentally from the effects produced by electricity in repose. First, they cease, as chemical decompositions do, as soon as we break the circuit. Second, in ordinary electric attractions and repulsions, opposite charges attract, and like charges repel; in the attractions and repulsions of electric currents, we have precisely the contrary; it is when the two conducting wires are placed parallel in such a way that their ends of the same sign are next to each other that there is attraction, and there is repulsion when the ends of the same sign are as far apart as possible. Third, in the case of attraction, when it is sufficiently strong to bring the movable conductor into contact with the fixed conductor, they remain attached to one another like two magnets, and do not separate after a while, as happens when two conducting bodies, oppositely electrified, come to touch."

We might add to Ampère's list of evidence still another item, namely that three *parallel* conductors carrying current in the same direction all attract *one another* simultaneously. No three electrically charged bodies will all attract one another; one pair will repel. (How do we know?)

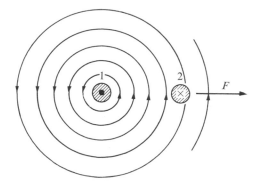

Fɪɢ. 23.7.2. End view of two wires carrying currents in opposite directions. Current in wire 1 is directed out of paper, current in wire 2 is directed into paper. Right-hand rule I (Fig. 23.5.2) predicts that magnetic field produced by wire 1 will be directed vertically upward in neighborhood of wire 2. Right-hand rule II (Fig. 23.6.1b) predicts that force on wire 2 will be in the direction indicated by *F* on the diagram; i.e., wire 2 is repelled by wire 1.

As a final check on the internal consistency of our information, let us see whether we can predict Ampère's results from the field direction observed in Oersted's experiment and from the direction of force experienced by a conductor in such a field. The analysis is given in Fig. 23.7.2, where we adopt a convention that will be frequently used throughout the rest of the book: An arrow directed toward us (out of the paper) will be denoted by a dot •, while an arrow directed away from us (into the paper) will be denoted by a cross ✕.

Pʀᴏʙʟᴇᴍ 23.5.   Redraw Fig. 23.7.2, showing wire 1 located in the magnetic field due to current in wire 2. Show that we expect wire 1 to be subjected to a force acting toward the *left*. Is this result consistent with the prediction made in Fig. 23.7.2 and with the experimental observations?

How would you change the connections in Fig. 23.7.1 to make the currents in *BC* and *GH* flow in the same direction?

Making appropriate sketches and using the two right-hand rules, predict the direction of force when the two currents flow in the same direction. Does this analysis of repulsion and attraction between the wires support the view that the effect is not electrostatic?

23.8   MEASUREMENT OF ELECTRIC CURRENT

Quantitative measurement of static electricity depended on the discovery of visible mechanical effects. Electrometers and electroscopes exhibited the deflection of a delicate metal leaf against gravitational force or depended on the twisting of a torsion balance suspension.

Ampère, in his communication to the Academy, went on to emphasize the significance of the mechanical effects associated with the newly discovered magnetic phenomena:

> ". . . there was lacking an instrument which would make it possible for us to detect the presence of an electric current in a pile or conductor and which would indicate its intensity and direction.* This instrument now exists; all that is necessary is that the pile, or any portion of the conductor, should be placed horizontally, oriented in the direction of the magnetic meridian [N–S], and that a compass needle should be placed above the pile or either above or below a portion of the conductor. . . . I think that in order to distinguish this instrument from the ordinary electrometer we should give it the name of 'galvanometer' and that it should be used in all experiments on electric currents, as we ordinarily use an electrometer on electrostatic machines, so as to see at every instant whether a current exists, and to indicate its intensity."

Using his galvanometer, Ampère went on to show that the intensity of the electric current was the same in every portion of the voltaic circuit, including the pile itself. He also showed that if the direction of current in the external circuit is taken by convention to be from the plus to the minus terminal of the pile, the current within the pile is in the opposite direction—from minus to plus. This, of course, strongly reinforced the concepts of circuit and of continuity of flow of charge that were embedded in the initial working hypotheses. Furthermore, Ampère gave a statement of what was qualitatively known to most "electricians" of the time, but remained to be quantitatively formulated by Georg Simon Ohm some years later:

> "Although the electric current so defined can be produced by an ordinary electrostatic machine by arranging it in such a way as to produce the two electricities, and by joining by a conductor the two parts of the apparatus where they are produced, we cannot, unless we use an exceedingly large machine, obtain an appreciable intensity of current except by the use of the voltaic pile, because the quantity of electricity produced by a frictional machine remains the same in a given time regardless of the conducting power of the rest of the circuit, *whereas that which the pile sets in motion during a given time increases indefinitely as we join the two extremities by a better conductor.*" [Italics ours.]

The galvanometer, as already used by Oersted and christened by Ampère, quickly became a vital tool in electrical research. Faraday used just such a device in his discovery of electromagnetic induction, and Ohm depended on it for his study of the conducting power of electric circuits. As time went by, the delicacy and sen-

---

* Recall how Volta had to invoke indirect evidence and the physiological sensations of his own body.

sitivity of the magnetic-needle galvanometer was tremendously increased, but variation of the effect with distance from, and orientation relative to, the conductor remained a fundamental limitation on accuracy and reproducibility of quantitative measurement. Ultimately this instrument gave way to a still more sensitive and reproducible device—one in which a moving coil, itself part of the electric circuit and carrying the current being measured, rotates in the field of a fixed magnet against the restoring torque of a coil spring. (See Section 24.9.)

Our present methods of measuring electric current and defining its unit evolved from Ampère's experiments; we pause to examine how this is achieved. From the start, it is tempting to assume a direct proportionality or linear relationship between the intensity of the current and its mechanical effects, such as the torque on the magnetic galvanometer needle. This assumption is already implicit in the early observations of Oersted and Ampère. We have a prior, intuitive notion of electric current in terms of quantity of charge and the rate at which it moves past a point in a conductor. It is entirely possible, in principle, that current, visualized in this way, is not linearly related to the torque on the compass needle. If this were the case, and if we followed Ampère's implied suggestion and defined current in terms of torque on the galvanometer, we would eventually run into inconsistencies and contradictions between the two points of view; i.e., we would have defined two entirely different "currents," and would be confusing the issue by using the same name for different operational concepts.

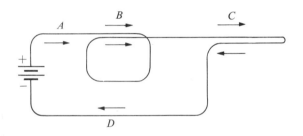

FIG. 23.8.1. Flexible conductor bent so that sections of the wire carry current in the same direction in region B and in opposite directions in region C. When current flows in the circuit and the galvanometer exhibits a given torque at positions A and D, it exhibits twice the torque in region B and zero torque in region C.

Accumulated experience, however, indicates that the linearity assumption is valid and that the concepts are not contradictory. We shall see all these ideas flow together in subsequent discussions, but for the time being we can reinforce the view with a very simple thought experiment: Suppose we connect the terminals of the battery with a wire sufficiently long and flexible to be coiled into various shapes, as in Fig. 23.8.1. When two loops of the wire are so arranged as to carry current in the same direction, as in region B, twice as much charge must flow past a point of observation per unit time as flows past a point of observation in regions A or D. If the magnetic effect is indeed proportional to the rate of flow of charge (i.e., if a simple superposition law is obeyed), we should observe at B twice the torque exerted on a galvanometer placed at A or D (at the same distance from the wire). If the wire is formed into three loops, we should observe three times the torque observed near a single strand, etc. Similarly, since the currents in region C are presumably equal and opposite to each other, and since the net transport of charge past a point of observation should be zero, we would expect the magnetic effect near region C to be zero. These anticipations can be tested in simple experiments and are found to be correct.

Experiments of the kind suggested above can be made with a device known as a current balance, a schematic diagram of which is shown in Fig. 23.8.2. In this form of the instrument, the force between two current-carrying coils of wire can be weighed directly by balancing the system in the absence of current and noting the additional weight necessary to rebalance it when current flows. If the coils have fairly large radii, they interact with each other very nearly like straight parallel wires.

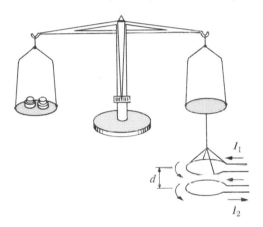

FIG. 23.8.2. Schematic diagram of a current balance. One loop or coil of wire is suspended from the pan of a balance. A second loop or coil of the same diameter is then placed directly below the first. When currents flow in the same direction through the two loops, the loops attract each other, and the force of attraction can be "weighed" directly by adding weights to the left-hand pan and rebalancing the system, which was initially balanced with zero current flowing in the wires.

The following quantitative effects and relations are observed in experiments with a current balance: (1) At a fixed separation d between the loops, the total force between them increases if either loop is connected to a larger voltaic pile; i.e., if the current in either loop is increased. If the current in each wire is kept fixed and one of them is coiled so as to make two loops, the observed force is doubled. If each wire is coiled into two loops, the observed force is four times that which obtains when the wires form single loops carrying the same current. Denoting the currents in the wires by I_1 and I_2, respectively, we are led to the conclusion that the total force between parallel wires is proportional to the product $I_1 I_2$ of the two currents. (2) For fixed current, the force between the wires is found to be inversely proportional to the separation d. (3) For fixed current and separation, the total force between the wires is found to vary with the length L over which the conductors are essentially parallel to each other. Measurements show that the total force F is directly proportional to L, and the ratio F/L then denotes the force per unit length of wire.

Summarizing in one algebraic equation the empirical results described above, we have the relation

$$F \propto \frac{I_1 I_2}{d} L; \qquad \frac{F}{L} \propto \frac{I_1 I_2}{d}; \qquad \frac{F}{L} = k_M \frac{I_1 I_2}{d}. \qquad (23.8.1)$$

If the two wires are connected in series with each other to the same battery, the two currents are identical, and Eq. (23.8.1) takes the form

$$\frac{F}{L} \propto \frac{I^2}{d}; \qquad \frac{F}{L} = k_M \frac{I^2}{d}. \qquad (23.8.2)$$

The subscript M attached to the proportionality constant will remind us that this constant is associated with a *magnetic* interaction.

The current balance thus provides a simple and direct way of relating an electric current to a measurable mechanical force. In our modern system of mks units, we take advantage of this fact to define the unit in which current is to be expressed. This unit is called the *ampere*, and is defined as: that unvarying current which, if present in each of two parallel conductors of infinite length one meter apart, causes each conductor to experience (in vacuum) a force of exactly 2×10^{-7} newton per meter of length. Given this definition, we can establish the value of any particular current by measuring with a current balance the force between wires of known length and known separation.

PROBLEM 23.6. Show that this definition amounts to choosing k_M in Eq. (23.8.2) to be equal to exactly 2×10^{-7}. (This particular choice was made in order to make the modern unit as nearly identical as possible with older units based on different standards.)

PROBLEM 23.7. In the calibration of a current meter (usually called an ammeter), the current from a battery is passed through the meter and a current balance connected in series with each other. In the current balance, it is found that for a length $L = 25.0$ cm, the total force between the wires is 15.3 mg at a center-to-center separation of the wires of 3.00 mm. What should this needle position on the meter be marked? Be sure to use mks units, and, remembering the "shorthand" mentioned in Chapter 5, note that milligrams are not a proper unit of force. [*Answer:* 3.00 amp.]

Having assigned k_M a specific numerical value (in vacuum) and thus established a unit of current and the calibration of current meters, it then becomes possible, in principle, to use a current balance to determine the force between conductors immersed in air, oil, or other media under conditions of known current. It is found experimentally that the force depends on the medium as well as on I and d, and that therefore k_M must be an intrinsic property of a given medium, just as k_E in Coulomb's law is also found to be such an intrinsic property. (Actually, measurements of this kind are made indirectly, with devices far more sensitive than a current balance, but the principle is unaltered.)

23.9   FORCE PATTERNS AROUND MAGNETS AND CURRENT-CARRYING CONDUCTORS

We have already alluded to the way in which iron filings in the neighborhood of a magnet tend to behave like small compass needles, and align themselves so as to show the pattern of directions of force that a compass needle would exhibit. Whereas, with a single compass needle we would have to make many individual observations, transporting the needle to different positions, and painstakingly drawing a map to represent the results, the iron filings immediately give us a "synoptic" view—an instantaneous picture of the pattern over an extended region.

Figure 23.9.1 shows iron filing patterns formed in the plane of a bar magnet, and between attracting and repelling magnetic poles. It is interesting to note that not only do the filings map out the directions of magnetic force, but they also give a rough qualitative indication of the local intensity: Where the intensity is very high, the filings tend to clump into heavy lines; where the intensity is lower, the filings form thinner lines, still clearly defined; at still weaker intensity, the alignment becomes more diffuse and less clearly connected. As you study the patterns in Fig. 23.9.1, imagine that you are holding a small compass needle, and visualize the force to which you would feel the N pole subjected as you moved the needle to different locations.

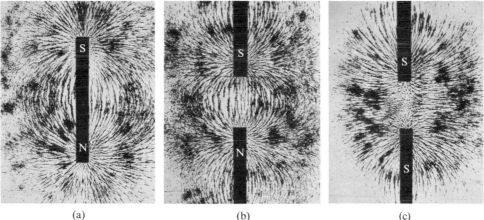

(a)	(b)	(c)
Bar magnet	Unlike poles	Like poles
	(attraction)	(repulsion)

FIG. 23.9.1. Patterns formed by iron filings sprinkled on a glass plate placed over a bar magnet or over attracting and repelling magnetic poles.

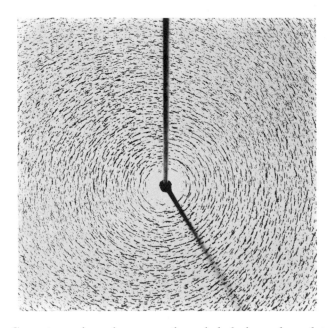

FIG. 23.9.2. Current-carrying wire passes through hole in a glass plate. Iron filings sprinkled on the plate align themselves to reveal circular pattern of direction of magnetic force, as deduced by Oersted from behavior of compass needle. (From *Physics*. Boston: D. C. Heath, 1960.)

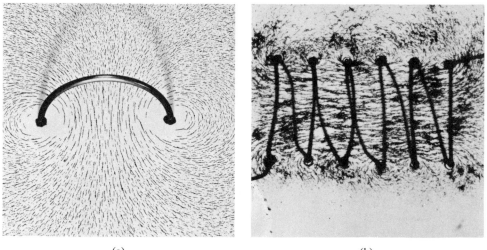

(a)   (b)
Current-carrying loop   Current-carrying solenoid

FIG. 23.9.3. Patterns formed by iron filings in planes passing through the center of a circular wire loop and through the axis of a solenoid. (Photograph (a) is from *Physics*. Boston: D. C. Heath, 1960.)

The pattern that Oersted deduced from the behavior of a compass needle near a current-carrying wire is shown in Fig. 23.9.2. Note how the circular pattern is most pronounced in the immediate vicinity of the wire and becomes more diffuse at greater radial distances, indicating a decrease of intensity with distance.

Another of the many questions suggested by Oersted's discovery is: What happens when a current-carrying wire is bent into various shapes? Do the magnetic effects superpose in a simple additive way, as we might anticipate from the fact that two turns of a current-carrying wire produce twice the magnetic effect of one turn (Fig. 23.8.1)? Figure 23.9.3 shows iron filing patterns in planes through the center of a circular loop of wire and through the axis of a solenoid. [When circular loops of wire are wound into a tight, toroidal (doughnut-like) shape, the resulting form is called a *coil*; when the wire is wound like a helix, i.e., the circular loops are spread out along a cylindrical axis, as shown in Fig. 23.9.3(b), the object is called a *solenoid*.]

PROBLEM 23.8. The whole idea of superposition in this context implies that each little length of current-carrying wire (called a "current element") is responsible for a magnetic effect throughout space (just as an electrical point charge is responsible for an electrical effect throughout space). Thus the total effect at a given point near a straight wire might be conceived of as the limit of the sum of the effects from each interval of length into which we visualize the wire to be subdivided, as the number of intervals is increased without limit. (The French physicists Biot and Savart formulated a mathematical statement of the magnetic effect of a current element within a few weeks after arrival of the news of Oersted's discovery.) Without exploring the full mathematical formulation, we can obtain some intuitive feeling for superposition of magnetic effects of current-carrying wires simply by visualizing each chunk of the wire as contributing its own effect at a given point, in accordance with right-hand rule I (Fig. 23.5.2). Verify that the force patterns exhibited in Fig. 23.9.3 are consistent with an application of this superposition principle. What would happen if the same current were passed through a coil formed by many circular turns of the same wire, instead of just one loop, as in Fig. 23.9.3(a)? The iron-filing pattern in Fig. 23.9.3(b) hints at both a high intensity and a substantial *uniformity* of the magnetic effect inside the solenoid, and this is ultimately confirmed quantitatively. How would you explain these results? In what direction would a compass needle point if placed at the center of the loop? if placed on the axis within the solenoid? Assuming a direction of current in Fig. 23.9.3(b), which end of the solenoid will attract the N end of a compass needle? What will happen at the opposite end? What will happen if the current is reversed? In the light of these results, what do you predict would happen to a current-carrying solenoid if it were freely suspended so that it could rotate with its axis in a horizontal plane?

23.10 THE SOLENOID AS A MAGNET

Part of the intent of Problem 23.8 was to lead the reader to perceive that a current-carrying solenoid (or a coil) behaves very much like a bar magnet, one end corresponding to an N and the other to an S pole. Ampère quickly seized upon this resemblance to suggest the possibility that *all* magnetism originates in the motion of electrical charge. He proposed the hypothesis that iron magnets have electric currents circulating around the axis of the magnet, just as the current circulates through the wires around the axis of the solenoid:

> " . . . from the simple comparison of facts it seems to me impossible to doubt that there are really such currents about the axis of a magnet, or rather that magnetization consists in a process by which we give to the particles of steel the property of producing currents in the sense that we have spoken. . . . It is thus that we come to this unexpected result, that the phenomena of the magnet are produced by electricity and that there is no other difference between the two poles of a magnet than their positions with respect to the currents of which the magnet is composed. . . "

Ampère formulated an elegant and powerful mathematical theory in which he treated the force between two current elements as an action at a distance having an inverse-square law of decay with distance of separation.* In Newtonian fashion, he avoided any hypothesis or model for the transmission of the force from one portion of wire to the other. Ampère's theory was very successful in accounting for all effects that were observable at that time. It is now recognized that his basic equation is applicable only to conditions of steady (or slowly varying) current, but with this restriction it is a valid description of the force between current-carrying conductors.

Coupled with the great unification and simplification afforded by the overall view of magnetism as fundamentally associated with electric current, Ampère's theory dealt a final blow to the still-lingering hypothesis of imponderable austral and boreal fluids. Mention of these soon vanished from the literature.

Modern research in magnetism, still a highly active and rapidly progressing branch of solid state physics, has gone far beyond Ampère and has yielded many deep insights into the atomic-molecular mechanisms that govern the magnetic behavior of various materials,† leading to an understanding of what characteristics of atomic structure make some substances ferromagnetic and others not, but Ampère's basic qualitative idea of the role of electricity in the magnetism of a bar magnet has been vindicated.

During the weeks while Ampère was performing his experiments with parallel wires, his friend and colleague Arago showed that iron could be weakly magnetized

---

* It is beyond the scope of this text to present the formulation of Ampère's theory. Elementary discussions of his law (or the closely related one formulated by his contemporaries Biot and Savart) will be found in references cited at the end of the chapter.

† Materials such as iron, nickel, and cobalt are capable of very strong permanent magnetization and are called *ferromagnetic*. Certain other materials, such as manganese compounds and the so-called rare-earth elements, do not acquire permanent magnetization at ordinary temperatures and are only weakly magnetized and attracted in the vicinity of a strong magnet; these materials are called *paramagnetic*. A third class of materials, exemplified by bismuth, are very weakly repelled by a strong magnet, and are called *diamagnetic*.

near the current-carrying conductor.* Ampère suggested that the effect might be greatly enhanced by placing an iron bar or steel needle within a solenoid where the magnetic influence would be stronger than near a single wire. This prediction was quickly confirmed. Since soft iron does not become permanently magnetized but readily shows induced magnetism when placed in a magnetic field, a soft iron bar inserted in a solenoid is magnetized when current flows in the solenoid, and not mangetized when the circuit is broken. This device is called an *electromagnet*, and finds innumerable practical uses in everything from doorbells, through automatic valves of washing machines, to control elements in elaborate machinery.

Almost as soon as these various discoveries were made, Laplace, Ampère, and others pointed out that if wires were run between two widely separated points, the closing of a circuit at the first point, and the consequent flow of current in the wire, could be used to produce motion at the second point by virtue of the effect on a compass needle, or still better, by energizing an electromagnet. After adoption of a code, information might thus be transmitted between widely separated places by means of electrical signals. In subsequent years many individuals attempted the construction of such a telegraph, the first fully successful long-distance operation being carried out between Baltimore and Washington in 1844 by Samuel F. B. Morse. The researches of Oersted, Ampère, and Arago, however, had been motivated by sheer curiosity concerning the phenomena of electricity and magnetism, and not by a plan to invent the electric telegraph. These men did not disdain the useful application of their discoveries, but the possibility of useful application played little or no direct role in their research.

From the 1820's and 1830's, applied and basic research in electricity and magnetism proceeded in closely related channels. Powerful electromagnets were being constructed by 1825; electric motors soon followed; more stable and reproducible voltaic batteries were manufactured; generators and dynamos made their appearance after Faraday's discovery of electromagnetic induction (Section 25.9) in 1831. Engineering applications of the basic discoveries not only accelerated technological development; they also fed back into the laboratory, providing steadier and more powerful sources of electricity, leading to more precise measurements and to the construction of experiments not possible with earlier devices. This in turn led to new empirical discoveries and to further efforts aimed at theoretical synthesis of the accumulating experimental knowledge.

PROBLEM 23.9. In the light of various preceding discussions, speculate on several mechanisms that could conceivably account for the magnetism of the earth. Do not assume that a pat answer is possible or available. This is an active field of research, and the last word is far from in. Certain suggestions can be eliminated on the basis of existing geophysical evidence; other ideas are still debatable, but it is not implied that you should possess a sophisticated background in the field. Simply bring to bear your own imagination and whatever knowledge you do possess. That some of your

---

* Humphry Davy made essentially the same discoveries independently at the Royal Institution at about the same time.

guesses might be incorrect is not the point at issue. If you become interested in the problem, you might find it interesting to pursue the matter further in a book on geophysics or terrestrial magnetism.

23.11   FORCE PATTERNS AROUND ELECTROSTATICALLY CHARGED BODIES

It is possible to map out synoptic patterns of electrostatic force by using small nonconducting particles that polarize, one end positive and the other end negative, under the influence of an electric field, and line up in the same manner as iron filings. The patterns shown in Fig. 23.11.1 were formed by grass seeds floating on oil. Similar patterns can be produced by allowing short, light, nonconducting fibers to align themselves on a glass plate in the presence of charged bodies.

(1) In studying the implications of Fig. 23.11.1, let us first note the similarities with and differences from the magnetic case. The patterns associated with like charges and unlike charges are very similar to the corresponding patterns with magnetic poles. On the other hand, magnetic poles are not observed to occur singly (they always occur in N–S pairs, even when a bar magnet is broken into many pieces, lending further support to Ampère's theory regarding the electrical nature of the phenomenon), while electrical charges do occur singly and give the spherically symmetrical force pattern implied in Fig. 23.11.1(a). Furthermore, in the electrical case, lines always begin and end on charged objects; while in the magnetic case, the lines are endless and always close on themselves—even in the bar magnet, where, in passing through the metal itself, they cannot be made visible by means of iron filings.

(2) Under steady conditions, the lines of the electrical force pattern are always found to be normal to the surface of a charged conductor (Figs. 23.11.1d, e, and f). If at some instant they were not normal to the surface, there would be a component of force acting parallel to the surface on electrical charge within the conductor. Since such charge is free to move (that is what we mean by "conductor"), the pattern would change from instant to instant, and the charge would redistribute itself until, at static equilibrium, tangential components would be zero, and lines would be normal to the surface.

(3) Close to the surface of a charged plate (Fig. 23.11.1f), the lines are parallel to each other, and the grass seeds give a qualitative indication of uniformity of field, similar to that of the magnetic effect within the solenoid. At larger distances from the plate, the lines begin to curve outward, hinting that at very large distances (large relative to the size of the plate itself) the plate would appear more and more like a point charge, giving a more nearly radially symmetrical pattern.

(4) When two equally and oppositely charged plates (one charged electrostatically by induction from the other, or each connected to opposite terminals of a battery) are placed parallel to each other to form a capacitor (Fig. 23.11.1e), the nearly uniform and oppositely directed forces outside the plates superpose so as to cancel each other. Between the plates, the forces act in the same direction and superpose to produce a very uniform pattern, confined almost entirely to this region. There is, of course, some distortion of the pattern and some slight influence beyond the plates

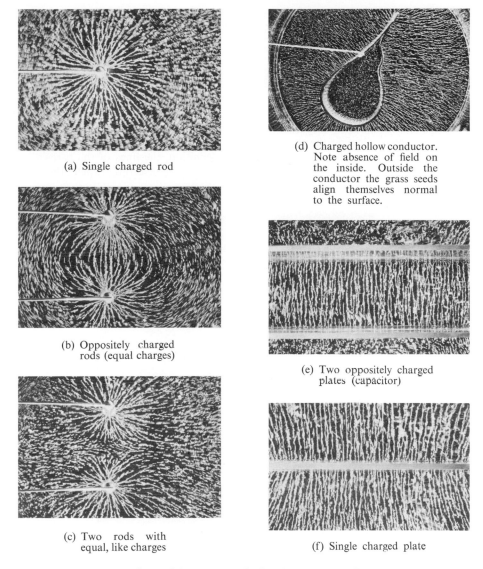

(a) Single charged rod

(b) Oppositely charged
rods (equal charges)

(c) Two rods with
equal, like charges

(d) Charged hollow conductor.
Note absence of field on
the inside. Outside the
conductor the grass seeds
align themselves normal
to the surface.

(e) Two oppositely charged
plates (capacitor)

(f) Single charged plate

FIG. 23.11.1. Patterns formed by grass seeds floating on oil surface under the influence
of electrostatic forces. (Courtesy Educational Services, Inc.)

near the edges of the capacitor. The larger the plates relative to the spacing, however,
the more uniform the pattern and the less pronounced are the edge effects.

(5) Note the absence of any tendency of the grass seeds to align themselves anywhere *inside* a hollow charged conductor of completely arbitrary shape (Fig. 23.11.1d).
This implies that, at equilibrium, the charge is so distributed over the surface, with
higher concentration in some areas and lower in others, that electrical forces from

all the charge elements superpose to cancel completely at every point *within* the conductor, while still producing net forces on the *outside*.

PROBLEM 23.10.   In the magnetic case, it is conventional to describe the force pattern in terms of direction of force on a N magnetic pole.   In the electrical case, the convention is to describe the direction of force on a small, positive "test charge," that is moved around to probe or sample various regions of the "field."   In each illustration of Fig. 23.11.1, assume a sign for the charge carried by various bodies, and resketch diagrams of your own, showing the direction of force on a positive charge at various points. As a consequence of the basic operational definition, the lines of the pattern cannot cross each other.   Why not?   Draw two lines of force intersecting; explain the absurdity that becomes manifest at the point of intersection.

FIG. 23.12.1.   Michael Faraday (about 1845).

23.12   MICHAEL FARADAY (1791–1867)

The nineteenth century saw two profound and far-reaching syntheses of scientific knowledge.   One of these was the science of energy, or thermodynamics; the other was the theory of electromagnetism.   Dominant figures in the latter development were Michael Faraday (Fig. 23.12.1) and James Clerk Maxwell (1831–1879).   Maxwell played a role corresponding to that of Newton, providing the imaginative analytical insights and mathematical formulation.   Faraday laid the ground-work for the Maxwellian synthesis by his brilliant experimental discoveries, by his deep intuitive, physical insights into the character of electromagnetic phenomena, and by his searching questions and speculations concerning possible mechanisms for the communication and establishment of electric and magnetic interactions.

Faraday was born near London in 1791, the son of a poor blacksmith. At the age of fourteen, with only a very rudimentary education behind him, he became apprentice to a bookbinder. The availability of books opened a new world to the young Faraday. He educated himself, reading widely and becoming particularly interested in science. This interest brought him in contact with the Royal Institution.

The Royal Institution had been founded in 1799 by Count Rumford during a period of residence in England. To establish the institution, Rumford sought subscriptions from well-to-do patrons for "forming in the metropolis of the British Empire, a public institution for diffusing the knowledge, and facilitating the general introduction of useful mechanical inventions and improvements, and for teaching by courses of philosophical lectures and experiments, the applications of science to the common purposes of life." In 1801 Rumford appointed to the directorship the then 22-year-old Humphry Davy, who came to Rumford's attention through having published a rather naive, but nevertheless vigorous, anti-caloric paper. Davy became one of England's great scientists (we have already alluded to some of his fundamental discoveries in chemistry and electricity elsewhere in this chapter), and brought great prestige to the Royal Institution.

In 1812, Davy, who was by then president of the Royal Society as well as director of the still young Institution, received an application for employment from Michael Faraday, whose bookbinding apprenticeship had just expired, and who submitted as evidence of his capability, notes that he had taken at some of Davy's public lectures.

Faraday was hired as a laboratory assistant on a weekly wage, thus beginning the distinguished career that he was to pursue at the Royal Institution until his retirement in 1861. Rumford, who had founded the Royal Institution as a projection of his own egoism and for the propagation of his interests in lamps, stoves, fireplaces, and heat, unwittingly initiated a sequence that led from Davy to Faraday, one of the most brilliant episodes in the history of experimental science. Faraday began publishing his first papers in 1816 and was elected to the Royal Society in 1824. In 1827 he began giving talks at the Royal Institution and soon developed a wide reputation as a brilliant and lucid lecturer. Among other activities, he organized the Christmas Courses of Lectures which were designed for young people. One of these, "The Chemical History of a Candle," presents in clear and unaffected terms the world of chemistry to be seen in the burning of a candle, if one watches with open eyes and senses. This lecture is widely reprinted and read to this day.

Faraday was very famous and could have become wealthy had he been willing to devote time to consulting and advising the new electrical industries which flourished as a result of his discoveries. This, however, he declined to do, electing instead a quiet life of research at the Royal Institution and modest financial circumstances.

Faraday was a meticulous worker. He had a deep intuitive understanding of physical phenomena, and his experiments, as he went about tracking down the answer to one problem after another, were models of cogency and relevance. Every paragraph of his writings is systematically numbered and cross-referenced to other paragraphs, in a carefully woven structure of growing knowledge and insight. Whittaker* closes his chapter on Faraday with this tribute:

"The closing period of his life was spent quietly at Hampton Court, in a house placed at his disposal by the kindness of the Queen; and here on 25 August 1867 he passed away. Among experimental philosophers Faraday holds by universal consent the foremost place. The memoirs in which his discoveries were enshrined will never cease to be read with admiration and delight; and future generations will preserve with an affection not less enduring the personal records and familiar letters, which recall the memory of this humble and unselfish spirit."

23.13 FARADAY'S CRITICISM OF ACTION AT A DISTANCE

Among Faraday's achievements were the recognition of several new chemical compounds; work on the liquefaction of gases; discovery of the laws of electrolysis; discovery of the phenomena of electromagnetic induction, diamagnetism, and of the rotation of the plane of polarization of a beam of light by a magnetic field. However, Faraday's great influence on subsequent scientific thought stemmed not only from the importance of his experimental discoveries but also from the influence of his theoretical speculations. His researches led him to reject the conception of action at a distance between bodies interacting electrically and magnetically and to assign a role to "lines of force" and to the intervening medium. He thus laid the basis for the concept of "field," which was elaborated mathematically by Maxwell and which remains one of the pivotal concepts in theoretical physics to this day.

Prior to the success and acceptance of the Newtonian theory of gravitation, the concept of action at a distance was anathema to most natural philosophers. In their revulsion against superstition, against the assignment of occult virtues and properties to inanimate substances, they rejected the thesis that a material object could exert an effect in a place where it was not. They tried to visualize clear-cut mechanisms for all interactions, and where an intervening medium was not apparent to the senses, they invented effluvia and continuous or corpuscular ethers through which effects could be propagated by contiguous action of layer on layer or particle on particle. The word "attraction," in certain contexts, implied action at a distance and was rejected as a yielding to occult beliefs. When Huygens was informed of the imminent publication of Newton's *Principia*, it is reported that he expressed the hope that the work would not be based on "attractions," as rumor had that it would be. Huygens and Leibniz never accepted the Newtonian theory on this account, but, as we have seen in other instances, opposition dies out with the older generation, and successful new methods are adopted and propagated by the young, sometimes with incomplete understanding of all the limitations and restrictions.

Newton himself had been careful to avoid commitment concerning models— "*Hypotheses non fingo*." He was clearly aware that he had discovered a mathe-

---

* *A History of the Theories of Aether and Electricity.* See reference at end of chapter.

matical formulation that correctly represented the facts of natural phenomena, but that might be subject to a variety of interpretations. (Situations of this kind have arisen frequently in the history of science. In 1822, for example, Fourier published a very complete and elaborate mathematical theory of the conduction of heat in solids, based on a differential equation that takes the rate of flow of heat through a unit area perpendicular to the x-axis to be proportional to the temperature gradient or space rate of change of temperature, dT/dx, in the x-direction. Fourier thought and wrote in terms of the caloric theory, which is quite incorrect, but his mathematical equation correctly represents the conduction of heat in solids, regardless of what hypothesis we hold as to the nature of heat itself, and his theory is therefore in complete agreement with observable facts concerning temperature distributions.)

Newton himself probably did not believe in action at a distance. He engaged in much speculation about ethers through which gravitational forces and other effects might be propagated, and there exist among his writings chapters that were originally intended for the *Principia* but that he withheld, possibly because he felt their speculative nature to be out of harmony with the Euclidean tone of the rest of the work. In any case, the *Principia* does without a mechanism for gravitational attraction, and, as Max Born writes, "... after Newton's theory ... had been established, the idea of a force acting directly at a distance gradually became a habit of thought. For it is indeed nothing more than a habit when an idea impresses itself so strongly on minds that it is used as the ultimate principle of explanation."

It was in this tradition that Ampère constructed his mathematical theory of magnetic interaction between current-carrying elements of wire. Faraday, in his *Experimental Researches in Electricity*, repeatedly expresses admiration for the "beautiful work" of Ampère and other members of the French school, but his own fundamental outlook was quite different. Lacking formal training, particularly in mathematics, he was never proficient in the abstract language of analysis (calculus). He tended to interpret his observations and formulate his concepts almost entirely in geometrical and physical terms. It is possibly because of this orientation that the geometrical patterns formed by iron filings impressed him so deeply. Faraday began to refer to "lines or curves of magnetic force" (a term that had already been used in connection with magnetism at least as early as the beginning of the seventeenth century): "By magnetic curves, I mean lines of magnetic forces, however modified by the juxtaposition of poles, which could be depicted by iron filings; or those to which a very small magnetic needle would form a tangent." Later he extended the concept to include lines of electric force.

Faraday's observations and experiments convinced him that the totality of electric and magnetic phenomena could not be explained in terms of action at a distance between particles, and that the intervening space must somehow be involved. Among the pieces of evidence that seem to have weighed most heavily with him are the following:

(1) The lines of force are curved in space and are not simply straight lines connecting the interacting magnetic poles or charged particles. Faraday could not conceive the curvature of lines of force in terms of action at a distance, particularly

in the case of lines around the current-carrying wire. He felt that the curvature either indicated a physical existence of the lines themselves, or else stemmed from a state or condition of an intervening ethereal medium.

(2) When a slab of dielectric (nonconducting) material—Faraday used discs of sulfur and shellac—was inserted between the plates of a charged capacitor, the quantity of charge on the plates was found to be different from what it had been when only air intervened. This experiment indicated that interaction between electrical charges on the plates was *not* the *exclusive* factor in such a situation, and that the intervening medium also played an important role. A similar effect (see end of Section 23.8) arises in magnetic phenomena.

(3) Among the phenomena that Faraday discovered was that of electromagnetic induction (see Section 25.9). One aspect of this phenomenon is that an electric current will flow in a wire when a portion of this wire is moved in a direction perpendicular to magnetic lines of force. "The mere fact of motion," contended Faraday, "cannot have produced this current: there must have been a state or condition around the magnet and sustained by it, within the range of which the wire was placed."

The most crucial question, that to which Faraday returned repeatedly, was whether or not finite time intervals were required for the propagation of changes in electric and magnetic forces: When current was abruptly changed in a wire, did a time interval elapse before the magnetic lines of force changed some distance away? When quantity of charge was abruptly changed on an electrically charged body, did a time interval elapse beofre a change in the force exerted on a test particle some distance away? An affirmative answer to these questions would have lent strong additional support to Faraday's views concerning the dubious status of any action-at-a-distance model, since it would have implied a propagation of action, perhaps in wavelike fashion, through the intervening space. (Although Maxwell's theory, developed over the decade 1856–1865, did answer these questions in the affirmative, direct experimental verification of the theory did not come until 1887, twenty years after Faraday's death.)

By Faraday's time, the experimental work of Young, Fresnel, and others (see Chapter 26) had shown that light behaves like a wave. It was far from clear as to just what was waving, but many physicists suspected and searched for a connection between light and electricity and magnetism. Faraday himself discovered the first such experimental effect (the rotation of the plane of polarization of light when propagating in a direction parallel to magnetic lines of force), and he entertained the idea that light might itself be the propagation of transverse vibrations of lines of force. He speculated on whether the velocity of propagation of magnetic effects might be of the same order as the velocity of light, and these thoughts provided further motivation for rejecting action at a distance and tentatively assigning a fundamental role in electromagnetic phenomena to lines of force or to an ethereal medium.

In his biography of Faraday, Tyndall writes, "During the evening of his life, he brooded on magnetic media and lines of force; and the great object of the last investigation he ever undertook was the decision of the question whether magnetic force requires time for its propagation. How he proposed to attack this subject we shall never know. But he left some beautiful apparatus behind; delicate wheels and pinions, and associated mirrors, which were to have been employed in the investigation."

> PROBLEM 23.11. From your own present point of view assess arguments (1), (2), and (3) against action at a distance. Do you find them convincing or unconvincing? (Do not hesitate to affirm the latter and present your reasons. This is a sophisticated inquiry, and it does not have a pat answer to the effect that Faraday was obviously right and that his views should have been accepted immediately. Action-at-a-distance theories would never have fallen on the basis of these arguments alone.) Why is the question of time of propagation so crucial? State its significance in your own words. If the time interval is finite, what can you say about the applicability of Newton's third law to electrically or magnetically interacting bodies? (Review Section 22.20 for relevant mechanical analogies.)

> PROBLEM 23.12. Following Faraday's general line of attack, what questions would you now raise about the phenomenon of gravitation? (Scientific literature contains much speculation on these matters. Definitive answers are *not* available. Some experiments one would like to perform are simply not possible with present techniques. The whole subject is one of great current interest.)

23.14 THE CONCEPT OF "FIELD"

Faraday, in his writings, carefully separated speculations regarding ethers and lines of force from factual reports of the results of his experiments, and he hedged these speculations almost apologetically:

> "It is not to be supposed for a moment that speculations of this kind are useless or necessarily hurtful in natural philosophy. They should ever be held as doubtful and liable to error and to change, but they are wonderful aids in the hands of the experimentalist and mathematician; for not only are they useful in rendering the vague idea more clear for the time, giving it something like a definite shape, that it may be submitted to experiment and calculation; but they lead on, by deduction and correction, to the discovery of new phenomena, and so cause an increase and advance of real physical truth, which unlike the hypothesis that led to it, becomes fundamental knowledge not subject to change."*

---

* We shall subsequently have occasion to recall the last part of this quotation. Faraday was by no means the only man of his time to believe that science advances "*real* physical truth" and leads us to "knowledge not subject to change." With only a few dissenting voices (among these, Ernst Mach's), many nineteenth-century scientists would have reflected similar attitudes. Their confidence is quite understandable. So wide in scope, so convincing were the successful applications of Newtonian mechanics and the new theories of thermodynamics and electromagnetism, that they indeed seemed to afford "knowledge not subject to change." The warnings of skeptical philosophers went largely unheeded.

When twentieth-century discoveries demonstrated the limited validity of Newtonian mechanics and electromagnetic theory, when it became necessary to revise attitudes toward concepts as fundamental as space, time, and mass, it is no wonder that these revelations came as a profound intellectual shock. But attitudes have changed in consequence, and today there are few scientists who would be inclined to use Faraday's confident phrases.

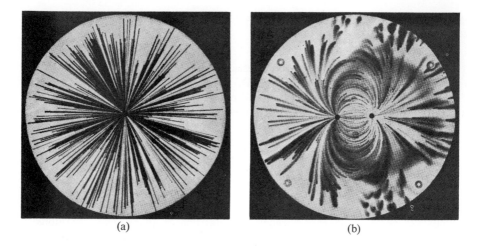

(a)   (b)

FIG. 23.14.1. Patterns of fluid flow made visible by streaks of dye carried by the fluid. (a) Fluid flow toward a point "sink." Fluid is being drawn out through small hole in bottom of tank. Note similarity to lines of force around electrical point charge. (b) Fluid flow from a point source to an equally strong point sink. Note similarity to pattern of lines of force around unlike electrical charges or unlike magnetic poles. (Photographs by Prof. A. D. Moore, University of Michigan. From *Introduction to Electric Fields*, by Rogers. New York: McGraw-Hill, 1954.)

Nevertheless, it is evident in much of Faraday's subsequent work that lines of force meant more to him than just an heuristic device. He used this idea so much and with such success that he clearly came to believe in "physical" lines of force. In this conception the lines filled all space and had distinct properties and modes of behavior. They acted like rubber bands, under tension longitudinally, and repelling each other laterally.

William Thomson (Lord Kelvin), in papers published in 1847 and 1854, called attention to mathematical analogies that exist between theories of fluid flow, heat flow, and elasticity on the one hand and electrostatics and magnetism, as described by lines of force, on the other. Faraday, taking mathematical analogy to other physical phenomena as evidence of physical reality, felt his view of lines of force to be strongly supported.

Figure 23.14.1(b) illustrates one such analogy, not by mathematical formulation, but by a picture that makes visible the flow of an incompressible fluid, in this case water. The water enters a tank by rising through a very small tube and flowing outward over the bottom. Nearby, water is drawn out at an equal rate through another small tube. The combination represents an idealized case of incompressible fluid flow involving a point source and a point sink of fluid. Spots of dye reveal the lines of flow, or directions of motion of the fluid at various points in the field. Note the complete geometrical similarity between this pattern of lines of flow and the lines of force associated with attracting electrical charges or magnetic poles.

(What pattern of flow lines would you expect if both points were simultaneously sources of fluid entering the tank?)

James Clerk Maxwell, then a young Fellow at Trinity College, Cambridge, was deeply impressed both with Faraday's conception of lines of force and with Thomson's revealing mathematical analogies. Gifted with great mathematical talent and with intuitive physical sense on a par with Faraday's, he embarked on an attempt to synthesize into one unified theory all the known phenomena of electricity and magnetism.

In his first two papers on this subject, published in 1856 and 1861, he developed an elaborate fluid model of Faraday's lines of force:

> "By referring everything to the purely geometrical idea of motion of an imaginary fluid, I hope to attain generality and precision, and to avoid the dangers arising from a premature theory professing to explain the cause of phenomena. If the results of mere speculation which I have collected are found to be of any use to experimental philosophers in arranging and interpreting their results, they have served their purpose, and a mature theory, in which physical facts will be physically explained, will be formed by those who by interrogating Nature herself can obtain the only true solution of the questions which the mathematical theory suggests."

(Note the similarity of this remark to the earlier one of Faraday, quoted at the beginning of this section.) In these papers Maxwell began to use the terms "electric field" and "magnetic field" in much the same sense in which we have already been using them elsewhere in this chapter.

In 1865 he published his final version of the theory:

> "I have preferred to seek an explanation [of electric and magnetic phenomena] by supposing them to be produced by actions which go on in the surrounding medium as well as in the excited bodies, and endeavoring to explain the action between distant bodies without assuming the existence of forces capable of acting directly at sensible distances.
>
> "The theory I propose may therefore be called a theory of the 'Electromagnetic Field' because it has to do with the space in the neighborhood of the electric and magnetic bodies, and it may be called a 'Dynamical' theory because it assumes that in that space there is matter in motion, by which the observed electromagnetic phenomena are produced.... [The space] may be filled with any kind of matter, or we may endeavor to render it empty of all gross matter, as in the case of Geissler [electrical discharge] tubes and other so-called vacua."

In this paper and in the *Treatise on Electricity and Magnetism* published in 1873, the elaborate heuristic device of fluid cells and vortices, the models of lines of force, are no longer presented. There remain only the mathematical equations, and the concept of "field" as a condition or state of an ethereal medium. Although some years elapsed before Maxwell's theory was widely accepted, it turned out to be, in the sphere of electricity and magnetism, as powerful a synthesis as Newton's. As Newton's laws of motion and gravitation proved applicable to the vast range of terrestrial and celestial mechanical phenomena, so Maxwell's mathematical equations encompassed the known laws and predicted observable effects in electricity and magnetism. In addition they revealed the nature of light as an electromagnetic phenomenon and gave a theoretical account of its behavior.

General acceptance of Maxwell's theory toward the end of the nineteenth century marked the transition from an era dominated by action-at-a-distance philosophy to the present era of field theories. Our quantitative description of electric and magnetic phenomena in the next chapter will therefore be conducted in the vocabulary of "fields."

23.15 PROBLEMS

23.13. Sketch the lines of force in the electric field surrounding a very long charged wire. How would you expect the pattern to compare with that around a charged sphere? The force on a test charge varies inversely as the square of the distance from the center of the sphere (Coulomb's law) and thus decreases very rapidly with increasing distances. How would you expect the force on the test charge to vary with the distance from the wire—more rapidly? less rapidly? in essentially the same way? Explain your line of reasoning.

23.14. A loop of wire, free to rotate if a torque acts on it, is placed with the plane of the loop parallel to the lines of force of a magnetic field, as shown in Fig. 23.15.1. A current is passed through the wire in the direction indicated. Using right-hand rule

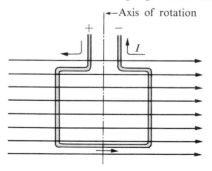

FIGURE 23.15.1

II, determine the direction of force exerted on each leg of the loop. What will happen to the loop? Is there an orientation of the loop relative to the magnetic field such that it will be in static equilibrium under balanced forces and will not tend to rotate?

23.15. Figures 23.9.1 and 23.11.1 show, among other cases, the patterns of lines of force between like and unlike magnetic poles and between like and unlike electrical charges. In each illustration the poles have essentially equal strength, and the electrical charges are of equal magnitude. Consider a situation in which you place a very small positive charge in the field of a sphere carrying a very large negative charge. Sketch a pattern of lines of force that you would expect in this case. What are the principal differences between this pattern and the one for equal charges? (Remember from Problem 23.10 that lines of force cannot intersect each other.)

23.16. (Possible subject for a paper for students interested in biophysics.) Look up the work of Galvani and Volta in some of the sources cited in the list of references below (e.g., Magie and Whittaker). Contrast the attitudes of Galvani and Volta toward the nature and origin of the "galvanic effect" and toward the most effective direction of research in this area. Why did

Galvani's work seem to "peter out" while Volta's yielded a rich harvest of results? Note that Galvani's track was not so much wrong as premature. What subsequent insights, discoveries, and theories can you identify as having contributed a necessary foundation for modern investigation of the role of electricity in biological processes?

SUPPLEMENTARY READING AND STUDY

"Alessandro Volta," G. de Santillana. *Scientific American*, **212**, 82 (1965)

Experimental Researches in Electricity, Volume I, Michael Faraday. London: R. and J. Taylor, 1839; Volume II, London: R. and J. Taylor, 1844; Volume III, London: Taylor and Francis, 1855

The Chemical History of a Candle, Michael Faraday. New York: Crowell-Collier Publishing Co., 1962; Collier Book *AS* 348

A History of the Theories of Aether and Electricity, Edmund Whittaker. London: Thomas Nelson & Sons, 1951, Chapters 3, 6, 8; New York: Harper & Brothers, 1960, Harper Torchbook 531

Forces and Fields, Mary Hesse. New York: Philosophical Library, 1961, Chapters 7, 8

The Edge of Objectivity, C. C. Gillispie. Princeton, N.J.: Princeton University Press, 1960, pages 435–477

Resource Letter FC-1 on Evolution of the Electromagnetic Field Concept. W. T. Scott, *Am. J. Phys.*, **31**, 819 (1963)

Excerpts from original sources: Galvani, Volta, Oersted, Ampère, Faraday, Maxwell.

Source Book in Physics, W. F. Magie. New York: McGraw-Hill, 1935

Great Experiments in Physics, edited by M. H. Shamos. New York: Henry Holt, 1959

Texts:

Physics, Physical Science Study Committee. Boston: D. C. Heath, 1960, Chapters 27, 28, 30

Physics for Students of Science and Engineering, R. Resnick and D. Halliday. New York: John Wiley & Sons, 1959, Chapters 27, 28, 33, 34

Physics, the Pioneer Science, L. W. Taylor. Boston: Houghton-Mifflin, 1941; New York: Dover Publications, 1959; Chapters 41, 42, 50

CHAPTER 24

Electric and Magnetic Fields II: Quantitative Laws and Relations

24.1 ELECTRICAL FIELD STRENGTH

If, in a given region in space, we find that an electrical force acts on a charged particle, we say that an electrical field exists in that region. Moving a positive test charge around from point to point and marking the direction of the force acting on it at each location, we could map out the lines of force, just as they are mapped out by the polarized grass seeds in Fig. 23.11.1, but we could also, in principle, measure the force $\mathbf{F}$ at each location P. If the test particle carries a small charge q_t, we would expect the magnitude of the force at P to be proportional to q_t,* and this fact can be confirmed experimentally.

Suppose that in a given situation we take a test particle with known positive charge q_t, measure $\mathbf{F}$ acting on it at point P and calculate the vector $\mathbf{E}$ defined by

$$\mathbf{E} \equiv \frac{\mathbf{F}}{q_t}. \tag{24.1.1}$$

Since $|\mathbf{F}|$ is proportional to q_t, we shall obtain the same value for $\mathbf{E}$ regardless of the charge q_t that we might happen to use. Thus $\mathbf{E}$ is a vector quantity uniquely associated with the electrical effect at point P and independent of the test object that we use for measuring the effect. It therefore seems reasonable to view $\mathbf{E}$ as a measure of the intensity of the electrical effect present at some point in space. $\mathbf{E}$ is called the "electrical field strength" at point P. If we were actually to carry out measurements of the kind described above, it would be very important to use small values of test charge q_t. A large value of test charge could induce redistribution of the charges producing the field (particularly if these charges reside on conductors)

---

* We saw in Chapter 7 that electrical forces superpose and add just as mechanical forces do. If the electrical field at P results from a known distribution of electrical charge in the vicinity, we can visualize dividing the distributed charge into small chunks, applying Coulomb's law between each chunk and the test particle, and evaluating $\mathbf{F}$ as the limit of the sum of all the forces acting on the test particle. Since q_t would appear as a factor in each term when we apply Coulomb's law, $\mathbf{F}$ itself must be proportional to q_t.

and could also induce polarization of surrounding media. If such changes were to occur, the effect measured would *not* be that of the original undisturbed charge distribution, and would not be a useful measure of the field at point *P*, since the resulting number would depend on the test charge; i.e., on the instrument we use to make the determination.

From definition (24.1.1), we see that **E** has dimensions of force per unit charge. In mks units this would be newtons/coulomb. By convention, the direction of **E** is taken to be the direction of force on a *positive* charge. If we are given the "field direction" at some point and we wish to deal with force expected to act on a *negative* charge, we must reverse the direction indicated. In words: the field strength **E** at any point in an electrical field is defined as the force per unit positive charge exerted on a charged particle at that point.

In cases of known charge distribution, we can compute **E** at any point without resorting to measurements. The simplest example is that of the field around a point charge at *A*. If the charge is positive and of magnitude q_A, the field is everywhere directed radially outward from *A*, and, in accordance with Coulomb's law, at a radial distance *r* from the charge, our test particle would experience a force

$$F = \frac{k q_A q_t}{r^2}. \tag{24.1.2}$$

The magnitude of the field strength would be given by

$$E \equiv \frac{F}{q_t} = \frac{k q_A}{r^2}. \tag{24.1.3}$$

Thus **E** at any point would be a vector of magnitude $k q_A / r^2$ n/coul, directed radially outward from the point charge q_A. If q_A were negative, the field vector **E** would have the same magnitude but would be directed radially inward. Equation (24.1.3) indicates that the field strength in the neighborhood of a point charge varies inversely as the square of the radial distance from the charge. The field around a point charge is frequently referred to as a Coulomb field. [See Fig. 23.11.1(a).]

If several point charges *A*, *B*, *C*, etc., produce a field at point *P*, we can calculate the resultant field by adding the individual vectors:

$$\mathbf{E} = \mathbf{E}_A + \mathbf{E}_B + \cdots \tag{24.1.4}$$

PROBLEM 24.1. Suppose you are told that the electrical field strength at a certain point is 20,000 n/coul, directed vertically upward. What force would be exerted at this point on a particle carrying a charge of -2.3×10^{-7} coul? [*Answer:* 4.6×10^{-3} n, vertically downward.]

PROBLEM 24.2. Make up several exercises in which you calculate the resultant field strength **E** in the neighborhood of two or three point charges. For example, evaluate **E** at point *C* in Problem 7.16. Evaluate **E** at several points on the perpendicular bisector of the line connecting two equal and opposite point charges. Make up additional exercises until you feel secure with the concept. In each case sketch the resultant field vector on the diagram.

PROBLEM 24.3. Using the definition of electrical field strength as a model, how would you define an analogous concept of gravitational field strength? Describe your idea in operational detail. What would be the dimensions of this quantity? What would be the mks units? What is the numerical value of gravitational field strength at the surface of the earth? How would the strength vary with radial distance from the center of the earth? What differences do you see between the electrical and the gravitational cases; for instance, is it necessary to adopt a particular convention for direction of field in the latter? Using appropriate information from Appendix B, calculate the location of the point of zero gravitational field strength on the line connecting the centers of the earth and moon. [This will require the solution of a quadratic equation. *Answer:* About one-tenth the distance from the moon to the earth, or 6 earth radii from the moon.] Sketch the pattern of lines of force around two gravitating spheres of equal mass.

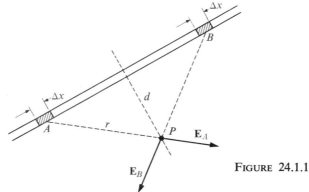

FIGURE 24.1.1

PROBLEM 24.4. Suppose we imagine a positive "line charge" (a uniformly charged thread) of λ coulombs/meter and of unlimited extent, as sketched in Fig. 24.1.1. Argue from the symmetry of the situation that the field must be "cylindrically symmetrical"; i.e., that lines of force must be radial lines perpendicular to the thread. [A hint as to how to go about the argument is given in the figure: Consider a point P at a distance d from the thread. A chunk of thread of length Δx at position A produces a field strength

$$E_A = \frac{k\lambda\,\Delta x}{r^2}$$

at point P, as shown. A symmetrically positioned chunk at B produces a field strength E_B of the same magnitude but of a different direction from that of E_A. How do the vectors E_A and E_B combine? How will other contributions combine if the line charge is of unlimited length?] Students having sufficient experience with methods of integration may wish to show that the resultant field strength at P has the magnitude $E = 2k\lambda/d$, but this is an additional task, and is *not* required in the qualitative argument about the symmetry of the field.

PROBLEM 24.5. Using an approach exactly parallel to that suggested in the preceding problem, argue that the field near a uniformly charged plane surface of unlimited extent must be everywhere directed perpendicular to the plane, and that the lines of force and the field vectors must be everywhere parallel to each other. (See Appendix G for an analytical formulation of this problem.)

24.2 THE FIELD BETWEEN CAPACITOR PLATES

In the electric field pattern illustrated in Fig. 23.11.1(f), the arrangement of the grass seeds near the charged plate implies a rather high degree of uniformity of the field in this region. It is possible to verify this indication analytically by calculating the electrical field for a corresponding, idealized situation—the vicinity of a plane of unlimited extent, carrying a uniform charge of σ coulombs per unit area. (This calculation is carried out in Appendix G.) By evaluating at any point P the limit of the sum of contributions from the "patches" into which we divide the plane, it can be shown that the field vector is everywhere perpendicular to the plane, and that the field strength is *uniform*, having the value $\mathbf{E} = 2\pi k\sigma$, where k is the Coulomb's law constant 8.99×10^9; that is, the field strength does *not* decrease as one moves away from a charged plane of unlimited extent. For a finite plane, $\mathbf{E}$ of course decreases at large distances, but at distances smaller than the linear dimensions of the plane itself, the field strength is given by

$$\mathbf{E} = 2\pi k\sigma \qquad\qquad (24.2.1)$$

to very good accuracy. If A is the area of the plate, then the total charge q is given by $q = A\sigma$, and we can use the alternative expression

$$\mathbf{E} = \frac{2\pi kq}{A}. \qquad\qquad (24.2.2)$$

Figure 24.2.1 illustrates the field in the neighborhood of positively and negatively charged plates. When two finite plates carrying equal and opposite charges, form a capacitor, the fields very nearly cancel each other outside the plates, and, with some

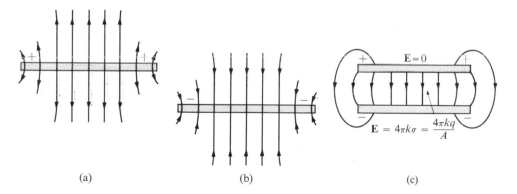

(a)   (b)   (c)

FIG. 24.2.1. Superposition of fields of oppositely charged plates. (a) Field lines directed outward from positively charged plate of area A. $\mathbf{E} = 2\pi k\sigma = 2\pi kq/A$. (b) Field lines directed inward toward negatively charged plate of area A. $\mathbf{E} = 2\pi k\sigma = 2\pi kq/A$. (c) Plates carrying equal and opposite charges q, placed so as to form a capacitor. Fields cancel each other outside the plates and reinforce each other in region between the plates. The letter q denotes the charge on *either* plate, and q (rather than $2q$) is called the charge on the capacitor.

slight fringe effects and distortion at the edges, add to give a very nearly uniform field strength

$$E = 4\pi k\sigma = \frac{4\pi kq}{A} \tag{24.2.3}$$

in the region between the plates.

Having developed a quantitative definition of field strength and used it to describe several electrostatic fields, we can perhaps set in clearer perspective some of the questions that puzzled Faraday. For example, we might wonder what happens at distant points if we start with an uncharged particle around which E is everywhere zero and then add charge to it, establishing a Coulomb field. In what way and how soon does the change in E take place at distant points? Or still another question that plays a very prominent role in Maxwell's theory: Suppose we start with an uncharged capacitor so that $E = 0$ between the plates and then connect the capacitor to the terminals of a battery so that it becomes charged, as in Fig. 24.2.1(c). What happens while E changes from zero to its final value of $4\pi kq/A$? In particular, is the change accompanied by any *magnetic* effects, such as those which accompany the flow of current in a wire? (We shall not try to answer these questions at this point; we raise them so that readers will become conscious of the ideas and better prepared for their discussion in later chapters. For some of the implications associated with the last question, for example, see Sections 27.10–12.)

24.3 FIELD WITHIN A UNIFORMLY CHARGED SPHERICAL SHELL

The most delicate and sensitive test of whether or not the electrical law of force is precisely of inverse square is afforded by examination of the electrical field inside a uniformly charged sphere. Let us examine the problem as though we do not know the actual law of force, but we do know that the force from a point charge decreases with increasing distance, and we expect a power function relation such as $F = K(q_1q_2/r^x)$, where x is an unknown exponent. Imagine that we place a positive test charge q_t at an arbitrarily chosen point P within the sphere (Fig. 24.3.1). Select a patch of charge A on the surface, and outline a corresponding patch B on the opposite side of the sphere by drawing straight lines through P from each point on the boundary of A. (The patches A and B then subtend equal "solid" angles at P.)

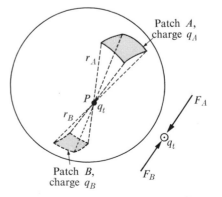

Fig. 24.3.1. Forces exerted on test charge q_t at point P by surface patches of charge at A and B. Surface of sphere carries a uniformly distributed positive charge. Free-body diagram of particle carrying q_t is shown at the right.

Patch A, charge q_A

Patch B, charge q_B

Charged patches A and B exert forces $\mathbf{F}_A$ and $\mathbf{F}_B$ on the test charge at P, as shown in the free body diagram. If r_A and r_B denote the distances of patches A and B from point P, our hypothetical force law gives the expressions

$$F_A = K\frac{q_A q_t}{r_A^x}, \qquad F_B = K\frac{q_B q_t}{r_B^x},$$

and the ratio of the magnitudes of the forces would be

$$\frac{F_A}{F_B} = \frac{q_A}{q_B}\left(\frac{r_B}{r_A}\right)^x, \tag{24.3.1}$$

where q_A and q_B denote the quantities of charge carried by the respective patches. The sphere is assumed to be uniformly charged with a surface charge density of σ coulombs/unit area, q_A and q_B are therefore directly proportional to the areas of the respective patches. Since the length of side of a patch is directly proportional to the first power of the radial distance r, the *areas* of the patches must be directly proportional to r_A^2 and r_B^2, respectively. (Note that this is a theorem in *geometry* and not a question of experimental physics.)

Therefore the charges q_A and q_B must be proportional to the squares of r_A and r_B:

$$\frac{q_A}{q_B} = \frac{r_A^2}{r_B^2}. \tag{24.3.2}$$

Combining (24.3.2) and (24.3.1):

$$\frac{F_A}{F_B} = \left(\frac{r_A}{r_B}\right)^2\left(\frac{r_B}{r_A}\right)^x. \tag{24.3.3}$$

By taking adjacent patches, constructed in the same way as A and B, we account for the effect at point P of all the charge on the sphere; for each corresponding pair of patches we would obtain an expression like (24.3.3).

Thus determination of the net force on a test charge at points within the sphere would yield information concerning the exponent x. In actual experiments, one would attempt to detect the presence of a field inside the sphere by using very sensitive electrometers to indicate whether charge is induced or displaced on conductors placed in this region. This is a far more sensitive indication than would be afforded by a direct attempt to measure force on a test charge, and is essentially the basis of all the methods that have actually been used. If no field can be detected anywhere within the charged sphere, the ratio F_A/F_B in Eq. (24.3.3) must equal 1 for all corresponding pairs of patches, and this, in turn, implies that $x = 2$; that is, that the law of force between point charges is of inverse square.

Experiments of this kind have had a long history. The law of electrical force is of such profound and fundamental importance in physical science that new and more searching tests of its accuracy are performed whenever technological developments open up a higher level of precision. To this date, all experiments have indicated that the electrical field within a charged sphere is zero and that the electrical law of force is of inverse square.

In Section 7.10 we have already referred to Priestley's (1767) crude test and perceptive guess concerning the inverse-square law. Priestley was motivated by the result of gravitational theory; namely that, given an inverse-square law of gravitational force, the field inside a spherical shell must be zero. (This theorem is proved analytically for the electrical case in Appendix G.) Cavendish, in the early 1770's, repeated Priestley's experiments with greater precision and concluded that $x = 2.00$ to within an accuracy of measurement of about $\pm 1\%$. (But Cavendish did not publish his results; much of his important and skillful work remained unknown until Maxwell edited and published Cavendish's papers almost a century later.) Maxwell himself repeated Cavendish's experiment, refining it so as to show that $x = 2.00000$, ± 5 parts in the last figure. Using still more precise techniques, Plimpton and Lawton showed in 1936 that $x = 2.000000000$ to within an accuracy of ± 2 in the last figure; i.e., to one part in a *billion!*

The search will not cease, however, even with this last result. If it were to be shown that the exponent definitely differed from 2, even by an exceedingly small amount, such knowledge would have profound, and possibly revolutionary, repercussions in physical theory.

(In this section we have confined ourselves to a discussion of the field inside the sphere. At points outside the sphere, the electrical field is exactly the one predicted by Coulomb's law, if we take all the charge to be concentrated at the center. We shall not discuss this theorem in detail, but those interested will find an analytical proof in Appendix G.)

24.4   POTENTIAL DIFFERENCE

In arriving at an operational definition of field strength, we visualized the force exerted on a positive test charge placed at the point in question. If we now visualize displacing the test charge from one location to another, we recognize that work will be done by or against the force exerted by the field, and, in accordance with definition (18.9.1), the system will undergo changes in potential energy

$$\Delta(\text{PE}) \equiv -\int_{s_1}^{s_2} \mathbf{F}_C \, ds, \qquad (24.4.1)$$

where $\mathbf{F}_C$ is the component of the force exerted on the test particle along the direction of displacement (that is, $\mathbf{F}_C$ is taken positive when acting in the direction of displacement and negative when it is directed opposite to the displacement).

From the definition of field strength, the component of force acting on a test charge q_t will be given by

$$\mathbf{F}_C = q_t \mathbf{E}_C, \qquad (24.4.2)$$

and therefore the potential-energy change resulting from the displacement of the test particle will be

$$\Delta(\text{PE}) = -\int_{s_1}^{s_2} q_t \mathbf{E}_C \, ds. \qquad (24.4.3)$$

As in the case of our definition of field strength, we can arrive at a number that depends only on the field characteristics and is independent of the test charge if we divide Eq. (24.4.3) by q_t:

$$\Delta V_{12} \equiv \frac{\Delta(PE)}{q_t} = - \int_{s_1}^{s_2} \mathbf{E}_C \, ds. \tag{24.4.4}$$

The quantity ΔV_{12} represents an amount of work *per unit positive charge* done in displacing a charged particle from point 1 to point 2 in an electric field and is called the *potential difference* between the two points. In the mks system the units of ΔV are newton-meters (or joules)/coulomb, and we give this combination the name *volts*. In the following we shall frequently use the abbreviation v for volts.

Consider the very simple case represented by the uniform field of a charged capacitor, as shown in Fig. 24.4.1. Suppose we displace a test charge along any line parallel to the plates (and therefore perpendicular to the lines of force). The component of the field strength in this direction is zero, and $\Delta V = 0$ for such displacement. Any surface which is drawn so as to be everywhere perpendicular to lines of force is one along which ΔV would be zero between any two points, and this is called an *equipotential surface*. The capacitor plates are themselves equipotential surfaces, and so is any other surface parallel to them. Displacing the test charge along such a surface is exactly analogous to displacing a body along a horizontal surface in the gravitational field of the earth. "Horizontal" or "level" surface is our name for an equipotential surface in the gravitational field. We displace a body along such a surface with zero work and zero change of potential energy.

Now suppose we displace a test charge from position s_1 to s_2 along a line parallel to the lines of force in Fig. 24.4.1. Denoting the magnitude of the field strength by E, the force exerted on the test charge by the field would be Eq_t toward the left, and we would have to push with force Eq_t toward the right. To displace the charge, we would have to do an amount of work

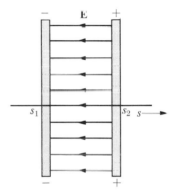

FIG. 24.4.1. Capacitor with uniform field strength E.

$$W = \int_{s_1}^{s_2} Eq_t \, ds = Eq_t \left[s \right]_{s_1}^{s_2} = Eq_t \, \Delta s, \tag{24.4.5}$$

where Δs is the separation between the plates, and the PE of the system would be increased by this amount. The work done per unit charge equals $E \, \Delta s$. If we let the charged particle go from rest at position s_2, it would "fall" toward the negative plate, acquiring kinetic energy equal to the PE stored in the original displacement.

Let us examine this same situation in terms of ΔV and Eq. (24.4.4). Since we are displacing the test charge toward the right, which is defined to be the positive direction of s, and since $\mathbf{E}$ is directed toward the left, we must take $\mathbf{E}_C = -E$ in (24.4.4). Then

$$\Delta V_{12} = \int_{s_1}^{s_2} E \, ds = E \, \Delta s. \tag{24.4.6}$$

The result agrees with the preceding calculation, which was made from a slightly different point of view. ΔV is positive for a displacement from the negative to the positive plate and negative for a displacement in the opposite direction.

A positively charged particle in an electrical field must be *pushed* to undergo a displacement in which ΔV is positive; if allowed to move freely under the influence of the field it will "fall" through displacements for which ΔV is negative. Given information about ΔV between points in a field, we can immediately calculate potential energy stored or work done between these points on a particle of charge q simply by calculating the number $q \, \Delta V$.

PROBLEM 24.6. In some cases (as with capacitor plates connected to opposite terminals of a battery), we shall see that ΔV is readily measured by means of a suitably calibrated meter. Suppose that a potential difference of 135 v is found to exist between a pair of plates spaced 3.0 cm apart. Making use of Eq. (24.4.6) and of information given in Section 24.2, calculate E, the field strength between the plates, and σ, the charge density on the plates. [*Answer:* $E = 4500$ n/coul; $\sigma = 4.0 \times 10^{-8}$ coul/m^2.]

PROBLEM 24.7. Suppose that we make the calculation of Eq. (24.4.6) along a slanted line in Fig. 24.4.1 instead of along a line parallel to the field. What will be the final expression for ΔV_{12} if we start at one plate and end at the other? (Recall that essentially the same problem has already been worked out for the gravitational case in Example 2 of Section 18.9.)

PROBLEM 24.8. Return to Problem 18.11 in Section 18.9, and, treating q_B as the test charge, find the expression for ΔV_{12}.

$$\left[Answer: \ \Delta V_{12} = kq_A \left(\frac{1}{r_2} - \frac{1}{r_1} \right) \cdot \right] \tag{24.4.7}$$

Suppose that in Problem 24.8 point 1 is taken to be very far away, so that $1/r_1$ is essentially zero. We can then write

$$\Delta V_{\infty 2} = \frac{kq_A}{r_2} \, . \tag{24.4.8}$$

When the reference point is very far away (or sometimes when the reference point is taken to be the earth itself), it is conventional to use the symbol V and to talk about "potential" rather than "potential difference." Thus Eq. (24.4.8) would become

$$V = \frac{kq_A}{r_A} \, , \tag{24.4.9}$$

and we would simply talk about the potential at a radial distance r_A from the point charge q_A instead of about the potential difference between this point and one very far removed, but one must remember that the simpler locution is only a shorthand for the latter concept. This code implies that we take the earth or the distant reference point to be at zero potential relative to the point in question.

24.5 MAGNETIC INDUCTION

It would be perfectly possible, in principle, to define a concept of magnetic field strength in terms analogous to those used in defining **E**. We would need a concept that corresponds to "magnetic charge," and such a concept was at one time defined and used under the name of "pole strength." It is clear, however, that a concept of magnetic charge is not arrived at as directly as the concept of electrical charge. The former is not transferable from one body to another on contact and cannot be divided equally between like bodies, as Coulomb did with electrical charge. Furthermore, Oersted's discovery and Ampère's theory of magnetism lead us to associate all magnetism with electric currents. In the light of this knowledge and experience, it becomes more natural to define a quantitative measure of strength of a magnetic field in terms of force on a current-carrying wire rather than in terms of the force on the pole of a compass needle or a bar magnet, and this is the procedure usually adopted in modern presentations of the science.

If we measure the force on a current-carrying section of wire placed in a magnetic field, we soon find that the force depends on a number of factors: the current in the wire, the length of wire in the field, and the orientation of the wire relative to the direction of the lines of force (we have seen that the force is zero on a section of wire parallel to the field, and is at a maximum when the wire is perpendicular to the field). The force on the wire also changes if we do something to alter the field; this might involve using a different magnet, or increasing the spacing between magnetic poles between which the wire is placed, or, if the field is produced electromagnetically, increasing or decreasing the current in the windings that produce the magnetization.

Before we can arrive at an operational prescription for assigning a number to the intensity of a magnetic field, we must have more detailed information as to how the force experienced by the wire depends on I, the current flowing on it, and on $L_\perp$, the length perpendicular to the field. A simple apparatus for making such measurements is shown schematically in Fig. 24.5.1. A section of heavy wire is bent into a rectangular shape, and the known length L of the bottom leg of the rectangle oriented in a horizontal plane, perpendicular to the lines of force between two large

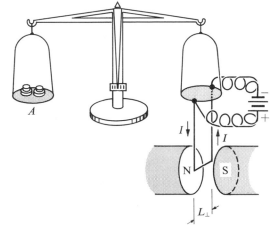

FIG. 24.5.1. Apparatus for measuring force on length $L_\perp$ of wire carrying current I in magnetic field. System is balanced at zero current. When current flows in direction shown, force is exerted downward on the wire (right-hand rule II), and displaces equal arm balance. The force is weighed by rebalancing the system with additional weights in pan A.

magnetic poles. When current flows in the wire, the horizontal leg $L_\perp$ experiences a vertical force, causing an up or down displacement of the pan of the equal arm balance to which the wire is attached. The forces on the vertical legs of the wire are horizontally directed, and do not affect the balance. Current is supplied to the wire through very flexible conductors, so arranged as not to have any appreciable influence on the balance as deflections occur. Keeping the length L fairly short and placing it near the central axis (rather than toward the edges of the field), we subject the wire to fairly uniform field conditions.

Now if we keep the current I fixed, and change $L_\perp$, either by rebending the wire or by using a different frame, we can explore the relation between $L_\perp$ and the force F on the wire. Experiments show that F is directly proportional to $L_\perp$ when all other factors are kept constant.

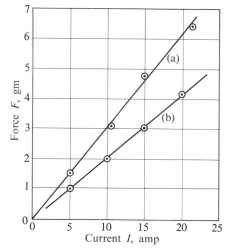

FIG. 24.5.2. Data for F versus I obtained in experiment set up as in Fig. 24.5.1. Here $L_\perp = 1.0$ cm. Line (a): Spacing between poles of magnet: 1.5 cm. Line (b): Spacing between poles of magnet: 2.0 cm.

In another set of experiments, we keep $L_\perp$ fixed and measure F for different values of the current I. Figure 24.5.2 shows actual numerical results obtained in a demonstration experiment of this kind. Since the points for each separate experiment fall on a straight line, it is indicated that F is proportional to I.

Combining the results described so far, we have that

$$F \propto IL_\perp, \tag{24.5.1}$$

where we use the symbol $L_\perp$ to emphasize that the segment of wire on which the force F is exerted has been oriented perpendicular to the lines of force of the magnetic field. Since we change the slope of the F-versus-I line when we change the spacing between the poles (Fig. 24.5.2), it appears that the slope is a property of the field and might be used to characterize its strength. We denote this constant by the symbol B and rewrite proportionality (24.5.1) in the form

$$F = BIL_\perp. \tag{24.5.2}$$

The symbol B is called *magnetic induction* or *magnetic flux density*. The former name was introduced by Maxwell, and this usage still continues.

In the mks system, B has units of

$$\frac{\text{newtons}}{\text{amperes} \cdot \text{meters}}, \text{ called "webers per square meter."}$$

(The reason for characterizing this quantity as a "flux density" or "something *per unit area*" is not apparent at this point but will emerge in the next chapter.)

To start establishing some sense for orders of magnitude, let us take note of the following figures: The flux density near a moderately powerful permanent magnet is of the order of 0.5 w/m². The flux density of the magnetic field of the earth at about 40°N latitude is of the order of 0.5×10^{-4} w/m².

> PROBLEM 24.9.　(a) Calculate the numerical values of B corresponding to the two lines (a) and (b) in Fig. 24.5.2. [*Answer:* 0.30; 0.20 w/m².] These are characteristic figures for the field of a moderately powerful laboratory magnet.
>
> 　(b) Comparing Eqs. (24.5.2), $F = BIL_\perp$, and (23.8.2), $F/L = k_M(I^2/d)$, show that the magnetic field around a long straight wire must be given by $B = k_M(I/d)$. Interpret this result.

24.6　MAGNETIC INDUCTION AS A VECTOR QUANTITY

When we defined electrical field strength in Section 24.1, it was immediately clear from the definition and from the knowledge that we already possessed concerning superposition of electrostatic forces that **E** must be a vector quantity. We might guess that magnetic induction, as defined in the preceding section, is also a vector quantity, but this fact does not follow from the definition alone. Separate experimental verification is necessary, just as in the case of superposition of mechanical forces, discussed in Chapter 5.

The problem may be approached in a variety of ways. For example, we might measure the values of B between two separate sets of magnetic poles. Then, bringing the poles into such an orientation that their fields cross at some known angle, we can measure B again and determine the resultant field. It is found that the observed resultant can be correctly predicted by vector addition of the separate values of B.

Another approach would be to superpose magnetic fields of current-carrying conductors. In that case B is found to be directly proportional to the current in the wire producing the field. [This is already to be expected from what we have learned about the force between parallel conductors in Section 23.8 and from Eq. (23.8.1). Why?] The field near the center of a circular coil of wire is found to be fairly uniform, and the geometrical arrangement offers a simple way of superposing magnetic fields while controlling their relative intensity. Two identical coils can be placed parallel to each other as in Fig. 24.6.1, and, by connecting them in series, the same current can be passed through each. When the connections are arranged so that the currents are in the same direction, as in Fig. 24.6.1(a), the field at the center is found to be twice that for one coil alone. When the currents are in opposite directions, as in Fig. 24.6.1(b), the field at the center is found to be zero. (This can be established simply by using a detecting device such as a delicate compass needle, and showing

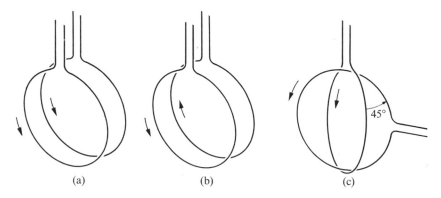

FIG. 24.6.1. Superposition of magnetic fields at center of circular coils carrying identical currents: (a) B at center is twice that of single coil; (b) B at center is zero; (c) B at center is 1.85 times that of single coil.

that it is not deflected from its normal N–S orientation when placed at the center of the two coils.) These experiments show that values of B add algebraically, as we would expect colinear vectors to do.

If identical coils carrying the same current are oriented at 45° to each other as in Fig. 24.6.1(c), vector addition would predict a resultant magnitude of **B** equal to 1.85 times the individual magnitudes, directed along the axis bisecting the larger angle between the coils. This prediction can be verified by introducing a third coil carrying a current 1.85 times that in the first two, placed so that its field near the center should cancel the resultant field of the original pair. A null indication by a compass needle placed at the center of the system confirms the prediction of vector superposition of the fields. Henceforth we shall always treat **B** as a vector quantity.

PROBLEM 24.10.   (a) Verify the number 1.85 quoted in the preceding paragraph. (b) Two identical coils, carrrying 1.00 and 1.73 amp, respectively, are placed at right angles to each other in the manner shown in Fig. 24.6.1. How must a third coil be oriented and what current must it carry in order to cancel the resultant field of the first two?

24.7   FORCE ON LENGTH OF WIRE NOT PERPENDICULAR TO B

If a segment of current-carrying wire is oriented parallel to the lines of force of a magnetic field **B**, as in Fig. 24.7.1(a), it is observed experimentally that the force acting on the segment is zero. When the segment is perpendicular to the field, as in Fig. 24.7.1(b), the force has a maximum value, and we used measurements made in this orientation to assign numerical values to |**B**|. If the segment is oriented at angle ϕ with respect to the magnetic lines of force, as shown in Fig. 24.7.1(c), we might make the reasonable guess that the force on the segment will be given by

$$F = BIL \sin \phi. \tag{24.7.1}$$

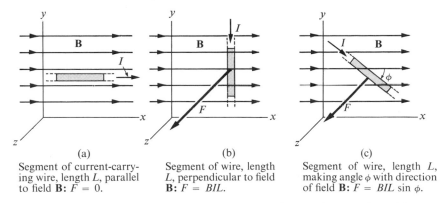

(a)
Segment of current-carry-
ing wire, length L, parallel
to field **B**: $F = 0$.

(b)
Segment of wire, length
L, perpendicular to field
B: $F = BIL$.

(c)
Segment of wire, length L,
making angle ϕ with direction
of field **B**: $F = BIL \sin \phi$.

FIG. 24.7.1. Segment of current-carrying wire oriented at various angles with respect
to lines of force of a uniform magnetic field.

The guess is motivated by the fact that sin ϕ is a simple, continuous function having
the value 0 when $\phi = 0$ and a maximum value of unity when $\phi = \pi/2$. Thus Eq.
(24.7.1) would give a continuous set of values of F at different angles and would
give the already established results for $\phi = 0$ and $\pi/2$. Equation (24.7.1) is readily
checked experimentally (after B is determined with the segment of wire perpendicular
to the lines of force) and correctly predicts the variation of force as the segment
is rotated away from the perpendicular orientation. Note that the force is always
perpendicular to the plane formed by **B** and the segment of wire, and the direction
of the force is always that given by right-hand rule II of Fig. 23.6.1.

We can interpret Eq. (24.7.1) in two equivalent ways. If we take it in the form
$F = BI(L \sin \phi)$, we can think of $(L \sin \phi)$ as $L_\perp$, the component of L in the direction
perpendicular to **B**. If we consider the form $F = (B \sin \phi)IL$, we can think of $B \sin \phi$
as $B_\perp$, the component of field vector **B** perpendicular to segment L. Thus we can
interpret Eq. (24.7.1) from either of two related points of view, denoted by the symbols

$$F = BIL_\perp \tag{24.7.2}$$

or

$$F = B_\perp IL. \tag{24.7.3}$$

PROBLEM 24.11. To obtain practice in using this conception, sketch a uniform magnetic field **B** oriented in a direction different from that shown in Fig. 24.7.1. Sketch
a segment of wire oriented at various angles to **B**; predict the direction of force F
and express its magnitude in terms of B, I, L, and a suitable angle appearing on your
new diagram.

24.8 TORQUE ON A CURRENT-CARRYING COIL

Many useful devices stem from practical application of knowledge concerning
currents and magnetic fields. Among these are two that operate on exactly the same
principle: the meter for measuring electric current and the motor for converting

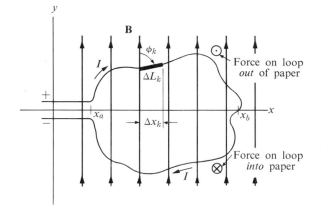

FIG. 24.8.1. Current-carrying loop of wire with plane of loop parallel to uniform magnetic field **B**. Loop experiences a torque around the *x*-axis.

electrical energy into mechanical work. We build up our understanding of these devices by starting with the general problem sketched in Fig. 24.8.1.

An arbitrarily shaped loop of wire is placed so that its plane is parallel to the direction of a uniform magnetic field **B**. If the loop is made part of an electric circuit and a current flows in the direction shown, each chunk of the loop is subject to a force perpendicular to the plane of the paper: out of the paper in the region above the *x*-axis and into the paper in the region below. The result is a net torque about the *x*-axis.

To compute this torque, imagine dividing the loop into many short chunks. The *k*th one, ΔL_k, is emphasized in the diagram. The force exerted on ΔL_k is given by

$$F_k = BI(\Delta L_k \sin \phi_k), \tag{24.8.1}$$

but $\Delta L_k \sin \phi_k$ is identical with Δx_k, the component of ΔL_k along the *x*-axis. Therefore we can write

$$F_k = BI \, \Delta x_k. \tag{24.8.2}$$

The torque exerted by this force around the *x*-axis is

$$\tau_k = BI y_k \, \Delta x_k. \tag{24.8.3}$$

To find the total torque exerted on the entire loop, we must evaluate the limit of the sum of all the τ_k's:

$$\tau = \lim_{n \to \infty} \sum_{k=1}^{n} \tau_k = \lim_{n \to \infty} \sum_{k=1}^{n} BI y_k \, \Delta x_k \tag{24.8.4}$$

$$\tau = BI \oint y_k \, dx_k \tag{24.8.5}$$

where the symbol $\oint$ is used to indicate that we must carry our summation all the way around the closed loop, running from x_a to x_b above the x-axis and returning from x_b to x_a below the axis. This is called a *cyclic integral*. An alternative way of writing Eq. (24.8.5) would be the more cumbersome form:

$$\tau = BI\left[\int_{x_a}^{x_b}\!\!\!\!\!\!\underset{\text{above }x\text{-axis}}{y_k\,dx_k} + \int_{x_b}^{x_a}\!\!\!\!\!\!\underset{\text{below }x\text{-axis}}{y_k\,dx_k}\right]. \tag{24.8.6}$$

Since the y_k's and Δx_k's are both positive above the axis and both negative on the reverse path below the axis, the sum in the brackets of Eq. (24.8.6) simply represents the total area A of the loop. Equation (24.8.5) therefore becomes

$$\tau = BIA. \tag{24.8.7}$$

If the conductor in Fig. 24.8.1 is a coil of N turns instead of a single loop of wire, the rate at which charge is moving in each section ΔL_k would be NI instead of I, and the final result for the torque would be $\tau = BNIA$.

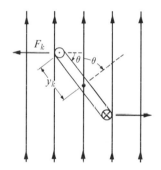

FIG. 24.8.2.   View from right of Fig. 24.8.1 when plane of coil is tilted so that its normal makes an angle θ with direction of the magnetic field. Lever arm of the force F_k on the kth segment of the coil becomes $y_k \sin \theta$.

If the coil is tilted so that its normal makes an angle θ with the magnetic lines of force, as shown in Fig. 24.8.2, the lever arm for the force on the kth chunk of wire becomes $y_k \sin \theta$, and $\sin \theta$ becomes a common factor of every term in the sum (24.8.4); that is, each lever arm is shorter than it was when the plane of the coil was parallel to the field. Thus the general expression for the torque on a current-carrying coil in a uniform magnetic field becomes

$$\tau = BNIA \sin \theta. \tag{24.8.8}$$

PROBLEM 24.12.   Sketch a coil with its plane perpendicular to the lines of force of a magnetic field. Using right-hand rule II, establish the direction of forces on various parts of the coil when a current flows in a specified direction. Is the coil subject to a torque? Is your answer in accord with the prediction contained in Eq. (24.8.8)? What happens to the forces acting on the coil if either the current or the magnetic field is reversed? In this problem you have examined the coil in two states of zero torque (one before and the other after reversal of the current); if the coil is free to turn, do you feel one of these states to be more stable than the other? Explain your conclusions.

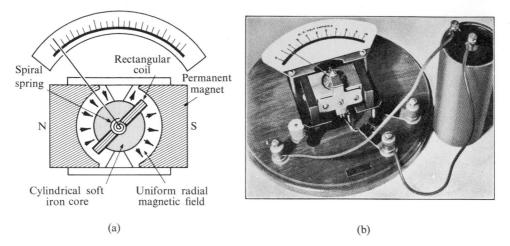

Spiral spring

Rectangular coil

Permanent magnet

N   S

Cylindrical soft iron core

Uniform radial magnetic field

(a)   (b)

FIG. 24.9.1.   (a) Schematic diagram of construction of galvanometer or ammeter.   (b) Photograph of an ammeter.

24.9 METERS AND MOTORS

Figure 24.9.1 shows a rectangular coil mounted on delicate pivot bearings between the poles of a permanent magnet.   The cylindrical soft iron core and the curved pole faces shape the magnetic field so that **B** is uniform and directed radially.   As the coil rotates, its plane remains parallel to **B**, keeping $\sin \theta = 1$ in Eq. (24.8.8). The coil is restrained by a hairspring (which is usually used as one conductor carrying current to the coil).   When current is passed through the coil, it experiences a torque which causes it to turn.   The coil turns until the torque due to the interaction of current and magnetic field is balanced by the opposing torque exerted by the hairspring.   Since the angle of deflection of the spring is proportional to the torque (Hooke's Law), the angular deflection of the pointer attached to the coil is a measure of the current in the coil.   By connecting the coil in series with a current balance (Fig. 23.8.2), we can calibrate the needle positions in amperes.   In very brief outline, we have described the principle and construction of an *ammeter*.   We shall repeatedly refer to this device in subsequent problems and discussions.   Ammeters are made in a wide variety of sizes and sensitivities.   Delicate and sensitive instruments will have small, light coils, sometimes mounted, like the balance wheel of a watch, on jewel bearings.

Another way of utilizing the torque on a current-carrying coil is in the construction of a motor.   (See Fig. 24.9.2.)

In a motor, a strong magnetic field is usually supplied by an electromagnet, the current for which comes from the source driving the motor.   A rugged coil is mounted on a shaft which is free to turn in a set of bearings.   When current is passed through the coil, it rotates to an orientation in which the torque becomes zero (see Problem 24.12); if, because of its inertia, it continues past this point with no alteration in the direction of current, it experiences a torque in the opposite direction and returns

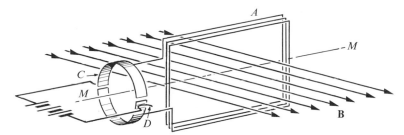

FIG. 24.9.2. Schematic diagram of electric motor. Coil (or armature) A rotates around axis MM. Current from battery flows to coil through brushes D and commutator strips C. As coil rotates, contact between commutator strips and brushes is interchanged, reversing direction of current and maintaining constant direction of torque.

to the equilibrium position. If, however, we arrange to reverse the battery connections to the coil just as it passes through the equilibrium position, the direction of current in the coil is reversed and the torque continues acting in the original direction (note arrangement of connections in Fig. 24.9.2). Under these circumstances, the coil can rotate continuously. With large currents in the coil and a strong magnetic field supplied by the electromagnet, a large torque will be available at the rotating shaft. By suitable connections of gears, belts, or pulleys, this torque can be utilized to run machinery and do other kinds of mechanical work.

PROBLEM 24.13. With the help of appropriate sketches, explain in your own words why it is necessary to reverse the direction of current in the motor coil in order to obtain continuous rotation in one direction. (The technical name for this coil is *armature*.)

24.10 FORCE ON A MOVING CHARGED PARTICLE IN A MAGNETIC FIELD

We have seen (Section 23.5) that when a body carrying an electrostatic charge is caused to move, the same magnetic effects are produced as when current flows in a wire. In the light of this fact, we would expect a charged particle, moving in a magnetic field, to experience a force just as the current-carrying conductor experiences a force when charge is displaced within it.

In order to examine this problem, let us try to transform the expression $F = B_\perp IL$ from one that refers to rate of flow of positive charge in a wire of length L to one that refers to a quantity of positive charge q moving at some velocity v.

Current I has been defined as the amount of positive charge moving past a point of observation in one second. If we let Q denote the amount of moving positive charge in each *unit length* of wire, and v the velocity at which the charge moves, an amount of charge equal to Qv passes our point of observation in each second (see Fig. 24.10.1). Therefore

$$I = Qv. \qquad (24.10.1)$$

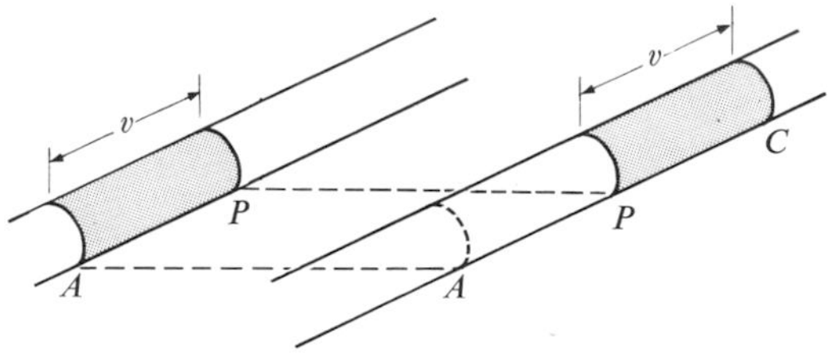

(a)   (b)
$t=0$ $t=1$ sec

FIG. 24.10.1. Charge moving past point of observation P in conductor at velocity v. Assume Q coulombs moving in each meter of wire. Charge which is in section of wire AP at $t = 0$ flows past point P and occupies section PC at $t = 1$ sec. Lengths $AP = PC = v$ meters. Amount of charge which moved past P in one second $= Q \times (PC) = Qv$.

In a length of wire L subjected to a magnetic field, the total amount of moving charge q must be given by

$$q = QL. \tag{24.10.2}$$

Eliminating Q from (24.10.1) and (24.10.2), we obtain $I = qv/L$ or $IL = qv$. Therefore we can write

$$F = B_\perp IL = B_\perp qv, \tag{24.10.3}$$

where the symbol $B_\perp$ is to be interpreted as the component of magnetic induction in the direction perpendicular to that of velocity v, and q is the total quantity of moving charge which is in the magnetic field at any instant of time. Right-hand rule II still applies, since v has the same direction as current I.

We now raise the question as to whether the new equation applies to charges moving *outside* a conducting wire as well as to charge within the conductor. Suppose we actually have an individual particle carrying electrostatic charge q, moving at velocity v perpendicular to the lines of force of a magnetic field. Does a force act on this particle, and if it does, is it correctly described by Eq. (24.10.3)? The experimental answers to these questions turn out to be yes. Several further deductions from the theory will help us understand the experimental evidence.

24.11   MOTION OF A CHARGED PARTICLE IN A UNIFORM MAGNETIC FIELD

If a free charged particle moving in a magnetic field experiences a force, the velocity of the particle cannot remain constant. What can we predict about the motion of the particle, assuming Eq. (24.10.3) to be applicable? Figure 24.11.1 shows a particle of mass m and positive charge q entering a region of uniform magnetic field at velocity **v**. With the field directed out of the plane of the paper, the instantaneous direction of force on the particle would be vertically downward, as indicated. The force, being perpendicular to the velocity, cannot change the magnitude of the latter, but can only alter its direction, just as a string alters the velocity of a rotating bob or the sun alters the velocity of a planet in a circular orbit. The force Bqv in Fig. 24.11.1 is thus recognized as a centripetal force, which would cause motion of the particle at tangential velocity v in a circle of radius R. Recalling that centripetal acceleration is equal to v^2/R, and applying Newton's second law:

$$F_{net} = ma,$$

$$Bqv = m\frac{v^2}{R},$$

$$R = \frac{mv}{Bq}. \qquad (24.11.1)$$

Our conjecture that the equation $F = Bqv$ might apply to charged particles not bound in a conductor leads to the prediction that such particles would move in a circular orbit in a uniform magnetic field, and that the radius of the orbit would be given by Eq. (24.11.1). These predictions have been fully verified experimentally and thus confirm the conjecture.

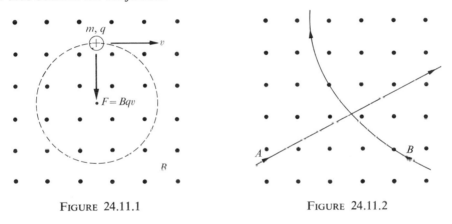

FIGURE 24.11.1   FIGURE 24.11.2

PROBLEM 24.14. Interpret Eq. (24.11.1). What changes would increase the radius of the orbit? What changes would decrease it? Try to give an intuitive explanation of each effect.

PROBLEM 24.15. How would the particle move in Fig. 24.11.1 if the direction of the magnetic field were reversed? (Assume the field to be of unlimited extent and not confined to the region indicated in the figure.) What would happen if the particle were negatively instead of positively charged? What would happen if the charged particle moved in a direction parallel to the lines of force instead of perpendicular to them?

PROBLEM 24.16. Two particles A and B enter a region of magnetic field and follow the trajectories shown in Fig. 24.11.2. What can you deduce about each particle?

If a positively charged particle enters a magnetic field with its velocity making an angle other than 90° with the lines of force, we can resolve its velocity into components: one perpendicular and one parallel to the field. The parallel component

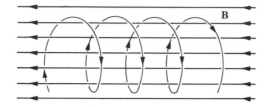

FIG. 24.11.3. Helical trajectory of positively charged particle with component of velocity parallel to lines of force of a uniform magnetic field.

will remain unaffected, since the force exerted in that direction is zero. The perpendicular component will determine the magnitude of the centripetal force $F = Bqv_\perp$ which causes circular motion in a plane perpendicular to the lines of force. Thus, if projected on a plane perpendicular to the lines of force, the trajectory of a particle would appear to be a circle, but since the velocity of the particle in the direction parallel to the field is unaffected, the trajectory is "stretched out" into a form called a *helix*. The pattern of such motion is illustrated in Fig. 24.11.3, and the particle is said to circulate around the lines of force.

24.12   MOTION IN NONUNIFORM MAGNETIC FIELDS

Analytical description of motion of charged particles in nonuniform magnetic fields becomes a mathematically complicated problem, but we can make a few interesting qualitative predictions in a very simple way.

If we float a magnet in a pan of water, the magnet will rotate until it aligns itself in a N–S direction, but it will not tend to accelerate translationally to one end of the pan or the other. This is to be interpreted as indicating that the magnetic field

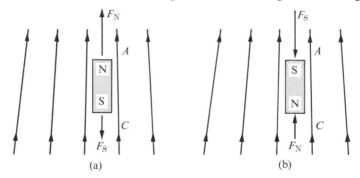

FIG. 24.12.1. (a) Bar magnet in nonuniform magnetic field. Field is stronger (B greater) at A than at C. F_N, force on north pole of magnet, is greater than F_S. If magnet were free to move (e.g., floating on water), it would be accelerated in direction from C to A. If it were given an initial velocity in the A-to-C direction, it would behave like a ball thrown into the air, slowing down and "falling back" toward A. (b) If magnet were oriented as shown, it would tend to rotate into position shown in (a), but if it were prevented from rotating, it would be accelerated translationally in the direction from A to C. Given an initial velocity in the CA direction, it would slow down and "fall back" toward C.

of the earth is very nearly uniform over a distance equal to the length of the magnet; i.e., that the forces exerted on the two poles of the magnet are very nearly equal and opposite.

If the field were nonuniform, as indicated schematically in Fig. 24.12.1 (nonuniformity is indicated by convergence or divergence of the lines of force), the poles of a magnet would be subject to unequal forces, and the magnet might be caused to accelerate in one direction or another.

What happens when an electrically charged particle enters a nonuniform field such as that in Fig. 24.12.1 and proceeds to circulate around the lines of force? We can best visualize this phenomenon if we recall that a moving charge is accompanied by a magnetic field just like that of a current in a wire. If a charge moves in a circular trajectory, it produces the same magnetic field as that of a current loop, and we have seen in Sections 23.9 and 23.10 that a coil or current loop behaves very much like a bar magnet perpendicular to the plane of the loop. Thus a positive charge circulating in one direction would be analogous to the magnet in Fig. 24.12.1(a), and a charge circulating in the opposite direction would be analogous to the magnet in Fig. 24.12.1(b). Depending on the direction in which it moves around the lines of force, the charged particle would be accelerated or decelerated in the direction of convergence of the magnetic field.

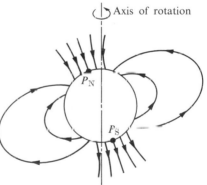

FIG. 24.12.2. Highly simplified sketch exhibiting nonuniformity of earth's magnetic field, which is strongest in polar and weakest in equatorial regions. The letters P_N and P_S denote positions of north and south magnetic poles.

Although the magnetic field of the earth appears to be very nearly uniform when observed over a very short distance with a bar magnet, it is, of course, not uniform on the geographical scale. The earth is a huge spherical magnet, with lines of force converging at the north and south magnetic poles, as illustrated in Fig. 24.12.2. Charged particles that enter the outer parts of the earth's magnetic field from the atmosphere or from outer space may get "trapped" in helical trajectories around the lines of force, if they happen to start circulating in the right direction. If a positively charged particle circulates counterclockwise as we look along the lines of force toward the north magnetic pole, its magnetic field is analogous to that of the bar magnet in Fig. 24.12.1(b). The particle will be accelerated toward the equator and start slowing down (in its motion parallel to the lines of force) as it approaches the south magnetic pole. Here it might be "reflected" before losing its energy in the atmosphere, and then accelerated back toward the equator to repeat the cycle over again.

This is a highly qualitative description of the physical basis of the phenomenon of trapped or *Van Allen* particle belts, first discovered in the early satellite experiments. Charged particles (principally protons and electrons) of very high kinetic energy are trapped in helical trajectories around the earth's lines of force, and bounce back and forth between the stronger regions of magnetic field at the poles, eventually losing their energy and "leaking" into the atmosphere.

24.13   PROBLEMS*

24.17. A uniform electrical field of strength E is directed as shown in the negative y-direction (Fig. 24.13.1). A particle of mass m carrying positive charge q is projected into the field with velocity v_{0x} in the x-direction. Take $t = 0$ at the instant the particle enters the field. Assume gravitational effects to be completely negligible.

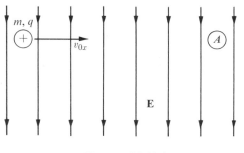

FIGURE 24.13.1

(a) What is the magnitude and direction of the force acting on the particle? (Explain your reasoning.) [*Answer:* $F_{y \text{ net}} = Eq$.]

(b) What is the acceleration of the particle in the x-direction? The y-direction? (Give an algebraic expression.) [*Answer:* $a_x = 0; a_y = -Eq/m$.]

(c) Using calculus language and symbols, derive expressions for v_x and v_y as functions of time. [*Answer:* $v_x = v_{0x}; v_y = -Eqt/m$.]

----

*Problems 24.17, 19, 20, and 24 are designed as preparations for the discussion of the Thomson and Millikan experiments in Chapter 31, and of atomic physics experiments in Chapter 33.

(d) Derive expressions for Δx and Δy as functions of time. Obtain the equation of the trajectory, and describe the motion on a Δx-versus-Δy diagram. [*Answer:* $\Delta x = v_{0x}t; \Delta y = -Eqt^2/2m$.]

(e) Note that we have already discussed a motion *exactly* like this one in a mechanical context. Go back to the earlier discussion and note all the similarities. Describe the motion which would take place if the particle were negatively instead of positively charged.

Suppose another particle of the same mass and charge is released at A at the same instant that the first particle is projected into the field. If we ignore the mutual repulsion between the two particles in comparison with the forces exerted by the field, what aspects of their motions will be similar? If the particle released at A had a different mass from the first particle, how would the motions compare? Contrast this situation with the events occurring in the corresponding gravitational problem.

24.18. In many experiments that we describe and study from now on, particularly experiments dealing with electrical phenomena on atomic and subatomic scales, we shall be concerned with the nearly uniform electrical field between capacitor plates in air or vacuum. A typical situation might involve a plate spacing of 1 to 2 cm and a potential difference of the order of tens or several hundreds of volts. Calculate the range of field strength represented. (Explain your calculation by defining each term in your own words and deriving the necessary relation.) Although our original definition of electrical field strength E indicates that its units in the mks system would be newtons/coulomb, field strength is often specified in units of volts/meter. Account for this usage.

24.19. A very small particle (mass $m = 6.67 \times 10^{-27}$ kgm), carrying a positive charge $q = 3.20 \times 10^{-19}$ coul, is released from rest at the positive plate of a capacitor, as shown in Fig. 24.13.2. The potential difference ΔV between the plates is 40,000 v, and the separation Δs between them is 3.00 cm. The electrical field between the capacitor plates is very nearly uniform. Gravitational effects are completely negligible. The whole system is in vacuum; i.e., no frictional forces act on the particle.

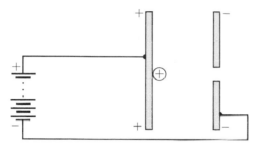

FIGURE 24.13.2

(a) Show by means of an arrow in the figure the electrical force F_E acting on the particle.

(b) Give the definitions of "electrical field strength" and "potential difference."

(c) Using the definitions given in (b) and explaining all steps, obtain an algebraic expression for the electrical field strength at any point between the plates, and an algebraic expression for the force F_E. Calculate the numerical values of the two quantities.

(d) Describe in words (using the ideas of force, acceleration, potential energy, kinetic energy) what happens to the particle after the instant of its release under the conditions indicated in the problem.

(e) Obtain an algebraic expression for the velocity acquired by the particle as it "falls" toward the negative plate and emerges

through the hole into the field-free region on the right. Calculate the numerical value of the velocity. [*Answer:* $v = \sqrt{2q\,\Delta V/m} = 1.96 \times 10^6$ m/sec.]

FIGURE 24.13.3

24.20. A pith ball with a conductive coating is placed on the lower of two horizontal capacitor plates, spaced 5.0 cm apart (Fig. 24.13.3). The plates can be charged by an electrostatic machine. As the potential difference between the plates is increased, the pith ball becomes more highly charged and finally is accelerated upward toward the positive plate. Suppose that the mass of the pith ball is 2.0 mg and that it acquires a charge of 3.0×10^{-10} coul. Calculate and compare the electrical and gravitational forces acting on the ball if the potential difference between the plates is 10,000 v. What will happen under these circumstances? What potential difference between the plates would cause an electrical force just balancing the gravitational force, keeping the ball suspended in midair between the plates? [*Answer:* 3300 v.] Suppose you could adjust the potential difference at will and determine its numerical value; how might you establish the magnitude of an initially unknown quantity of charge on the pith ball?

24.21. A conducting sphere with a radius of 3.00 cm carries a positive charge of 12.6×10^{-8} coul. Explaining steps and using notation and methods of the calculus, calculate the work that must be done in displacing a positive charge of 3.6×10^{-10} coul from a point very far to the right on the line shown in Fig. 24.13.4 to point A, 5 cm from the center of the sphere. Calculate the potential difference between the

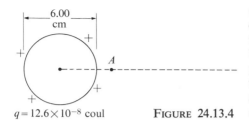

$q = 12.6 \times 10^{-8}$ coul   FIGURE 24.13.4

two points. What is the potential at point A?
At the surface of the sphere? [*Answer:*
Potential at $A = 22,700$ v; at surface,
37,800 v.]

24.22. In a paper published in the *Philosophical Magazine* in 1843, Faraday described the following experiment: "Let A [in Fig. 24.13.5] represent an insulated pewter ice pail ten inches high and seven inches diameter, connected by a wire with a delicate gold-leaf electrometer E, and let C be a round brass ball insulated by a dry thread of white silk, three or four feet in length, so as to remove the influence of the hand holding it from the ice pail below. Let A be perfectly discharged, then let C be charged by a machine or Leyden jar, and introduced into A as in the figure. If C be positive, E will diverge positively; if C be taken away, E will collapse perfectly.... As C enters the vessel A, the divergence of E will increase until C is about three inches below the edge of the vessel and will then remain steady and unchanged [as C is moved around to various positions inside A]."

Faraday went on to show that if C is touched to the inside of A it becomes

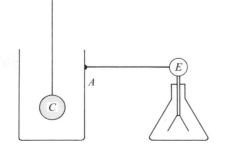

FIGURE 24.13.5

completely discharged without any further change in the deflection of E. He also showed that charge could be transferred or shared between conducting bodies within the ice pail (the bodies not touching the pail and therefore not becoming discharged) without any alteration in the deflection of E. (These are very simple experiments that a student can readily repeat and verify in the laboratory during dry weather, when experiments in electrostatics are not seriously influenced by humidity. He might also try additional variations, such as touching charged sphere C to the outside of A instead of to the inside, etc.)

These experiments led Faraday to the conclusions that (a) the charge induced on the outside of A is exactly equal to the charge carried by C, regardless of the position of C on the inside; (b) that after C touches the inside of A, the net charge on A is equal to that originally on C, and resides on the outside surface.

Present in your own words the arguments which support these conclusions. What relevance do these experiments have with respect to the concept of conservation of electrical charge? What evidence do they provide concerning the electrical field inside a charged, hollow conductor?

24.23. Describe in your own words how "magnetic induction" or "magnetic flux density," B, is defined. Indicate which aspects of the operational definition are arbitrary and which aspects involve appeal to experiment.

24.24. Suppose that in the situation described in Fig. 23.13.1 the uniform electrical field is produced by capacitor plates with potential difference ΔV and spacing Δy. Current-carrying coils are now arranged so that a uniform magnetic field B is directed into the plane of the paper, and its strength can be adjusted by varying the current in the coils. (Sketch a possible arrangement of the coils and capacitor plates, and indicate the way in which the coils must be connected to a battery to cause the current to flow in the proper direction.)

Continuing to neglect gravitational effects entirely, describe qualitatively what will happen to the motion of the charged particle as the current in the coils, and therefore the strength of B, is increased in successive experiments from zero to very high values. Obtain an algebraic expression for B_0, the value of B at which the electric and magnetic forces on the particle are exactly balanced. How will the particle move under these circumstances? Suppose that ΔV and Δy are known, so that B_0 can be determined from the current in the coils; what could you learn about the velocity of the particle? about its charge and mass? [*Answer:* $B_0 = (\Delta V / \Delta y)/v$.]

24.25. Return to Eq. (24.11.1), which describes the radius of the circle in which a charged particle would move in a plane perpendicular to a uniform magnetic field:

$$R = \frac{mv}{qB}.$$

Obtain an algebraic expression for the *period* T of this circular motion. Interpret the result. How does the period depend on the size of the circle? How do you account physically for this seemingly strange result? This idea was very ingeniously utilized by Ernest Lawrence in 1931, in the development of one of the early high-energy particle accelerators (the cyclotron). Look up a description of this device in a reference text, and present an explanation in your own words.

24.26. Suppose that a small, electrically charged sphere is rotating around an axis coinciding with a diameter of the sphere.

(a) Make a rough sketch of the magnetic field you might expect to find around the sphere. (Note that it will behave like small magnet with north and south poles.)

(b) Describe qualitatively what would happen if the rotating sphere were free to move and were placed in a uniform magnetic field with its axis of rotation at various different angles to the direction of the field.

(c) Suppose that a magnetic field is directed parallel to the x-axis but is nonuniform in the sense that B varies (increases or decreases) in the x-direction. The rotating, charged sphere (free to move) is placed with its axis also parallel to the x-axis. Describe qualitatively what will happen.

For more advanced work, here is a problem utilizing calculus:

24.27. Following the basic pattern of analysis illustrated in Appendix G, evaluate algebraic expressions for the potential $V(r)$ at points outside and inside a uniformly charged sphere. Sketch graphs of $V(r)$ and $E(r)$ versus r.

SUPPLEMENTARY READING AND STUDY

Physics, Physical Science Study Committee. Boston: D. C. Heath, 1960, Chapters 29, 30

Physics for Students of Science and Engineering, R. Resnick and D. Halliday. New York: John Wiley & Sons, 1960, Chapters 27, 29, 33, 34

Physics, the Pioneer Science, L. W. Taylor. Boston: Houghton Mifflin, 1941; New York: Dover Publications, 1959, Chapters 42, 43, 46

Resource Letter FC-1 on Evolution of the Electromagnetic Field Concept. W. T. Scott, *Am. J. Phys.* **31**, 819 (1963)

CHAPTER 25

Current Electricity

25.1 INTRODUCTION

Well before the discovery of the voltaic battery, it was realized that electrical conductors were not identical in their conducting powers, and that some substances offered more "resistance" to the passage of electricity than others. The evidence for this was essentially qualitative, although Cavendish, in the 1770's, succeeded in making remarkably accurate comparisons of the relative conducting power of various metals and liquids. Cavendish's technique consisted in discharging a Leyden jar through his own body, in series with a length of the conductor being investigated. Adjusting the lengths of different conductors until they gave him the same intensity of shock from a reproducibly charged jar, he took these lengths to be a direct measure of the relative conducting power per unit length.

In 1821 Davy, using a rough comparison of electric currents, studied the relative conducting powers of metallic wires of different lengths and cross sections in voltaic circuits and concluded that, for wires made of any one metal, the conducting power was inversely proportional to the length, directly proportional to the cross-sectional area, and independent of the shape of the cross section when the area was fixed. From the latter observations he concluded that voltaic currents pass through the body of the conducting wire and not along its surface.

> PROBLEM 25.1. State in your own words the line of reasoning that supports this conclusion. [*Hint:* What happens to the surface area of the wire as the shape of the cross section is changed while the cross-sectional area is kept constant?]

Making use of Oersted's recent discovery of the magnetism of current-carrying wires, Davy also remarked that the effect on a compass needle was the same at every point in a circuit, even though the circuit was formed of wires of different conducting powers pieced together in series. He interpreted this to mean, just as Ampère had (Section 23.8), that the current was the same at every point in a voltaic circuit.

Throughout this era of investigation, however, it was clear that the current in a circuit depended not only on the conductors but also on a strength or intensity of the source itself. Stronger shocks were obtained through a given conductor from more highly charged Leyden jars; larger magnetic effects were evident when current was supplied by a voltaic pile consisting of a larger stack of plates.

Thus, by the mid 1820's, there existed clear physical motivation for concepts of "electrical resistance" of conducting materials and "strength" of sources of electric current; the problem was to achieve operational definitions of the concepts and to establish the mathematical law describing their relation to the current in a given circuit. The necessary experimental groundwork was laid in Cologne in 1826–27 by Georg Simon Ohm (1789–1854).

25.2 OHM'S INVESTIGATION OF CONDUCTION IN METALLIC CIRCUITS

Ohm attempted to make precise measurements of current supplied by voltaic batteries with different numbers of plates to conductors of different length and conducting power. Despite the invention of the galvanometer in 1820 and its availability as a sensitive current-measuring device, he found it impossible to obtain reproducible experimental observations because of erratic fluctuations in the voltaic piles themselves. [Although modern knowledge and techniques of construction have made electric batteries highly stable and reproducible sources of electricity, early construction failed to control important factors such as cleanness of metallic surfaces, uniformity in concentration of the electrolyte (conducting liquid between the plates), effects of temperature and pressure on the contact between layers of the pile, etc.]

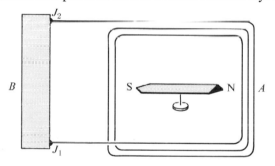

FIG. 25.2.1. Seebeck or thermoelectric effect: Coil of copper wire, A, is connected to ends of a bar, B, of bismuth or some other metal. If the two junctions, J_1 and J_2, are maintained at different temperatures, the compass-needle galvanometer shows a deflection, giving evidence of a continuous flow of current in the coil.

Ohm found a way out of this difficulty, however, by capitalizing on a discovery made a few years earlier (1822) by a fellow countryman, Thomas Johann Seebeck (1770–1831). In experiments with voltaic batteries, Seebeck had discovered that he could dispense with the conducting liquid entirely and still obtain a feeble but continuing electric current if he firmly connected the two ends of a copper wire to a bar of some other metal and maintained the two junctions at different temperatures (Fig. 25.2.1). This is called the *Seebeck* or *thermoelectric* effect.

The thermoelectric effect turned out to be highly stable and reproducible so long as the two temperatures were kept constant. Ohm set up an improved and very sensitive galvanometer (using a thin gold ribbon suspension of a magnetized steel needle held in carefully fixed position over the current-carrying wire), and measured the torque exerted on the needle for different currents in the wire. He took the torque, τ, to be a direct indication of the magnitude of the current.

Ohm made the following experiments: (a) Choosing a particular bar of metal, B, and keeping the temperature of the two junctions (Fig. 25.2.1) fixed, he inserted different lengths x of copper wire, A, of uniform cross section, and found that the torque on the needle could be represented by the empirical equation

$$\tau = \frac{a}{b + x},$$ (25.2.1)

where a and b were numerical constants.

(b) Changing the temperature difference between the two junctions and repeating the experiments, he found that the numerical value of b remained unchanged, but that the value of a was altered in direct proportion to the temperature *difference*.

Ohm proposed a very simple interpretation of these observations: (a) The quantity $R \equiv b + x$ represents a direct measure of the total "resistance" of the circuit, with x representing the varying contribution of the different lengths of conducting wire and b the constant contribution of bar B and the junctions at which the wire is connected. "Resistance" is a suitable name for the property being measured, since an increase in its value results in a decrease of the observed electric current.

(b) The quantity a is not affected by changes in the conducting properties of the circuit, but increases with increasing temperature difference between the junctions, and is zero when the temperature difference is zero. Thus a is a unique property of the electric source itself and a measure of its driving strength or intensity.

In a very famous paper published in 1822, the French mathematician Fourier had developed the analytical theory of conduction of heat in solids, based on the assumption that the rate of flow of heat through a slab of material is directly proportional to the temperature difference between the opposite sides of the slab. Motivated by this successful model, Ohm visualized the quantity a in the electric circuit as having a role analogous to that of temperature difference in heat flow. He also went on to show that a small electrometer, charged by connecting one side of the thermoelectric source to the leaves and the other to the case, exhibited a proportionately stronger charge or "tension" as the temperature difference between the junctions, and therefore a, was increased.

With our present knowledge and perspective, we might immediately be led to ask about any possible connection between a and the concepts of electrostatics discussed in Chapters 23 and 24. As we shall see very shortly, a can be identified directly with the concept of potential difference defined in Section 24.4, but it must be remembered that these concepts had not been clarified when Ohm performed his farsighted experiments. The significance of the energy concepts was not to be appreciated until twenty years later.

25.3   JOULE'S INVESTIGATION OF HEAT EVOLVED IN ELECTRIC CIRCUITS

We have referred several times to the heating of conducting wires as one of the characteristic effects of current electricity. With his profound interest in all thermal phenomena, it is not surprising to find Joule making this the subject of one of his early investigations in 1841.

Joule first determined the ratio of the resistances of two different samples of wire. He then wound the wires on glass tubes, immersed the windings in cylinders of water, connected them in series with each other and with a voltaic battery, so that the same current would flow through each one, and determined the temperature rise of the water in each cylinder during a fixed interval of time. A schematic diagram of Joule's experiment is shown in Fig. 25.3.1.

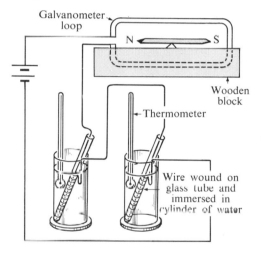

Fig. 25.3.1. Schematic diagram of Joule's apparatus for the determination of the rate of evolution of heat in current-carrying wires.

Joule showed that for a fixed current (indicated by a constant deflection of the galvanometer needle), the rate at which heat was evolved in each cylinder was proportional to the resistance R of each wire. The next step was to determine the effect of the current; Joule had already made a guess as to what the relationship might be: "I thought the effect produced by the increase of the intensity of the electric current would be as the square of that element ... arising from the increase of the *quantity* of electricity passed in a given time, and also from the increase of the *velocity* of the same." His experiments showed that the rate of evolution of heat in each cylinder was indeed proportional to the square of the current, I.

Combining the two results into one functional relationship, we would summarize Joule's experimental observations in the statement:

In a conductor of resistance R carrying current I, the rate of evolution of heat is proportional to I^2R, or, denoting by Q the total heat (not electrical charge) evolved over the time interval between t_1 and t_2:

$$Q \propto \int_{t_1}^{t_2} I^2 R \, dt. \tag{25.3.1}$$

The functional relationship described in these equations is still frequently referred to as *Joule's law*, and the heat evolved in an electrical circuit as the *Joule heat*.

A proportionality sign has been used in Eq. (25.3.1) to emphasize the fact that we have not yet specified a set of units that would allow us to assign values to I and R such as to give numerical values of Q in previously defined energy units (joules or calories).

25.4 OHM'S LAW

During the twenty years that followed Ohm's experiments of 1826–27, his results were repeated and confirmed with increasing precision by a number of investigators, but the connection between the law of current electricity and other electrical concepts remained obscure until the essential unity of all the various phenomena was grasped through growing appreciation of the significance of the law of conservation of energy.

Roget as early as 1832 and Faraday in 1840 had both pointed to the chemical changes taking place within voltaic batteries as evidence that something was being used up within the system while electricity was being displaced. In Roget's words, "All the powers and sources of motion, with the operation of which we are acquainted, when producing their peculiar effects, are expended in the same proportion as those effects are produced; and hence arises the impossibility of obtaining by their agency a perpetual effect; or, in other words, a perpetual motion." And from Faraday came the remark that one never found in nature "a pure creation of force; a production of power without a corresponding exhaustion of something to supply it."*

In 1849, just as the accumulated impact of the work of Mayer, Joule, and Helmholtz was being grasped by the scientific community, the German physicist Kirchhoff pointed out that existing knowledge of electricity fell together beautifully and consistently if the quantity a in Ohm's empirical relation [Eq. (25.2.1)] were identified with the magnitude of the potential difference, $|\Delta V|$, giving the algebraic form

$$I = \frac{|\Delta V|}{R} \tag{25.4.1}$$

$$\Delta V = IR. \tag{25.4.2}$$

(We shall normally drop the absolute-value signs, as we have in Eq. (25.4.2), but it is necessary to remember that conventional positive current flows in the direction of decreasing potential; i.e., through potential differences we defined as negative in Section 24.4.)

---

* It is interesting to note that both of these statements preceded the papers of Mayer and Joule in the 1840's. The idea of conservation of energy was "in the air," in the form of a postulate of impotence. In limited, qualitative ways it had been invoked and used by many investigators to guide their thoughts and speculations. (See Section 20.9.)

The identification of a with $|\Delta V|$ would readily account for the previously established fact that the difference of electric "tensions" between the terminals of a voltaic battery (measured by means of an electrometer) was proportional to Ohm's quantity a. Furthermore, since ΔV represents the work per unit positive charge displaced between two points, and since I represents the rate of displacement of charge, the product $I\,\Delta V$ must be interpreted as the total rate at which work is done on moving electrical charge between two points. (The modern name for "rate of doing work" is *power*; in the mks system the units of power are joules/sec or *watts*.)

Thus, pursuing Kirchhoff's interpretation, if work is being done at the rate

$$P = I\,\Delta V, \tag{25.4.3}$$

and if the current is connected with ΔV by the relation (25.4.2), then

$$P = I(IR) = I^2 R. \tag{25.4.4}$$

If all the work done in an electrical circuit of this kind is converted into heat, then the rate of evolution of heat should be proportional to the product $I^2 R$, which is precisely what had been observed empirically by Joule [relation (25.3.1)].

In effect, just as we have found an electric battery capable of maintaining a fixed potential difference and constant electrostatic field between a pair of capacitor plates connected to its terminals, so we extend this conception and visualize the battery as maintaining a fixed potential difference and electrical field *within* a conductor. With a charged pith ball bouncing back and forth between the capacitor plates (Section 23.4), we saw the work done on the charge being converted into KE of the moving pith ball and then into heat on inelastic collision with the plates. Within the conductor, uniformity of the current throughout the circuit and the uniform evolution of heat everywhere along a wire combine to indicate that work done on the moving charge is being converted directly into heat, without being stored in kinetic or potential form to be released at particular points.

This gives us the intuitive sense that resistance in an electric circuit is in some manner analogous to friction in mechanical motion: The work we do in pushing an object over a rough surface at constant velocity is converted into heat at the same rate that the work is done. If we exert force F in the direction of the velocity v, the rate of doing work and producing heat is given by the product $F \cdot v$. When a raindrop of mass m falls at terminal velocity v_t in the atmosphere (Section 6.8), work is done by the gravitational field, and this work is converted into heat at the uniform rate mgv_t. In Ohm's resistive circuit, electrical work is converted into heat at the rate $(\Delta V)I$.

In honor of his pioneering investigations, Eq. (25.4.1) is called Ohm's law, although, as we have seen, Ohm himself did not provide the full interpretation of its significance and did not perceive the relation between his parameter a and the electrostatic concept of potential difference. Having already given the modern definitions of the units of ΔV (volts) and I (amperes), it follows from (25.4.1) that the units of resistance, $R = \Delta V/I$, must be volts/ampere. The name given this combination is *ohms*.

Implicit throughout our discussion of Ohm's law has been the idea that R is a constant property of any particular conducting object (called a *resistor*); i.e., that a graph of the potential difference ΔV between the ends of the resistor versus the current I flowing in it would be a straight line of slope R. Although this linear relation indeed obtains in many instances, particularly with metallic resistors, as demonstrated by Ohm and other investigators, there are also instances in which the relation is not at all linear. Among the latter cases are electrical conduction in gases and the behavior of the filament of an electric light bulb. Here the ratio $\Delta V/I$ is not constant, and, although we can define an "instantaneous" resistance by this ratio, we say that the object does not obey Ohm's law.

PROBLEM 25.2.   Sketch hypothetical graphs that you might expect to obtain in plotting measured values of ΔV-versus-I for two objects obeying Ohm's law. Which object has the greater resistance? In the case of an electric light filament, the instantaneous resistance increases with increasing current. Sketch a hypothetical ΔV-versus-I graph for such a filament.

PROBLEM 25.3.   Suppose we wrote Eq. (25.4.2) in the form $I = G\,\Delta V$. Is there anything wrong with this representation; does it still convey the idea contained in Ohm's original equation? What might be some suitable names for G that would appropriately characterize its physical significance?

PROBLEM 25.4.   In Problem 7.1 you were asked to contrast the laws represented by $F_{\text{net}} = ma$, $F_f = \mu N$, $F = kx$ (Hooke's law). Let us add $Q = mc_p\,\Delta t$, $F = BIL_\perp$, and $\Delta V = IR$ to the group, and continue the original discussion. Do all of these statements have anything in common? Are all of them "laws" in the same sense? Do you consider some to be more general and fundamental than others? Why? Which proportionality constant in the other equations do you feel to be most nearly analogous to R?

25.5   RESISTIVE CIRCUITS

In Fig. 25.5.1 we summarize the code of graphical representation and some of the terminology we have already been using in talking about simple electric circuits. Electrical connections of negligible resistance between points in a circuit diagram are shown by lines. Any object that has appreciable resistance is designated by the symbol $\sim\!\!\bigvee\!\!\bigvee\!\!\sim$, and sources of current $\;\dashv\vert\vdash\;$. Let us predict some of the effects that might occur when we connect resistors in series as in Fig. 25.5.1(a). The battery maintains a constant potential difference ΔV_{ab} between the points a and b. Since the current is known to be the same at every point between a and b, the rate at which work is being done on moving electrical charge is $I\,\Delta V_{ab}$. Part of this work, $I\,\Delta V_{a1}$, however, is done as charge is displaced from a to 1, and an additional amount $I\,\Delta V_{1b}$ is done in the displacement from 1 to b. The law of conservation of energy demands that, in the absence of additional batteries or other sources of potential difference between a and b:

$$I\,\Delta V_{ab} = I\,\Delta V_{a1} + I\,\Delta V_{1b}$$
$$\Delta V_{ab} = \Delta V_{a1} + \Delta V_{1b}. \tag{25.5.1}$$

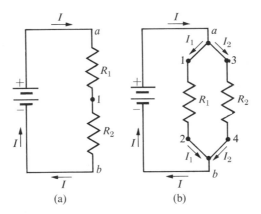

FIG. 25.5.1. (a) Resistors R_1 and R_2 connected consecutively or "in series," with $\Delta V_{ab} = \Delta V_{a_1} + \Delta V_{1b}$. (b) Resistors R_1 and R_2 connected "in parallel," with $I = I_1 + I_2$ and $\Delta V_{ab} = \Delta V_{12} = \Delta V_{34}$.

Suppose that we wish to replace the combination of resistors R_1 and R_2 by a single resistor R that would have the same overall effect; i.e., leave I unchanged. What should be the value of R?

If each of the resistors obeys Ohm's law, $\Delta V_{ab} = IR$, $\Delta V_{a1} = IR_1$, and $\Delta V_{1b} = IR_2$. Substituting these relations into (25.5.1) we obtain $IR = IR_1 + IR_2$, or

$$R = R_1 + R_2, \tag{25.5.2}$$

$$I = \frac{\Delta V_{ab}}{R_1 + R_2}. \tag{25.5.3}$$

PROBLEM 25.5. Interpret these results in words, and explain them in a simple, intuitive way. Suppose that initially $R_1 = R_2$. What are the relative values of ΔV_{a1} and ΔV_{1b}? Now suppose that R_2 is kept constant but R_1 is varied. What happens to the current I and the potential difference ΔV_{1b} as R_1 is increased? As it is decreased? Show algebraically that

$$\Delta V_{1b} = \frac{R_2}{R_1 + R_2} \cdot \Delta V_{ab}.$$

What happens if R_1 is made very much larger than R_2? If it becomes very nearly zero? What would be the formula for R if more than two resistors were connected in series?

Suppose that you wish to devise a laboratory experiment in which various different values of ΔV are imposed across the ends of a resistor, but that you have available only one battery of fixed potential difference. How might you set up your experiment? (Draw a diagram of the circuit.)

In circuits such as that in Fig. 25.5.1(a) we frequently speak of "potential drops" between various points. The potential drop between the positive terminal of the battery and point a is zero, since the resistance of this portion of the circuit is indicated by our code of representation to be zero. From a to 1 the potential drop is $\Delta V_{a1} = IR_1$, etc. The potential drop between any pair of points can be calculated from the current and the total resistance between the points. Two points with essentially zero resistance between them must be at very nearly the same potential, and the potential drop between them is zero. This would, for example, be true of any pair of points along the wire connecting the battery and point a in Fig. 25.5.1.

In Fig. 25.5.1(b), points a, 1, 3 are at one potential and points b, 2, 4 at another. Therefore

$$\Delta V_{ab} = \Delta V_{12} = \Delta V_{34}. \tag{25.5.4}$$

Since no accumulation of charge of one sign or the other is observed to build up anywhere in the circuit, the principle of conservation of charge requires that

$$I = I_1 + I_2. \tag{25.5.5}$$

If we ask what single value of resistance R will produce the same effect as the parallel combination, we have [by substituting for I from Ohm's law into (25.5.5)]:

$$\frac{\Delta V_{ab}}{R} = \frac{\Delta V_{12}}{R_1} + \frac{\Delta V_{34}}{R_2}$$

and, because of Eq. (25.5.4),

$$\frac{1}{R} = \frac{1}{R_1} + \frac{1}{R_2}. \tag{25.5.6}$$

*PROBLEM 25.6.   Interpret Eq. (25.5.6). What happens to the effective resistance of a combination as more and more resistors are connected in parallel? What happens to the current drawn from the source? What relevance does this analysis have to the situation in which more and more appliances are connected to a household electric outlet until a fuse blows? (What is a fuse and why does it blow under these circumstances?)

PROBLEM 25.7.   Suppose that we start with $R_1 = R_2$ in a parallel combination. How does the total current I divide between the two resistors? If we keep R_2 constant but change R_1, what happens to the relative values of I_1 and I_2 as R_1 is increased? As it is decreased? Suppose we wish exactly one-tenth of the total current to flow through R_2, what should we take as the value of R_1? [*Answer:* $R_1 = \frac{1}{9}R_2$.]

25.6   AMMETERS AND VOLTMETERS

In Section 24.9 we described how to make use of the torque exerted on a current-carrying coil in a magnetic field in order to construct a meter in which angular deflections would be proportional to the current flowing in the coil. An immediate

---

* *Note to students and teachers:* Developing an understanding of Ohm's law and of simple resistive circuits is an eminently suitable task for independent study coupled with laboratory experience. For this reason, this text will contain very few numerical problems and exercises on this material. The problems that are given are meant to guide the student to the most important conceptual aspects. Further practice in handling calculations should be acquired in the course of laboratory work or by seeking out additional exercises in other texts.

consequence of the analysis carried out in the preceding section is an insight into how one might design one type of meter to give a direct measure of the current flowing in a circuit, and another type to give a direct measure of the potential difference between two points.

To make an ammeter—a meter that measures current flowing at some point or in a branch of a circuit—we wish the unknown current to pass through the meter and register its effect, but we want the meter itself to alter or "perturb" conditions in the circuit as little as possible. For the unknown current to pass through the meter, we must insert the meter into the circuit at a point (or points) of interest, as shown in Fig. 25.6.1. Since the coil of the meter will always have slight resistance, the discussion of the series circuit (Fig. 25.5.1a) indicates that insertion of the meter will always cause a slightly smaller current than that which flows in the absence of the meter.

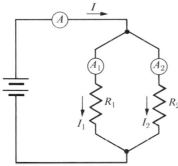

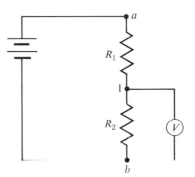

FIG. 25.6.1. Ammeters inserted at various points in a simple resistive circuit. Ammeter A measures total current, I, flowing from the battery. Ammeter A_1 measures current I_1 flowing through resistor R_1.

FIG. 25.6.2. Voltmeter connected to measure potential difference ΔV_{1b} across resistor R_2.

Thus, in general, we should design ammeters to have as small an effective resistance as possible. If the meter resistance is much smaller than that of the rest of the circuit, the meter has no significant effect on the current. If the meter resistance is higher than that of the circuit, the current that we observe is essentially determined by the meter itself rather than by the circuit resistance.

Now suppose that we wish to measure the potential difference between two points, say across the ends of a resistor, rather than the current within the circuit. Ohm's law suggests how this might be done by proper use of a meter.

If we connect a meter across the ends of resistor R_2 as shown in Fig. 25.6.2, a current $I_m = \Delta V_{1b}/R_m$ will flow through the meter (where R_m is the effective resistance of the meter coil), and the meter will indicate a corresponding deflection. If R_m is much larger than R_2, ΔV_{1b} will be essentially unaffected by the presence of the meter, and the meter deflection, caused by the smaller current I_m, will be proportional to ΔV_{1b}. By appropriate calibration or by calculations based on the precisely determined values of R_m, currents I_m can be converted into potential differences, and the scale of the meter marked directly in volts instead of amperes.

PROBLEM 25.8.   In the light of the analysis carried out in Problem 25.7, describe what would happen under the conditions of Fig. 25.6.2 if the meter had a low rather than a high resistance.   Note that the essential difference between an ammeter and a voltmeter is that the former must be designed to have as low an effective resistance as possible, while the latter must have as high an effective resistance as possible.   Explain these requirements in your own words.

PROBLEM 25.9.   If you are furnished with a particular meter, there is nothing you can do to alter the resistance of the coil; this is a fixed, intrinsic property of the meter. It is perfectly possible, however, to adapt the meter to serve *either* as an ammeter or as a voltmeter by proper use of additional resistors of low or high value connected *externally*.   Describe what you would do to make each conversion.   What information would you wish to have with respect to the meter itself?   Explain the physics behind your strategy in each case.

25.7   EMF

If we were to release a positively charged particle at some point in the uniform electrical field between capacitor plates, or in a nonuniform field, such as one of those mapped out by the grass seeds in Fig. 23.11.1, the particle would be displaced toward positions of lower and lower potential. In general, it would not spontaneously go around a closed path and return to its starting point.

Suppose that we visualize transporting the particle around a closed path, however, as illustrated in Fig. 25.7.1.   We imagine doing this under conditions of balanced force and essentially zero acceleration, as in our calculations of potential energy change and potential difference in Sections 18.9 and 24.4.   (The reader might find it helpful to review these two sections at this point.)   Recalling our previous experi-

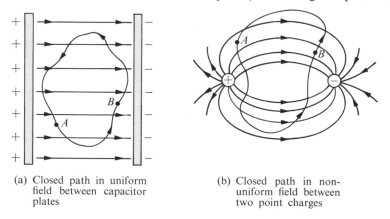

(a) Closed path in uniform field between capacitor plates

(b) Closed path in non-uniform field between two point charges

FIG. 25.7.1.   In each case the net work done per unit charge in displacing a charged particle around a closed path (starting at point A and returning to this point) is zero.   In mathematical symbols, $\oint \mathbf{E}_c \cdot ds = 0$.

ence with such calculations, we note that the work done by the field in displacing the particle to positions of lower potential would be exactly equal in magnitude to the work we would have to supply from the outside to bring the particle back to its initial position. In other words, the *net* work done on the particle in transporting it around a closed path would be zero; we could store the work done while moving to regions of lower potential by arranging to raise a weight, and we restore exactly this amount of work as the weight is lowered in returning the particle to its starting point at the higher potential.

If the quantities of work were not balanced in this fashion, we might arrange to have the particle "fall" while raising a weight along that part of the path yielding the larger amount of energy, and we would return the particle to its starting point along the part of the path requiring less energy. We would then have a quantity of work left over; we could pump water or operate machines, extracting a continuous supply of energy from the electrostatic field without producing any changes or any "running down" in the system. The conviction that nature does not permit our getting something for nothing in this sense has been pointed out repeatedly, and was seen to play a role in the evolution of the concept of conservation of energy.

To express in symbols the statement that the net work done in moving a charged particle around a closed path is zero, we visualize calculating small quantities of work $\mathbf{E}_{ck} \cdot \Delta s_k$ per unit charge, where $\mathbf{E}_{ck}$ is the component of electric field in the direction of the kth small displacement Δs_k. Then we evaluate the limit of the sum (around the closed path) of all these small quantities of work as the Δs_k tend toward zero.

Introducing the symbol $\oint$ to denote a limit of the sum or integral taken around a closed path, we would write $\oint \mathbf{E}_c \cdot ds$ as the symbol for the net work per unit charge in such a displacement. The assertion that the net work per unit charge must be zero is then embodied in the statement,

$$\text{For an electrostatic field:} \quad \oint \mathbf{E}_c \cdot ds = 0. \tag{25.7.1}$$

Another way of interpreting Eq. (25.7.1) is to point out that along some parts of the path the force component $\mathbf{E}_c$ is in the same direction as the local displacement Δs, and work is then done *by* the field (that is, $\mathbf{E}_c \cdot \Delta s$ is positive). Along other parts of the path, $\mathbf{E}_c$ is directed oppositely to the local displacement Δs, and work must then be supplied externally (i.e., work is done *against* the field, $\mathbf{E}_c \cdot \Delta s$ is negative). The positive and negative quantities of work add up to zero as we evaluate the limit of the sum around the closed path.

Still another way of interpreting this restriction is to imagine that we construct a frictionless track forming the closed path, and that we impart an initial kinetic energy to the particle so that it keeps sliding around and around the "circuit." If we give the particle sufficient energy to negotiate the "highest" point in the track, it will keep going around indefinitely so long as we make no attempt to extract energy. If we extract work, however, or if we introduce friction and cause kinetic energy to be continuously transformed into heat, the motion will quickly run down; the particle will end up at the position of lowest potential along the track; its motion will cease, and there will be no tendency for it to keep going around the circuit.

PROBLEM 25.10.   Suppose that you transport a body of mass m around some arbitrary closed path in the gravitational field of the earth, with up-and-down and horizontal motions, returning it eventually to the starting point. Argue that $\oint (mg)_c \cdot ds$ must equal zero. What connection do you see between this situation and that referred to in Eq. (25.7.1)? (See Section 18.9.)

Displacement of electrical charge in a circuit associated with a voltaic battery or a thermoelectric effect (Section 25.2) presents a sharp contrast to the case of the electrostatic field we have described above. In the battery system, charge is continuously displaced around a closed path—the very name "circuit" is a recognition of this special aspect—while heat is continuously evolved in all parts of the circuit (including the battery) as the current flows. Thus the battery and thermal junctions appear to be seats of electrical effects capable of maintaining the flow of charge and supplying the work which is transformed into the observed Joule heat.

But the battery and thermoelectric junction are not perpetual-motion devices or sources of infinite amounts of energy. In the battery, energy is stored in a potential form associated with the chemicals that react and are used up as the battery runs down. In the Seebeck effect, energy is drawn from the source of heat which maintains the temperature difference between the junctions; in the absence of such a source, the temperature difference drops to zero and current ceases to flow.

We shall not attempt to describe the electric fields set up within the conductors in voltaic or thermoelectric circuits, or the mechanisms by means of which these fields are set up and maintained. (As a matter of fact, there is still much to be understood about the detailed mechanisms, and these phenomena are subjects of research and investigation to the present day.) As we have seen in a variety of other complicated situations, however, the energy concepts frequently allow us to make definitive statements about the overall behavior of a physical system even when we remain ignorant of the details of intervening events or processes.

It is a readily observable experimental fact that for a given battery, or for a particular thermoelectric junction with fixed temperature difference, the current I flowing in the circuit is always inversely proportional to the *total* circuit resistance R_T, comprised of the sum of the external resistance R_{ext} and the internal resistance R_{int} of the battery or thermal junction itself. This experimental fact can be stated

$$I \propto \frac{1}{R_T} \qquad \text{or} \qquad IR_T = \text{a constant, denoted by } \varepsilon, \qquad (25.7.2)$$

where the constant ε is a fixed number for any particular battery. The number is different for different batteries, increasing as more cells are stacked in series; it increases in a thermoelectric junction when the temperature difference in the junction is increased.

In the light of our discussion of Ohm's law and the definition of the concept of resistance in Section 25.4, we note that the quantity $\varepsilon = IR_T$ must represent a work per unit charge and must be measured in joules per coulomb or volts in the mks system. Furthermore, $\varepsilon I = I^2 R_T$ represents the rate at which Joule heat is evolved in the entire circuit while current I is flowing. Thus the constant, ε, uniquely associated with each voltaic or thermoelectric source, is the direct quantitative measure of the ability of the source to deliver energy through the continuous displacement of electrical charge—an ability that we described only in qualitative terms in the first part of our discussion.

The constant ε represents the work per unit charge made available by the electrical phenomena, which we make no attempt to describe, but which are nevertheless assumed to be present, maintaining the flow of charge around the closed conducting path and the simultaneous evolution of Joule heat. The quantity ε has the same units as potential difference (volts). It is given the name EMF,* and we speak of batteries and thermal junctions as *seats* or *sources* of EMF.

Figure 25.7.2 shows how we represent, in a simple circuit diagram, some of the ideas we have just discussed. When an external resistance R_{ext} is connected across the battery, the ammeter A registers current I. It follows from Eq. (25.7.2) that

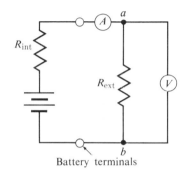

$$\varepsilon = IR_T = IR_{int} + IR_{ext}, \qquad (25.7.3)$$

$$\varepsilon - IR_{int} = IR_{ext} = \Delta V_{ab}. \qquad (25.7.4)$$

Voltmeter V registers the potential drop ΔV_{ab} across the external resistance. Note that, in the light of Eq. (25.7.3), ε must always be *larger* than ΔV_{ab}, which, in accordance with Ohm's law, is equal to IR_{ext}.

FIG. 25.7.2. Battery circuit, showing internal and external resistances.

PROBLEM 25.11. In our earlier discussions we avoided making a specific commitment as to whether ΔV_{ab} was a constant quantity, independent of the size of the current drawn from the battery. Since the EMF, denoted by ε, is found to be a constant property of any given source, Eq. (25.7.4) tells us that ΔV_{ab} cannot be constant. Interpret Eq. (25.7.4): What happens to the potential difference at the terminals of a battery as the external resistance is decreased and a larger current flows? What happens in such a case if the internal resistance of the source of EMF happens to be extremely low? What value does ΔV_{ab} approach as R_{ext} is made extremely high? When a battery is connected to a pair of capacitor plates, how is the potential difference between the plates related to the EMF of the battery? (Explain your answer.) Interpret the statement: "The open-circuit voltage of a battery is identical with its EMF." (You might find it interesting to design and execute your own laboratory experiment to explore some of these ideas and relationships, and to determine the EMF of a particular battery.)

———————

* We shall read this simply as the letters "ee em ef." The letters were originally an abbreviation for the term *electromotive force*, a name introduced before clarification of the energy concepts and the establishing of a clear distinction between force and energy. Since EMF is, like potential difference, work per unit charge, the word force is inappropriate, and hence we shall avoid the words of the original name.

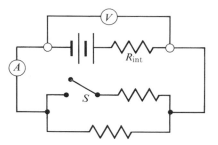

FIGURE 25.7.3

PROBLEM 25.12.   Suppose that the switch S in Fig. 25.7.3 is closed.   The battery has a small but significant internal resistance.   Will the readings of the respective meters increase, decrease, or remain unchanged?   Explain your reasoning.   [*Answer: A* increases; *V* decreases.]

25.8   ELECTROLYSIS AND CONDUCTION OF ELECTRICITY

In the entire discussion of electricity up to this point, we have said nothing about the mechanism of conduction, and have covered our ignorance of detail by use of the convention that positive charge is displaced.   It is clear—from phenomena such as the decomposition of water and other substances when electricity is passed through them, from the chemical changes that take place in a voltaic battery, from the spark that passes through air when a sufficiently intense field is built up between the terminals of an electrostatic machine—that electricity is intimately associated with the very structure of matter itself.   It was inevitable that study of the mechanisms of conduction of electricity would lead to deeper knowledge of the structure of matter. The detailed fruits of theoretical speculation and research in this area did not ripen until the end of the nineteenth century, but in the meantime, evidence accumulated.

It was clear from the time of discovery of the voltaic cell and of the phenomenon of electrolysis that there was a basic difference between conduction in metals, within which no chemical changes occur when current passes through, and conduction in liquids such as water or other "electrolytes," in which characteristic chemical changes invariably accompany the flow of current.

During the 1830's Faraday devoted a major effort to the quantitative study of electrolysis of different compounds.   It was well established by this time than many chemical compounds could be decomposed in solution or in the molten state by passage of an electric current, and that certain chemical elements (hydrogen in the decomposition of water, lead in the decomposition of lead chloride, copper in the decomposition of water solution of copper sulfate) always appeared at the electrode connected to the negative terminal of the battery, and that other elements (oxygen in decomposition of water, chlorine in decomposition of lead chloride) always appeared at the opposite electrode* connected to the positive battery terminal.

---

* Electrode is the name given to plates of metal (frequently platinum) or other conducting objects used to establish electrical contact with a conducting fluid.

Faraday showed that the amounts of material liberated at the electrodes were exactly proportional to the amount of electricity passed through the system. He showed that fixed masses of hydrogen and oxygen were liberated by a fixed amount of electricity, regardless of whether the water being decomposed was made conducting by acidification or by the addition of salt. He showed that free materials were always evolved at the electrodes in exactly the ratios in which they combined to form the compounds being decomposed. At one point he remarks, "In some of these experiments several substances were placed in succession [series], and decomposed simultaneously by the same electric current: [molten] chloride of tin and chloride of lead, and water, were thus acted on at once . . . the tin, lead, chlorine, oxygen, and hydrogen evolved being *definite in quantity* and [appearing in their known combining proportions] to each other." (Metals such as copper, lead, and tin plated out on the negative electrode, and the quantity liberated over a measured period of time could be determined by weighing the electrode before and after a run. Gases such as hydrogen, oxygen, and chlorine were trapped in tubes surrounding the respective electrodes, and the volume of gas was determined at known temperature and pressure.)

Faraday began using a cell in which hydrogen and oxygen released in the decomposition of water were trapped in separate tubes and accurately measured. Inserted in series with any circuit, this cell served as a *coulometer*, a device for measuring the total transport of electricity over a period of time. It was, in other words, an integrating device, capable of giving, in terms of hydrogen and oxygen released, the values of $\int_{t_2}^{t_1} I(t)\, dt$. Faraday showed—to express it in modern units—that a total of 96,500 coul of electricity displaced through water would evolve 1.00 gm of hydrogen at the negative electrode and simultaneously liberate 8.00 gm of oxygen at the positive electrode. This quantity, 96,500 coul, will be referred to frequently in later discussions, and will play an important role in numerical calculations concerning electrical properties of matter. It is called "one faraday" of electrical charge.

In order to cut through the welter of confusion that resulted from the use of nonstandard terminology, Faraday suggested a nomenclature for aspects of electrolytic conduction that remains in use to this day. He suggested the name *cathode* for the negatively charged electrode in an electrolytic cell and the name *anode* for the positive electrode. For the substances that migrated through the liquid to be evolved at the electrodes he suggested the general name *ions*, and for ions of hydrogen, copper, lead, etc., that migrated to the cathode he used the specific designation *cations*, while for those migrating to the anode he used the designation *anions*.

Faraday visualized cations and anions as migrating in opposite directions through the solution, transporting charge toward the respective electrodes, but keeping the body of the solution electrically neutral as they displaced past each other. When later investigators found that gases, such as air and other common substances, exhibit electrical conductivity on being subjected to strong heating, electrical discharge (particularly at low pressures in an evacuated tube), or in the presence of a flame, or (still later) under the influence of X rays and radioactivity, they were almost automatically led to speak of the gas as becoming "ionized" under these influences and to visualize ions as being attracted to the respective electrodes. As time went by the word ion was, of course, redefined; its meaning became sharper and more specific than Faraday may have visualized. The refinements came with further detailed discoveries concerning the atomic and electrical constitution of matter, discoveries foreshadowed and anticipated in the speculations of many scientists early in the nineteenth century.

Faraday himself was a strong believer in the then still young atomic theory of Dalton (see Chapter 28). In trying to express his own feeling about the ultimate significance of his laws of electroylsis, he wrote:

"The theory of electrolytical or electrochemical action appears to me to touch immediately on the *absolute quantity* of electricity or electric power belonging to different bodies. It is impossible, perhaps, to speak on this point without committing oneself beyond what present facts will sustain; and yet it is equally impossible, and perhaps would be impolitic not to reason upon the subject. Although we know nothing of what an atom is, yet we cannot resist forming some idea of a small particle, which represents it to the mind; and though we are in equal, if not greater, ignorance of electricity, so as to be unable to say whether it is a particular matter or matters, or mere motion of ordinary matter, or some third kind of power or agent, yet there is an immensity of facts which justify us in believing that the atoms of matter are in some way endowed or associated with electrical powers, to which they owe their most striking qualities, and amongst them their mutual chemical affinity."

Faraday was not the first to voice such ideas (Humphry Davy, the Swedish chemist Berzelius, and many others held similar views) but the quotation is a particularly clear articulation of the attitude and spirit of the times.

25.9   INDUCTION OF ELECTRIC CURRENTS

Motivated by the fact that current-carrying conductors are surrounded by a magnetic field, Faraday suspected that an inverse effect might exist—that conductors, appropriately exposed to the influence of a magnetic field, might have a flow of current induced in them—and he made a deliberate search for such an effect in investigations begun as early as 1825. His first positive results were reported to the Royal Society in 1831.

Winding two helices of wire, one over the other on a wooden core (Fig. 25.9.1a), Faraday connected one helix to a sensitive galvanometer and the other to a battery, thus subjecting the first helix to the magnetic field of the second. Under these circumstances he observed no permanent deflection of the galvanometer, but he noticed very slight kicks of the instrument in opposite directions as contact to the battery was made and broken. Following up this slight indication, he made the basic discovery that electric currents are indeed induced in conductors, but only by changing, rather than by constant, magnetic fields.

Faraday's first report concerning induced electric currents describes three types of experiments, illustrated in Fig. 25.9.1. In case (a), a magnetic field is produced by a

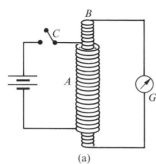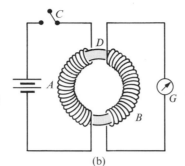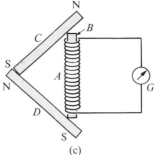

(a)	(b)	(c)

Solenoid *A* is wound over solenoid *B*. When switch *C* is closed, galvanometer *G* shows pulse of current in one direction, and then registers zero current until switch *C* is opened; galvanometer then shows pulse of current in opposite direction. Pulses of current are induced in *B* only when field of solenoid *A* is increasing or decreasing.

Two coils of wire are wound on opposite sides of soft iron ring *D*. When switch *C* is closed, current in coil *A* magnetizes iron ring, and galvanometer *G* shows a pulse of current in coil *B* as ring becomes magnetized. Galvanometer then shows zero current in *B* until switch is opened. As magnetization of ring disappears, galvanometer shows pulse of current in opposite direction.

Solenoid *A* is wound on soft iron rod *B*. When rod is magnetized by contact with permanent magnets *C* and *D*, galvanometer shows pulse of current in *A* as magnetization occurs, and then registers zero current until permanent magnets are removed; a pulse of current then flows in opposite direction.

FIG. 25.9.1. Faraday's three experiments, showing induced current when magnetic field through a coil or solenoid is changed by different agencies.

solenoid; in case (b) by an electromagnet; in case (c) by inducing magnetization of a soft iron bar by the proximity of permanent magnets. In each instance the magnetic field passes *through* another coil or solenoid connected to a galvanometer, and in each instance current flows in this second circuit when the magnetic field directed along its axis is increased or decreased. By opening and closing the switch in a steady alternation, it is possible to make pulses of current flow back and forth through the galvanometer (alternating current). By opening and closing the switch at the same frequency as the natural frequency of oscillation of his rather sluggish and slow-moving galvanometer, Faraday was able to excite the galvanometer into swings of large amplitude, and thus magnify the otherwise very small deflection, barely observable with a single pulse.

Let us relate Faraday's observation to our preceding discussion of electric circuits: Faraday's experiments show that when a *closed* conducting loop surrounds a region of changing magnetic field, an electric current is induced in the circuit formed by the conductor. In this case we have none of the complexities associated with voltaic cells or thermal junctions; we have nothing but a homogeneous conducting path, containing no *internal* seats of EMF. Since a current is induced by the changing magnetic field, we conclude that an electrical field must be set up within the conductor, and that the lines of force of this electric field must circulate around the loop and close upon themselves, as sketched in Fig. 25.9.2. Such a field would be capable of causing charge to be displaced continuously around the loop. (Although the attention of Faraday and other contemporary investigators was concentrated

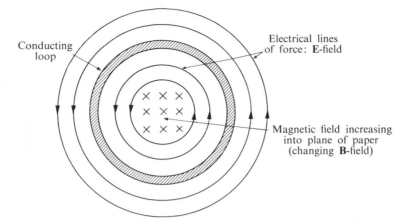

Fig. 25.9.2. Region of changing **B**-field is surrounded by electrical lines of force (E-field) circulating around the **B**-field in manner analogous to circulation of magnetic field around a current-carrying conductor.   Presence of counterclockwise E-field causes positive charge to be displaced in counterclockwise direction within the conducting loop.

on the current induced in the conducting loop, Maxwell subsequently called attention to the likelihood that the conducting loop only served to reveal the presence of an electrical field which was always induced around a changing magnetic field, whether or not the conducting loop happened to be present. This hypothesis turned out to be correct, and Fig. 25.9.2 is sketched accordingly.) In describing his observations Faraday remarked that

> "All these results show that the power of inducing electric currents is circumferentially exerted by a magnetic resultant or axis of power, just as circumferential magnetism is dependent upon and is exhibited by an electric current."

Since the circumferential flow of charge results in the evolution of Joule heat in the conductor, we again infer, as in the case of the voltaic circuit, the availability of an amount of work per unit charge and hence the presence of an EMF. In the same context, let us note that the field pattern sketched in Fig. 25.9.2 is fundamentally different from that of the static fields we discussed previously. In previous instances we encountered only situations in which lines of force in the electrical field began and ended on static charges, while the lines of force in the "dynamically" induced electrical field of Fig. 25.9.2 close circumferentially upon themselves.

If in this latter case we proceed to evaluate $\oint \mathbf{E}_c \cdot ds$, we note that the field components $\mathbf{E}_c$ and the local displacements Δs are always in the same direction all the way around the loop. Thus we do not have positive and negative values balancing each other in the summation, and we obtain a *nonzero* final value for the work per unit charge in contrast to the zero value always obtained in the case of the static field.

The concepts of induced EMF and of nonvanishing $\oint \mathbf{E}_c \cdot ds$ in the case of circumferentially closing electrical lines of force are perfectly consistent with each other; as a matter of fact they are simply different ways of saying essentially the same thing, namely, that work is available to drive charge around a closed resistive circuit. We are thus led to identify ε, the EMF induced by the changing magnetic field, with the nonzero value of the closed integral of the electrical field,

$$\text{Surrounding a changing magnetic field:} \quad \varepsilon = \oint \mathbf{E}_c \cdot ds. \qquad (25.9.1)$$

25.10 FARADAY'S LAW OF ELECTROMAGNETIC INDUCTION

Having established the existence of induced current and EMF, Faraday went on to determine the direction of the current and the factors governing the magnitude of the effect.

The observed direction of induced current or electric field is easily remembered by means of the left-hand rule described in Fig. 25.10.1.

The quantitative aspects of the phenomenon of electromagnetic induction are described in the following statements:

(1) In Section 25.9 we conjectured that the fundamental phenomenon associated with the changing magnetic field is the induction of a particular value ε of EMF. If this is the case, and if we then keep ε constant by conducting experiments in which all factors inducing current I in a conducting loop are kept the same while the total resistance R_T of the loop is varied, we would expect the observed current to be inversely proportional to R_T, since I should be equal to ε/R_T. It is observed that I actually does behave in this fashion, confirming our conjecture.   In subsequent

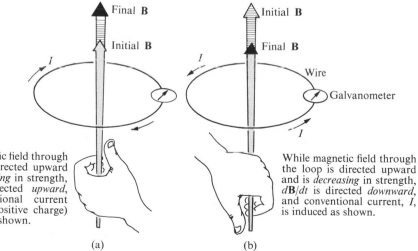

While magnetic field through the loop is directed upward and is *increasing* in strength, $d\mathbf{B}/dt$ is directed *upward*, and conventional current (motion of positive charge) is induced as shown.

While magnetic field through the loop is directed upward and is *decreasing* in strength, $d\mathbf{B}/dt$ is directed *downward*, and conventional current, I, is induced as shown.

(a)   (b)

FIG. 25.10.1. Mnemonic device for recalling direction of induced current in accordance with Faraday's law (left-hand rule): Point thumb of left hand in direction of $d\mathbf{B}/dt$. Curl of fingers shows direction of induced current and induced electrical field.

discussion we shall therefore focus attention on ε rather than on I as the fundamental quantitative measure of the phenomenon.

(2) If the conducting loop consists of N turns of wire instead of a single turn, our accumulating experience with superposition of electric and magnetic effects leads us to expect that the same EMF will be induced in each turn and that the total EMF would be the sum of the EMF's in the individual turns; i.e., we would expect an effect similar to that observed when voltaic cells are connected in series.   In electromagnetic induction we would thus expect the total EMF and the induced current I to be proportional to N, and this is indeed found to be the case experimentally.

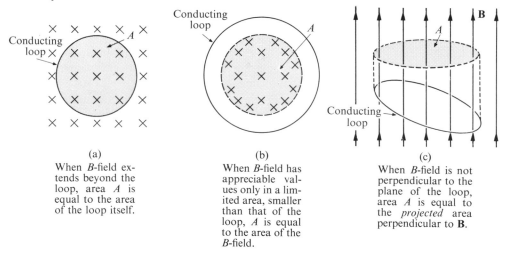

(a)   (b)   (c)
When B-field ex-   When B-field has   When B-field is not
tends beyond the   appreciable val-   perpendicular to the
loop, area A is   ues only in a lim-   plane of the loop,
equal to the area   ited area, smaller   area A is equal to
of the loop itself.   than that of the   the *projected* area
                             loop, A is equal   perpendicular to $\mathbf{B}$.
                             to the area of the
                             B-field.

FIG. 25.10.2.   Definition of area A relevant to description of induced EMF in a conducting loop.

(3) Quantitative observation of induced current in a loop of fixed resistance R_T shows that the induced EMF depends on two aspects associated with the magnetic field: the *rate* at which the field changes, and the *area* of the field perpendicular to the plane of the loop.   The relevant area, A, is defined in Fig. 25.10.2.   For a given rate of change of B, the induced EMF increases with increasing A.

(4) The number defined by

$$\Phi_B \equiv BA \tag{25.10.1}$$

is called the *magnetic flux* passing through the loop.*   Faraday's experiments showed

* In definition (25.10.1) it is implicitly assumed that $\mathbf{B}$ is uniform (i.e., the same at each point over the area in question).   This is, of course, rarely the case, and Φ_B is more rigorously defined by a limit of the sum calculation:

$$\Phi_B \equiv \lim_{\substack{\|\Delta\|\to 0 \\ n\to\infty}} \sum_{k=1}^{n} B_k \cdot \Delta A_k.$$

that the induced EMF in a conducting loop is directly proportional to the time rate of change of the magnetic flux.

Summarizing the preceding verbal statements in mathematical form, we say that the total induced EMF in a conducting loop of N turns through which the magnetic flux is changing is given by

$$\varepsilon = -N\frac{d\Phi_B}{dt}.$$
(25.10.2)

This equation is called *Faraday's law*. The minus sign has specific mathematical significance with respect to the arithmetic of vectors in three dimensions. We shall not have time to discuss these aspects of vector algebra, but we shall retain the minus sign to remind us that a *left-* (rather than a right-) hand rule is associated with induced EMF; the induced electrical field circulates in the counterclockwise direction when we look along the direction of increasing magnetic flux.

In mks units, ε is expressed in volts (joules/coul) and Φ_B in webers. (It now becomes apparent why, in Section 24.5, we referred to B as "magnetic flux density" and named its units "webers/m^2." We are frequently interested in the product defined in Eq. (25.10.1) and we think of it as a total "flux." In this context, B becomes a flux per unit area, and the names have evolved accordingly.)

PROBLEM 25.13.   (a) Sketch some situations showing orientations of conducting loops and direction of changing magnetic field different from those employed in Fig. 25.10.1, and determine the direction of flow of induced current by the left-hand rule.

(b) Using mks units, verify that Eq. (25.10.2) is dimensionally consistent; i.e., verify that EMF has the same dimensions as time rate of change of magnetic flux. (See Section 24.5 for a discussion of the dimensions of B.)

25.11 INDUCED EMF IN A MOVING CONDUCTOR

Varying B is not the only way of changing the total magnetic flux Φ_B passing through a conducting loop; Φ_B can also be changed by keeping B constant and increasing or decreasing the total area of the loop itself. Does Faraday's law apply in this case? To examine this question we can employ a simple theoretical analysis that tests the internal consistency of a number of different ideas and concepts.

In Fig. 25.11.1 we predict that motion of part of a conducting circuit should result in a flow of induced current. While the moving conducting wire *ef* is located to the left of the region of magnetic field B, no effects are observed in the conducting circuit, but when *ef* enters the region of magnetic field, the galvanometer indicates a flow of current in the direction shown on the diagram. Note that this direction is consistent with the left-hand rule of Fig. 25.10.1: the flux through the conducting loop is directed into the plane of the paper and is increasing, since the area of the loop is increasing as *ef* moves to the right; this has the same effect as an increase in the magnitude of B.

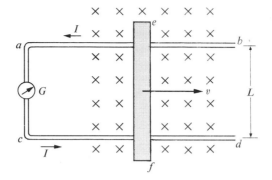

FIG. 25.11.1. Uniform magnetic field **B** between pole pieces of a magnet is directed into plane of paper. Conducting wire *ef* slides at velocity *v* on parallel conductors *ab* and *cd*. Plane of conducting loop is perpendicular to **B**.

Let us examine this problem in terms of forces acting on electrical charge within the moving wire *ef*. We visualize the wire as containing equal quantities of uniformly distributed negative and positive charge. This charge is at rest within the wire, but moves to the right with the wire as a whole. While the wire is to the left of the region of magnetic field and is not "cutting" any lines of force, the charges within the wire experience no forces other than those which carry them along with the wire itself, and no current flows along the wire. When *ef* enters the region of magnetic field, however, we can think of the charges as moving with the wire toward the right through the **B** field, and, in accordance with right-hand rule II (Fig. 23.6.1), positive charge experiences a force *upward* along the wire *ef*, while the negative charge is subjected to a force downward. In our conventional representation of electric current, we take negative charge to be fixed and positive charge to be free to move; therefore we predict a flow of positive charge upward in *ef* and counterclockwise around the circuit, and this is confirmed in the actual experiment. Thus we find the qualitative effects in the case of a moving conductor to be consistent with those observed in the experiments described in Fig. 25.9.1, where only magnetic flux density was altered and no motion of conductors was involved. Can we also make a prediction of the quantitative effects?

When induced current *I* flows in the direction shown in Fig. 25.11.1, the wire *ef* is subjected to a force of magnitude *BIL* directed toward the left; to keep the wire moving at constant velocity $v = dx/dt$, we must exert an equal and opposite force T to the right. A force diagram of *ef* under these circumstances is shown in Fig. 25.11.2.

Pulling the wire with force T at velocity dx/dt, we do work at the rate

$$P = T\frac{dx}{dt} \text{ joules/sec.} \tag{25.11.1}$$

Simultaneously, the induced current *I* flows through the circuit. If the total resistance is denoted by R, heat is evolved in the circuit at the rate I^2R joules/sec, there being no observable storage of energy in any other form. Conservation of energy

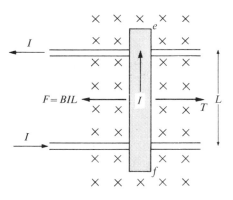

FIG. 25.11.2. Free-body diagram of sliding wire *ef* of Fig. 25.11.1. When current *I* flows in the wire, it experiences a force *BIL* toward the left. To keep the wire moving at constant velocity we must exert force $T = BIL$ toward the right.

requires that the work we do be equal to the heat evolved:

$$I^2R = T\frac{dx}{dt}. \tag{25.11.2}$$

But, since $T = BIL$:

$$I^2R = BIL\frac{dx}{dt},$$

$$IR = BL\frac{dx}{dt}. \tag{25.11.3}$$

In Eq. (25.11.3) we recognize IR as equal to ε, induced EMF, and we recognize the quantity $L(dx/dt)$ as being the rate of change dA/dt of the area of magnetic field within the current loop. Introducing the minus sign of Eq. (25.10.2) to remind us that the induced current obeys the *left*-hand rule, we write (25.11.3) in the form

$$\varepsilon = -B\frac{dA}{dt}. \tag{25.11.4}$$

Noting that $N = 1$ in this instance, suppose we apply Faraday's law,

$$\varepsilon = -\frac{d\Phi_B}{dt} = -\frac{d(BA)}{dt}, \tag{25.11.5}$$

directly to the problem suggested in Fig. 25.11.1. Carrying out the differentiation, we obtain

$$\varepsilon = -B\frac{dA}{dt} - A\frac{dB}{dt}. \tag{25.11.6}$$

Since B was taken to be uniform and unchanging, $dB/dt = 0$, and Eq. (25.11.6) reduces to

$$\varepsilon = -B\frac{dA}{dt},$$

in agreement with (25.11.4). Similar experiments and analyses of more complex geometrical situations yield exactly the same results. Faraday's law is found to be a completely general statement, applicable to *all* cases in which magnetic flux changes through a conducting loop, regardless of what combination of motions and changes of **B** produces the change in flux. Furthermore, having examined the problem of the moving conductor from two very different points of view, we note that Faraday's law, the law of conservation of energy, and the laws of force on moving charges and current-carrying conductors form a completely consistent set of statements and requirements, exhibiting no contradictions among each other.

As we have already seen (Section 23.13), Faraday was fully aware of the induction of current in a moving wire, and this phenomenon played an important role in his rejection of action-at-a-distance. Knowing that motion alone would not induce the current, he felt it necessary to assign a role to the "medium" through which the wire moved.

PROBLEM 25.14. Something similar to the idealized experiment suggested in Fig. 25.11.1 is frequently performed in lecture demonstrations: A portion of flexible wire, connected to a sensitive meter, is swept between the pole pieces of a magnet. Let us estimate the order of magnitude of I and ε induced under such circumstances. Reasonable orders of magnitude are: 0.2 w/m^2 for B, 5 cm for L, 1 ohm for R, and 1 m/sec for v. [*Answer:* $\varepsilon \sim 0.01$ v; $I \sim 0.01$ amp.] What would happen if the wire were coiled in 5 turns instead of forming a single loop? What would happen if the magnet were moved past the wire, instead of vice versa?

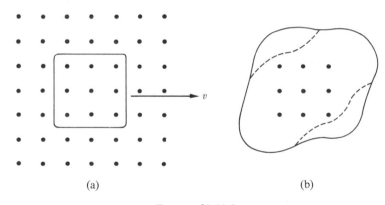

(a)   (b)

FIGURE 25.11.3

PROBLEM 25.15. Suppose that a rigid conducting loop were moved translationally through a uniform magnetic field, as shown in Fig. 25.11.3(a). What effects would be induced within the loop? Explain your answer carefully. [*Answer:* ε and I equal zero.]

Suppose that a large loop of wire surrounds a small region of magnetic field, as shown on Fig. 25.11.3(b). What effects would be induced in the loop if the wire were deformed in various ways, changing the area of the loop (as shown by the dashed lines) without allowing the wire to cut any lines of force of the magnetic field? [*Answer:* ε and I equal zero.]

25.12   THE ELECTRIC GENERATOR

Another way of changing the total magnetic flux passing through a conducting loop is to *rotate* the loop in a magnetic field, as shown in Fig. 25.12.1.

The terminals of the loop are connected to separate metal rings. Wires from an external circuit make contact with the rings through "brushes." As the loop and the rings rotate, induced current flows in the circuit, reversing its direction after every 180° of rotation of the loop. The rings act as though they were terminals of a battery that periodically reverses its polarity.

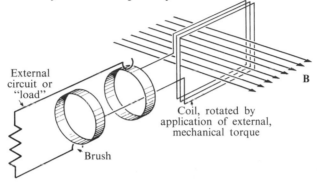

FIG. 25.12.1. Alternating-current generator: As conducting loop is rotated in a magnetic field, total magnetic flux through the loop varies with time. Induced current flows if the circuit is completed by an external "load." As the coil rotates, the current in the load periodically changes direction.

The device sketchily idealized in Fig. 25.12.1 illustrates the basic principle of the *alternating-current generator*. If we supply work by application of an external torque to the shaft of the rotating armature, we can cause induced current to flow in the coil and its external circuit, supplying electricity to lights, heating elements, motors, etc. The operation of the generator is essentially the inverse of that of the electric motor.

PROBLEM 25.16.   At what orientations of the loop relative to the magnetic field does the current reverse direction in the external circuit? Assume a direction of rotation of the coil in Fig. 25.12.1, and establish the instantaneous direction of flow of current in the external circuit. What will be the direction of torque exerted on the coil by the magnetic field? What must be the direction of the applied external torque driving the generator? What will happen if we give the coil a spin on its axis and let it coast with the external circuit closed? (Assume negligible frictional forces.) What will happen if we perform the same experiment with the external circuit open? Describe these phenomena in the vocabulary of the law of conservation of energy.

PROBLEM 25.17.   The device shown schematically in Fig. 24.9.2 would become a *direct-current generator* if its operation were reversed by driving the coil by application of an external mechanical torque and connecting an external load to the terminals. Explain the difference between this generator and the type illustrated in Fig. 25.12.1.

The discovery of electromagnetic induction greatly enhanced Faraday's already substantial fame and reputation and represents one of his foremost achievements. Like Oersted's discovery, Faraday's was immediately appreciated and seized upon by the rest of the scientific world. Primitive electric generators were in use for various experimental purposes very soon after Faraday's discovery of 1831. We have already seen (Section 19.10) that one of Joule's first experimental determinations of the mechanical equivalent of heat was based on comparing the work done in driving a generator with the heat evolved in flow of the induced current. Not far ahead lay the development of electrical technology. But we might note that Faraday had not put in a research proposal outlining his intention to invent the dynamo; he had simply been curious as to whether there existed an effect inverse to that of Oersted's —whether a magnetic influence could induce an electric current.

25.13 AN HISTORICAL FOOTNOTE

In these last three chapters we have tried to give the reader a feeling for the sweep and interplay along an advancing front of scientific knowledge. Discovery of the basic phenomena of electricity and magnetism did not come through deep penetration of one separate channel at a time—electricity and electrical fields first, magnetism next, chemistry afterward. As in a wave rolling upward along an irregular beach, penetrations along one part of the front paved the way for immediate advances along adjacent parts, and held together by this interdependence, the leading edge of knowledge moved forward in many areas at the same time.

While employing the working hypothesis that "common" electricity, animal electricity, thermoelectricity, voltaic electricity, "magneto" (Faraday's induction) electricity were all manifestations of an identical property of matter, researchers progressed in their investigations, but they did not allow themselves to forget that many of their conceptions were predicated on this assumption of identity. In 1833, fifty years after Galvani's first experiments and more than thirty years after introduction of the voltaic battery, Faraday published a definitive paper on *Identity of Electricities Derived from Different Sources*. Here he constructed a table, listing the different sources along one side and various effects such as sparks, shocks, heating powers, magnetic deflection of a galvanometer, chemical action, magnetization of a steel needle, charging of electrometer, etc., along the other side. Quoting results of previous investigators and presenting results of delicate and skillful experiments of his own, he tried to check off as many squares in the table as possible, showing that each electricity was capable of producing each one of the effects that had come to be associated with electrical phenomena. Some squares in the table he left blank, indicating that the given electricity was apparently too feeble to produce the corresponding effect, but concluding that the evidence amassed over the years convincingly demonstrated the basic identity of the phenomena. That a man of Faraday's stature should have devoted himself to this problem is some indication of how large it must have loomed at the time. In the present day many of us accept casual assertions regarding the identity of electricities (simply because the name "electricity" is applied to all of them) without being fully aware of the work and the evidence that make this assertion scientifically tenable.

Static electricity had been explored early because of its observable and measurable mechanical effects. Chemical effects from the transient discharge of Leyden jars had been noticed but had engaged little interest because of their minuteness. The spectacular chemical effects of voltaic electricity gave impetus to a new era of chemical research, but progress on the study of electricity itself was delayed until the work of Oersted, Ampère, Faraday, and others revealed new *mechanical effects* to serve as points of departure for further observation and quantitative measurement. The study of electricity established a bridge of conceptual connections between physics and chemistry, and even indicated links to physiology, demonstrating in a hitherto unprecedented manner the deep underlying unity among natural phenomena.

Imponderable electricity, revealed to the human senses by interaction with ponderable matter, ceased to be regarded as an "accidental property" in the Aristotelian sense, and came to be recognized as an essential component, inseparable from matter itself, clearly responsible for chemical organization and behavior, and probably intimately associated with physical structure as well. Much of the remainder of this book will be concerned with the extension of this insight.

25.14 PROBLEMS

25.18. The household electric meter is essentially an integrating device. It measures the instantaneous power $P = I\Delta V$ supplied to the household circuit, and calculates the total energy supplied over a period of time:

$$W = \int_{t_1}^{t_2} P(t)\, dt = \int_{t_1}^{t_2} I\Delta V\, dt. \quad (25.14.1)$$

Shown in Fig. 25.14.1 is an hypothetical plot of $P(t)$ versus t. If the potential difference were essentially constant at about 120 v, what would have been the appearance of the $I(t)$-versus-t graph? Counting squares to obtain the relevant area, estimate numerically from Fig. 25.14.1 the total energy supplied over the time interval shown. [*Answer:* 3.6×10^7 joules or 10 kilowatt hours.]

25.19. Draw on whatever common knowledge you possess to estimate the order of magnitude of resistance and of current drawn by household items such as various wattage light bulbs, toasters, irons, etc.

25.20. A constant potential difference $\Delta V = 120$ v is maintained across a certain resistor. The resistance changes with time, and the current is observed to vary according to the relation

$$I = 20.0 - 0.01t,$$

where I is in amperes and t is in seconds.

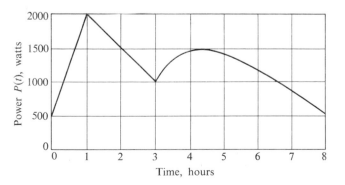

FIGURE 25.14.1

(a) Was the resistance increased or decreased? Explain.

(b) Define "power," and write an expression for the power being delivered by the battery at any instant t. (Explain your expression by going back to the definitions of ΔV and I.)

(c) Explaining steps, evaluate the total amount of energy taken from the source in the time interval between $t = 0$ and $t = 800$ sec. If 1 cal $= 4.19$ joules, how many calories of heat are generated? [*Answer:* 1.54×10^6 joules.]

25.21. A small 12-ohm resistor can be connected across the terminals of a battery maintaining a constant potential difference of 60 v. The resistor is placed in a calorimeter containing 300 gm of water at 20°C. A switch is closed and current allowed to flow for 45 sec. Predict the final temperature of the water. Explain your work, indicating what definitions and laws are applied and what idealizations and approximations are being made. What additional information should you really have about the calorimeter itself? Describe the entire phenomenon in terms of energy transformations.

Suppose that some heat will actually be lost to the surroundings during the 45-sec period. Argue *from the algebra of your solution* whether the predicted final temperature calculated above will be higher or lower than the final value which would actually be observed. [*Answer:* Predicted final temperature $= 30.7$°C.]

25.22. Suppose that you have an ammeter of sensitivity such that it reads 1.00 amp at full-scale deflection. You wish to measure larger currents than this, and would like to have a meter reading 10.0 amp at full scale. You have at your disposal heavy wire of low resistance that you can cut to different lengths, thus obtaining a resistor having any precisely selected, low value of resistance you might wish. How might you go about converting the given meter into one reading 10.0 amp at full-scale

deflection? What additional information or instruments would you wish to have, and how would you use them? (See Problem 25.7.)

25.23. In an experiment in which you wish to determine the unknown, fairly high resistance of a given conductor, you have available a suitable ammeter, but the voltmeter resistance is not as many times greater than that of the conductor as you would like it to be. What difficulty does this pose? Consider two possible ways (Fig. 25.14.2) of connecting the meters into the circuit. Which of these connections would you consider preferable in the given circumstances? Why?

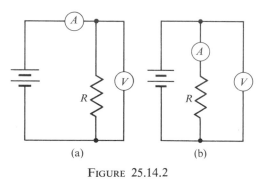

(a)   (b)

FIGURE 25.14.2

25.24. Consider the resistive circuit with ammeters and a voltmeter connected as shown in Fig. 25.14.3. (The symbol ⌁⌁⌁ denotes a *variable resistor*, the resistance it contributes to the circuit being increased or decreased simply by sliding a contact toward one end or the other and changing the effective length.) Suppose that the sliding

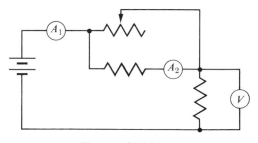

FIGURE 25.14.3

contact is shifted toward the left, decreasing the resistance contributed by the variable resistor. If the battery maintains an essentially constant potential difference across its terminals, what will happen to the respective meter readings A_1, A_2, and V? Explain your reasoning. [*Answer*: A_1 increases, A_2 decreases, V increases.]

25.25. One of Faraday's early experiments with induction of current in moving conductors led to the following result: If one of two straight, mutually parallel conductors is carrying a current, and if we move the other parallel to and *toward* the first, then during the motion there will be induced a current in the moving conductor which is *opposite* in direction to the current in the fixed conductor; if the second conductor is moving away, however, then the induced current is in the *same* direction as that in the fixed conductor. Sketch the situation described and verify that this result is consistent with the left-hand rule defined in Section 25.10.

25.26. In 1834 a Russian physicist, Heinrich Lenz, after repetition of some of Faraday's experiments, advanced the following rule which is still widely referred to as *Lenz's law*: "Whenever a metallic conductor is moved in the vicinity of a galvanic current or of a magnet, a galvanic current will be induced, which has a direction such that it would have caused the wire, if it were at rest, to move in a direction opposite to the one given...." Verify that the effects described in Figs. 25.11.2 and 25.12.1 and in Problem 25.25 are indeed consistent with this rule. An extension of Lenz's law consists of the general assertion that an induced effect always acts so as to oppose the change that produces it. Test this statement on the induction effects described in Section 25.10, where no motion of conductors is involved, but only changes in magnetic flux through the conducting loop.

25.27. Consider a simple circuit in which a solenoid (or even just a single wire) is

connected to the terminals of a battery. While the circuit is open, there is zero magnetic flux through the conducting loop, but after the circuit is closed and a current flows, a magnetic flux has been established. In the light of preceding discussions and analyses, what effects do you expect within the circuit during the short interval of time in which the magnetic flux increases from zero to its final value? Be specific as to the direction of the effect. What happens when the circuit is suddenly broken? (If you wish to pursue in more detail the ideas suggested to you by this question, you will find them discussed in more advanced texts under the name of "self inductance." You may also be interested in the role of the American physicist Joseph Henry in the discovery of this phenomenon.)

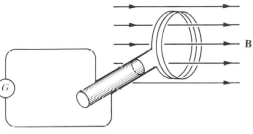

FIGURE 25.14.4

25.28. Suppose that a small coil of N turns of wire and total resistance R is connected to a galvanometer and is placed with its plane perpendicular to the direction of a magnetic field **B** (such as that of the earth), as shown in Fig. 25.14.4. The area of the loop is A, and the flux passing through it is Φ_B. The coil is quickly flipped over through an angle of 180° in a short time interval Δt, and the flux now passes through it in the opposite direction. Argue that the average current flowing through the galvanometer during the time interval Δt must be given by

$$\bar{I} = \frac{N}{R} \cdot \frac{2BA}{\Delta t}, \qquad (25.14.2)$$

and that the total charge displaced through

the galvanometer must be

$$q = \frac{N}{R} \cdot 2BA. \qquad (25.14.3)$$

The "flip coil" is actually an important instrument for measuring magnetic induction B. There are more sophisticated aspects to such an instrument than are apparent in the basic hints given above, but, utilizing whatever knowledge you possess and ideas that occur to you as you think about the problem, go as far as you can in the direction of outlining how such an instrument might work and what problems are likely to be encountered in its design. Do not be satisfied with a glib, off-the-cuff response; but on the other hand, do not expect to penetrate all the levels of sophistication that are involved.

SUPPLEMENTARY READING AND STUDY

Physics, Physical Science Study Committee. Boston: D. C. Heath, 1960, Chapter 29; Chapter 31 (Sections 1–9)

Physics, the Pioneer Science, L. W. Taylor. Boston: Houghton Mifflin, 1941; New York: Dover Publications, 1959, Chapters 43, 44, 45

Physics for Students of Science and Engineering, R. Resnick and D. Halliday. New York: John Wiley & Sons, 1960, Chapters 31; 32 (Sections 1–7); 35

A History of the Theories of Aether and Electricity, E. T. Whittaker. New York: Harper Torchbook 531, 1960, Chapter 3

Source Book in Physics, W. F. Magie. New York: McGraw-Hill, 1935, pages 465–513, 524–528

The Edge of Objectivity, C. C. Gillispie. Princeton, N. J.: Princeton University Press, 1960, pages 435–477

CHAPTER 26

The Nature of Light

26.1 INTRODUCTION

In the concluding paragraph of his treatise on "Opticks," published in 1704, Newton speaks of his study of light in particular and of the role of natural philosophy in general:

> "In this . . . Book I have only begun the Analysis of what remains to be discovered about Light and its Effects upon the Frame of Nature, hinting several things about it, and leaving the Hints to be examined and improved by the farther Experiments and Observations of such as are inquisitive. And if natural Philosophy in all its Parts, by pursuing this Method, shall at length be perfected, the Bounds of Moral Philosophy will also be enlarged. For so far as we can know by natural Philosophy what is the first Cause, what Power he has over us, and what Benefits we receive from him, so far our Duty towards him, as well as that towards one another, will appear to us by the Light of Nature."

Many intellectuals from Hellenic times onward had worked in the long-range hope that deeper knowledge of nature, together with the enlightenment supplied by reason, would illuminate moral philosophy and bring progress in the ways of man to man. It is not surprising that questions concerning the nature of light should have occupied their minds simultaneously with questions concerning the laws of mechanics, the behavior of the heavenly bodies, and the structure of the universe. Light plays a major role in almost every element of our consciousness of the physical world, in our perceptions of process and change, in our awareness of, and communication with, each other. But light turned out to pose even more subtle and elusive problems than did the other elements of physical experience. We now understand it to be fundamentally electromagnetic in nature; we know it to be inextricably involved in our measurements of space and time; we find its emission and absorption to be intimately connected with changes in atomic and subatomic structure of matter; in certain well-defined contexts it exhibits a wavelike behavior, and in others it takes on a corpuscular character. In this chapter we shall be concerned with the first part of the story—the evolution of the concepts of the nature of light through the period of classical physics which ends with the closing years of the nineteenth century.

26.2 PROPAGATION OF LIGHT

Attempts to develop a model for the nature and behavior of light were preceded by accumulation of experimental evidence on the basis of which such a structure might be philosophically erected. In this and several following sections, we assemble the primary factual knowledge.

First, the behavior of light strongly implies some kind of motion, process, or propagation. It has its origin in bodies that we describe as being self-luminous, such as a lamp, a candle, or the sun. Other bodies reflect light when subjected to illumination and, although not self-luminous, are to be regarded as secondary sources. Light from any body can be cut off or intercepted by interposition of an opaque shield, and this shows that light comes from, or travels in, a particular direction.

If a source of light is very small, an opaque object placed in the beam will cast a very sharp shadow. To early investigators this clearly implied that light travels in straight lines emanating from the source, and these lines are referred to as rays of light.

PROBLEM 26.1. If an opaque object is placed near a large or extended source, the shadow cast by the object is not sharp but has a fuzzy gradation from the darkest region within the main part of the shadow to a bright region outside. Sketch such a situation (for example, a pencil near an electric light bulb, casting a shadow on a piece of paper), and draw rays emanating from various parts of the source. Referring to your sketch, explain why the shadow cast from the extended source cannot be sharp, even though light must travel in perfectly straight lines. Draw lines that establish geometrically the boundaries of the darkest region of the shadow. Draw lines that establish the outermost boundary of the shadow.

As we shall see, it was eventually established that, when examined on an appropriately small scale, light does not propagate in straight lines and actually does bend slightly around edges and into regions of shadow, but, on the scale of observation implied in Problem 26.1, straight-line propagation gives an entirely valid picture of its behavior.

The concept of propagation of light immediately invites the question as to its velocity, and many individuals addressed themselves to this problem. Descartes speculatively assumed the velocity of light to be infinite, while Galileo, with his deeper commitment to experimental philosophy, gives the following description at one point in the First Day of the *Two New Sciences*:

Salviati: "[I devised] a method by which one might accurately ascertain whether illumination, i.e., the propagation of light, is really instantaneous. The fact that the speed of sound is as high as it is, assures us that the motion of light cannot fail to be extraordinarily swift.... Let each of two persons take a light contained in a lantern, or other receptacle, such that by the interposition of the hand, the one can shut off or admit the light to the vision of the other. Next let them stand opposite each other at a distance of a few cubits and practice until they acquire such skill in uncovering and occulting their light that the instant one sees the light of his companion he will uncover his own. After a few trials the response will be so prompt that without sensible error the uncovering of one light is immediately followed by the uncovering of the other, so that as soon as one exposes his light he will instantly see that of the other. Having acquired skill at this short distance let the two experimenters, equipped as before, take up positions separated by a distance of two or three miles and let them perform the same experiment at night, noting carefully whether the exposures and occultations occur in the same manner as at short distances; if they do, we may safely conclude that the propagation of light is instantaneous; but if time is required at a distance of three miles which, considering the going of one light and the coming of the other, really amounts to six, then the delay ought to be easily observable. . . . In fact I have tried the experiment only at a short distance, less than a mile, from which I have not been able to ascertain with certainty whether the appearance of the opposite light was instantaneous or not; but if not instantaneous, it is extraordinarily rapid."

Galileo's experiment did not resolve the question of whether light propagated with finite or infinite velocity, but it at least indicated that the velocity, if finite, was too large to be determined by experiments that depended on the quickness of physiological reception and response. The first direct indication that the velocity was indeed finite and the first estimate of its numerical value came from astronomical evidence.

In 1675, Olaf Roemer, a Dane who was then resident in Paris, pointed out that an observed variation in the time of eclipse of Jupiter's moons was best explained in terms of the time taken by light to propagate a distance of the diameter of the earth's orbit. This was a plausible and convincing interpretation, and it was immediately accepted by many of Roemer's contemporaries. Huygens incorporated the idea, with due credit to Roemer, in the first draft of his *Treatise on Light* in 1678:

"Let A [Fig. 26.2.1] be the Sun, *BCDE* the annual orbit of the Earth, *F* Jupiter, *GN* the orbit of the nearest of his Satellites, for it is this one which is more apt for this investigation than any of the other three, because of the quickness of its revolution. Let *G* be this Satellite entering into the shadow of Jupiter, *H* the same satellite emerging from the shadow. Let it be then supposed, the Earth being at *B*, . . . that one has seen the said Satellite emerge from the shadow; it must

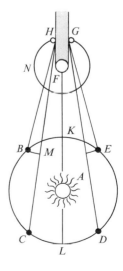

FIG. 26.2.1. Roemer's determination of the velocity of light from variation of the time of eclipse of the innermost moon of Jupiter. (Figure taken from Huygens' *Treatise on Light*.)

needs be, if the Earth remains at the same place, that, after $42\frac{1}{2}$ hours, one would again see a similar emergence, because that is the time in which it makes the round of its orbit. . . . And if the Earth, for instance, were to remain always at B during 30 revolutions of this Satellite, one would see it again emerge from the shadow after 30 times $42\frac{1}{2}$ hours. But the Earth having been carried along this time to C, increasing thus its distance from Jupiter, it follows that if Light requires time for passage, the illumination of the little planet will be perceived later at C than it would at B, and that there must be added to this time of 30 times $42\frac{1}{2}$ hours that which the light has required to traverse the space MC, the difference of the spaces CH, BH. Similarly at the other quadrature when the Earth has come to E from D while approaching toward Jupiter, the immersions of the Satellite ought to be observed at E earlier than they would have been seen if the Earth had remained at D.

"Now in quantities of observations of these Eclipses, made during ten consecutive years, these differences have been found to be very considerable . . . and from them it has been concluded that in order to traverse the whole diameter of the annual orbit KL, which is double the distance from here to the Sun, Light requires about 22 minutes of time."

PROBLEM 26.2. The *radius* of the earth's orbit is close to 93 million miles. Calculate the velocity of light implied by Roemer's figure of 22 minutes for transit of the diameter of the orbit.

Within a few years, other observers (Newton among them) gave figures ranging from 15 minutes to 28 minutes for the transit time across the earth's orbit. [Some of this scatter was due to instrumental errors and uncertainties in measurement of time; some stems from an uncertainty in the exact moment of eclipse due to apparent irregularities in the "limb" or edge presented by Jupiter itself (see Fig. 15.10.2).] Furthermore, the radius of the earth's orbit was not accurately known in the seventeenth century. By 1680, however, it was well known to the scientific community that the velocity of light in interstellar space was somewhere between 100,000 and 200,000 mi/sec, and this figure served for order-of-magnitude estimates and calculations. It is now known that the correct value of the velocity of light in vacuum (or air) is very close to 186,000 mi/sec, or roughly 1000 ft/μsec (1 μsec $= 10^{-6}$ sec). The velocity of sound in air is about 1000 ft/sec; the velocity of light is a million times greater! (In metric units, the velocity of light is 3.00×10^8 m/sec.)

26.3 REFLECTION AND REFRACTION

Men were aware of reflection and refraction of light from very early times. It was recognized that reflection from irregular (or matte) surfaces was diffuse. It was also known that a coherent or regular reflection occurs at smooth, shiny, metallic surfaces, that the incident and reflected rays of light lie in a plane perpendicular to the reflecting plane, and that the angle of incidence is equal to the angle of reflection ($\theta_i = \theta_r$ in

Fig. 26.3.1). Euclid made use of this empirical knowledge in constructing theorems concerning the effect of mirrors.

Concerning refraction, it was also established that the incident and refracted rays lie in a plane perpendicular to the refracting plane, and it was known that the extent of refraction at a given angle of incidence depends on the two transparent media in contact with each other. Some investigators (Ptolemy among them) constructed empirical tables of angle of refraction θ_t versus angle of incidence θ_i for various media. Then it was discovered that the ratio θ_t/θ_i seemed to be a constant for any given pair of media; i.e., that each set of tabulated data could be well represented by the simple equation

$$\frac{\theta_t}{\theta_i} = k_{12}, \tag{26.3.1}$$

where k_{12} is a constant for a given pair of media forming an interface (Fig. 26.3.1).

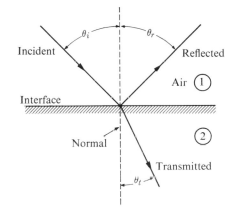

FIG. 26.3.1. Simultaneous reflection and refraction of a narrow beam of light at a plane interface such as air–glass or air–water. Note that the refracted ray is bent toward the normal; $\theta_t < \theta_i$.

About 1621, Willebrord Snell, professor of mathematics at Leyden, found that this equation did not represent the experimental data closely at large values of angle of incidence, and discovered the correct, general law. Snell's work was circulated privately in manuscript form and was not published, but it apparently came to the attention of both Descartes and Huygens. Descartes published the relation in its modern form in 1637:

$$\frac{\sin \theta_t}{\sin \theta_i} = n_{12}, \tag{26.3.2}$$

that is, the ratio of the *sines* of the angles of refraction and incidence (rather than the ratio of the angles themselves) is a constant for a given pair of contiguous media. This empirical equation is known as *Snell's law*, although Snell stated his original discovery in somewhat less convenient algebraic form. In our notation we shall represent the constant on the right-hand side by the symbol n_{12} or n_{21}, depending on whether the ray passes from medium 1 to medium 2, as in Fig. 26.3.1, or in the opposite direction. If it passes in the opposite direction, the angle of incidence is in medium 2 and the angle of refraction is in medium 1.

TABLE 26.3.1

INDICES OF REFRACTION OF VARIOUS MATERIALS RELATIVE TO VACUUM
(For light of wavelength $\lambda = 5890$ A)

Material	Index relative to vacuum
Vacuum	1.0000
Air (1 atm; 20°C)	1.0003
Water	1.33
Ethyl alcohol	1.36
Canada balsam	1.53
Quartz (crystalline)	1.54
Quartz (fused)	1.46
Rock salt	1.54
Glass (ordinary crown)	1.52
Glass (dense flint)	1.66

An experimentally observed fact about incident, reflected, and refracted rays of light is that their passage is perfectly *reversible*: If a narrow pencil of parallel rays in medium 1 comes in along what is the path of the reflected beam in Fig. 26.3.1, it is reflected *outward* along the path shown for the incident beam. If a beam is incident in medium 2 along the path indicated for the refracted beam in Fig. 26.3.1, it emerges in medium 1 along the path shown for the incident beam. From this reversibility it follows that $n_{21} = 1/n_{12}$. The number n_{21} is called the "index of refraction of medium 2 relative to medium 1"; similarly, n_{12} would be referred to as "the index of refraction of medium 1 relative to medium 2." A table of indices of refraction of various substances relative to vacuum is given in Table 26.3.1. The indices correspond to values of $1/n_{12}$ for the direction of transmission illustrated in Fig. 26.3.1.

PROBLEM 26.3. Interpret Snell's law, Eq. (26.3.2): What happens to the angle of refraction as the angle of incidence is increased from zero? It is an experimental fact that, in passing from air (medium 1) into glass or water (medium 2), a ray of light is bent *toward* the normal to the interface (that is, $\theta_t < \theta_i$ as in Fig. 26.3.1). Is n_{12} larger or smaller than 1.00 for this case? Explain in your own words and with the aid of a diagram why it was asserted that $n_{21} = 1/n_{12}$. What will happen to a ray of light passing from water to air? Describe the behavior of the refracted ray in passage from water to air as the angle of incidence is increased. The numerical value of n_{21}, the index of refraction of water relative to air, is 1.33; as θ_i is increased, it attains a critical value θ_c beyond which Eq. (26.3.2) ceases to give meaningful information. Find the numerical value of θ_c and interpret its physical significance. [*Answer:* $\theta_c = 48.6°$.]

In the last part of Problem 26.3 it is found that when the angle of incidence for a ray passing from water to air has a particular critical value θ_c, defined by $\sin \theta_c =$

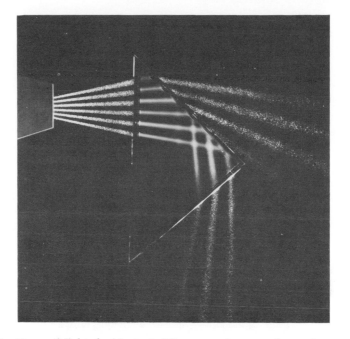

FIG. 26.3.2. Rays of light, incident at different angles, pass from glass to air through the upper right-hand face of the glass prism. Note that the refracted ray is bent *away* from the normal. Note also the critical angle at which the emerging ray becomes parallel to the interface, and observe that the incident ray is then totally reflected within the prism. (Courtesy Educational Services, Inc.)

$1/n_{21}$, the angle of refraction is 90°, and the emerging ray is parallel to the interface. Snell's law gives no information beyond this point, and cannot be used as a basis for deducing what happens at larger angles of incidence. Experimentally, it is observed that when θ_i exceeds θ_c, the incident ray is completely reflected and remains within the water or glass. Because of this, θ_c is called the "critical angle for total internal reflection."

A number of the effects we have described in this section are illustrated in Fig. 26.3.2.

26.4 REFRACTION THROUGH SUCCESSIVE INTERFACES

By passing a ray of light through a succession of surfaces, it is possible to alter its direction in systematic ways. When a ray passes through a glass plate or block with plane parallel surfaces (Fig. 26.4.1), it is refracted in one direction on entering the first surface and in the opposite direction on leaving the second. It emerges parallel to its original direction but displaced laterally by a distance that depends on the thickness of the glass plate and on the index of refraction of glass relative to air. (For different kinds of glass, this index varies from about 1.5 to 1.7.)

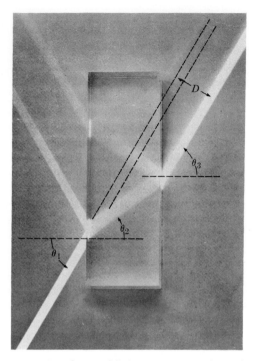

FIG. 26.4.1. Displacement, D, of ray of light on passage through a block of glass with parallel sides. Note simultaneous reflections. (From *Physics*. Boston: D. C. Heath, 1960.)

PROBLEM 26.4. Applying Snell's law at each surface in Fig. 26.4.1, give a general proof that $\theta_3 = \theta_1$; that is, that the emerging ray is parallel to the incident ray.

PROBLEM 26.5. A ray of light is incident at an angle of 40.0° at the first surface of a glass plate 1.00 in. thick and having an index of refraction relative to air of 1.60. Sketch the passage of the ray through the plate, and calculate the displacement D of the ray on emerging from the second surface. [*Answer: D* = 0.307 in.) What happens when the incident ray is normal to the first surface?

If the glass is in the shape of a triangular prism, and a ray of light is incident, as in Fig. 26.4.2, the ray is deviated from its original direction by an angle δ. (Verify in Fig. 26.4.2 that the ray is bent *toward* the normal on entering the glass, and *away* from the normal on leaving the glass.) Calculating the angle of the emerging ray in this case is a somewhat tedious process, but it is nevertheless a straightforward application of Snell's law and of elementary trigonometry. The same effect is illustrated in the photograph of Fig. 26.3.2.

A particularly useful systematic refraction is produced by lenses with spherical surfaces and either convex or concave shapes, as illustrated in Fig. 26.4.3. If we trace several incident rays through each lens (qualitatively) as we did through the prism

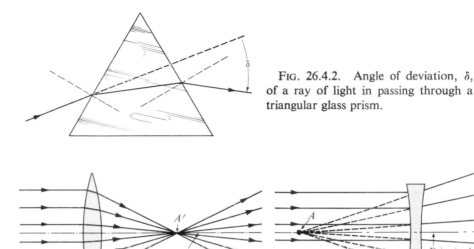

FIG. 26.4.2. Angle of deviation, δ, of a ray of light in passing through a triangular glass prism.

(a)   (b)

FIG. 26.4.3. (a) Convex or "converging" lens. Incident rays parallel to principal axis are refracted so as to converge to a point A' on the principal axis; A' is called a "principal focal point" of the lens. (b) Concave or "diverging" lens. Incident rays parallel to principal axis are caused to diverge in such a way that, on emerging from the lens, they appear to diverge from a point A on the principal axis.

FIG. 26.4.4. Photograph of the converging-lens effect sketched in Fig. 26.4.3(a). (From *Physics*.   Boston: D. C. Heath, 1960.)

in Fig. 26.4.2, it is readily apparent that a convex lens will cause a bundle of parallel rays to tend to converge, while a concave lens will cause a bundle of parallel rays to diverge. It is not at all obvious, however, that the convergence or divergence will be associated with sharply defined points, such as A' and A in Figs. 26.4.3(a) and (b). This effect and its limitations are discussed in more detail in Appendix H. A photograph of the effect sketched in Fig. 26.4.3(a) is shown in Fig. 26.4.4.

26.5   IMAGES

When we look obliquely through a water surface at an object below, the object appears to be located at a depth shallower than the actual. Objects viewed in a mirror appear to be some distance behind the mirror, although we know that the light reaching our eyes does not originate in that region. If we stand within the beam of a slide projector, well beyond the point at which a sharply focused picture would appear on a screen, we can see the picture as though it were hanging in empty space in the plane where the screen would have been.

In our normal experience, light reaches our eyes along straight lines from the source, and we mentally locate the source at an appropriate distance out along the direction from which light appears to arrive. In each one of the instances cited above, the direction of propagation of light from a self-luminous or illuminated source has been altered by reflection or refraction, and the light coming to our eyes does not actually originate from the direction or from the point from which it seems to come. Under such circumstances we speak of the formation of "images."

The study of image formation is essentially a geometrical problem. By applying the laws of reflection and refraction we can calculate what happens to rays of light at various interfaces and determine the final path followed by any ray from a given source. This branch of science is called *geometrical optics.*

We shall not attempt to discuss geometrical optics or the nature of optical instruments in the body of this text. The basic concepts are simple and straightforward. This material is eminently well suited for a project of independent study, directly connected with laboratory work.

Appendix H contains an outline that leads the student step by step through the geometrical theory of image formation by simple (thin) lenses. It is suggested that this material be studied and worked with as part of a laboratory program, in which the student sets up the physical counterparts of his pencil-and-paper diagrams, verifies predictions, tries out his own ideas, solves problems, and develops his understanding of the concepts of elementary optics with a minimum of classroom instruction. (Take-home kits of simple optical equipment would serve the same purpose as more conventional laboratory setups.)

26.6   THE CORPUSCULAR MODEL

As the idea of mathematicizing the description of natural phenomena gained strength and adherents during the seventeenth century, attempts were made to invent models or mental pictures of the nature of light from which one might derive mathematically the empirically known behavior summarized in the preceding sections.

One model that showed considerable promise and was espoused by many scientists (Newton among them) was based on visualizing light as consisting of a stream of countless, minute, subtle particles or corpuscles emanating from the luminous source, being reflected specularly or diffusely from various objects, and stimulating the sensation of sight by action on the retina and optic nerve after entering the eye.

In the corpuscular model, reflection from a mirror is visualized in the manner illustrated in Fig. 26.6.1. In an elastic collision with a smooth surface as shown

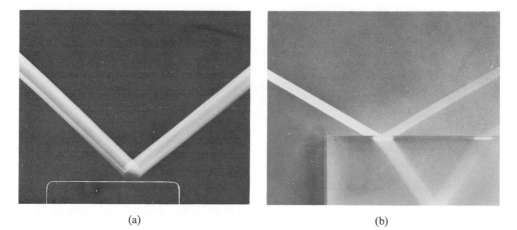

(a)   (b)

FIG. 26.6.1. (a) Continuous-exposure photograph of reflection of a steel ball from surface of a steel block. Essentially elastic collision. (Courtesy Educational Services, Inc.)
(b) Narrow beam of light reflected from surface of a glass block. (From *Physics*. Boston:
D. C. Heath, 1960.)

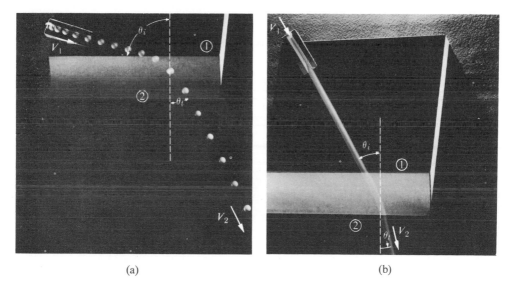

(a)   (b)

FIG. 26.6.2. (a) Ball rolls at uniform velocity V_1 along horizontal surface in region ①.
On reaching sloping surface, it is accelerated in direction parallel to the normal. Component of velocity parallel to the normal increases, while component parallel to the interface remains unaltered. After reaching second horizontal surface in region ②, ball rolls
with new velocity V_2, greater than V_1. (b) Continuous-exposure photograph of behavior
of ball in (a). Compare these photographs with refraction of light beam on passing from
air to glass, as illustrated in Fig. 26.6.1(b). In the corpuscular model of light, it is assumed
that corpuscles of light are accelerated in an extremely thin transition region close to the
interface, undergoing a change in velocity analogous to that of the rolling ball in (a) and
(b). (From *Physics*. Boston: D. C. Heath, 1960.)

in (a), the component of momentum of the particle parallel to the reflecting surface remains unchanged, while the component of momentum perpendicular to the wall is unchanged in magnitude but reversed in direction. (See Section 17.7 and Problem 17.6.) The net result is that $\theta_i = \theta_r$, and we are led to think of the stream of corpuscles in the light beam as behaving in essentially the same way. Thus we derive the already well-known law of reflection, $\theta_i = \theta_r$, from this model or hypothesis.

Refraction is visualized by assuming that the corpuscles of light travel at different constant velocities in various transparent media, and that, in approaching an interface, they are attracted or repelled in such a way that the component of velocity perpendicular to the interface is changed. This concept is illustrated in Fig. 26.6.2.

It is pictured that the corpuscles of light are subjected to an appreciable net force only in an extremely narrow region in the immediate neighborhood of the interface. Since the plane of the interface extends very far on either side of the point of incidence of a ray, the net force acting on the particles must be normal to the surface, components of force parallel to the surface canceling each other because of the symmetry. The velocity component of the corpuscles parallel to the surface would then remain unaltered, while that perpendicular to the surface would increase or decrease. A physical analog, in which the region of acceleration is enormously expanded to make the effect visible, and in which gravity is deliberately invoked as the accelerating force, is shown in Fig. 26.6.2(a) and (b). Note that this is just an *analog*, and no hypothesis is made concerning the specific nature of the force accelerating or retarding the corpuscles of light.

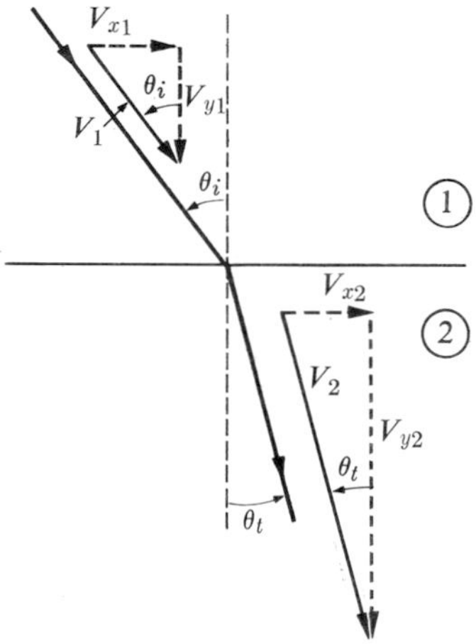

FIG. 26.6.3. Velocity in each medium is resolved into components parallel and normal to the interface. Component parallel to interface remains unaltered ($V_{x2} = V_{x1}$), while component normal to interface is increased ($V_{y2} > V_{y1}$).

In Fig. 26.6.3 we show velocity vector diagrams corresponding to refraction of the kind illustrated in Fig. 26.6.2.

From the diagram we have the following relations for components of propagation velocity parallel to the interface:

$$V_{x1} = V_1 \sin \theta_i, \tag{26.6.1}$$

$$V_{x2} = V_2 \sin \theta_t. \tag{26.6.2}$$

In our model of refraction, the normal component V_{y1} is changed to a new value

V_{y2}, while the x-component remains unaltered. Therefore $V_{x1} = V_{x2}$ and

$$V_1 \sin \theta_i = V_2 \sin \theta_t,$$

$$\sin \theta_t / \sin \theta_i = V_1/V_2. \tag{26.6.3}$$

Equation (26.6.3) immediately invites comparison with Snell's law, Eq. (26.3.2):

$$\sin \theta_t / \sin \theta_i = n_{12}.$$

We can say that we have derived Snell's law from our corpuscular model if we identify the empirical constant n_{12} with the velocity ratio V_1/V_2. Since n_{12} is *observed* to be less than unity for passage of light from air to glass ($\theta_t < \theta_i$, and the ray is bent toward the normal as in Fig. 26.6.1b), the model implies that $V_1 < V_2$; that is, that the hypothetical corpuscles of light have higher velocities in glass than in air.

> PROBLEM 26.6. In deriving Eq. (26.6.3) and identifying it with Snell's law, we have extracted certain physical predictions from the corpuscular model. In principle these predictions are subject to experimental tests, the results of which might support the model or place it in doubt. What tests would you wish to perform in this case, and how would you react to various possible results? (For example, what would be your reaction if the velocity of propagation in glass were found to be higher than that in air, but the ratio of velocities was not exactly equal to the empirically known value of n_{12}? What would be your reaction if V_2 were found to be less than V_1, etc.?)

So far the particle model holds up fairly well. It correctly predicts the law of reflection, and it yields a law of refraction that has the same algebraic form as Snell's law. To be sure, there is a troublesome physical aspect, in that reflection and refraction of light are observed to occur *simultaneously* at interfaces between transparent media (Figs. 26.3.2 and 26.4.1). This is not consistent with our knowledge of the behavior of particles; we know these to be either reflected or transmitted, but not both simultaneously. Newton, however, rationalized even this behavior in a corpuscular model (see Section 26.9).

It is worthy of note that Descartes, Newton, and others who exploited the corpuscular model had no intention of being specific about such matters as the nature, shape, size, or other properties of the hypothetical corpuscles. They endowed the corpuscles only with those properties (such as elasticity and propagation velocity) that were necessary to account for what was then known about the behavior of light. New and more detailed knowledge concerning light could conceivably lead to the visualization of more detail concerning the corpuscles, but such detail was not injected gratuitously.

26.7 THE WAVE MODEL

While an analogy to particle motion constituted one way of picturing the behavior of light, it is reasonable to suppose that an analogy to wave motion might be an alternative possibility. This view had strong supporters in the seventeenth century among men such as Hooke and Huygens, and the latter's *Treatise on Light* of 1678 is a skillful presentation of the wave point of view. Let us acquire some of the flavor of Huygens' mode of thought:

"It is inconceivable to doubt that light consists in the motion of some sort of matter . . . one sees that here upon the Earth it is chiefly engendered by fire and flame which contain without doubt bodies that are in rapid motion, since they dissolve and melt away many other bodies, even the most solid. . . . When light is collected as by concave mirrors it has the property of burning as a fire does, that is to say it disunites the particles of bodies. This is assuredly the mark of motion, at least in the true Philosophy, in which one conceives the causes of all natural effects in terms of mechanical motions. . . .

"[Since] light takes time for its passage* it will follow that this movement, impressed on the intervening matter, is successive; and consequently it spreads, as Sound does, by spherical surfaces and waves. . . .

"The agitation, moreover, of the particles which engendered the light ought to be much more prompt and rapid than is that of the bodies which cause sound, since we do not see that the tremors of a body which is giving out a sound are capable of giving rise to Light, even as the movement of the hand in the air is not capable of producing Sound.

"Now if one examines what this matter may be in which the movement coming from the luminous body is propagated, which I call Ethereal matter, one will see that it is not the same that serves for the propagation of Sound. For one finds that the latter is really that which we feel and which we breathe, and which being removed from any place still leaves there the other kind of matter that serves to convey Light. This may be proved by shutting up a sounding body in a glass vessel from which the air is withdrawn by the machine which Mr. Boyle has given us [i.e., the vacuum pump]. . . ."

Thus Huygens postulates an ether, consisting of particles that impinge on each other, causing a wave to propagate away from the source. Visualizing each point on a wave front as the source of a small disturbance propagating into the ethereal medium ahead, he works out a rather detailed mechanical model and a geometrical way of constructing new wave fronts as envelopes of the wavelets from the point sources along a previous wavefront. This geometrical construction is known as *Huygens' construction*. Huygens' construction is slightly different in detail from the bow-wave concept we employed in Section 22.11, but it is the same in principle; and with it, Huygens derived the laws of reflection and refraction at an interface, corresponding exactly to the results we obtained in Eqs. (22.11.4) and (22.11.6):

$$\text{For reflection:} \qquad \theta_i = \theta_r, \tag{26.7.1}$$

$$\text{For refraction:} \qquad \sin \theta_t / \sin \theta_i = V_t / V_i, \tag{26.7.2}$$

---

* Here Huygens presents Roemer's results, discussed above in Section 26.2, and uses them to support his physical model.

where V_i denotes the propagation velocity in the medium in which the wave is incident and V_t the velocity in the medium into which the wave is transmitted.

Equation (26.7.2) has the algebraic form of Snell's law, and one would identify the constant n_{12} with the ratio of wave velocities:

$$n_{12} = V_t/V_i = V_2/V_1. \qquad (26.7.3)$$

Since θ_t is known to be less than θ_i on passage of light from air to glass, the wave model requires that V_2 be less than V_1; that is, that light propagate more slowly in glass than in air.

Although the wave and particle models predict the same law of reflection and the same algebraic form of the law of refraction, we now discern a crucial difference. One model predicts a higher and the other a lower velocity of light in glass than in air. Such differences in prediction are eagerly looked for in alternative physical theories; they invite the construction of crucial experiments to resolve the discrepancy and eliminate one theory or the other.

In this instance, however, the direct comparison of the velocity of light in air with the velocity in water or glass did not become technically feasible until the middle of the nineteenth century. The French physicist Foucault showed in 1850 that the velocity of light in air is greater than that in water, but by this time the wave model had already become very widely accepted for other reasons, and Foucault's result was simply a confirmation that was confidently anticipated.

26.8   COLOR

An unavoidable question that forces itself on any investigator of the behavior of light concerns the nature of color. One of the most direct ways of obtaining different colors of light is to allow a narrow beam of sunlight (or light from a lamp) to pass through a triangular prism, as sketched in Fig. 26.8.1. The emerging light is not in the form of a narrow beam, equal in width to the incident beam, but is spread out over an appreciable angle with a regular sequence of colors, identical with those seen in a rainbow. Red always lies closest to the original direction of the incident beam, exhibiting a smaller angle of deviation (δ_r) than does the blue color with angle of deviation δ_b.

Many individuals studied and wrote of this phenomenon, attempting to account for the origin of colors from originally white light. Hooke, who thought in terms

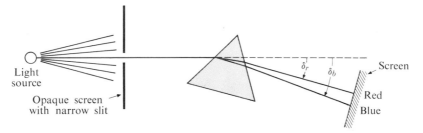

FIG. 26.8.1. Formation of spectrum on passage of narrow beam of white light through a triangular prism.

of waves in an ether, convinced himself that colors originated when the prism caused the wave front of incident white light to be slanted over at various angles relative to the "direction of thrust" or motion of the ether particles. He therefore believed that color was an artifact of the prism (or of the raindrops producing a rainbow), and was not an intrinsic property of the original white light. He might have tested this hypothesis by introducing another narrow slit at the position of the screen in Fig. 26.8.1, separating out a beam of pure red, or yellow, or green light and passing this through a second prism to see whether the color changed again on further distortion of the wave front.

Apparently this experiment did not occur to Hooke, but it did occur to Newton, who reports it as part of one of his earliest published researches. Newton found that the color did not change on passing through a second prism, but that the beam was deviated once more through exactly the same angle (say δ_r or δ_b) that was associated with the given color on passage through the first prism; i.e., each color is associated with a different numerical value of index of refraction.

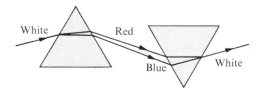

Fig. 26.8.2. Schematic diagram of Newton's experiment demonstrating the recombination of the spectral colors.

In another crucial experiment, Newton showed that, by inserting a second prism oriented as in Fig. 26.8.2, the beam emerging from the first prism could be recombined into a single beam of white light, equal in width to the original beam.

As a result of these experiments Newton concluded that color was an intrinsic property of light itself and that white light was a mixture of all the colors. He communicated his results to the Royal Society in 1671:

"Colors are not *Qualifications of Light* derived from Refraction or Reflection of natural Bodies (as 'tis generally believed), but *Original and connate properties*, which in divers Rays are divers. Some rays are disposed to exhibit a red colour and no other, and so of the rest. Nor are there only Rays proper and particular to the more eminent colours, but even to all their intermediate gradations.

"To the same degree or Refrangibility ever belongs the same colour, and to the same colour ever belongs the same degree of Refrangibility.

"The species of colour, and degree of Refrangibility proper to any particular sort of Rays, is not mutable by Refraction, nor by Reflection from natural bodies, nor by any other cause, that I could yet observe . . . notwithstanding my utmost endeavours to change it."

Newton's conclusions were simple and straightforward, easily verified by experiment, and independent of whether one adhered to a corpuscular or wave model. They were soon widely accepted, but their original communication drew an acid response from Hooke, then secretary of the Royal Society, and the ensuing controversy is said to have been largely responsible for Newton's subsequent reluctance to publish new discoveries. He withheld publication of his treatise on *Opticks* until 1704, following Hooke's death in 1703.

26.9   RINGS AND FRINGES

In the *Opticks*, Newton gives extensive consideration to two phenomena he felt to be of fundamental importance in the study of light. The first was the observation of colors that are seen when light falls on a thin film (such as a soap bubble) or on a thin layer of air between glass plates. This effect had been previously observed and studied qualitatively by Boyle and by Hooke, but because of the intensive quantitative study carried out by Newton, the circular pattern observed from the film of air between a spherical lens and a flat glass plate (Fig. 26.9.1) is usually referred to as "Newton's rings."

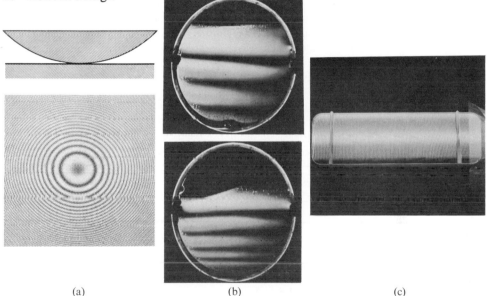

(a)   (b)   (c)

Fɪɢ. 26.9.1. Regions of brightness and darkness when a single color of light is reflected from thin films of varying thickness. Note that each ring or band follows a locus of constant thickness of the film. (a) Newton's rings. Observed when light of a single color is reflected from a thin film of air between a spherically curved glass and a flat glass plate. Dark spot in center is located at region where the glass surfaces are essentially in contact and the film thickness is practically zero. The central dark spot is surrounded by concentric dark rings, the spacing between which decreases with increasing radius. (b) Single color of light reflected from a vertically oriented soap film. Under influence of gravity, film becomes wedge-shaped—very thin at the top and thicker at the bottom. Note dark region (zero reflection) where film is extremely thin at the very top of the ring. The lower photograph was taken some seconds after the upper one. As the film drains, it becomes still more wedge-shaped, as indicated by the expansion of the upper dark region and the narrowing of the lines near the bottom. (c) Single color of light reflected from a wedge-shaped film of air between two flat glass surfaces. [Part (a) is from Sears and Zemansky, *University Physics*, Addison-Wesley, 1964. Parts (b) and (c) are from *Physics*. Boston: D. C. Heath, 1960.]

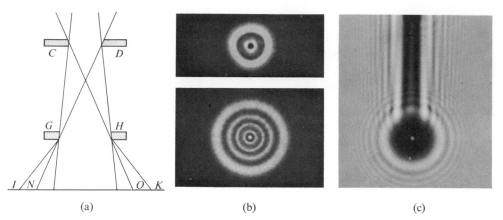

(a)   (b)   (c)

FIG. 26.9.2. Effects observed when light from a small source passes through small apertures or forms shadows of opaque objects. (a) Grimaldi's experiment: *CD* was a small
aperture admitting sunlight through a window shutter; *GH* another aperture quite far removed from *CD*. Light passing through *GH* fell on white paper producing illuminated
region *IK*. Grimaldi found the total illuminated region to be significantly greater than the
region *NO* to be expected if light passed through the two apertures in straight lines with
no bending. He observed colored bands in the region between *NO* and *IK*. (b) Dark and
bright rings observed when a single color of light from a very small source passes through
apertures of different sizes in an opaque plate. In both cases the apertures have diameters
significantly smaller than the diameter of the illuminated region. (c) Shadow of a sphere
supported by a thin rod. (Single-color light from very small source.) Note bright spot in
center of sphere and bright line in center of shadow of rod. Also note bright and dark bands
extending far out beyond the geometrical boundaries of the rod and the sphere.

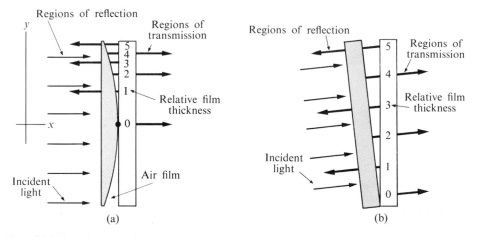

(a)   (b)

FIG. 26.9.3. Newton observed that when light shines on a thin film, a given color is
alternately reflected or transmitted, depending on the thickness of the film in a given region.
Denoting the thickness of film at the first reflection maximum as 1, other reflections are
found to occur at thicknesses of 3, 5, 7, etc., and transmissions are observed at thicknesses
of 0, 2, 4, 6, 8, etc. (a) Side view of air film in Newton's experiment with rings, as in Fig.
26.9.1(a). (Thickness of film is greatly exaggerated.) (b) Side view of wedge-shaped air
film between glass plates, as in Fig. 26.9.1(c).

The second phenomenon that commanded Newton's attention was the discovery, first described in 1665 in a posthumous work of an Italian Jesuit, Francesco Maria Grimaldi, that light bends slightly, but distinctly, around the edges of opaque obstacles illuminated by a very small source of light. (Grimaldi gave this phenomenon the name *diffraction*; Hooke independently discovered and studied the effect around 1670.) Grimaldi made a very small hole in a window shutter facing the sun and allowed light from this source to cast the shadow of a small opaque object on a piece of white paper. He observed the edge of the shadow to be diffuse rather than sharp and noticed bands of color in the region outside the shadow. In another experiment (Fig. 26.9.2a) he allowed light from the source to illuminate a small aperture in an opaque screen and allowed the light coming through the aperture to fall on the white paper. Here he observed illumination in the region that should have been in shadow if light passed through the aperture in straight lines, and he noticed bands of color within the illuminated region of the aperture itself. Examples of modern experiments of this kind are shown in Fig. 26.9.2(b) and (c).

From our experience with waves and the concept of interference, we are perhaps already motivated to associate regions of brightness and darkness with constructive and destructive interference of light. But the concept of interference remained to be developed and exploited by Thomas Young a century later, and Newton thought in rather different terms.

If we sketch the air films of Figs. 26.9.1(a) and (c) as viewed from the side, showing the variation in thickness, we obtain the diagrams shown in Fig. 26.9.3.

Newton went far beyond his predecessors in subjecting the ring phenomenon to careful quantitative measurement. By establishing with precision the radius of curvature R of the spherical surface, he could calculate accurate values of film thickness at various distances y from the central point at which the thickness is zero. He observed that a given color of light was alternately reflected and transmitted with increasing film thickness, forming the circular patterns of Fig. 26.9.1(a). Taking the film thickness at the first bright region of reflection as a reference unit, he found that reflection occurred systematically at thicknesses that stood in the ratios 1, 3, 5, 7, etc., and that maximum transmission (zero reflection) occurred at the thicknesses of 0, 2, 4, 6, 8, etc. Each color was found to have a different thickness of film at which the first bright reflection was observed.

These observations force the inescapable conclusion that there is something periodic in the behavior of light, and Newton rationalized this by the conception that a ray of light of a given color is alternately "disposed" to be reflected from or transmitted through an interface:

> "The returns of the disposition of any Ray* to be reflected I will call its *Fits of easy Reflection*, and those of its disposition to be transmitted its *Fits of easy Transmission*, and the space it passes between every return and the next return, the *Interval of its Fits*.
>
> "What kind of action or disposition this is; Whether it consists in a circulating or a vibrating motion of the Ray, or of the Medium, or something else, I do

---

* By "rays" Newton meant particles or corpuscles of light.

not here enquire. Those that are averse from assenting to any new Discoveries, but such as they can explain by an Hypothesis, may for the present suppose, that as Stones by falling upon Water put the Water into an undulating Motion, and all Bodies by percussion excite vibrations in the Air; so the Rays of Light, by impinging on any refracting or reflecting Surface, excite vibrations in the refracting or reflecting Medium or Substance, and by exciting them agitate the solid parts of . . . the Body . . . and cause the Body to grow warm and hot; that the vibrations thus excited are propagated in the reflecting or refracting Medium or Substance, much after the manner that vibrations are propagated in the Air for causing Sound, and move faster than the Rays so as to overtake them; and that when any Ray is in that part of the vibration which conspires with its Motion, it easily breaks through a refracting Surface, but when it is in the contrary part of the vibration which impedes its Motion, it is easily reflected. . . . But whether this Hypothesis be true or false I do not here consider. I content myself with the bare Discovery that the Rays of Light are by some cause or other alternately disposed to be reflected or refracted. . . ."

Different colors he associated with the excitation of different vibrations in the medium and with different intervals between fits of reflection and transmission:

". . . if by any means those [vibrations] of unequal bigness [length] be separated from one another, the largest beget a Sensation of a *Red* Colour, the least or shortest a deep *Violet*, and the intermediate ones, of intermediate colours; much after the manner that bodies, according to their several sizes, shapes and motions, excite vibrations in the Air of various bignesses, which according to those bignesses, make several Tones in Sound."

However, despite his conservative disclaimer with respect to the truth of his hypothesis, it is clear that Newton's thinking was strongly shaped by this heuristic device. He recognized that some kind of periodic effect was present, but he was never willing to abandon the concept that rectilinear motion of particles was also involved; this because he did not believe that light bent around obstacles in the manner of sound waves and ripples.

As we have seen, he was fully aware of Grimaldi's observation of diffraction, but he felt that the effect was too small to be attributed to wave behavior and inclined to explain it as a refraction effect: He believed the ethereal medium to be less dense in water or glass than in air (thus accounting for the prediction of a higher velocity of light particles in the denser media), and he conceived Grimaldi's effect to arise in the region near the edge of an obstacle where the ethereal medium was changing density from one region to the other and a net force was exerted on the light particles, as in refraction. It was not yet realized at that time that the extent to which a wave "bends" around an obstacle depends on the ratio of the wavelength to the size of the obstacle (see Section 22.6) and that light exhibits so little bending because its wavelength is so very short.

Newton made no pretense that his work on light was definitive. He closes the *Opticks* with the statement, "When I made the foregoing Observations [concerning the fringes formed on diffraction], I designed to repeat most of them with more care and exactness, and to make some new ones for determining how the Rays of Light are bent in their passage by Bodies.... But I was then interrupted, and cannot now think of taking these things into farther Consideration. And since I have not finished this part of my Design, I shall conclude with proposing only some Queries, in order to farther the search to be made by others." There then follow the 31 famous queries in which Newton set forth his bold and imaginative speculations about the nature of light, heat, electricity, magnetism, and the structure of matter.*

PROBLEM 26.7. At one point in the *Opticks* Newton says that, for yellow rays passing into air, "The Intervals of their Fits of easy Reflexion are the 1/89,000th part of an Inch." Since the interval for the fit of easy transmission is of equal length, the length of a complete cycle must be 2/89,000ths of an inch. In the most commonly used modern system, we express such lengths in Angstrom units, where $1 A = 10^{-8}$ cm. Convert Newton's figure for the interval of a complete cycle of yellow light into Angstrom units. [*Answer:* 5700 A; this is very close to the modern value for the wavelength of yellow light.] Using a film of water instead of air, Newton observed that the rings decreased in radius and that the various colors now occurred at regions where the film thickness was three-fourths the thickness of the corresponding region in the air film. What significance do you see in this observation? From what point of view is this ratio consistent with the known value of the index of refraction of water relative to air, 1.33?

26.10 INTERFERENCE OF LIGHT

Although, as we have seen, Newton's comments concerning his model of the nature of light were ambivalent and strongly qualified, and although he endowed light with the clear-cut periodicity of regularly recurring fits of transmission and reflection, he inclined to view the periodicity as a secondary effect in the medium rather than an intrinsic property of light rays themselves. His speculative position in the queries is quite strongly against a wave model and in favor of a corpuscular one. Assisted by the enormous prestige and authority of Newton's name, the corpuscular view prevailed during the eighteenth century, although essentially no progress was made toward putting the model on a more secure foundation. The few proponents of the wave model (Franklin and Euler among them) also did not succeed in connecting it convincingly with quantitatively observable phenomena, and this area of science remained static until the beginning of the nineteenth century, when it was suddenly revivified by a protean Englishman by the name of Thomas Young (1773–1829).

---

* Many of these queries form very interesting links and contrasts between seventeenth-century views and modern concepts. Analysis and commentary on some of the more important ones could be the subject of stimulating essays or term papers. Newton's *Opticks* is available in paperback (Dover Publications, Inc., New York, 1952).

Young was a practicing physician, a medical researcher, member of the Royal Society at the age of twenty, and an Egyptologist who contributed to the deciphering of the hieroglyphics, and to archeology and philology as well. He was a lecturer at the Royal Institution for several years in the early days after its founding by Rumford, and his contributions to physics included research on the elastic properties of materials, early advances toward the concept of energy (he was one of the first to use this name for the quantity mv^2), and, in the years between 1799 and 1803, major advances in support of the wave model of light.

Young argued that, to account for the same propagation velocity of light from different sources, the corpuscular theory had to assume, rather implausibly, that particles were emitted at the same velocity from feeble sources (such as the spark obtained in striking stones) and from the sun. In a wave model this difficulty does not arise, since the propagation velocity is a property of the medium and is independent of the source. Furthermore, he emphasized how much more naturally the wave model accounts for simultaneous reflection and refraction at an interface.

For the purpose of interpreting experimental observations on light, Young revived a principle that Newton himself had invoked to explain the anomalous behavior of tides in certain bays and channels, and which other scientists had used more or less qualitatively in connection with wave phenomena for many years: If we suppose waves of equal height to be produced by two separate sources on the quiet surface of a lake, the series of waves, on arriving at a channel at one end,

"will not destroy each other, but their effects will be combined; if they enter the channel in such a manner that the elevations of one series coincide with those of the other, they must together produce a series of greater joint elevations; but if the elevations of one series are so situated as to correspond to the depressions of the other, they must exactly fill up those depressions, and the surface of the water must remain smooth. Now I maintain that similar effects take place whenever two portions of light are thus mixed; and this I call the general law of the interference of light."

Young went on to give a mathematical analysis of interference of waves and to interpret Newton's rings as an interference phenomenon, in which, because of the path difference introduced by travel back and forth through the film, the light reflected from the front and back surfaces interfered destructively or constructively, depending on the local film thickness. In Fig. 26.10.1, the incident beam, I, is partly reflected (R_1) at surface 1 and partly transmitted (T_1). Beam T_1 is partly reflected (R_2) at surface 2 and partly transmitted (T_2). From the standpoint of a wave model, if R_1 and R_2 are in phase with each other, one should observe a bright reflection. If R_1 and R_2 are out of phase, they should interfere destructively, giving essentially zero reflection and, consequently, essentially complete transmission. Note that R_2 will be partially reflected when it returns to surface 1, but this effect is neglected in the present analysis. Note also that if the angle between the surfaces were really as great as that indicated in the diagram, the reflected rays would not be practically

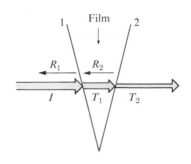

FIG. 26.10.1.   Schematic diagram of reflection and transmission at surfaces of a thin film (thickness of film greatly exaggerated).

parallel to each other and would not exhibit a sharply defined interference. In very thin films, however, the rays *are* essentially parallel to each other, and the interference effects are clear-cut.

PROBLEM 26.8.   Utilizing the interference concepts developed in Chapter 22, give your own explanation of Newton's rings as an interference phenomenon. Make your explanation quantitative and algebraic. At what thickness of film would you expect constructive and destructive interference of the two reflections? What must happen in films of varying thickness (as in Fig. 26.9.1)? It is a fact that different colors show constructive interference at different film thicknesses. What does this imply concerning the wavelength of different colors of light? How would you decide which color had the shortest and which the longest wavelength? Note that this is how Newton concluded that red light had the longer interval between "fits" of transmission and reflection.

One troublesome feature of the attempt to explain Newton's rings with a wave model was the fact that the reflection pattern for a film of air between glass boundaries was observed to be *dark* at the center, where the film thickness was essentially zero and where the incident and reflected waves should interfere constructively rather than destructively if the phase difference between them is zero.

It occurred to Young that the analogy to mechanical behavior should be pursued still further—that perhaps light undulations kept the same phase or were inverted in phase depending on whether they were reflected from "less-dense" or "more-dense" interfaces, something like the waves on strings in Fig. 22.10.2; or in analogy to elastic impact, in which a heavy body colliding with a stationary, lighter one keeps moving in its original direction, while a lighter body colliding with a heavier one bounces backward.

To test this idea, he utilized a lens of crown glass having an index of refraction of about 1.5, and a flat plate of flint glass having a higher index of refraction (about 1.7). Between the glasses he placed a film of oil of sassafras with an index of refraction falling *between* that of the two different kinds of glass. Young predicted that, if his wave analogy was correct, the reflected pattern should now be bright in the center, and this indeed turns out to be the case. (That is, Young was suggesting that perhaps the phase of the reflection would be the same at each interface if each interface involved transmission from a less-dense to a more-dense medium.)

PROBLEM 26.9. Explain in your own words the point of Young's experiment with the sassafras oil. What do you think it proves? In your present state of knowledge, in what ways does it leave you in doubt? Why do you suppose Young used index of refraction as a criterion of "density" of the media in this context? What must happen to the rest of the pattern of Newton's rings when the center is bright instead of dark? The modern technique of reducing loss of light by reflection from the surfaces of lenses in optical instruments involves coating the lens with a thin film of material of appropriate thickness and index of refraction. Given this hint, can you now deduce the principle involved—what must be the thickness of the film and the approximate magnitude of its index of refraction?

PROBLEM 26.10. Newton had observed that when the film between the glasses is water rather than air, the rings contract in radius (see Problem 26.7). Young confirmed the effect, and argued that the wavelength must be shorter in water than in air and that therefore the propagation velocity must be lower in water, supporting the wave hypothesis (Section 26.7). Explain this line of reasoning in your own words. What assumption must be made about the frequency? Do you find this assumption reasonable or unreasonable? Why?

26.11   TWO-SOURCE INTERFERENCE

In Newtonian tradition, Young performed many other quantitative observations to support the wave hypothesis. A Dutch physicist had cast serious doubt on Newton's explanation (see Section 26.9) of Grimaldi's diffraction patterns by showing that the latter were completely independent of the index of refraction of the medium that cast the shadow. Young went a step further to show that the fringes on the inside of a region of shadow disappeared when the light coming around one side of the obstacle was blocked off; i.e., that a combination of light arriving along different paths was necessary to produce the effect. From these results he argued that diffraction could not be caused by refraction of light at the edges of objects, as the corpuscular theory held, but was more likely a bending of waves as in water or sound. Invoking what was for these cases a primitive and incomplete theory, he nevertheless deduced a numerical value of the wavelength that would produce interference effects such as the observed fringes, and showed this value to be of the same magnitude as that deduced from Newton's rings (see Problem 26.7).

Young's most famous experiment consisted of a demonstration deliberately designed to illustrate wave behavior. Referring to water ripples and sound waves, he cites a diagram similar to Fig. 22.14.3 to illustrate the pattern of two-source interference, and then continues:

"We are now to apply the same principles to the alternate union and extinction of colors. In order that the effects of two portions of light may be thus combined, it is necessary that they be derived from the same origin, and that they arrive at the same point by different paths in directions not much deviating from each other. [The simplest case that satisfies these requirements] appears to be when a beam of homogeneous light falls on a screen in which there are

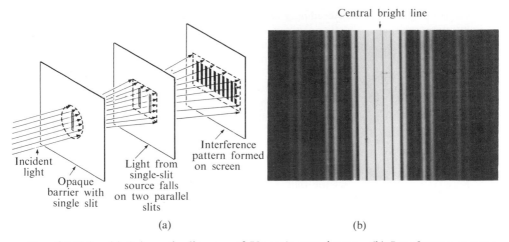

FIG. 26.11.1. (a) Schematic diagram of Young's experiment. (b) Interference pattern observed in Young's experiment with two slits.

two very small holes or slits [spaced very close to each other], which may be considered as centers of divergence from whence light is diffracted in every direction. . . . [See Fig. 26.11.1(a).] When the two newly formed beams are received on a surface placed so as to intercept them, their light is divided by dark stripes . . . so as to subtend nearly equal angles from the apertures at all distances, and wider also in the same proportion as the apertures are closer to each other. The middle . . . is always light, and the bright stripes on each side are at such distances, that the light coming to them from one of the apertures must have passed through a longer space than that which comes from the other by an interval which is equal to the breadth of one, two, three or more of the supposed undulations [i.e., an integral number of wavelengths], while the intervening dark spaces correspond to a difference of half a supposed undulation, of one and a half, of two and a half, or more. From a comparison of various experiments, it appears that the breadth of the undulations constituting the extreme red light must be supposed to be, in air about one 36 thousandth of an inch, and those of the extreme violet about one 60 thousandth; the mean of the whole spectrum being about one 45 thousandth."

Figure 26.11.1(b) illustrates the pattern observed in Young's experiment when light is passed through two parallel slits.

PROBLEM 26.11. Why does Young insist on the necessity that light striking the two openings be "homogeneous"; i.e., from virtually a point source? (In his own demonstration, he made this source a single slit or a pinhole through which he passed sunlight or light from a bright lamp.) What would happen in the ripple tank if two point sources vibrated randomly, unconnected with each other, instead of vibrating in unison on the same rigid mounting? (See Problem 22.20.)

PROBLEM 26.12.   In an exceedingly simple, qualitative experiment, you can see Young's interference fringes directly.   Take a card or piece of stiff paper and with a needle, the point of a compass, or other sharp instrument, puncture two very small holes as close together as you can get them without breaking the separation in between. Hold the openings directly in front of your eye and look at a small bright source of light (a flashlight bulb with the reflector removed or a distant street lamp at night). You will see parallel bright and dark lines perpendicular to the line connecting the two holes.   Puncture additional pairs of holes, closer together and farther apart than the first pair, and compare the spacing of the fringes as seen through the different pairs of holes.   Estimate the width of the spacing between the holes and note how small is the angle subtended by the individual fringes.

PROBLEM 26.13.   Convert the numerical values of wavelength given in the preceding quotation from Young into Angstrom units, and compare with Newton's result for yellow light (Problem 26.7), and with the modern values in Table 26.11.1.   [*Answer:* red: 7100 A; blue: 4200 A; mean: 5600–5700 A.]   Calculate the frequencies that must be associated with these wavelengths, and make up some illustrations to show how fantastically large they are.

TABLE 26.11.1

WAVELENGTHS OF VISIBLE LIGHT IN VACUUM (OR AIR)
(Angstrom units)

Extreme visible violet	4000 A
Violet	<4500
Blue	4500–5000
Green	5000–5700
Yellow	5700–5900
Orange	5900–6100
Red	>6100
Extreme visible red	~7000

In discussions from now on we shall frequently have occasion to compare other microscopic lengths (distances between atoms, atomic diameters, wavelengths of other disturbances, etc.) with the wavelengths of visible light.   The reader will find it worthwhile to memorize temporarily the order of magnitude of these wavelengths so as to possess this useful basis of comparison.   To facilitate the memorization, make up some problems in which you measure a few very small lengths in numbers of wavelengths of light.

Modern values of wavelengths of light in various portions of the visible spectrum are given in Table 26.11.1.   Note that the values given by Young and Newton were of very respectable accuracy.

26.12   THE DIFFRACTION GRATING

The two-slit interference effect can be greatly sharpened and enhanced by construction of a diffraction grating, a technique developed after Young's time, in the latter part of the nineteenth century.   This consists of scratching very fine parallel lines, very close together and very uniformly spaced, on a glass or metal surface. The unscratched regions act as parallel slits that transmit or reflect incident plane waves. The source is usually made to consist of a narrow slit oriented parallel to the lines on the grating.

The grating produces very sharply defined regions of constructive interference at a different angle for each incident wavelength, as outlined in Section 22.17. Thus white light is separated into spectra of different orders, symmetrically spaced around the principal axis, as illustrated in Fig. 26.12.1.

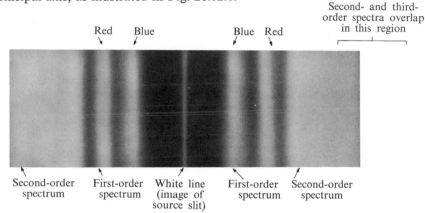

FIG. 26.12.1. Diagram of continuous spectra observed when white light is passed through a diffraction grating and focused on a screen. Source of light is a narrow slit oriented parallel to the lines of the grating.

In any given order, blue light always lies closer to the principal axis than red, indicating that blue has the shorter wavelength. Recall that in the spectrum formed by dispersion in a prism (Fig. 26.8.1), the blue light is deviated more strongly and lies further than red light from the axis defined by the direction of the original beam. These two devices for separating white light into spectra are fundamentally different from each other. The grating involves no refraction effects, and separates colors by constructive and destructive interference of the respective wavelengths. The prism gives no direct information about wavelength, but separates colors because of the phenomenon of *dispersion*: different propagation velocities for different wavelengths of light in glass. Accepting light as a wave phenomenon, and noting the fact that blue light is more strongly refracted than red, we infer that blue light has the lower propagation velocity in glass.

PROBLEM 26.14. In the light of the analysis given in Section 22.17, interpret and describe the things one might observe with an optical grating in more detail: What would you expect to see if the incident light were a single pure color? only two or three sharply defined colors? (Note that each separate line is a sharp image of the original source slit, and that if the incident light is white, these sharp images become smeared out into the appearance of a continuous spectrum.) What do you predict will happen to the positions of any given color if the grating is ruled with a finer spacing? a coarser spacing?

PROBLEM 26.15. Assume that you are preparing to perform an experiment in which you will determine the wavelengths of different colors of light with the help of a diffraction grating. What observations will you want to make? What additional information will be required? How will you calculate the wavelength? Assume that you will have a grating ruled 15,000 lines to the inch. What is the spacing between the lines of the grating in A? Predict the angular positions of blue, yellow, and red lines in the first few orders of spectra. How many orders of spectra will actually be visible with this fine a grating? Compare the predicted angular positions of the *second*-order red and third-order violet. How do you interpret these results?

26.13   POLARIZATION

About 1670 Erasmus Bartholinus published an account of a peculiar optical property exhibited by a transparent crystalline mineral called Iceland spar or calcite. The nature of the effect, frequently called "double refraction," is illustrated in Fig. 26.13.1. An incident narrow pencil of light, in passing through a flat plate of the crystal, is separated into two distinct beams instead of remaining a single beam as it does in glass or water. Subsequently, other crystalline materials were found to exhibit similar effects.

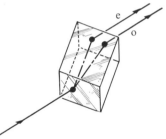

FIG. 26.13.1. Double refraction in calcite. Incident pencil of light is refracted and separated into two pencils. If one looks through a transparent calcite crystal, he sees two images of any source of light, each image being associated with one of the two emerging beams. The beams are designated "ordinary" (o) and "extraordinary" (e), respectively.

Huygens sensed that the phenomenon of double refraction had important implications with respect to both the nature of light and the structure of matter, and devoted considerable space in his *Treatise on Light* to an ingenious but imperfect attempt to explain the phenomenon in terms of his model of longitudinal waves in a corpuscular ether. Newton was also fully aware of the effect and recognized its importance.

It is beyond the scope of this text to engage in a rigorous and detailed description of double refraction and its consequences, but we shall concentrate attention on one simple and particularly significant experimental aspect, which we shall, for convenience, describe in modern rather than seventeenth-century terms.

Either one of the two separated beams in double refraction can be blocked off after emergence from the plate of calcite, and the remaining beam can be studied alone. If we take a plate of polaroid (such as that used in polaroid sunglasses) or a plate of a transparent crystalline mineral called tourmaline, place either plate perpendicular to the emerging beam and observe the transmission, we find that the intensity of the transmitted beam varies as we rotate the polaroid plate around the beam as an axis, as sketched in Fig. 26.13.2. We can find an orientation of the polaroid

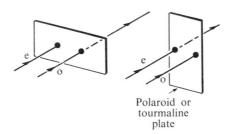

Polaroid or
tourmaline
plate

FIG. 26.13.2. Pencils of light emerging from a calcite crystal (Fig. 26.13.1) intercepted by a plate of polaroid or tourmaline. It is possible to find an orientation of the plate such that pencil e is extinguished while pencil o is transmitted. If the plate is then rotated through an angle of 90° around the pencil as an axis, it is found that pencil e is transmitted, while pencil o is extinguished. In intermediate orientations of the plate, both pencils are partly transmitted.

at which the transmission is a maximum. If we then rotate the polaroid, we find the intensity of transmission decreasing until, after an angular displacement of 90°, the transmitted beam is extinguished. After another displacement of 90°, the transmitted intensity returns to a maximum, etc. The other beam emerging from the calcite exhibits the same properties but appears to be rotated through 90° relative to the first; i.e., it is extinguished by that orientation of the polaroid which fully transmits the first beam.

An analogous effect, discovered by Etienne Louis Malus in 1808, is illustrated in Fig. 26.13.3. One of the beams from the calcite crystal is obliquely reflected from a glass plate which is rotated to various different positions around the beam as an axis, the angle of incidence remaining fixed during the rotation. It is possible to find a position of the glass plate at which the incident beam is reflected with maximum intensity. Then, as the plate is rotated around the beam, the intensity of reflection decreases, reaching a minimum when the reflecting plate has been rotated 90°. These

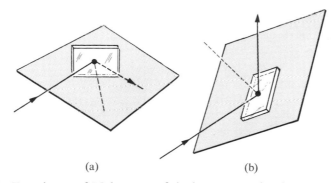

(a)   (b)

FIG. 26.13.3. Experiment of Malus: one of the beams emerging from a calcite crystal is obliquely reflected from a glass plate. If the angle of incidence remains constant, but the glass plate is rotated into different orientations around the incident beam as an axis, the intensity of the reflected beam is found to vary, passing through a minimum, as shown in (a), and a maximum, as in (b), separated by angular displacements of 90°.

experiments clearly imply that the beams of light emerging from the calcite crystal have acquired properties that vary in different directions at *right angles* to the direction of propagation.

Huygens and Newton were, of course, not aware of any material such as polaroid, and did not know about the variation of intensity of reflection from a glass plate. The experiments they knew consisted of allowing the beam emerging from the first calcite crystal to pass at various angles of incidence through a second calcite crystal, which was rotated about the incident beam as an axis. The transmitted beam then exhibits certain variations, more complex than the ones we have described, but analogous in the sense that properties of the beams appear to vary in directions *perpendicular* or *transverse* to the direction of propagation.

As in his experiments with color, Newton concluded that this property of directionality transverse to the direction of propagation was intrinsic to the original, mixed beam of light incident on the first crystal, and that the crystal only separated the effects (as a prism separated colors) without itself endowing the light with new properties.

Malus introduced the term *polarized* to describe the ordinary and extraordinary beams emerging from the calcite. Newton described the light as having "sides": "Every ray of light has therefore two opposite Sides, originally endued with a Property on which the unusual Refraction depends, and the other two opposite Sides not endued with that Property."

Subsequently it was discovered by Malus and others that light could be polarized not only by transmission through crystals but by reflection from water and glass surfaces. The phenomenon of polarization remains to this day an important mechanism for studying the interaction between light and matter, and during the nineteenth century it played an important role in elucidation of the nature of light.

26.14   ACCEPTANCE OF THE WAVE MODEL

Not being able to rationalize the "sides" or transverse behavior of light in terms of a wave model that visualized longitudinal condensations and rarefactions in a fluid medium, and recognizing transverse or shear waves to be impossible in a fluid, Newton adduced the polarization phenomenon as one of the strongest pieces of evidence against the wave model.

When Young embarked on his revival of wave theory around 1800, he forcefully reminded his readers of the periodicity (regular fits of reflection and transmission) Newton had associated with light and contended that he was only extending and improving the Newtonian ideas. Like Newton, Young inclined to believe in an ethereal medium, and even suggested a connection between the electric and luminiferous ethers: "Whether the electric ether is to be considered the same with the luminiferous ether, if such a fluid exists, may perhaps at some future time be discovered; hitherto I have not been able to observe that the refractive power of a fluid undergoes any change by electricity." The idea of the identity of electric and luminiferous ethers had already been in the air for some time, Leonhard Euler having proposed similar speculations as early as 1760.

In his early work, Young did not succeed in formulating a really convincing explanation of polarization, and this left a gap in his scheme. Recognizing the limitations of his wave model, Young, around 1807, defended it as follows:

"It is presumed that the accuracy with which the general law of the interference of light has been shown to be applicable to so great a variety of facts, in circumstances the most dissimilar, will be allowed to establish its validity in the most satisfactory manner. The full confirmation or decided rejection of the theory, by which this law was first suggested, can be expected from time and experience alone; if it be confuted, our prospects will again be confined within their ancient limits, but if it be fully established, we may expect an ample extension of our views of the operations of nature, by means of our acquaintance with a medium so powerful and so universal as that to which the propagation of light must be attributed."

Young's work, however, was somewhat ahead of the time. It was virulently attacked by self-styled Newtonians and largely ignored by other investigators, until it was rediscovered and brilliantly advanced about a decade later by the French engineer and physicist, Augustin Fresnel. Young had constructed some of his theoretical analyses on the assumption that diffraction fringes depended on the *reflection* of light from the edges of apertures or obstacles. Fresnel disproved this notion by showing that blunt and sharp edges produce identical effects, and went on to develop a more sophisticated model, using Huygens' basic idea that every point on a wave front is the origin of forward-moving wavelets.

When Poisson pointed out that Fresnel's wave theory of diffraction contained the unlikely implication that there must be a bright spot in the center of the shadow cast by an opaque circular disc, Fresnel set up the experiment and showed that this is exactly what is observed. [See Fig. 26.9.2(c).] In 1816 Fresnel and Arago showed that two pencils of light polarized at right angles (such as the beams emerging from the calcite crystal) do not interfere with each other under circumstances in which ordinary light exhibits interference, and that interference of beams of polarized light can be obtained only with beams of the same polarization.

When Young heard of these experiments, he suggested that "If we assume as a mathematical postulate, on the undulating theory, without attempting to demonstrate its physical foundation, that transverse motion may be propagated in a direct line, we may derive from this assumption a tolerable illustration of the subdivision of polarized light by reflection in an oblique plane." In 1818, in a letter to Arago, Young compared the polarization of light to the undulations of a string, vibrating in one plane or another depending on the direction of motion imposed by a driving mechanism at one end (Fig. 26.14.1). Fresnel seized on this idea and went on to exploit it in additional theory and experiments. Over a period of years, in cleverly devised experiments, Fresnel showed that light could be made to exhibit all the effects one might imagine to be associated with transverse waves, and he succeeded in giving a simple and convincing theory of double refraction and of other aspects of the propagation of light in crystals.

Throughout all these developments it remained beyond the scope of science to give a physical foundation to the wave model. Neither Young nor Fresnel could say what it was that was "waving" in a light wave. They constructed a beautifully complete and convincing analogy to mechanical experience and were fully aware of the limited nature of their construct.

With the persuasive and incredibly detailed work of Fresnel, the wave theory swept aside former objections and obstacles. By the 1830's and 1840's, when Faraday was writing the *Experimental Researches*, the wave model was taken for granted and the way was paved for the acceptance of a universal ether and for the development of the field concept. When in 1850 Foucault showed by direct measurement that light propagated at lower velocity in water than in air, his experimental *tour de force* was virtually an anticlimax. Everyone knew how the result had to come out.

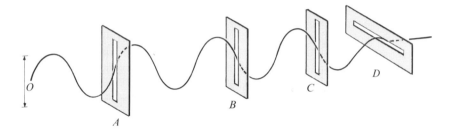

FIG. 26.14.1. Young's suggestion of a mechanical analog for the polarization of light. If a string is vibrated up and down at O, the transverse wave that is generated will pass through slots A, B, C parallel to the deflections of the string, but will be extinguished at D, where the horizontally oriented slot prevents vertical deflection. Barriers C and D, which respectively transmit or extinguish the propagating wave at orientations of 90° relative to each other, are analogous to the polaroid plates in Fig. 26.13.2. The transverse wave with deflections confined to a single plane is said to be polarized; the complicated jiggling wave with horizontal and vertical deflections not confined to a single plane is described as unpolarized. If an unpolarized disturbance were incident at barrier A, only a vertically polarized wave would be transmitted.

Thus after many years the wave model prevailed, and it prevailed in the absence of any clear notion of what property was varying in the wave train or how it could possibly vary in a direction transverse to the direction of propagation. The model was accepted not as a revelation stemming from one or two brilliant experiments, but as a conclusion arrived at after a painstaking series of predictions, tests, and cross checks—after elaborations of detail and complexity that we have only outlined and hinted at in this necessarily brief description. The inquiry, however, had only begun, and in subsequent years the ablest theoreticians concentrated their efforts on attempts to understand in more precise physical detail the nature of the waves that constitute light.

26.15 PROBLEMS

26.16. Occasionally there occurs in the heavens an explosion of a star, producing what is known as a supernova. The star suddenly becomes many times brighter than before. The stars are so far away that the light from them takes many years to reach us. An explosion that we observe must have occurred a long time ago, and the light has been traveling toward us ever since. We see the explosion as a bright white light, not as a series of different colors arriving at different times. What does this show about the speed of light of different colors in vacuum?

26.17. A narrow pencil of light enters the top surface of the water in a rectangular aquarium at an angle of incidence of 40°. The refracted pencil continues to the bottom of the tank, striking a horizontally placed plane mirror which reflects it back again to the surface, and it is again refracted as it emerges into the air. Compare the directions of the incident ray entering the water and the refracted ray emerging from it. If the water in the tank is 10 cm deep, what is the distance between the points on the water surface where the ray enters and where it emerges? Predict what happens to the ray as the original angle of incidence is increased from 40° to successively larger values.

FIGURE 26.15.1

26.18. A wedge-shaped air film is formed between two glass microscope slides by tilting one slide slightly with respect to the other. The slides are then illuminated with yellow light, and interference fringes are observed by reflection (Fig. 26.15.1). Now suppose that one slide is moved slowly forward or backward (in or out of the paper)

without changing its angle relative to the other slide. The film retains its wedge shape but increases uniformly in thickness. If you were watching the interference fringes during this motion, what would you expect to see? Why?

26.19. Could you "see" an object 5000 A in diameter? Why or why not? (This is a fairly complex question, put forth to stimulate thought and discussion. It does not have a one-phrase pat answer.)

26.20. How would you set up an optical experiment which is an analogy of the ripple experiment described in Problem 22.30? (The name "Lloyd's mirror" actually derives from the optical rather than the mechanical case.) Make your answer quantitative, suggesting dimensions and spacings that might be used and predicting locations of regions of constructive interference for some particular color of light.

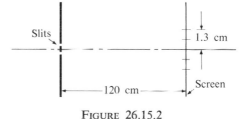

FIGURE 26.15.2

26.21. In a Young's double-slit experiment, the slits are spaced 0.10 mm apart; a screen is placed 120 cm away. With a particular color of light, the second-order maximum is observed to be 1.3 cm from the principal axis (Fig. 26.15.2). Estimate the wavelength of the incident light and indicate its color. [*Answer:* 5400 A.]

26.22. In Section 22.18 we discussed the single-slit diffraction pattern of ripples, but we have not taken time in this chapter to say anything in detail about single-slit diffraction of light. You can observe this phenomenon qualitatively for yourself in a very simple

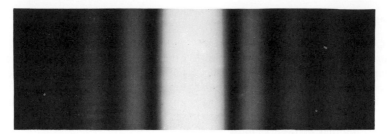

FIGURE 26.15.3

way. When you have the opportunity to view a line source of light (a light bulb such as a showcase bulb with a long, straight filament observed at a distance of 10 or 15 ft, or a long fluorescent or neon light at greater distance), make a slit directly in front of your eye by looking between a pair of fingers held close together. Align the slit parallel to the light source and change its width by squeezing the pair of fingers closer together with your other hand. You will readily see the single-slit diffraction pattern and its rapidly increasing width as the slit is made narrower. A photograph of such a single-slit pattern is shown in Fig. 26.15.3. What connection do you discern between this figure and the broad variations in intensity visible in Fig. 26.11.1(b)?

SUPPLEMENTARY READING AND STUDY

Text material:

Physics, Physical Science Study Committee. Boston: D. C. Heath, 1960, Chaps. 11–15, 19

Physics, the Pioneer Science, L. W. Taylor. Boston: Houghton Mifflin, 1941; New York: Dover Publications, 1959, Chapters 29–36

Physics for Students of Science and Engineering, R. Resnick and D. Halliday. New York: John Wiley & Sons, 1960, Chapters 41–46

Light and Colour in the Open Air, M. Minnaert. New York: Dover Publications, 1954

Historical and philosophical:

A History of the Theories of Aether and Electricity, E. T. Whittaker. New York: Harper Torchbook 531, 1960, Chapters 1, 4

Source Book of Physics, W. F. Magie. New York: McGraw-Hill, 1935, pages 265–344

Great Experiments in Physics, M. H. Shamos. New York: Henry Holt, 1959, pages 93–120

The Scientific Revolution 1500–1800, A. R. Hall. New York: Longmans, Green, 1954; Boston: Beacon Press (paperback BP 29), 1956, Chapter 9

The Principles of Physical Optics, an Historical and Philosophical Treatment, E. Mach. New York: Dover Publications, S178. (Reprint of 1926 edition.)

The Edge of Objectivity, C. C. Gillispie. Princeton, N.J.: Princeton University Press, 1960, pages 117–134; pages 406–435

Original sources:

Opticks: or, a Treatise of the Reflexions, Refractions, Inflexions and Colours of Light, Isaac Newton. New York: Dover Publications, 1952

CHAPTER 27

Light, Matter, and Electricity

27.1 INTRODUCTION

Light is emitted when matter is made self-luminous by heat from a flame, heat from the passage of electric current, or by the transient passage of an electric spark or continuous electrical discharge in gases. Light is reflected, refracted, and absorbed in different ways by different substances. Its absorption is invariably accompanied by heating of the absorbing material. It is apparent that both the emission and absorption of light are intimately connected with transformations of energy and that, in general, emission occurs at high temperatures when we would expect the particles of matter to be excited into violent motion.

A host of questions is stimulated by these observations: By what mechanism is light emitted and absorbed? Are emission and absorption essentially inverse processes having some simple relation to each other? From observed differences in the light emitted by various substances, what can be inferred concerning the interaction between matter and light? In what way is light connected with electricity? Does it respond in any observable way to electric and magnetic forces?

Most of these questions, and many others, were raised in one form or another during the latter part of the eighteenth and the beginning of the nineteenth century, and the investigation has been vigorously pursued to this day. Light and electricity turned out to be keys to knowledge of atomic and molecular structure. The study of the interaction between light and matter on a microscopic scale begins with the study of spectra.

27.2 CONTINUOUS SPECTRA

The first spectra we are likely to become familiar with are those of sunlight or of incandescent solids. If the slit through which the light passes is made very narrow and oriented parallel to the axis of the dispersing prism or to the lines of a diffraction grating, there is a minimum of overlap of each successive colored image of the slit. The colors then appear bright and pure and merge continuously, one into the next, from one end of the visible spectrum to the other. This is called a *continuous spectrum*.

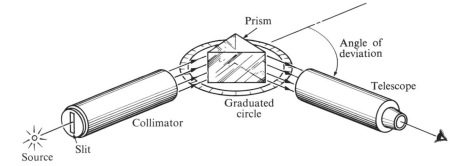

FIG. 27.2.1. Schematic diagram of prism spectroscope.

High-precision instruments have been designed in which light from a source is accurately collimated (formed into parallel rays by a lens system) before being passed through a prism or grating (Fig. 27.2.1). Portions of the emerging spectrum can then be viewed through a telescope (or focused on a photographic plate), the telescope being mounted on a graduated arc, so that angular positions of the color of light being viewed can be accurately determined. Depending on whether it is set up for optical viewing or for photographic recording, such an instrument is called a *spectroscope* or a *spectrograph*.

In 1800 the English astronomer William Herschel took thermometer readings in different positions of the spectrum formed by a prism and found not only that the thermometer showed higher readings when exposed to the red light than when exposed to the violet, but also that the indicated temperature continued to rise as the thermometer was moved to points beyond the region of visible red light. In subsequent experiments with these "invisible rays," Herschel showed that they obeyed Snell's law and the law of reflection.

As the wave model of light gained acceptance, it was recognized that this region of the spectrum (called the *infrared*) must consist of longer wavelengths and lower frequencies than those that excite the sense of sight, just as it is possible to generate in the air compressions and rarefactions of long wavelength and low frequency which do not excite the sense of hearing and which we call "subsonic" vibrations.

Later investigators discovered that rock salt is much more transparent to infrared light than glass is. With rock-salt prisms and with very much more sensitive thermal detectors than Herschel's, the solar spectrum was observed and measured out to wavelengths of tens of thousands of Angstrom units.

A year after Herschel's discovery, J. W. Ritter of Jena found that invisible rays, capable of producing chemical effects such as the blackening of white silver chloride, existed in the spectral region beyond the visible violet. With the advent of photography in the 1840's, the chemical effects of light were utilized to produce permanent pictorial records in black and white, and it was realized that much of the sensitivity of photographic plates lay in the "ultraviolet" region. Photographic techniques were almost immediately applied to spectroscopy, the first photograph of the solar spectrum being made in 1842.

In 1825 Sir G. G. Stokes discovered that quartz was more transparent to ultraviolet light than glass was. With quartz prisms and photographic plates, ultraviolet spectra were observed and measured out to about 2000 A. With more modern techniques, utilizing improved photographic emulsions and vacuum systems to prevent absorption of ultraviolet light by the air, observations in the "far ultraviolet" were carried to wavelengths of the order of hundreds of A.

Such discoveries imply that there is no reason for assuming that spectra end abruptly at the wavelength where particular detecting techniques cease to be adequate, and they invite speculation concerning the possibility of generating and detecting still broader ranges of wavelength and frequency.

27.3 EMISSION SPECTRA OF GASES

During the second half of the eighteenth century, after pioneering observations in 1752 by Thomas Melvill, a Scottish physicist, it came to be realized that luminous gases exhibited spectra that were markedly different from the continuous spectra of incandescent solids. When different substances are volatilized in a hot flame, the flame takes on a color characteristic of the added substance (bright yellow for table salt, purple for potassium compounds, blue-green for copper, etc.).

Melvill allowed the light from such flames to pass through a small circular aperture in a pasteboard and examined it with a prism. Instead of a continuous spectrum, he observed one or several spots (separate images of the aperture), each in a particular color and with dark regions, devoid of light, in between. He further noted that the colors that were present (and the corresponding positions of the bright spots) were different for each different substance added to the flame.

In 1823 the astronomer John Herschel (son of William Herschel, discoverer of infrared light) suggested that particular substances in unknown mixtures might be identified by the spectra of their luminous gases and with this suggestion initiated the science of spectrum analysis. This technique played a vital role in the evolution of chemistry, making it possible to determine the chemical constitution of small samples or of complex materials that would have been difficult to analyze in any other way.

Investigators began using a system of lenses to focus the dispersed light emerging from the prism into a sharp image that could be viewed by eye or projected on a screen or on a photographic plate. They found that the image was easier to observe and locate precisely if the light from the luminous source were passed through a narrow slit instead of a round aperture. Under these circumstances one sees each image of the slit as a bright line in the separate colors that are present, and for this reason the spectra of luminous gases are called "bright-line" spectra. Figure 27.3.1 shows several typical bright-line spectra of different substances.

In the 1850's the physicist Gustav Kirchhoff and the chemist Robert Bunsen at the University of Heidelberg constructed the prototype of the modern spectroscope, and went on to a number of important discoveries. Kirchhoff identified the yellow line in the flame of table salt as being associated with the element sodium, and Kirchhoff and Bunsen jointly discovered two hitherto unknown elements, cesium and rubidium, by observing their emission lines in the spectra of vaporized mineral waters.

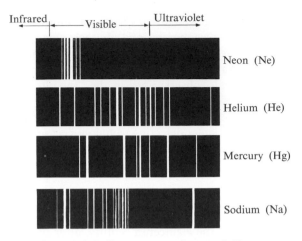

Fig. 27.3.1. Portions of the bright-line spectra of neon, helium, mercury, and sodium (resketched from spectrographic records). Note that lines vary markedly in intensity.

The systematic use of spectroscopy in chemical analysis led to observations and accumulation of data of profound physical significance. It was found, for example, that lines in the visible and ultraviolet regions were invariably associated with materials that had been chemically identified as "elements," substances that combined with each other to form the more complex materials called "compounds." Later it was established that specific gaseous compounds were associated with complex sharp line groupings in both the near and the far infrared. It was established that the bright lines of a particular spectrum remained unaltered in number or wavelength as the density of the gas was altered; only the intensity of the lines decreased as the gas concentration was reduced.

The density independence of the bright-line spectra was interpreted as indicating that individual particles, acting independently of each other, were responsible for emission of these specific frequencies of light, and that any one particle was capable of emitting any one of the bright lines, the total intensity in a given instance depending on the number of particles present. Differences between spectra and the complexity of some of them (there are thousands of lines in the visible spectrum of iron) were believed to imply complexity in behavior or structure of the particles themselves.

As the energy concepts came to be accepted and used in the 1850's and 1860's, questions could be put in still another form: What are the processes, motions, changes of potential and kinetic energy by means of which the particles of a given gas receive energy from a source of heat or electricity and emit it in the form of sharply restricted frequencies of light?

27.4 FRAUNHOFER LINES

By the time the preceding question could be articulated in the vocabulary of energy, it was known that gases could receive energy not only from heat and electricity but by absorption of light itself—a process precisely inverse to that of emission. The first hint of this experimental fact came in an observation by William Wollaston in 1802 that the spectrum of sunlight was crossed by seven irregularly spaced dark lines. Wollaston labored under the impression that these lines marked separations between different colors and did not pursue their origin and significance any further.

Some years later, the German physicist Joseph Fraunhofer found himself in need of a very sharply defined and reproducible wavelength for the measurement of indices of refraction of different kinds of optical glass used in the manufacture of lenses. He had discovered that he could use the very bright yellow line associated with the flame of certain lamps (later shown by Kirchhoff to be due to sodium), but wanting greater intensity than that available from the lamp, he used his early version of the spectroscope to see: "whether a bright line such as that in the lamp spectrum could be seen in the spectrum of sunlight. With the telescope, I found instead of this, an almost countless number of strong and weak lines, which, however, were darker than the other parts of the spectrum, some appearing almost perfectly black."

These sharp dark lines, always reproducible, and liberally scattered through the visible spectrum, were exactly what Fraunhofer needed to establish landmarks or reference points at various wavelengths for his index measurements. To identify the lines for his work and records, he assigned the letters $A, B, C, D \ldots$ to the most prominent ones. The line labeled D (later shown by higher-resolution spectroscopes to be a "doublet," or two lines very close together in wavelength) was observed to occupy exactly the same position as the bright yellow line he had used in his flame spectra. An illustration of the Fraunhofer dark-line spectrum of sunlight is shown in Fig. 27.4.1.

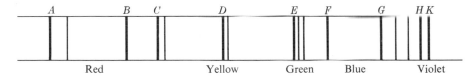

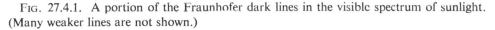

FIG. 27.4.1. A portion of the Fraunhofer dark lines in the visible spectrum of sunlight. (Many weaker lines are not shown.)

Between 1814 and 1824 Fraunhofer published three papers concerning his discovery. He examined the spectra of moonlight and of several planets and found lines identical to those observed in sunlight. In the spectra of stars he found clear-cut differences, together with many lines that were identical. This observation demonstrated that at least some of the lines were of extra-terrestrial origin, even if the earth's atmosphere were responsible for others.

But neither Fraunhofer himself nor the rest of the scientific community was ready to appreciate the full significance of these observations. Chemical analysis by spectroscopy awaited Bunsen and Kirchhoff, and a theory of the nature and origin of the dark lines had to precede recognition of the possibility of chemical analysis of the sun and stars.

27.5 ABSORPTION SPECTRA OF GASES

An explanation of the dark lines came from Kirchhoff in 1859:

> "I have made some observations which give an unexpected explanation of the origin of the Fraunhofer lines and allow us to draw conclusions from them about the composition of the sun's atmosphere and perhaps also of that of the brighter fixed stars. . . .
>
> "I arranged a solar spectrum and allowed the sun's rays, before they fell on the slit, to pass through a flame heavily charged with salt. When the sunlight was sufficiently weakened there appeared in place of the two dark *D* lines, two bright lines; if its intensity, however, exceeded a certain limit, the two dark *D* lines showed much more plainly than when the flame charged with salt was not present."

It was well known at this time that the spectrum of white light from an incandescent solid does not exhibit the Fraunhofer lines. Kirchhoff made use of such light in another crucial experiment:

> "If an alcohol flame in which salt is introduced is placed [between the source of white light and the slit of the spectroscope], then in place of the bright lines two dark lines appear, remarkably sharp and fine, which in every respect correspond to the *D* lines of the solar spectrum. Thus the *D* lines of the solar spectrum have been artificially produced in a spectrum in which they do not naturally occur."

Kirchhoff went on to introduce an artificial dark line not present in the solar spectrum by passing sunlight through a flame colored by lithium chloride, and showed that the line disappears as soon as the flame is removed.

From these experiments he concluded that gases absorb from passing light exactly the same sharply defined wavelengths they emit in their own luminosity, and,

> "I conclude further that the dark lines of the solar spectrum, which are not produced by the earth's atmosphere, occur because of the presence of those elements in the glowing atmosphere of the sun which would produce in the spectrum of flame bright lines in the same position."

Based on his laboratory experiments, Kirchhoff suggested a model for the origin of the Fraunhofer lines: Light emanating from the extremely hot deeper layers of the sun passes through a relatively cooler outer atmosphere. The content of chemical elements in this atmosphere determines the dark absorption lines of solar origin. Other absorption lines arise in a similar way as the light passes through the earth's atmosphere. Kirchhoff initiated a chemical analysis of the sun, and explicitly identified the

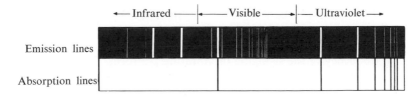

FIG. 27.5.1. Comparison of the emission and absorption spectra of sodium vapor. Note that the spectra are not identical, in that many of the emission lines do not have counterparts in the absorption spectrum.

presence of sodium and potassium and noted the apparent absence of lithium. When, around 1870, a set of prominent lines was found that did not correspond to those of any element known on earth, the element was christened helium, denoting its association with the sun. In the 1890's helium was recognized terrestrially as one of the group of "noble gases." It was detected in small traces in the atmosphere and as a gas trapped within solid radioactive minerals.

Absorption spectra can be studied in the laboratory by causing a beam of white light to pass through a transparent cell of the absorbing gas before falling on the slit of the spectroscope. Figure 27.5.1 illustrates both the emission and absorption spectra of sodium vapor. Note that the spectra are not identical. All the lines of the absorption spectrum are to be found in emission, but there are many emission lines that do not appear on the absorption spectrum. Any successful theory of the structure of matter and its interaction with light, in addition to accounting for the sharp lines themselves, would have to account for this somewhat puzzling difference between the spectra.

PROBLEM 27.1. In the light of the very fragmentary knowledge we have developed so far, attempt to construct an explanation for bright-line and dark-line spectra, and a discussion of some of their properties. (Do not feel that there is a pat answer to this question, and do not plunge into what you might happen to know about modern theories. Try to construct a reply in terms of the primitive concepts we have outlined so far. The fact that some of your ideas will be incorrect from a modern point of view is entirely beside the point.) How would you account for the fact that spectra of glowing solids are continuous and that only the spectra of gases are discrete? Through what observations and experiments might you determine which lines in the Fraunhofer spectrum are due to terrestrial atmospheric absorption and which originate in the sun (or stars)? (Consider the possibility of introducing cells in which the gas content can be controlled.)

27.6 THE RESONANCE MODEL OF DARK-LINE SPECTRA

Several years before Kirchhoff's systematic and conclusive demonstration that the Fraunhofer lines are due to absorption, G. G. Stokes, impressed by the already well-known identity of wavelengths of the yellow line in flames and the Fraunhofer D-line, had adopted an absorption–emission hypothesis and suggested a mechanical analogy.

To grasp the concept being involved, recall the physical sensation associated with "pumping" a swing or with obtaining an impulse from a springboard or trampoline. To obtain a large amplitude of motion, one must time his own kicks or impulses to the natural frequency of the swinging or vibrating platform. The basic situation can be reproduced in a very simple laboratory experiment: Suspend a weight on a helical spring (Fig. 27.6.1) and try to set it into large vertical oscillation, not by pulling it down and letting it go, but by tapping it at regular intervals. If you press the mallet against the weight and move it up and down very slowly, the weight simply follows the action of your hand without going into an oscillation of its own. If you tap the weight at a very high frequency, it will hardly respond at all, remaining very nearly stationary in its equilibrium position. If you tap the weight, however, at a frequency that is identical with the frequency at which it oscillates naturally when plucked and let go, the weight is readily excited into vigorous oscillation, and the oscillation increases violently if the tapping is continued. In such instances we say that the oscillating system is in resonance with the driving effect. Energy is supplied by the motion of the mallet in exactly the right phase to be absorbed as kinetic and potential energy of the vibrating system, instead of being converted into heat of inelastic collision, or simply reflected in a bouncing away of the mallet.

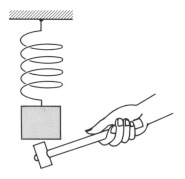

FIG. 27.6.1.   Resonance of weight on spring.

In his experiments designed to test the identity of the different kinds of electricity, Faraday wished to show that a wire used to discharge a Leyden jar was surrounded by a magnetic field while the discharge took place. Since the pulse of current is very brief, however, he could not expect to observe, in a single discharge, an appreciable deflection of the sluggish, slow-moving galvanometer needle. (This would be analogous to giving a large weight on the spring a single quick tap with a very light hammer.) To get around this difficulty, Faraday utilized the phenomenon of resonance, charging and discharging the Leyden jar repeatedly at regular intervals and exciting an oscillation of the needle: "During the time the needle completed its vibration in the first direction and returned, the [electrostatic] machine was worked and the jar recharged; and when the needle in vibrating resumed its first direction, the discharge was made again. By repeating this action a few times, the vibrations soon extended to above 40° on each side of the line of rest." (See also Section 25.9.)

An analogous situation, in which wave motion plays an intermediate role and replaces the direct collision associated with the tapping of a hammer, can readily be set up with two identical tuning forks: Set the forks some distance apart and strike one of them without touching the other; then put your hand on the first fork to extinguish its sound. You will now hear a weaker sound emanating from the second fork. The second fork has been set into oscillation by *resonance*, the waves of the first fork impinging upon it at its own natural frequency. Some energy was absorbed by the second fork from the passing wave, and that energy is now being reradiated in all directions.

Suppose we place a number of identical tuning forks between us and the source of a plane wave of sound having the same frequency as the forks. In principle, the intensity of the sound reaching us will be weakened as the tuning forks are excited into vibration: Each tuning fork removes some energy from the beam coming straight toward us, and although the tuning fork then reradiates this energy, it does not redirect all of it in the direction of the original beam; it radiates spherically in all directions. If the original beam contains a continuous spectrum of acoustic frequencies, it will be weakened in only that one which the forks absorb and reradiate; we would thus hear a "dark line" at this wavelength. If the sound source were cut off, we would hear a "bright line," the weaker sound of the excited tuning forks themselves.

This was the mechanical analogy that Stokes suggested as a possible approach to thinking about the origin of optical emission and absorption spectra. It was a useful and fruitful idea, but still very far removed from a specification of the nature of light waves or the mechanism of radiation and absorption of specific wavelengths by material particles. It also failed to explain the presence of lines in the emission spectrum (Fig. 27.5.1) that do not have counterparts in the absorption spectrum.

27.7 NUMEROLOGY OF LINE SPECTRA

As the power of chemical analysis through observation of spectra came to be fully appreciated, careful studies and photographs were made of the spectra of various pure substances so that they could be readily recognized and identified in unknown samples. It was soon realized that in many instances the lines of a spectrum formed orderly patterns or repeating groups. Note some of the repetitions apparent in the emission spectrum of sodium and the orderly sequence, with decreasing spacing of the lines, in the absorption spectrum (Fig. 27.5.1).

The emission spectrum of atomic hydrogen (Fig. 27.7.1) presents another striking case of an orderly sequence of lines.

As Kepler searched for numerical order in the accumulated tables of astronomical observations, so nineteenth-century investigators searched for systematic empirical relations in the spectroscopic data. If simple empirical relations could be discovered

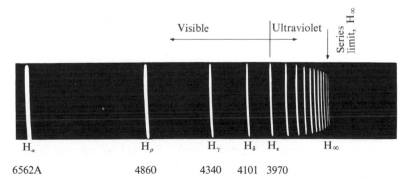

FIG. 27.7.1. Emission spectrum of atomic hydrogen in the visible and near ultraviolet (the Balmer series).

TABLE 27.7.1

COMPARISON OF WAVELENGTHS IN HYDROGEN SPECTRUM CALCULATED FROM BALMER'S
FORMULA WITH THE VALUES EXPERIMENTALLY OBSERVED BY ANGSTRÖM*

Symbol	Value of n	Wavelength, λ (A)	
		According to formula (27.7.1)	Measured by Angström
H_α	3	6562.08	6562.10
H_β	4	4860.8	4860.74
H_γ	5	4340	4340.1
H_δ	6	4010.3	4101.2

* From Balmer's paper in *Ann. Phys. Chem.*, **25,** 1885.

in the spectra, they might be the clue to new laws of light and matter, leading perhaps to another synthesis as embracing as the Newtonian one. Hydrogen attracted particular attention because of the simplicity of its visible spectrum and because the hydrogen atom, having the smallest mass among the known atoms, offered promise of the greatest simplicity in structure or behavior.

In 1885, a Swiss schoolteacher, Johann Balmer, published *A Note on the Spectrum Lines of Hydrogen.* Balmer had discovered that the wavelengths of the first four lines in the visible spectrum (Fig. 27.7.1) could be very accurately represented by the formula

$$\lambda = b \left(\frac{n^2}{n^2 - 2^2} \right), \tag{27.7.1}$$

where b is an empirically determined constant, equal to 3645.6 A, and n corresponds to the integers 3, 4, 5, 6. To illustrate the accuracy of the representation, Balmer gave the figures shown in Table 27.7.1.

PROBLEM 27.2.   Verify one or two of Balmer's calculated values. Calculate the wavelength of a possible fifth line ($n = 7$). What values of λ are obtained from formula (27.7.1) as n becomes very large? (The limit value, denoted by H_∞, is called the *series limit.*)

Balmer writes that he was initially unaware of the existence of a fifth line, but he calculated the value corresponding to $n = 7$ in his formula, obtaining $\lambda = 3969.65$ A. A friend then informed him that not only was the fifth line (in the violet) well known, but that a great many additional lines had also been detected photographically in the ultraviolet region in the spectra of certain stars. Further calculation showed that the formula predicted the wavelength of the additional lines! Because of the success of this empirical representation, the group of lines shown in Fig. 27.7.1 is called the *Balmer series.*

27.8 OTHER SERIES IN THE SPECTRUM OF HYDROGEN

In his paper, Balmer remarked that

> "None of the hydrogen lines which correspond to the formula when [2^2 is replaced by 3^2, 4^2, etc.] and which may be called lines of the third or fourth order, are found in any spectrum as yet known; they must develop themselves under entirely new relations of temperature and pressure if they are to become perceptible."

Although there was no physical basis whatsoever to Balmer's formula, and no reason why such additional lines should exist, it is apparent that Balmer must have been deeply convinced that there was more to his formula than just numerology.

It turned out that Balmer's prediction of additional spectra was essentially correct, but that his formula had to be modified slightly to make it more general. By 1890 the Swedish physicist Johannes Rydberg had discovered a more complicated formula that was capable of describing series of lines in spectra other than that of hydrogen. For the case of the Balmer series, Rydberg's formula reduced to

$$\frac{1}{\lambda} = R_{\mathrm{H}} \left(\frac{1}{2^2} - \frac{1}{n^2} \right), \tag{27.8.1}$$

where $n = 3, 4, 5 \ldots$ and, according to modern measurements, $R_{\mathrm{H}} = 109{,}677.58$ cm^{-1}. The symbol R_{H} is called the Rydberg constant for hydrogen. (If λ is measured in centimeters, the quantity $1/\lambda$ represents the number of waves per centimeter, and is called the wave number.)

PROBLEM 27.3. Show that Eq. (27.8.1) follows from algebraic rearrangement of (27.7.1) if R_{H} is set equal to $2^2/b$.

PROBLEM 27.4. Suppose that hydrogen spectral series exist for which 2^2 in formula (27.8.1) is replaced by 1^2 and by 3^2. Calculate the wavelength of the first line and of the series limit in each case, and indicate the region of the spectrum in which each series should be looked for.

With formula (27.8.1), Balmer's suggestion of replacing 2^2 by the squares of the other integers gives formulas such as

$$\frac{1}{\lambda} = R_{\mathrm{H}} \left(\frac{1}{1^2} - \frac{1}{n^2} \right); \quad n = 2, 3, 4, \ldots,$$

$$\frac{1}{\lambda} = R_{\mathrm{H}} \left(\frac{1}{3^2} - \frac{1}{n^2} \right); \quad n = 4, 5, 6, \ldots,$$

and so forth. We can accord this scheme a general representation in the form

$$\frac{1}{\lambda} = R_{\mathrm{H}} \left(\frac{1}{n_f^2} - \frac{1}{n_i^2} \right), \tag{27.8.2}$$

where n_f can be given specific integer values, and n_i then takes on values of $n_f + 1$, $n_f + 2, n_f + 3, \ldots$.

In researches beginning in 1906, Theodore Lyman at Harvard discovered a series of lines in the far ultraviolet spectrum of hydrogen corresponding to the case $n_f = 1$. In 1908, F. Paschen in Germany reported a series in the infrared corresponding to $n_f = 3$. Additional series in the far infrared, corresponding to $n_f = 4$ and 5, were observed by Brackett and by Pfund in 1922 and 1924, respectively.

> PROBLEM 27.5.   Map out a wavelength scale to run from about 10^5 to 10^3 A, and shade in the regions between the first line and the series limit of various hydrogen series we have mentioned above.   Determine what is wrong with Balmer's original formula [Eq. (27.7.1)]; in what way does it fail to coincide with the experimental data for series other than the Balmer series?

The existence of the additional series of lines in the spectrum of hydrogen, describable by an identical formula with just a change of integers, would have delighted a Platonist like Galileo.   The discovery of related formulas describing more complex spectral series of other elements and the appearance of the Rydberg constant in all these equations all combined to point to the probability of some common physical basis for the emission and absorption of light by gases.

Poincaré once wrote that "Science is built up with facts, as a house is with stones. But a collection of facts is no more science than a heap of stones is a house." We have outlined a large collection of facts that were accumulated during the nineteenth century concerning the behavior of light and its interaction with matter.   An understanding of these facts—the capacity to rationalize and predict them in a theoretical structure, based on concepts and ideas that one would accept as fundamental— still remained to be achieved, but it was becoming quite clear that theories which would successfully organize this heap of stones into a house would constitute a major scientific development, and would inevitably yield an insight into both the nature of light and the structure of matter deeper than any which had hitherto been attained.

A parallel situation exists at the present time in the area of knowledge concerning high-energy physics and elementary particles.   Facts are being rapidly accumulated, but the facts are puzzling and are not unified and understood in terms of existing physical theories.   Physicists are scrutinizing the observed discrete spectra of the masses of so-called elementary particles, trying, like Kepler and Balmer, to discover numerical relations in the empirical data, and hoping that such relations will be the keys to a higher theoretical synthesis.

In the case of the data concerning the behavior of light, the quest for order and understanding gave birth in the twentieth century to the new sciences of atomic physics and quantum mechanics.   Our story moves in this direction, but we must first return to follow another crucial part of the interlocking sequence: the theory of the transmission of electric and magnetic influences through space.

27.9   MAXWELL

James Clerk Maxwell (1831–79) was born in Edinburgh in the year of Faraday's discovery of electromagnetic induction (Fig. 27.9.1). He studied at Trinity College, Cambridge, maturing during the years that saw the development of the law of conservation of energy, terrestrial determination of the velocity of light, the triumph of the atomic-molecular theory of the constitution of matter, rapid growth of the science of spectroscopy, and many important discoveries in electricity and magnetism. He held a deep veneration for Faraday, and made a careful study of the latter's *Experimental Researches* before embarking on his own theoretical investigation.

Fig. 27.9.1. James Clerk Maxwell (1831–1879).

During his most productive years, from 1856 to about 1870, Maxwell published an important paper on the stability of the rings of Saturn, developed a theory of color, and made contributions to the kinetic theory of gases and to the new science of thermodynamics that alone would have made his name famous among future generations of scientists. In his theory of the electromagnetic field, however, he produced a synthesis that rivals Newton's, incorporating in one elegant, symmetrical system of differential equations all that is known concerning light, electricity, and magnetism on the macroscopic scale of ordinary experience.

This theory, like Newton's, has been found inadequate to the description of phenomena on an atomic and subatomic scale, but the range of validity of the two syntheses is equally broad. Together, as "classical physics," they form the most powerful and complete mathematical description of macroscopic mechanics and electromagnetism that natural philosophy has produced. The theories of relativity and quantum mechanics, formulations that deal successfully with the realm of extremely high velocities and the microscopic structure of matter, were carefully designed to reduce to the theories of Newton and Maxwell in the limit of low velocities and macroscopic dimensions.

In 1873 Maxwell summarized his electrical researches in the publication of his famous *Treatise on Electricity and Magnetism*. From 1871 until his untimely death at the age of forty-eight in 1879, he was professor of experimental physics at Cambridge, and the first director of the newly established Cavendish Laboratory, in the founding of which he himself had played a significant role. The Cavendish Laboratory was destined to become one of the most important centers of research contributing to the evolution of modern atomic physics.

27.10 FIELDS IN THE ABSENCE OF CONDUCTORS

Maxwell's concern with the propagation of electric and magnetic influences through space was not new. Speculation on such matters dated at least from Descartes, and in the nineteenth century prominent theoretical physicists and mathematicians such as Gauss, Riemann, Weber, F. Neumann, Helmholtz, Kirchhoff, and William Thomson (Lord Kelvin) made various contributions with incomplete success. Unsuccessful work is not necessarily fruitless, however: the preliminary mathematical explorations, discussions, and attempts at formulation all combined to clarify many issues regarding correct and proper ways of converting experimental information contained in Coulomb's law, Oersted's discovery, Faraday's law of induction, Ohm's law, etc., into mathematical statements about quantities such as E and B at position x at time t.

Strongly influenced by previous mathematical work and inspired by Faraday's intuitive speculations about lines of force and the role of an intervening medium in electromagnetic phenomena, Maxwell proceeded to rewrite and reinterpret the mathematical statements.

Faraday's law of induction [Eq. (25.10.2), with N taken equal to 1],

$$\varepsilon = \oint \mathbf{E}_c \cdot ds = -\frac{d\Phi_B}{dt},\qquad (27.10.1)$$

was based on measurements of current induced *within* a *conductor* when the total magnetic flux is changed through the conducting loop. Maxwell conceived the idea that an electrical field may *always* be induced around a region of varying magnetic flux (in accordance with the left-hand rule, indicated by the minus sign), even in a vacuum and regardless of whether or not a loop of wire happens to be present. The conducting loop, he held, simply acts as a detector and *reveals* the presence of a circulating electrical field because charge is free to move within the conductor.

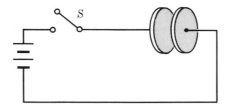

FIG. 27.10.1. When switch S is closed, pulse of current flows through circuit as capacitor is charged. Wires are surrounded by magnetic field while current is flowing. Is region between capacitor plates similarly surrounded by a magnetic field? If so, can this field be related to an equivalent current between the capacitor plates as the magnetic field around a wire is related to current in the wire?

According to Maxwell's conjecture, Eq. (27.10.1) would be applicable in any region in empty space. The integral on the left-hand side is to be taken around any arbitrarily chosen closed loop in empty space, and the symbol Φ_B on the right-hand side refers to the total magnetic flux passing through this loop.

Given the conjecture that a varying magnetic flux is always surrounded by an induced electrical field, one might be led to wonder about the inverse effect: Is a varying electrical flux surrounded by an induced magnetic field? We already know from Oersted's work that a current-carrying conductor *is* surrounded by a magnetic field. What must happen, then, in the vicinity of a capacitor as it is being charged by a battery (Fig. 27.10.1)*?

As the capacitor is charged, the electrical field between the plates increases from zero to

$$E = \frac{4\pi k_E q}{A}. \tag{27.10.2}$$

[See Section 24.2 and Eq. (24.2.3).] The expression k_E denotes the constant appearing in Coulomb's law. We have introduced the subscript E to emphasize that this is the constant associated with electrical force and to distinguish it from the magnetic constant k_M of Eq. (23.8.2).

Maxwell suggested that, while the electrical field is changing, the capacitor is surrounded by a magnetic field just as are the wires carrying the pulse of current, and extended this idea to the broader conjecture that a varying electrical field will *always* be surrounded by an induced magnetic field, even in a vacuum, in regions far removed from the immediate influence of moving charges.

The next step is to formulate this hypothesis algebraically, and one might anticipate the development of an equation analogous to Faraday's law [Equation (27.10.1)], an equation that describes a *magnetic* field looped around a changing *electrical* flux.

27.11 AMPÈRE'S LAW

To formulate the hypothesis enunciated at the end of the preceding section, let us return to what we know about the magnetic field surrounding an electric current. We learned that the magnetic lines of force have the circular pattern shown around wire 1 in Fig. 27.11.1, and we associate a magnetic induction $\mathbf{B}_1$ with each position in the field. Thus a second wire, oriented parallel to the first and carrying current I_2, would experience a force per unit length given by

$$\frac{F_2}{L_2} = B_1 I_2, \tag{27.11.1}$$

in accordance with the basic relation $F = BIL_\perp$, [Eq. (24.5.2]. But we have the

---

* In raising this question and proposing an answer, Maxwell was motivated by problems of continuity of the electrical system and the proper mathematical form of the descriptive equations. We are here somewhat oversimplifying the discussion by stripping it of its mathematical sophistication.

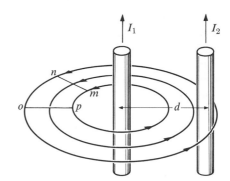

FIG. 27.11.1. Wire 2, carrying current I_2, is placed in magnetic field B_1 of wire 1. (Magnetic field shown in the diagram is that due to wire 1 alone.) Wire 2 is subjected to a force per unit length F_2/L_2.

additional relation, based on Eq. (23.8.1):

$$\frac{F_2}{L_2} = k_M \frac{I_1 I_2}{d}, \tag{27.11.2}$$

which we used in defining the ampere, assigning k_M a value of exactly 2×10^{-7} in vacuum.

Comparing Eqs. (27.11.1) and (27.11.2), we note that the magnetic field around wire 1 must be given by the expression:

$$B_1 = \frac{k_M I_1}{d}. \tag{27.11.3}$$

For the general case of the magnetic field around a straight wire carrying current I, we would simply drop the subscripts. From the symmetry of the problem, it is apparent that at a distance d from a long, straight wire, the magnetic induction $\mathbf{B}$ must lie in the plane perpendicular to the wire and be tangent to the circle of radius d. The magnitude of $\mathbf{B}$ is the same everywhere on this circle and is determined by relation (27.11.3).

Let us evaluate the "circulation" of the magnetic field, $\oint \mathbf{B}_c \cdot ds$, around a closed loop enclosing the wire. The simplest loop to take is a circle of radius d, since the component $\mathbf{B}_c$ in the direction of displacement is equal to $\mathbf{B}$ itself, and $|\mathbf{B}| = k_M(I/d)$ is constant all the way around. Making use of Eq. (27.11.3), and taking displacements in the direction of $\mathbf{B}$, defined by the right-hand rule,

$$\oint \mathbf{B}_c \cdot ds = \oint k_M \frac{I}{d} \, ds = k_M \frac{I}{d} \oint ds. \tag{27.11.4}$$

Since the limit of the sum of displacements represented by $\oint ds$ is simply the circumference of the circle, $2\pi d$, the final result is

$$\oint \mathbf{B}_c \cdot ds = k_M \frac{I}{d} \cdot 2\pi d = 2\pi k_M I \quad \text{or} \quad \oint \mathbf{B}_c \cdot ds = (4\pi \cdot 10^{-7})I, \tag{27.11.5}$$

where I is the current flowing *through* the loop. Currents outside the loop do not contribute to the integral (see Problem 27.6). The algebraic sign of our result is positive only because we elected to take displacements in the direction of $\mathbf{B}$ consistent with the right-hand rule. We shall retain the positive sign, in contrast with the negative sign in Eq. (27.10.1), to keep track of this relation among the directions involved.

Although we have tried to make Eq. (27.11.5) plausible by connecting it with the very special case of the long straight wire, it is actually a very powerful general relation, frequently referred to as Ampère's law. We have neither the time nor the space to explore and demonstrate its generality, but we can perhaps make this assertion more plausible by pointing out that Ampère's law is analogous to Faraday's law [Eq. (27.10.1)]. The induced magnetic field around a loop is determined by the total rate of flow of electrical charge through the loop, the moving charge being bound in a metallic conductor or being transported by freely moving particles in air or vacuum.

PROBLEM 27.6. Evaluate the quantity $\oint \mathbf{B}_c \cdot ds$ by carrying an integration around the loop marked *mnop* in Fig. 27.11.1. The legs *mn* and *op* lie on radial lines. Do not forget that along one of the two circular arcs displacements will be made in a direction *opposite* to that of **B**. The result of this integration is zero. This illustrates in a very simple special case the general theorem that $\oint \mathbf{B}_c \cdot ds = 0$ if the closed loop does not encircle a current.

27.12 DISPLACEMENT CURRENT

Ampère's law, as expressed in Eq. (27.11.5), contains a hint as to how we might formulate Maxwell's conjecture that a varying electrical field is surrounded by an induced magnetic field. Consider the capacitor in Fig. 27.10.1 as it is being charged at the rate dq/dt. From Eq. (27.10.2) we have the rate of change of electrical field:

$$\frac{dE}{dt} = \frac{4\pi k_E}{A} \cdot \frac{dq}{dt}.$$ (27.12.1)

Thus we might think of the rate of change of electrical field between the plates as corresponding to an "equivalent current":

$$I_{eq} \equiv \frac{dq}{dt} = \frac{A}{4\pi k_E} \frac{dE}{dt},$$ (27.12.2)

where A is the area of the plates and therefore the area over which the field strength E is changing. Noting that the product AE can be thought of as an electrical flux Φ_E, in the same sense that we thought of the product AB as a magnetic flux Φ_B, we might guess that, in general, the equivalent current corresponding to a varying electrical field is given by

$$I_{eq} \equiv \frac{1}{4\pi k_E} \cdot \frac{d\Phi_E}{dt}.$$ (27.12.3)

In order to simplify the presentation, we have not followed Maxwell's original argument, but Maxwell obtained the same result and suggested that I_{eq} must be included in Ampère's law, together with the actual conduction current I, to give a complete prediction of the induced magnetic field:

$$\oint \mathbf{B}_c \cdot ds = 2\pi k_M (I + I_{eq}) = 2\pi k_M \left(I + \frac{1}{4\pi k_E} \frac{d\Phi_E}{dt} \right). \qquad (27.12.4)$$

If the conduction current through the loop is zero and only the electric flux changes, Eq. (27.12.4) reduces to

$$\oint \mathbf{B}_c \cdot ds = \frac{2\pi k_M}{4\pi k_E} \cdot \frac{d\Phi_E}{dt} = \frac{k_M}{2k_E} \frac{d\Phi_E}{dt}. \qquad (27.12.5)$$

Note that the reasoning we have outlined is essentially *inductive* rather than deductive. There is no guarantee that the conception is valid; it will become acceptable only if it is found to "work" in explaining and predicting physical phenomena.

The quantity $(1/4\pi k_E)(d\Phi_E/dt)$ has the dimensions of current, in coulombs/second; and Maxwell called it *displacement current*. He assumed that Eq. (27.12.5) describes the magnetic field around the charging or discharging capacitor and that it also describes a magnetic field surrounding changing electrical flux in *any* region, even when remote from current-carrying conductors and moving charges. (Strictly speaking, the numerical values of the constants, $k_M = 2 \times 10^{-7}$ and $k_E = 8.99 \times 10^9$, have been given for vacuum, but their values in air are only very slightly different, negligibly so for the present context of discussion.)

Right-hand rule I still applies to Eq. (27.12.5) in the sense that when the thumb of the right hand is pointed in the direction of the changes in $\mathbf{E}$ the curl of the fingers shows the direction of the induced magnetic field. (See Fig. 27.12.1.)

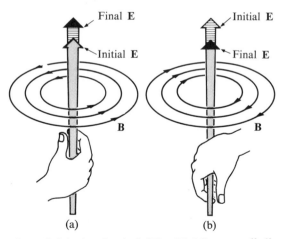

Fig. 27.12.1. Extension of right-hand rule I (Fig. 23.5.2) to recall direction of magnetic field induced around a displacement current (changing electrical field). (a) While electrical field is directed upward and is *increasing* in strength, $d\mathbf{E}/dt$ is directed *upward*, and magnetic field $\mathbf{B}$ circulates around the electrical field in direction shown. (b) While electrical field is directed upward and is *decreasing* in strength, $d\mathbf{E}/dt$ is directed *downward*, and magnetic field $\mathbf{B}$ circulates around the electrical field in direction shown.

There being no experimental basis or evidence to support the invention of the concept of displacement current, this was the boldest and most imaginative of Maxwell's conjectures. It was also the one that most sharply distinguished his theory from other contemporary attempts at a synthesis of electromagnetism. The delay in acceptance of Maxwell's work was in large measure due to doubts concerning this strange new concept.

In subsequent years, as theoretical physicists began to lay increasing stress on the symmetries that come to be revealed in mathematical formulations of natural laws, it was noticed that the equations

$$\oint \mathbf{E}_c \cdot ds = - \frac{d\Phi_B}{dt} , \qquad (27.10.1)$$

$$\oint \mathbf{B}_c \cdot ds = \frac{k_M}{2k_E} \frac{d\Phi_E}{dt} , \qquad (27.12.5)$$

are neatly symmetrical in the inverse effects they describe, and that this symmetry disappears if the displacement current is not included. Oliver Heaviside, the British physicist and electrical engineer who applied Maxwell's theory to a wide range of physical problems and did much to make it better understood by his contemporaries, was among the first to emphasize the significance of the symmetry, but Maxwell himself never invoked this particular argument in support of his revolutionary idea.

27.13   THE CONSTANT $2k_F/k_M$

The combination $2k_E/k_M$, appearing in Eq. (27.12.5), turns out to have surprisingly simple dimensions and a very interesting numerical value.

The dimensions of k_E can be determined from Coulomb's law:

$$k_E = \frac{Fr^2}{q_1 q_2} ; \qquad \text{dimensions:} \quad \frac{\text{n·m}^2}{\text{coul}^2} .$$

The dimensions of k_M can be determined from the force law between parallel wires [Eq. (23.8.2)]:

$$k_M = \frac{Fd}{LI^2} ; \qquad \text{dimensions:} \quad \frac{\text{n·m·sec}^2}{\text{m·coul}^2} = \frac{\text{n·sec}^2}{\text{coul}^2} .$$

The dimensions of k_E/k_M are then

$$\frac{\text{n·m}^2}{\text{coul}^2} \cdot \frac{\text{coul}^2}{\text{n·sec}^2} = \frac{\text{m}^2}{\text{sec}^2} .$$

Therefore the dimensions of $2k_E/k_M$ are those of velocity squared, and $\sqrt{2k_E/k_M}$ has the dimensions of velocity. Using the presently accepted numerical values of the constants:

$$\sqrt{\frac{2k_E}{k_M}} = \sqrt{\frac{2(9.00)(10^9)}{2(10^{-7})}} = \sqrt{9.00(10^{16})} = 3.00 \times 10^8 \text{ m/sec.}$$

In 1856, Weber and Kohlrausch performed a series of laboratory measurements in which they effectively determined the numerical value of $\sqrt{2k_E/k_M}$,* obtaining the result 3.1×10^8 m/sec. Kirchhoff pointed out the identity (within experimental uncertainty) of this value with that of the known velocity of light in vacuum.

It is extremely unlikely that results of this kind are a matter of pure coincidence. Here was another indication of an intimate connection between light and electricity. An explanation of the connection lay in Maxwell's theory.

27.14   ELECTROMAGNETIC WAVES

Maxwell introduced the concept of displacement current in 1861, in the second of his sequence of three papers on electromagnetic theory. In this paper he went on to show that when Faraday's law and the generalized form of Ampère's law [Eqs. (27.10.1) and (27.12.5)] are rewritten in the form of differential equations and solved simultaneously to describe $\mathbf{E}$ and $\mathbf{B}$ separately as functions of position and time, the final result is a differential equation that has exactly the same algebraic form as the differential equations describing deflections of a string, deflections of a water surface, or pressure variations in the air as functions of position and time.

In other words, Maxwell's results implied that if one created an appropriate disturbance (variations of $\mathbf{E}$ and $\mathbf{B}$) at some position in space, variations in $\mathbf{E}$ and $\mathbf{B}$ would propagate from this boundary or region of disturbance outward through the vacuum, just as ripples propagate away from the vibrating bar in a ripple tank or sound waves from the vibrating tuning fork.

Furthermore, Maxwell's results showed that the disturbance must propagate with a velocity $V = \sqrt{2k_E/k_M}$ and that the variations in $\mathbf{E}$ and $\mathbf{B}$ must be directed transversely (at right angles) to the local direction of propagation.

The only really correct way of obtaining these results is to perform the mathematical analysis and interpret the equations. Such a treatment, however, is beyond the scope of the present text, and we shall adopt a far less rigorous approach—one that becomes possible only in retrospect, after the correct answers have been established by more advanced methods, but nevertheless one that gives us some modest insight into the implications of the theory.

27.15   ELECTRIC FIELD ASSOCIATED WITH MOVING MAGNETIC DISTURBANCE

Without inquiring how we would generate such a pulse, let us suppose that a uniform magnetic field B_{0z} is set up in the region to the left of x_0, as shown in Fig. 27.15.1(a). The field forms a front of unlimited extent in the y-versus-z plane; the effect to the right of x_0 is still zero. We now assume that this front will propagate in

---

* They were not thinking in terms of the language and symbols we have adopted in our discussion, but were comparing units of charge defined electrostatically by Coulomb's law, with units of charge defined electrodynamically in terms of the interaction between current carrying conductors. The quantity involved, however, is identical with the one we have denoted by $\sqrt{2k_E/k_M}$.

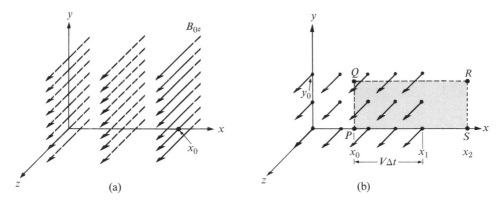

Fig. 27.15.1. (a) Uniform magnetic field B_{0z} parallel to z-axis and of indefinite extent in yz-plane. Edge of plane wave advances at velocity V in the x-direction into the initially undisturbed region. (b) In time interval Δt, edge of plane wave advances from x_0 to x_1, a distance $V \Delta t$. (To simplify the diagram, only a few B-vectors associated with points in the xy-plane are shown.)

the x-direction at some velocity V just as a kink in a stretched string or a compression in the air would propagate into the undisturbed region ahead. (This is what we also assume, without rigorous proof that the disturbance must propagate, in the treatment of sound waves and waves on strings in Appendix F.)

Let us pursue the consequences of this assumption· In a time interval Δt, the edge of the region of magnetic field would advance from x_0 to x_1, a distance $V \Delta t$ (Fig. 27.15.1b). During this time interval the magnetic flux through the loop $PQRS$ must have increased, the magnetic field having been initially zero and then having taken on the positive value B_{0z} in part of the loop, and, in accordance with Faraday's law, an electrical field and EMF, $\varepsilon = \oint \mathbf{E}_c \cdot d\mathbf{s}$ must be induced clockwise around the loop. We have deliberately taken the right-hand leg of the loop, RS, well to the right of the advancing front, so that no disturbance can have reached this region. Let us calculate $\oint \mathbf{E}_c \cdot d\mathbf{s}$ step by step around $PQRS$ in the clockwise direction:

$$\text{Along } PQ: \int_0^{y_0} E_{0y} \, dy = E_{0y} y_0. \qquad (27.15.1)$$

Since we have assumed the magnetic field to be completely uniform throughout the yz-plane, all points along PQ are subjected to identical effects as the disturbance propagates to the right. Therefore the induced field E_{0y} should be the same at all points along PQ, and we have used this constancy of E_{0y} in evaluating the integral in Eq. (27.15.1).

Along RS the contribution to our total integral is zero, since this leg is well to the right of the advancing disturbance.

Along the legs QR and SP, we would have to calculate the contribution of any induced x-components of electrical field E_x. The complete mathematical analysis in Maxwell's theory rigorously indicates that these contributions are zero because

$E_x = 0$ in a wave front perpendicular to the x-axis; i.e., the induced electrical field associated with the B_{0z} disturbance has *only* the transverse component E_{0y}, and has *zero* longitudinal components. In our present treatment, we might argue (somewhat less rigorously) that even if the E_x components were not zero, they would have to be equal and in the same direction along the legs QR and SP because B_{0z} does not vary in the y-direction. Because of this symmetry, there should be no difference between any effects occurring at corresponding positions along these two legs. Then, since in carrying out our integration clockwise around the loop we traverse the two legs QR and SP in opposite directions, the contributions to the total integral must cancel each other.

We therefore conclude that the total cyclic integral $\oint \mathbf{E}_c \cdot ds$ around $PQRS$ must be $E_{0y}y_0$, as given by Eq. (27.15.1).

At the beginning of the time interval Δt, the magnetic flux Φ_B through $PQRS$ was zero, and at the end of the time interval it is $\Phi_B = B_{0z}(y_0 V \Delta t)$, since the flux now occupies the area $y_0 V \Delta t$. Therefore the rate at which the flux is changing is given by:

$$\frac{d\Phi_B}{dt} = B_{0z}y_0 V. \tag{27.15.2}$$

Applying Faraday's law [Eq. (27.10.1)], and dropping the minus sign because we have carried out our integration in the clockwise direction as demanded for a positive result by the left-hand rule, we obtain

$$E_{0y}y_0 = B_{0z}y_0 V,$$

$$E_{0y} = B_{0z}V. \tag{27.15.3}$$

Since this result is independent of the position x_1 to which the wave front has advanced, we find that the uniform, induced electrical field E_{0y} is associated with all positions enveloped by the advancing uniform disturbance B_{0z}. If B_{0z} is directed in the positive z-direction, as shown in Fig. 27.15.1, the induced electrical field E_{0y} must be directed in the positive y-direction.

27.16   MAGNETIC FIELD ASSOCIATED WITH MOVING ELECTRICAL DISTURBANCE

The results of the preceding section imply that a uniform electrical field E_{0y} accompanies the advancing magnetic disturbance B_{0z}. Let us examine the consequences associated with the advance of this uniform electrical disturbance (Fig. 27.16.1).

We note that in the time interval Δt the electrical flux through the loop $PTUS$ has increased, and, in accordance with the concept of displacement current, a circulation of the magnetic field $\oint \mathbf{B}_c \cdot ds$ must have been induced around the loop in the direction indicated by the sequence of letters $PTUS$. By arguments exactly parallel to those used in the preceding section, we note that the contribution to this integral along the leg US must be zero, and that the contributions along TU and SP must cancel each other. (The latter contributions are actually zero *separately*, since the rigorous analysis shows that $B_x = 0$ just as $E_x = 0$.)

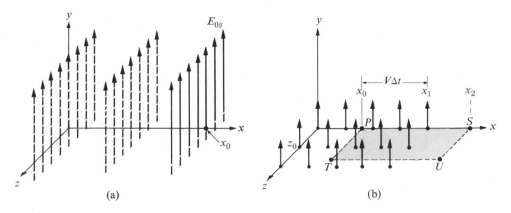

FIG. 27.16.1. (a) Uniform electrical field E_{0y} parallel to y-axis and of indefinite extent in yz-plane. Edge of plane wave advances at velocity V in the x-direction into the initially undisturbed region. (b) In time interval Δt, edge of plane wave advances from x_0 to x_1, a distance $V \Delta t$. (To simplify the diagram, only a few E-vectors associated with points in the xz-plane are shown.)

Thus the only contribution to the integral derives from the leg PT:

$$\int_0^{z_0} B'_{0z} \, dz = B'_{0z} z_0, \tag{27.16.1}$$

where B'_{0z} denotes the uniform magnetic field induced along the leg PT and accompanying the uniform electric field E_{0y}.

From an argument exactly parallel to that which yielded eq. (27.15.2), the rate of change of electrical flux Φ_E through loop $PTUS$ is given by

$$\frac{d\Phi_E}{dt} = E_{0y} z_0 V. \tag{27.16.2}$$

Applying Maxwell's generalized form of Ampère's law [Eq. (27.12.5)], we obtain

$$B'_{0z} z_0 = \frac{k_M}{2k_E} E_{0y} z_0 V,$$

$$B'_{0z} = \frac{k_M}{2k_E} \cdot E_{0y} V. \tag{27.16.3}$$

27.17 VELOCITY OF AN ELECTROMAGNETIC PULSE

From our application of Maxwell's equations to the propagating disturbance, we have obtained two relations

$$E_{0y} = B_{0z} V, \tag{27.15.3}$$

$$B'_{0z} = \frac{k_M}{2k_E} E_{0y} V. \tag{27.16.3}$$

We now interpret these as representing one unified effect: The leading edge of the magnetic disturbance B_{0z} propagates into an initially unperturbed region, inducing an associated electrical field E_{0y}. The leading edge of the induced field, E_{0y}, propagates into the undisturbed region, regenerating a magnetic field B'_{0z} in the same direction as the original magnetic field which started the sequence. Visualizing these self-sustaining effects to comprise a stable pulse, at the edge of which a total magnetic field B_{0z} is associated with a total electric field E_{0y}, we identify B'_{0z} with B_{0z} and simply write Eq. (27.16.3) in the form

$$ B_{0z} = \frac{k_M}{2k_E} E_{0y} V. \tag{27.17.1}$$

This gives us two simultaneous equations in the quantities E_{0y}, B_{0z}, and V. If we substitute (27.15.3) into (27.17.1), we obtain

$$ B_{0z} = \frac{k_M}{2k_E}(B_{0z}V)V, \qquad V^2 = \frac{2k_E}{k_M}, $$

$$ V = \sqrt{2k_E/k_M} = 3.00 \times 10^8 \text{ m/sec}. \tag{26.17.2}$$

Thus, subject to the validity of our model and the interpretations we have imposed, the quantity $\sqrt{2k_E/k_M}$ does indeed turn out to be a propagation velocity, as surmised in Section 27.13. It is the propagation velocity of what Maxwell called an "electromagnetic" wave in vacuum. The wave is called electromagnetic because it consists of *interdependent* changes in electric and magnetic fields propagating together. Since we now know V in terms of fundamental constants, Eq. (27.15.3) gives us the relation between the two fields associated with the pulse:

$$ \frac{E_{0y}}{B_{0z}} = V. \tag{27.17.3}$$

27.18   GENERATION OF ELECTROMAGNETIC WAVES

Although the preceding analysis has been far from rigorous or complete, it does give us some feeling for the nature of Maxwell's results and some useful qualitative insights into various important phenomena. Let us ask ourselves, for example, how a propagating electromagnetic wave might be generated: What electromagnetic effect corresponds to the plucking of a string or the vibrating of a tuning fork?

A wire, oriented vertically as shown in Fig. 27.18.1, and carrying a steady current I, will be surrounded by a magnetic field that decreases in intensity with increasing radial distance from the wire but that does not vary with time. No pulses or waves propagate under these circumstances; i.e., when electric charges move at uniform velocity. If we start with zero current and zero field, however, and abruptly increase the current to the value I in the downward direction, an electromagnetic pulse, similar to that discussed in Sections 27.15 and 27.16, will be propagated outward. If we vary the current in the wire sinusoidally with time at frequency ν, a train of sinusoidal waves of the same frequency will be emitted, as sketched in Fig. 27.18.1. The wavelength of this train will be given by $\lambda = \nu/V$.

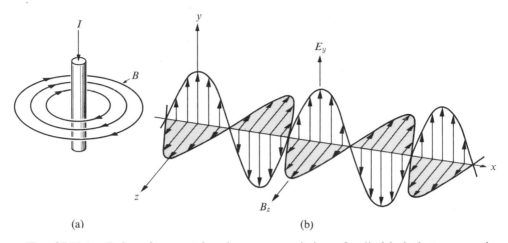

(a)   (b)

FIG. 27.18.1.   Pulse of current in wire causes emission of cylindrical electromagnetic pulse, propagating radially outward from the wire. Sinusoidal variation of current in the wire causes emission of sinusoidal wave train, as sketched in (b). To simplify the diagram, sinusoidal variations in E and B are shown only along a single radial line, indicated by the x-axis; the wave fronts are actually coaxial cylindrical surfaces, with the wire as a common axis. The electromagnetic wave is polarized, with all E-vectors parallel to the wire and all B-vectors lying in planes perpendicular to the wire. A radio transmitting antenna emits radio waves in essentially this fashion.

The electromagnetic wave illustrated in Fig. 27.18.1 is polarized, just as the vibration of a string is polarized when it is confined to a single plane. In Fig. 27.18.1 the magnetic vector varies sinusoidally in the z-direction (that is, in the x-z plane) while the electric vector is confined to variation in the x-y plane.

Thus we see that a source of electromagnetic waves, an analog to the vibrating tuning fork, must be an oscillating current—a system in which electrical charge is accelerated, either in a transient fashion to produce a pulse or periodically to produce a continuous periodic wave train. Since moving electrical charges are surrounded by magnetic fields whether the charge is bound within a metallic conductor or transported by freely moving particles in empty space, the theory suggests that electromagnetic waves will be emitted whenever electrical charge is accelerated, regardless of whether or not it is confined within conducting wires.

Thus Maxwell's theory unequivocally answered the questions that Faraday considered so important and found so perplexing. Changes in electric and magnetic forces should indeed be propagated from one region to another in finite time, and the velocity of propagation should be 3.00×10^8 m/sec, as given by

$$\sqrt{2k_E/k_M}.$$

Furthermore, Maxwell showed that one can think of energy as being stored in any region of space in which there exist electric and magnetic fields, and that electromagnetic waves transport energy outward from a source just as do water ripples or sound waves. Hence we speak of electromagnetic radiation of energy in the same sense that we speak of acoustic radiation. If such radiation is absorbed by matter, it should cause an increase in temperature.

Since energy is radiated outward in the electromagnetic wave, an oscillating electrical charge will lose energy, just as the tuning fork loses energy, and the oscillation will die down unless work is supplied to maintain the oscillation at a fixed amplitude.

The theory indicates that electromagnetic waves transport momentum as well as energy. This implies that they must exert pressure on surfaces at which they are absorbed, and twice this pressure if the wave is reflected (analogous to inelastic and elastic collisions, respectively).

Thus the theory implies that both energy and momentum are conserved in electromagnetic phenomena. When electric charges are accelerated at some point, forces on distant charges do not change immediately through an action at a distance in which the charges exert equal and opposite forces on each other instant by instant. Rather, momentum is conserved by propagation through the intervening region, and this propagation is associated with variations in electric and magnetic field strengths, just as propagation of momentum and energy in a sound wave is associated with variations of density (compressions and rarefactions) in the material through which the sound wave passes.

According to the conceptual model being constructed, electromagnetic waves emitted by an alternating current in a wire (as in Fig. 27.18.1) should be detectable. If we take another wire, part of a conducting circuit, and place it parallel to the first, the vertically directed variations in electrical field E_{0y} in the passing wave will exert forces on electric charge in the second wire and cause an alternating current to flow in the circuit of which it is a part. (In such circumstances the first wire is called a transmitting and the second a receiving antenna, and the reader should recognize that we have given a highly simplified description of the transmission and reception of radio waves.)

27.19   ELECTROMAGNETIC WAVES AND LIGHT

Maxwell did not hesitate to interpret his results as indicating that light must be an electromagnetic wave. Pointing to the predicted wave velocity, $V = \sqrt{2k_E/k_M} = 3.00 \times 10^8$ m/sec, he wrote:

> "This velocity is so nearly that of light, that it seems we have strong reason to conclude that light itself (including radiant heat and other radiations if any) is an electromagnetic disturbance in the form of waves propagated through the electromagnetic field according to electromagnetic laws."

The supporting evidence was also strong: Qualitatively, the theory explained the association of light with electric sparks and other electrical phenomena. It gave an explicit statement of precisely what might be "waving" in the previously undefined wave model of Young and Fresnel. It showed that electromagnetic waves were inherently *transverse* and therefore capable of polarization (as illustrated in Fig. 27.18.1). This could dispel the doubts of those who, like Newton, could not see how light could possibly have "sides."

This evidence supported the hypothesis that light consisted of high-frequency electromagnetic waves, emitted by rapidly oscillating electrical charges present in material substances. Here was a starting point for models and speculations concerning interactions among light, matter, and electricity that could conceivably lead to an explanation of the highly specific and organized powers of emission and absorption exhibited in the discrete line spectra of gases and an insight into the detailed microscopic structure of such substances.

But Maxwell's theory is mathematically complex and sophisticated; the field concept represented a revolutionary departure from conventional nineteenth-century action-at-a-distance interpretations of the by then almost sacrosanct Newtonian theory; the notion of displacement current was new and unfamiliar. Few physicists grasped the full import of Maxwell's theoretical formulations, and direct experimental confirmations of his predictions concerning electromagnetic waves were not achieved until 8 years after his death and 25 years after the first publication of his theory.

27.20 EXPERIMENTAL CONFIRMATION OF THE ELECTROMAGNETIC THEORY

In the nineteenth century, before the invention of vacuum tubes and the birth of electronic technology, there was no readily available way of exciting an alternating current of sufficiently high frequency to cause a wire to emit detectable electromagnetic waves, as suggested in Fig. 27.18.1. In 1887, however, the young physicist Heinrich Hertz (1857–1894) seized upon what was known about electric sparks that occurred between the terminals of an induction (or "spark") coil—a device frequently used to produce high potential differences and maintain electrical discharge in gases at low pressure.

It had been observed that when an induction coil produced intermittent sparks in air, the sparks themselves were oscillatory, implying a motion of charge back and forth between the terminals. Hertz saw this oscillation as a possible mechanism for the generation of electromagnetic waves.

As a detector he tried a "receiver" made of a piece of wire with spherical terminals at each end. The wire was bent into a circle with the terminals fairly close together. A passing electromagnetic wave should induce an electrical field, exerting forces on electrical charge in the wire. If the induced effects are sufficiently strong, a spark should jump across the terminals.

Hertz found that this system worked. Not only could he detect electromagnetic waves qualitatively by observing the spark in his receiver at distances of many meters from the induction coil, but he showed that the waves were reflected by metallic conductors, that they could be focused by a concave metallic mirror, that they could be refracted in passing through nonconducting materials. He estimated the frequency

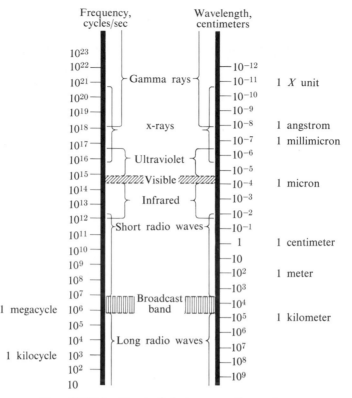

FIG. 27.20.1. Chart of electromagnetic spectrum.

of his source to be about 3×10^7 cycles/sec and determined that the waves had a wavelength of about 10 m. This gave a velocity of propagation of about $(3 \times 10^7)(10) = 3 \times 10^8$ m/sec!

Here was a direct demonstration of the generation of electromagnetic waves of a particular frequency and wavelength, produced at will by causing the oscillation of electrical charges. There was no reason why the electromagnetic spectrum should not include all wavelengths, from the very low to the very high. Visible light, embracing a very small region of short wavelengths, would be that part of the continuous spectrum capable of producing the chemical effects at the retina that excite the sense of sight (just as the restricted range of acoustic frequencies between about 50 and 20,000 cycles/sec is capable of exciting the sensation of sound). Infrared and ultraviolet radiations would take their place in the electromagnetic spectrum on either side of the visible, etc.

A schematic diagram of the electromagnetic spectrum is shown in Fig. 27.20.1. Modern electronic techniques have made it possible to generate, detect, and explore almost the entire range of wavelengths longer than about one millimeter. The discovery of X-rays and gamma rays extended knowledge of the spectrum beyond the ultraviolet.

Hertz's experiments made an immediate impact and led to rapid acceptance and appreciation of Maxwell's synthesis.   The theory was taken up by mathematical physicists and applied to detailed analysis of a vast range of phenomena—the details of reflection and refraction at conducting and nonconducting interfaces, the mechanism of polarization, the transport of energy, the effect of magnetic fields in rotating the plane of polarization of light—all with dramatic success.

In 1899, Lebedev in Russia and in 1901, Nichols and Hull in the United States, supplied another important experimental confirmation.   Using mirrors and sensitive torsion balance techniques in very high vacua (to eliminate complicated effects due to heating in the presence of gases), they succeeded in showing that light did indeed exert measurable pressure on a mirror from which it was reflected and that this pressure, a function of the intensity of the incident light, was equal to the value predicted by Maxwell.

By the beginning of the twentieth century, Maxwell's electromagnetic theory stood on a par with Newton's among enunciations of fundamental laws of physics.   It was disappointing, perhaps, to have two separate descriptions—one for mechanics and gravitation and another for electromagnetism.   But theoreticians could dream of an ultimate unification of the theories, and, in the meantime, experimentalists could search for more concrete evidence of the Maxwellian ether, in which electric and magnetic field variations were propagated at the velocity of light and through which the earth and solar system must be flying on their course through interstellar space.

Imagine how challenging and attractive this line of investigation must have been. In mechanics we have found no fundamental or "absolute" frame of reference with respect to which we can describe all forces and motions.   A frame attached to the earth allows simple description of much everyday experience, but when we consider motions profoundly influenced by the rotation of the earth (motions of satellites and of the oceans and atmosphere), we must modify the simple Newtonian equations by introducing fictitious forces associated with the rotation.   The fictitious forces can be eliminated only if we detach our frame of reference from the earth and fix it with respect to the "fixed" stars, but in what sense are these stars themselves fixed?   The chain of questioning is obviously endless, yet Newton had convinced himself that there must exist an "absolute space" with respect to which the equations of mechanics would always take their simplest form, a space that would constitute an absolute frame of reference for the description of dynamical phenomena, even though he could not specify how this space was to be identified.

Then the Maxwellian synthesis invoked the presence of an all-pervasive ether, one that has numerical properties k_E and k_M, a medium that carries electromagnetic waves by contiguous action from one "layer" to the next at velocity 3.00×10^8 m/sec, a medium with respect to which one should measure the velocity of moving charges, a frame of reference with respect to which Maxwell's equations, the laws of electricity and magnetism, appear to take their fundamental form.

Nineteenth-century experience, with its ever-deepening perception of unity in nature, invited the exciting conjecture that the ether of electromagnetic theory might also constitute the basic frame of reference for the laws of mechanics, and men would certainly have been willing to characterize so fundamental a frame as in some sense absolute. Attempts to detect the motion of the earth relative to the ether were made repeatedly by skillful experimenters. The failure of all these experiments laid the groundwork for understanding the profound limitations of both Newtonian mechanics and electromagnetic theory, precipitating the conceptual revolution that we call the Theory of Relativity. (See Chapter 36 for a continuation of this discussion.)

27.21 PROBLEMS

27.7. It has been remarked that lines well known in terrestrial and solar spectra are found in the spectra of distant stars, making it possible to draw inferences concerning the chemical composition of the latter. It is frequently observed that in certain stars within our galaxy the lines are displaced or shifted slightly to shorter wavelengths than those observed for the same lines in the laboratory. For other stars the shift may be toward longer wavelengths. For light coming from other galaxies, the shift is always found to be toward longer wavelengths (the "red shift"), and is systematically larger the more distant the galaxy. Interpret these observations in terms of the discussion given for sound waves in Section 22.8. What do you infer from the facts that have been stated? How would you go about computing the velocity of a star or galaxy relative to us?

27.8. Neglecting the fact that the pulse emitted when the current in the wire of Fig. 27.18.1 is abruptly increased from zero to a final value I is cylindrical rather than plane, Figs. 27.15.1 and 27.16.1 give a reasonably adequate sketch of the propagation of this pulse into the initially undisturbed surroundings. Suppose now that we start with a steady current I in the wire and a steady magnetic field B established around it. The circuit is broken, and the current in the

wire drops abruptly to zero. Sketch diagrams similar to 27.15.1 and 27.16.1, illustrating the propagation outward of the pulse that drops all the surrounding field values to zero.

27.9. Examine the sinusoidal wave illustrated in Fig. 27.18.1 and verify whether or not the directions of the E and B vectors are correctly indicated and consistent with the analysis carried out in the preceding sections. Which parts of the sinusoid were emitted when the current in the wire was flowing upward, and which were emitted when it was flowing downward?

27.10. In terms of the concepts of electromagnetic waves and the energy radiated with them, describe what must happen if a charged particle is set into very rapid oscillation. (Visualize it as a small mass on a very stiff spring, executing an oscillation of very small amplitude.) Sketch the wave that would be emitted, and describe what would happen to the kinetic and potential energy of the particle and to the amplitude of the oscillation as time went by. What would determine the frequency of the emitted wave? In an exactly parallel fashion, discuss the behavior that would be expected in the case of a charged particle set into circular motion around a stationary charged particle, as in Problem 18.18.

SUPPLEMENTARY READING AND STUDY

On spectra:

Foundations of Modern Physical Science, G. Holton and D. H. D. Roller. Reading, Mass.: Addison-Wesley, 1958, Chapter 33

Source Book in Physics, W. F. Magie. New York: McGraw-Hill, 1935, pages 354–365

A History of the Theories of Aether and Electricity, E. T. Whittaker. New York: Harper Torchbook TB 531, 1960, Chapter 12

Physics, the Pioneer Science, L. W. Taylor. Boston: Houghton Mifflin, 1941; New York: Dover Publications, 1959, Chapter 37

On Maxwell:

Physics, the Pioneer Science, op. cit., Chapter 50

The Edge of Objectivity, C. C. Gillispie. Princeton, N. J.: Princeton University Press, 1960, pages 458–492

"Electromagnetic Waves in an Introductory Physics Course," H. Y. Carr and R. L. Sells. *Am. J. Phys.*, **28,** 727–732 (1960)

Resource Letter FC-1 on Evolution of the Electromagnetic Field Concept, W. T. Scott. *Am. J. Phys.*, **31,** 819 (1963)

CHAPTER 28

Atomic-Molecular Theory I:

FROM PHILOSOPHICAL ATOMISM TO QUANTITATIVE SCIENCE

28.1 THE ATOMISM OF DEMOCRITUS

Motivated by a desire to reduce the multiplicity and apparent disorder of nature to simplicity and intelligibility, trying to imagine how phenomena that transcended their senses might be operating, the earliest Greek philosophers addressed themselves to questions such as: What is matter? In what characteristics reside the identities of various material substances and what are the essential differences among them? What is the explanation of material changes that are everywhere apparent to the senses —changes associated with combustion, with evaporation and solution, with growth and decay? Is there a limit to which a material substance can be subdivided without obliterating its identity?

One response to these queries lay in the conception of the four qualitatively different primordial elements—earth, water, air, and fire—the composition of which, in different proportions, led to the formation of other material substances. (See the brief description of Greek science in Chapter 2.) In this tradition, outlined by Empedocles (*c.* 490–430 B.C.) and elaborated in great philosophical detail by Aristotle, change was explained teleologically in terms of the natural goals and tendencies of the elements commingling in material systems.

A radically different tradition originated with Leucippus and was elaborated in considerable logical detail by Democritus* (*c.* 460–370 B.C.) of Abdera in Thrace.

Democritus visualized all substance to consist of indivisible (Greek word *atomos*) entities or "atoms." Atoms he assumed to be qualitatively identical and distinguishable from each other only in the geometrical properties of size and shape. Any object evident to the senses is composed of many atoms, individual atoms being

---

* None of Democritus' works have survived, and our knowledge of his thought comes primarily from Aristotle, who quoted Democritus in order to attack his doctrine, and from Epicurus and Lucretius, who embraced the doctrine and made it basic to their respective philosophies.

so small as to transcend sense perception. To make change intelligible, Democritus seized on the concept of local motion and proposed that change in a thing is based on change of position of atoms. He visualized motion as a primitive, intrinsic atomic property, and, in order that atoms could be separate entities and also have room in which to move, he assumed the existence of a *void:* "By convention there is sweet; by convention there is bitter; by convention there is warm and by convention there is cold; by convention there is color. But in sooth there are atoms and the void," he is quoted as saying.

Like the system of Aristotle, the theory of Democritus was an attempt to present nature as a complete, self-contained whole. By their combinations and movements, atoms produced the infinite complexity of the universe, accounting not only for objective physical phenomena but psychical, mental, and spiritual as well.

28.2 ATOMISM AND ATHEISM

Impelled by belief that a sound system of philosophy could relieve at least some measure of human misery by freeing men from superstitious fears, Epicurus (340–270 B.C.) and the Roman poet Lucretius (*c.* 100–50 B.C.) incorporated the atomism of Democritus into a system of ethics—a moral and religious scheme in which nature, freed from the omens and taboos of organized religions of the time, was to be accepted in her majesty and beauty, without gratuitous attributions of vindictiveness and caprice.

But although neither Epicurus nor Lucretius denied the existence of the gods, the theory of Democritus was essentially atheistic in character because its basic argument dispensed with the *necessity* of God as creator and molder of substance and change. Atoms were conceived to be permanent and indestructible; their combinations and motions could produce infinite variety—the earth, the stars, and living beings. The soul was thought to consist of more subtle atoms, very mobile, round, and polished. Thoughts which traverse the mind are movements of component atoms. In this completely self-sufficient picture of nature, the world may have arisen by chance. Mind and soul and emotion are explained in purely materialistic terms. It is not necessary to postulate a Creator.

While Aristotle's teleological physics and philosophy could be, and were, reconciled with Christian dogma and incorporated into the teachings of the church, it is understandable that the concepts of Democritus as transmitted by Epicurus and Lucretius were anathema to Christian doctrine. Reflecting the attitudes of his time, Dante places Democritus among the ancient sages in the first circle of the Inferno, and refers to him as one "who ascribes the world to chance." Until well into the seventeenth century, "atomism," in the eyes of scholars and philosophers, connoted an essentially materialistic, atheistic belief.

It must be emphasized that divergence between the traditions of Aristotle and Democritus lay in different attitudes toward the nature of process and change, toward the origin and character of natural and spiritual phenomena, rather than in disagreement concerning the corpuscular structure of matter or limits of its subdivisibility.

The human mind has always found the concepts of continuity and infinity to be among the most difficult and subtle ideas it encounters (witness the long and complicated intellectual struggle surrounding continuity and infinity in the development of the concepts of "number" in arithmetic and of "function" and "limit" in the calculus), and very few philosophers found a tenable position in a view that matter is continuous and infinitely divisible. Aristotle believed that the elements consisted of "minima" or ultimate particles, but in his teleological philosophy, built around vague universal notions of forms and qualities, he did not find it necessary to elaborate the properties and behavior of the particles as Democritus and the Epicureans were impelled to do, and he rejected the concept of the void and therefore of the essential *separateness* of the particles.

28.3 ATOMISM IN THE SEVENTEENTH CENTURY

With the advent of the scientific revolution in the seventeenth century, with the gradual sharpening of scientific questions coupled with conscious restriction of their scope, natural philosophers addressed themselves more explicitly to inquiry concerning the nature of physical and chemical change: What happens when a solid expands on heating? when water is evaporated? when acid eats away a metal? What is the essential difference between matter that is solid and matter that is gaseous? And in facing these questions they began to find a corpuscular model increasingly useful in visualizing and explaining various phenomena. Evaporation and condensation of water, as well as changes in density of solids, were, with increasing frequency, described in terms of increasing or decreasing separation of constituent corpuscles.

Descartes, who like the Aristotelians refused to accept the conception of an absolute vacuum, populated his plenum with particles of equal size in constant circular motion. The "grinding" of the particles against each other generated fine spherical particles and filled the interstices with still more finely ground "splinter matter." These two classes of subtle particles provided a "relative vacuum" for a third class of coarser, slower particles that possessed appreciable inertia and that, in aggregation, exhibited the properties of gross matter.

In 1649 the Catholic priest and natural philosopher Peter Gassendi (1592–1665) published a treatise that embraced the Epicurean doctrine of atoms, expurgating its atheistic connotations by asserting that atoms were not eternal, but created by God. Gassendi then invoked a simile that reappears frequently in discussions of atomism:

> "As letters are the elements of writing and from letters are formed first syllables, and then successively words, phrases, and speeches, so also atoms are the elements of all things. From the atoms the smallest molecules are joined together first, and then successively somewhat bigger ones, still bigger ones, the finest and the coarsest bodies, and finally the biggest bodies."

The major figures among the seventeenth-century English scientists—Boyle, Hooke, and Newton—were all convinced atomists. In his *Opticks*, Newton allowed himself speculations that he had carefully avoided in the *Principia:*

> "It seems probable to me that God in the beginning form'd matter in solid, massy, hard, impenetrable, movable particles, of such sizes and figures and with such other properties, and in such proportion to space, as most conduced to the end for which he form'd them; and that these primitive particles being solids, are incomparably harder than any porous bodies compounded of them; even so very hard, as never to wear or break in pieces; no ordinary power being able to divide what God himself made one in the first creation. . . . And therefore, that nature may be lasting, the changes of corporeal things are to be placed only in the various separations and new associations of these permanent particles. . . .
>
> "Now by the help of these principles, all material things seem to have been composed of the hard and solid particles above mention'd, variously associated in the first creation by the counsel of an intelligent agent. For it became him who created them to set them in order. And if he did so, it's unphilosophical to seek for any other origin of the world, or to pretend that it might arise out of a chaos by the mere laws of nature: *though being once form'd, it may continue by those laws for many ages.*" [Italics ours.]

It is apparent that, like Gassendi, Newton was concerned with dispelling the cloud of atheistic materialism associated with the atomic doctrine, and with making it theologically more acceptable to his contemporaries. Note also how he articulates the mechanistic view that became so widely accepted in the eighteenth century: The Deity creates the initial mechanism, which then runs for ages, without tinkering or attention, governed by the mathematical laws of gravity, force, and motion.

28.4 THE CONCEPT OF ELEMENT

As chemistry arose out of alchemy during the seventeenth and eighteenth centuries, researchers became more explicitly conscious of what it meant to recognize, identify, and name a material substance. Boyle gives a virtually modern operational account:

> "If you ask a man what gold is, if he cannot shew you a piece of gold, . . . he will describe it to you as a body that is extremely ponderous, very malleable and ductile, fusible and yet fixed in the fire, and of a yellowish color; and if you offer to put off to him a piece of brass for a piece of gold, he will presently refuse it, and . . . tell you, that though your brass be colored like it, it is not so heavy nor so malleable, neither will it like gold resist the utmost brunt of the fire, or resist aqua fortis. And if you ask men what is meant by a ruby, or nitre, or a pearl, they will still make you [similar] answers. . . ."

The science of biology began with taxonomy (systematic description and *classification* of forms and species of plants and animals), facilitating identification and recognition of particular specimens and the perception of broad biological relation-ships. Similarly, chemistry began with qualitative description, identification, and classification of material substances, and the way was prepared for discovery of quantitative relationships, far from obvious on casual observation.

Identification of chemical substances required increasingly precise physical meas-urements of weights, volumes, and temperatures, leading to more accurate determi-nations of densities, melting and boiling points, and quantities of material participating in chemical changes. It is understandable that chemists drew eagerly on improved physical techniques and frequently contributed to instrumental development and improvement.

With improved ability to recognize and classify substances and to produce desired results in specific chemical reactions, with acceptance of the impossibility of chemical transmutation of baser metals into gold, came the sober recognition that the four elements of Aristotle provided no help in organizing chemical knowledge or in reveal-ing connections and relationships among changing material substances. The concept of "element," however, was too suggestive and attractive to be abandoned; it was gradually redefined. As early as 1661, Robert Boyle had written in the *Sceptical Chymist:*

> ". . . I now mean by elements . . . certain primitive and simple, or perfectly unmingled bodies; which not being made of any other bodies, or of one another, are the ingredients of which all those call'd perfectly mixed bodies are immediately compounded, and into which they are ultimately resolved. . . ."

But, with the knowledge available in his day, Boyle was not prepared to single out particular substances and support an argument that these and not others were to be recognized as elements. A century later, as the development of physics and physical techniques made it possible for Lavoisier to demonstrate the conservation of mass in many different chemical reactions, the concept of stability, immutability, and perma-nence of matter, as measured by the property "mass," became the framework for further hypotheses. Through his own discoveries and his wide knowledge of chemical reactions, Lavoisier was led to sharpen the concept of element:

> ". . . if, by the term 'elements,' we mean to express those simple indivisible atoms of which matter is composed, it is extremely probable we know nothing at all about them; but, if we apply the term 'elements' or 'principles of bodies' to express our idea of the last point which chemical analysis is capable of reach-ing, we must admit, as elements, all the substances into which we are capable, by any means, to reduce bodies by decomposition. Not that we are entitled to affirm that these substances we consider as simple may not be compounded of two, or even a greater number of principles; but, since these principles cannot be separated, or rather since we have not hitherto discovered the means of separating them, they act with regard to us as simple substances, and we ought never to suppose them compounded until experiment and observation have proved them to be so."

On the basis of this conservative definition, Lavoisier and his contemporaries in 1787 could point to specific substances to be classified as elements. The list included the common metals such as copper, zinc, iron, lead, tin, mercury, substances such as sulfur and carbon, and the newly identified gases, oxygen, nitrogen, hydrogen. The list also included the entirely hypothetical caloric fluid, and a number of substances such as salt, lime, soda, and potash that cannot be decomposed by ordinary chemical means and that awaited the discovery of electrolysis to be identified as compounds.

In this manner, water came to be recognized as a combination of the elements hydrogen and oxygen, the red powder now called mercuric oxide as a compound of the elements mercury and oxygen, and so forth.

28.5 THE LAW OF DEFINITE PROPORTIONS

During the years 1797–1807, the French chemist J. L. Proust published the results of numerous analyses of the composition (by weight) of various compound substances. Had it not been for the introduction into chemistry of accurate gravimetric (weighing) techniques and the establishment of the law of conservation of mass by Lavoisier, it is unlikely that there would have been any motivation for Proust's painstaking experiments. But the knowledge that total mass is conserved in chemical changes gave meaning to the experimental science of "gravimetric analysis"—determination of the weights of different materials reacting to form specific compounds.

Proust developed numerical evidence to show that in many substances the constituent elements are always present in a fixed ratio or definite proportion by weight, and he used this property to define what might be meant by "true compound" as opposed to ordinary "mixture":

> "... a compound ... is a privileged product to which nature assigns fixed ratios; it is, in short, a being which nature never creates even when through the agency of man, otherwise than with her balance in hand. ... Let us recognize that the properties of true compounds are invariable as is the ratio of their constituents. Between pole and pole, they are found identical in these two respects; their appearance may vary owing to the manner of aggregation, but their [chemical] properties never. No differences have yet been observed between the oxides of iron from the South and those from the North. The cinnabar of Japan is constituted according to the same ratio as that of Spain. Silver is not differently oxidized or muriated in the muriate* of Peru than in that of Siberia. ...
>
> "If we find it impossible to make an ounce of nitric acid, an oxide, a sulfide, a drop of water, in ratios other than those which nature had assigned to them from all eternity, we must recognize that there is a balance which ... regulates even in our laboratories the ratios of compounds."

Note how Proust seeks to reinforce his position by pointing to the *universality* of the relationship, the identity of properties and composition of samples of widely different

---

* The modern name is chloride.

geographic origin, and from both naturally occurring and artificial (laboratory synthesis) sources.

PROBLEM 28.1.   The red powder, mercuric oxide, with which Lavoisier performed some of his crucial experiments is formed when mercury is gently heated in the presence of oxygen. It is known to have the definite composition by weight: 92.6% mercury, 7.4% oxygen. (a) Calculate the "fixed ratio" of mercury to oxygen. How much oxygen combines with 10.0 gm of mercury? [*Answer:* 12.5; 0.80 gm.] (b) Suppose that 15.0 gm of mercury are heated in a vessel containing 11.0 gm of air (which consists of about 21% oxygen and 79% nitrogen). When the chemical reaction has been completed, what substances, and what mass of each, will be present in the vessel? [*Answer:* 16.2 gm mercuric oxide; 1.1 gm oxygen; 8.7 gm nitrogen.]

In 1801 Proust's conclusions were challenged by the eminent French chemist C. L. Berthollet (1748–1822), who pointed to numerous instances in which chemical change appeared to occur in continuously variable proportions up to some fixed maximum value. For example: sugar and salt dissolve in water in continuously variable proportions, until saturation is attained; oxygen appears to combine with copper in variable proportions, forming an indefinite series of oxides of progressively varying color.

Proust responded with careful experiments, showing that the reaction between oxygen and copper always resulted in the production of just two distinct compounds, each containing oxygen and copper in fixed proportions, and that the variability pointed to by Berthollet stemmed from a mechanical mixture containing variable amounts of the two specific compounds. Proust regarded solutions in similar terms:

"The attraction which causes sugar to dissolve in water may or may not be the same as that which makes a fixed quantity of carbon and of hydrogen react with another quantity of oxygen to form the sugar of our plants, but what we do see clearly is that these two kinds of attractions are so different in their results that it is impossible to confound them."

The controversy between Proust and Berthollet continued over a period of years, until about 1807. It served to clarify the conceptual distinction between mixtures and true chemical compounds, and was ultimately resolved in Proust's favor. The idea that chemical compounds, as opposed to mixtures, are characterized by fixed and invariable proportions of their constituents came to be generally accepted.

28.6   JOHN DALTON (1766–1844)

Among early adherents to the law of definite proportions was a Manchester teacher of mathematics and chemistry, John Dalton, the self-educated son of a poor handloom weaver. Dalton was a devoted admirer of Newton, deeply impressed with the latter's success in explaining terrestrial and celestial mechanics in terms of forces between particles, and thoroughly steeped in Newtonian atomism. Dalton trans-

FIG. 28.6.1. (a) John Dalton (1766–1844). (b) Robert Boyle (1627–1691). (c) Antoine Laurent Lavoisier (1743–1794).

formed the atomic concept from a philosophical speculation into a scientific theory—framed to explain quantitative observations, suggesting new tests and experiments, and capable of being given quantitative form through the establishment of relative masses of atomic particles.

Dalton's first scientific research was concerned with the atmosphere. He made numerous meteorological observations and published a book on this subject in 1793. His interest in the atmosphere led him to a question that had also been asked by Priestley: Why is the atmosphere vertically homogeneous, so that samples from different altitudes show the same proportions of water vapor, nitrogen, and oxygen? It was well known that these three gases, when pure, had distinctly different densities, increasing in the order listed. Why did not the fluids separate as oil from water, with the atmosphere consisting of a lowest layer of oxygen, followed by a layer of nitrogen, with a layer of water vapor floating on top?

In the *Principia*, Newton proves a theorem to the effect that *if* a gas is made up of stationary particles that mutually repel each other, with forces inversely proportional to the distances between their centers, the pressure of the *gas* is inversely proportional to the total volume; i.e., the gas obeys Boyle's law, a relation which was already well established experimentally. (See Chapter 30.)

Dalton jumped to the mistaken conclusion that Newton had *proved* that, under equilibrium conditions, gas particles are stationary and repel each other, and he proceeded to develop a model of the atmosphere on this basis. He visualized the repulsion to be provided by layers of caloric fluid surrounding individual particles. He then developed an argument to the effect that if the water, nitrogen, and oxygen were not initially uniformly mixed, the particles would repel each other with unbalanced forces and would rearrange themselves into a uniform distribution, providing the different particles were not of the same size. Several years later, in studying the solution of gases in water, he convinced himself that different gases exhibited different solubilities because of the different sizes of their constituent particles.

Dalton's reasoning was based on a variety of misconceptions and was not internally consistent. We shall not try to follow his erroneous arguments in detail, but his notions of the structure of gases and of the difference in size between different species of particles are significant because of the role they played in the evolution of the atomic theory; they directed his attention to the desirability of establishing the relative sizes and masses of atomic particles, but they later led him to reject the important hypothesis, advanced by several other investigators, that equal volumes of different gases at the same temperature and pressure contain equal numbers of particles.

28.7 DALTON'S POSTULATES

Dalton's basic work on the atomic theory seems to have been done between 1803 and 1807,* and was brought together in 1808 in his book *A New System of Chemical Philosophy*. The following excerpts summarize his postulates and objectives:

"Matter, though divisible in an extreme degree, is nevertheless not infinitely divisible. That is, there must be some point beyond which we cannot go in the division of matter. . . . I have chosen the word 'atom' to signify these ultimate particles. . . .

"If some particles of water were heavier than others, if a parcel of liquid on any occasion were constituted principally of these heavier particles, it must be supposed [that one would observe variations in density of different samples of water], a circumstance not known. Similar observations may be made on other substances. Therefore we may conclude that the ultimate particles of all homogeneous bodies are perfectly alike in weight, figure, &c. In other words, every particle of water is like every other particle of water; every particle of hydrogen is like every other particle of hydrogen, &c. . . .

"Chemical analysis and synthesis go no farther than to the separation of particles one from another, and to their reunion. No new creation or destruction of matter is within reach of chemical agency. We might as well attempt to introduce a new planet into the solar system, or to annihilate one already in existence, as to create or destroy a particle of hydrogen. All the changes we can produce consist in separating particles that are in a state of cohesion or combination, and joining those that were previously at a distance.

"In all chemical investigations, it has justly been considered an important object to ascertain the relative weights of the simples [elements] which constitute a compound. But unfortunately the enquiry has terminated here; whereas from the relative weights in the mass, the relative weights of the ultimate particles or atoms of the bodies might have been inferred, *from which their number and weight*

---

* The period in which Young published his work on the wave theory of light; the period of controversy between Proust and Berthollet; the period of growing use of the voltaic pile and the application of electrolysis in chemical research. (In 1807 Davy, by electrolysis of fused soda and potash, discovered the hitherto-unknown metallic elements sodium and potassium.)

*in various other compounds would appear, in order to assist and to guide future
investigations and to correct their results.* [Italics ours.]

"Now it is one great object of this work to shew the importance and advantage
of ascertaining the relative weights of the ultimate particles, both of simple and
compound bodies, and the number of simple elementary particles [atoms]
which constitute one compound particle [molecule]. . . ."

The last paragraph indicates Dalton's own vital, original contribution to the theory.
Instead of being diverted by considerations of shape, color, hardness, texture, he
concentrated attention on weight (or, more precisely, *mass*) as the relevant and significant property of atoms. It was this specific choice that gave the theory a quantitative
basis and made testing, prediction, and validation possible.

28.8 THE RULE OF GREATEST SIMPLICITY

In effect, Dalton's postulates denoted acceptance of the law of definite proportions
and represented an attempt to account for the observed regularity. Many materials,
such as hydrogen and oxygen, have a strong "affinity" for each other and combine
vigorously, even explosively, forming compounds that are not easily separated into
the original constituents. It is very difficult to visualize a process or mechanism in
which such substances, if they are continuous or infinitely divisible, would combine
only in fixed proportions by weight. Since they have a strong tendency to react, why
would they not merge with each other in *all* proportions? What property or mode of
behavior would determine that one or another material was in excess and cause it to
remain unused in a reaction?

Dalton's corpuscular model, however, suggests a simple and comprehensible
mechanism: Reaction between elements A and B to form a true chemical compound is
distinguished from solution or mechanical mixing by the *combination* of atoms to
form molecules. The molecules of any given compound are identical, and contain
fixed numbers of atoms of A and B, characterized by different atomic masses m_A and
m_B. If one of the elements is in excess, as illustrated in Fig. 28.8.1, the excess atoms
are left over, while the compound contains materials A and B in fixed *proportions* by
weight, regardless of how many molecules of the compound are formed.

The atomic-molecular model immediately suggests a specific question: Is it possible
to infer the *formulas* of compounds (number of atoms of each element in the molecule)
from the available chemical data? Defining the basic problem, Dalton wrote:

"If there are two [elements], A and B, which are disposed to combine, the
following is the order in which combinations may take place, begining with the
most simple: namely,

1 atom of A + 1 atom of B = 1 [molecule] of C, binary [compound AB],

1 atom of A + 2 atoms of B = 1 [molecule] of D, ternary [compound AB_2],

2 atoms of A + 1 atom of B = 1 [molecule] of E, ternary [compound A_2B],

. . . etc."

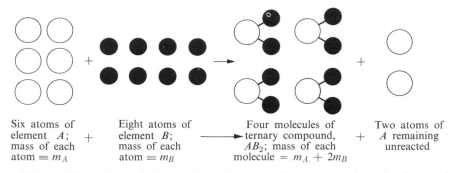

Six atoms of element A; mass of each atom $= m_A$ $+$ Eight atoms of element B; mass of each atom $= m_B$ $\longrightarrow$ Four molecules of ternary compound, AB_2; mass of each molecule $= m_A + 2m_B$ $+$ Two atoms of A remaining unreacted

FIG. 28.8.1. Illustration of chemical reaction according to atomic-molecular model, assuming that the compound formed consists of one atom of element A associated with two atoms of element B to form ternary molecule AB_2. Since element A is in excess, some of its atoms are left unreacted. The composition of the compound would have the definite proportions:

$$\text{Fraction of } A = \frac{m_A}{m_A + 2m_B}; \qquad \text{fraction of } B = \frac{2m_B}{m_A + 2m_B}.$$

Recognizing the infinite number of possibilities, yet requiring some reasonable starting point for numerical analysis and interpretation, Dalton made a bold assumption:

"The following general rules may be adopted as guides in all our investigations respecting chemical synthesis:

"1st. When only one combination of two [elements] can be obtained, it must be presumed to be the *binary* one, unless some cause appear to the contrary.

"2nd. When two combinations are observed, they must be presumed to be a *binary* and a ternary.

"3d. When three combinations are obtained, we may expect one to be a *binary* and the other two *ternary.* . . ."

In 1808 water was the only known compound of hydrogen and oxygen (hydrogen peroxide was discovered subsequently); ammonia was the only known compound of hydrogen and nitrogen. Two gaseous oxides of carbon had been identified and were named "carbonic oxide" and "carbonic acid," respectively.* Carbonic oxide was known to be the less dense of the two and was known to yield carbonic acid on burning. The compositions of these various compounds as they were known to Dalton, together with accurate modern values, are given in Table 28.8.1.

In his treatise, Dalton writes:

"From the application of these rules [quoted above] to the chemical facts already well ascertained, we deduce the following conclusions: That water is a

---

* The modern names of these compounds are carbon monoxide and carbon dioxide, respectively.

TABLE 28.8.1

COMPOSITIONS OF SEVERAL COMPOUNDS REFERRED TO BY DALTON

Name used by Dalton	Composition by weight	
	Quoted around 1808	Modern Values
Water	12% hydrogen; 88% oxygen	11.2% hydrogen; 88.8% oxygen
Ammonia	17% hydrogen; 83% nitrogen	17.8% hydrogen; 82.2% nitrogen
Carbonic oxide	44% carbon; 56% oxygen	42.9% carbon; 57.1% oxygen
Carbonic acid	28% carbon; 72% oxygen	27.3% carbon; 72.7% oxygen

binary compound [HO] of hydrogen and oxygen, and the relative weights of the two elementary atoms are as 1:7, nearly; that ammonia is a binary compound [NH] of hydrogen and azote [nitrogen], and the relative weights of the two atoms are as 1:5, nearly; . . . that carbonic oxide is a binary compound [CO], consisting of one atom of charcoal and one of oxygen, together weighing nearly 12; that carbonic acid is a ternary compound . . . consisting of one atom of charcoal and two of oxygen [CO_2], [together] weighing 19. . . . In all these cases the weights are expressed in atoms of hydrogen, each of which is denoted by unity. . . ."

PROBLEM 28.2. Analyze Dalton's conclusions in the light of the data given in Table 28.8.1. Verify his values for the relative atomic masses, including that of carbon, noting how he rounded off the final values to the nearest whole number, apparently not deeming the accuracy greater. Assuming the same formulas, revise the values in the light of the modern data. Note how sensitive the results are to relatively small errors in the composition measurements. Why is this the case? (Analyze the error algebraically in terms of the calculus of differentials developed in Section 8.12, if you are familiar with this mode of analysis.)

PROBLEM 28.3. Calculate the atomic mass of oxygen, relative to hydrogen, assuming water to be the ternary compound containing two atoms of oxygen. Make the same calculation for the ternary compound containing two atoms of hydrogen. Show algebraically that if a compound consisting of elements A and B has the formula A_xB_y, the ratio of atomic masses m_B/m_A is given in terms of the percentage composition by

$$\frac{m_B}{m_A} = \frac{x}{y} \cdot \frac{\%B}{\%A}.$$ (28.8.1)

Verify your preceding arithmetical calculations in the light of this general formula.

PROBLEM 28.4. What justification is there for taking "carbonic oxide" rather than "carbonic acid" to be the binary compound? How might you argue that the least dense compound should be the binary one? What would be the formula of carbonic oxide and the relative atomic mass of carbon if carbonic acid were assumed (erroneously) to be the binary compound? [*Answer:* C_2O, relative mass of C $= 2.5$.]

PROBLEM 28.5.   Assemble in one concise list, stated in your own words, all the basic postulates and assumptions you discern in Dalton's theory.

PROBLEM 28.6.   Accurate data on the composition of water (Table 28.8.1) indicate that very nearly 8.0 gm of oxygen combine with 1.0 gm of hydrogen. Let us denote the number of atoms in 3.0 gm of hydrogen by n. (Note that the atomic theory, at this stage of development, affords us no way of estimating the numerical value of n, although, with Dalton and his contemporaries, we would suppose it to be extremely large.) If we adopt Dalton's guess that water is the binary compound HO, what can we say about the number of atoms of oxygen in 24.0 gm of oxygen? [*Answer: n.*] About the number of molecules of water in 27.0 gm of water? [*Answer: n.*] What would the answer to these questions be if we assumed water to be the ternary compound H_2O? As a further exercise, make up a similar question about "carbonic acid." According to the modern tables, the relative masses of the atoms of hydrogen (H), carbon (C), nitrogen (N), and oxygen (O) are very nearly as 1.0, 12.0, 14.0, and 16.0. Suppose we weigh out 1.0 lb H, 12.0 lb C, 14.0 lb N, 16.0 lb O. What would these very different quantities of different substances have in common with each other?

Dalton's rule of greatest simplicity has no basis in fact and is now rejected. Although he guessed some formulas correctly (as in the case of the oxides of carbon), many of his guesses were wrong; water and ammonia, for example, are not binary compounds. Most of the entries in his original table of atomic and molecular weights relative to hydrogen are far from the now well-established values. (See Table 28.11.1.) Yet, without an audacious pioneering attempt of this variety, it is unlikely that the science would have progressed. Successful scientific developments often begin with ingenious but imperfect speculations from which the errors and inconsistencies are gradually eliminated by self-correcting processes of testing and validation, truth being eventually distilled from error. Dalton's theory makes an excellent illustration of this curious facet of the scientific enterprise.

28.9   SYMBOLS AND NOTATION

Dalton made the notable contribution of introducing a system of notation for elements, compounds, and reactions. He represented atoms of elements by circles with various symbols (such as dots, lines, and letters) inside; molecules of compounds were indicated by appropriate groupings of the circles.

Mathematical discourse would be hopelessly complicated if it were based on words alone and did not take advantage of the economy and clarity of symbols. Dalton helped bring the same economy and clarity to chemical calculation and communication of chemical information. The importance of this contribution is not diminished by the fact that his notation was somewhat cumbersome and was soon superseded; it helped motivate the simpler notation, suggested in 1813 by the Swedish chemist Jöns Jacob Berzelius (1779–1848), and still in use today.

In this system, elements are represented by letters taken from their common, or sometimes Latin, names. Molecules are represented by forms such as A_xB_y, already indicated in preceding sections; the subscripts x and y represent, respectively, the numbers of atoms of elements A and B in the molecule.

Chemical reactions are represented by equations of the form

$$xA + yB = A_xB_y \quad \text{or} \quad xA + yB \rightarrow A_xB_y.$$

For purposes of further discussion, we shall adopt the modern notation immediately, discussing even Dalton's work in this notation rather than in his own.

28.10 LAW OF MULTIPLE PROPORTIONS

Dalton's atomic model led him to examine the data already available in a new way. Where two distinct compounds of the pair of elements, A and B, were known, the theory assumed that molecules of the less-dense compound were binary, of the form

$$A\text{—}B \quad (1)$$

while molecules of the other compound possessed one of the two possible ternary forms

$$(2) \qquad\qquad (3)$$

Suppose the two forms happen to be the ones denoted by (1) and (3). The amount of B that combines with one gram of A in the definite proportions of compound (3) should then be just twice the amount of B that combines with one gram of A to form compound (1). Similarly, if the two compounds happen to be of types (1) and (2), the amount of B combining with one gram of A to form compound (2) should be just half the amount combining with one gram of A to form compound (1).

TABLE 28.10.1

COMPOSITION OF DIFFERENT COMPOUNDS OF THE SAME PAIR OF ELEMENTS

Substance		Composition by weight	
Name used by Dalton	Modern name	Quoted around 1808	Modern value
Carbonic oxide	Carbon monoxide	44% C; 56% O	42.9% C; 57.1% O
Carbonic acid	Carbon dioxide	28% C; 72% O	27.3% C; 72.7% O
Olefiant gas	Ethylene	83% C; 17% H	85.6% C; 14.4% H
Carburetted hydrogen	Methane	71% C; 29% H	74.9% C; 25.1% H

Let us illustrate this idea numerically, just as Dalton did, using the original data given in Table 28.10.1 and noting that its accuracy does not justify keeping more than two significant figures.

In "carbonic oxide":

$$1.0 \text{ gm C combines with } \tfrac{56}{44} = 1.3 \text{ gm O.}$$

In "carbonic acid":

$$1.0 \text{ gm C combines with } \tfrac{72}{28} = 2.6 \text{ gm O.}$$

Thus, for a given amount of carbon, the second compound contains just twice as much oxygen as the first.

Alternatively, we might calculate the carbon associated with a fixed amount of oxygen in each compound.

In "carbonic oxide":

$$1.0 \text{ gm O combines with } \tfrac{44}{56} = 0.79 \text{ gm C.}$$

In "carbonic acid":

$$1.0 \text{ gm O combines with } \tfrac{28}{72} = 0.39 \text{ gm C.}$$

Thus, for a given amount of oxygen, the first compound contains just twice as much carbon as the second.

PROBLEM 28.7.   Analyze the remaining data in Table 28.10.1, both old and modern values for the carbon-oxygen and carbon-hydrogen compounds, in the same way. Note that you are entitled to retain three significant figures in the modern data.

Recognizing the existence of more complex cases (such as the series of oxides of nitrogen illustrated in Table 28.10.2 below) Dalton pointed out that one would not

TABLE 28.10.2

COMPOSITION OF OXIDES OF NITROGEN (MODERN VALUES)

Substance				Composition	
Name used by Dalton	Modern name	Character and appearance at ordinary conditions of temperature and pressure	Density relative to air at same temperature and pressure	% N	% O
Nitrous gas	Nitric oxide	Colorless gas	1.03	46.7	53.2
Nitrous oxide	Nitrous oxide	Colorless gas	1.52	63.6	36.4
Nitric acid	Nitrogen dioxide	Reddish-brown gas	1.59	30.4	69.6
Oxynitric acid	Nitrogen peroxide	Bluish gas	2.14	22.6	77.4
Nitrous acid	Nitrous anhydride	Reddish-brown gas	2.62	36.9	63.1
—	Nitric anhydride	White crystalline solid	—	25.9	74.1

always expect ratios of just 2:1 in comparing pairs of compounds, but might observe ratios such as 3:1, 4:1, 3:2, 4:3, etc.; that is, ratios of *small, whole numbers*. We refer to this regularity as "the law of multiple proportions."

Prior to the publication of Dalton's theory, it had not occurred to chemists to examine the composition data in this way. The facts were there but did not speak for themselves. As L. K. Nash remarks,

"Not knowing what there was to see, diverted by a mode of percentage calculation that hid the inner harmony of their data, distracted by results that only approximated the correct values, Proust and his contemporaries held the critical data in their hands and failed to see the significance of what they 'knew.' With the advent of Dalton's atomic theory, the new beliefs it encouraged brought about a remarkable sharpening of the empiricists' vision. They were told what to look for and how to look for it—and, behold, it was there."

Dalton's prediction of the law of multiple proportions was a powerful stimulus to further investigation. With better analysis and a knowledge of what to look for, numerous additional examples were soon found, providing firm support for the law and a major triumph for the new theory.

"The [law] of multiple proportions," wrote Berzelius to Dalton in 1812, "is a mystery but for the Atomic Hypothesis, and as far as I have been able to judge, all the results so far obtained have contributed to justify the hypothesis." And Dalton, replying to Berzelius, remarked, "It [the law of multiple proportions] appears like the mystical ratios of Kepler, which Newton so happily elucidated."

PROBLEM 28.8. Because of their multiplicity, the oxides of nitrogen afforded Dalton an interesting opportunity to assign a sequence of molecular formulas and to test the law of multiple proportions. Six oxides (one of them unknown to Dalton) are listed in Table 28.10.2, together with accurate modern values of composition.

In accordance with the rule of greatest simplicity, Dalton assigned the formula NO to nitric oxide, the least-dense member of the series. It happens that this guess is correct, in the light of modern knowledge; therefore the other formulas he deduced also turn out to be correct. From the data given in the table, deduce the formulas of the remaining compounds and examine the composition data for adherence to the law of multiple proportions. In the latter examination, do not just compare all the other compounds with nitric oxide; compare arbitrarily chosen pairs and note the occurrence of ratios such as 3:2, 4:3, 5:3, etc. (Note that tables of atomic masses, such as Table 28.11.1, should *not* be used in this problem. Find the formulas by using *only* the composition data and the assumption that nitric oxide has the formula NO. *Hint:* Tabulate the amount of oxygen combining with 1.00 gm nitrogen in each case.)

PROBLEM 28.9. Starting with the compositions of the carbon-hydrogen compounds given in Table 28.10.1, calculate two or three other sets of percentage compositions that would satisfy the law of multiple proportions with respect to each other and with respect to the given compounds.

TABLE 28.11.1

RELATIVE ATOMIC MASSES

Element	Modern symbol	Dalton's value* of atomic mass (Scale H ≡ 1)	Modern value (Scale C ≡ 12)‡
Hydrogen	H	1	1.00797
Carbon	C	5	12.01115
Nitrogen	N	5	14.0067
Oxygen	O	7	15.9994
Sodium† (Natrium)	Na	—	22.9898
Aluminum†	Al	—	26.9815
Phosphorous	P	9	30.9738
Sulfur	S	13	32.064
Chlorine†	Cl	—	35.453
Iron (Ferrum)	Fe	38	55.847
Copper (Cuprum)	Cu	56	63.54
Zinc	Zn	56	65.37
Silver (Argentum)	Ag	100	107.870
Gold (Aurum)	Au	140	196.967
Mercury (Hydrargyrum)	Hg	167	200.59
Lead (Plumbum)	Pb	96	207.19
Lime**	—	23	—
Soda**	—	28	—

  * From *New System of Chemical Philosophy*, published in 1808.
  † Not known as elements when Dalton was writing his treatise.   (Sir Humphry Davy discovered sodium by electrolysis of soda in 1807.)
  ** Dalton and his contemporaries mistook these oxides of calcium and sodium as elements because they could not be decomposed by ordinary chemical means.
  ‡ The modern chemical system assigns the carbon isotope ^{12}C, a relative mass of exactly 12, giving the lightest element, hydrogen, a relative mass just slightly greater than 1.   (See Section 33.7 for details.)

28.11   MOLECULAR FORMULAS AND RELATIVE ATOMIC MASSES

Table 28.11.1 shows some of the entries appearing in one of Dalton's early tables of relative atomic masses. Presently accepted values are listed for comparison, and it is readily apparent that the rule of greatest simplicity did not lead Dalton to many correct results. Ignoring the discrepancies for the moment, however, let us work out some simple examples in order to develop a better feeling for Dalton's objective in constructing the table in the first place.* (For this purpose we shall make use of the modern data.)

───────────

  * Note Dalton's definition of his objectives in the italicized passage of the quotation given in Section 28.7.

Example 1. Establishing an unknown formula from new composition data: Suppose that we find that an oxide of iron of unknown molecular formula has a composition of 70.0% Fe and 30.0% O. Given the previously established table of atomic masses, we note (rounding off to two significant figures) that 56 gm Fe and 16 gm O contain the same numbers of atoms; let us denote this number by N_0. Now consider the combining proportions: 70 gm Fe combine with 30 gm O. Thus

$$70 \text{ gm Fe contain } \tfrac{70}{56} \cdot N_0 = 1.25 \ N_0 \text{ atoms,}$$

$$30 \text{ gm O contain } \tfrac{30}{16} \cdot N_0 = 1.88 \ N_0 \text{ atoms.}$$

The numerical ratio of atoms is

$$\frac{1.88 N_0}{1.25 N_0} = 1.50 = \frac{3}{2}.$$

That is, the compound contains three oxygen atoms for every two iron atoms. Therefore the simplest formula would be Fe_2O_3, although any formula such as Fe_4O_6, Fe_6O_9, etc., would satisfy the arithmetical conditions.

Example 2. Calculating amounts of material to be used or produced in chemical reactions: It is known that mercury and chlorine combine to form mercuric chloride (corrosive sublimate), a salt having the molecular formula $HgCl_2$ (white powder, poisonous if ingested, vaporizes at 302°C). In symbols we write $Hg + 2Cl \rightarrow HgCl_2$. (Note the convention of writing chemical reactions so that they are balanced; the number of atoms of *each element* is made equal on either side of the "equation" in order to provide a visible accounting of all particles, in accordance with the law of conservation of mass.) Suppose that we wish to calculate the amount of mercury that would react with 10.0 gm chlorine and the amount of mercuric chloride that would be formed. According to the table, 35.5 gm Cl and 201 gm Hg contain the same number of atoms, N_0. The reaction therefore informs us that $2(35.5) = 71.0$ gm Cl combine with 201 gm Hg, producing 272 gm $HgCl_2$. Then:

$$10.0 \text{ gm Cl would combine with } 10.0 \times \tfrac{201}{71} = 28.3 \text{ gm Hg,}$$

$$10.0 \text{ gm Cl would produce } 10.0 \times \tfrac{272}{71} = 38.3 \text{ gm } HgCl_2.$$

To check the calculation, we note that 28.3 gm Hg + 10.0 gm chlorine = 38.3 gm of the compound, agreeing with the second number calculated above.

Dalton's fundamental objective was to systematize the quantitative aspects of chemistry, making calculations and predictions, such as those we have just illustrated, possible. He was aware that his table contained errors and contradictions, because he encountered various inconsistencies that could not be blamed on errors in the available gravimetric analyses. He did not regard the rule of greatest simplicity as being above suspicion, remarking:

"After all, it must be allowed to be possible that water may be a ternary compound. In this case, if two atoms of hydrogen unite with one of oxygen, then an atom of oxygen must weigh 14 times as much as one of hydrogen. . . ."

Dalton was unable to find a sounder, more objective basis for the selection of molecular formulas, but further progress of the theory rested on the necessity of discovering just such a basis. As we shall see in the next chapter, resolution of the puzzle came through additional factual information, gained from study of the chemical behavior of gases.

PROBLEM 28.10.   Given the percentage compositions by weight of the following two compounds:

Compound A: 32.4% sodium; 22.5% sulfur; 45.1% oxygen,

Compound B: 43.7% phosphorous; 56.3% oxygen.

Using the concepts illustrated in Example 1 above, and explaining all steps of the reasoning in your own words, determine the simplest molecular formulas that can be assigned to these compounds in the light of the modern atomic mass data of Table 28.11.1.

PROBLEM 28.11.   Carbon, having a strong tendency to combine with oxygen, can in many cases be used to "reduce" metallic oxides to the pure metal. For example, copper oxide, having the molecular formula CuO, might be heated with carbon, resulting in the formation of free metallic copper and the liberation of carbon dioxide gas, CO_2. Translate this verbal statement into a balanced chemical reaction. Calculate the amount of carbon that must be supplied to reduce 25 kg of copper oxide, and the amount of copper metal that would result. Explain all steps of the arithmetic in your own words.

SUPPLEMENTARY READING AND STUDY

On atomism before the nineteenth century:
De Rerum Natura (The Nature of the Universe), Lucretius. Baltimore: Penguin Books, L18, 1960
   Essay on Atomism, L. L. Whyte. Middletown, Conn.: Wesleyan University Press, 1961
   From Atomos to Atom, A. G. Van Melsen. New York: Harper Torchbook TB517, 1960
   The Architecture of Matter, S. Toulmin and J. Goodfield. New York: Harper & Row, 1962

For textbook presentations of the laws of definite and multiple proportions and of the atomic-molecular concepts, see references listed at the end of Chapter 29.

Atomic–Molecular Theory II:

MOLECULAR FORMULAS AND ATOMIC MASSES

29.1 CHEMICAL REACTIONS BETWEEN GASES; THE LAW OF COMBINING VOLUMES

During the first years of the nineteenth century, while Dalton was developing and publishing his atomic theory, substantial progress was being made in laboratory techniques for preparing, purifying, containing, and measuring different gases. In 1809, a young French chemist, Joseph Gay-Lussac (1778–1850), who was associated with the group surrounding Berthollet, published a memoir in which he set forth his "intention to make known some new properties of gases, the effects of which are regular, by showing that these substances combine amongst themselves in very simple proportions, and that the contraction of volume which they experience on combination also follows a regular law."

Together with the famous naturalist, Alexander von Humboldt, Gay-Lussac had performed experiments on the formation of water vapor by passing sparks through mixtures of hydrogen and oxygen. In these experiments they had observed that, for any given volume of oxygen completely utilized in the reaction, exactly *twice* this volume of hydrogen was required (the measurements were so precise that they pointed to a ratio of two to one, within an accuracy of the order of 0.1%!). The volume of water vapor produced, when recalculated to the same temperature and pressure that obtained before the reaction, was found to be equal to that of the hydrogen utilized. Putting this verbal statement in a shorter form, we can write:

2 volumes hydrogen + 1 volume oxygen → 2 volumes water vapor,

all volumes being measured at the same temperature and pressure.

Not only did the experiments reveal a law of definite proportions by *volume*; they indicated that the reacting and resulting volumes themselves bore small whole-number ratios to each other. Gay-Lussac was strongly impressed by the regularity; Galileo was neither the first nor the last scientist to be fascinated by the occurrence of integers in quantitative descriptions of natural phenomena.

Gay-Lussac proceeded to investigate volume relations in other gas reactions, and also recomputed on a volume basis the gravimetric data on gas reactions previously

TABLE 29.1.1

GAY-LUSSAC'S SUMMARY OF VOLUME RELATIONS IN A NUMBER
OF REACTIONS BETWEEN GASEOUS SUBSTANCES

2 volumes hydrogen + 1 volume oxygen → 2 volumes water vapor	(1)
3 volumes hydrogen + 1 volume nitrogen → 2 volumes ammonia gas	(2)
2 volumes sulfur dioxide + 1 volume oxygen → sulfur trioxide (solid)	(3)
1 volume ammonia + 1 volume hydrochloric acid gas → ammonium chloride (solid)	(4)
2 volumes carbon monoxide gas + 1 volume oxygen → 2 volumes carbon dioxide gas	(5)
1 volume nitrogen + 1 volume oxygen → 2 volumes nitric oxide gas	(6)
1 volume oxygen + carbon (solid) → 2 volumes carbon monoxide gas	(7)

reported by other investigators. Among the results assembled in his paper (but stated in more cumbersome tables) are those summarized in Table 29.1.1.

In reporting the results, Gay-Lussac rounded them off to the integer values; in only a few instances was the evidence as precise as that in the hydrogen-oxygen reaction. In some cases such as the oxides of nitrogen, rather difficult to work with experimentally, the indicated ratios departed from integer values by as much as 6 or 8%. Gay-Lussac, being deeply convinced of the correctness of his insight, chose to ignore such discrepancies, assuming them to stem from experimental uncertainties, just as Dalton ignored similar discrepancies in developing his table of atomic masses and in assuming the general validity of the laws of definite and multiple proportions.

Summarizing his view of the significance of the data, Gay-Lussac enunciated a law of combining volumes.

"Thus it appears evident to me that gases combine in the simplest proportions [by volume] when they act on one another.... In all the preceding examples the ratio of combination is 1 to 1, 1 to 2, or 1 to 3. It is very important to observe in considering weights that there is no simple [integral] relation between the elements of any one compound; it is only when there is a second compound between the same elements that the new proportion of the element that has been added is a multiple of the first quantity. [Gay-Lussac was already fully aware of the work of Dalton and others on the law of multiple proportions, work that had become available only during the preceding year.] Gases, on the contrary, in whatever proportions they may combine, always give rise to compounds whose [constituents] by volume are [integral] multiples of each other.

"Not only, however, do gases combine in very simple proportions ... but the apparent contraction of volume which they experience on combination has *also* a simple relation to the volume of the gases. . . .

"These ratios by volume are not observed with solid or liquid substances, nor when we consider weights, and they form a new proof that it is only in the gaseous state that substances are in the same circumstances and obey regular laws."

Gay-Lussac simply presented his results and refrained from explicit interpretation of their significance, although at first glance one would be impelled to regard them as providing strong evidence in favor of Dalton's theory. Gay-Lussac was aware of the work of Proust and Dalton and referred to both these men in his paper. Being beholden, however, to Berthollet who was his senior and his patron, and being appreciative of various sound and important aspects of Berthollet's work, Gay-Lussac was inclined to be cautious.

PROBLEM 29.1.   In what sense does the law of combining volumes seem to lend support to Dalton's theory? How would you be inclined to interpret the significance of the small whole numbers in Gay-Lussac's data? If the volume of a gas at a given temperature and pressure is directly related to the number of particles present, what seems to be implied concerning the number of particles present in equal volumes of different gases? Interpreted in this light, what does the two-to-one ratio in the hydrogen-oxygen reaction suggest concerning the binary or ternary character of the water molecule?

29.2 DALTON'S REJECTION OF THE LAW OF COMBINING VOLUMES

The suggestion that equal volumes of different gases at the same temperature and pressure might contain equal numbers of particles was not new, having been first proposed by Bernoulli as early as the 1750's. Later it had been advanced to account for the identical behavior of different gases in response to changes in temperature and pressure. It was implicit in the thinking of many scientists who accounted for the striking differences between the gaseous state on the one hand and the solid and liquid states on the other by supposing the constituent particles to have become so widely separated in gases that they exerted negligible influence on each other. Dalton was invoking this idea (at least in rough approximation) when he decided that the least dense of all gases, hydrogen, must have the lightest atoms and when he selected the less dense of two gases, "carbonic oxide" and "carbonic acid," as the binary compound with the simpler, lighter molecules.

Gay-Lussac's law of combining volumes would seem to support the view that equal volumes of gases contain equal numbers of particles, thus accounting for the definite proportions and simple numerical ratios of reacting volumes. This in turn appears to be very favorable to the atomic-molecular theory; but Dalton, when he became aware of Gay-Lussac's paper, rejected the results completely.

The conception that, in gases, molecular size was negligible and equal volumes contained equal numbers of particles conflicted with his (erroneous) explanation of the homogeneity of the atmosphere, an explanation that depended on the assumption that the different sizes of oxygen, nitrogen, and water molecules were responsible for the uniform mixing of these constituents in the atmosphere (see Section 28.6).

More cogently, he pointed to the hydrogen-oxygen reaction. Water vapor was well known to be considerably less dense than oxygen. If equal volumes contain equal numbers of particles, how, asked Dalton, can hydrogen atoms be *added* to oxygen, producing water molecules of higher mass than the mass of oxygen atoms alone, and still yield a compound less dense than oxygen? (Recall that Dalton's thinking was controlled by one of the basic assumptions of his theory: namely, that the fundamental particles of all elements consist of individual, unassociated atoms.)

With respect to the reaction

1 volume nitrogen $+$ 1 volume oxygen $\rightarrow$ 2 volumes nitric oxide gas,

Dalton raised the question: If equal volumes contain equal numbers of particles, how can one atom of oxygen combine with one atom of nitrogen to form *two* molecules of nitric oxide?

These various contradictions weighed very heavily with Dalton, and he refused to accept the implications of Gay-Lussac's results. To bolster his view he pointed to the various departures from integral ratios appearing in Gay-Lussac's data and argued that these departures must be significant, while at the same time he was perfectly willing to ascribe to experimental uncertainty much more glaring discrepancies in his own calculations. Thus Dalton and Gay-Lussac differed in their evaluation of what constituted major fact and minor error in the same set of data.

Again we have an illustration that numerical data do not necessarily speak unequivocally for themselves. They must frequently be *interpreted* in the light of various uncertainties, and in the context of some framework of theory or hypothesis. Equally honest and objective scientists may accord the same data radically different interpretations by approaching the information from different theoretical frames of reference and with different presuppositions. Even the *uncertainties* in the data may be interpreted in different ways. When the interpretations carry social or political consequences (as they frequently do today in such instances, for example, as the assessment of the effect on human beings of atmospheric contamination from atomic bomb tests) the disagreements are likely to be strongly intensified.

29.3 AVOGADRO'S HYPOTHESIS

A very ingenious attempt to reconcile conflicting views and rationalize the apparent contradictions in the chemical data was made in 1811 by Amedeo Avogadro (1776–1856), professor of physics at Turin.

Avogadro was anxious to preserve the simple and attractive "equal volumes–equal numbers" hypothesis and showed that this might be done by relaxing Dalton's assumption that the "particles" in which elements occur consist exclusively of individual atoms.

Reexamining each one of Dalton's calculations, he pointed out, for example, that the nitric oxide reaction [(6) in Table 29.1.1] might be easily explained if one supposed that both nitrogen and oxygen gases consist of "particles" or molecules composed of two atoms each; i.e., having the formulas N_2 and O_2, respectively. Then, if the chemical combination of the particles N_2 and O_2 broke up into separate molecules NO instead of remaining in the form N_2O_2, one would obtain two molecules of nitric oxide from each pair of nitrogen and oxygen molecules, resolving the contradiction that appeared insuperable to Dalton. Let us depict Avogadro's suggestion graphically, according to the diagram at the top of the opposite page.

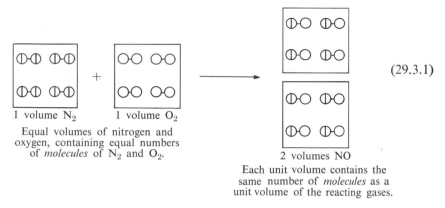

1 volume N$_2$ 1 volume O$_2$

Equal volumes of nitrogen and
oxygen, containing equal numbers
of *molecules* of N$_2$ and O$_2$.

2 volumes NO

Each unit volume contains the
same number of *molecules* as a
unit volume of the reacting gases.

(29.3.1)

In the case of the hydrogen-oxygen reaction, Avogadro pointed out that the
two-to-one ratio implies that water is the ternary compound H$_2$O (rather than the
binary HO as assumed by Dalton) and that Gay-Lussac's volume ratios could be
accounted for by assuming that hydrogen and oxygen gases both consist of diatomic
molecules:

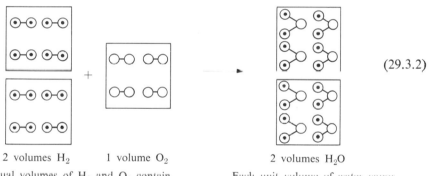

2 volumes H$_2$ 1 volume O$_2$

Equal volumes of H$_2$ and O$_2$ contain
equal numbers of diatomic molecules.

2 volumes H$_2$O

Each unit volume of water vapor
contains as many molecules as are
present in equal volumes of either
hydrogen or oxygen.

(29.3.2)

Of course, the hydrogen-oxygen reaction could also be explained if one assumed
hydrogen to be monatomic, oxygen diatomic, and water to have the formula HO in
accordance with the following representation:

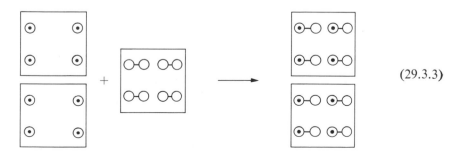

(29.3.3)

But taking hydrogen to be monatomic would give results inconsistent with the ammonia reaction:

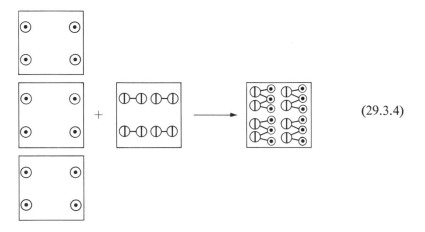

(29.3.4)

Nitrogen was already taken as diatomic, to explain reaction (29.3.1). The only way in which three volumes of monatomic hydrogen could react completely with one volume of diatomic nitrogen to form identical molecules would be through the formation of N_2H_3, as shown in Eq. (29.3.4), but only *one* volume of this compound would be formed, corresponding to the one volume of nitrogen. The predicted volume ratios would agree with Gay-Lussac's results, however, if both hydrogen and nitrogen are taken to consist of diatomic molecules:

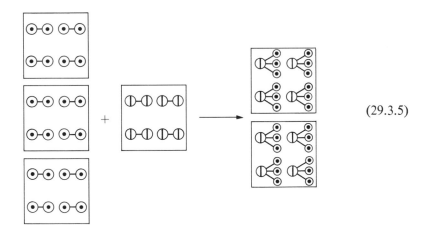

(29.3.5)

Avogadro's assumption that the molecules of the gaseous elements were diatomic was motivated at least in part by a regularity he noted in reactions such as those summarized in Table 29.1.1: "On reviewing the various compound gases most generally known, I only find examples of *duplication* of the volume relative to the volume of that one of the constituents which combines with one or more volumes of the other."

Note the effect that Avogadro's hypothesis has on the vocabulary referring to the number of "particles" in a given volume of gas. Assuming oxygen to be diatomic as Avogadro suggests, a volume that contains a total of N atoms will contain $N/2$ *molecules*. The same volume of ammonia gas will contain the same number, $N/2$ *molecules* of ammonia. Since each molecule of ammonia contains four atoms (one nitrogen and three hydrogen), this volume of ammonia will contain a total of $2N$ atoms. Thus equal volumes of different gases at the same temperature and pressure are *not* assumed to contain equal numbers of atoms. The "equal volumes–equal numbers" hypothesis refers to *molecules*, even when dealing with elements rather than compounds.

Avogadro's hypothesis makes it possible to select molecular formulas for water and other compounds on a somewhat more objective basis than Dalton's rule of greatest simplicity. Choice of a formula, in turn, makes possible the calculation of relative atomic masses from the gravimetric data.

PROBLEM 29.2.   Return to the gravimetric data of Table 28.8.1 and add the composition of nitric oxide from Table 28.10.2. Selecting molecular formulas that are consistent with Avogadro's hypothesis, recalculate the relative atomic masses of H, O, C, and N, using the modern composition data and the scale on which C $\equiv$ 12. Check the results for internal consistency.

PROBLEM 29.3.   Examine the two conceivable reactions

$$H + O \rightarrow HO, \qquad 2H_3 \mid O_2 \rightarrow 2H_3O,$$

in the light of Gay-Lussac's results and Avogadro's hypothesis. [Draw diagrams of the reactions similar to (29.3.1) *et seq.*] Are the reactions consistent with the volume data given in Table 29.1.1? Would the assumption of a triatomic molecular formula, H_3, for hydrogen give results consistent with the volume data of the ammonia reaction?

PROBLEM 29.4.   Assume the molecular formula of oxygen to be O_4 and those of hydrogen and nitrogen to be H_2 and N_2, respectively. Using diagrams such as (29.3.1), show that you can write reactions agreeing with the volume data by selecting appropriate formulas for water, nitric oxide, and ammonia. [*Answer:* H_2O_2, NO_2, and NH_3, respectively.] What would have to be assumed regarding the formulas of the two oxides of carbon? [*Answer:* CO_2 and CO_4, respectively.] Suppose that you were a contemporary of Avogadro's, confronted with the necessity of evaluating his suggestions. What would be your reaction to the theory in the light of the existence of alternative solutions as exhibited in this problem? (See Section 29.4.)

PROBLEM 29.5.   The reaction between hydrogen and chlorine exhibits the following volumetric relations:

1 volume hydrogen + 1 volume chlorine gas $\rightarrow$ 2 volumes hydrogen chloride gas.

Using Avogadro's hypothesis, what molecular formulas would you select for chlorine and hydrogen chloride?

PROBLEM 29.6.   In accordance with Avogadro's hypothesis, we take the formula of nitric oxide to be NO. On this basis, the calculations in Problem 28.8, based on Table 28.10.2, gave the formula N_2O for the compound nitrous oxide. Predict the volume ratios in the reaction in which *nitrous* oxide is oxidized to nitric oxide:

$$N_2O + O_2 \rightarrow NO.$$

[Note that it is first necessary to "balance" the equation.]

29.4   OBJECTIONS TO AVOGADRO'S PROPOSALS

Within several years after the publication of Avogadro's paper, Ampère independently advocated utilizing and testing the "equal numbers" hypothesis. Despite Ampère's perceptive arguments, and despite the fact that Avogadro's suggestions ultimately turned out to be the correct solution to the puzzle of molecular formulas and relative atomic masses, the scientific community paid little attention to Avogadro's ideas for almost 50 years. Although in the deceptive illumination of hindsight this neglect might seem strange, it becomes quite understandable when viewed in the context of its own time.

Until the writings of Mayer and Joule in the 1840's, followed by the recognition of heat as a form of energy, and the development of a quantitative physical theory of gases (the kinetic theory) in which widely separated particles were viewed as possessing kinetic energy of random thermal motion, there was no persuasive physical evidence to support the "equal volumes–equal numbers" hypothesis; this was just as speculative as Dalton's concept of static atoms of different sizes.

Furthermore, the period from 1800 to 1820 witnessed revolutionary developments in chemistry, stemming from the discovery of electrolysis: the realization that an electric current might be a more powerful agent of chemical action than the strongest acid or alkaline reagents, the dawning awareness that electrical and chemical effects were inextricably connected, and that the forces leading to chemical combination and recombination were most likely electrical in character. (See Section 25.8.)

In the evolving conceptions it was natural to view molecules of compounds as being formed through the attraction of opposite electrical charges on different species of atoms. What then would hold identical atoms together to form molecules such as H_2 and O_2 when atoms of the same element should presumably carry like charges and repel each other? If there *were* forces attracting identical atoms to each other, why should they stop at H_2? Why not go on to H_3, H_4, etc., forming any number of different polyatomic molecules, or eventually just clumping all the atoms together in one mass? In the light of this possibility, how could the gaseous state exist at all?

These are not trivial objections. Although internally consistent chemical evidence eventually forced scientists to accept as a fact the occurrence of molecules such as H_2, O_2, N_2, P_4, S_6, etc., the tantalizing puzzle of how such associations could occur was not resolved until the late 1920's, with the development of the new science of quantum mechanics and its attendant theories of atomic structure and chemical bonding.

Other objections to Avogadro's proposals stemmed from the fact that they did not supply *unique* solutions. The combinations

$$2H_2 + O_4 \rightarrow 2H_2O_2$$

and many others would agree just as well with the weight and volume data as the proposed reaction

$$2H_2 + O_2 \rightarrow 2H_2O.$$

(See Problem 29.4.) At the time Avogadro published his papers, only four elements (hydrogen, oxygen, nitrogen, and chlorine) were known to be gaseous under conditions of temperature and pressure such that it was possible to study their chemical reactions with existing laboratory techniques. Therefore, only a very limited test of Avogadro's ideas was possible. The scarcity of data seems to have led Avogadro to indulge in rather remote and erroneous speculations concerning the atomic behavior of liquids and solids, and this aspect of his papers reduced the confidence of readers in the respectability of the rest of his work.

Berzelius, for example, rejected Avogadro's notion of diatomic molecules of elements and held to the idea that elements were intrinsically monatomic. He explained Gay-Lussac's integral ratios of reacting volumes by supposing that the "equal volumes–equal numbers" hypothesis applied *only* to elements, while compounds departed from this rule because of effects of the size of their molecules.

By 1827 progress in laboratory techniques made possible the study of densities and chemical reactions of gases at elevated temperatures. The French chemist J. B. A. Dumas and other investigators produced evidence that the vaporized elements mercury, sulfur, phosphorous, arsenic could not be considered diatomic without leading to contradictions with other chemical and physical data. Thus it appeared that the general behavior of gaseous elements could not be explained by one simple hypothesis, assuming the formation of diatomic molecules, and there seemed to be no way of modifying the hypothesis to select other possible formulas on an objective, unequivocal basis. These difficulties served to cast additional doubt on the usefulness of Avogadro's conception.

29.5 MARKING TIME

In the face of these contradictions and the resulting impasse in unequivocal identification of molecular formulas and relative atomic masses, the atomic theory underwent a period of eclipse. Scientific vocabulary of the 1830's and 1840's retained the long-employed atomistic and corpuscular terms (witness the quotations from Joule in Chapter 20 and Faraday in Chapter 25), but many scientists gave up hope that the atomic theory would develop into a powerful quantitative synthesis in the Newtonian sense, or that it would do more than "save the phenomena," as the Ptolemaic system did, within a narrowly limited range of experience.

During this period, data concerning chemical combining powers of the elements were expressed principally in terms of equivalent weights rather than in terms of atomic masses and molecular formulas. The term "equivalent weight" of a substance

denotes the weight that combines with 1.008 gm of hydrogen. If the substance does
not combine with hydrogen directly, its equivalent weight is determined by the amount
that combines with an equivalent weight of a third substance that does combine
with hydrogen. For example:

1.008 gm H combines with 8.00 gm O,

1.008 gm H combines with 35.45 gm Cl,

8.00 gm O combine with 32.69 gm Zn.

Also, 35.45 gm Cl combine with 59.35 gm Sn to form stann*ous* chloride, and with
29.68 gm Sn to form stann*ic* chloride. In the compound copper sulfate, 63.54 gm Cu
take the place of 2.016 gm H originally present in sulfuric acid.

The relative equivalent weights of the various elements referred to are:

O   8.00,

Cl   35.45,

Zn   32.69,

Sn   29.68 (or 59.35, depending on the state of combination),

Cu   31.77.

In his quantitative study of electrolysis* in the 1830's, Faraday showed that,
when the same current was passed through several electrolytic cells in series, the
amounts of material liberated at each electrode were always in the ratio of their
equivalent weights, dramatizing the more direct relation of quantity of electrical
charge to equivalent proportions than to the hypothetical atomic masses of Dalton
and Berzelius.

For a time, molecular formulas and atomic masses seemed relatively unimportant,
but rapid development of the new science of organic chemistry revived demand
for resolution of the problem. "Organic" compounds are those associated with
living systems (plants and animals) and contain carbon in combination with hydrogen,
oxygen, nitrogen, and other elements. Organic compounds exist in tremendous
number and variety. Entire series of compounds with obviously different properties
such as solubility, melting point, reactivity with other substances, etc., are found
to have identical percentage compositions. For example, a series of carbon-hydrogen
compounds called olefins all have the identical combining proportions of 1.008 gm H
to 6.005 gm C, and cannot be distinguished on the basis of composition alone.
(It is established that molecular formulas of members of the series are given by
C_nH_{2n}, where n is an integer.) Knowing the equivalent weight of carbon in this
instance is of no help in identifying a particular compound or predicting any of its
distinctive properties.

---

* The reader may find it useful at this point to reread Section 25.8.

By the 1850's chemists sensed their science to be in a period of crisis, and in September 1860 the first International Chemical Congress was convened at Karlsruhe, with Dumas as chairman, in the hope of resolving the question of formulas and atomic masses. The conference itself made little progress, but toward the end of the meetings an Italian chemist distributed reprints of a paper that had been published two years earlier by his friend Stanislao Cannizzaro (1826–1910), professor of chemistry at the University of Genoa.

This paper describes how Cannizzaro taught his students the elements of chemistry, including the derivation of a clear and unambiguous system of molecular formulas and relative atomic masses. Cannizzaro had been present at the meetings, but his talks drew no more attention that did those of other participants. Only after people went home and studied his presentation at leisure did the pamphlet begin to show its impact.

As in previous instances in the history of science, all the necessary numerical facts had been available for some time, but they had not spoken for themselves. A particular approach to the data—the insight provided by Cannizzaro—was necessary to reveal the order not apparent to the superficial glance.

29.6   CANNIZZARO'S RESOLUTION OF THE PROBLEM

Cannizzaro's paper starts with an historical review of the ups and downs of atomic-molecular theory, very much as we have related it in previous sections, and then calls forcefully for a revival of the hypotheses of Avogadro and Ampère. There follows an analysis (of the type illustrated in Table 29.6.1*) in which Cannizzaro systematically investigates the known densities and compositions of a substantial list of gases and vapors for which data were available.

To understand Cannizzaro's contribution, it is necessary to develop some feeling for the origin and content of Table 29.6.1. The densities listed in the second column are the results of direct physical measurement. Some of the substances listed are gaseous at ordinary conditions, but substances such as sulfur, phosphorous, mercury calomel, etc., are vaporized only at elevated temperatures. To make the densities comparable to each other, it is necessary to "reduce" observed values to a common temperature and pressure. This has been done by calculating the density each gas or vapor would have if it were confined at 0°C and 1.00 atmosphere pressure. (The density of gases and vapors is known to be directly proportional to the confining pressure and inversely proportional to the absolute temperature, defined as Celsius temperature +273.) All the numbers in the table, therefore, refer to masses associated with one particular volume of gas—one liter, at 0°C and 1.00 atm pressure.

---

* Table 29.6.1 is not identical with Cannizzaro's, in that it displays the data in a simpler way and uses modern values of densities of gases and compositions of compounds. The elements and compounds cited, however, are taken from Cannizzaro's somewhat longer list (except for hydrogen cyanide, which has been added to illustrate numbers obtained with a compound containing three elements). By Cannizzaro's time, the accuracy of the analytical data was such that his final results for relative atomic masses are in essential agreement with modern values, to three significant figures.

TABLE 29.6.1

ILLUSTRATION OF CANNIZZARO'S ANALYSIS OF THE DENSITY AND COMPOSITION DATA FOR VARIOUS GASES

Name of gas or vapor	Density ρ, recalculated to 0°C and 1 atm pressure (grams/liter)	Grams/liter of each constituent element, based on composition data								Molecular formula and relative molecular mass; scale O ≡ 16
		H	O	S	P	Cl	N	Hg	C	
Hydrogen	0.090	0.090								H_2, 2.02
Oxygen	1.43		1.43							
Sulfur (<1000°C)	8.59			8.59						
Sulfur (>1000°C)	2.86			2.86						
Phosphorus	5.53				5.53					P_4, 124
Chlorine	3.16					3.16				
Nitrogen	1.25						1.25			
Mercury	8.96							8.96		
Water	0.803	0.090	0.713							H_2O, 18.02
Hydrogen chloride	1.63	0.045				1.58				
Ammonia	0.760	0.135					0.625			NH_3, 17
Phosphine	1.52	0.135			1.38					
Hydrogen sulfide	1.52	0.090	1.43							

Hydrogen cyanide	1.20	0.045					0.625		0.53
Chloride of phosphorus	6.13				1.38	4.74			
Calomel	10.54					1.58		8.96	
Corrosive sublimate	12.12					3.16		8.96	
Nitrous oxide	1.96		0.713				1.25		
Nitric oxide	1.34		0.713				0.625		
"Carbonic oxide"	1.25		0.713						0.54
"Carbonic acid"	1.96		1.43						0.53
Oxide of sulfur	2.86		1.43	1.43					
Ethylene	1.25	0.180							1.07
Alcohol	2.05	0.270	0.71						1.07
All numbers in the vertical column are integral multiples of:		0.045	0.715	1.43	1.38	1.58	0.625	8.96	0.535
Converted to scale O ≡ 16, numbers in preceding row become:	1.01	16.000	32.1	31.0	35.4	14.0	201	12.0

The numbers in the adjacent columns, representing the number of grams of each constituent element in one liter of the gas, are obtained by applying the known composition values to the density data. For example:

(1) Oxygen gas is 100% oxygen; therefore the number 1.43, identical with the density in column 2, appears in the column headed O.

(2) From Table 28.8.1, we have the composition of ammonia as 17.8% H and 82.2% N. Therefore, in one liter of ammonia there will be

$$0.760 \times 0.178 = 0.135 \text{ gm H,}$$
$$0.760 \times 0.822 = 0.625 \text{ gm N.}$$
$$\text{Total} = 0.760 \text{ gm ammonia.}$$

(3) Note that the numbers on any horizontal line must add up to equal the density number in column 2.

PROBLEM 29.7. Using composition data from Tables 28.8.1, 28.10.1, and 28.10.2, verify some of the other numbers in Table 29.6.1.

With reference to a table similar to Table 29.6.1, Cannizzaro says:

"Once my students have become familiar with the importance of the numbers as they are exhibited in the following table, it is easy to lead them to discover the law which results from their comparison. Compare, I say to them, 'the various quantities of the same element contained in the molecule of the free substance and in those of all its different compounds, and you will not be able to escape the following law: *The different quantites of the same element contained in different molecules are all whole multiples of one and the same quantity, which, always being entire, has the right to be called an atom.'* ... The law enunciated in the form just indicated is a direct deduction from the facts: but who is not led to assume from this same law that the weights of equal volumes represent the molecular weights, although other proofs are wanting? ..."

All the numbers in the column under hydrogen in Table 29.6.1 are integral multiples of 0.045; all the numbers in the column under sulfur are integral multiples of 1.43, etc. These numbers are listed in the next-to-last row of the table, and are converted to the scale based on oxygen = 16 in the last row. Cannizzaro interpreted the numbers in the last row as representing the relative atomic masses on the O $\equiv$ 16 scale.

PROBLEM 29.8. Verify the numbers in the last two rows of Table 29.6.1.

PROBLEM 29.9. When we assume that the smallest number appearing in a column (Table 29.6.1) is associated with the presence of a single atom of the given element in a molecule of the compound, the formulas and relative molecular masses of the various gases follow directly. Several formulas and molecular weights have been entered in the last column as guides and examples. Fill in the rest of the column in a similar way.

PROBLEM 29.10. Using the density data in column 2 of Table 29.6.1 and the relative molecular masses evaluated in the preceding problem, calculate the volume occupied at 0°C and 1 atm pressure by that number of grams of each gas numerically equal to its relative molecular mass. How do you interpret your results? [*Answer:* 22.4 liters.]

A typical reaction to Cannizzaro's paper is apparent in the following remarks by the eminent German chemist Lothar Meyer, one of the participants in the Karlsruhe conference:

"I . . . was astonished at the clarity with which the booklet illuminated the most important points of controversy. The scales seemed to fall from my eyes. Doubts disappeared, and a feeling of quiet certainty took their place. . . . It must have affected many others who attended the conference as it affected me. The big waves of controversy began to subside, and more and more the old atomic weights of Berzelius came to their own."

Cannizzaro's way of handling the data did not supply direct proof of the equal volumes—equal numbers hypothesis, as his own statement readily admits; nor did it resolve the question of how elements could form polyatomic molecules (H_2, N_2, S_6, P_4, etc.) without "clumping" together. It did, however, reveal a completely consistent pattern, free of internal contradictions and ambiguities, and made possible the assignment of formulas and relative atomic masses on the basis of objective numerical data alone, without subjective guesswork or a dubious "rule of greatest simplicity." The resulting system of atomic masses and molecular formulas proved to be free of internal contradictions. Furthermore, it was so fruitful and consistent in its predictions, so powerful an instrument for explaining and understanding chemical phenomena, that confidence in its basic validity grew despite the absence of independent evidence to support the numerical values of relative atomic mass, and despite the lack of a clear explanation of chemical bonding. While waiting for growing knowledge of the structure of matter to resolve these problems, the scientific community made fruitful use of the atomic-molecular theory. General acceptance of the theory was accompanied, in turn, by deepening belief in the "reality" of atoms and molecules—by the view that these conceptions were something *more* than mere heuristic devices arbitrarily invented to explain observable effects originating on a scale beyond that of direct sense perception; by the view that there exist microscopic entities having reproducible, understandable, predictable properties and behavior, however imperfectly the detailed features may be conceived or visualized.

29.7   RELATIVE ATOMIC MASSES AND NUMBERS OF ATOMS

With the establishment of a consistent scale of relative atomic and molecular masses, it immediately becomes possible to compare the number of particles in different quantities of various substances. For example, suppose that we weigh out into separate boxes the quantities of various elements illustrated in Fig. 29.7.1. Although each box contains a very different number of grams of material, the boxes have something in common: Each one contains the *same total number of atoms* of its particular species. In honor of Avogadro's contribution to atomic-molecular science, this number is called "Avogadro's number"; we shall denote it by the symbol N_0. In the 1860's scientists did not know the numerical value of N_0, and it was not at all obvious that the value could be determined. Subsequent developments in atomic physics, however, made it possible to determine N_0 by several entirely independent methods. Agreement among these different methods presents us with a beautiful and convincing verification of the entire theory. These results and developments will be discussed in Chapters 33 and 34.

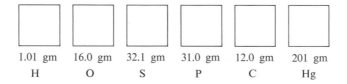

1.01 gm	16.0 gm	32.1 gm	31.0 gm	12.0 gm	201 gm
H	O	S	P	C	Hg

FIG. 29.7.1. Into each box we weigh out that number of *grams* of an element equal to the relative mass number established in Table 29.6.1.

If in Fig. 29.7.1 we weigh out half as many grams of each element, each box would contain $N_0/2$ atoms; if we weigh out twice as many grams of each element, each box would contain $2N_0$ atoms, and so forth. We refer to quantities such as 16.0 gm oxygen, 12.0 gm carbon, 35.4 gm chlorine as "one gram-atomic mass" of each element. One gram-atomic mass of any element contains N_0 atoms. Similarly we would refer to 32 gm oxygen, 24 gm carbon, or 70.8 gm chlorine as "two gram-atomic masses" of each element. Five grams of mercury contain 5/201 gram-atomic mass of mercury and a total of $5 N_0/201$ atoms.

PROBLEM 29.11. Suppose that we weigh 100 gm of the respective elements into each box in Fig. 29.7.1. Do the boxes now contain the same number of atoms? Why or why not? Calculate the number of gram-atomic masses contained in each box. [*Answer:* 99, 6.24, 3.11, 3.23, 8.33, 0.497.] Express the number of atoms in each box in terms of N_0.

PROBLEM 29.12. Suppose that, in Fig. 29.7.1, we had weighed 1.01 kg H, 16.0 kg O, 32.1 kg S, etc., into the respective boxes; i.e., suppose that we had placed one kilogram atomic mass in each box. How would the number of atoms in each box be related to N_0? What would be your answer to the same question if we had put one pound atomic mass into each box?

PROBLEM 29.13. We shall see later that N_0 is established to have the unimaginably large numerical value of 6.02×10^{23} atoms per gram-atomic mass. Given this value, calculate the mass in grams of each species of atom referred to in Fig. 29.7.1. [*Answer:* S atom $= 5.32 \times 10^{-23}$ gm.]

PROBLEM 29.14.   How many grams of hydrogen, oxygen, sodium, and copper, respectively, contain the same number of atoms as 140 gm of carbon?   How many atoms is this?   [*Answer:* 11.8 gm H; 187 gm O; 268 gm Na; 741 gm Cu; 7.02×10^{24} atoms.]

29.8   RELATIVE MOLECULAR MASSES AND NUMBERS OF MOLECULES

Consider several of the molecular formulas and relative molecular masses established in Section 29.6 and Problem 29.9 (Table 29.8.1).

TABLE 29.8.1

Molecule	Formula	Relative molecular mass
Hydrogen gas	H_2	2.02
Oxygen gas	O_2	32.00
Phosphorus vapor	P_4	124
Water	H_2O	18.02
Hydrogen chloride	HCl	36.4
Ammonia	NH_3	17.0
Nitrous oxide	N_2O	44.0

Suppose that we weigh out 2.02 gm hydrogen, 32.0 gm oxygen, 124 gm phosphorus vapor, 18.0 gm water, etc., into separate boxes. Our boxes now contain very different numbers of *atoms*, but they still have something in common: each one contains the *same total number of molecules* of its particular species, namely, N_0. For example: The box of hydrogen contains $2N_0$ atoms, but each molecule consists of 2 atoms, and therefore there are N_0 *molecules*. The box of water contains 16.0 gm of oxygen and therefore N_0 atoms of oxygen; since one atom of oxygen is present in each molecule of water, there must be N_0 molecules of water. (The number of *atoms* in this box is N_0 oxygen and $2N_0$ hydrogen, giving a total of $3N_0$ atoms altogether.)

PROBLEM 29.15.   Examine other molecules listed in Table 29.8.1 in a similar way, and verify that each box would indeed contain N_0 *molecules*.

Using a nomenclature similar to that of the preceding section, we refer to the quantities 2.02 gm hydrogen, 18.0 gm water, 17.0 gm ammonia, 36.4 gm hydrogen chloride as "one gram-molecular mass" of each substance. This lengthy name is commonly shortened to the single word *mole*. Thus one-half mole of phosphorus vapor has a mass of 62 gm and contains $N_0/2$ molecules of formula P_4. One hundred grams of nitrous oxide gas correspond to $100/44.0 = 2.27$ moles and contain 2.27 N_0 molecules of N_2O.

PROBLEM 29.16.   Table salt (sodium chloride) has the molecular formula NaCl. Find its relative molecular mass. If you were asked to weigh out 4.50 moles of salt, how many grams would you take? How many moles of salt are contained in one kilogram? [*Answer:* 58.45; 263 gm; 17.1 moles.]

PROBLEM 29.17. Taking $N_0 = 6.02 \times 10^{23}$, calculate the number of molecules present in 100 gm of each of the substances listed in Table 29.8.1. Calculate the total number of atoms of all species present in each case. Calculate the mass in grams of each molecule. [*Answer:* N_2O molecule has mass of 7.31×10^{-23} gm.]

PROBLEM 29.18. Reinterpret the results obtained in Problem 29.10 in the vocabulary we have just developed—particularly in terms of the word "mole" and the number N_0.

29.9 CHEMICAL CALCULATIONS

Having established an unambiguous way of comparing the number of molecules present in various masses of different substances, let us examine the quantities of material participating in a chemical reaction. Consider as a specific example the reaction for synthesis of ammonia:

$$3H_2 + N_2 \rightarrow 2NH_3. \tag{29.9.1}$$

Previously we interpreted this statement as saying, "Three molecules of hydrogen combine with one molecule of nitrogen to form two molecules of ammonia." Now, in the light of our realization that the same number of molecules are present in one mole of any substance, we can also interpret this statement as saying, "Three *moles* of hydrogen (consisting of $3 \times 2.0 = 6.0$ gm) combine with one *mole* (28 gm) of nitrogen to form two *moles* (34 gm) of ammonia."

The last statement forms the basis for very simple arithmetical calculations of quantities of material utilized or produced in the reaction: Suppose that we have 1500 gm hydrogen available; how many grams of nitrogen must be supplied and how much ammonia will be formed if all the hydrogen is utilized?

Answer: (a) We start with 1500/2.0 moles of hydrogen. Since $\frac{1}{3}$ mole of nitrogen reacts with each mole of hydrogen, and since each mole of nitrogen contains 28 gm, the amount of nitrogen required is

$$\frac{1500}{2.0} \times \frac{1}{3} \times 28 = 7000 \text{ gm.}$$

(b) Since $\frac{2}{3}$ mole of ammonia is produced for each mole of hydrogen used, and since each mole of ammonia contains 17 gm, the amount of ammonia produced is

$$\frac{1500}{2.0} \times \frac{2}{3} \times 17 = 8500 \text{ gm.}$$

(c) The last result is checked by noting that 1500 gm hydrogen reacting with 7000 gm nitrogen would yield 8500 gm of product, in accordance with the principle of conservation of mass.

PROBLEM 29.19. When metallic copper is treated with hot, concentrated sulfuric acid (formula H_2SO_4), the copper is dissolved to form copper sulfate; water and sulfur dioxide are also formed in the process. The balanced reaction is written

$$Cu + 2H_2SO_4 \rightarrow CuSO_4 + 2H_2O + SO_2\uparrow.$$

(The vertical arrow indicates that sulfur dioxide is liberated as a gas.) Suppose that you start with 200 gm of metallic copper. Ask some questions and carry out numerical calculations similar to those illustrated in the preceding example. Explain the basis of the calculations in your own words.

PROBLEM 29.20. In the neighborhood of a platinum surface, ammonia can be made to burn (unite with oxygen) to form water vapor and nitric oxide, according to the reaction

$$NH_3 + O_2 \rightarrow NO + H_2O.$$

The reaction, as written, is not balanced. Balance it with appropriate coefficients and make up some problems of your own concerning quantities of material involved in the reaction.

29.10   CHEMICAL FORMULAS AND THE LAW OF ELECTROLYSIS

During the 1830's Faraday showed that, in decomposition of chemical compounds by electrolysis, a fixed amount of charge always liberated a fixed amount of material at each electrode,* and that the amounts liberated were in the ratio of their equivalent proportions. Let us now examine some typical electrolysis data in the light of known atomic masses and chemical formulas, as illustrated in Table 29.10.1.

TABLE 29.10.1

AMOUNTS OF VARIOUS ELEMENTS LIBERATED AT CATHODE AND ANODE IN ELECTROLYSIS

Substance electrolyzed	Molecular formula	Cathode			Anode		
		Element	Number of grams	Number of gram-atomic masses	Element	Number of grams	Number of gram-atomic masses
Water	H_2O	H	1.0	1	O	8.0	$\frac{1}{2}$
Hydrogen chloride	HCl	H	1.0	1	Cl	35.4	1
Sodium iodide (fused salt)	NaI	Na	23.0	1	I	127	1
Copper sulfate (water solution)	$CuSO_4$	Cu	31.7	$\frac{1}{2}$	O	8.0	$\frac{1}{2}$
Calcium bromide (fused salt)	$CaBr_2$	Ca	20.0	$\frac{1}{2}$	Br	80.0	1
Aluminum chloride (fused salt)	$AlCl_3$	Al	9.0	$\frac{1}{3}$	Cl	35.4	1
Stannic (tin) chloride (fused salt)	$SnCl_4$	Sn	29.7	$\frac{1}{4}$	Cl	35.4	1

Amounts of material liberated by passage of one faraday (96,500 coul)

---

* See Section 25.8 for the initial discussion of these concepts.

PROBLEM 29.21.   Look up the relative atomic masses of the various elements listed in Table 29.10.1, and verify the fractions listed in the columns labeled "number of gram-atomic masses."

When one examines the molecular formulas of compounds formed by various elements, it becomes apparent that certain elements exhibit an intrinsic one-ness in their ability to enter combinations. This characteristic is evident for example, in hydrogen and in the alkali metals (lithium, Li; sodium, Na; potassium, K; cesium, Cs; rubidium, Rb) as well as in another group of elements called the *halogens** (fluorine, F; chlorine, Cl; bromine, Br; and iodine, I). Let us denote hydrogen and the alkali metals by A and the halogens by X; we note that these two groups of elements combine with each other only on a one-to-one basis to form compounds with formula AX; there exist no compounds having formulas AX_2 or A_2X, etc.

Similarly, if we denote by B the members of another group of elements called *alkali earth metals*, (magnesium, Mg; calcium, Ca; strontium, Sr; barium, Ba), we find that these elements combine with the halogens to give compounds having the formula BX_2. Thus the alkali earths exhibit a "two-ness" relative to the halogens.

On the other hand, oxygen, sulfur, and the group (SO_4), called the *sulfate radical*, form compounds such as H_2O, H_2S, $H_2(SO_4)$, Na_2O, Na_2S, $Na_2(SO_4)$, CaO, CaS, $CaSO_4$. Thus oxygen, sulfur, and the sulfate radical exhibit a two-ness relative to hydrogen and sodium and match the two-ness of calcium.

Other elements (exemplified by aluminum, Al, and tin, Sn, in Table 29.10.1) exhibit a three-ness or four-ness in their combination with the halogens. (This numerical combining capacity relative to hydrogen and the alkali metals was named *valence* in the early days of chemistry. The concept has since been redefined and elaborated into a powerful, complicated quantum-mechanical theory of chemical bonding, the discussion of which is beyond the scope of this text.)

If we return to the data shown in Table 29.10.1, we note that the one-ness, two-ness, or three-ness exhibited by any given element in forming chemical combinations is directly connected with the number of atoms of this element liberated in electrolysis by passage of 96,500 coulombs of charge. Thus 96,500 coulombs always liberate exactly one gram-atomic mass, or N_0 atoms, of hydrogen, the alkali metals, or the halogens. The same amount of charge liberates one-half gram-atomic mass, or $N_0/2$ atoms, of oxygen, copper, or calcium, and $N_0/3$ and $N_0/4$ atoms of aluminum and tin, respectively.

Many prominent nineteenth-century scientists pointed to the logical implications of these results. A typical example is the following statement by Helmholtz in a Faraday lecture at the Royal Institution in 1881:

> "Now the most startling result of Faraday's law [of electrolysis] is perhaps this: if we accept the hypothesis that the elementary substances are composed of atoms, we cannot avoid concluding that electricity also, positive as well as negative, is divided into elementary portions which behave like atoms of electricity."

---

* "Halogen" means "salt-former."

This was the simplest and most natural way of explaining the fact that a fixed quantity of electrical charge liberates a fixed number of atoms of various elements at both the positive and negative electrodes. The different valences of one, two, three, etc., exhibited by various elements would be directly related to the number of "corpuscles" or "packets" of charge associated with each atom. The systematic one-ness in the chemical behavior of the atoms of hydrogen, the alkali metals, and the halogens would appear to reside in the capacity of each atom to transport, or gain or lose, or in some way be associated with, only one elementary packet of electrical charge.

PROBLEM 29.22. We saw in previous problems that, if we knew the numerical value of Avogadro's number N_0, we could evaluate the mass m of an individual atom of an element of relative atomic mass M:

$$m = \frac{M}{N_0} \text{ gm} \quad \text{or} \quad \frac{M}{1000 N_0} \text{ kg.}$$

If we denote the amount of charge associated with each hypothetical elementary "packet" by q_e, the data given in Table 29.10.1 imply that $q_e = 96{,}500/N_0$ coul. Explain and justify this statement in your own words. How many packets of size q_e seem to be associated with oxygen, copper, calcium, aluminum, and tin atoms, respectively? If N_0 is not known numerically, we cannot calculate m and q_e separately, but we can in any case calculate the hypothetical *charge-to-mass* ratio of individual atoms. Explain how this is to be done. Calculate the charge-to-mass ratio associated with each of the atoms (or ions) referred to in Table 29.10.1. [*Answer:* For hydrogen, $q_e/m_H = 96{,}500/1.008 = 9.57 \times 10^7$ coul/kg; for oxygen, $2q_e/m_O = 1.21 \times 10^7$ coul/kg, etc.]

Toward the end of the nineteenth century a number of different measurements and new physical discoveries coalesced to give quantitative information regarding the corpuscular nature of electrical charge and the entities with which corpuscles of charge are associated on a microscopic scale. The atomic charge-to-mass ratios calculated in Problem 29.22 played an important role as checks and cross checks in the network of theory and hypothesis through which the new discoveries were interpreted. We shall return to these ideas in Chapter 31.

29.11 THE PERIODIC TABLE OF THE ELEMENTS

Just as Kepler combed Tycho's data for evidence of numerical regularity in the behavior of the planets, just as Balmer sought an empirical formula for the line spectrum of hydrogen, nineteenth-century chemists searched for numerical order in the accumulating list of elements.

As early as 1815 an English physician and chemist, William Prout, advanced the suggestion that higher elements might all be constituted by combination of various numbers of atoms of the lightest element, hydrogen. This implied that relative atomic masses should all be integral numbers, with hydrogen taken as 1. As increasingly accurate determinations showed that the relative masses departed significantly from integer values, the idea was abandoned.

TABLE 29.11.1

PERIODIC TABLE OF THE ELEMENTS

The atomic weights, based on the exact number 12 as the assigned atomic mass of the principal isotope of carbon, are the most recent (1961) values adopted by the International Union of Pure and Applied Chemistry. (For artificially produced elements, the approximate atomic weight of the most stable isotope is given in brackets.)

Period	Series	I	II	III	IV	V	VI	VII	VIII			0
1	1	1 H 1.00797										2 He 4.0026
2	2	3 Li 6.939	4 Be 9.0122	5 B 10.811	6 C 12.01115	7 N 14.0067	8 O 15.9994	9 F 18.9984				10 Ne 20.183
3	3	11 Na 22.9898	12 Mg 24.312	13 Al 26.9815	14 Si 28.086	15 P 30.9738	16 S 32.064	17 Cl 35.453				18 A 39.948
4	4	19 K 39.102	20 Ca 40.08	21 Sc 44.956	22 Ti 47.90	23 V 50.942	24 Cr 51.996	25 Mn 54.9380	26 Fe 55.847	27 Co 58.9332	28 Ni 58.71	
4	5	29 Cu 63.54	30 Zn 65.37	31 Ga 69.72	32 Ge 72.59	33 As 74.9216	34 Se 78.96	35 Br 79.909				36 Kr 83.80
5	6	37 Rb 85.47	38 Sr 87.62	39 Y 88.905	40 Zr 91.22	41 Nb 92.906	42 Mo 95.94	43 Tc [99]	44 Ru 101.07	45 Rh 102.905	46 Pd 106.4	
5	7	47 Ag 107.870	48 Cd 112.40	49 In 114.82	50 Sn 118.69	51 Sb 121.75	52 Te 127.60	53 I 126.9044				54 Xe 131.30
6	8	55 Cs 132.905	56 Ba 137.34	57–71 Lanthanide series*	72 Hf 178.49	73 Ta 180.948	74 W 183.85	75 Re 186.2	76 Os 190.2	77 Ir 192.2	78 Pt 195.09	
6	9	79 Au 196.967	80 Hg 200.59	81 Tl 204.37	82 Pb 207.19	83 Bi 208.980	84 Po [210]	85 At [210]				86 Rn [222]
7	10	87 Fr [223]	88 Ra [226.05]	89–Actinide series**								

*Lanthanide series: | 57 La 138.91 | 58 Ce 140.12 | 59 Pr 140.907 | 60 Nd 144.24 | 61 Pm [147] | 62 Sm 150.35 | 63 Eu 151.96 | 64 Gd 157.25 | 65 Tb 158.924 | 66 Dy 162.50 | 67 Ho 164.930 | 68 Er 167.26 | 69 Tm 168.934 | 70 Yb 173.04 | 71 Lu 174.97 |

**Actinide series: | 89 Ac [227] | 90 Th 232.038 | 91 Pa [231] | 92 U 238.03 | 93 Np [237] | 94 Pu [242] | 95 Am [243] | 96 Cm [245] | 97 Bk [249] | 98 Cf [249] | 99 Es [253] | 100 Fm [255] | 101 Md [256] | 102 No | 103 |

In subsequent years other investigators looked for regularities among numerical values of atomic masses, but many of the tabulated values were incorrect, and these attempts were doomed to failure until the 1860's, when acceptance of Cannizzaro's views led to the establishment of what proved to be a correct atomic mass table.

A number of investigators had pointed out the existence of groups of elements such as the alkali metals, the alkali earth metals, and the halogens. Members of any one group increased regularly in atomic mass, had very similar chemical properties, and exhibited the same valence in combining with other elements. In 1869 the Russian chemist Dmitri Ivanovich Mendeléev (1834–1907) and the German chemist Lothar Meyer (1830–1895) simultaneously and independently (Meyer published his first paper a few months after Mendeléev's) presented an ingenious tabulation of the elements in order of increasing atomic mass. The table was not simply a vertical listing but was organized in such a way as to collect elements with similar properties into visibly separate groups and to emphasize the systematic periodicity with which chemical properties were found to be repeated with increasing atomic mass. At the same time the table called attention to similarities in chemical behavior that had not been noted previously and revealed gaps implying the existence of still-undiscovered elements. How were these insights achieved?

Table 29.11.1 shows a modern version of the periodic system of the elements. Let us follow Mendeléev's procedure by making reference to this table. Hydrogen is listed by itself in the first row; in the second row are listed the elements lithium, beryllium, boron, carbon, nitrogen, oxygen, and fluorine in increasing order of atomic mass.*

The next element is sodium, an alkali metal with properties very similar to lithium. Therefore, instead of continuing the first row, sodium is placed beneath lithium in the table, indicating the beginning of a new "period" or repetition of properties. The sequence then continues from sodium through chlorine, each element showing properties similar to that of the element above it, chlorine falling below the lightest member of the halogen group, fluorine. A similar sequence begins with the next element, potassium, but is somewhat more complicated, running through two series (as shown in the table) before being completed with the next halogen, bromine. To Mendeléev, however, the next known element after calcium (Ca) was titanium (Ti). He recognized that calcium belonged under magnesium, but he also noted that titanium had properties similar to carbon and silicon (Si) rather than boron and aluminum. Furthermore, if he placed titanium under aluminum, all the subsequent elements would be out of place, falling in columns to which their properties were not similar. Thus Mendeléev left a gap between calcium and titanium, predicting the existence of an element not yet discovered, one that would exhibit a valence of three, similar to boron and aluminum, and with an atomic mass between 40 and 48. In a similar fashion Mendeléev spotted other vacancies, two for example between zinc (Zn) and arsenic (As).

---

* In Mendeléev's day the elements in column 0 at the right-hand side of the table were unknown. These are called the *noble gases*, and were discovered by Ramsay and Rayleigh during the closing years of the nineteenth century.

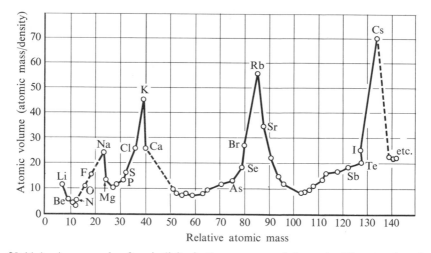

FIG. 29.11.1. An example of periodicity in the sequence of elements. The atomic volumes vary periodically with the atomic masses. (After Lothar Meyer, but using modern values.)

One of the great triumphs of the periodic system lay in the subsequent discovery of the predicted elements. Not only were these elements discovered, but they were found to have the density, appearance, and chemical properties predicted by Mendeléev by interpolation between the properties of adjacent elements.

Lothar Meyer adduced additional support for the periodic system by showing that other properties besides chemical behavior were also periodic with increasing atomic mass. For example, a graph of atomic volume (volume of one gram-atomic mass in the solid or liquid state; i.e., volume occupied by N_0 atoms) is shown in Fig. 29.11.1; the periodicity of this graph clearly follows that of the periodic table.

Mendeléev was deeply convinced that increasing atomic mass was the basic criterion for ordering the elements. When he found a few instances in which placing elements in their proper columns of chemical behavior led to a reversal in the order of increasing mass, he unhesitatingly asserted that the masses were in error, and that improved gravimetric redeterminations of atomic mass would lead to a steadily increasing sequence. In some instances he was correct, but if we look at the modern data in Table 29.11.1, we note that argon (A) has an atomic mass of 39.9, slightly greater than that of the next element, potassium. Also, tellurium (Te) has a slightly greater atomic mass than that of its successor, iodine (I). Apparently, the so-called *atomic number*—the number of the element in the periodic sequence—is for some reason more fundamental than the atomic mass. Physical explanation of the periodic system and of the significance of atomic number was subsequently one of the great triumphs of twentieth-century physics.

In the construction of the periodic system, we see still another instance in which the data existed but had to be looked at in a particular way before order was revealed. Here it was a matter of how the information was actually written down. A particular form of tabulation, that introduced by Mendeléev and Meyer, turned out to be a discovery in itself, a discovery that revitalized the chemical science of the day, revealed unsuspected similarities and relationships among elements, predicted new compounds, and precipitated purposeful search for new elements of predicted properties and atomic mass. In addition this discovery presented physics with a profound new challenge, calling for a physical explanation of the whole atomic system. However, with only 63 elements known in 1869, the discovery of the periodic system by Mendeléev and Meyer was not a matter of stumbling upon the self-evident. In achieving their insight, they brought to bear a profound and far-reaching knowledge of the literature and facts of chemical science, and to this knowledge they added the ingredients of boldness and imagination.

SUPPLEMENTARY READING AND STUDY

Textbook presentations:
Foundations of Modern Physical Science, G. Holton and D. H. D. Roller. Reading, Mass.: Addison-Wesley, 1958, Chapters 23, 24
Physical Science: Men and Concepts, G. C. Omer, H. L. Knowles, B. W. Mundy, W. H. Yoho. Boston: D. C. Heath, 1962, Chapters 26–31
Principles of Physical Science, F. T. Bonner and M. Phillips. Reading, Mass.: Addison-Wesley, 1957, Chapters 7–9

Historical studies and excerpts from original papers:
The Atomic-Molecular Theory, Case 4 in the Harvard Case Histories in Experimental Science, L. K. Nash. Cambridge, Mass.: Harvard University Press, 1957
Readings in the Literature of Science. Excerpts from Dalton, Gay-Lussac, Avogadro, Mendeléev, and Faraday, edited by W. C. and M. Dampier. New York: Harper, 1959, Harper Torchbook TB512, pages 93–126
A Source Book in Chemistry, 1400–1900. Selections from Avogadro, Gay-Lussac, Mendeléev, edited by H. M. Leicester and H. S. Klickstein. New York: McGraw-Hill, 1952
The World of Mathematics, J. R. Newman. Selection from Mendeléev. New York: Simon and Schuster, 1956, pages 910–931

CHAPTER 30

Kinetic Theory of Gases

30.1 INTRODUCTION

It has been repeatedly illustrated in preceding chapters that a successful theory in physical science contains far more than just a descriptive verbal component. An essential feature resides in the development of a mathematical structure—the capacity to reveal, explain, and predict relations among observable physical quantities. In the course of such mathematization by nineteenth-century scientists, the atomic-molecular theory achieved not only the systematization of chemistry described in Chapters 28 and 29, but also a model in which gross macroscopic physical properties of material substances are quantitatively accounted for in terms of the kinetic behavior, on the microscopic scale, of the huge population of constituent corpuscles.

In this chapter we shall follow several elementary aspects of the kinetic theory, showing how previously developed concepts such as force, mass, velocity, and energy are invoked in order to create a picture of molecular behavior. We shall not attempt an historical development, but shall present the ideas in modern terms with a few historical asides.

As is usual in the development of a new theory or set of concepts, we start with the simplest possible case. Much of our accumulated physical evidence points to the gaseous state of matter as probably the simplest from the atomic-molecular point of view. The fluidity and compressibility of gases support the idea that molecules are, under these conditions, relatively free and independent of each other. (The rigidity and structural regularity of crystals, on the other hand, suggest a dominant role for interatomic and intermolecular forces in determining the structure and properties of solid materials, while liquids might be viewed as exhibiting a complex behavior intermediate to the gaseous and solid extremes.) This qualitative evidence is supplemented, furthermore, by quantitative evidence (Chapter 29) that equal volumes of gas contain equal numbers of molecules regardless of chemical nature or composition, indicating that the molecules themselves might be very much smaller than the average spacing between them.

On the hypothesis that the gaseous state is probably the simplest state of matter, our inquiry begins with an attempt to visualize the observable properties of gases in terms of the behavior of individual molecules.

30.2 ALTERNATIVE MODELS

In visualizing the role of molecules in a gas, a number of different points of view can be taken, and the following were all seriously entertained at various times:

(1) *The static model.* Some atomists, Newton and Dalton among them, held the view that the corpuscles of a stationary, nonflowing gas occupied fixed positions and filled the entire space available to them, expanding and contracting and remaining in contact with each other as the total volume occupied by the gas was increased or decreased. In the *Principia*, Newton showed that *if* the corpuscles repelled each other with a force inversely proportional to the distance between their centers, the pressure of the gas would decrease as volume increased according to the inverse relation $p \propto (1/V)$. Robert Boyle had shown that gases do indeed exhibit this relation between pressure and volume at constant temperature, and the regularity is referred to as *Boyle's law*.

(2) *The Boscovich model.* In 1758 the Serbian scientist Roger Boscovich suggested a model in which matter was to be viewed as composed of indivisible point centers of force. The point centers possess inertia and interact with each other, in principle, to infinite distances as do gravitating bodies. However, the force between two point centers is repulsive when they are very close together, alternates between attraction and repulsion as the points are moved farther apart, and becomes a $1/r^2$ attractive force when the points are widely separated. Thus, in a sense, Boscovichean atoms are infinite in extent. The whole conception involves an attempt to describe material substances only in terms of centers of force and to dispense with naïve notions of "stuff" and "matter." Although Boscovich's theory was not fruitful enough to achieve wide acceptance, it did influence the thinking of a number of prominent scientists, among whom were figures such as William Hamilton, Michael Faraday, and Joseph Henry.

(3) *The vortex model.* Early in the nineteenth century, Humphry Davy proposed a qualitative dynamical theory of heat, suggesting that in solids the vibration of atoms or molecules increased as the material was heated, while in gases the atoms rotated about their axes or possessed rotating "atmospheres." For a brief time Joule and other investigators turned to this model and attempted to account for the tendency of gases to expand by visualizing the atoms as spinning, fluid vortices, tending to expand centrifugally when external confining forces were relaxed.

(4) *The kinetic model.* In his treatise on the mechanics of fluids, published in 1738, Daniel Bernoulli suggested an atomistic model based on visualizing gases as consisting of minute corpuscles, vastly smaller than their average distances of separation, moving freely and eternally at high velocities in the volume in which they are confined, exerting a steady average pressure on any boundary by virtue of their extremely high frequency of bombardment. This model, neglected for about a century, was revived quite independently by ninteenth-century scientists—Joule and Maxwell prominent among them—who now had the additional motivation of seeking to construct a dynamic theory of heat (see the discussion of the evolution of the concept of conservation of energy in Chapter 20). The kinetic theory, simple and enormously successful in a wide range of applications, became the basis of our modern view.

30.3   THE KINETIC MODEL

Let us first attempt to visualize the kinetic picture entirely qualitatively, without formulas or calculations. In the process we shall identify the basic assumptions which it seems reasonable to adopt in developing the model.

(1) We start with Bernoulli's picture of minute corpuscles in rapid translational motion. The molecules move freely, colliding with each other and with the walls of the container at all possible angles in a complete chaos of changing directions of motion and changing magnitudes of velocity. This immediately incorporates into our model a way of accounting for the immense fluidity of a gas, for its tendency to fill uniformly all the space available to it, and for the tendency of different gases to diffuse through each other and form a uniform mixture even if they are initially separated.

(2) We interpret the steady pressure (force per unit area) measured at any wall or boundary as arising from the enormous number of individual molecular impacts at each element of area, each collision being associated with an impulse delivered to the reflected molecule and to the wall (see Section 17.7 and Problems 17.6 and 17.26).

(3) Invoking the concept of conservation of energy, we associate the addition or removal of heat from the gas with increasing or decreasing kinetic energy of the molecules. (This leads us to anticipate a possible connection between temperature and molecular motion, and a mathematical expression for such a connection will indeed emerge in the analytical development of the theory. At this point, however, we only advance the idea as a conjecture.) Supposing that the fluidity and compressibility of gases arises from the fact that molecules are on the average very far apart, we assume that long-range forces of mutual attraction or repulsion among the molecules are negligible and that interaction between them occurs only in collisions. An alternative way of expressing the same idea is to say that we assume negligible any quantities of potential energy stored or released when gases are expanded or compressed. (Note that potential energies are by no means negligible in all molecular systems. The latent heat of vaporization of a liquid is stored in separating the molecules against the attractive forces that hold them together in the liquid state. See Joule's remarks in Section 20.6.)

(4) Since the pressure of an isolated gas does not decrease with time, and since the gas remains uniformly distributed throughout its container (it does not end up condensed on the bottom of the box), we must, to be consistent with our kinetic model, accept the proposition that the velocity and kinetic energy of the molecules do not diminish with time. This requirement has deeper implications than may be apparent superficially: It requires that molecular collisions be perfectly elastic.

It is probable that this more than any other aspect of the kinetic model made the theory seem implausible to early investigators. If the reader has initial doubts about this assumption, he finds himself in good company. All our ordinary macroscopic experience indicates that collisions between material objects are to some extent inelastic; the bodies move more slowly after collision, some kinetic energy is lost, and an equivalent amount of heat appears in the process. But we must remember that we are now carrying our investigation far beyond the realms of ordinary experience and are trying to construct a mental picture of a physical world that lies beyond our senses. We ourselves, as well as our sense organs, are composed of huge aggregations of the very atoms and molecules whose individual microscopic behavior we try to visualize in our theory. It is important to realize that in our present endeavor we must not lean too heavily on sense impressions or extrapolate unwarily from ordinary experience.

Recall how a collision between pith balls carrying like charges or between carts carrying opposing magnets can take place without the bodies touching each other, and extend this notion to what might conceivably happen in molecular collisions where potential energy is perhaps stored against electrical forces on close approach of the particles and is returned to kinetic energy as they fly apart.

It is in this way that we rationalize the elasticity of individual molecular collisions. We shall see inelastic behavior to be associated not with individual molecular interactions but with the conversion of "organized" or "orderly" kinetic energy, such as that held in common by a huge group of molecules moving as a single unit in a moving ball, into the random, disorderly kinetic energy of completely chaotic motion of individual molecules.

(5) Simple observations with a pressure gauge and with a thermometer indicate that pressure and temperature are *uniform* throughout a gas at equilibrium in its container. From this evidence we might make the guess that the density is also uniform, and this indeed proves to be the case. We can account for this uniformity by the very plausible assumption that no particular direction of molecular motion is preferred over any other; all directions of motion are equally likely in the molecular chaos. If we were capable of moving through the gas and observing, say in each cubic millimeter, the number of molecules colliding and moving in various directions at various velocities, we would expect to observe exactly the same catalog of behavior in each region that we explore, and in each coordinate direction. A system which has properties that are independent of directions in space is said to be *isotropic*, and we assume isotropy in our gas model. (Note that a very tall vertical column of gas, such as a portion of the atmosphere, decreases in pressure and density in the vertical direction and is therefore described as *anisotropic*. In many crystalline solids the spacing and arrangement of atoms or molecules is different in different directions. Such solids have different compressibilities and exhibit different propagation velocities for sound and light in these different spatial directions. This is still another form of anisotropy.)

(6) In the isotropic chaos of collisions, velocity changes, bombardment of walls, we would scarcely expect all molecules to have the same speed. At any instant of time some might be virtually stationary, others might be moving very rapidly after being hit from behind, others would have speeds of every conceivable value between the two extremes. Although we would never be able to construct a table by taking an actual count, molecule by molecule, in our unimaginably large population, we can at least conceive of a catalog that would list the number of molecules lying in various *ranges* of speed: for example, the number that have speeds between 0 and 1 m/sec, the number between 1 and 2 m/sec, etc., over the entire relevant spectrum of velocities. In such circumstances we say that there exists a "distribution" of molecular veloci-

ties. The catalog we mentioned would be a complete arithmetical description of the distribution. From such information we could, for example, immediately calculate the average speed of the group of molecules.

PROBLEM 30.1. Suppose that a parallel beam of atoms or molecules is directed into a container of gas. (A parallel beam consists of a stream of molecules all moving in the same direction. Such a beam can be produced by allowing gas to escape from a very small opening in a heated enclosure, and further "collimating" the beam by passing it through a succession of narrow slits. Only molecules moving in a direction parallel to that of the series of openings can get through in the final beam.) Describe in your own words, in the light of the kinetic model, what will happen to the beam as it penetrates the gas. What will be the subsequent history of the molecules originally in the beam? What would happen if the density of the gas into which the beam penetrated were decreased? What would happen if the space the beam entered were extremely highly evacuated?

PROBLEM 30.2. Suppose that a burner is lighted under a box containing a gas. In terms of the kinetic model, how do you visualize the sequence of events and transfers of energy that end up with the heating of the gas; i.e., with the increase in the kinetic energy of the gas molecules?

PROBLEM 30.3. Consider a very simple distribution in which there are three groups of particles having three different ranges of velocity:

Number of particles in each group	Approximate velocity of each particle in group
$N_1 = 3$	$v_1 = 4.0$ m/sec
$N_2 = 7$	$v_2 = 6.0$ m/sec
$N_3 = 5$	$v_3 = 8.0$ m/sec

(a) Calculate the average velocity $\bar{v}$ of the particles in this system. [*Answer:* $\bar{v} = 6.9$ m/sec. Note that the answer is *not* simply 6.0 m/sec. It is necessary to calculate the *weighted* average, taking into account the number of particles in each velocity range.]

(b) Translate your previous calculation into symbols and argue that

$$\bar{v} = \frac{N_1 v_1 + N_2 v_2 + N_3 v_3}{N_1 + N_2 + N_3}$$

or that, in a more general case:

$$\bar{v} = \frac{\sum_i N_i v_i}{\sum_i N_i}, \tag{30.3.1}$$

where the symbol $\sum_i$ denotes summation over all the groups or categories into which the population has been divided. If N is the total number of particles in the system, argue that

$$N\bar{v} = \sum_i N_i v_i. \tag{30.3.2}$$

(c) If each particle in the distribution tabulated above has a mass $m = 0.01$ kg, calculate the average kinetic energy $\bar{\varepsilon}$ of the particles. [*Answer:* $\bar{\varepsilon} = 0.21$ j.] Verify the fact that the quantity $\frac{1}{2}m(\bar{v})^2 = 0.24$ j and is *not* equal to $\bar{\varepsilon}$.

(d) Generalize your calculation of $\bar{\varepsilon}$ in symbols, and argue that

$$\bar{\varepsilon} = \frac{\sum_i N_i(\frac{1}{2}mv_i^2)}{N}. \tag{30.3.3}$$

What interpretation can you assign to the quantity $2\bar{\varepsilon}/m$? Note that

$$\frac{2\bar{\varepsilon}}{m} = \frac{\sum_i N_i v_i^2}{N}. \tag{30.3.4}$$

(The quantity on the right-hand side of (30.3.4) is the weighted average of the *square* of the velocity. It is usually called the *mean square velocity*. The square root of this quantity is not, in general, equal to $\bar{v}$, the mean first power of the velocity.)

30.4 VISUALIZING GAS PRESSURE ON A WALL

Figure 30.4.1 is an idealized sketch of a region near the wall of a container of gas, illustrating the molecular bombardment that results in a steady pressure against the wall [see item (2) in Section 30.3]. Using this sketch as a basis for visualization of the problem, we shall try to derive an expression for the pressure in terms of molecular properties such as molecular mass, velocity, and numbers of particles. To calculate the pressure, we must calculate the force per unit area on the wall, recognizing that this, in turn, is equal to the rate of change of momentum imparted to the molecules at each unit area (see Section 17.7 and Problems 17.6 and 17.26).

First let us concentrate our attention on one group of molecules with some particular small range of values of *x-component* of velocity toward the wall (say the range between 824 and 826 m/sec) and denote the representative value of velocity in this group by the symbol v_{xi}. We might take $v_{xi} = 825$ m/sec in the illustration cited.

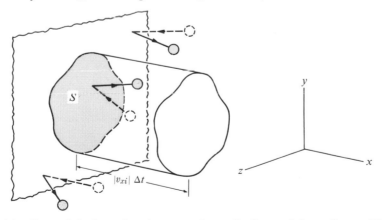

FIG. 30.4.1. Expanded view of region near the wall of a container of gas. The *x*-axis of the coordinates is taken perpendicular to the wall.

(Members of this group might have very different y and z velocity components.) Now in some short time interval Δt, a molecule with this x-component of velocity will be displaced a distance $|v_{xi}| \Delta t$ in the x-direction. Therefore, if at the beginning of the time interval the molecule is closer to the wall than the distance $|v_{xi}| \Delta t$, it will strike the wall *within* the time interval. If it is initially farther from the wall than $|v_{xi}| \Delta t$ it will get to the wall *after* the interval Δt is over and will not contribute to the force on the wall during this interval. Thus molecules that strike the wall with velocity components v_{xi} within the assumed time interval Δt must come from within a "pillbox" of altitude $|v_{xi}| \Delta t$, such as that sketched in Fig. 30.4.1, and cannot originate from farther away.

Now let us consider the molecules that actually strike the shaded area S. Some of these molecules arrive from within the sketched pillbox, depending on their angles of incidence, but we would also expect others to arrive at oblique angles from the sides, originating outside the pillbox. However, some of the molecules, originally in the pillbox with velocity components v_{xi}, may have y and z velocity components such as to make them go off at oblique angles and strike the wall far outside area S.

Here we add a refinement to our model in order to cover the new insight we have attained: We shall assume that for every molecule that leaves the pillbox at an oblique angle and does not strike area S, there is another molecule with the same velocity that comes in obliquely from outside the pillbox, striking area S and essentially "replacing" the first molecule so far as the effect at the wall is concerned.

A little reflection will show that this assumption must be closely connected with the concepts of isotropy and uniformity of the gas discussed in paragraph (5) of Section 30.3. If compensating molecular events of the kind we have just described were not equally likely to occur in the huge population of gas molecules, if such restoration of initial conditions and replacing of one molecular action by another were not continually taking place, it would be difficult to see how the isotropy or uniformity of the gas as a whole could be preserved. The hypothesis we are introducing is sometimes called the "principle of detailed balancing." (This principle can be accorded a rather sophisticated mathematical analysis and a more rigorous basis in terms of probability concepts than we shall attempt here.)

The principle of detailed balancing thus suggests that we can make our calculation of what happens at area S *as though* all the molecules striking it with velocity component v_{xi} originated in the sketched pillbox, despite the fact that some of the molecules striking S do not actually originate in the box and some of the molecules initially in the box never get to S.

Furthermore, the principle of detailed balancing helps us rationalize another problem: Since the wall itself is made of atoms and molecules, it can hardly be a perfectly smooth plane on the scale of molecular size. From the point of view of the dimensions of the gas molecules, the wall is a very rough surface, full of hills, valleys, and bumps of molecular size. Under such circumstances, the individual reflections of the incident molecules can hardly be specular (see Section 22.11 for definition of relevant concepts). The angle of reflection of any single collision event will rarely be equal to the angle of incidence. On the average, however, we might expect that the deviations from specular reflection cancel each other out in such a way that the entire system behaves *as though* angle of incidence were equal to angle of reflection in each collision at the wall. In the next section, in calculating momentum changes at the wall, we shall treat each collision as though the angles of reflection and of incidence were equal.

30.5 DERIVATION OF THE PRESSURE FORMULA

Now let us use the concepts and assumptions developed in the preceding section to make a step-by-step calculation of the pressure against the wall in Fig. 30.4.1. Consider first the group of molecules with x velocity components lying in a small range in the neighborhood of a particular magnitude of velocity $|v_{xi}|$, as illustrated numerically in the preceding section. Let us denote the total number of molecules (in the entire gas) having velocities in the given interval by the symbol $\Delta N(|v_{xi}|)$. If we divide the molecules into nonoverlapping groups [the number $\Delta N(251)$ with velocity components between $v_x = 250$ and 252 m/sec, the number $\Delta N(253)$ between 252 and 254 m/sec, etc., with each group characterized by an "interval number" i] and add up all the ΔN's, the result of the addition must give us the total number of molecules, N, in the box. Stating this arithmetic in symbols, we have

$$N = \sum_i \Delta N(|v_{xi}|). \tag{30.5.1}$$

If we denote the mass of each molecule by m, the x-component of momentum of a molecule arriving at shaded area S in Fig. 30.4.1 is $-m|v_{xi}|$. Using the assumption that, on the average, each reflection is specular, the molecule rebounds from the wall with x-component of momentum reversed in direction but unchanged in magnitude: final momentum is $+m|v_{xi}|$. Therefore the *change* of momentum experienced by each molecule that strikes S with x-component of velocity $|v_{xi}|$ is

$$+m|v_{xi}| - (-m|v_{xi}|) = 2m|v_{xi}|. \tag{30.5.2}$$

How many such molecules strike S in a short time interval Δt? We agreed, when we applied the principle of detailed balancing, that we could treat all molecules striking S in the time interval Δt *as though* they arrived from the pillbox sketched in Fig. 30.4.1. The pillbox has an altitude $|v_{xi}| \Delta t$ and a base area S; therefore its volume is $|v_{xi}| S \Delta t$, and it occupies the fraction $|v_{xi}| S \Delta t/V$ of the total volume of the box, where V denotes the total volume.

Since the gas is assumed uniform and isotropic, the number of molecules with x-component of velocity $|v_{xi}|$ in the pillbox must be

$$\underbrace{\Delta N(|v_{xi}|)}_{\substack{\text{Total number of} \\ \text{molecules in the} \\ \text{box with } x\text{-com-} \\ \text{ponent of velocity} \\ \text{near } |v_{xi}|}} \cdot \underbrace{\frac{|v_{xi}| S \Delta t}{V}}_{\substack{\text{Fraction of total} \\ \text{volume occupied} \\ \text{by pillbox}}}.$$

Because we know that the gas remains uniform and isotropic, we assume that half these molecules are moving to the left toward S and the other half toward the opposite wall on the right.

PROBLEM 30.4. Suppose that more than half the molecules were moving toward the left all the time in any region of the gas. What would happen within the box as time went by? What would happen to pressure and density readings in various places?

The number of molecules with x-component $|v_{xi}|$ that actually arrive at S in time interval Δt must be given by

$$\tfrac{1}{2} \Delta N(|v_{xi}|) \cdot \frac{|v_{xi}| S \, \Delta t}{V} . \tag{30.5.3}$$

Combining Eqs. (30.5.2) and (30.5.3), we obtain the total change of momentum experienced by molecules with velocity components $|v_{xi}|$ at area S in time interval Δt:

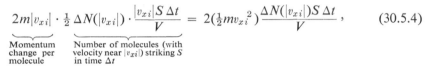

$$\underbrace{2m|v_{xi}|}_{\substack{\text{Momentum} \\ \text{change per} \\ \text{molecule}}} \cdot \underbrace{\tfrac{1}{2} \Delta N(|v_{xi}|) \cdot \frac{|v_{xi}| S \, \Delta t}{V}}_{\substack{\text{Number of molecules (with} \\ \text{velocity near } |v_{xi}|) \text{ striking } S \\ \text{in time } \Delta t}} = 2(\tfrac{1}{2}mv_{xi}{}^2)\frac{\Delta N(|v_{xi}|)S \, \Delta t}{V} , \tag{30.5.4}$$

where $\tfrac{1}{2}mv_{xi}^2$ is the kinetic energy associated with the x-component of motion of each molecule in the group. (Note that the absolute-value signs can be dropped because the velocity is squared.) To obtain the *total* change of momentum for all the different intervals of velocity, we must sum the expression (30.5.4) over all the intervals or categories denoted by i:

$$\begin{array}{l}\text{Total change of momentum} \\ \text{experienced by all molecules} \\ \text{striking area } S \text{ in time} \\ \text{interval } \Delta t\end{array} = \frac{2}{V} \sum_i (\tfrac{1}{2}mv_{xi}^2)\, \Delta N(|v_{xi}|)S \, \Delta t. \tag{30.5.5}$$

This momentum change must be equal to the total *impulse* imparted to the wall over area S in time Δt (see Section 17.7). Therefore the average force acting on area S is calculated by finding the impulse delivered per second; that is, by dividing expression (30.5.5) by the time interval Δt. Since pressure p is defined as the force per unit area, we must also divide by S, obtaining from (30.5.5) the equation

$$p = \frac{2}{V} \sum_i (\tfrac{1}{2}mv_{xi}^2)\, \Delta N(|v_{xi}|). \tag{30.5.6}$$

The right-hand side of (30.5.6) has a simple interpretation in terms of kinetic energy (this is why we avoided canceling the factors of 2 appearing in the expression): It represents the total translational kinetic energy E_x associated with the x-component of molecular motion. We can thus rewrite (30.5.6) as

$$pV = 2E_x. \tag{30.5.7}$$

PROBLEM 30.5. Explain the preceding assertion in your own words: First identify (in words) the meaning of $\frac{1}{2}mv_{xi}^2$, then of the product $(\frac{1}{2}mv_{xi}^2)\,\Delta N(|v_{xi}|)$, and finally of the summation carried over i. Check (30.5.7) for dimensional consistency on each side of the equation (use mks units).

If we had elected to orient the y-axis perpendicular to area S in Fig. 30.4.1, we would, of course, have obtained the expression $pV = 2E_y$; there is no special significance to be ascribed to any particular axis. Since the gas is known to be uniform and isotropic, we would expect that the total kinetic energies associated with translational motion in the three independent coordinate directions would be equal. (What would be observed happening if this were not the case?) In other words, our model requires that

$$E_x = E_y = E_z. \tag{30.5.8}$$

This is referred to as a statement of *equipartition of energy*. The total KE of the system is equally divided among the three independent translational motions.

These three equal quantities of energy must, in turn, add up to equal the total translational kinetic energy E (regardless of direction of motion) of all the molecules in the box; that is,

$$E = E_x + E_y + E_z = 3E_x. \tag{30.5.9}$$

In the light of (30.5.9) we can transform (30.5.7) into

$$pV = \tfrac{2}{3}E. \tag{30.5.10}$$

Furthermore, if we denote the average translational KE per molecule as $\bar{\varepsilon}$, we have that $\bar{\varepsilon} = E/N$ and

$$pV = \tfrac{2}{3}N\bar{\varepsilon}. \tag{30.5.11}$$

PROBLEM 30.6. Let us denote the magnitude of the *total* vector velocity of any given molecule by v. Imagine dividing the population into groups of molecules with the jth group having velocities near $\mathbf{v}_j$. Using a notation similar to that adopted earlier in this section, set up an expression for the total kinetic energy E of the entire population. [*Answer:* $E = \sum_j(\frac{1}{2}mv_j^2)\,\Delta N(|\mathbf{v}_j|)$.] Is this way of looking at the total KE consistent with Eqs. (30.5.6) and (30.5.9), or is it in conflict with the latter? Explain your line of reasoning. (Note that previously we were classifying molecules by magnitude of velocity *component*, whereas now we are classifying by magnitude of *total* velocity.)

30.6 EXPERIMENTAL FACTS REGARDING PRESSURE–VOLUME RELATIONS: BOYLE'S LAW

In order to interpret the results derived in the last section we must become familiar with the experimentally known facts regarding the pressure–volume behavior of gases. A simple way of stating these facts is to describe the behavior of the pressure–volume product pV under various circumstances. We first consider the case of constant temperature.

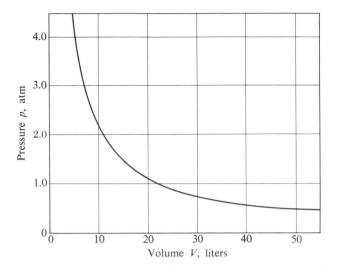

FIG. 30.6.1. A p-V isotherm for one mole of gas at 0°C. Note that curve is an equilateral hyperbola. (See Problem 30.7 for other curves to be sketched on this diagram.)

If a gas is expanded or compressed while the temperature is held constant, it is found experimentally that the pressure varies inversely as the volume. In algebraic form, we say that

$$pV = C, \tag{30.6.1}$$

where C is a constant for a given temperature and a fixed quantity of the gas. This empirical relation is known as Boyle's law.

We have seen in Section 29.6 and Problem 29.10 that one mole of any gas at 0°C and 1 atm pressure occupies a volume of 22.4 liters. Two moles would occupy twice this volume, etc. If we express pressure in atmospheres and volume in liters, the pV product for one mole of gas at 0°C would have the fixed numerical value

$$pV = 22.4 \text{ liter} \cdot \text{atm} \qquad (1 \text{ mole at } 0°C). \tag{30.6.2}$$

Similarly, we would obtain

$$pV = 44.8 \text{ liter} \cdot \text{atm} \qquad (2 \text{ moles at } 0°C),$$

$$pV = n(22.4) \text{ liter} \cdot \text{atm} \qquad (n \text{ moles at } 0°C). \tag{30.6.3}$$

Figure 30.6.1 shows a graph of (30.6.2). A p-V curve at constant temperature is called an *isotherm*.

PROBLEM 30.7.   Sketch on Fig. 30.6.1 the isotherms for 0.5 and 2 moles of gas at 0°C. For one mole of gas at some temperature higher than 0°C, the value of C in Eq. (30.6.2) will no longer be 22.4. Would you expect it to be a larger or a smaller number? Explain your reasoning in detail. Where would the resulting graph lie in Fig. 30.6.1?

It is to be emphasized that Boyle's law is an idealization, as are many other empirical laws we have encountered. The pV product of a gas is *not* absolutely constant as pressure is changed at constant temperature, but varies somewhat with the pressure. Over very wide ranges of compression this variation becomes quite appreciable, particularly with gases composed of relatively large and complex molecules. Boyle's law is, however, a very useful *first-order* description of the isothermal behavior of gases at ordinary temperatures and pressures.

30.7 EXPERIMENTAL FACTS REGARDING PRESSURE–VOLUME RELATIONS: THE LAW OF CHARLES AND GAY-LUSSAC

In the preceding section we saw that the pV product of a fixed amount of gas remains very nearly constant as a gas is expanded or compressed at constant temperatures, and in Problem 30.7 we surmised that if the temperature of this same amount of gas is increased the pV product will take on a new, larger value. We can comprehend this intuitively since we sense that p would increase if we raised the temperature while holding V constant, or that V must be allowed to increase if we are to keep p constant. In either case the numerical value of pV would increase. This is only a qualitative prediction, however, and there remains the question of the actual functional relationship between the pV product and the temperature.

Figure 30.7.1 illustrates schematically the results of experimental observations for several different quantities of gas. We note that the pV product is found to be a *linear* function of the Celsius temperature τ; this linear variation is referred to as the "law of Charles and Gay-Lussac" or frequently simply as *Charles's law*. Like Boyle's law, this is a very useful first-order approximation at ordinary temperatures

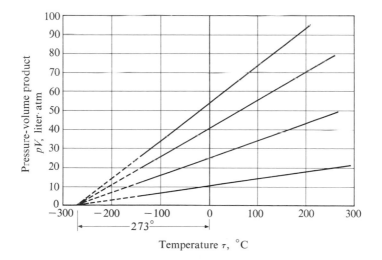

Fig. 30.7.1. Schematic diagram of the results of experimental observations on the temperature dependence of the p-V product of different amounts of gas. The observed linear relation, extrapolating to $-273°C$, is referred to as the law of Charles and Gay-Lussac.

and pressures.   Substantial departures from linearity are encountered over very large changes in these variables.

At sufficiently low temperatures (different for different gases) all gases condense into a liquid state, and an entirely different mathematical relation among p, V, and τ takes over. Thus the straight lines of Fig. 30.7.1 cease to have physical meaning below whatever the condensation temperature happens to be, and this fact is indicated schematically by the dashed portions of the lines in the diagram.

It is a very interesting fact, however, that all the straight lines extrapolate to the same point: They all radiate from the point $(-273, 0)$ on the τ-axis. That is, the straight lines, in the region in which they have physical meaning, all behave as though the pV product (or the volume of the gas itself) would vanish at a temperature of $-273°C$. Of course such vanishing does not occur physically; after the gas condenses, the liquid contracts only very slightly as the temperature continues to decrease.

Let us set up a quantitative expression of the law exhibited in Fig. 30.7.1 by finding an equation for the family of straight lines. The intercept of any line on the pV-axis is the numerical value of the pressure-volume product at a temperature of $0°C$; let us denote the intercept by $(pV)_0$. In Section 30.6 [see Eq. (30.6.3)], we indicated that it is an experimental fact that for *all gases*

$$(pV)_0 = n(22.4) \text{ liter} \cdot \text{atm,} \tag{30.7.1}$$

where n is the number of moles of gas in the container. The differing intercepts in Fig. 30.7.1 indicate that each line refers to the behavior of a different number n of moles of the gas. Since all the lines intersect at $\tau = -273$, the slope of any line with intercept $(pV)_0$ is $(pV)_0/273$. Using the slope-intercept form of the equation of a straight line [Section 3.3, Eq. (3.3.2)], we can write the equation of any line in Fig. 30.7.1 as

$$pV = \frac{(pV)_0}{273}\tau + (pV)_0$$

or, substituting Eq. (30.7.1), we obtain

$$pV = n\left(\frac{22.4}{273}\right)\tau + n(22.4),$$

$$pV = n\left(\frac{22.4}{273}\right)(\tau + 273). \tag{30.7.2}$$

The numbers 22.4 and 273 are applicable to *all* gases and are not the special properties of any particular substance. Their ratio, occurring in Eq. (30.7.2), has the numerical value 0.0821 and the dimensions of liter $\cdot$ atm/mole $\cdot$ °C. This quantity is conventionally denoted by the symbol R. Thus

$$R \equiv 0.0821 \text{ liter} \cdot \text{atm/mole} \cdot °C.$$

The numerical value is of course different if we elect to use different units: In the mks system,

$$R = 8.32 \text{ j/mole} \cdot °C.$$

If energy is measured in calories,

$$R = 1.99 \text{ cal/mole} \cdot {}°C.$$

The term $(\tau + 273)$ in Eq. (30.7.2) suggests that we shift the origin of our temperature scale from the point we called 0°C to the point at which the straight lines intersect in Fig. 30.7.1. If we call the intersection point 0 on our new scale, then room temperature or 20°C becomes 293°K, 100°C becomes 373°K, etc. This new scale, with origin at -273°C, is referred to as the *absolute* or the *Kelvin* scale; hence the K following the numerical values quoted above.

Let us adopt the notation

$$T \equiv \tau + 273,$$

so that T denotes temperature on the Kelvin scale. (Note that the *sizes* of degrees on the Kelvin and celsius scales are identical. It is only the *origin* that differs.) Equation (30.7.2) in our new symbols takes the form

$$pV = nRT. \tag{30.7.3}$$

As we have pointed out above, no real gas obeys this empirical equation with complete precision. The behavior described by this equation is called "ideal," and the equation itself is referred to as the ideal-gas law or the ideal-gas equation of state.

Since in the kinetic model we are making reference to the total number of molecules N in volume V, it is convenient to introduce N into the ideal-gas equation of state. Recall that Avogadro's number, denoted by N_0, is the number of molecules in one gram-molecular mass (one mole) of any material. We then have that the number of moles of gas associated with N molecules is given by $n = N/N_0$, and the ideal-gas equation takes the form

$$pV = N \frac{R}{N_0} T. \tag{30.7.4}$$

The quantity R/N_0 is a universal constant since R and N_0 are both universal constants. This quantity is usually denoted by k and is called *Boltzmann's constant*. In this notation the ideal-gas equation becomes

$$pV - NkT. \tag{30.7.5}$$

PROBLEM 30.8. Charles's law is sometimes described by the statement that "if the pressure of a fixed quantity of gas is held constant, the volume of the gas decreases by 1/273 of its volume at 0°C for every degree of decrease in temperature (up to the point at which the gas condenses)." Show that this statement is consistent with the information presented in Fig. 30.7.1.

PROBLEM 30.9. To obtain practice with a very elementary manipulation of Eq. (30.7.3), calculate the volume that would be occupied by 1.50 moles of ideal gas at 52°C and 2.35 atm pressure. [*Answer:* 17.0 liters.]

PROBLEM 30.10.   Using Eq. (30.7.3) as a point of departure, deduce how the *density* of an ideal gas would vary (a) with temperature if pressure were held constant, (b) with pressure if temperature were held constant. Check to see whether your results make sense intuitively.

30.8   INTERPRETATION OF TEMPERATURE BY MEANS OF THE KINETIC MODEL

In Section 30.5 we derived, from the kinetic model of a gas, the *theoretical* result

$$pV = \tfrac{2}{3}E = \tfrac{2}{3}N\bar{\varepsilon} \qquad \text{(theory)}, \tag{30.8.1}$$

where E denotes the total translational KE of all the N molecules, and $\bar{\varepsilon}$ denotes the average KE per molecule.

In Section 30.7 we asserted that experimental observations on behavior of gases yield the *empirical* equation of state

$$pV = N\frac{R}{N_0}T \qquad \text{(experiment)}. \tag{30.8.2}$$

By putting these different statements together, we can begin testing our theoretical model to see whether it yields consistent, sensible results. Suppose that we equate the right-hand sides of (30.8.1) and (30.8.2) and solve for the temperature T; we obtain

$$T = \frac{2}{3}\frac{N_0\bar{\varepsilon}}{R}. \tag{30.8.3}$$

This result suggests an *interpretation* of the concept of temperature, an interpretation which is not contained in the physical, empirical facts forming the background of Eq. (30.8.2). It is suggested that the physical property we called absolute temperature of the gas is directly related to the translational kinetic energy of the molecules. It is further suggested that temperature is, in this interpretation, like pressure, an intrinsically *statistical* quantity. It is related to the *average* kinetic energy of the molecules or, alternatively, to the total kinetic energy ($N_0\bar{\varepsilon}$) of the 6.02×10^{23} molecules that comprise a mole. A thermometer comes to equilibrium with the steady average KE of billions of billions of surrounding molecules, just as a pressure gauge registers the steady average force exerted by the molecular hailstorm at the boundary with the gas. In this context terms such as "the pressure of a single molecule" or "the temperature of a single molecule" have no meaning. Pressure and temperature have meaning as uniquely defined, steady values only in the overall behavior of an astronomically huge number of individual molecules.

The association of temperature with the vigor of molecular motion makes good sense qualitatively. Virtually all the atomists from Newton to Davy and Faraday supposed that heating a body increased the motion or vibration of its corpuscles. Equation (30.8.3), however, suggests a more specific interpretation; it indicates a direct connection between temperature and molecular KE rather than just some unknown function of molecular velocity. It further suggests that increases in temperature are associated with definite increases in molecular kinetic energy and thus provides a specific mechanism for explaining what happens to the energy supplied when a gas is heated: energy supplied as heat is conserved in increasing the total KE of the molecules.

> PROBLEM 30.11. Consider a box of gas in which one side is at a higher temperature than the other. This means that the average molecular KE is higher on the one side than the other. Visualize and describe in words what must happen to the kinetic energies as a result of random molecular motions and collisions as time goes by. What must happen to the temperatures? In the light of this description, how would you visualize the mechanism of transfer of heat from one body to another in general? How do you account for the fact that heat flows only from bodies at higher to bodies at lower temperature and never in the opposite direction? (See Section 30.14 for help with this discussion, but first try to carry it out by yourself.)

These qualitative results give us a new level of insight into the nature of heat as opposed to that of other forms of energy. If we do work to accelerate a body, the work is conserved in the form of the organized KE of the body as a whole, its macroscopic velocity being superposed on the individual random motions of its constituent molecules. The KE of the body can be stored as work or as PE if we allow it to slow down by raising a weight, compressing a spring, or turning an electric generator. But if we allow the body to slow down under the influence of friction, its organized macroscopic KE is converted into the random, chaotic KE of molecular motion, and these random motions will not become spontaneously reorganized into an orderly KE of motion of the body as a whole, even though the latter effect would involve no violation of the conservation law. On the microscopic scale, this is what lies behind processes we previously described as involving a dissipation of work or KE into heat. We thus come to speak of random molecular motions as "thermal motion" and the associated energy as "thermal energy."

All these deductions and insights tie together in a consistent and plausible way, strengthening our confidence in the kinetic model and in the interpretations we draw from it.

30.9 ORDER OF MAGNITUDE OF MOLECULAR VELOCITY

Having given a plausible kinetic interpretation of temperature, we now proceed to turn Eq. (30.8.3) around and examine the information it affords concerning molecular motions:

$$\bar{\varepsilon} = \frac{3}{2} \frac{R}{N_0} T, \qquad (30.9.1)$$

where $\bar{\varepsilon}$ denotes the average translational KE per molecule or the average value of $\frac{1}{2}mv^2$ (m being the mass of an individual molecule). In calculating the average value of $\frac{1}{2}mv^2$, adding up over all the molecules (see Problem 30.3 and Section 30.5), the quantity $\frac{1}{2}m$ is a constant factor in each term. The resulting average can be denoted by $\frac{1}{2}m\overline{v^2}$, where $\overline{v^2}$ is called the *mean-square velocity* and the quantity $\sqrt{\overline{v^2}}$ is called the *root-mean-square velocity*. We can therefore write Eq. (30.9.1) in the form

$$\tfrac{1}{2}m\overline{v^2} = \frac{3}{2}\frac{R}{N_0}T. \tag{30.9.2}$$

Solving for the root-mean-square velocity and noting that the product $N_0 m$ (number of molecules per mole times the mass of a single molecule) must equal the total mass M of a mole of gas, we obtain

$$\sqrt{\overline{v^2}} = \sqrt{3RT/M}. \tag{30.9.3}$$

Let us obtain the numerical value of this velocity for air at 20°C ($T = 293°$K). One mole of air has a mass of 29 gm or 0.029 kg. In mks units (see Section 30.7 for appropriate value of R):

$$\sqrt{\overline{v^2}} = \sqrt{\frac{3(8.31)(293)}{0.029}} = 500 \text{ m/sec}.$$

The velocity of sound in air at 20°C is 340 m/sec, which is of the same order of magnitude as the value of $\sqrt{\overline{v^2}}$ just obtained. We might expect that the velocity with which a macroscopic pressure pulse is communicated from layer to layer of gas molecules would be of a magnitude similar to that of a characteristic molecular velocity, and our model does not disappoint us. We must remember, however, that $\sqrt{\overline{v^2}}$ is in no sense *the* velocity of the molecules. Actual velocities must range from essentially zero to very high values, and $\sqrt{\overline{v^2}}$ is only a single number, a particular kind of average, a skimpy but significant bit of information about the distribution.

PROBLEM 30.12.   Evaluate $\sqrt{\overline{v^2}}$ for hydrogen and carbon dioxide at 20°C and compare with the value for air. Give a general statement of how $\sqrt{\overline{v^2}}$ varies with molecular mass at a given temperature. [*Answer:* Root-mean-square velocity is inversely proportional to square root of molecular mass.]

As we concentrate our attention on these velocities, it must be emphasized that the root-mean-square velocity $\sqrt{\overline{v^2}}$ is *not* the same number as the ordinary average first power of velocity denoted by $\overline{v}$ (see Problem 30.3). Knowledge of the entire distribution of molecular velocities in a gas (a result we shall not have time to derive in this text) shows that $\overline{v}$ is actually about 8% smaller than $\sqrt{\overline{v^2}}$, or equal to about $0.92\sqrt{\overline{v^2}}$.

It has been established experimentally that when gases are confined in a chamber closed by a thin porous plug and allowed to escape slowly through the plug (the process is called *diffusion*), different gases escape at different rates, measured in moles/sec of escaping gas. Gases with lower molecular weight are found to diffuse through the plug more rapidly than gases of higher molecular weight at the same temperature and pressure. This is what one would expect on the basis of a corpuscular model, providing the molecules of higher mass had, on the average, lower velocities than those of lower mass. This is precisely what the kinetic theory predicts. As a matter of fact, the experimentally measured rates of diffusion are found to be inversely proportional to the square root of the molecular mass of the gas. This is quite in accord with our kinetic theory result in Problem 30.12 and with the assertion made above concerning the relation between $\bar{v}$ and $\sqrt{\overline{v^2}}$. Here is an instance in which the kinetic model yields quantitative results in accord with direct experimental measurements.

30.10   THE HEAT CAPACITIES OF GASES*

Since the constant-volume and constant-pressure heat capacities of gases (c_v and c_p) are experimentally measurable quantities, it is a matter of considerable interest to determine what prediction the kinetic theory makes concerning these properties.

In Sections 19.6 and 20.5 we saw that the numerical values of c_v and c_p for air are quite different from each other ($c_v = 0.172$ cal/gm · °C; $c_p = 0.241$ cal/gm · °C) and that Mayer interpreted this difference as a measure of the amount of heat converted into work during constant-pressure heating of a gas. On the basis of this interpretation Mayer obtained one of the early estimates of the conversion factor between units of work and units of heat. Stated another way, Mayer's interpretation implies that, for one gram of air, 0.172 cal are required to change the temperature by one celsius degree under any circumstances, and that an additional 0.069 cal are required to supply the energy associated with the work done in the constant-pressure expansion.

Let us first consider the problem of constant-volume heating. Here no energy is transformed into work, and our kinetic model, subject to the law of conservation of energy, demands that all the heat put into the system must go into energy of individual molecules. Our model visualizes the molecules as possessing KE of translational motion (this aspect formed the basis of our theoretical equation for the gas pressure), but we must now recognize the possibility that molecules might also take up energy in other forms (or *modes of motion*, as they are sometimes called). For example, as the molecules collide with each other at all angles and velocities, we might expect them to acquire motions of rotation as well as translation. We might also expect collisions to excite vibration of atoms relative to each other within the molecule.

In the chaos of molecular collisions, individual molecules would be continually undergoing changes in translational, rotational, and vibrational motion, and energy could never be confined to one particular mode. Heat energy supplied to the system would thus become "smeared out" or distributed over all the different possible forms, and could never be retained in just one mode such as translation.

The kinetic model now suggests the following approach to the concept of heat capacity:

(1) Instead of taking grams or kilograms as units of mass, it would seem wise to think in terms of heat supplied per *mole* of gas. We would then, when we discussed

---

* A reader not satisfied with his grasp of the concepts of heat and heat capacity would find it profitable at this point to reread relevant sections of Chapters 19 and 20.

TABLE 30.10.1

EXPERIMENTALLY MEASURED VALUES OF c_v FOR DIFFERENT GASES
IN THE NEIGHBORHOOD OF ROOM TEMPERATURE

Type of gas	Name and formula		Molecular mass, grams/mole	c_v, j/gm · °K	c_v, j/mole · °K
Monatomic	Helium,	He	4.00	3.13	12.5
	Neon,	Ne	20.2	0.62	
	Argon,	A	39.9	0.313	
	Mercury vapor,	Hg	201	0.0626	
Diatomic	Hydrogen,	H_2	2.02	10.1	20.4
	Oxygen,	O_2	32.0	0.654	
	Nitrogen,	N_2	28.0	0.735	
	Carbon monoxide,	CO	28.0	0.743	

different gases, be comparing the energy supplied to equal numbers of molecules instead of to otherwise unrelated or uncomparable quantities of material.

(2) We have interpreted temperature as a direct measure of the average translational KE of the molecules [Eq. (30.8.3)]. If the molecules are complicated in their structure, we have to supply enough energy to increase the average rotational and vibrational energies simultaneously with the average translational energy before the temperature can be changed by one degree. Comparing energy supplied to equal numbers of molecules, we would expect gases composed of complex molecules to have higher heat capacities than those composed of simple molecules.

Table 30.10.1 presents some experimental facts concerning the constant-volume heat capacities of a number of different gases.

PROBLEM 30.13.   Fill in the blank spaces in the last column of Table 30.10.1 by calculating the remaining numerical values of c_v in units of j/mole · °K, from the data given in the two preceding columns. Note that the data in units of j/gm · °K reveal no special pattern other than a decreasing value of c_v with increasing molecular mass. A very particular pattern is revealed in the last column, however. What is the significance of switching from grams to moles as the units of mass? In the light of the discussion carried out so far, how do you interpret the numerical regularities revealed in the last column of the table?

30.11   THEORETICAL CALCULATION OF c_v OF MONATOMIC GASES

The experimental data presented in Table 30.10.1 indicate that if the constant-volume heat capacity, c_v, is measured per mole instead of per gram of the gas, all monatomic gases exhibit the same numerical value: $c_v = 12.5$ j/mole · °K. Let us attempt to construct a kinetic theory of the constant-volume heat capacity, using the experimental results as a test of the validity of the theory.

We start with the simplest possible assumption: that the atoms of the monatomic gas exchange kinetic energy of translation *only*. We previously ruled out potential energy associated with long-range forces of interaction between the atoms. We now add the assumption that, in collisions of individual atoms, none of the translational KE is converted into other forms of energy such as might be associated with KE of rotation of the atoms around their own diameters, or with vibrations of the internal structure of the atoms if such a structure exists; that is, if we add heat to the system, this energy is stored exclusively as increased KE of translational motion of the atoms.

At this point we have no way of judging the validity of the last assumption. We are going through a phase of development of the theory in which we are making a guess. We shall judge the guess to be a good one if the theoretical results agree with experiment; we shall have to revise our thinking if the results disagree. Thus our model evolves by interaction between theory and experiment; we work back and forth to devise a theory that agrees with experimental facts. Then we see whether the theory can predict some additional experimental facts we have not already used as guides in developing the theory. If the theory works for the new case, our confidence in it is strengthened.

To return to our theory: In the case of the monatomic gas we are tentatively assuming that heating the system affects only the translational KE of the atoms. If we denote the average translational KE per atom by $\bar{\varepsilon}$ and Avogadro's number by N_0, the total "internal" energy, u, associated with the motion of atoms in one mole of a monatomic gas is given by

$$u = N_0\bar{\varepsilon} = N_0(\tfrac{1}{2}m\overline{v^2}), \tag{30.11.1}$$

and from the relations developed in Sections 30.8 and 30.9 [Eqs. (30.8.3) and (30.9.1)], we have

$$u = N_0\left(\frac{3}{2}\frac{R}{N_0}T\right) = \frac{3}{2}RT. \tag{30.11.2}$$

If we heat the monatomic gas at constant volume, all the energy supplied must go into increasing the translational KE of the atoms and therefore into increasing u. No energy is utilized in the work of expansion. Therefore the constant-volume heat capacity c_v per mole of monatomic gas should be equal to the amount by which u changes for a one-degree change in temperature; that is,

$$c_v = \frac{du}{dT} = \frac{3}{2}R. \tag{30.11.3}$$

Our derivation has applied to *any* monatomic gas (no particular substance has been specified; the mass m of individual molecules does not appear in our final equation), and R is a universal constant, determined empirically for all gases exhibiting the ideal behavior defined in Section 30.7. Equation (30.11.3) therefore says that, subject to the assumptions we have introduced earlier in this section, the value of c_v

in units of j/mole · °K should be identical for all monatomic gases and equal to $\frac{3}{2}(8.32) = 12.5$ j/mole · °K. This is precisely the value found experimentally, as shown in Table 30.10.1. The agreement leads us to accept the tentative assumptions introduced at the beginning of this section, and encourages an effort to extend the theory to a more complicated system.

30.12   THEORETICAL CALCULATION OF c_v of DIATOMIC GASES

Returning to the last column of Table 30.10.1 and the values calculated in Problem 30.13, we note that the diatomic gases have constant-volume heat capacities very close together, averaging about 20.7 j/mole · °K as opposed to 12.5 j/mole · °K for the monatomic group. The larger value of heat capacity for the diatomic gases implies that more heat must be supplied to N_0 diatomic molecules (before their average translational KE is increased by an amount corresponding to 1°K change in temperature) than must be supplied to exactly the same number of atoms to produce a 1°K temperature change in a monatomic gas. We are faced with the question of what happens to the additional energy in the diatomic case.

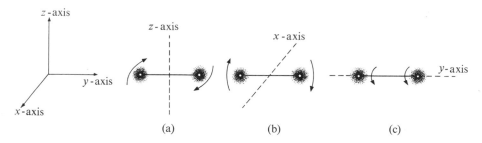

Fig. 30.12.1. Three independent ways in which a diatomic molecule can rotate around the three Cartesian axes.

A possible answer suggests itself if we visualize a diatomic molecule as a dumbbell-shaped object, capable of rotating around any of the three independent Cartesian axes, as illustrated in Fig. 30.12.1. In the random chaos of molecular collisions, some molecules will be struck in such a way that they will emerge from the collision rotating more rapidly, their rotational KE being increased at the expense of translational KE in the collision. In other instances there will be a reverse effect as a rapidly rotating molecule strikes a neighbor in such a way as to increase the translational velocity of the latter. Since energy supplied to the molecules becomes shared between the translational and rotational motions, more heat must be supplied to the rotating dumbbells of the diatomic gas to raise the temperature one degree than must be supplied to produce the same temperature change of the monatomic gas, whose atoms seem to exchange translational energy only.

How much energy should we ascribe to the rotation of our hypothetical diatomic dumbbells? One hint supplied by the monatomic gas model developed in the preceding section is that we should rule out exchange of kinetic energy with the component or "degree of freedom" of rotational motion depicted in Fig. 30.12.1(c). This is a rotation about the axis through the dumbbell—a rotation of the atoms about their own diameters—and we saw in Section 30.11 that there is apparently no excitation of this mode of KE in a monatomic gas.

In the case of the monatomic gas [Eqs. (30.11.1) and (30.11.2)], we found that the total translational KE of the atoms is given by

$$u = N_0(\tfrac{1}{2}m\overline{v^2}) = N_0 \frac{m}{2}(\overline{v_x^2} + \overline{v_y^2} + \overline{v_z^2}) = \tfrac{3}{2}RT. \qquad (30.12.1)$$

The plausible assumption regarding isotropy of the gas suggested that the average KE associated with each independent component of translational motion must be the same, and that the three equal values

$$\frac{N_0}{2}\,m\overline{v_x^2}, \qquad \frac{N_0}{2}\,m\overline{v_y^2}, \qquad \frac{N_0}{2}\,m\overline{v_z^2}$$

should add up to the total KE of $(N_0/2)m\overline{v^2}$. Since the total KE is also expressed as $\tfrac{3}{2}RT$, we are led to associate one-third of this amount or $\tfrac{1}{2}RT$ with each of the three independent translational motions, or *translational degrees of freedom*, as they are frequently called.

Now, returning to Fig. 30.12.1(a) and (b), we note the possibility of two independent rotational degrees of freedom for the diatomic molecule. If we assume that energy continues to be shared *equally* among all independent motions (as it seems to be in the three translations of the monatomic gas), we are led to the hypothesis that, for the diatomic gas, the total internal energy of one mole is given by

$$u = \tfrac{5}{2}RT, \qquad (30.12.2)$$

where an amount $\tfrac{1}{2}RT$ is associated with each of the three translations and two rotations.*

Now the amount of energy necessary to change the temperature of one mole by one degree would be given by

$$c_v = \frac{du}{dT} = \tfrac{5}{2}R = \tfrac{5}{2}(8.32) = 20.8 \text{ j/mole} \cdot {}^\circ\text{K}. \qquad (30.12.3)$$

This result is in excellent agreement with the experimental values for diatomic gases given in Table 30.10.1.

Before we jump to conclusions, however, let us examine another possibility. Suppose that our diatomic molecule is not at all a rigid dumbbell, but consists of a pair of atoms held together by electrical forces so that the atoms are free to *vibrate* toward and away from each other as though connected by a spring obeying Hooke's law.

---

* This supposition concerning the uniform sharing of energy among independent degrees of freedom can be given a sound analytical basis, rooted in the laws of classical mechanics. The discussion, however, is beyond the scope of this text. Interested readers should explore more advanced texts for discussions of the principle of equipartition of energy.

In such a vibration, there is always some KE associated with the velocities of the particles; there is also PE associated with extension and compression of the "spring." We shall not attempt to prove the following assertion, but it can be shown that, when averaged over time, the average amount of KE is equal to the average amount of PE. Each of these energies constitutes an independent degree of freedom in the system.

Suppose our diatomic molecules are not capable of changing their KE of rotation, but can change their *vibrational* energies on collision. Uniform sharing of energy among the independent degrees of freedom would require $\frac{1}{2}RT$ for each of the translational components, $\frac{1}{2}RT$ for KE of vibration and $\frac{1}{2}RT$ for PE of vibration, again giving $u = \frac{5}{2}RT$, as in Eq. (30.12.2), and predicting a value of $c_v = 20.8$ j/mole $\cdot$ °K. Which of the two alternatives is correct?

This question is not resolved in any simple, obvious, or pat way. It turns out that our first supposition regarding the rotation of the dumbbell molecule is the correct description of the behavior of diatomic gases at ordinary temperatures, but this conclusion is reached after the examination of heat capacity data for more complex molecules, the way in which c_v varies over a wide range of temperature, information concerning size and structure of molecules, etc. Deeper inquiry into this range of problems—an area still fascinating to chemists and physicists interested in the structure of molecules—would lead us too far afield. We shall stop our story at this point, though it is only partly told, hoping that the reader has become aware of how this part of the theory got its start, what questions have been convincingly answered, and how many questions remain to be pursued.

> PROBLEM 30.14.   In the light of the discussion of constant-volume heat capacities in Sections 30.11 and 30.12, what guesses would you make about the behavior of a triatomic molecule at ordinary temperatures? [Consider two possible cases: (1) The centers of the three atoms lie on a straight line. (2) The centers form the vertices of a triangle.] Look up c_v of some triatomic molecules and compare with your predictions.

> PROBLEM 30.15.   In the kinetic model we have implicitly assumed that the rotation of diatomic or more complex molecules does not influence the pressure they exert on the wall of the container. What experimental facts justify this assumption?

30.13   VARIATION OF c_v WITH TEMPERATURE; FAILURE OF THE CLASSICAL THEORY

Our model of the rotating diatomic molecule developed in the preceding section led to the result $c_v = 20.8$ j/mole $\cdot$ °K—a prediction that c_v should be independent of temperature. Experimental investigation, however, reveals that c_v is not constant; a graph of observations for hydrogen gas, H_2, is shown in Fig. 30.13.1. It is evident that the curve is quite flat and that c_v is nearly constant at a value of 20.8 j/mole $\cdot$ °K between about 250 and 500°K (that is, between about -20 and 200°C). Above this range the curve rises to a new flat region at 29.1 j/mole $\cdot$ °K, while below this range it falls to a flat region in which the heat capacity becomes identical with the monatomic gas value: $c_v = 12.5$ j/mole $\cdot$ °K.

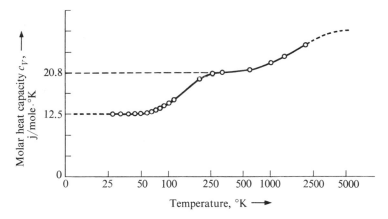

FIG. 30.13.1.   Experimental measurements of the constant-volume heat capacity of hydrogen (H_2) as a function of temperature. (Temperature is plotted on a logarithmic scale in order to compress the graph to a reasonable width.)

These experimental measurements seem to imply that below about 50°K, the rotational mode of the hydrogen molecules is no longer excited, and the molecules behave as though they gained or lost translational KE only. Similarly, the behavior at high temperatures might be interpreted as indicating that the vibrational mode, unexcited below about 500°K, begins to participate in the energy exchanges and absorbs energy as heat is added to the system.

Such behavior clearly contradicts the principle of equipartition of energy, since, in the temperature ranges in which c_v is changing, energy is *not* uniformly distributed in the amount of $\frac{1}{2}RT$ for each independent degree of freedom. The distribution apparently changes with T in some complex way so that the derivative $du/dT = c_v$ is not a constant.

Thus the kinetic theory we have developed appears to contain a very serious flaw, despite some of its other plausible results and dramatic successes. Experimental observations such as those represented in Fig. 30.13.1 confronted the scientific community at the turn of this century with a very fundamental unresolved problem. Ultimately, resolution of the problem came through a reexamination of the most basic assumptions of physical theory and the invention of a new mechanics of atoms and molecules.

Deeply embedded in all the analyses and calculations we have made with the kinetic theory is the assumption that, in their translational, rotational, and vibrational motions, atoms and molecules behave just like macroscopic objects, changing their energies in various degrees of freedom *continuously* through every conceivable arithmetic value. One of the most unsettling discoveries of twentieth-century science was the realization that molecules, atoms, and subatomic particles do not behave in this way at all. It was found that behavior on the microscopic scale differs profoundly and qualitatively from that on the macroscopic scale: Individual atoms or molecules can take on only discrete values of energy. A particular kind of molecule, say H_2, can exist only in certain fixed *energy levels*, as these discrete values are usually called.   Changes in energy involve transitions from one discrete level to another, and intermediate values of energy are never assumed by any molecules in the system. We speak of the energy of the molecules as being *quantized* in discrete levels, and we say that quanta of energy are absorbed or emitted in transitions from one level to another.

The laws of classical mechanics assume that continuous values of velocity, energy, etc., are possible, and the principle of equipartition of energy holds only under these conditions.   Given the quantum concept, however, we can begin to see qualitatively how the equipartition principle breaks down.   Suppose we start with H_2 molecules at very low temperatures where $c_v = 12.5$ j/mole $\cdot$ °K.   Apparently, as heating takes place, only translational motion is increased and no energy is transferred to rotational motion.   This effect can readily be explained if there is a large difference between the lowest allowed rotational energy level and the next higher one.   Under such circumstances, with molecules moving at relatively low translational velocities because of the low temperature, collisions would not be energetic enough to kick molecules from the lowest rotational level to the next higher one, and no energy would be transferred into rotational KE.   As the temperature is increased, however, some translational velocities would become high enough to kick a few molecules into the next rotational level, but no higher.   This would result in a slight increase in c_v, but we would be very far from an equipartition of energy among translational and rotational degrees of freedom.   The process would continue with increasing T until so many molecules had motions distributed over a wide spectrum of allowed rotational energy levels that the system would be very close to obeying the equipartition principle.   Then c_v would level off at 20.8 j/mole $\cdot$ °K.

PROBLEM 30.16.   It is known that in diatomic molecules the energy difference between the lowest and next higher vibrational energy levels is considerably larger than the energy difference between the first two rotational levels. Starting with this information, justify the assertion that the first rise in Fig. 30.13.1 is due to excitation of molecular rotations, while the second is due to excitation of vibrations. Describe in your own words what happens in hydrogen gas as temperature is increased in the region above 500°K.

Not only did the quantum theory resolve the specific problems we have indicated above; it also made possible the determination and elucidation of molecular structure in a detail that seems astounding even at this time.   Physicists and chemists have been able to determine the average spacings between atoms in various molecules to three or four significant figures.   It is also possible to determine the precise arrangement of the atoms in three dimensions, the frequencies of the discrete vibrational energy levels, the rotational energy levels, etc.   It is possible to predict a complete heat-capacity curve such as that of Fig. 30.13.1 on the basis of the kinetic theory and of knowledge of molecular structure, without reference to any other experimental information about the particular substance.

The reader will find fragments of the story of the advent of the new science of quantum mechanics in Chapters 34 and 35, and descriptions in greater detail in many other texts.

30.14 STATISTICAL BASIS OF THE MACROSCOPIC PROPERTIES OF MATERIAL SUBSTANCES

A very simple arithmetical calculation will give us a frame of reference in which to visualize the behavior of the crowd of molecules in a gas. Let us calculate the order of magnitude of the average spacing between molecules under ordinary conditions of temperature and pressure: We have seen in Table 29.6.1 and Problem 29.10 that one mole of any gas occupies around 20,000 to 30,000 cm^3, depending on temperature and pressure. We have also asserted that the number of molecules N_0 in one mole of any substance is equal to about 6×10^{23}. (See Chapters 31, 33 and, in particular, Section 33.8 for a discussion of how this information is obtained.) The average volume associated with each molecule is therefore about

$$\frac{250 \times 10^2}{6 \times 10^{23}} \cong 40 \times 10^{-21} \ \text{cm}^3.$$

If we imagine each molecule encased in a little cube of this volume, we see that the average spacing between molecules must be equal to the length of one side of the cube, which is equal to

$$(40 \times 10^{-21})^{1/3} - 3.4 \times 10^{-7} = 34 \times 10^{-8} \ \text{cm} = 34 \ \text{A}.$$

Thus the average spacing between molecules of a gas at ordinary conditions of temperature and pressure must be of the order of 30 to 40 A. This is of the order of $\frac{1}{200}$ of the wavelength of visible light! As we shall see in later chapters, the size of an individual molecule is of the order of 1 or 2 A.

PROBLEM 30.17.   Sketch a cube 1 mm to a side on the paper. Show that the number of molecules of gas in 1 mm^3 at ordinary temperature and pressure is of the order of 2 to 3×10^{16}. Try to visualize how large this number is; then calculate and try to sketch the size of a cube that contains only one billion (10^9) molecules.

It has been argued in Sections 30.5 and 30.8 that pressure on the wall of the container is an essentially *statistical* quantity. It is interpreted as the average effect of the unimaginably large number of molecular collisions taking place every second on each unit area of the wall, and we begin to recognize that, under ordinary conditions, our measuring devices record a steady, unfluctuating pressure because of the enormous number and frequency of the collisions.

If we try to visualize what would happen in a box containing only a few molecules, we immediately see that any small area of the wall would receive only an occasional impulse from an individual molecule. Since an instrument is composed of atoms and molecules itself, it is not capable of detecting such a single collision. But if it were, it would indicate individual blows spread out randomly in time; it would not register a steady force. Thus our concept of pressure loses meaning if we examine too rarefied a gas or if we focus our attention on too small a wall area, even under ordinary conditions.

In an exactly similar sense, the kinetic model [see Eq. (30.8.3)] also shows temperature to be a statistical quantity, depending on the average translational KE of the molecules. If we were able to examine events taking place in a very small volume, say 100 A to a side, we would find both the number of molecules in this volume and their average KE fluctuating violently from moment to moment. Under these circumstances, we could not describe the temperature within the small volume as a single number, constant in time.

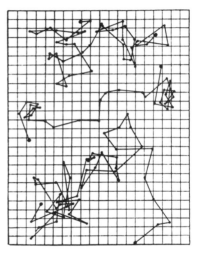

FIG. 30.14.1. Brownian motion. Positions (on a highly enlarged scale) of three grains suspended in water and observed at 30-sec intervals. Note that unplotted, equally jerky motions were occurring between the observations. (After J. Perrin.)

The effect of fluctuations and nonuniformity on a very small scale can actually be exhibited visually in quite simple experiments. Tiny specks of dust, pollen grains, or other so-called "colloidal" particles suspended in a transparent liquid can be made visible, like motes of dust in a sunbeam, by shining a bright light through the suspension. When watched through a microscope, the specks are seen to move around perpetually in a jerky dance. (This phenomenon, first observed in 1827 by the English botanist Robert Brown, is called *Brownian motion*.) Figure 30.14.1 is a sketch, on a highly enlarged scale, of positions of several grains observed at 30-sec intervals.

The suspended particles are so small that, in experiencing the irregular bombardment of molecules of the surrounding liquid, they are accelerated and displaced first one way and then another. In other words, they detect for us the irregular, pulsating effects of relatively small numbers of molecular impacts in a manner our usual pressure-measuring instruments are quite incapable of doing. And yet it must be kept in mind that even these minute grains have sizes that are enormous relative to molecular dimensions and spacing.

The discovery of Brownian motion caused a certain amount of consternation because it implied the existence of perpetual motion, a phenomenon that seemed to be prohibited on the macroscopic scale of ordinary sense experience. The kinetic theory now helps us understand that perpetual motion is not at all prohibited on the atomic-molecular scale. It is an essential feature of the behavior of atoms and molecules and determines most of the prominent macroscopic properties of bulk matter. Considering the readiness with which some individuals jumped to hasty conclusions by extrapolating ordinary experience to the microscopic level, we might now better appreciate the profundity of Newton's intuition as exhibited in the quotation from the *Opticks* cited in the first paragraph of Section 19.8.

Not only are atoms and molecules in constant motion (vibrational motion around fixed positions in solids) in material substances of any kind, but they are constantly passing in and out of bodies in the course of various physical and chemical processes. The apparently steady equilibrium between a liquid and its vapor is not an inert, static condition but an active, *kinetic* equilibrium in which molecules randomly break out of the liquid and enter the vapor phase, while molecules of vapor collide with the liquid and reenter it at an equal and opposite rate. In living systems, atoms and molecules are continually incorporated and released from the structure as respiration, metabolism, and other biological processes take place. On the atomic-molecular level, these systems participate in eternal flux and motion and change. Many atoms that constitute our bodies now are not the ones that were there some time ago, and these will in turn be exchanged for others.

Our qualitative discussion of the statistical, kinetic behavior of aggregations of molecules can now give us an insight into the character of certain common spontaneous processes. Consider, for example, a situation in which we heat the top of a container of gas and the temperature in that region is higher than it is elsewhere in the container; the heating is then stopped. We know from a wealth of accumulated experience that heat will flow from the higher to the lower temperature regions until the temperature becomes uniform throughout the gas. How do we account, in terms of the kinetic theory, for this spontaneous change which invariably takes place in one particular direction? Note that the process is essentially statistical; it takes place as an average, overall effect: faster-moving molecules in the higher temperature region collide with slower molecules in adjacent regions and more translational KE tends to be transferred, *on the average*, from higher KE to lower KE regions than is transferred in the opposite direction.

It is not *impossible* for all the faster molecules to move after collisions toward one side of the container, giving that side a higher temperature than the other; it is just extremely improbable—vastly less probable, for example, than having the entire human population of the earth spontaneously walk to the north at some instant of time. Similarly, it is just as improbable that vast numbers of molecules will head toward one end of the container, increasing the density in that region and causing a pressure difference that can be utilized to do external work.

Thus the random motion and collisions of atoms and molecules seem to obey the rules of probability and lead to spontaneous changes that *obliterate* nonuniformities in properties such as temperature and pressure. Heat never flows spontaneously from regions of lower to regions of higher temperature, even though the conservation-of-energy principle would *not* be violated in such a process! It is quite apparent that these ideas are intimately connected with the laws of thermodynamics, which were very briefly mentioned in Section 20.9. Our present cursory discussion can do no more than give the reader a notion of the channels into which this discussion leads. Further exploration in more advanced references can be very rewarding.

PROBLEM 30.18. Consider the familiar physical situation in which a block, initially sliding on a level floor, comes to rest under the influence of friction. In the language and concepts of the kinetic theory, describe in detail what happens to the initial orderly KE of the body as a whole. Where does this energy end up? Through what sequence of processes? Why cannot this energy be *spontaneously* returned to the form of translational KE of the block as a whole?

SUPPLEMENTARY READING AND STUDY

Elementary discussion:
  Physics, Physical Science Study Committee. Boston: D. C. Heath & Co, 1960, Chapters 8, 9
  The Restless Universe, M. Born. New York: Harper 1936; Dover 1951

Other presentations of kinetic theory:
  Physics for the Inquiring Mind, Eric Rogers. Princeton, N.J.: Princeton University Press, 1960, Chapter 25
  Physics for Students of Science and Engineering, R. Resnick and I. Halliday. New York: John Wiley & Sons, 1960, Chapters 23, 24
  Introduction to Mechanics, Matter, and Waves, U. Ingard and W. L. Kraushaar. Reading, Mass.: Addison-Wesley, 1960, Chapters 15, 16

Historical background:
  "A Sketch for a History of the Kinetic Theory of Gases," E. Mendoza. *Physics Today*, **14**, 36 (1961)
  A Source Book in Physics. Selections from Joule, Bernoulli, Brown, and Maxwell, edited by W. F. Magie. New York: McGraw-Hill, 1935

CHAPTER 31

Subatomic Particles and the Corpuscular Nature of Electricity

31.1 INTRODUCTION

The years around 1890 marked a plateau in the evolution of physical science. Tested and verified over an incredible range of phenomena, the Newtonian laws seemed to provide an unassailable foundation for the description of mechanical processes and gravitation. Maxwell's theory of the electromagnetic field unified the description of electric and magnetic effects, explained the propagation, reflection, refraction, and polarization of light, predicted radio waves, and, in the hands of mathematical physicists such as Hertz, Heaviside, Poynting, and Lorentz, led to the solution of many detailed and complex problems in the generation and propagation of electromagnetic disturbances and the interaction of such disturbances with distributions of electrically charged particles. Bridging mechanical, electromagnetic, and chemical phenomena were the laws of thermodynamics, pointing to energy as the characteristic of regularity and permanence in transformations involving these diverse effects and, through the second law of thermodynamics, predicting the direction of spontaneous processes and the conditions under which equilibria would be attained.

Embedded in these theoretical structures one can discern two primary, distinct conceptions of physical process. On one hand, there is the concept of *particle*—a localized, corpuscular entity, possessing inertial mass, having geometrical dimensions, moving in a clearly defined trajectory described by positions s occupied at instants of time t, not superposable on another particle in a given position at the same instant, subject to mechanical, electrical, or magnetic forces, and, under the influence of these forces, obeying the Newtonian laws of motion. On the other hand, there is the concept of *wave*—a nonlocalized process, spreading out in all directions, with pulselike or oscillatory variations, exhibiting diffraction in passing around obstacles, and interference in superposition of more than one wave at a given place. Complex physical phenomena were being analyzed very successfully in terms of these two distinct conceptions, and further progress was to be expected.

In 1890 there was no scarcity of unsolved problems. Bright line spectra of gases remained to be explained, and their relation to the atomicity of matter and the vibration of electrically charged atomic particles had not advanced significantly beyond the level of conjecture. Knowledge of relative atomic masses revealed but did not explain periodicities in the behavior of the chemical elements. It was suspected but not yet experimentally demonstrated that, on an atomic scale, electrical charge was corpuscular rather than continuously distributed. Attempts to observe the motion of the earth relative to Maxwell's electromagnetic ether had so far been unsuccessful, and puzzling problems remained to be resolved in connection with the description of electromagnetic phenomena viewed from frames of reference moving at different velocities relative to each other.

There was, however, no reason to suspect that these problems could not be solved within the existing structure of concepts and theories. On the contrary, previous experience gave strong support to the supposition that solutions would soon be forthcoming. No one could foresee that the decade 1895–1905 would bring a flood of experimental discovery, revealing a new world of unanticipated physical phenomena on the subatomic scale; few would have imagined a conceptual crisis and conceptual revolution to be imminent.

The conceptual revolution had two principal branches. One, stemming from problems posed by the concept of an electromagnetic ether and considerations of frames of reference for the description of electromagnetic phenomena, led to the theory of relativity, rejection of Newton's conception of absolute space and absolute time, and realization of the limited range of validity of the Newtonian laws of mechanics and gravitation. The second branch, stemming from discoveries of subatomic phenomena, led to models of atomic structure and theories of bright line spectra and chemical bonding, but these theories were achieved only at the expense of abandoning, on the microscopic scale, important elements of the Maxwellian synthesis and by creating an entirely new and strange mechanics of microscopic phenomena.

In this and several following chapters, we shall be concerned with the revolution stemming from the discovery of subatomic effects. The story begins in 1895 with the achievement of sudden new insights into a phenomenon that had been under study for many years—the discharge of electricity through rarefied gases.

31.2 CATHODE RAYS

A simple apparatus for illustrating phenomena observed in electrical discharge through gases is sketched in Fig. 31.2.1. Initially the glass tube contains air or some other gas at atmospheric pressure. When the voltage source (potential differences of the order of tens of thousands of volts) is connected to the electrodes, no effects are observed in the tube, but as the pressure in the tube is lowered by means of a vacuum pump, one first observes flickering, lightning-like discharges between the electrodes, followed at lower pressures by the establishment of a more or less uniform glow throughout the tube. As the pressure is lowered further, the glow becomes interspersed with darker vertical striations, and a region in which the glow is absent

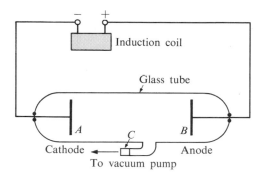

FIG. 31.2.1. Sketch of apparatus to illustrate phenomena associated with electrical discharge in gases. Metal electrodes A and B are sealed into a glass tube. Tube can be evacuated through outlet C. Electrodes are connected to high-voltage source such as an induction coil. Using Faraday's terminology, electrode A is called the cathode and B the anode.

(so-called *dark space*) develops to the right of the cathode. The gas immediately around the cathode glows with an intense bluish-purple color.

As the evacuation continues to still lower pressures (of the order of 10^{-5} mm of mercury), the dark space expands to fill the entire tube, all visible glow of gas is extinguished, and only a greenish-yellow fluorescence of the glass itself is visible at the end of the tube opposite the cathode. If the polarity of the applied voltage is reversed, the greenish-yellow glow appears on the glass at the other end of the tube, opposite the electrode which has now become the cathode.

Various minerals and different types of glass inserted into the tube between cathode and anode fluoresce brightly with colors characteristic of their respective compositions. Metal objects cast sharply defined shadows on a glass wall opposite the cathode, regardless of the location of the anode.

These experiments suggest that something proceeds in straight lines from the neighborhood of the cathode and is cut off by obstacles. The emission was given the name "cathode rays" or "cathode discharge." Our further discussion will be concerned with research that led to elucidation of the nature of the cathode rays. (The phenomena of gas glow occurring at somewhat higher pressures are very much more complex than the phenomenon of cathode rays, and even today are only partly understood.)

31.3 CROOKES' EXPERIMENTS WITH CATHODE RAYS

In a Bakerian lecture delivered in 1879, Sir William Crookes (1832–1919) summarized the available experimental knowledge concerning the behavior of cathode rays. Much of the work described was done in his own laboratory with the assistance of a highly skilled glassblower, to whom Crookes paid high tribute for making the delicate experiments possible.

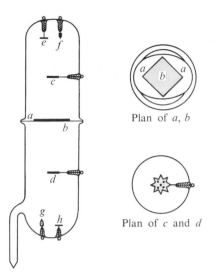

FIG. 31.3.1.   Schematic diagram of
tube used by Crookes to observe
shadows of objects in a beam of cathode
rays.

Plan of a, b

Plan of c and d

Crookes reported on a careful investigation of the formation of shadows in a tube
constructed as shown in Fig. 31.3.1. Two types of electrodes were built into the tube:
flat disc electrodes e and h and pointed electrodes f and g. At ab there was fastened
a piece of uranium glass that acted as a screen, exhibiting a greenish glow under
incidence of cathode rays.   Metal plates of various shapes (stars, rectangles, or
discs with holes in them) could be mounted at c or d.   Crookes reported that objects
at c cast very sharp shadows on the screen when the cathode was the flat disc denoted
by e, and that the shadows were diffuse when the cathode was the sharp pointed
electrode f. (Either g or h was the anode in these experiments.) Crookes interpreted
these results as indicating that the cathode rays emanate in straight lines perpendicular
to the cathode surface, and he subsequently designed other experiments based on
this idea.   The geometrical shape and the location of the anode* were found to have
no observable effect on the cathode beam or on the shadow produced.   Reversing
polarity and making g or h the cathode would cause the screen ab to glow, but the
shadow would be that of obstacle d, the obstacle c no longer intercepting the beam
ahead of the screen.†

---

* The anode can be placed almost anywhere in the tube without affecting the fluorescence
of the screen or the behavior of the rays.

† The reader should recognize the fundamental connection between this primitive tube
and the much more efficient modern television tube, in which rays emanate from a heated
cathode coated with substances that greatly enhance the intensity of the discharge.   The
anode is usually located in the side of the tube not far from the cathode.   The screen at
the viewing end of the tube corresponds to Crookes' screen of uranium glass; it is coated
with special mineral "phosphors" that exhibit a bright fluorescence under incidence of the
cathode rays.   In the television tube, the beam is sharply focused so as to strike the screen
at only one very small spot at any instant of time.   The beam is then rapidly swept back
and forth and displaced up or down while being increased and decreased in intensity, thus
producing the picture seen on the screen.

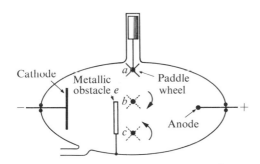

FIG. 31.3.2. Schematic diagram of paddle-wheel experiment.

In another experiment, Crookes showed that cathode rays could produce mechanical effects. A small paddle wheel "8 millimeters in diameter, furnished with clear mica vanes . . . and delicately supported on a glass cup and needle point" was suspended in the tube by means of flexible glass fibers. The paddle wheel could be brought into various positions inside and outside the shadow cast by a metal plate *e*, as sketched in Fig. 31.3.2. When the wheel was outside the shadow, exposed to the unobstructed beam at position *a*, it did not rotate. In positions *b* and *c*, with some vanes in the shadow and others exposed to the beam, the wheel rotated in the directions shown by the arrows. Questions regarding the significance of this experiment are raised in Problem 31.2 below.

Observing what he thought to be evidence of heating effects in certain experiments, Crookes conceived of concentrating or focusing the cathode beam by using a curved instead of a flat electrode, basing his idea on the previous observation that cathode rays seem to emanate along straight lines normal to the cathode surface:

> "A nearly hemispherical cup of polished aluminum *a* [Fig. 31.3.3] is made one [electrode] in a bulb, and a small disc of aluminum *b* is made the other [electrode]. At *c* a strip of platinum is held by a wire passing through the glass, and forming another electrode at *d*. The tip of the platinum strip is brought to the center of curvature, and the whole is exhausted to a very high point. On first turning on the [high-voltage source], the cup being made the [cathode], the platinum strip entered into a very rapid vibration. This soon stopped, and the platinum quickly rose to white heat and would have melted had I not stopped the action of the coil. The same phenomena of ignition take place if the platinum strip itself is made the [anode]."

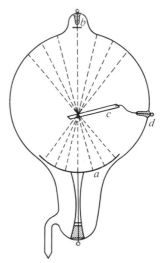

FIG. 31.3.3. Crookes' tube in which a curved cathode at *a* focuses the cathode rays on a platinum strip *c*.

31.4 EFFECT OF MAGNETIC FIELDS ON CATHODE RAYS

Having observed that the presence of a magnet caused a deflection of the position of the fluorescent region on the glass opposite the cathode, Crookes designed a tube to display and study this effect more clearly (Fig. 31.4.1).

He made visible the path of a narrow beam of cathode rays by allowing the beam to fall along the diagonally oriented screen *f*, a small portion of the beam remaining unintercepted and forming a spot at *k* on screen *d*. In the presence of a magnetic field directed into the plane of the paper (Fig. 31.4.1b), the beam was observed to be deflected downward. The beam, however, is not appreciably broadened under these circumstances, and the spot originally at *k* on screen *d* is shifted downward to *n* with only very slight change in size, or elongation in the vertical direction.

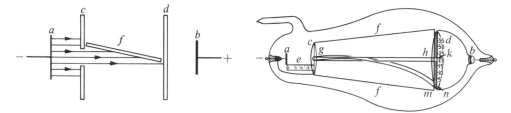

(a) Top view of tube construction: *c* is an aluminum plate with a hole near the center; *f* is a vertical screen of mica covered with a fluorescent powder. The screen cuts diagonally across the beam emerging from the hole in *c*. Another fluorescent screen is placed at *d*.

(b) Front view of tube construction: In absence of magnetic field, narrow beam formed by hole in *c* is visible because of fluorescence along band *gh*, and causes fluorescent spot on screen at *k*. When magnetic field is directed *into* plane of paper, beam is deflected downward so as to form fluorescent band *gm* and spot at *n*.

Fig. 31.4.1. Schematic diagram of Crookes' tube for studying effects of magnetic field on narrow beam of cathode rays.

In an experiment with a tube having a curved cathode similar to that shown in Fig. 31.3.3, Crookes used a magnet to deflect the point of focus of the rays until it fell on the side of the tube: "To ascertain if heat were developed here, I touched it with my finger and immediately raised a blister. The spot where the focus fell was nearly red hot."

Crookes was firmly convinced that the cathode rays consisted of charged particles shot off from the cathode. All his descriptions, comments, and interpretations of experiments are indeed based on this mental picture. In the following problems let us tentatively adopt Crookes' point of view, and explain the experimental observations in terms of a corpuscular model:

PROBLEM 31.1. In discussing the experiments with shadows cast by metallic objects, Crookes remarks, "The sharpness of the shadows, when projected from a wide [electrode proves them to be formed by particles]. Had the projection from the negative pole radiated in all directions, after the manner of light radiating from a luminous disc, the shadows would not be perfectly sharp, but would be surrounded by a penumbra.

Being, however, projected material particles in the same electrical state, they do not cross each other, but travel on in slightly divergent paths, giving sharp shadows with no penumbrae. . . ." Elaborate on Crookes' comments: Drawing appropriate rays, sketch the umbra and penumbra of the shadow that would be observed if each point on the cathode sent out rays in all directions. What is the direction of the lines of force of the electrical field near a flat metallic cathode? If electrically charged material particles are accelerated in this region of the field, what trajectories would you expect them to have? How do you account for the focusing effect produced by the curved cathode in Fig. 31.3.3?

PROBLEM 31.2. Explain the results of the paddle-wheel experiment described in Fig. 31.3.2. How do you account for the fact that it does not rotate at all in position a? What inferences are to be drawn about properties of the cathode rays from the paddle-wheel experiment and from the heating of the platinum foil (Fig. 31.3.1)? Couch your answer in terms of the concepts of momentum and energy.

PROBLEM 31.3. If the cathode rays consist of charged particles accelerated away from the cathode, what charge must the particles carry? Is this conjecture consistent with the results of the magnetic deflection experiment described in Fig. 31.4.1(b)? Describe your reasoning in detail. It is readily established that the presence of a powerful magnet has no deflecting effect on a beam of light or radio waves. What relevance does this fact have to the choice of a model for the nature of cathode rays?

PROBLEM 31.4. Return to consideration of the fact that, under magnetic deflection, the spot at position k in Fig. 31.4.1(b) is shifted to position n with only very slight spreading or elongation. Using Crookes' corpuscular model and tentatively assuming that all the particles in the beam are identical in charge and mass, what inference would you draw concerning the velocities of the particles in the beam? Explain your reasoning. What effect would you expect on the location of spot n if the potential difference between the electrodes is increased? (This effect is readily observed.) How would you account for the fact that the beam in Fig. 31.4.1(b) shows no detectable downward deflection under the influence of gravity?

The German physicist P. Lenard (1862–1947) at the University of Heidelberg adopted a different point of view from that of Crookes. He conducted numerous careful experiments on the transmission of cathode rays through very thin metal foil "windows" in the end of the cathode-ray tube and on the penetration of the rays through different gases after passing through the foil. Finding that the rays penetrated the foil and continued on for another centimeter or two, still in straight lines, Lenard became convinced that the cathode rays could not be corpuscular or material in character, but must be wave disturbances in the ether. He could not conceive material charged particles penetrating a substance as dense as the metal foil without being deflected from straight-line paths. The opposing points of view of Crookes and Lenard exemplify the sharp distinction between corpuscular and wave phenomena that had emerged in nineteenth-century scientific thought. It was believed that these two kinds of behavior were mutually exclusive, that any given phenomenon must be of either one class or the other, that no manifestation could exhibit both corpuscular *and* wavelike aspects.

31.5 THE DISCOVERY OF X-RAYS

In December 1895, Wilhelm Karl Roentgen (1845–1923), professor of physics at Würzburg, reported a discovery that aroused world-wide interest among both lay-men and scientists and stimulated a flurry of research activity not unlike that generated by Oersted's discovery of the magnetic field around a current-carrying conductor three-quarters of a century earlier. Roentgen had observed that a paper screen covered with a sensitive fluorescent material (barium platino-cyanide) glowed brightly in a darkened room when placed at distances as great as two meters from a cathode-ray tube operating under large potential difference. The fluorescence was observed when the tube was tightly covered with black cardboard!

Roentgen's initial observation was accidental, but it changed the entire direction of his research; he embarked on a careful sequence of experiments designed to de-termine the nature of the new phenomenon. He showed that the brightness of the glow could be varied by placing different objects between the tube and the fluorescent screen, and he concluded that rays of some sort emanated from the tube. He found that photographic film was sensitive to the rays. He reported that objects such as paper, wood, sheets of hard rubber, and thin sheets of aluminum, all opaque to ordinary light, attenuated the new rays only slightly or not at all. He found that lead of a thickness of 1.5 mm was virtually opaque to the rays, and started using lead as a shield to block off the rays and to protect photographic plates until he wished to expose them.

"If the hand be held between the discharge tube and the screen," he wrote in his first paper, "the darker shadow of the bones is seen within the slightly dark shadow image of the hand itself." Photographs of this effect soon made a public sensation, and it was not long before physicians were using such photographs for diagnostic purposes.

Being in doubt about the physical nature of the emanations, Roentgen called them X-rays, and the name persists to this day.

Roentgen showed that X-rays were not measurably refracted by prisms of various materials, and pointed out that it would therefore be impossible to focus them by means of lenses.

An important question was whether cathode rays and X-rays were the same or different manifestations. Roentgen pointed out that Lenard had shown that cathode rays penetrate only a centimeter or two into air at atmospheric pressure, while X-rays penetrate several meters. He then adduced other evidence:

> "A further difference, and a most important one, between the behavior of cathode rays and of X-rays lies in the fact that I have not succeeded, in spite of many attempts, in obtaining a deflection of the X-rays by a magnet, even in very intense fields. . . .
>
> "According to experiments designed to test the question, it is certain that the spot on the wall of the discharge tube which fluoresces the strongest is to be considered as the main center from which X-rays radiate in all directions. . . . If the cathode rays within the tube are deflected by means of a magnet, it is observed

that the X-rays proceed from another spot—namely, from that which is the new terminus of the cathode rays. . . . For this reason, therefore, the X-rays, which it is impossible to deflect, cannot be cathode rays simply transmitted or reflected without change by the glass wall. . . .

"I therefore reach the conclusion that the X-rays are not identical with cathode rays, but that they are produced by the cathode rays at the glass wall of the discharge apparatus. This production does not take place in glass alone, but, as I have been able to observe in an apparatus closed by a plate of aluminum 2 mm thick, in this metal also. Other substances are to be examined later."

It was soon demonstrated that many substances emit X-rays when exposed to the cathode beam. Subsequent study of X-rays and their properties led to many basic discoveries in the suddenly emerging field of atomic physics. (See Chapter 34.) The first Nobel prize in physics, awarded in 1901, went to Roentgen for his epoch-making discovery.

31.6 CONDUCTION OF ELECTRICITY IN GASES

In his earliest experiments Roentgen found that X-rays caused the discharge of electrified bodies such as a charged sphere or an electroscope. The discharge took place more rapidly when the X-rays were more intense, as indicated by the glow of the fluorescent screen. Several indirect pieces of evidence led him to suspect that the discharge occurred because X-rays rendered air around the charged bodies conducting. He confirmed this hypothesis by drawing air through a tube past a charged object; when X-rays were passed through the moving air at points as much as 20 cm ahead of the charged body, the body was discharged as though the air were a conductor. The conductivity of the air disappeared if it were passed through a plug of wadding before reaching the electroscope.

Similar experiments were being performed almost simultaneously by J. J. Thomson and his associates at the Cavendish Laboratory at Cambridge. They showed that conductivity induced by X-rays disappeared when a gas was sucked through glass wool. They also showed that the conductivity was removed by passing the gas between capacitor plates connected to a battery of sufficiently high potential difference.

In other experiments they showed that a steady current flowed through the circuit while X-rays were being passed through the air between the capacitor plates. The current increased to a maximum or "saturation" value as the potential difference between the plates was increased, and then remained fixed despite further increase in the potential difference. More intense X-rays caused a higher saturation current. The current dropped off to zero over a period of several seconds after the X-rays were turned off.

These experiments strongly supported the hypothesis that X-rays induced the formation of ions (electrically charged atoms or molecules) within the gas, and that migration of these ions accounted for the observed conductivity. In other words, it appeared that conductivity in gases was essentially "electrolytic" in character—

similar to conduction observed in electrolysis of liquid solutions. (See Section 25.8.) However, in the gaseous state relatively rapid recombination of positive and negative ions to re-form neutral molecules apparently necessitated a steady supply of energy from the X-rays to maintain a high population of ions, and thereby sustain the conductivity.

> PROBLEM 31.5. Elaborate the proposed model of gas conductivity somewhat further in your own words. How would you account for the observation of a maximum or "saturation" current—why might the current cease to increase despite further increase in potential difference between the capacitor plates? Why does increasing the X-ray intensity increase the saturation current? In your present state of knowledge, how do you visualize the difference between conduction in the ionized gas and conduction in a metallic conductor obeying Ohm's Law?

31.7 SIGNIFICANCE OF THE DISCOVERY OF IONIZATION OF GASES

Prior to the discovery of X-rays, it had not been possible to study conductivity of gases in controlled and reproducible fashion.* The new experimental tool opened up a wide field of investigation, one that is far from exhausted even to this day. Among other things, it was soon shown that the order of magnitude of electric charge carried by ions in gaseous conduction was the same as that observed in electrolysis, namely about 10^5 coulombs (about one faraday) per mole.

Robert A. Millikan, in describing the history of these events,† summarizes the new insights and the flood of new questions:

> "...up to this time the only type of ionization known was that observed in solution, and here it is always some compound molecule like sodium chloride (NaCl) which splits up spontaneously into a positively charged sodium ion and a negatively charged chlorine ion. But the ionization produced in gases by X-rays was of a wholly different sort, for it was observable in pure gases like nitrogen or oxygen, or even in monatomic gases like argon and helium. Plainly, then, the neutral atom even of a monatomic substance must possess minute electrical charges as constituents. Here was the first direct evidence (1) that an atom is a complex structure, and (2) that electrical charges enter into its makeup. With this discovery, due directly to the use of the new agency, X-rays, the atom as an ultimate, indivisible thing was gone, and the era of the constituents of the atom began. ...

---

* It was well known that flames rendered gases conducting, but flames involved chemical reactions, introduced new products into an initially pure gas, caused convection currents and extraneous effects due to temperature differences. A steady, controlled, reproducible electrical process was virtually impossible to achieve under these circumstances.

† *Electrons (+ and −), Protons, Photons, Neutrons, and Cosmic Rays*, Robert A. Millikan. Cambridge: Cambridge University Press, 1935.

"Physicists began at once to seek diligently and to find at least partial answers to questions like these:

(1) What are the masses of the constituents of the atoms torn asunder by X-rays and similar agencies?

(2) What are the values of the charges carried by these constituents?

(3) How many constituents are there?

(4) How large are they; i.e., what volumes do they occupy?

(5) What are their relations to the emission and absorption of light and heat waves; i.e., of electromagnetic radiation?

(6) Do all atoms possess similar constituents? . . ."

A partial answer to the first question came through J. J. Thomson's quantitative experimental study of the behavior of cathode rays.

FIG. 31.8.1. J. J. Thomson (1856–1940).

31.8 J. J. THOMSON (1856–1940)

Joseph John Thomson (Fig. 31.8.1) was born near Manchester, the son of a bookseller and publisher. Thomson started the study of engineering at Manchester, but his interests soon turned to mathematics and physics. At the age of 19, with the help of a scholarship, he entered Trinity College at Cambridge, where he distinguished himself in mathematical studies. After taking his degree, he entered the Cavendish Laboratory, which Maxwell had been instrumental in founding, and worked under Lord Rayleigh, who had succeeded Maxwell as director.

In his early theoretical work Thomson carried out several important extensions of Maxwell's electromagnetic theory. He started conducting experiments on gaseous discharge in 1886, and, as his son remarks, "... for about fifty years afterwards he was rarely, if ever, without some work on gaseous discharge in one form or another on hand."

In 1894, at the age of 28, Thomson succeeded Rayleigh as director of the Cavendish Laboratory, which, under his leadership, became the world's foremost center of research in atomic, and later nuclear, physics. Among the men who studied and worked under Thomson's influence were Rutherford, C. T. R. Wilson, Aston, Geiger, Chadwick, Bohr, G. P. Thomson (J. J.'s son, and a Nobel prize winner in his own right), and many others whose names will arise in the course of our story.

Thomson was awarded the Nobel prize in physics in 1906, and eight of his students later became Nobel laureates. He resigned the directorship of the Cavendish Laboratory in 1919 and served as master of Trinity College from 1918 until his death at the age of 84 in 1940.

31.9 NEGATIVE CHARGE OF CATHODE RAYS

In 1897 Thomson made a concerted attack on the question of the nature of cathode rays; his paper,* a classic of modern physics, proved to be a decisive treatment of the problem. Referring to the conflicting corpuscular and wave hypotheses, Thomson revealed some of the factors that had moulded his thought:

> "The electrified particle theory has, for purposes of research, a great advantage over the aetherial theory, since it is definite and its consequences can be predicted; with the aetherial theory it is impossible to predict what will happen under any given circumstances, as on this theory we are dealing with hitherto unobserved phenomena in the aether, of whose laws we are ignorant.
>
> "The following experiments were made to test some of the consequences of the electrified-particle theory."

Thomson first repeated and extended a very fundamental experiment carried out by the French physicist Perrin two years earlier. Perrin had inserted an electrometer cup (a metal cup, acting as a Faraday "ice pail,"† connected to an electroscope through the wall of the tube) into the tube opposite the cathode. When the tube was turned on, the cathode beam entered the cup, and the electroscope registered the collection of negative charge. When the beam was deflected magnetically so that it did not fall into the cup, no further charge was collected by the electrometer. Thomson extended this experiment by putting the electrometer cup at the *side* of

---

* "Cathode Rays," *Philosophical Magazine*, **44**, 5, 1897, page 293. Excerpts from this paper are quoted in Magie, *Source Book in Physics*; New York: McGraw-Hill, 1935. Also in Shamos, *Great Experiments in Physics*; New York: Henry Holt & Co., 1959.

† See Problem 24.22.

the tube instead of opposite the cathode (Fig. 31.9.1). When the tube was turned on, the electrometer showed no charge; when the cathode beam was deflected magnetically so that it entered the cup, the electrometer indicated collection of negative charge. "This experiment shows," wrote Thomson, "that however we twist and deflect the cathode rays by magnetic forces, the negative electrification follows the same path as the rays, and that this negative electrification is indissolubly connected with the cathode rays."

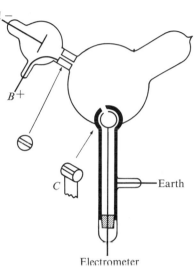

Fig. 31.9.1.   Thomson's tube for demonstrating that cathode rays continue to transport negative charge even when deflected from their original path.

Although the magnetic-deflection experiments of Crookes and others had supplied *indirect* evidence that cathode rays were associated with moving negative charge, the experiments of Perrin and Thomson provided the first *direct* confirmation.

31.10 ELECTROSTATIC DEFLECTION OF CATHODE RAYS

Thomson then attacked another crucial problem:

"An objection very generally urged against the view that the cathode rays are negatively electrified particles is that hitherto no deflexion of the rays has been observed under a small electrostatic force. . . . Hertz made the rays travel between two parallel plates of metal placed inside the discharge tube, but found that they were not deflected when the plates were connected with a battery of storage cells; on repeating this experiment I at first got the same result, but subsequent experiments showed that the absence of deflexion is due to the conductivity conferred on the rarefied gas by the cathode rays. On measuring this conductivity it was found that it diminished very rapidly as the exhaustion increased; it seemed then that on trying Hertz's experiment at very high exhaustions there might be a chance of detecting the deflexion of the cathode rays by an electrostatic force."

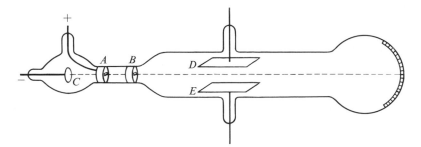

FIG. 31.10.1. Thomson's tube with capacitor plates D and E for producing electrical deflection of cathode beam.

Great discoveries have more than once hinged on basic insights like the one modestly advanced by Thomson. The insights may appear obvious or almost trivial in retrospect, but at the critical moment they were far from apparent to other individuals working in the same field. As a result of his preceding year and a half of experimenting and thinking about conductivity induced in gases by X-rays, Thomson was very sensitive to the possible role of this phenomenon. He realized that cathode rays as well as X-rays induce conductivity in gases, and he was well prepared to visualize the possible consequence. As it happened, newly developed vacuum techniques made it possible for him to test his ideas by achieving sufficiently high vacuum to suppress the conductivity:

"The rays from the cathode C [Fig. 31.10.1] pass through a slit in the anode A, which is a metal plug fitting tightly into the tube and connected with earth; after passing through a second slit in another earth-connected metal plug B, they travel between two parallel aluminum plates about 5 cm long and 2 broad and at a distance of 1.5 cm apart; they then fall on the end of the tube and produce a narrow well-defined fluorescent patch. A scale pasted on the outside of the tube serves to measure the deflexion of this patch.

"At high exhaustions the rays were deflected when the two aluminum plates were connected with a battery of small storage cells; the rays were depressed when the upper plate was connected with the negative pole of the battery, the lower with the positive, and raised [when the connections were reversed]. The deflexion was proportional to the difference of potential between the plates, and I could detect the deflexion when the potential difference was as small as two volts.

"It was only when the vacuum was a good one that the deflexion took place, but that the absence of deflexion is due to the conductivity of the medium is shown by what takes place when the vacuum has just arrived at the stage at which the deflexion begins. At this stage there is a deflexion of the rays when the plates are first connected with the terminals of the battery, but if this connexion is maintained the patch of fluorescence gradually creeps back to its undeflected position. This is just what would happen if the space between the plates were a conductor, though a very bad one, for then the positive and negative ions between the plates would slowly diffuse until the positive plate became coated with negative ions, the negative plate with positive ones; thus the electric intensity between the plates would vanish and the cathode rays be free from electrostatic force. . . .

"As the cathode rays carry a charge of negative electricity, are deflected by an electrostatic force as if they were negatively electrified, and are acted on by a magnetic force in just the way in which this force would act on a negatively electrified body moving along the path of these rays, I can see no escape from the conclusion that they are charges of electricity carried by particles of matter."

PROBLEM 31.6.   In your own words and with appropriate sketches, explain Thomson's theory of how conductivity of the gas prevented electrostatic deflection of the cathode beam. Why does the effect cease at higher vacua?

31.11   CHARGE-TO-MASS RATIO ASSOCIATED WITH THE CATHODE BEAM

Thomson's keen intuition had led him to an experiment that added significantly to the qualitative evidence concerning the nature of cathode rays, but also he saw in this experiment a further possibility, one that makes his name immortal in experimental physics:

"The question next arises, What are these particles? Are they atoms, or molecules, or matter in a still finer state of subdivision? To throw some light on this point, I have made a series of measurements of the ratio of the mass of these particles to the charge carried by [them]."

Thomson's strategy was to measure the deflection of the beam under the influence of a known electrical field between the capacitor plates and to find the value of magnetic field B that exactly opposed the effect of the electrical field. These two measurements made it possible to calculate the velocity of the particles in the beam as well as their charge-to-mass ratio.

Using concepts and results developed in previous chapters, let us describe algebraically, in notation and terms now familiar to us, the motion of negatively charged particles through Thomson's tube. (The analysis will be carried out as an extended problem with steps to be filled in by the reader. A review of Problems 24.17 and 24.24 will prove very helpful at this point.)

PROBLEM 31.7.   Figure 31.11.1 is a schematic diagram of the trajectory of a negatively charged particle after it emerges from the slit B in the tube shown in Fig. 31.10.1. We shall neglect the influence of gravity and assume that there is no appreciable "fringing field" beyond the ends of the capacitor plates.

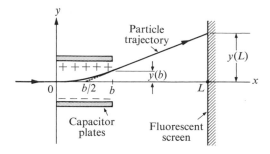

FIG. 31.11.1. Schematic diagram of particle trajectory in Thomson's tube: (1) The x-axis is taken along direction of initial velocity of particle. Origin is located at point at which particle enters region between capacitor plates. (2) Capacitor plates have length denoted by b. Fluorescent screen is located at distance L from origin. (3) In absence of electrical field between the plates, negatively charged particle moves along x-axis, striking the center of the screen at the point $(L, 0)$. When potential difference exists between the plates with polarity indicated, particle is deflected upward, following parabolic path until it emerges from between the plates at point $[b, y(b)]$. Particle then follows straight-line trajectory until it strikes the fluorescent screen at point $[L, y(L)]$.

(a) Explain in your own words the assertions made concerning the trajectory of the particle in item (3) of the caption of Fig. 31.11.1: How do we know that one part is parabolic and the other straight?

(b) Assuming that a particle arriving at 0 has charge q, mass m, and velocity v_{0x}, and denoting the electrical field strength between the capacitor plates by E, show that the equation of the trajectory for the region $0 \le x \le b$ between the plates is given by

$$y(x) = \frac{1}{2} \frac{Eq}{m} \frac{x^2}{v_{0x}^2}. \tag{31.11.1}$$

(See Problem 24.17.)

(c) Show that at $x = b$, the slope of the trajectory is given by

$$\left(\frac{dy}{dx}\right)_{x=b} = \frac{Eq}{m} \frac{b}{v_{0x}^2}. \tag{31.11.2}$$

Using the point-slope form of the equation of a straight line, show that the trajectory in the region $x > b$ is given by

$$y(x) = \frac{Eq}{m} \frac{b}{v_{0x}^2} \left(x - \frac{b}{2}\right). \tag{31.11.3}$$

That is, prove that the straight line must pass through the point $(b/2, 0)$. Prove that the y-deflection of the particle from the point at which it would strike the screen in the absence of electrical field between the plates is given by:

$$y(L) = \frac{Eq}{m} \frac{b}{v_{0x}^2} \left(L - \frac{b}{2}\right). \tag{31.11.4}$$

(d) Now consider a narrow beam of particles formed by the slits in Thomson's tube. The spot formed on the fluorescent screen is not appreciably spread out in the y-direction when the beam is deflected by the field E. Argue that this observation shows that the quantity q/mv_{0x}^2 is very nearly the same for all particles in the beam, but does not prove that the particles all have the same charge, mass, and velocity. (Thomson analyzed and interpreted the significance of this result several months before making the additional measurements described below.)

(e) With the negatively charged particle being deflected under influence of field E between the capacitor plates, a uniform magnetic field B is now superposed on the region between the plates in such a way that the magnetic force acting on the particle is opposite in direction to the electric force. Argue that the magnetic field must be directed into the plane of the paper. How would you arrange a set of coils or solenoids so as to produce the required magnetic field? How would you control and vary the magnetic induction B? (See Problem 24.24.) The size of the coils is so designed that the diameter of the region of effective magnetic field is very nearly equal to b.

(f) In the presence of a fixed electrical field E, the current in the coils is increased until the magnetic field B acquires a particular value B_0 such that a negatively charged particle moving along the x-axis experiences no net deflection and strikes the screen at point $(L, 0)$. Draw a force diagram of the particle while it is between the plates, label the forces, and show that

$$v_{0x} = \frac{E}{B_0}. \tag{31.11.5}$$

(g) In performing this operation on the cathode beam, we start with the spot deflected to $[L, y(L)]$ by the electrical field. As the current in the coils is increased and the magnetic field reaches a value designated by B_0, the spot returns to the center of screen at $(L, 0)$ *without* being spread out appreciably in the y-direction. Argue that this proves that all the particles in the beam have very nearly the same velocity. (What would be observed if there were a distribution of velocities?) Argue that all the particles in the beam must have the same charge-to-mass ratio. Thomson calculated the value of v_{0x} from his measurements of E and B_0 and found it to be of the order of one-tenth the velocity of light. What relevance does this result have with respect to the suggestion that cathode rays consisted of an electromagnetic disturbance in the ether? (What would be the velocity of such a disturbance?) Thomson himself placed considerable stress on this quantitative result, arguing in subsequent lectures and papers that, since their velocities were very much lower than that of light, it was very unlikely that cathode rays might be some form of electromagnetic radiation.

(h) Show that the charge-to-mass ratio is given by the expression

$$\frac{q}{m} = \frac{E}{B_0^2 b}\frac{y(L)}{L - b/2}. \tag{31.11.6}$$

Define all the terms appearing on the right-hand side of the equation and note that they are either fixed quantities or are observable in any particular experiment. Suppose that in a given tube b and L are 4.00 and 20.0 cm, respectively, and that the spacing between the capacitor plates is 1.50 cm. Under a potential difference of 150 v the deflection of the spot is observed to be 2.6 cm. The magnetic field that restores the the spot to the center of the screen is 4.5×10^{-4} weber/m^2. Calculate the charge-to-mass ratio and the velocity of the particles in the beam. (Be sure to use consistent units.) [*Answer:* $q/m = 1.8 \times 10^{11}$ coul/kg; $v_{0x} = 7.4\%$ of the velocity of light.]

(i) Note the velocity of the particles calculated in the preceding section. Calculate the vertical deflection the particles sustain under the influence of gravity as they traverse the tube. Would this deflection be observable? Compare it with some small lengths such as wavelengths of light and diameters of atoms. (The diameter of atoms is of the order of 1 A.) [*Answer:* $\sim 4 \times 10^{-16}$ m.]

PROBLEM 31.8. Suppose that the accelerating potential between electrodes c and A in Fig. 31.10.1 were increased while the potential difference between capacitor plates D and E were kept fixed. What would happen to the spot position denoted by $y(L)$? Would the required value of B_0 remain unchanged? Explain your reasoning clearly in each instance.

31.12 THOMSON'S OBSERVATIONS

Using the method described in the preceding section, Thomson made measurements of the charge-to-mass ratio of the cathode beam in tubes with electrodes of different metals (aluminum, platinum, iron) and with different gases (air, hydrogen, carbon dioxide) initially present and remaining in small amounts after evacuation.

In his paper Thomson remarks on certain systematic errors which he believed made his values of q/m somewhat lower than the true ones. At this juncture, however, he was not striving for high accuracy. He was pioneering new experimental techniques, and quite a few years were to elapse before their accuracy became such that they were reliable to within a few percent. Rather, he was interested in orders of magnitude, and he was trying to establish whether the charge-to-mass ratio associated with cathode rays varied over a wide range of values, as it was known to do with different ions in electrolysis and in conducting gases (see Section 29.10, Problem 29.22), or whether it was essentially constant.

The results of all his different measurements fell between 0.67 and 0.9×10^{11} coul/kg. This being a very much narrower range of variation than that observed for different ions in electrolysis, and also being within the range of uncertainty of his experimental measurements, Thomson was led to the conclusion that the negatively charged particles have the same charge-to-mass ratio in all cathode beams regardless of electrode material and surrounding gas and that, very likely, the particles would all be found to have the same charge and the same mass when it would become possible to determine these two properties separately. On this account he denoted the charge of the particles by a particular symbol, e, rather than by a general symbol for an arbitrary quantity of charge. We shall follow his notation from now on and use the symbol e/m for the charge-to-mass ratio observed in cathode rays.

More refined measurements fully confirm Thomson's conclusion concerning the constancy of e/m in different tubes with different gases and electrodes. It has been established that, to three significant figures,

$$e/m = 1.76 \times 10^{11} \text{ coul/kg,}$$

which is about twice the value originally reported by Thomson. Since the particles moving freely in the cathode beam (under a fixed potential difference between cathode and anode) all seem to have very nearly the same velocity v_{0x}, it would appear that they all originate in the immediate neighborhood of the cathode, perhaps being ejected from the cathode itself or being formed when gas around the cathode is ionized.

PROBLEM 31.9. Explain in somewhat greater detail the logical basis of the inference made in the preceding paragraph.

On the basis of the experimental evidence and theoretical interpretation outlined in the preceding sections (Sections 31.9–31.12), Thomson felt that the particle nature of cathode rays was fully demonstrated and any possibility of a wave interpretation excluded. This view was quickly accepted by the scientific community.

31.13 SIGNIFICANCE OF THE NUMERICAL VALUE OF e/m

We have seen in Section 29.10 and Problem 29.22 that the charge-to-mass ratio of ions in electrolysis was well known by 1897. For example, for hydrogen,

$$\frac{q_\mathrm{H}}{m_\mathrm{H}} = \frac{96{,}500}{0.001008} = 9.57 \times 10^7 \text{ coul/kg,}$$

and for oxygen,

$$\frac{q_\mathrm{O}}{m_\mathrm{O}} = \frac{2(96{,}500)}{0.0160} = 1.21 \times 10^7 \text{ coul/kg.}$$

The charge-to-mass ratio of ions induced in gases by passage of X-rays was much less precisely established, but was known to be of a similar order of magnitude. Thus the e/m value of cathode-ray particles (1.76×10^{11} coul/kg) is seen to be roughly 2000 times larger than the largest known ionic charge-to-mass ratio, that of hydrogen.

Thomson remarked on this result as follows:

"Thus for the carriers of electricity in the cathode rays [e/m is very large] compared to its value in electrolysis. The [size of e/m] may be due to the smallness of m or the largeness of e, or to a combination of these two. That the carriers of the charges in cathode rays are small compared with ordinary molecules is shown, I think, by Lenard's results as to the rate at which the brightness of the [fluorescence] produced by these rays diminishes with the length of path traveled by the ray."

Here he was making reference to the following set of ideas:

From experimental study of the rate of conduction of heat through gases and the rate of diffusion of one gas through another, it had been established, with the help of the kinetic-molecular theory, that molecules of gases at ordinary conditions of temperature and pressure must have *mean free paths* (i.e., average distance of flight between collisions with other molecules) of the order of 10^{-5} cm. It was also inferred from these experimental results and from the theory that the molecules themselves must have diameters of the order of 1 A or 10^{-8} cm. Thus, in this unvisualizably large population, an individual molecule goes bumping around randomly among its neighbors, sometimes traveling only a few molecular diameters between successive collisions and sometimes many thousands of diameters and, on the average, traveling about 1000 diameters or only 10^{-5} cm between collisions. If we imagine starting off a group of molecules in a parallel beam traveling through the surrounding gas, one after another the molecules will undergo collisions with other molecules in the gas and will be scattered out of the beam. The beam will therefore decrease in "intensity" (number of molecules still in it) as it travels through the gas, and after a distance of several mean free paths will become virtually undetectable. A beam of molecules would therefore cease to be detectable after traveling a distance of the order of 10^{-4} cm.

PROBLEM 31.10. How would you expect the mean free path of molecules in a gas to change with the pressure of the gas? Explain your reasoning.

Lenard had shown, however, that cathode rays penetrating into a gas at ordinary pressure cause detectable fluorescence of a screen over path lengths of the order of 1 cm, thousands of times the distance that might conceivably be penetrated by a beam of molecules! Thomson interpreted this result as signifying that the cathode-ray particles must be very small compared with ordinary molecules and unhesitatingly ascribed the largeness of e/m to the smallness of m rather than to a much larger value of charge e than that associated with ions in electrolytic solutions or conducting gases.

This interpretation, of course, implies the existence of particles of subatomic size, particles with only one two-thousandth the mass of atoms of hydrogen—entities with determinable and reproducible properties to which one might begin to assign a specific role in the internal structure of atoms.

31.14   OBSERVATION OF e/m IN OTHER PHYSICAL CONTEXTS

Were the value $e/m = 1.76 \times 10^{11}$ coul/kg observed only in cathode rays, one would be cautious in ascribing a broad general significance to the cathode-ray particles, but in the years between 1897 and 1900 several entirely different observations pointed to the occurrence of the same charge-to-mass ratio in entirely different physical situations.

In 1897 the Dutch physicist Pieter Zeeman (1865–1943), working at the University of Leyden, reported observations of the broadening of the D-lines of the sodium spectrum when glowing sodium vapor was subjected to a strong magnetic field, and a translation of Zeeman's paper was published in England at just about the time Thomson was engaged in his own experiments. Placing a tube of glowing vapor between the poles of a powerful electromagnet, Zeeman showed that the spectrum lines became measurably broader when the current in the coils was turned on; the broadening disappeared when the current was off; i.e. the presence of a strong magnetic field changed by a small amount the frequency and wavelength of light emitted by the sodium atoms. (The effect of a magnetic field on spectrum lines is still generally called the *Zeeman effect.*)

Zeeman was working at Leyden under the eminent theoretical physicist H. A. Lorentz (1853–1928). Oliver Heaviside in England and Lorentz on the continent had both done much to extend Maxwell's electromagnetic theory, to make it more widely understood, and to demonstrate its power and fruitfulness.

In particular, Lorentz developed an intricate and detailed theory to which Zeeman alludes briefly in his paper:

"... it is considered that, in all bodies, there occur small entities charged with electricity, that all electrical processes are to be referred to the equilibrium or motion of these charged particles and that undulations of light are caused by vibrations of these particles. It seems to me that in the magnetic field the forces directly acting on the particles suffice for the explanation of the phenomena [the effect of the magnetic field in broadening the sodium D-lines].

"Prof. Lorentz, to whom I communicated my idea, was good enough to show me how the motion of the charged particles might be calculated, and further suggested that if my application of the theory be correct there would follow [the consequence] that the magnitude of the effect would lead to the determination of the ratio of the electric charge the particle bears to its mass. We may designate the ratio e/m ..."

From his initially rough measurements of the line broadening, Zeeman estimated e/m to be of the order of 10^{11} coul/kg. Later, improved techniques and more refined measurements showed that e/m deduced from the Zeeman effect was identical with that observed in cathode rays. Lorentz and Zeeman shared the Nobel physics prize of 1902 for their work on the influence of magnetism on electromagnetic radiation. (The Zeeman effect is a rather complex physical phenomenon, and we shall not try to analyze it in this text. It involves not simply a "smearing out" of a sharp spectral line but a "splitting" of this line into three or more closely spaced lines. Classical electromagnetic theory only gave a partial explanation of the observed effects, and a full explanation was achieved only in the new science of quantum mechanics. Readers who become interested in this problem are referred to the more advanced references cited at the end of the chapter.)

The Zeeman effect provided a convincing demonstration that particles with $e/m = 1.76 \times 10^{11}$ coul/kg existed not only in a free state in cathode-ray tubes but were bound, as such, into the very structure of atoms themselves.

In 1899 Thomson published a paper* in which he showed that the electrical charge set free and repelled from a negatively charged metal plate upon which ultraviolet

---

* *Philosophical Magazine,* **48**, 547 (1899).

light was incident (photoelectric effect, see Chapter 34) was associated with ions having the same e/m as cathode rays. His son, G. P. Thomson, remarked in a lecture in 1956:

"He also showed in the same paper that the negative particles emitted from a hot wire had approximately the same e/m. This really completed the proof. Opposition to the idea of particles smaller than atoms did indeed continue, but it was merely the spasmodic dying kicks of the older physics, a matter of muscular contraction rather than brain."

Identifying negatively charged particles with $e/m = 1.76 \times 10^{11}$ coul/kg as subatomic implies that they are separated from initially neutral atoms, leaving the far more massive atomic fragment with a net positive charge; i.e., making the remaining fragment a positive ion. This realization motivated the development of techniques for the study of positive ions in gases, experiments that involved forming beams of these ions and measuring their charge-to-mass ratio by methods essentially similar to those used by Thomson in studying cathode rays. We shall return to this problem in Chapter 33.

It is interesting to note how much could be inferred from measurements of e/m without knowing the values of e and m separately. This does not mean that the latter question was ignored or deemed unworthy of investigation. While studying cathode rays, Thomson and his associates at the Cavendish Laboratory were simultaneously working on the determination of the quantities of charge carried by individual gaseous ions. Their motivation is explained in the next section.

31.15 THE "CORPUSCLE" OF ELECTRICAL CHARGE

From the one-ness, two-ness, etc., of different ions in electrolysis, it seemed reasonable to believe that both positive and negative ions carried electrical charge in discrete "packages" or "corpuscles," and that these corpuscles, both positive and negative, consisted of identical quantities of charge. This in turn implied the possible existence of a fundamental corpuscle or elementary unit of charge common to the structure of all matter. The behavior of cathode rays and of ions in gases did not contradict this hypothesis, and, if anything, lent it additional support. Hence intensive efforts were directed toward the determination of the magnitude of what was possibly a universal constant—the elementary unit of charge. There are few better illustrations of the expectation scientists hold of discovering order and simplicity in nature— an expectation that governs their plans and actions long before proof, or at times even substantial evidence, is achieved.

During the same months that Thomson himself was working on the e/m ratio of cathode rays, associates of his at the Cavendish Laboratory were attempting to establish the order of magnitude of the charge carried by the individual ions produced in gases by passage of X-rays.

It had been discovered that in humid air the ions seemed to serve as "nuclei" on which water vapor would condense to form tiny droplets. J. S. Townsend determined with the aid of an electrometer the total electrical charge per cubic centimeter of gas. From the total amount of water per cc, and from an estimate of the average size of droplets based on their rate of fall, he calculated the number of cloud droplets in the cubic centimeter, and, making the admittedly rough assumption that each ion, and therefore each droplet, carries only one corpuscle of charge, he calculated the order of magnitude of the elementary charge to be of the order of 10^{-19} coul. Shortly afterward, Thomson himself conducted similar experiments with somewhat improved methods and reported values ranging from 1.8 to 2.8 $\times$ 10^{-19} coul. In his work of 1899 in which he determined e/m for charges released from heated wires and in the photoelectric effect, he also applied the cloud-droplet method, and obtained values of e similar to those found for gaseous ions formed by X-rays.

An immediately relevant question is whether or not these values of charge are at all comparable with the charge carried by the hydrogen ion in electrolysis. It was well known that 96,500 (about 10^5) coul of charge liberated 1 gram-atomic mass of hydrogen. From a knowledge of Avogadro's number, N_0 (the number of atoms per gram-atomic mass), one could calculate the charge associated with a single hydrogen ion. Around 1900, the value of N_0 was estimated with a wide range of uncertainty by application of kinetic theory to the interpretation of data on heat conduction, diffusion, and viscosity of gases; it was bracketed in the range between 2 and 20 $\times$ 10^{23}.

Taking N_0 as about 10^{24}, in the middle of the range, one obtains

$$\frac{10^5 \text{ coul/gram-atomic mass}}{10^{24} \text{ ions/gram-atomic mass}} = 10^{-19} \text{ coul/ion}$$

as the order of charge on the hydrogen ion, a magnitude agreeing with that observed for gaseous ions and for Thomson's subatomic particles. These were encouraging results that invited further investigation.

Order-of-magnitude calculations of the kind we have just illustrated play a vital role in new fields of scientific research. They guide the direction of investigation, reveal promising channels, show others to be unpromising, and indicate specific areas in which greater precision of measurement has become necessary or desirable. The research worker strives to make such calculations wherever possible, and to draw tentative conclusions that guide the next steps of research. There are pitfalls here, as in all intellectual adventure, but high imagination, a careful critical faculty, and the checks and balances supplied by other workers in the field combine to make this a viable and effective aspect of scientific thought.

31.16 MILLIKAN'S INVESTIGATION OF THE ATOMICITY OF ELECTRICITY

Robert A. Millikan (1868–1953) was born the son of a minister in a small Illinois town (Fig. 31.16.1). He attended Oberlin College where he became interested in physics, took his doctorate at Columbia University, and after a year of post-doctoral

FIG. 31.16.1. Robert A. Millikan (1868–1953).

study at Göttingen and Berlin, joined the staff of the physics department at the University of Chicago. There, in the years between 1907 and 1913, he did his classic work on electrical charge, demonstrating its discreteness and determining the magnitude of the elementary unit. Later, he turned to work on the photoelectric effect and after that to cosmic rays. From 1921 to 1945 he was president of the California Institute of Technology. He received the Nobel prize in physics in 1923.

Millikan approached his study of electrical charge with the objective of obtaining

"... direct and tangible demonstration ... of the correctness of the view advanced many years ago and supported by evidence from many sources that all electrical charges, however produced, are exact multiples of one definite, elementary, electrical charge, or in other words, that an electrical charge instead of being spread uniformly over the charged surface [of macroscopic objects] has a definite granular structure, consisting, in fact, of an exact number of specks or atoms of electricity, all precisely alike. ..."

He began his research by working with clouds of charged water droplets (the technique developed by Townsend, Thomson, and C. T. R. Wilson at the Cavendish Laboratory), but soon discovered that it was possible to concentrate observations on one single charged droplet, balancing it against the downward force of gravity by means of the electrical field between charged capacitor plates (see Problem 24.20). Finally, to avoid scatter and uncertainty caused by gradual evaporation of the droplet under observation, he turned to the use of oil instead of water. In a paper published

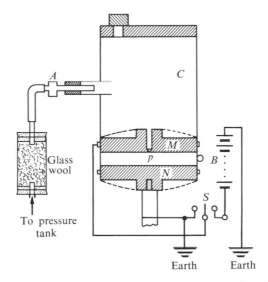

FIG. 31.16.2. Millikan's oil-drop apparatus (1911).

in 1911,* he described the current status of his technique as follows:

"By means of a commercial atomizer A [Fig. 31.16.2], a cloud of fine droplets of oil is blown with the aid of dust-free air into the dust-free chamber C. One or more droplets of this cloud is allowed to fall through a pinhole p into the space between the [circular] plates M and N of a horizontal capacitor, and the pinhole is then closed by means of an electromagnetically operated cover not shown in the diagram. If the pinhole is left open, air currents are likely to pass through it and produce irregularities. The plates M and N [with very flat surfaces] are held exactly 16 mm apart by means of three small ebonite posts. ... A strip of thin sheet ebonite passes entirely around the plates, thus forming a completely enclosed air space. Three glass windows, 1.5 cm square, are placed in this ebonite strip at the angular positions 0°, 165°, 180°. A narrow parallel beam of light from an arc lamp enters the capacitor through the first window and emerges through the last. The other window serves for observing, with the aid of a short-focus telescope placed about 2 feet distant, the illuminated oil droplet as it floats in the air between the plates. The appearance of this drop is that of a brilliant star on a black background. It falls, of course, under the action of gravity,† toward the lower plate; but before it reaches it, an electrical field strength of between 3000 and 8000 volts/cm is created between the plates by means of the battery B, and, if the droplet had received a frictional charge of the proper sign and strength as it was blown out of the atomizer, it is pulled up

---

* *Physical Review*, **32**, 349 (1911).

† At a uniform terminal velocity, with the gravitational force on the droplet balanced by the opposing force of fluid friction. See Section 6.8 and Problem 6.10.

by this field against gravity toward the upper plate. Before it strikes [the plate], the plates are short-circuited by means of switch S, and the time required by the drop to fall under gravity the distance corresponding to the space between the cross hairs of the observing telescope is accurately determined. Then the rate at which the droplet moves up under the influence of the field is measured by timing it through the same distance when the field is on. This operation is repeated and the speeds checked an indefinite number of times, or until the droplet catches an ion from among those which exist in the air or which have been produced in the space between the plates by any of the usual ionizing agents like radium or X-rays. The fact that an ion has been caught and the exact instant at which the event happened is signaled to the observer by the change in speed of the droplet under the influence of the field.* ... The experiment is particularly striking when, as often happens, the droplet carries but one elementary charge and then by the capture of an ion of an opposite sign is completely neutralized so that its speed is altogether unaffected by the field. In this case the computed charge is itself the charge on the captured ion."

31.17 RESULTS OF MILLIKAN'S EXPERIMENT

Let us first analyze the physical problem posed by the behavior of the charged drop with and without the electrical field. For this purpose we make use of the ideas developed in Section 6.8 and Problem 24.20. The analysis will be carried out, as in the case of the Thomson experiment, in the form of a problem with steps to be filled in by the reader.

PROBLEM 31.11. Figure 31.17.1 shows force diagrams for a charged oil drop between the capacitor plates. Explain each algebraic expression given on the diagrams. In some of his earlier experiments, Millikan measured the downward terminal velocity v_{tD} of the droplet in the absence of electrical field and then adjusted the field (by changing the potential difference ΔV between the plates) to a value E_0 such that the electrical force exactly balanced the gravitational force as in Fig. 31.17.1(b). From this figure we have:

$$E_0 q = \tfrac{4}{3}\pi r^3 \rho g,$$

$$q = \frac{4}{3}\frac{\pi r^3 \rho g}{E_0}. \tag{31.17.1}$$

The quantity q, the charge on the droplet, is what we wish to calculate. We know the density ρ of the oil, and have measured E_0 by balancing the drop; to complete the calculation we must establish the mass m or the radius r of the drop. This is the

---

* Capturing an ion has an unobservably small effect on the mass of the droplet. The droplets were of the order of 10^{-3} mm in radius, and, small though this size seems to be, the mass of the droplet is still millions of millions of times the mass of an individual atom or ion.

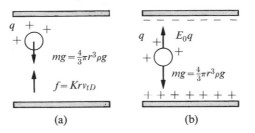

(a)   (b)

FIG. 31.17.1. (a) Plates are shorted. Electrical field $E = 0$. Droplet falls at terminal velocity v_{tD}. The quantity q denotes charge on droplet, m its mass, r its radius, and ρ the known density of the oil. (Effect of buoyancy of the air is neglected.) (b) Electrical field is directed upward. Positively charged droplet is balanced and remains stationary at a particular field value E_0.

point of measuring the terminal velocity: From Fig. 31.17.1(a), we have:

$$\tfrac{4}{3}\pi r^3 \rho g = K r v_{tD} \tag{31.17.2}$$

an expression that can be solved for r in terms of the known quantities ρ, g, K, and the measured terminal velocity v_{tD}. Eliminating r from (31.17.1), we obtain

$$q - \left(\frac{3}{4\pi \rho g}\right)^{1/2} K^{3/2} \frac{v_{tD}^{3/2}}{E_0}. \tag{31.17.3}$$

Fill in the algebraic steps.

Thus the charge carried by the droplet can be calculated from the experimental data. (The accuracy of the result is significantly improved if correction is made for the buoyancy of the air and for the fact that the value of K for droplets as small as 10^{-3} mm radius is somewhat different from that which applies to larger spheres or droplets.)

PROBLEM 31.12. In his later experiments, Millikan did not try to balance the droplet with the electrical field, but, as described in the quotation given in Section 31.16, applied an upward field E larger than E_0 so that the droplet moved upward at a terminal velocity v_{tU}, which was measured in the experiment. Draw the force diagram appropriate to this case, and show that

$$Eq = K r v_{tU} + \tfrac{4}{3}\pi r^3 \rho g. \tag{31.17.4}$$

Then eliminate r and show that

$$q = \left(\frac{3}{4\pi \rho g}\right)^{1/2} \frac{K^{3/2}}{E} (v_{tU} + v_{tD}) v_{tD}^{1/2}.$$

Why do you think Millikan turned to this method in favor of the one described in Problem 31.11? What effect would Brownian motion have on attempts to observe the perfectly balanced droplet?

TABLE 31.17.1

SELECTION FROM ONE OF MILLIKAN'S SERIES OF
OBSERVATIONS OF DIFFERENT CHARGES CARRIED
BY AN OIL DROPLET OVER A PERIOD OF TIME*

Total charge, $q\dagger$ (coul)	Number of elementary charges
8.20×10^{-19}	5
11.49	7
13.13	
11.49	
9.87	
8.20	
6.55	
9.87	
8.20	
6.55	
9.87	
8.20	

* Values are expressed in coulombs rather than in the cgs electrostatic units used in Millikan's paper.

† In this instance the total charge on the droplet was negative. In other
series of observations net charge was positive.

Table 31.17.1 shows a small selection from one of Millikan's long series of observations.

PROBLEM 31.13. Examine the *differences* between charges listed in Table 31.17.1,
and show that the smallest difference averages about 1.64×10^{-19} coul. Then show
that all the differences are very nearly integral multiples of this quantity. Fill in the
remainder of the second column in Table 31.17.1, indicating the number of "packets"
of size 1.64×10^{-19} coul in each one of the total quantities of charge. How do you
interpret the fact that sometimes the negative charge increased while at other times
it decreased; i.e., what kind of ions were being captured by the droplet at various
points?

Millikan observed electrification of droplets not only under the influence of ionizing radiation from X-rays and radium but also from ordinary friction in the
atomizer itself. Discussing his large accumulation of data of the kind illustrated
in Table 31.17.1, Millikan remarks:*

"Relationships of exactly this sort have been found to hold absolutely without
exception, no matter in what gas the drops have been suspended or what sort of

---

* *Electrons (+ and −)*, by R. A. Millikan. Cambridge: Cambridge University Press, 1935.

droplets were used upon which to catch the ions. In many cases a given drop has been held under observation for five or six hours at a time and has been seen to catch not [four to eight] ions, as in the experiment above, but hundreds of them. . . . In no case have I ever found [a change in charge] which, when tested as above, did not have either exactly the value of the smallest charge ever captured or else a very small multiple of that value. *Here, then, is direct unimpeachable proof that the [elementary charge] is not a statistical mean, but rather that the electrical charges found on ions all have either exactly the same value or else small exact multiples of that value.*"

To three significant figures, the value of the elementary charge is now known to be 1.60×10^{-19} coul. Compare this result with the earlier estimates described in Section 31.15.

31.18 CONCEPT OF "ELECTRON"

Millikan's measurements did not furnish direct proof that the elementary charge observed in his experiments was identical with the charge e of Thomson's cathode-ray particles, but the reproducibility and universality of his results made the identification more plausible than ever. In all further theory and investigation it was tacitly assumed that $e = 1.60 \times 10^{-19}$ coul, and, as we shall see in subsequent chapters, one cross-check after another substantiated this hypothesis.

We have now established the behavior and properties of a reasonably clearly defined entity: a particle with $e/m = 1.76 \times 10^{11}$ coul/kg; found in the cathode-ray beam and ejected from metals under the influence of heat or ultraviolet light; present within atoms as indicated by its connection with the emission of bright line spectra; carrying an elementary negative charge $e = 1.60 \times 10^{-19}$ coul and possessing an inertial mass

$$m = \frac{1.60 \times 10^{-19} \text{ coul}}{1.76 \times 10^{11} \text{ coul/kg}} = 9.1 \times 10^{-31} \text{ kg}.$$

To this entity, operationally defined by the above list of properties and the circumstances under which it is observed, we give the name "electron."

As time went by, further details were added to the list, and the properties and occurrence of electrons became more sharply specified: The hypothesis that electrons were present in the structure of all atoms was substantiated. It was found that electrons are ejected from atoms by X-rays; that a fraction of the electrons associated with the atoms of a metal are free to move within the metal like molecules of a gas, and, being displaced under the influence of an electrical field, are responsible for the high electrical conductivity of metallic substances. It was found that electrons possess a "magnetic moment"; i.e., they behave like minute magnets with north and south magnetic poles.

But the electron is an entity very far removed indeed from direct sense perceptions. Our inferences concerning its occurrence and properties are based on observations, not of "electrons" as such, but deflection of spots on fluorescent screens and of readings on dials that indicate potential difference in an electrical field or current in coils establishing a magnetic field. In what sense, if any, are electrons "real"; to what extent is it meaningful to say that they "exist"?

In raising this question, we go beyond the immediate problem of the electron and touch on a philosophical subject, concerning which there are widely divergent views among both scientists and philosophers and concerning which there is an extensive, and frequently abstruse, literature. The present author does not profess to be qualified to give a definitive discussion of the problem, but the issue is a fundamental and interesting one and goes to the heart of questions concerning the character of the information science gives us about the world in which we live—questions fundamental to the intellectual enterprise of "natural philosophy."

To most practising scientists an entity is "real" or "exists" if at least some of its properties seem to be definite and reproducible and if it has physical effects that can be predicted and then confirmed by observation. The British philosopher-historian, Dr. Mary Hesse, remarks that "we try to investigate the further properties we expect [our models] to have, and if we are correct in our expectations we shall conclude that the model, at least as far as we have gone, is a description of reality and not an illusion arising from our previous partial knowledge."

So it is with electrons and, similarly, with atoms and molecules. Although as late as 1910 a few eminent scientists still had serious doubts about the "reality" and "existence" of such entities and were inclined to consider them mental artifacts, invented to account for scintillations, dial readings, and mass changes observed in chemical reactions, most scientists of the present day would probably accept the assertion that these entities are real—real in the sense of producing repeatable and observable effects, ranging from individual tracks in cloud or bubble chambers to pictures on a television screen and the random "Brownian motion" of tiny, visible particles (such as Millikan's oil drop) suspended in still air or in a liquid.

The assertion of "reality," however, should not mislead us into gratuitously ascribing to something like an electron all sorts of additional properties that form part of our familiar, everyday conception of "particle"—properties, such as color, luster, texture, shape, hardness, that the scholastic philosophers called accidents. We should furthermore not be surprised if our new entities exhibit unfamiliar modes of behavior that we do *not* associate with ordinary macroscopic particles. After all, our conception of the electron as a particle is a model based on a certain limited correspondence to ordinary particles in observable properties and behavior, and there is really no reason to expect complete correspondence in every conceivable aspect. As Robert Oppenheimer remarks,

"We come to our new problems, full of old ideas and old words, not only the inevitable words of daily life, but those which experience has shown fruitful over the years. ... We ... love the old words, the old imagery, and the old analogies, and we keep them for more and more unfamiliar and more and more unrecognizable things."

The conservative attitude enunciated here stems, however, from the benefit of hindsight. This epistemological view was not prevalent and clearly articulated early in this century. It emerged later, after electrons and atomic particles were found in certain clear-cut experiments to exhibit effects that could only be interpreted as constructive and destructive interference. In later chapters we shall have occasion to return to these phenomena and to the questions that they pose.

31.19   PROBLEMS

31.14. In his paper of 1897, Thomson actually describes determinations of the charge-to-mass ratio of cathode-ray particles by two different methods, and indicates that they give results in essential agreement with each other. One was the method we have analyzed in detail in Section 31.11. The other, independent method involved the following steps:

(1) The cathode beam was allowed to fall on an electrometer at the end of the tube and the total charge Q collected during a fixed interval of time was measured. (2) The cathode rays entering the electrometer struck very thin strips of copper and iron which were connected to very fine insulated wires leading out of the tube. These strips formed a thermocouple of known mass and heat capacity, and the temperature rise of the thermocouple was measured while the charge Q was being collected. The temperature rise made it possible to calculate the total amount of heat H transferred to the thermocouple by the incident rays. (3) If N particles, each with charge e, arrive during the given time interval:

$$Q = Ne, \qquad (31.19.1)$$

$$H = N(\tfrac{1}{2}mv_{0x}^2). \qquad (31.19.2)$$

Explain these two equations. (4) Thomson made it possible to eliminate v_{0x} from these equations by measuring the radius of curvature R of the cathode beam in a magnetic field of known induction B:

$$\frac{mv_{0x}^2}{R} = Bev_{0x}. \qquad (31.19.3)$$

Explain this equation. (See Section 24.11.) (5) Combining the above equations, show that

$$\frac{e}{m} = \frac{\cdot 2H}{QR^2 B^2}. \qquad (31.19.4)$$

Explain the point and significance of the last equation in your own words.

31.15. Suppose that a particle with negative charge e and mass m rotates in a circular orbit of radius r around a massive particle with positive charge q (Fig. 31.19.1).

(a) If ω_0 is the angular velocity of the particle, argue that

$$mr\omega_0^2 - k\frac{qe}{r^2}. \qquad (31.19.5)$$

(b) Now suppose that a uniform magnetic field B is imposed in a direction perpendicular to the plane of the orbit. Assume that r remains essentially unchanged. Argue that

$$mr\omega^2 = k\frac{qe}{r^2} \pm Ber\omega, \qquad (31.19.6)$$

where ω is the new angular velocity of the particle. Draw a free body diagram of the particle. Explain Eq. (31.19.6). Why

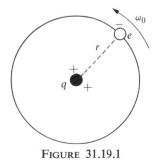

FIGURE 31.19.1

is the $\pm$ sign introduced? (c) Show that

$$\frac{e}{m} = \frac{|\omega^2 - \omega_0^2|}{B\omega}, \qquad (31.19.7)$$

and when the change in angular velocity, $\Delta\omega = \omega - \omega_0$, is very small, the charge-to-mass ratio is given to a very good approximation by the simpler expression

$$\frac{e}{m} = \frac{2|\Delta\omega|}{B}. \qquad (31.19.8)$$

Although this highly simplified analysis does not constitute an explanation of the observed complex features of the Zeeman effect, it does give some crude inkling of its basic character. Explain the connection. How might Zeeman have made his estimate of the order of magnitude of e/m?

SUPPLEMENTARY READING AND STUDY

Readers are urged to refer to the original papers by Thomson and Millikan cited in the text. The papers are by no means difficult or abstruse; they are lucid and very illuminating in many details of evidence and reasoning.

The Discovery of the Electron, D. L. Anderson. Princeton, N.J.: Van Nostrand Momentum Book No. 3, 1964

Electrons (+ *and* −), *Protons, Photons, Neutrons, and Cosmic Rays*, Robert A. Millikan. Cambridge: Cambridge University Press, 1935, Chapters 1–9

Great Experiments in Physics. Excerpts from Roentgen, Thomson, and Millikan, edited by M. H. Shamos. New York: Henry Holt, 1959, Chapters 14, 16, 18

Source Book in Physics. Excerpts from Roentgen, Thomson, and Millikan, edited by W. F. Magie. New York: McGraw-Hill, 1935

Physics, the Pioneer Science, L. W. Taylor. Boston: Houghton Mifflin, 1941, Chapters 51, 52. New York: Dover Paperback S566, 1959

"Centenary of J. J. Thomson," *Science*, **124**, 1191 (1956). An article by Sir G. P. Thomson, reminiscing about his father's career and discoveries. A similar article appears in *Physics Today*, August 1956.

For an introductory discussion of the classical theory of the Zeeman effect:

Optics, F. W. Sears. Reading, Mass.: Addison-Wesley, 1958, Chapter 11

CHAPTER 32

Radioactivity

32.1 BECQUEREL'S DISCOVERY

Lecturing on the history of radioactivity shortly before his death in 1937, Ernest Rutherford, whose own research on the nature of radioactivity had won a Nobel prize, recounted the story of the original discovery in the following terms:*

"Few of you can possibly realize the enormous sensation produced by the discovery of X-rays by Roentgen in December 1895. It interested not only the scientific man, but also the man in the street, who was excited by the idea of seeing his own inside and his bones. Every laboratory in the world took out its old Crookes' tubes to produce X-rays. . . . These old tubes of Crookes showed that cathode rays have the power of causing brilliant phosphorescence† in a great number of substances, and it was also observed that X-rays appeared to come from the points which were struck by the rays. This led many people to think that X-rays might be connected with phosphorescence in some way, perhaps that phosphorescent substances might emit X-rays. A number of observers on the continent did experiments on this subject, among others Henri Becquerel of Paris. [This was within two months of the announcement of Roentgen's discovery.] His father, a professor before him, had been very interested in phosphorescence, particularly in measuring its duration, and he had also been interested in the rather unusual properties shown by uranium compounds. Henri helped in his father's work, and fifteen years before, in 1880, he had amused himself by making some crystals of the double sulfate of uranium and potassium, which glowed beautifully when exposed to light.

"In his search for a connection between phosphorescence and X-rays, Becquerel placed a number of phosphorescent substances, enveloped in black paper, over

---

* *Backgrounds to Modern Science*, J. Needham and W. Pagel. New York: Macmillan, 1938.

† The term "phosphorescence" as opposed to "fluorescence" is used to describe the phenomenon in which a substance *continues* to emit visible light for some time after the cathode ray, sunlight, or other excitation is cut off.

a photographic plate, but his results were entirely negative. It then occurred to him to try crystals of uranium salt. He first exposed them to [sunlight] so as to make them phosphoresce and then wrapped them in black paper and placed them over a photographic plate. After an exposure of several hours and development, a distinct photographic effect was observed. The experiment was repeated with a thin piece of glass between the uranium salt and the photographic plate in order to cut off effects due to possible vapours, but the photographic effect was again obtained.

"At first Becquerel assumed that the emission of rays which could penetrate the black paper was in some way connected with the phosphoresence, but later he showed that the effects were just as marked if the uranium salt had previously been kept in the dark for several weeks, so that there was no sign of phosphorescence. He later showed that all the salts of uranium and even the metal itself have the power of producing radiation which penetrates black paper. In this way he discovered the phenomenon which today we call 'radioactivity'."

By early March of 1896 Becquerel had shown that the radiation from uranium, like X-rays, was capable of ionizing air, thereby causing the discharge of an electroscope, a more rapid rate of discharge indicating a higher intensity of radioactivity. Both the photographic and ionizing effects were considerably weaker than those produced by X-rays, and Becquerel initially assumed that the radiations from uranium consisted of weak X-rays.

32.2   OTHER RADIOACTIVE SUBSTANCES

The earlier discovery and more spectacular effects of X-rays pre-empted scientific attention, and at first relatively little attention was paid to the radiation from uranium. The discovery, however, captured the interest of Marie Sklodowska Curie (1867–1934), Polish-born wife of one of Becquerel's colleagues at Paris. Checking other substances, she found that thorium was the only other known element that was radioactive, but she also noticed that certain ores of uranium, particularly pitchblende, showed a much higher intensity of radiation than uranium itself. Pierre Curie, who was noted for his work on the electric and magnetic properties of solids, recognized the importance of the discovery, gave up his previous line of research, and joined his wife in further investigation. In the July 1898 issue of *Comptes Rendus*, the Curies reported the discovery of a new element:

"The study of the compounds of uranium and of thorium has shown, in fact, that the property of emitting rays which make air conducting and which act on photographic plates, is a specific property of uranium and thorium, which appears in all the compounds of these metals, being so much the more feeble as the proportion of the active metal in the compound is itself less. The physical state of the substances seems to be of altogether secondary importance. Various experiments have shown that if the substances are mixed with others, their condition seems to have no effect except as it varies the proportion of the active body and the absorption produced by the inert substance. . . . Impurities, which have so great an effect on phosphorescence or fluorescence, are here altogether without effect. [In other words, the intensity of radioactivity is directly proportional to the amount of uranium or thorium present and is completely unaffected by other conditions such as combinations or admixture with other materials.] It therefore becomes very probable that if certain minerals are more active than uranium and thorium, it is because they contain a substance more active than these metals. We have attempted to isolate this substance in pitchblende, and the experiment has confirmed our expectations.

"[By carrying out successive chemical operations to separate and concentrate the active material in the ore] we obtained products which were more and more active. Finally we obtained a substance whose activity is about 400 times greater than that of uranium. . . . We believe, therefore, that the substance we removed from pitchblende contains a metal which has not yet been known, similar to bismuth in its chemical properties. If the existence of this new metal is confirmed, we propose to call it 'polonium' [after Mme. Curie's native country]."

In the same journal in December 1898, the Curies reported a second discovery. In separating radioactive materials from pitchblende, they had found evidence of a substance with chemical properties quite different from polonium and so similar to barium that it proved very difficult to separate it from compounds of the latter. Experimenting with a mixture of chlorides, they found that

". . . by dissolving these chlorides in water and precipitating a part of them by alcohol, the precipitated part is much more active than the part which remains dissolved. By starting with this fact we may carry out a series of fractionations, from which we may obtain more and more active chlorides. We have thus obtained chlorides which have an activity 900 times greater than that of uranium . . . These facts can be explained by the presence of a radioactive element of which the chloride is less soluble in alcoholic solution than is barium chloride."

A colleague of the Curies', examining the bright line spectrum of the increasingly active chlorides, observed in the ultraviolet region a hitherto unreported spectral line that increased in intensity with increasing radioactivity of the sample, providing further support for the Curies' thesis: "The various reasons which we have presented lead us to believe that the new radioactive substance contains a new element, to which we propose to give the name *radium*."

Through successive chemical reactions, solutions, and crystallizations, the Curies had followed the element by its telltale radioactivity, the amount of radium actually present being much too small to weigh or work with chemically. In many ways this episode is analogous to Bunsen's discovery of the elements cesium and rubidium by means of the spectroscope. (See Section 27.3.)

During four succeeding years of backbreaking physical labor, without technical or financial assistance, the Curies proceeded to treat several tons of ore, obtaining larger samples of active salts with which to perform more detailed chemical and physical investigations at higher levels of activity. In 1902 Marie Curie could report the isolation of 100 mg of very pure radium chloride.

Pure radium metal, isolated by Marie Curie in 1910 by electrolysis of fused radium chloride, was subsequently shown to exhibit over 10^6 times the radioactivity of uranium.

Between 1898 and 1902 the researches of Rutherford and other investigators (researches that will be described in the following sections) had demonstrated that radioactivity was associated with deep-seated transformations of atomic structure—the transmutation of one element into another. The importance of radioactivity in the study of atomic physics was clear to the entire scientific world. In the light of these parallel developments and after the successful isolation of radium chloride in 1902, the Curies found both recognition and support for their work. With Becquerel they shared the 1903 Nobel prize in physics for the discovery of radioactivity. Marie Curie continued these researches for the rest of her life. After Pierre's untimely death in a street accident in 1906, she succeeded him at his post at the Sorbonne. In 1911 she enjoyed the unusual distinction of a second Nobel award—that in chemistry, for the discovery of the elements polonium and radium.

32.3 THE NATURE OF "BECQUEREL RAYS"

Uranium and thorium are rather weak sources of radioactivity. Photographic detection with plates and emulsions available at the turn of the century took hours of exposure time. The ionization effects were detected more readily but required very sensitive electrometers. It is not surprising that Becquerel first considered the radiation to be very weak X-rays.

In 1898 Rutherford, then at McGill University in Montreal, performed an experiment in which he placed successive layers of aluminum foil over a layer of powdered uranium compound spread on a capacitor plate. An electrometer connected to the capacitor showed the rate of decay of charge on the capacitor as radiation from the uranium ionized the air between the plates. He found that the ionization decreased sharply with the first few layers of aluminum foil and then very slowly with superposition of additional layers. These results led him to the conclusion that uranium radiation was complex and consisted of two components, one capable of penetrating only a few centimeters of air or a few layers of the aluminum foil and the other capable of penetrating much greater thicknesses of either air or aluminum. Reporting these results early in 1899, Rutherford suggested that the two radiations be designated α and β, respectively. When another investigator (Villard in France in 1900) later discovered a third, still more penetrating component, he followed Rutherford's nomenclature and designated it as γ-radiation.

The implied question is clear: Are these various rays entirely new physical manifestations or are they related to already known entities or physical phenomena? As one might anticipate, early experiments centered on determining the influence

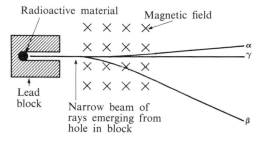
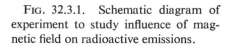

FIG. 32.3.1. Schematic diagram of experiment to study influence of magnetic field on radioactive emissions.

of electric and magnetic fields on the rays. A schematic diagram, illustrating how such experiments might be performed, is shown in Fig. 32.3.1. A narrow beam of radiation is formed by placing radioactive material at the bottom of a long, very small diameter hole drilled in a lead block. The lead absorbs all rays except those emerging from the hole. If desired, the system can be encased in an evacuated glass tube. The narrow beam of rays can be subjected to electric and magnetic fields in the same manner as the narrow beam of cathode rays formed in a cathode-ray tube.

In 1899 Becquerel showed that part of the radiation from radium was deflected by electric and magnetic fields in the manner expected of negatively charged particles. Using Thomson's technique of "crossed" electric and magnetic fields, he showed that these rays exhibited the same charge-to-mass ratio as cathode rays, but possessed considerably higher velocities. This component of the radiation was quickly identified with Rutherford's β-rays, and thus β-rays (or, more precisely, β-particles) came to be identified as electrons. This identification, however does not account for the *origin* of the electrons in the radioactive material any more than Thomson's earlier discovery accounted for the origin or source of the particles in the cathode-ray tube. Investigation at this point was still concentrated on the more restricted question of the identity or physical nature of the rays; questions as to their origin would become the subject of later research.

At first it was reported that α- and γ-rays were both undeviated by electric and magnetic fields. This indeed turned out to be correct for γ-rays; like X-rays and light they are not deflected by the strongest fields. Ultimately, X-rays and γ-rays were shown to be electromagnetic radiation—like light but of increasingly greater frequency and shorter wavelength. Rutherford showed, however, in 1903 that attempts to deflect α-rays had failed because the fields used in the earlier experiments had been too weak. (The relative effects are shown schematically, but not to scale, in Fig. 32.3.1.)

Working with strong electromagnets, Rutherford showed that α-rays were deflected as though positively charged, and using Thomson's crossed-field technique, he obtained a charge-to-mass ratio, q_α/m_α, of about 4.8×10^7 coul/kg, and velocities of the order of 2×10^7 m/sec, or one-tenth the velocity of light.

PROBLEM 32.1. Compare the charge-to-mass ratio of α-particles with that of electrons and of hydrogen ions in electrolysis. Starting with the charge-to-mass ratio of H^+ calculated in Problem 29.22, calculate the charge-to-mass ratio for a hydrogen *molecule* that is "singly ionized"; i.e., has the formula H_2^+ indicating that it carries one elementary packet of charge. [*Answer:* 4.78×10^7 coul/kg.] Calculate the charge-to-mass ratio of a "doubly ionized" helium atom He^{++} (helium has an atomic mass about four times that of the hydrogen atom and twice that of the hydrogen molecule). [*Answer:* 4.78×10^7 coul/kg.] Calculate the charge-to-mass ratio of He^+. In the light of the values you have quoted above, what might α-particles be? What possibilities must be rejected? Why? How would you explain the very small deflection of α-particles in a magnetic field that produces large deflection of β-particles?

32.4 ERNEST RUTHERFORD (1871–1937)

The name of Ernest Rutherford (Fig. 32.4.1) arises continually as we follow the lines of discovery leading to the elucidation of atomic structure; his was one of the dominant figures in experimental physics during the first part of this century. Born the son of a flax farmer near Nelson, New Zealand, he took honors in mathematics and physics at college and in 1894 came to England to work under J. J. Thomson. The discoveries of X-rays and radioactivity drew him, with others at the Cavendish Laboratory, to the study of ionization and electrical conduction in gases.

FIG. 32.4.1. Ernest Rutherford (1871–1937). Photograph courtesy *Physics Today*.

From 1898 to 1907 Rutherford was research professor of physics at McGill University in Montreal. Here he did the work that led to the classification of α- and β-radiation from uranium, made detailed chemical and physical studies of the activity of uranium and thorium, and, with his colleague, the chemist Frederick Soddy, proposed a theory of the nature of radioactivity that ultimately proved to be the correct explanation of the phenomenon.

In 1907 Rutherford became professor of physics at Manchester University. At Manchester he carried out research that unequivocally proved α-particles to be doubly ionized helium atoms and, in interpreting the α-particle scattering experiments of his colleagues Geiger and Marsden, put forth his famous theory of the nuclear structure of the atom.

During World War I he devoted himself to work on government projects; in 1919 he succeeded J. J. Thomson as director of the Cavendish Laboratory. Rutherford was president of the Royal Society from 1925 to 1930. In 1931 he was elevated to the peerage with the title of Baron Rutherford of Nelson. He received the Nobel prize in chemistry in 1908.

32.5 RADIOACTIVITY AND THE CONSERVATION LAWS

After the isolation of radium in 1902, the Curies found that radium compounds, kept in a small tube, maintain themselves continually at a higher temperature than their surroundings, an effect that had not been noticed with the much weaker radio-active sources previously available:

> "When a tube of radium is placed in the calorimeter, there is observed a con-tinual evolution of heat, which ceases when the radium is withdrawn. Measure-ments [show] that each gram of radium gives off about 80 calories per hour. Thus radium gives off sufficient heat in an hour to melt its own weight of ice. This evolution of heat produces no change in the appearance of the salt, nor can any ordinary chemical reaction be pointed out as the source of heat evolved. . . .
>
> "Radium therefore gives us an example of a body which, while remaining in the same state, evolves continuously a considerable amount of energy. This fact is apparently in contradiction to the fundamental principles of ener-getics. . . ."*

Not only was the law of conservation of energy challenged. What was the source of continuous, spontaneous emission of α- and β-particles? These particles were shown to possess measurable mass. Atomic theory held that atoms merely combined or separated from each other in chemical changes, remaining otherwise unaltered, thus accounting for conservation of mass in chemical reactions. How could one account for the continuous emission of material particles in the apparent absence of chemical changes or other alterations in the state of the radioactive materials? How, in particular, could such effects arise in a pure *element* such as metallic radium or uranium, without interaction with atoms of other substances?

Since it was well known that changing the temperature and the pressure at which a chemical reaction takes place changes the rate of the reaction, numerous efforts were made to determine whether changes of temperature and pressure had any in-

---

* Pierre Curie, quoted in the *Smithsonian Treasury of Science*, Volume I. New York: Simon and Schuster, 1960, page 253.

fluence on the intensity of radiation from various materials, but no effect was observed, even at very large pressures and high temperatures.

One of Rutherford's first experiments at Manchester was described many years later by his technical assistant:

> ". . . we had a thing for measuring the explosive power of cordite . . . which was a great big iron bomb, and you got the pressure by the explosion in this 3-inch wall thickness—and the temperature by the thermocouple. Well, Rutherford hadn't been here, oh a week or two, I think, perhaps a few weeks, and then he suddenly thought: 'To hell with our [radioactive material]. It's never been under pressure like that.'—That will make it go up to 1000 atmospheres and 1000 degrees Centigrade—'What will emanation do in it?' And straightaway he fitted it up with no trouble at all. He fitted it up, and put the emanation in, and got his electroscopes up, and got the decay, and exploded it. . . . But no, no difference, you see, and he dropped it straightaway. . . ."*

By the time this experiment was performed, Rutherford really did not expect to observe any positive effect. He was quite sure that radioactivity was not affected by external conditions. It was clear that the source of heat and of material particles in radioactivity was very deep-seated in atomic systems, since it did not appear to have any of the usual characteristics of chemical reactions. Did the atomic theory and the laws of conservation of mass and energy fail in this new range of phenomena? A critical reexamination of the theory and of all the chemical and physical evidence was clearly demanded.

32.6 RADIOACTIVE TRANSFORMATIONS

After the success of the Curies in 1898 in discovering polonium and radium by tracing characteristic radioactivity in minute quantities of residues extracted through chemical treatment of pitchblende, other investigators applied similar techniques to what were thought to be highly purified compounds of uranium and thorium. Sir William Crookes, in 1900, separated a radioactive constituent of great activity and chemical nature distinct from uranium and called it "uranium X." In 1902 Rutherford and Soddy confirmed Crookes' work and showed that:

> "The major part of the radioactivity of thorium—ordinarily about 54 percent— is due to a non-thorium type of matter, Th X, possessing distinct chemical properties, which is temporarily radioactive, its activity falling to half value in about four days. The constant radioactivity of thorium is maintained by the production of this material at a constant rate. Both the rate of production of the new material and the rate of decay of its activity appear to be independent of the physical and chemical condition of the system."

------

* "Recollections of Rutherford," by William Alexander Kay, in *The Natural Philosopher*, Volume I. New York: Blaisdell Publishing Co., 1963.

These results led Rutherford and Soddy to put forth a revolutionary hypothesis:

> "... It is well established that [radioactivity] is the function of the atom and not the molecule. Uranium and thorium, to take the most definite cases, possess the property in whatever molecular condition they occur [as well as] in the elementary state. . . .
>
> "Since, therefore, radioactivity is at once an atomic phenomenon and accompanied by chemical changes in which new types of matter are produced, these changes must be occurring within the atom, and the radioactive elements must be undergoing spontaneous transformation. The results that have so far been obtained, which indicate that the velocity of this reaction is unaffected by the [physical and chemical] conditions, makes it clear that the changes in question are different in character from any that have been before dealt with in chemistry. It is apparent that we are dealing with phenomena outside the sphere of known atomic forces. Radioactivity may therefore be considered as a manifestation of subatomic chemical change. The changes brought to knowledge by radioactivity, although undeniably material and chemical in nature, are of a different order of magnitude from any that have before been dealt with in chemistry. The course of the production of new matter which can be recognized by the electrometer, by means of the property of radioactivity, after the lapse of a few hours or even minutes, might conceivably require geological epochs to attain to [large enough quantities to be detected by weighing]."*

During succeeding years, the transformation theory proposed by Rutherford and Soddy was fully substantiated in almost every detail. Ingenious chemical detective work succeeded in identifying the products of disintegration of uranium, thorium, polonium, and radium. The first step involves emission of an α-particle from a single atom. The new atoms of lower mass resulting from the first disintegration are themselves radioactive, and the result is a "cascade" of disintegration, each new element emitting either α- or β-particles and becoming transformed into still another element of the periodic system. The cascade eventually ends with lead, the atoms of which are "stable" and terminate the sequence of spontaneous transformations. The sequence beginning with uranium, for example, passes through fourteen steps before terminating with lead. (Detailed listings of the steps of disintegration, the branchings that occur, the zigzags back and forth in the atomic numbers of elements formed in the sequence of α- and β-emissions will be found in any text that discusses the phenomenon of radioactivity in greater detail than we attempt here.)

These results showed finally and conclusively that the chemical atom lived up to its name of "indivisible" only in a relative sense: the energy transformations of chemical reaction and electrolysis, large changes in temperature and pressure, did not probe the internal structure, allowing atoms of different elements to behave as indivisible, unalterable entities. Natural radioactivity, however, involved deep-seated

---

* *Philosophical Magazine*, September 1902.

atomic transformations, taking place spontaneously in a certain few inherently unstable elements of large atomic mass. Here was a new "chemistry" with its own set
of reactions—*not* connected with chemical reactions as hitherto understood.

This realization soon led to the question as to whether atomic transformations
and radioactivity could be produced *artificially* by probing deeply into atoms through
"bombardment" with particles of very high kinetic energy. Such questions led to
the design of experiments in which α-particles from radium or polonium were used
as projectiles against atoms of other substances and eventually to the design of
"accelerators" to develop "projectiles" of still higher kinetic energy. Along
this path lay the study of nuclear structure and the development of modern
nuclear technology. The first *artificial* nuclear reaction or transmutation was
accomplished by Rutherford at Manchester just before he moved to the Cavendish
Laboratory.

32.7   THE IDENTIFICATION OF α-PARTICLES

At the time he and Soddy suggested the theory of radioactive transformations
in 1902, Rutherford was still under the impression that β-particles were the only
"deviable" component (deflected by magnetic fields) of radioactive emission. He
spoke of both α- and γ-radiations as "undeviable." Perhaps the theory of subatomic
transformation impelled him to study the disintegration products more closely;
at any rate, in 1903 he risked the then great expense of constructing an unusually
powerful electromagnet and reported the results already stated in Section 32.2:
that the α-radiation consisted of *positively* charged particles with $q_\alpha/m_\alpha \cong 4.8 \times 10^7$ coul/kg.

As we noted in Problem 32.1, this charge-to-mass ratio might apply equally well
to singly ionized hydrogen molecules or to doubly ionized helium atoms. Rutherford's
intuition immediately turned him to the hypothesis that α-particles were helium.
He had previously been strongly impressed by the discovery that helium gas was
always found trapped in small quantities in the pores and interstices of radioactive
materials and ores.

At this point Rutherford had one rough check of the hypothesis: In using the
crossed-fields technique to determine q_α/m_α, he had also determined the *velocity* of
the α-particles, just as Thomson in a precisely similar situation had determined
the velocity of electrons in cathode rays. Thus he could calculate the kinetic energy
of the particles either on the assumption that they were hydrogen molecules or on
the assumption that they were helium atoms. In the latter case the KE would be
twice as great as in the former. [Why?] He had determined (by observation of
scintillations on a fluorescent screen) the number of particles emitted per unit mass
of radium per unit time. From this he could estimate the total energy of emitted
particles and calculate the heat generated by one gram of radium per hour, a value
that the Curies had reported to be about 80 cal/gm-hr. Rutherford found that his
calculation agreed well with the Curies' result if he assumed α-particles to have
the atomic mass of helium.

PROBLEM 32.2. Set up Rutherford's calculation in algebraic symbols. What quantities must be known in addition to the ones mentioned in the preceding paragraphs? How do you visualize the generation of heat in this situation; i.e., what happens to the α-particles and their KE?

In 1903 Ramsey and Soddy presented evidence that as the gas radon* decays in a tube, the spectrum of helium appears in the residual gases and becomes more intense. Rutherford and Royds eventually (1909) used this indication to set up the conclusive experiment† which is illustrated schematically in Fig. 32.7.1.

Radon gas (obtained by pumping it away as it emanates from a radium compound) is placed in the inner, extremely thin-walled (0.001 cm) glass tube. This tube is sealed within a larger heavy-walled evacuated tube, as shown in the diagram. The α-particles from the decaying radon have enough energy to penetrate the thin-walled tube but are trapped in the thick-walled outer container over a "seal" of mercury. After a sufficient period of time (about a week), enough gas accumulates in the outer container to allow a spectroscopic test. Additional mercury is let into the tube, raising the level of the liquid until the small amount of gas above it is compressed into the small capillary which is fitted with electrodes. Electrical discharge through the gas causes the emission of a line spectrum.

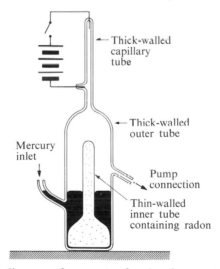

FIG. 32.7.1. Schematic diagram of apparatus for showing spectroscopically that helium is formed from α-particles.

---

* Radon is a member of the column of the periodic table containing the family of "noble" gases: helium, neon, argon, krypton, and xenon. It is the first product of the sequence of disintegration of radium, being formed when a radium atom emits an α-particle. Radon itself is also radioactive, and decays with emission of α-particles.

† See paper by Rutherford and Royds, *Philosophical Magazine*, **17**, 281 (1909). Also reprinted in *Rutherford at Manchester*, Edited by J. B. Birks. New York: W. A. Benjamin Inc., 1963.

Rutherford showed that the characteristic lines of helium were observed under these circumstances, and he showed that ordinary helium gas (neutral helium atoms) stored in the inner tube does *not* penetrate through its thin walls—only the far more energetic α-particles are capable of this penetration.

This experiment, combined with the previous evidence, demonstrated conclusively that α-particles must be doubly ionized helium atoms.

32.8 DETECTION OF RADIOACTIVE EMISSIONS

Radioactivity was originally discovered by virtue of its photographic effects, and Becquerel and a few others continued to use photographic techniques of detection in various experiments. The photographic technique was slow, and required hours of exposure time. Rutherford, the Curies, and other investigators turned to the more rapid and sensitive method of observing the decay of charge on an electrometer.

It was eventually discovered that α-particles, on striking a zinc sulfide fluorescent screen, caused individual flicks or scintillations that could be seen in a darkened room after the eyes became dark adapted. Viewing a very small area of the fluorescent screen through a low-powered microscope, and using a radioactive source of sufficiently low intensity, it was possible to count the individual flashes of light as they occurred in various regions of the screen. Thus, for example, it was possible to form a narrow beam of particles (Fig. 32.3.1), allow the beam to strike and penetrate a target of very thin metal foil, and count the α-particles scattered to various angles away from their initial direction. Rutherford and his associates performed many of their most important experiments using this technique. One of the best known of these experiments (see Section 33.12) led Rutherford to propose the nuclear model of atomic structure.

Note that this technique is very different from the first two we have mentioned. It involves the observation and counting of *individual events* and strengthens the view that α-radiation is not a continuous phenomenon but consists of discrete, corpuscular effects. Photographic and electrometer methods yield what is essentially a summation or integration of total ionization produced over the period of observation and do not allow the counting or recording of individual events.

In 1911 C. T. R. Wilson, one of J. J. Thomson's associates at the Cavendish Laboratory, capitalizing on earlier work with the clouds of water droplets formed on ions in a gas containing water vapor (see Section 31.15), developed another device for the recording of individual radioactive events. The device, called a cloud chamber, is illustrated schematically in Fig. 32.8.1.

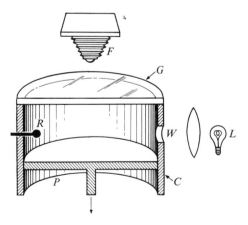

FIG. 32.8.1.   Schematic diagram of Wilson cloud chamber.

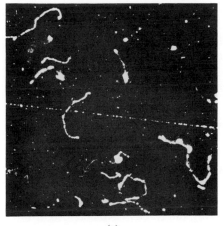

(a)

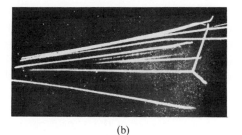

(b)

Alpha particles cross the view field from left to right. One has hit an oxygen atom and has glanced off to the upper right corner, while the oxygen atom moves away toward the lower right corner.

Beady track produced by a high-energy electron. Broader tracks are due to low-energy photoelectrons. (Courtesy of C. T. R. Wilson and the Royal Society of London.)

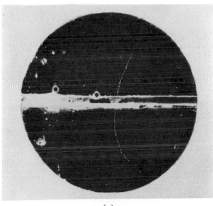

(c)

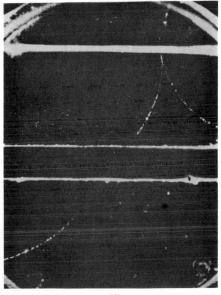

(d)

Cloud chamber photograph in which a particle, leaving a beaded track similar to that of high-energy electrons, originated in the lower right-hand part of the cloud chamber, passed through a 6-mm-thick lead plate, and then continued on with decreased speed. A magnetic field is directed out of the plane of the paper toward the reader. Direction of curvature of the track indicates particle was positively charged. This photograph, marking the discovery of the positron, was taken by C. D. Anderson in 1932.

A γ-ray entering the cloud chamber from above strikes a lead plate. A magnetic field is directed perpendicular to the plane of the photograph. Two particles emerge from the lead plate, leaving tracks that curve in opposite directions. One particle is an electron, the other a positron. This photograph illustrates the phenomenon called "pair production" in which the energy of the γ-ray, after interaction with an atom in the lead plate, is converted into energy of the electron-positron pair.

FIGURE 32.8.2

A cylinder C is covered with a glass plate G. The interior of the cylinder can be illuminated through window W by bright light from lamp L. A radioactive source R is placed within the cylinder (or ionizing radiation enters from the outside). The air in the cylinder is not quite saturated with water vapor. Ions formed in the gas can be cleared or swept away by an electric field maintained between capacitor plates not shown in the diagram. The α, β, or other ionizing particles passing through the gas in the chamber leave a track of many pairs of ions (positive and negative), the kinetic energy of the α- or β-particles being transformed into potential energy of separation of the electrical charge on the ions along the track. When the chamber is to be operated, the clearing field is turned off so as not to sweep away the ions being formed. Piston P is rapidly displaced a short distance downward, causing the air in the chamber to cool by expansion and to become supersaturated with water vapor. The water vapor condenses rapidly, forming tiny water droplets around the ions in the tracks left by the ionizing particles, and making the tracks visible as bright lines against a dark background (just as the oil droplet was made visible by side illumination in Millikan's experiment). The camera is triggered and the tracks photographed as they become visible. The entire operation takes a fraction of a second; the tracks must be photographed immediately after they are formed, since they become diffuse and fade away rapidly as the tiny droplets are dispersed by free fall and by motion of the gas in the cylinder. Typical cloud chamber photographs are shown in Fig. 32.8.2. A recently invented instrument, called the bubble chamber, operates in a manner inverse to that of a cloud chamber. The trail formed by passage of an energetic particle through a fluid such as liquid hydrogen is made visible by the formation of tiny bubbles of gas around the ions (Fig. 32.8.3).

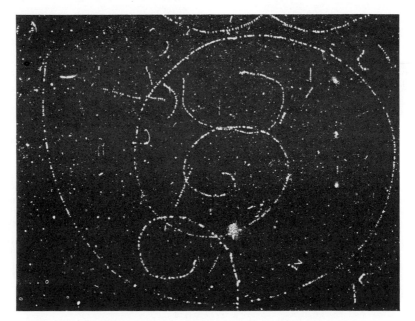

FIG. 32.8.3. A very high energy electron slowing down in a liquid hydrogen bubble chamber traversed by a magnetic field. (Courtesy Radiation Laboratory, Univ. of California.)

Numerous electronic devices have been developed for recording total ionization and for counting individual radioactive events. Descriptions of such instruments will be found in references cited at the end of the chapter.

32.9   RATE OF DECAY OF A PURE RADIOACTIVE ELEMENT

In the preceding sections we have referred to the discoveries that intensity of radioactivity of a sample of material is completely unaffected by temperature, pressure, or chemical conditions and that the intensity of radioactivity (i.e., number of disintegrations taking place per second) is directly proportional to the mass of the radioactive element present. These observations imply that the number of disintegrations per second depends *only* on the number of atoms of the radioactive element present at any given time, and that the rate must itself decrease with time as the number of remaining atoms decreases. Let us translate this verbal statement into mathematical symbols, denoting by N the number of undisintegrated atoms of the radioactive element present at any instant of time t:

$$\frac{dN}{dt} = -kN. \qquad (32.9.1)$$

The symbol k represents a proportionality constant, having different values for different radioactive substances. Note that the minus sign must be introduced in order to have the algebraic statement make physical sense: N is inherently a positive quantity and, for convenience, we shall agree to make k positive also. Then, if we do not introduce the minus sign, the equation would say that dN/dt is positive; i.e., that the number of undisintegrated atoms *increases* as time goes by. This is not the case we are trying to describe. In radioactive decay, N *decreases as time* goes by, meaning that dN/dt is inherently negative. Introduction of the minus sign satisfies this *physical* requirement.

Equation (32.9.1) is a "differential equation" that, even at first glance, tells us a great deal about the function $N(t)$; that is, about how the number of radioactive atoms varies with time.

PROBLEM 32.3. Interpret the information contained in Eq. (32.9.1) by answering the following questions: (a) Let us sketch a graph of N versus t, taking $N = N_0$ at $t = 0$. What is the direction or slope of the graph near $t = 0$? What happens to the slope of the graph as t increases? What happens to the value of N as t increases? Can N become zero or negative? Sketch the general shape of the curve. (b) Give a physical interpretation of the proportionality constant k: Which element decays more rapidly—one with lower or higher value of k? What are the dimensions of k? [*Answer:* reciprocal time: $\sec^{-1}$, yr^{-1}, etc.] (c) Starting at the same value of N_0 used in part (a), sketch curves for decays having first a higher, then a lower, value of k than that of

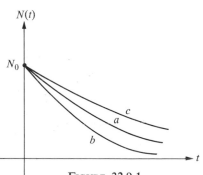

FIGURE 32.9.1

the first curve drawn. Your final sketch should have the appearance of Fig. 32.9.1. If we denote the curves by letters a, b, c, respectively, the "decay constants" fall in the numerical sequence $k_b > k_a > k_c$. (The larger the value of k, the more rapid is the decay of the element.) (d) Equation (32.9.1), stated in the language and notation of the calculus and implying that N is a continuous function of t, is physically valid only if we are applying it to systems containing enormous numbers of atoms. Why?

32.10 NONDIMENSIONAL FORM OF EQ. (32.9.1)

The mathematical problem that now confronts us is that of "solving" differential equation (32.9.1)—finding algebraic expressions for functions $N(t)$ that behave in the manner described by this equation and sketched in Fig. 32.9.1. First we note that we have a different curve for each different value of N_0, as well as for each different value of k. Our task would be very tedious indeed if it were necessary to treat each new combination of N_0 and k as a new problem, but we are saved by the use of a simple and powerful technique that plays an important role in the methods of mathematical physics: we introduce "scaled" or "dimensionless" variables. For example, let us introduce a scaled or dimensionless time defined by

$$\tau \equiv kt. \tag{32.10.1}$$

(How do we know that kt is dimensionless?)

Then, making use of the chain rule of differentiation (see Section 8.10), we have

$$\frac{dN}{dt} = \frac{dN}{d\tau}\frac{d\tau}{dt} = k\frac{dN}{d\tau}. \tag{32.10.2}$$

Substituting (32.10.2) into (32.9.1), we obtain $k(dN/d\tau) = -kN$, and hence

$$\frac{dN}{d\tau} = -N. \tag{32.10.3}$$

Dividing both sides of the last equation by N_0:

$$\frac{1}{N_0}\frac{dN}{d\tau} = \frac{d}{d\tau}\left(\frac{N}{N_0}\right) = -\frac{N}{N_0}. \tag{32.10.4}$$

Note that N/N_0 represents the *fraction* of the initial number of molecules, N_0, left at time t. Denoting this fraction by f, Eq. (32.10.4) becomes

$$\frac{df}{d\tau} = -f, \tag{32.10.5}$$

where f has the value 1 at $\tau = 0$. (Why?)

This is our basic nondimensional form of the differential equation of radioactive decay. The arbitrary numbers N_0 and k have been used to "scale" the variables; they no longer appear explicitly in the equation but, as we shall see, they can be brought back into our calculations whenever we wish to do so.

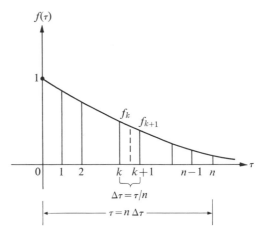

FIG. 32.11.1. Sketch of $f(\tau)$ versus τ. Along the abscissa a time interval τ is divided into n equal intervals $\Delta\tau$, so that $\Delta\tau = \tau/n$ or $\tau = n\,\Delta\tau$. Note the initial condition: $f(0) = 1$.

32.11 NUMERICAL ANALYSIS OF THE NONDIMENSIONAL DIFFERENTIAL EQUATION

The function $f(\tau)$ of Eq. (32.10.5) must have the form sketched in Fig. 32.11.1. By an essentially numerical method, we now proceed to establish its algebraic chacacter. Let us divide a time interval τ along the abscissa into n equal intervals Δt. These intervals are numbered $1, 2, 3, \ldots k, k + 1, \ldots n$ in Fig. 32.11.1.

Consider interval number $(k + 1)$ as marked in the figure, with ordinates f_k and f_{k+1} at the beginning and end of the interval, respectively. The slope of the secant of the curve in this interval is

$$\frac{f_{k+1} - f_k}{\Delta\tau}. \tag{32.11.1}$$

Since $f(\tau)$ is a continuous function (its derivative exists wherever values of f exist), the mean value theorem assures us that (32.11.1) represents a value of the derivative at some point within the $(k + 1)$ interval. Therefore, in accordance with the fact that

$$\frac{df}{d\tau} = -f, \tag{32.11.2}$$

expression (32.11.1) must be the negative of a value of the ordinate f occurring within the same interval. As a reasonable guess let us take the latter value to be the average of f_k and f_{k+1}:

$$\frac{f_{k+1} - f_k}{\Delta\tau} \cong -\left(\frac{f_{k+1} + f_k}{2}\right). \tag{32.11.3}$$

Let us rearrange Eq. (32.11.3) to find how f_{k+1} is related to f_k:

$$f_{k+1} - f_k \cong -\frac{\Delta\tau}{2}f_{k+1} - \frac{\Delta\tau}{2}f_k, \quad \left(1 + \frac{\Delta\tau}{2}\right)f_{k+1} \cong \left(1 - \frac{\Delta\tau}{2}\right)f_k,$$

$$f_{k+1} \cong \left[\frac{1 - (\Delta\tau/2)}{1 + (\Delta\tau/2)}\right]f_k. \tag{32.11.4}$$

To simplify our notation, let us introduce the symbol β for the more cumbersome ratio in (32.11.4):

$$\beta \equiv \frac{1 - (\Delta\tau/2)}{1 + (\Delta\tau/2)},$$

$$f_{k+1} \cong \beta f_k. \tag{32.11.5}$$

Equation (32.11.5) tells us that, in the uniform subdivision of the curve shown in Fig. 32.11.1, each succeeding value of f is obtained from the one preceding it by always multiplying by the same constant fraction β. This statement is illustrated in symbols in the following table, which starts with the initially prescribed condition that $f = 1$ when $\tau = 0$:

$$f_0 = 1,$$

$$f_1 \cong \beta f_0 = \beta,$$

$$f_2 \cong \beta f_1 = \beta^2,$$

$$f_3 \cong \beta f_2 = \beta^3,$$

$$\vdots \quad \vdots \quad \vdots$$

$$f_{k+1} \cong \beta f_k = \beta^{k+1},$$

$$\vdots \quad \vdots \quad \vdots$$

$$f_n \cong \beta f_{n-1} = \beta^n, \quad \text{where } n = \tau/\Delta\tau.$$

But f_n is what we mean by $f(\tau)$, the value of f at the end of the full interval τ. Therefore

$$f(\tau) \cong \beta^n = (\beta^{1/\Delta\tau})^\tau. \tag{32.11.6}$$

Our arithmetical statement, which began with the approximation made in setting up Eq. (32.11.3), should become more and more precise as we make n (the number of intervals) larger and $\Delta\tau$ smaller. Let us examine what happens to the numerical value of $\beta^{1/\Delta\tau}$ in such a sequence. (See Table 32.11.1.)

PROBLEM 32.4. Make the appropriate calculations and fill in all the blank spaces that remain in Table 32.11.1. Plot a graph of $\beta^{1/\Delta\tau}$ versus $\Delta\tau$ to get a better feeling for how the function behaves.

TABLE 32.11.1

EVALUATION OF $\beta^{1/\Delta\tau}$ FOR VARIOUS VALUES OF $\Delta\tau$

$\Delta\tau$	$1 - \Delta\tau/2$	$1 + \Delta\tau/2$	β	$\beta^{1/\Delta\tau}$
1.0				0.333
0.5	0.75	1.75	0.600	$(0.600)^2 = 0.360$
0.25				$(0.777)^4 = 0.365$
0.20				0.367
0.10				0.368

From the results of Table 32.11.1 and Problem 32.4 it appears that, to three significant figures,

$$\lim_{\Delta\tau\to0}\left[\frac{1-(\Delta\tau/2)}{1+(\Delta\tau/2)}\right]^{1/\Delta\tau}=0.368. \tag{32.11.7}$$

We shall accept this result without giving it a rigorous mathematical examination. (It can be shown that the limit exists and that it is an irrational number. The analysis will be found in more advanced mathematics texts.) From Eq. (32.11.6) we now infer that, as we make $n\to\infty$ and $\Delta\tau\to0$, we obtain the function

$$f(\tau)=(0.368\ldots)^\tau=\left(\frac{1}{0.368\ldots}\right)^{-\tau}. \tag{32.11.8}$$

An almost universal mathematical convention is to introduce the *reciprocal* of the quantity 0.368 arising in the preceding calculations. This number is denoted by the symbol ϵ, and when calculated to a larger number of significant figures it is found that

$$\epsilon=2.71828\ldots.$$

Thus, Eq. (32.11.8) becomes

$$f(\tau)=\left(\frac{1}{\epsilon}\right)^\tau=\epsilon^{-\tau}. \tag{32.11.9}$$

This function is said to be a "solution" of differential equation (32.11.2): it is the function such that

$$\frac{d\epsilon^{-\tau}}{d\tau}=-\epsilon^{-\tau}, \tag{32.11.10}$$

and it satisfies the initial condition that $f=1$ when $\tau=0$.

The function $\epsilon^{-\tau}$ is a special case of a broad class called "exponential" functions, the name being applied to functions in which the variable appears in the exponent. Exponential functions of this type arise in many physical problems—wherever a rate of change of a given quantity is proportional to the instantaneous value of the quantity itself. This occurs in the case of leakage of electrical charge from a capacitor, flow of gas from a hole in a compression chamber, the behavior of certain simple chemical reactions, variation of pressure with altitude in a gas at uniform temperature, and countless other physical situations. Exactly the same mathematical equation must be solved in each instance. Thus the analysis we have carried out in this section applies to far more problems than just that of radioactive decay.

32.12 THE LAW OF RADIOACTIVE DECAY

Having obtained a general solution to the nondimensional differential equation, let us return to our original symbols. Introducing $f\equiv N/N_0$ and $\tau\equiv kt$, Eq. (32.11.9) becomes

$$\frac{N}{N_0}=\epsilon^{-kt}\qquad\text{or}\qquad N=N_0\epsilon^{-kt}. \tag{32.12.1}$$

Let us verify that we can get back to our original differential equation (32.9.1): Taking the derivative of (32.12.1) and making use of (32.11.10) in the intermediate steps, we obtain

$$\frac{dN}{dt} = \frac{d}{dt}(N_0\epsilon^{-kt}) = N_0\frac{d\epsilon^{-kt}}{dt} = N_0\frac{d\epsilon^{-\tau}}{d\tau}\frac{d\tau}{dt} = N_0(-\epsilon^{-\tau})k.$$

Therefore

$$\frac{dN}{dt} = -kN_0\epsilon^{-\tau} = -kN, \tag{32.12.2}$$

which was indeed our original starting point.

Equation (32.12.1) is called the *law of radioactive decay*. The result informs us that, as we might have guessed from our preliminary sketches in Fig. 32.9.1, it is useless to talk about the "total life" of a radioactive substance, since $N \to 0$ only as $t \to \infty$. Our analysis now reveals, however, that we can still characterize "life time" or rate of decay in a very simple way. We have seen from the analysis in Section 32.11 that f decreases by exactly the same fraction in each succeeding uniform interval of τ. Thus, for example, if we find the value of τ over which f falls from 1 to, say, $\frac{3}{4}$ (this value of τ is calculated to be 0.288, since $\epsilon^{-0.288} = 0.75$; verify this numerical result by use of logarithms or slide rule), in another equal interval f would fall from $\frac{3}{4}$ to $\frac{3}{4} \times \frac{3}{4} = \frac{9}{16}$, and in still another equal interval would be reduced to $\frac{9}{16} \times \frac{3}{4} = \frac{27}{64}$. The interval $\Delta\tau = 0.288$ would be called the "three-quarter life" of the decay.

The convention actually adopted in describing radioactivity is to talk about the *half-life* of the decay. The value of τ at which f drops from 1 to $\frac{1}{2}$ is calculated to be 0.693 (verify that $\epsilon^{-0.693} = 0.5$). An illustration of the meaning of these numbers is given in Table 32.12.1.

TABLE 32.12.1

SIGNIFICANCE OF THE DIMENSIONLESS HALF-LIFE INTERVAL $\Delta\tau = 0.693$

τ	$f(\tau) = \epsilon^{-\tau}$
0.693	1/2
2 × 0.693	1/4
3 × 0.693	1/8
4 × 0.693	1/16
$\vdots$	$\vdots$
n × 0.693	$1/2^n$

PROBLEM 32.5.   Illustrate the meaning of Table 32.12.1 graphically by making a sketch of $f(\tau)$ versus τ, marking off equal intervals with $\Delta\tau = 0.693$, and showing how the value of f at the end of each interval is related to 1, the initial value at $\tau = 0$.

If we now establish the numerical value of the constant k for any given material, we can immediately calculate its half-life, denoted by $t_{1/2}$. Since τ was defined as kt, we have

$$t_{1/2} = \frac{\tau_{1/2}}{k} = \frac{0.693}{k}. \tag{32.12.3}$$

Example: It is established by α-particle counting that about 3.6×10^{10} disintegrations occur in each second among the atoms in one gram of radium; the number of atoms in one gram is 2.66×10^{21}. From our original differential equation, we have

$$k = \frac{-dN/dt}{N} = \frac{3.6 \times 10^{10}}{2.66 \times 10^{21}} = 1.36 = 10^{-11} \text{ sec}^{-1}.$$

The half-life of radium is then obtained from

$$t_{1/2} = \frac{0.693}{1.36 \times 10^{-11}} = 5.1 \times 10^{10} \text{ sec} = 1600 \text{ yr.}$$

(Verify the calculations, including the last step.)

If we start with one gram of pure radium, the number of undisintegrated radium atoms left after 4860 years (3×1620) would be $1/2^3 \times 2.66 \times 10^{21} = 3.33 \times 10^{20}$.

Let us examine this aspect of radioactivity in still another way: We have indicated that, regardless of when we start with a group of atoms, half of them will decay in a time interval $t_{1/2} - 0.693/k$. Thus it does not matter at all how "old" the radioactive atoms are. Their chances of surviving for an additional time interval of length $t_{1/2}$ are fifty-fifty. Note that this is not a universal kind of behavior; for example, living organisms have less and less chance of survival for an additional length of time as they get older. The radioactivity decay law describes the behavior of atoms whose chances of disintegrating over any succeeding time interval seem to be governed only by random conditions within the structure itself, and not on the preceding age or history.

If it were possible to observe the behavior of a system containing only a few hundred or thousand radioactive atoms, we would expect to find that dN/dt was far from steady, and showed violent, random fluctuations. In a sense, this is analogous to our expectation that if millions of coins were flipped in a given experiment, the result would be very, very close to 50% heads and 50% tails. But if only a few coins are flipped, we are not surprised to find fairly large departures from the fifty-fifty ratio in any given experiment.

In a very rapidly decaying radioactive material—one with a half-life of hours, minutes, or even seconds—it may well be impossible to determine the total number of atoms initially present, simply because the chemical measurements could not be made in a short enough time. It is still possible, however, to determine the half-life in a fairly simple way. Equation (32.12.2) reveals a very interesting property of the exponential function: not only do N and f decrease exponentially with a half-life of $0.693/k$, but the intensity or rate of disintegration dN/dt *also decreases in exactly the same way.* Thus when a substance decays so rapidly that we can follow the *decrease* in dN/dt (we cannot do this with radium, for example, because dN/dt does not change appreciably over many years), we can measure the time over which dN/dt drops to $\frac{1}{2}$ its value at the beginning of the interval, and thereby have the half-life of the substance itself. Many laboratory determinations are made in just this way.

Final note of caution: The decay law we have derived applies to the behavior of a single, pure radioactive element. Complicated mixtures of radioactive substances and samples containing products of initial disintegrations that are themselves radioactive do *not* obey the simple exponential decay law.

32.13 PHYSICS IN THE NINETEENTH CENTURY

Having brought our story up to the conceptual revolution that occurred at the turn of the twentieth century, we pause briefly to view from this perspective some of the events and changes that occurred in the character of the scientific enterprise during the nineteenth.

During this period the results of pure scientific inquiry and knowledge began to have their rapidly deepening and accelerating impact on technology. Such effects are small and hard to trace during the eighteenth century, but they are obvious in the nineteenth. The science of thermodynamics was used to improve steam engines and develop steam power to unprecedented heights of flexibility and efficiency. Engineers began to make systematic use of the science of mechanics in the design of machinery. Discovery of electromagnetic phenomena led to the development of an entirely new technology of electrical power—the construction for industrial purposes of large and powerful motors and generators. Knowledge of electro-magnetism was exploited to provide new means of communication—the telegraph, transoceanic cable, telephone, and wireless. From chemistry came the rapid growth of chemical technology—the manufacture of a vast variety of substances for industrial, agricultural, and domestic use.

While technology was growing out of science, science itself underwent subtle and profound changes. Physical problems that were relatively simple mathematically had been solved. The problems that remained required powerful and sophisticated mathematical techniques. Lagrange, Laplace, Poisson, Gauss, and Fourier in less than two generations developed mathematical physics to such a point that little room was left for the gifted amateur who had contributed so much during the seventeenth and eighteenth centuries. Hamilton, Kelvin, Maxwell, and Rayleigh carried the process still further. Not only did science become professionalized, requiring lengthy and specialized training of new recruits; it simultaneously became more arcane behind its mathematical walls and less accessible to the nonscientific intellectual.

This fragmentation rapidly penetrated into science itself. Where the nineteenth-century physicist could hope to know and understand virtually all developments in physical science, his twentieth-century counterpart is usually happy to be able to hold his own in one specialized branch, such as elementary particles or a section of solid state physics or the phenomena of shock waves, with only a fairly sketchy knowledge of progress and developments in other areas. Similarly, the modern chemist, instead of having the entire range of the subject at his disposal, operates within the confines of some branch of organic chemistry or of molecular structure or the properties of conducting solutions. A few highly gifted individuals have the range and scope to cross the artificial boundaries that have arisen, but their number is all too small.

The rise of the scientific professional has taken place side by side with the growth of opportunity for employment. During the nineteenth century came the expansion of science in the universities, the growth of research institutions, the increase of employment opportunities in industry. Where in previous times the rewards for success in science were limited to scholarly prestige and the respect and accolade of one's peers, the nineteenth century saw the addition of economic rewards and the power that goes with administration of institutes and influence in government circles. With these developments came the growth of specialized professional societies, functioning as agencies of communication and publication of results and of discipline and control of professional standards.

Increase in the number of professional scientists was inevitably accompanied by increased competition for recognition and for priority in scientific discovery. Newton and his contemporaries were very sensitive concerning priority and the honor attached thereto, as their angry polemics liberally testify. Although in modern times the language has become more temperate and restrained, the competition for priority has, if anything, intensified, the economic rewards having become more tangible and significant.

In the last few chapters the reader must have sensed the rapidly accelerating pace of acquisition of scientific knowledge. Where, in describing scientific advances of the seventeenth and eighteenth centuries, we spoke of developments that are frequently separated by many years, we find events in the early nineteenth century coming only a few years apart—witness the work of Dalton, Gay-Lussac, Avogadro, and Berzelius in chemistry and that of Young, Malus, Brewster, and Fresnel in optics.

In outlining the events that followed the discovery of X-rays, however, we referred to a cascade of important developments separated by only months or weeks, with work on X-rays, conduction in gases, radioactivity, cathode rays, corpuscular nature of charge, all influencing and interacting with each other in a complex pattern of cross current and cross fertilization of ideas. The accelerating pace can be traced in part to the fact that many more people than ever before were devoting themselves to professional pursuit of science, and in part to the intrinsically more rapid pace of discovery, stimulated by the large body of scientific theory synthesized and clarified during the nineteenth century, and by rapid progress in experimental techniques of electrical measurement and of high vacuum.

At the turn of the century the discovery of the new radiations, of electrons, of transmutation of elements, the failure of delicate experiments to detect motion of the earth through the ether as predicted by electromagnetic theory, all conspired to leave physics in a state of crisis. The most firmly established theories were being challenged; no one knew what strange phenomenon might be discovered next.

In this climate the American historian Henry Adams issued his despairing cry that "Chaos is the law of nature; order is the dream of man." In this climate, also, René Blondlot, professor of physics at the University of Nancy, announced in 1903 the discovery of an entirely new kind of radiation which he designated as N-rays in honor of his university. Many individuals throughout the scientific community were drawn into research in this field or into efforts to verify Blondlot's strange results. It was more than a year before N-rays were exposed by the American physicist R. W. Wood as either a hoax or a self-deception on the part of Blondlot.*

---

* For a description of this fantastic episode, see Chapter 4, "Mutations in Science," in *Science Since Babylon*, by Derek Price. New Haven: Yale University Press, 1961.

Physics, as we shall see in the remainder of our story, weathered the conceptual crisis of the early 1900's only to encounter and then weather others. It is passing through a crisis now, centered around the problem of inability of present theories to account for the numerous "elementary" particles observed in high-energy phenomena. Few scientists would claim that "final" knowledge is within our grasp, but, despite some of the limitations we begin to discover on our ability to "know" or describe nature, our view of the order it manifests seems something more than a dream.

32.14   PROBLEMS

32.6. In the analysis carried out in Sections 32.9–32.12, we treated N, the number of radioactive atoms present at any instant of time, as a *continuous* function of t. Since atoms are discrete entities, and since N can therefore take on only integer values, the actual physical quantity is clearly *not* continuous in the mathematical sense. How is it that we can get away with a calculus treatment and obtain a result in agreement with experimental observations? Under what circumstances would we expect the analysis to fail us? In what way?

32.7. A radioactive material obeying the exponential decay law is found to decrease in intensity of radioactivity to 0.6 its initial value after a period of one day. What would be the intensity relative to initial value at the end of three days? At the end of n days? [*Answer:* 0.22; $(0.6)^n$.]

32.8. A radioactive form of the element carbon, C^{14}, with atomic mass 14 rather than 12, is found in the atmosphere at fairly uniform but extremely low concentration, and is incorporated with ordinary carbon into the structure of plants while the plants are growing. When plants die, the exchange of chemicals with the atmosphere ceases; the C^{14} atoms decay with a half-life of 5600 yr and are no longer replaced. The average activity of C^{14} per gram of total carbon in living plants has been carefully established. Suppose that a sample of charcoal from an archeological site is found to have about $\frac{1}{4}$ the C^{14} activity per gram of carbon found in living wood. How old

is the archeological site? What is the value of k for C^{14}? [*Answer:* About 11,000 yr; $k = 1.24 \times 10^{-4}$ yr.]

A sample of papyrus from an ancient document is found to have 0.78 the C^{14} activity of the living plant. What is the age of the document? [*Answer:* Since $\epsilon^{-0.25} = 0.78$, $\tau = 0.25$, and age is about 2000 yr.]

32.9. You are likely to hear much now and in future years about radiation damage to living body tissues from excessive exposure to X-rays or radioactivity. In the light of what has been said about detection of X-rays and radioactivity by means of the ionization effects produced in a gas, what effect do you imagine such rays would have on the materials constituting living cells and tissues which depend on the structure and properties of very complex molecules? (Detailed mechanism of radiation damage is a highly specialized study in its own right. Your answer to the preceding question is not expected to be a professional answer, but a speculation based on the limited knowledge you have acquired so far.) Draw on whatever biological information you have acquired in previous study or general reading to speculate on the mechanism by which exposure to X-rays or radioactivity might have hereditary effects.

32.10. Starting with the differential equation

$$\frac{df}{d\tau} = +f,$$

perform an analysis parallel to that carried

out in Section 32.11, showing that $f = \epsilon^\tau$ is a solution, subject to the condition $f = 1$ at $\tau = 0$. Note that the exponential function is characterized by an unusual property: It is its own derivative! Do you see any connection between this function and the series of Problem 8.26(d)?

SUPPLEMENTARY READING AND STUDY

Foundations of Modern Physical Science, G. Holton and D. H. D. Roller. Reading, Mass.: Addison-Wesley, 1958, Chapter 36

Physics of the Atom, M. R. Wehr and J. A. Richards. Reading, Mass.: Addison-Wesley, 1960, Chapter 9

Atomic Physics, L. Kerwin. New York: Holt, Rinehart, and Winston, 1963, Chapter 11

Experimental Atomic Physics, G. P. Harnwell and J. J. Livingood. New York: McGraw-Hill, 1933, Chapter 10

Radiation from Radioactive Substances, Rutherford, Chadwick, and Ellis. New York: Macmillan, 1930

CHAPTER 33

Physics of Atoms: The Nuclear Model

33.1 INTRODUCTION

Study of conduction in gases began with *qualitative* observation of rays in discharge tubes, glow of gases at different degrees of vacuum, fluorescence of glass and other materials exposed to the rays. Then suddenly, within the few years at the end of the nineteenth century, the discovery of X-rays, the electron, radioactivity, and the corpuscular nature of electrical charge marked the emergence of a new *quantitative* science—one that yielded numerical information concerning a submicroscopic scale far below that of direct sense perception, and generated radically new conceptions of the structure of matter.

Interweaving in a fabric of ingenious experiments, new hypotheses, checks and cross checks, these discoveries made possible the study of the physics of atoms, exposing to direct investigation from an entirely new direction these entities, whose properties and existence had so far been only indirectly inferred from the data of chemistry and from the kinetic theory of gases.

The first penetration of this area came through further study of that remarkably seminal phenomenon—electrical discharge in gases.

33.2 CANAL RAYS

In 1886, some years after Crookes' careful summary of the qualitative properties of cathode rays, Eugen Goldstein at the University of Berlin reported discovery of a hitherto unnoticed form of radiation in a cathode ray tube. Using a tube consisting of two chambers or compartments separated by a perforated metallic disc cathode, as illustrated in Fig. 33.2.1, Goldstein found that electrical discharge between cathode and anode in chamber *A* was accompanied by the passage of rays through each hole in the cathode into chamber *B*. The rays were made visible by the glow of residual gas along their paths. If the cathode was not perforated, no effects were apparent in chamber *B*. These rays were named *canal rays* because of their apparent connection with perforations or "canals" in the cathode. Attempts to cause electric or magnetic deflection of the rays were unsuccessful.

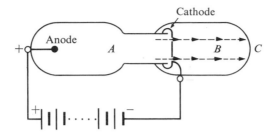

FIG. 33.2.1. Canal-ray tube. When the cathode disc is perforated by holes or "canals," a cathode-ray discharge in chamber A is accompanied by the appearance of rays coming from each hole in the cathode into chamber B. These rays are made visible by the glow of gas along their paths in chamber B. At sufficiently high vacuum, the rays penetrate to the end of the glass tube and excite fluorescence at C.

In 1886 there was still no clear way of visualizing or understanding the primary discharge phenomena themselves, and, as might be expected, little attention was paid to Goldstein's rather incomprehensible secondary effect. By 1897, however, with the demonstration by Perrin and Thomson that cathode rays transported negative charge, with Thomson's first quantitative results supporting the view that cathode rays consisted of negatively charged particles of subatomic mass, the formation of hypotheses about the nature of canal rays became possible. In 1898, shortly after the impact of Thomson's work, Wilhelm Wien published a paper in *Annalen der Physik und Chemie* addressed to the problem:

> "After the negative charge of the cathode rays was demonstrated, the thought came to me that the canal rays observed by Goldstein, which cannot be deflected appreciably by ordinary magnets, and proceed backwards through a pierced cathode, might carry the positive charge."

33.3 WIEN'S EXPERIMENTS

Wien surmised that previous attempts to observe electric and magnetic deflection of canal rays may not have utilized sufficiently strong fields. He was also concerned about the fact that strong electric and magnetic effects applied to chamber B (Fig. 33.2.1) might disturb or alter the effects taking place in discharge tube A. He shielded tube A from such influence by surrounding it with a heavy iron shell, a plate of which formed the cathode itself:

> "I was able to observe the electrostatic deflection in a simple way. A hole 2 mm in diameter was bored in the cathode plate. ... When the exhaustion was sufficient, there came out from the hole a beam of canal rays which brought out a spot of fluorescence, of the well-known yellow-green color, on the glass wall at a distance of 9 cm from the plate.

"This beam of rays passed between two [capacitor plates inserted into chamber *B*] and was deflected when the plates were brought to a difference of potential of 2000 volts. . . . The deflection amounted to 6 mm. The stream was attracted by the negative electrode."

Using what was for that time a very powerful electromagnet (giving a **B**-field of the order of 0.3 weber/m^2), Wien showed that the canal rays were deflected in the direction expected for positively charged particles moving from left to right in Fig. 33.2.1. In both the electric and magnetic deflections, the spot of fluorescence was spread out into a line instead of remaining a coherent spot as in the deflection of cathode rays (see Fig. 33.3.1).

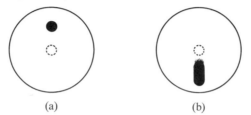

(a)   (b)

FIG. 33.3.1. (a) Cathode-ray beam deflected upward by electric or magnetic field. Spot is shifted from its initial central position on the screen, but is not significantly broadened or smeared out in the vertical direction. (b) Beam of canal rays deflected by electric or magnetic field. Instead of retaining form of a coherent spot, region of fluorescence is spread out into a vertical line, as illustrated in the diagram.

This observation led Wien to remark that the canal rays or "positive" rays, as they soon came to be called, are a mixture, showing a *range* of deflections when subjected to fixed values of electric or magnetic field strengths.

Applying Thomson's technique of crossed electric and magnetic fields, Wien obtained average order-of-magnitude values of charge-to-mass ratio and velocity for the particles associated with the positive beam:

$$q/m \sim 3 \times 10^6 \text{ coul/kg}, \qquad v \sim 3.6 \times 10^5 \text{ m/sec} \sim 0.001\, c,$$

where *c* denotes the velocity of light. (The residual gas in Wien's tube was air.)

PROBLEM 33.1. Return to the equations derived in Section 31.11, Problem 31.7, in connection with Thomson's experiment. Interpreting these equations, point out all the factors that might conceivably be responsible for the range of deflection or the "smearing out" of the positive ray spot, as illustrated in Fig. 33.3.1(b). How might you account for the origin of the positive rays? (Note previous information to the effect that cathode rays *ionize* residual gas in the tube; note also that the electric field in the discharge tube would accelerate positively charged particles toward the cathode.) What inferences do you draw from the fact that the cathode must be *perforated* for the positive rays to be formed? In the light of prior evidence concerning the corpuscularity of electrical charge and the atomic theory of matter, what factors causing continuous smearing out of the positive ray spot would you be inclined to rule out, at least tentatively? What factors would you retain? How might you account for the particles in the beam having a continuous range of velocities?

PROBLEM 33.2. In previous chapters we have encountered the following charge-to-mass ratios:

$$\text{Electron: } e/m = 1.76 \times 10^{11} \text{ coul/kg,}$$

$$\text{Hydrogen ion in electrolysis: } q_H/m_H = 9.6 \times 10^7 \text{ coul/kg,}$$

$$\text{Alpha particles: } q_\alpha/m_\alpha = 4.8 \times 10^7 \text{ coul/kg.}$$

Note the value of 3×10^6 coul/kg reported by Wien as a rough average for positive rays (in a tube containing air as the residual gas). Note also the large potential difference (2000 volts) and the large magnetic field (0.3 weber/m^2) needed to produce sensible deflection of the positive rays. Compare these values of potential difference and **B** with the values given for a typical cathode ray experiment cited in Problem 31.7(h). Note further that the crossed-field experiment showed electrons in the cathode rays to have velocities of the order of $0.1\,c$ (one-tenth the velocity of light) while Wien reported positive ray velocities of the order of $0.001\,c$. While cathode rays were known to penetrate very thin metal foils, Wien found that positive rays would not penetrate these foils at all.

Discuss the relevance and significance of each bit of information cited above. What inferences concerning the qualitative nature and origin of positive rays would you draw from this collection of information? What quantitative inferences? (Is Wien's reported magnitude of charge-to-mass ratio consistent with what you might expect for singly ionized nitrogen or oxygen molecules?)

33.4 THOMSON'S RESEARCH ON POSITIVE RAYS

The evidence described in the preceding sections strongly suggests that positive ray particles are formed at various distances from the cathode through ionization of the residual gas by the beam of electrons. The positive ions are attracted toward the cathode, "falling" from various distances and acquiring a distribution of kinetic energies and velocities. Whereas electrons appear to have subatomic mass, the positive ions appear to carry essentially the entire atomic mass. Combined with the evidence (supplied by the Zeeman effect) that electrons are present within the structure of atoms and molecules, the results suggest the model that ionization occurs when electrons are knocked out of this structure by ultraviolet light, X-rays, radioactive emanations, or by the cathode beam. Left behind are positive ions carrying virtually the entire mass of the original atom or molecule, while the free electrons drift around as negative ions, occasionally recombining with a positive ion to re-form a neutral atom, or attaching themselves to neutral particles to form negative ions of atomic or molecular mass (such negative ions are indeed observed in ionized gases).

Evolution of this conception of ionization motivated further quantitative studies of the positive rays; atomic and molecular particles were for the first time accessible

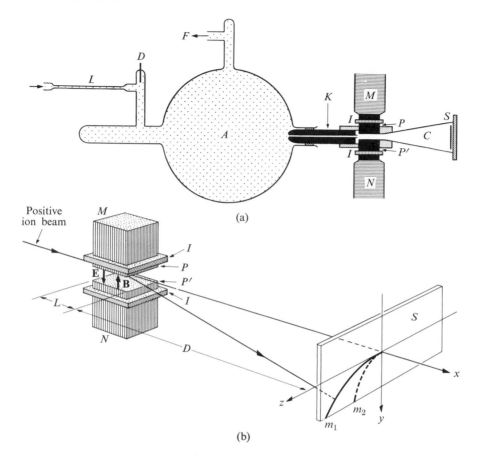

FIG. 33.4.1. (a) Schematic diagram of Thomson's positive ray tube. (b) Diagram of deflection of positive ion beam. The E-field deflects ions downward, while parallel B-field causes lateral deflection in z-direction. Ions with different velocities but same charge-to-mass ratio all fall on the same nearly parabolic arc on screen or photographic plate at S. (See Problem 33.19 at end of chapter.)

to direct physical investigation. Prior to this their properties could be inferred only indirectly from their collective behavior in gases or in chemical reactions.

In a long and painstaking series of investigations initiated by Thomson in 1907 and subsequently pursued by him, by his associate F. W. Aston, and by many other investigators, the techniques for studying positive rays were refined and improved. The groundwork was laid for the highly developed modern experimental science of mass spectrometry.

Over the years 1907–1910 Thomson developed the device illustrated in Fig. 33.4.1. A narrow beam of positive rays is passed through a region of *parallel* electric and magnetic fields. All particles having a particular value of charge-to-mass ratio q/m fall along a single parabolic arc on the screen S, despite the fact that they all

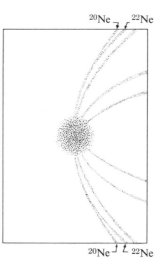

^{20}Ne $\quad$ ^{22}Ne

^{20}Ne $\quad$ ^{22}Ne

FIG. 33.4.2.   Sketch of parabolic arcs formed on photographic plate in Thomson's positive ray tube, neon (Ne) being the residual gas. Symmetrical pattern above and below central axis of photograph is obtained by reversing the **B**-field through reversal of the direction of current in the electromagnet.

have different velocities. Particles with a different charge-to-mass ratio fall along a different arc, etc. (An algebraic analysis of the behavior of particles in this tube is left for Problem 33.19 at the end of the chapter.)

Thomson inserted photographic plates *within* the tube. On development of the plates, the parabolic arcs (together with various other secondary effects due to ions produced by the positive rays themselves) showed up as dark lines. To take full advantage of all the possible data and average out some of the asymmetries inevitably present in the fields and in the structure of the tube, he took two exposures, one with the **B**-field as shown in Fig. 33.4.1 and the other with the **B**-field reversed. The result was a more or less symmetrical set of parabolic arcs, as sketched in Fig. 33.4.2. From the location and spread of the arcs under known values of B, E, and tube dimensions, it is possible to identify the q/m of the ions producing the arc.

Starting with hydrogen as the residual gas in the tube, Thomson was able to identify two arcs: One was associated with $q/m = 9.6 \times 10^7$ coul/kg, identical with the charge-to-mass ratio of the hydrogen ion in electrolysis, and thus presumably due to the singly ionized hydrogen atom H^+. The other arc was associated with $q/m = 4.8 \times 10^7$ coul/kg, and was interpreted as due to the singly ionized hydrogen molecule H_2^+. When helium was the residual gas, Thomson identified ions with $q/m = 2.4 \times 10^7$ coul/kg, the ratio one would expect for singly ionized helium, He^+. In air Thomson observed arcs associated with O^+, O_2^+, N^+ and N_2^+. Once the various arcs were identified and had become familiar, they could be recognized at a glance and identified in gaseous mixtures, their relative intensity giving a clue to the concentration of various components in the mixture.

PROBLEM 33.3.   The fact that the positive rays are separated in Thomson's tube into sharply distinct arcs constitutes an independent confirmation of Millikan's conclusion that electrical charge comes in discrete packets of identical size. Why? What would happen if either q or m (or both quantities) were continuously distributed over some appreciable range of values?

PROBLEM 33.4. Thomson found that doubly ionized particles such as He^{++}, O_2^{++}, N^{++}, etc., could indeed be detected, but that their lines were very faint and were not formed unless the potential difference producing the electron beam were greatly increased. What do you infer from this observation? Thomson noted that there was *never* any evidence, even under very energetic electron beams, of doubly ionized hydrogen atoms, H^{++}, and he found this result "strongly suggestive." How do you interpret this remark? What hint is given concerning the structure of the hydrogen atom?

PROBLEM 33.5. What implication do you see in the fact that the charge-to-mass ratio of hydrogen ions in the positive ray tube is found to be identical with the value calculated in electrolysis?

33.5 MASS SPECTROGRAPHS

After Thomson's pioneering work, more accurate and refined instruments were developed for studying the characteristics of ions in the positive rays. The basic strategy in most of these devices was to select from the positive beam a group of ions having very nearly the same velocity and to "focus" these ions on a photographic plate or on an "exit slit" where they might be detected with a sensitive electrometer. As an example, we shall describe a particularly simple and elegant instrument designed by Prof. K. T. Bainbridge of Harvard University in 1930.

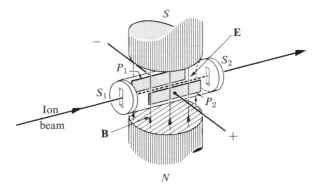

FIG. 33.5.1. Velocity selector: Ion beam passes through crossed electric and magnetic fields. Only the ions with velocity $v = E/\mathbf{B}$ emerge undeflected through slit S_2.

The schematic diagram of a velocity selector is shown in Fig. 33.5.1. The beam of positive ions passes through a slit S_1 into a region of crossed electric and magnetic fields of strength E and B, respectively. Those ions with the particular value of velocity

$$v = E/B, \tag{33.5.1}$$

pass through without deflection and emerge from the slit S_2. Ions with other values of velocity are deflected to one side or the other and are removed from the beam. Thus the "homogeneous" beam emerging from S_2 is very much weaker in intensity than the original beam.

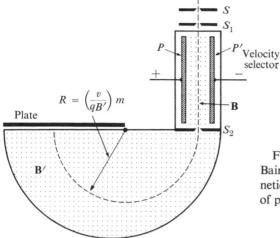

Fig. 33.5.2.   Schematic diagram of Bainbridge's mass spectrograph. (Magnetic fields **B** and **B'** directed out of plane of paper.)

The beam of ions with velocity $v = E/B$ then enters another region of uniform magnetic field, B', as sketched in Fig. 33.5.2. Here the ions move in circular arcs of radius

$$R = \frac{m}{qB'}\, v. \tag{33.5.2}$$

After traversing a semicircle, they strike a photographic plate; the radial distance R can be accurately measured after development of the plate. If the field strengths E, B, and B' are also known, the charge-to-mass ratio of ions can be calculated from

$$\frac{q}{m} = \frac{E}{B'BR}. \tag{33.5.3}$$

PROBLEM 33.6.   Derive Eqs. (33.5.1, 2, 3), explaining the steps of reasoning in your own words. On the velocity selector in Fig. 33.5.2, sketch the paths of ions with velocities less than E/B; with velocities greater than E/B. Check whether or not the circular path is curved in the right direction for the given directions of ion velocity and magnetic field B'. Where on the photographic plate will impinge ions with q/m greater than that of the ions associated with the dashed trajectory sketched in the figure? Sketch the appearance you would expect the photographic plate to have after exposure to a beam of singly ionized atoms and molecules with a number of different masses.

A photographic plate exposed to the ion beam from a mixture of gases will show a series of sharp lines, each one an "image" of slit S_2 at the exit of the velocity selector. The resulting photograph looks like the photograph of a bright line emission spectrum. F. W. Aston began calling a device of this kind a *mass spectrograph*. An instrument in which the location of the final ion beam is determined electrically instead of photographically is usually called a *mass spectrometer*.

33.6   ISOTOPES

In the course of his work on positive rays, Thomson made a systematic examination of a large number of gases and gaseous mixtures, identifying by their charge-to-mass ratios the various ions that left tracks on his photographic plates.   In addition to the primary ions of the pure gases (listed in Section 33.4) Thomson noted the presence of compound ions such as OH, CN, CH_4, C_2H_2, O_3, CO_2, etc.   In an important paper he called attention to the fact that positive ray analysis promised to become a significant new tool of chemical investigation—one that would allow chemical analysis of ionized and reacting gases, quite beyond the range of conventional chemical techniques.   (Note the analogy to spectrum analysis.)

In 1912, while engaged in these investigations, Thomson examined the noble gas neon (atomic mass 20.2) and obtained the photographic record sketched in Fig. 33.4.2.   Instead of a single arc for the ion Ne^+ at a mass number of approximately 20, he observed two arcs very close together, one much fainter than the other.   The more intense arc lay very close to the expected mass number 20, while the fainter arc corresponded to a mass number of about 22.

Thomson's first inclination was to ascribe the mass 22 line to the compound ion NeH_2^+ even though neon, a noble gas, was not known to enter into chemical combination with the other elements under ordinary conditions.   He also toyed with the idea that "we may be interpreting Mendeléev's law too rigidly," and that "in the neighborhood of the atomic weight of neon there may be a group of two or more elements with similar properties, just as in another part of the table we have the group iron, nickel, and cobalt."

There was still another interpretation that had to be entertained.   Ever since the pioneer work of Rutherford and Soddy in 1902, accumulating evidence concerning the chemical transmutations associated with radioactive decay invited the hypothesis that there might exist different forms of the same element—different in relative atomic mass but essentially identical in chemical properties.   For example, it is established that the following steps form part of the sequence of decay of uranium atoms (atomic number 92, mass number 238, denoted by the shorthand $^{238}_{92}U$):

$$^{238}_{92}U \xrightarrow{\alpha} {}^{234}_{90}Th \xrightarrow{\beta, \gamma} {}^{234}_{91}Pa \xrightarrow{\beta, \gamma} {}^{234}_{92}U, \qquad (33.6.1)$$

where the symbols Th and Pa denote the elements thorium and protactinium, respectively.   The emission of an α-particle (loss of 2 positive charges and 4 atomic units of mass) followed by the successive emission of two β-particles (equivalent to the regaining of two positive charges with negligible loss of mass) resulted in the formation of atoms with the chemical properties of uranium, despite the fact that 4 atomic units of mass had been lost in the process.

Years later Rutherford wrote:

"Many people had observed that there was an incredible difficulty, amounting almost to an impossibility, in separating certain radioactive bodies from one another. Soddy became very interested in this phenomenon and found there were some radioactive substances which he could not separate. These bodies were completely distinct and had characteristic radioactive properties, yet they could not be separated by chemical operations. He also pointed out that there was not enough room in the periodic table for the great group of radioactive elements, and he suggested that there were elements which from the chemical point of view were inseparable, but from the radioactive point of view showed different properties. Soddy called the related elements of this kind 'isotopes,' and that was the beginning of that great field of investigation which has owed so much to Dr. Aston. . . ."

Thomson's observations on neon could also be interpreted as an indication that atoms of the same chemical element occurred with different atomic masses. When Aston developed the first high-precision mass spectrograph, he showed that no ions of neon struck the plate at a position corresponding to mass 20.2, but that the intense line fell at 20.00 and the less-intense one at 22.00. This result eliminated the possibility that the intense line was due to ions of pure neon (Ne^+) with atomic mass 20.2, and the faint line to ions of NeH_2^+ with mass 22.2. The observed atomic mass of 20.2 seemed to be more nearly a weighted average of the masses of two groups of neon atoms, with masses of 20 and 22, respectively.

It is now well established that atoms of a given chemical element do indeed occur with different masses. Following Soddy's suggestion, such atoms are called *isotopes*. Naturally occurring neon is found to consist of nearly 91% of the mass 20 isotope, 8.8% of the isotope of mass 22, and a very small amount (0.26%) of an isotope of mass 21. As an additional illustration, a modern mass-spectrograph record of the lines associated with the element germanium, indicating five isotopes with masses 70, 72, 73, 74, 76, is shown in Fig. 33.6.1.

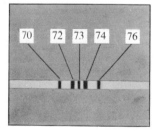

FIG. 33.6.1. The mass spectrum of germanium, showing the isotopes of mass numbers 70, 72, 73, 74, 76. (Courtesy of K. T. Bainbridge.)

The discovery of isotopes finally eliminated one of the most tenaciously held assumptions of the atomic-molecular theory—the assumption that all atoms of a given element are identical in every respect, including mass. Prior to introduction of the physical electromagnetic techniques, it had not been possible to subject this assumption to a critical test. The assumption seemed very plausible, introduced no contradiction into the theory, and was universally accepted because of the simple, intelligible model it afforded. The crucial physical test, however, showed the assumption to be untenable and left the question as to what characteristics *did* determine the chemical properties and therefore the position of an element (i.e., its atomic *number*) in the periodic system. More and more the accumulating evidence pointed to organization of electrical charge within the atomic structure as the dominating feature—more significant than the total mass of the structure itself.

33.7 SOME FACTS ABOUT ISOTOPES AND MEASUREMENT OF ATOMIC MASS

Table 33.7.1 shows modern values of atomic mass of several naturally occurring isotopes, together with an indication of their relative abundance; i.e., the proportions in which they are found in natural sources.

This table illustrates the astounding precision achieved in modern mass spectrometry when atomic masses are compared *with each other*. The uncertainty in the tabulated values is in the last significant figure! The absolute values in kilograms, however, are known to a somewhat lower accuracy—about one part in 10^5.

With the discovery of the isotopes of oxygen in 1929, it was realized that the chemical scale of atomic masses (which had assigned the value of exactly 16 to natural oxygen) was based on a slightly variable mixture of three different isotopes rather than on a single atomic species. As the precision of mass spectrometry increased rapidly during the 1930's and 1940's, a new physical scale was set up in which the isotope $^{16}_{8}O$ was taken as the physical standard and assigned the value of exactly 16. This practice made the chemical and physical scales of atomic masses slightly different (by a factor of 1.000276). In 1960 and 1961 the International Union of Pure and Applied Physics and the International Union of Pure and Applied Chemistry agreed to unify the scales by adopting the standard $^{12}_{6}C$ = 12 exactly.*

Atomic masses according to both the old and new standards are shown in Table 33.7.1. The average chemical atomic masses based on the $^{12}_{6}C$ = 12 scale are tabulated in Appendix D. Where originally atomic masses were determined by measurement of chemical combining proportions, most of them are now determined by mass spectrometric measurement of isotopic masses and relative abundances, the weighted average atomic mass being calculated from these measurements.

It is conventional to speak of the relative atomic masses as being measured in "atomic mass units," abbreviated amu. Thus 1 amu on the new international scale corresponds to exactly $\frac{1}{12}$ the mass of a $^{12}_{6}C$ carbon atom, and the mass of the isotope $^{1}_{1}H$ is 1.0078252 amu.

PROBLEM 33.7. Making use of the abundances given in Table 33.7.1, indicate how you would calculate the average atomic mass of naturally occurring oxygen and neon. Calculate the value for neon to four significant figures. [*Answer:* 20.15.]

PROBLEM 33.8. The discovery of isotopes reveals that a molecule of a chemical compound may be formed in many ways by combinations of isotopes. For example,

---

* For a clear and simply told story of how and why this was done, see the article "The New Unified Scale of Atomic Masses and Weights," by A. O. C. Nier, in *The Physics Teacher*, **1**, 11 (1963).

TABLE 33.7.1

Naturally Occurring Isotopes of Several Elements

Element	Isotopes	Relative atomic masses*		Abundance: Naturally occurring percent of atoms of each isotope
		$^{16}O = 16$ scale	$^{12}C = 12$ scale†	
Hydrogen	$^{1}_{1}H$	1.0081456	1.0078252	99.985
	$^{2}_{1}H$	2.0147425	2.0141022	0.015
Helium	$^{3}_{2}He$	3.0169888	3.0160299	$\sim 1.5 \times 10^{-4}$
	$^{4}_{2}He$	4.0038761	4.0026036	~ 100
Lithium	$^{6}_{3}Li$	6.017039	6.015126	7.52
	$^{7}_{3}Li$	7.018236	7.016005	92.48
Beryllium	$^{9}_{4}Be$	9.015051	9.012186	100
Carbon	$^{12}_{6}C$	12.0038150	12 exactly (standard)	98.892
	$^{13}_{6}C$	13.007488	13.0033543	1.108
Nitrogen	$^{14}_{7}N$	14.0075262	14.0030744	99.635
	$^{15}_{7}N$	15.004877	15.000108	0.365
Oxygen	$^{16}_{8}O$	16 exactly (standard)	15.9949149	99.759
	$^{17}_{8}O$	17.004538	16.999133	0.037
	$^{18}_{8}O$	18.0048821	17.9991598	0.204
Neon	$^{20}_{10}Ne$	19.9987964	19.9924404	90.92
	$^{21}_{10}Ne$	21.000524	20.993849	0.257
	$^{22}_{10}Ne$	21.9983759	21.9913845	8.82
Uranium	$^{234}_{92}U$	234.1154	234.0410	0.006
	$^{235}_{92}U$	235.11866	235.04393	0.715
	$^{238}_{92}U$	238.12644	238.05076	99.28

* Everling, König, Mattauch, and Wapstra, *Nuclear Physics*, **18**, 529 (1960); König, Mattauch, and Wapstra, *Nuclear Physics*, **31**, 18 (1962).
† International unified scale adopted in 1961.

we have implicitly thought of water as $(^{1}_{1}H)_{2}\,^{16}_{8}O$, and indeed the vast majority of water molecules are of this variety. But molecules such as $^{1}_{1}H\,^{2}_{1}H\,^{16}_{8}O$, $(^{2}_{1}H)_{2}\,^{18}_{8}O$ are readily detected. List several other possible water molecules. Would these molecules be more likely or less likely to occur than the first two listed? Why? Tabulate the formulas and the corresponding approximate molecular masses (two significant figures).

PROBLEM 33.9. Is there any other mass standard (such as taking $^{1}_{1}H = 1$ exactly or $^{4}_{2}He = 4$, etc.) that would make the atomic masses all come out to be exactly integer values? What significance do you see in your conclusion? Note, however, that the relative masses are *very close* to integer values—invariably closer than one percent. For this reason it is conventional to refer to isotopes by the integer close to their atomic mass; i.e., "helium 3," "oxygen 18," "uranium 235," etc.

About 20 of the 92 naturally occurring elements occur as only one atomic species without additional isotopes (note beryllium in Table 33.7.1). Over 300 isotopes of the other elements have been observed. Hundreds of additional unstable (radio-active) isotopes are produced in the nuclear reactions occurring in atomic reactors or in nuclear explosions.

It is found that atoms and molecules composed of different isotopes do not have quite identical physical and chemical properties. Lighter molecules take part in chemical reactions just a bit more rapidly than their heavier counterparts, and their liquids have slightly higher vapor pressure. Many chemical reactions taking place in geological and biological processes cause continual separation and changes in concentration of isotopes of hydrogen, carbon, nitrogen, oxygen, sulfur and many other elements. By observing these "fractionations" by means of a mass spectrometer, it has been possible to learn about ages of certain kinds of rocks, temperatures of ancient seas, steps of complicated chemical reactions in biological processes.

Naturally occurring stable isotopes reveal a numerology all their own: The elements of odd atomic number in the periodic system have only a few isotopes or occur in only one species; elements of even atomic number tend to have larger numbers of isotopes. Numerical data are still combed for hints of empirical order and relation-ship, just as Kepler combed Tycho's data and Balmer scanned the wavelengths of bright lines in the hydrogen spectrum. The even-odd number relations in the occur-rence of isotopes are now known to have something to do with the nuclear structure of atoms, but at this juncture are far from being thoroughly understood. One of the tests of a theory of nuclear structure is its ability to predict the observed stability of isotopes.

33.8   AVOGADRO'S NUMBER FROM ELECTROLYTIC DATA AND FROM SPECTROMETRIC CHARGE-TO-MASS RATIOS

In discussing the decomposition of chemical compounds in electrolysis (Section 29.10), we referred to the experimentally established fact that passage of 96,500 coul of electrical charge would liberate one gram equivalent of an element at each elec-trode—for example, one gram-atomic mass (1.008 gm) of hydrogen at the cathode. From this we inferred a possible charge-to-mass ratio of hydrogen ions in electrolytic solution:

$$\frac{q_H}{m_H} = \frac{96,500}{1.008 \times 10^{-3}} = 9.58 \times 10^7 \text{ coul/kg.} \tag{33.8.1}$$

It is very encouraging to find exactly the same value emerging for gaseous hydrogen ions in the analysis of positive rays, supplemented by Thomson's suggestive evidence that doubly ionized hydrogen ions are never observed. Thus the one-ness of hydrogen in its capacity to combine chemically with other atoms appears to be directly correlated with the one corpuscle of positive charge it appears to carry as an ion; the charge-to-mass ratio 9.58×10^7 coul/kg is a fundamental property of the hydrogen ion, regardless of whether it occurs in an acid solution or in an ionized gas.

Given Millikan's determination of the corpuscle of electrical charge, 1.60×10^{-19} coul, it is immediately possible to calculate the number of hydrogen atoms in one gram-atomic mass—this is the number we have called "Avogadro's number" and denoted by N_0. On the assumption that one corpuscle of charge is associated with each ion, we calculate the number of such corpuscles in 96,500 coul:

$$N_0 = \frac{96,500}{1.60 \times 10^{-19}} = 6.02 \times 10^{23}. \qquad (33.8.2)$$

PROBLEM 33.10. An equivalent calculation starts with the charge-to-mass ratio of hydrogen ions obtained in the mass spectrometer: Taking $q_H/m_H = 9.58 \times 10^7$ coul/kg and $q_H = 1.60 \times 10^{-19}$ coul, calculate m_H. Calculate N_0, the number of ions in 1.008 gm hydrogen.

In the above calculations we have used modern values of the various quantities; by about 1910 these values were known to within a few percent, and were well known to the scientific community. In 1908 Perrin had obtained entirely independent values of Avogadro's number from a beautiful set of experiments in which he observed the behavior of minute colloidal particles of gum suspended in water.* His results placed N_0 between 6 and 8×10^{23}, in good agreement with values obtained from interpretation of the electrical data.

33.9 THE SIZES OF ATOMS AND MOLECULES

Gases are highly compressible substances of very low density, and the kinetic model of their behavior visualizes atoms or molecules, on the average widely separated from each other, free to move translationally, colliding with one another and with the walls of the container. Solids and liquids, on the other hand, are much denser than gases and are relatively incompressible. We are immediately led to infer that in liquids and solids the atoms or molecules have been brought quite close together. Furthermore, many solids take on various crystalline forms with definite

---

* Perrin observed the random Brownian motion of the colloidal particles (made visible by scattered light, as in Millikan's experiment) under the influence of irregular bombardment by the invisible surrounding water molecules. From kinetic theory, combined with the analysis of the random displacements of the particles in successive equal intervals of time as well as from their gradual stratification under the influence of gravity, he was able to deduce numerical values of Avogadro's number. These were the experiments that convinced the last doubters of the "reality" of atoms and molecules. For a more detailed discussion of Perrin's work, see references cited at the end of the chapter. (The theory of Brownian motion, including the equation connecting Avogadro's number and the random displacements of colloidal particles, had been published by Einstein in 1905.)

symmetries of shape and with clearly defined cleavage planes. These observations early invited the conjecture that the particles of solids are probably arranged in regular patterns or "lattices."

If we accept the proposition that the constituent particles are very close together in liquids and solids, the spacing between centers of adjacent particles must be a measure of their size or "diameter." (Molecules are in general not spherical in shape, but we shall nevertheless talk of their average "diameter" in our rough calculations. Atoms tend to have an essentially spherical symmetry.)

Let us calculate the average spacing between water molecules in ordinary liquid water: The density of water is 1.00 gm/cm^3. One mole of water (18 gm) occupies a volume of 18 cm^3 and contains N_0 molecules. The volume associated with each molecule is therefore about

$$\frac{18}{N_0} = \frac{18}{6 \times 10^{23}} = \frac{180}{6} \times 10^{-24} \text{ cm}^3.$$

If we imagine each molecule encased in a little cube with length of side σ, we have

$$\sigma^3 = \frac{180}{6} \times 10^{-24} \text{ cm}^3, \qquad \sigma \sim 3 \times 10^{-8} \text{ cm} = 3 \text{ A},$$

where 1 angstrom unit is defined as 10^{-8} cm. Thus the average spacing between the centers of the water molecules must be about 3 A, and, if we assume the molecules to be very close together, this must also be the order of magnitude of the molecular diameter. The radius of the water molecule should be of the order of 1.5 A.

PROBLEM 33.11. Turn to the periodic graph of atomic volumes versus atomic mass in Fig. 29.11.1. Note that the atomic volumes (volume of one gram-atomic mass) of elements in liquid or solid form all fall between 5 and 70 cm^3 for the range of atomic masses shown. Calculate the upper and lower values of the average spacing between atomic centers, and the upper and lower values of atomic *radii* that are indicated. [*Answer:* atomic radii fall between 1 and 2.5 A.]

PROBLEM 33.12. It was shown in Problem 29.10 that one mole of any gas occupies a volume of 22.4 liters or 22,400 cm^3 at 0°C and 1 atm pressure. (These conditions are usually referred to as standard temperature and pressure, abbreviated STP.) Calculate the average spacing between molecules of a gas at STP. [*Answer:* 30–40 A.] Would you take this to be the average diameter of gas molecules? Why or why not? What would happen to the average spacing as the pressure decreased? What would you expect to be the functional relationship between average spacing and pressure? Why?

The reader is urged to memorize the range of magnitudes encountered in the preceding problems. In subsequent discussions we shall have many occasions to compare these lengths with various others. For example, how does the order of magnitude of interatomic distance in liquids and solids compare with the wavelength of visible light? Ultraviolet light?

33.10 THE CONCEPT OF ATOMIC STRUCTURE

With the discovery of the electron and the realization that the bulk of the mass of an atom must be associated with the positively charged portion, it became possible to invent and test models of atomic structure; one of the leaders, publishing numerous papers in this field, was J. J. Thomson. In lectures delivered at Yale* in 1903 and at the Royal Institution† in 1906, Thomson summarized some of his ideas:

"We have seen that whether we produce the corpuscles** by cathode rays, by ultraviolet light, or from incandescent metals, and whatever may be the metals or gases present, we always get the same kind of corpuscles. Since corpuscles similar in all respects may be obtained from very different agents and materials, and since the mass of the corpuscles is less than that of any known atom, we see that the corpuscle must be a constituent of the atom of many different substances. . . .

"We are thus confronted with the idea that atoms of the chemical elements are built up of simpler systems, an idea which in various forms has been advanced by more than one chemist. Thus Prout‡ in 1815 put forward the view that the atoms of all the chemical elements are built up of atoms of hydrogen; if this were so, the combining weights of all the elements would, on the assumption that there was no loss of weight when the atoms of hydrogen combined to form the atom of some other element, be integers; a result not in accordance with observation. To avoid this discrepancy Dumas suggested that the primordial atom might not be the hydrogen atom, but a smaller atom having only one half or one quarter of the mass of the hydrogen atom Further support was given to the idea of the complex nature of the atom by the discovery by Newlands and Mendeleeff of what is known as the periodic law. . . . Further evidence in the same direction is afforded by the similarity in the structure of the spectra of elements in the same group in the periodic series, a similarity which recent work on the existence in spectra of series of lines whose frequencies are connected by definite numerical relations§ has done much to emphasize and establish. . . .

"The phenomenon of radioactivity . . . carries the argument still further, for there seem to be good reasons for believing that radioactivity is due to changes going on within the atoms of the radioactive substances. If this is so, we must face the problem of the constitution of the atom, and see if we can imagine a model which has in it the potentiality of explaining the remarkable properties

* *Electricity and Matter.* New York: Charles Scribner's Sons, 1904.

† *The Corpuscular Theory of Matter.* New York: Charles Scribner's Sons, 1907.

** During this period Thomson was using the term "corpuscle" for the entity we have designated by the name "electron."

‡ William Prout (1785–1850), an English chemist.

§ See Sections 27.7 and 27.8.

shown by radioactive substances. It may thus not be superfluous to consider the bearing of the existence of corpuscles on the problem of the constitution of the atom; and although the model of the atom to which we are led by these considerations is very crude and imperfect, it may perhaps be of service by suggesting lines of investigation likely to furnish us with further information about the constitution of the atom."

Note how Thomson pulls together all the threads of evidence, revealing the motivation of his constructs. Note also the cautious qualification at the end—how similar its tone to Faraday's remark about lines of force (quoted in Section 23.14.) Thomson's model turned out not to be correct, but it suggested experimental tests that led to the evolution of a more successful picture.

33.11   THOMSON'S ATOMIC MODEL

From data on the extent to which a narrow electron beam is scattered (broadened) by passage through a very thin metal foil, and from data on the scattering by gases of visible light and X-rays, Thomson (and other contemporary investigators, notably Barkla) had estimated that the number of electrons in a single atom must be roughly one-half the relative atomic mass.

Thomson went on to outline his conjectures quantitatively:

"The form in which positive electricity occurs in the atom is at present a matter about which we have very little information. No positively electrified body has yet been found having a mass less than that of an atom of hydrogen. All the positively electrified systems in gases at low pressures seem to be atoms which, neutral in their normal state, have become positively charged by losing a corpuscle. In default of exact knowledge of the nature of the way in which positive electricity occurs in the atom, we shall consider a case in which the positive electricity is distributed in the way most amenable to mathematical calculation; i.e., when it occurs as a sphere of uniform density throughout which the corpuscles are distributed.*

"The positive electricity attracts the corpuscles to the center of the sphere, while their mutual repulsion drives them away from it; when in equilibrium they will be distributed in such a way that the attraction of the positive electrification is balanced by the repulsion of the other corpuscles.

"Let us now consider the problem as to how 1, 2, 3, . . . n corpuscles would arrange themselves if placed in a sphere filled with positive electricity of uniform density, the total negative charge on the corpuscles being equivalent to the positive charge in the sphere. When there is only one corpuscle the solution is very simple: the corpuscle will evidently go to the centre of the sphere . . . [Fig. 33.11.1(a)].

_____

* Thomson took the radius of the sphere to be of the order of 1 A or 10^{-8} cm—the well-established order of magnitude of atomic size. See Section 33.9.

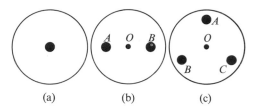

FIG. 33.11.1. Thomson's atomic model. One, two, and three electrons at equilibrium positions within a sphere of uniformly distributed positive charge (radius ~ 1 A).

"When there are two corpuscles inside a sphere of positive electricity they will, when in equilibrium, be situated at two points A and B, in a straight line with O the centre of the sphere and such that $OA = OB = a/2$, where a is the radius of the sphere... [Fig. 33.11.1(b)]. Three corpuscles inside a single sphere will be in stable equilibrium when at the corners of an equilateral triangle whose centre is at the centre of the sphere and whose side is equal in length to the radius of the sphere... [Fig. 33.11.1(c)]."

Thomson went on to work out equilibrium configurations (in three dimensions) of still larger numbers of electrons within the sphere of positively charged "fluid." He argued that external disturbances (heat, electrical discharge) would set the electrons vibrating about their equilibrium positions and radiating electromagnetic waves (see Sections 27.17–27.20). He found that the frequencies of oscillation should be of the order of magnitude of the frequency of visible light. This was an encouraging result, but the theory did not predict discrete frequencies or bright lines, as observed in the spectra of gases.

PROBLEM 33.13. From the velocity of light and the wavelengths of violet and red light, calculate the range of frequencies of visible light. This is the order of magnitude obtained in Thomson's calculations. Suppose that the electron in Fig. 33.11.1(a) is pulled away somewhat from point O by close passage of an α-particle and then "released" as the α-particle moves further away. Describe the subsequent behavior of the electron. (Describe the whole process in terms of the vocabulary of energy transformations. Do not ignore the effect on the α-particle or the electromagnetic radiation of the electron.) In what respects does this simple model correctly represent what is known about the hydrogen atom? In what respects does it fail? (Could the model possibly account for the Balmer spectrum of atomic hydrogen? Why?)

Thomson went on, however, to examine the equilibrium patterns formed as more electrons were placed within the positive globule. He found that certain patterns tended to re-form and repeat themselves with increasing numbers of electrons, and thus indicated a possible avenue toward explanation of the periodic system. He also worked out, on the basis of this atomic model, very ingenious qualitative explanations of chemical reaction, formation of molecules, and radioactive disintegration.

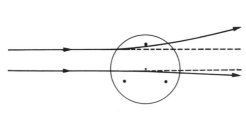

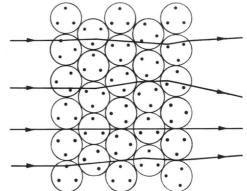

(a) Deflections of α-particles passing through Thomson atom. Particle passing close to center undergoes very little deflection.

(b) Schematic diagram (enormously enlarged) of narrow beam of α-particles passing through thin foil made up of Thomson atoms. After cumulation of many small, random deflections, α-particle emerges from foil with only a small angle of deflection from its original path.

FIG. 33.11.2. The α-particles, on passing through the large positive spheres of Thomson atoms, would be only slightly deviated because of repulsion of the distributed positive charge. Being about 7300 times more massive than electrons, the α-particles would not be appreciably deviated by attractive forces of the electrons; rather the electrons would be displaced and set into oscillation after passage of an α-particle. The oscillating electrons would radiate light as their oscillations died down.

Having used data on the scattering of electrons, light, and X-rays in developing his atomic model, Thomson was keenly sensitive to the fact that improved quantitative study of scattering might give better and more detailed information on atomic structure. In 1910 he published a theoretical analysis of the scattering of α- and β-particles to be expected when such particles passed through thin foils made of atoms that had the "plum-pudding" structure described in the preceding paragraphs. He showed in particular that an α-particle passing through an array of the positively charged spheres should emerge with very little deflection from its original path. (See illustration in Fig. 33.11.2.)

33.12 SCATTERING OF α-PARTICLES BY THIN FOILS

Meanwhile, Rutherford and his associates at Manchester were also interested in α-particle scattering. Shortly before his death in 1937, Rutherford said in a lecture* delivered at Cambridge:

"Now I myself was very interested in the next stage, . . . and I would like to use this example to show how you often stumble upon facts by accident. In

---

* *Background to Modern Science*, edited by J. Needham and W. Pagel. New York: Macmillan, 1938.

the early days I had observed the scattering of α-particles, and Dr. Geiger in my laboratory had examined it in detail. He found, in thin pieces [foils] of heavy metal, that the scattering was usually small, of the order of one degree. One day Geiger came to me and said, 'Don't you think young Marsden, whom I am training in radioactive methods, ought to begin a small research?' Now I had thought that too, so I said, 'Why not let him see if any α-particles can be scattered through a large angle?' I may tell you in confidence that I did not believe that they would be, since we knew that the α-particle was a very fast massive particle, with a great deal of energy, and you could show that if the scattering was due to the accumulated effect of a number of small scatterings the chance of α-particles being scattered backwards was very small. Then I remember two or three days later Geiger coming to me in great excitement and saying, 'We have been able to get some of the α-particles coming backwards. . . .' It was quite the most incredible event that has happened to me in my life. It was almost as incredible as if you fired a 15-inch shell at a piece of tissue paper and it came back and hit you. On consideration I realized that this scattering backwards must be the result of a single collision, and when I made calculations I saw that it was impossible to get anything of that order of magnitude unless you took a system in which the greater part of the mass of the atom was concentrated in a minute nucleus. It was then that I had the idea of an atom with a minute massive center carrying a charge."

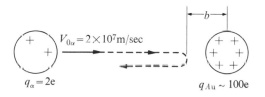

FIG. 33.12.1. An α-particle with initial velocity of 2×10^7 m/sec in head-on collision with Au nucleus. The value b is the distance of closest approach of centers of the spheres.

Geiger and Marsden published their first observations in 1909.* They found that the vast majority of particles in a beam of α-particles passed through a 0.00004-cm-thick gold foil with very little deflection. A very small fraction of the particles, about 1 in 20,000, were turned through an average angle of 90°. Rutherford felt that these large deflections could not possibly be due to a random accumulation of angular deflection by passage through many Thomson atoms but must be due to single atomic encounters between the α-particles and the very much more massive atoms of gold (Au) in the foil. On this assumption, he estimated in a very simple calculation the closest distance of approach between an α-particle and the center of positive charge in the Au atom in a head-on collision (Fig. 33.12.1).

The initial kinetic energy $(\frac{1}{2})m_\alpha v_{0\alpha}^2$ of the α-particle is converted into potential energy as it approaches the hypothetical nucleus, the kinetic energy being zero at a

---

* *Proc. Roy. Soc.*, lxxxii, 495 (1909).

distance of closest approach b between centers. Then

$$\tfrac{1}{2}m_\alpha v_{0\alpha}^2 = \frac{kq_\alpha q_{Au}}{b},\qquad(33.12.1)$$

$$b = \frac{2kq_\alpha q_{Au}}{m_\alpha v_{0\alpha}^2}.\text{*}\qquad(33.12.2)$$

The charge-to-mass ratio of the α-particle was known to be 4.8×10^7 coul/kg. By means of the crossed-field technique, the velocity $v_{0\alpha}$ of the α-particles was established as 2.09×10^7 m/sec. Using the current estimates of Thomson and other investigators, Rutherford took the positive charge of the $^{197}_{79}$Au atom to be of the order of half the atomic mass, or about 100 e. Substituting these numerical values into Eq. (33.12.2), with e $= 1.60 \times 10^{-19}$ coul, we have

$$b = \frac{2(9)(10^9)(4.8)(10^7)(100)(1.60)(10^{-19})}{4(10^{14})},\qquad(33.12.3)$$

$$b = 3.4 \times 10^{-14}\text{ m} = 3.4 \times 10^{-12}\text{ cm}.$$

Thus if the positive charge on the Au atom and α-particle is visualized as concentrated in small massive spheres, the centers of the spheres must approach to within about 3×10^{-12} cm of each other in a head-on collision, while the overall atomic radius is known to be of the order of 10^{-8} cm—about 10,000 times larger!

On the basis of this model, the α-particle must encounter a tiny but massive positive nucleus deep within the atomic structure. Presumably the overall atomic size of 10^{-8} cm is then determined by a distribution of electrons in the relatively enormous volume outside the nucleus, and the atom is mostly empty space!

PROBLEM 33.14. Return to the discussion of elastic collisions in Sections 17.8 and 18.13 and Problems 17.9 and 18.13. Using and interpreting the algebraic equations obtained in these discussions, explain Rutherford's surprise at the backward scattering of α-particles. On what grounds does he say, "Remember that the mass, momentum, and kinetic energy of an α-particle are very large compared with the corresponding values for an electron in rapid motion, it does not seem possible from dynamic considerations that an α-particle can be deflected through a large angle by a close approach to an electron." In light of the equations of elastic collision, what can you say about the effect of the α-particle collision on the nucleus of an Au atom?

PROBLEM 33.15. Suppose that an α-particle with a velocity of 2×10^7 m/sec moves toward a positively charged sphere carrying a uniformly distributed positive charge of 100 e, as in Fig. 33.12.1, but the positively charged sphere is a penetrable globule with a radius of 10^{-8} cm. Assume that no negative charges are present. What fraction of the initial KE of the α-particle will have been converted into PE at the instant the center of the α-particle arrives at the periphery of the globule? How far away from the

* The reader wishing to review relevant concepts and derivations should refer to Section 18.6 and to Problems 18.20, 24.8, and 24.21.

center of the globule is a "remote" starting point for the α-particle? [*Answer:* α-particle KE $= 1.3 \times 10^{-12}$ joule; potential at globule surface $= 1400$ v; fraction of KE converted into PE $= 0.00035$. A remote starting point would be a millionth of a cm away.] What interpretation do you place on the result? How much KE remains? How would the α-particle continue to move after arrival at the periphery of the globule?

PROBLEM 33.16. After making the "distance of closest approach" calculation given in Eq. (33.12.3), Rutherford says, "[With the radius of the atom known] to be of the order of 10^{-8} cm, it is obvious that the α-particle, before being turned back, penetrates so close to the central charge that the field due to the uniform distribution of negative electricity [the electrons] may be neglected." Interpret this remark. What assumptions are implied? What is the significance of this idea in the overall line of reasoning? Why can the effect of the negative charge be considered negligible? (See Section 24.3.) How far away from the nucleus is a "remote" starting point for the α-particle? How does this distance compare with an atomic radius?

33.13   RUTHERFORD'S NUCLEAR MODEL

In May 1911, Rutherford published a classic paper in the *Philosophical Magazine*.* Here he put forth his new conception of atomic structure, arguing that Thomson's model was quite incapable of explaining the diffuse scattering of α-particles observed by Geiger and Marsden, making the calculations illustrated in the preceding section, and deriving an equation for the angular distribution of the scattered particles to be expected on the basis of the nuclear model.

Consider the individual encounter illustrated in Fig. 33.13.1. An α-particle traveling along line AOB would miss the nucleus by distance p; that is, it undergoes a "glancing" rather than a head-on collision. If the nucleus is much more massive than the

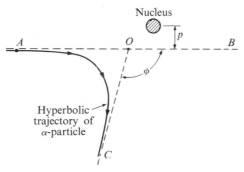

FIG. 33.13.1.   "Glancing collision" between α-particle and massive atomic nucleus. Initial direction of motion of α-particle is along line AOB, missing nucleus by distance p. Under influence of repulsive central force (see Section 17.14 and Problem 17.17), particle moves in hyperbolic trajectory with asymptotes AO and OC. Direction of motion of particle is deflected through angle ϕ.

* "The Scattering of α and β Particles by Matter and the Structure of the Atom." *Phil. Mag.*, **21,** 669 (1911). Reprinted in *Rutherford at Manchester*, edited by J. B. Birks. New York: W. A. Benjamin, 1963.

α-particle, it remains essentially stationary, undergoing very little recoil in the collision. The α-particle on the other hand, repelled by the Coulomb force from the nucleus, moves in the hyperbolic* trajectory illustrated in the diagram, undergoing an angular deflection ϕ from its original direction of motion. Lines AO and OC are asymptotes of the hyperbola.

We shall not attempt to derive Rutherford's scattering equation, but we shall state his result and interpret its significance. Rutherford showed that if N alpha particles fall on a thin metal foil, the number of α-particles, y, that strike a unit area of the detecting screen after deflection through an angle ϕ is given by

$$ y = \frac{N n t Z^2 e^4}{4R^2(\tfrac{1}{2}m_\alpha v_{0\alpha}^2)^2 \sin^4(\phi/2)} , \tag{33.13.1} $$

where: $n =$ the number of atoms per unit volume in the scattering foil,
 $t =$ the thickness of the foil,
 $Z =$ the number of elementary charges on the scattering nucleus,
 $e =$ the electronic charge,
 $R =$ the radial distance between the scattering foil and the detecting screen,
 $\tfrac{1}{2}m_\alpha v_{0\alpha}^2 =$ the initial KE of the α-particles.

A schematic diagram of the scattering visualized in this theory is shown in Fig. 33.13.2.

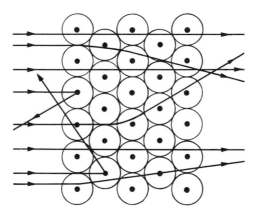

FIG. 33.13.2. Schematic diagram of Rutherford's model of α-particle scattering. Vast majority of α-particles in narrow beam pass through the thin metal foil with very small or zero deviation. A small fraction of the α-particles is deviated through large angles by individual encounters or collisions with massive atomic nuclei. Contrast this model with the small-angle scattering illustrated in the Thomson model (Fig. 33.11.2).

---

* As proved by Newton, a particle under the influence of a central inverse-square force moves in a trajectory that is a conic section. If the force is repulsive, the particular conic section is the hyperbola.

The critical test of the nuclear model lay in whether or not the observed particle scattering obeyed Eq. 33.13.1. For example, the number of particles scattered to any angle ϕ should be directly proportional to the thickness of the foil, whereas in the Thomson model it was shown that this number should be proportional to the square root of the thickness. Still more unique requirements lay in the fact that the number of α-particles scattered to angle ϕ should be inversely proportional to the *fourth power* of sin $(\phi/2)$! As Rutherford remarked when reminiscing in 1937, "These deductions were later verified by Geiger and Marsden in a series of beautiful experiments."

33.14 VERIFICATION OF RUTHERFORD'S THEORY

In 1913 Geiger and Marsden published the results of investigations testing the predictions of Eq. (33.13.1).* They described their apparatus as follows:

"The apparatus [Fig. 33.14.1] consisted of a strong cylindrical metal box B, which contained the source of α-particles R, the scattering foil F, and a microscope M to which the zinc-sulphide screen S was rigidly attached. The box was fastened down to a graduated circular platform A, which could be rotated by means of a conical airtight joint C. By rotating the platform the box and microscope moved with it, whilst the scattering foil and radiating source remained in position, being attached to the tube T, which was fastened to the standard L. The box B was closed by the ground-glass plate P, and could be exhausted through the tube T.

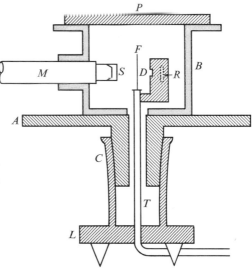

FIG. 33.14.1. Apparatus of Geiger and Marsden for testing Rutherford's theory of α-particle scattering.

---

* "The Laws of Deflexion of Particles Through Large Angles." *Phil. Mag.*, **25**, 604 (1913). Reprinted in *Rutherford at Manchester*.

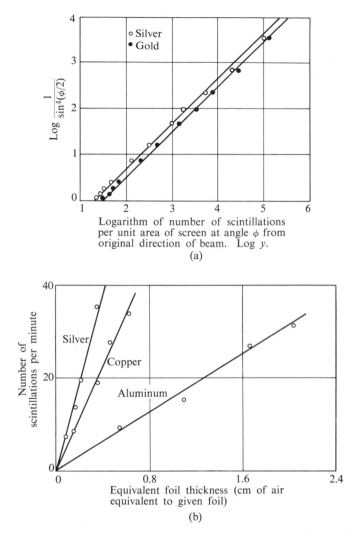

FIG. 33.14.2. Graphs of selected data from paper by Geiger and Marsden (Problem 33.17). (From *Introduction to Modern Physics*, by F. K. Richtmeyer. New York: McGraw-Hill, 1934.)

"The source of α-particles employed was similar to that used originally by Rutherford and Royds in their experiments on the nature of the α-particle [see Section 32.7]. It consisted of a small thin-walled glass tube about 1 mm. in diameter, containing a large quantity of well purified radium emanation [radon]. The α-particles emitted by the emanation and its active deposit could pass through the glass walls without much reduction of range."

PROBLEM 33.17. Two graphs of sets of data published by Geiger and Marsden are shown in Fig. 33.14.2. What does each graph demonstrate? In what way does each graph provide evidence in support of Eq. (33.13.1) and the theory and assumptions behind this equation? Why is the *logarithm* of $1/\sin^4(\phi/2)$ plotted against the *logarithm* of the number of scintillations, instead of just $1/\sin^4(\phi/2)$ against the number of scintillations directly?

33.15 ACCEPTANCE OF RUTHERFORD'S MODEL

Rutherford's model implies that electrons, carrying the negative charge of the atom, are distributed around the nucleus at distances of the order of 10,000 times the effective radius of the nucleus itself. Since the electrons would be attracted toward the nucleus by the inverse-square Coulomb force, one would immediately be led to visualize a planetary system with electrons revolving around the nuclear "sun" in circular or elliptical "planetary" orbits.

This model had been thought of before but was not seriously entertained because it should be inherently unstable. We showed in Sections 27.18, 19, 20 that, according to Maxwell's electromagnetic theory, accelerated (oscillatory or revolving) charged particles are associated with the production of electromagnetic waves and must therefore be continually radiating energy into space. Electrons in planetary orbits should continually radiate energy, spiraling in toward the nucleus like a satellite toward earth, resulting in ever-decreasing atomic radii unless energy were continually supplied from the outside. Atoms radiate light after intense excitation by heat or electrical discharge, but after this energy is emitted, they do not show further net emission of radiation and do not exhibit continual decrease in size, with electrons collapsing toward the nuclei. This problem of atomic collapse was deliberately avoided in Thomson's theory by the invention of a model in which electrons occupy stationary equilibrium positions, are set oscillating by external disturbances, and are not required to execute orbits in which they would have to radiate continually.

Despite this very substantial theoretical and conceptual problem, Rutherford's model was very quickly accepted. Not only was the theory elegantly simple and the experimental results of Geiger and Marsden profoundly convincing, but there were also other attractive features. For example, there was a hint of possibly simple explanations of some aspects of radioactivity. As Rutherford pointed out, "If the central charge be positive, it is easily seen that a positively charged mass if released from the center of a heavy atom would acquire a great velocity in moving through the electric field. It may be possible in this way to account for the high velocity of expulsion of α-particles without supposing that they are initially in rapid motion within the atom."

With acceptance of the model came an increasingly intense search for a more complete theory—a theory that would describe the organization of the electrons in the atomic structure and account for the bright line emission spectra. But at the same time it became increasingly clear that it might be necessary to give up some of the hard-won concepts and theories of classical physics. Hints as to the direction a new theory must take came from other lines of physical investigation. We shall first pursue these new lines of inquiry, and return to the question of atomic structure in Chapter 35.

33.16   PROBLEMS

33.18. Draw a very small dot on a sheet of paper. Measure its radius, and then locate in the room or building the position of a concentric circular arc with a radius 10,000 or 20,000 times as large as that of the dot. You now have a roughly scaled representation of a nucleus and the periphery of the atom of which it is a part. If atoms are indeed largely composed of empty space, how would you account for the fact that condensed matter (liquids and solids) is so very incompressible?

33.19. Consider Thomson's early mass spectrograph, as sketched in Fig. 33.4.1. Complete the following outline of the analysis of its operation. Suppose that the beam consists of positive ions of mass m, charge q, and various initial velocities v_{0x}:

(a) The E- and B-fields deflect the ions downward and sideways. The time of travel of the distance L between the plates is very nearly L/v_{0x}. Show that the y-component of velocity imparted to the ions is very nearly

$$v_y = \frac{q}{m} \cdot \frac{EL}{v_{0x}} \qquad (33.16.1)$$

and that the z-component of velocity imparted to the ions is very nearly

$$v_z = \frac{q}{m} \cdot BL. \qquad (33.16.2)$$

(b) What approximation is made in the preceding calculations; i.e., why is the phrase "very nearly" used several times? [Hint: Does the velocity component v_{0x} actually remain unchanged? Is the acceleration in the z-direction uniform?] Under what conditions do the approximations introduce very little error?

(c) Taking D/v_{0x} as the time for the particles to traverse the distance D, argue that the vertical and horizontal deflections at the screen are given very nearly by:

$$y = \frac{q}{m} \cdot \frac{ELD}{v_{0x}^2}, \qquad (33.16.3)$$

$$z = \frac{q}{m} \cdot \frac{BLD}{v_{0x}}, \qquad (33.16.4)$$

and that the equation of the trace on the screen is

$$z^2 = \frac{q}{m} \cdot \frac{B^2LD}{E} y. \qquad (33.16.5)$$

What approximations are introduced in this part of the analysis? Interpret the final result; how must Thomson have made use of it? Sketch the trace that would be made by an ion of higher mass than the one indicated in Fig. 33.4.1. What would happen to the traces if the E-field were reversed? if the B-field were reversed?

SPECIAL PROBLEM FOR MORE
ADVANCED WORK

33.20. Consider the Thomson model of a hydrogen atom, in which a single electron occupies an equilibrium position at the center of a uniformly distributed sphere of positive charge. The radius of the sphere is a and the total charge is e (Fig. 33.16.1).

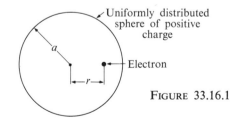

FIGURE 33.16.1

(a) Show that if the electron is displaced to a radial position r, the force restoring it toward the center of the sphere is given by

$$F(r) = \frac{ke^2}{a^3} r, \qquad (33.16.6)$$

where k is the Coulomb's law constant.

(b) If necessary, go to another physics text and make yourself sufficiently acquainted with the problem of simple harmonic motion to show that if the electron is let go from its displaced position it will undergo simple harmonic oscillation at a frequency

$$\nu = \frac{1}{2\pi} \sqrt{\frac{ke^2}{ma^3}}, \qquad (33.16.7)$$

where m is the mass of the electron.

(c) Calculate the numerical value of the oscillation frequency for an appropriate value of a and compare the result with the range of frequencies of visible light. What features of this model do you consider plausible and successful? What features unsuccessful?

SUPPLEMENTARY READING AND STUDY

Foundations of Modern Physical Science, G. Holton, D. H. D. Roller. Reading, Mass.: Addison-Wesley, 1958, Chapters 34, 37

Introduction to Atomic Physics, H. Semat. New York: Rinehart, 1946, Chapter 2. (See Appendix VII for derivation of Rutherford scattering formula.)

Physics of the Atom, M. R. Wehr, J. A. Richards. Reading, Mass.: Addison-Wesley, 1960, Chapter 2

Introduction to Modern Physics, F. K. Richtmyer. New York: McGraw-Hill, 1934, pages 346–362; pages 614–627

Introduction to Modern Physics, C. H. Blanchard, C. R. Burnett, R. G. Stoner, R. L. Weber. Englewood Cliffs, N. J.: Prentice-Hall, 1958, pages 133–145

Rutherford at Manchester, edited by J. B. Birks. New York: W. A. Benjamin, 1963

Structure of Atomic Nuclei, C. S. Cook. Princeton, N.J.: Van Nostrand Momentum Book No. 8, 1964

CHAPTER 34

Interaction of Electromagnetic Radiation with Matter

34.1 NATURE OF X-RAYS

Between 1897 and 1905 the electric and magnetic deflection experiments of Thomson, Rutherford, and others brought about general acceptance of the view that cathode, alpha, and beta rays consisted of streams of charged particles. Attempts to deflect X-rays and γ-rays by very strong fields remained unsuccessful. Various hypotheses were advanced to account for their nature (e.g., the suggestion that X- and γ-rays might consist of electrons to which some positive electricity had been added, neutralizing the charge without appreciably affecting size or mass), but the simplest interpretation which was consistent with experience among macroscopic phenomena was to regard as an electromagnetic wave any radiation that is undeflected on passage through electric or magnetic fields. Thomson seems never to have wavered in this point of view; the vocabulary of his published lectures and papers, from 1897 on, simply takes these distinctions for granted.

Acceptance of the electron model of cathode rays in turn made an electromagnetic interpretation of X-rays increasingly plausible and inviting. Since X-rays were always emitted when rapidly moving electrons struck a solid target, one could suppose that X-rays represented electromagnetic pulses associated with the extremely rapid deceleration to be expected when electrons were slowed down and stopped by the target material.

When X-rays were directed against other materials, in addition to producing ionizing effects and being absorbed, they were also observed to be diffusely *scattered*, i.e., scattered in all directions (see Fig. 34.1.1).

Thomson worked out a quantitative theory based on a model in which the scattered radiation was generated when the electric and magnetic field variations in incident X-rays excited the vibration of, and transferred energy to, electrons bound within the atoms of the scattering material. The vibrating electrons in turn re-emitted this absorbed energy by sending out electromagnetic waves. A leading experimental investigator, the English physicist Charles Barkla (1877–1944), interpreted the results

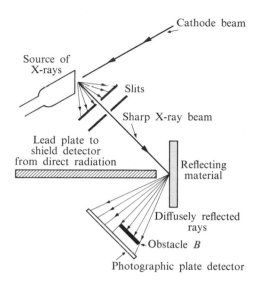

FIG. 34.1.1. Schematic diagram of apparatus demonstrating diffuse reflection of X-rays. Sharp beam of X-rays incident on a block of reflecting material (carbon, paraffin, etc.) is observed to be diffusely scattered rather than specularly reflected; i.e., X-rays are detected at all angles, not just at an angle of reflection equal to the angle of incidence. A shadow of obstacle *B* is formed on the photographic plate regardless of the position of *B*.

of scattering measurements in the light of Thomson's theory, estimating that about six scattering electrons (i.e., a number approximately equal to half the relative atomic mass) were associated with each atom of carbon.

In other elegant experiments Barkla showed that scattered X-rays behaved as though they were at least partially polarized. In absorption experiments he found evidence that pointed indirectly, but nevertheless strongly, to the presence of *bright lines*, or wavelengths at which the radiations had unusually high emission and absorption intensities in particular materials.*

Various other investigators attempted to observe diffraction of X-ray beams passing through extremely narrow slits, a few thousandths of a millimeter wide. Results were marginal and not very convincing. It was concluded that, if X-rays were indeed wavelike, the wavelengths must be of the order of 0.1 to 1 A. In 1907 Wien, applying Einstein's recently advanced heuristic model of the photoelectric effect (see Sections 34.11, 12), interpreted measurements of the energy of electrons ejected from materials by X-rays as indicating an X-ray wavelength of the order of 0.3 A.

* We do not have the space in which to discuss Barkla's interesting and important contributions in adequate detail. For at least an introductory sketch, the reader is referred to Section 2–4 of Chapter 13, *Introduction to Modern Physics* (second edition), by F. K. Richtmeyer. New York: McGraw-Hill, 1934. Barkla was awarded the Nobel prize in physics in 1917.

Thus, by 1912, it was widely accepted as a working hypothesis that X-rays were very short electromagnetic waves, with wavelengths of the order of a fraction of an angstrom unit, or about one thousandth of the wavelength of visible light. The time was ripe for direct experimental verification, and an idea for a suitable experiment was stimulated by the rapidly emerging conceptions of atomic structure.

34.2 X-RAY DIFFRACTION

It had long been assumed that the characteristic shapes and sharp cleavage planes of crystalline materials stemmed from highly regular arrangements of atoms or molecules in a lattice structure, with fixed, orderly spacing of atoms in various planes and directions. Rutherford's nuclear model suggested an atomic structure in which groups of electrons, capable of scattering X-rays, were somehow grouped around minute but massive nuclei. Thus a crystal structure should contain regularly spaced "scattering centers" several angstrom units apart (see the atomic spacing calculations made in Section 33.9).

Seizing on the idea that X-ray wavelengths seemed to be of the order of tenths of angstroms, the German physicist Max von Laue (1879–1960) suggested in 1912 that a thin crystalline plate should act as a three-dimensional diffraction grating: passage of a narrow pencil of X-rays through a crystal might lead to the formation of a diffraction pattern analogous to that obtained when visible light is passed through an optical grating. [Note that if two ruled optical gratings are placed one over the other so that the lines are at right angles and form an array of square openings, an incident pencil of light is diffracted so as to produce a pattern of *spots* (instead of lines) in a regular arrangement around the central beam as the principal axis. See Problem 34.17 at the end of this chapter.]

The experiment with X-rays was a matter of strategy and deliberate design rather than an accidental discovery. It was performed by Friedrich and Knipping, and the results were reported in July 1912. On passing a narrow pencil of X-rays through a crystal of zincblende and exposing a photographic plate to the emerging rays for several hours, Friedrich and Knipping obtained a photograph showing numerous fainter spots lying on an orderly arrangement around the intense central beam (Fig. 34.2.1). From a series of photographs taken with the crystal oriented at different angles, and from estimates of the atomic spacing in the crystal, they concluded that there were present in the X-ray beam wavelengths ranging from 0.13 to 0.48 A.

The importance of these experiments was immediately appreciated by the scientific community, and Laue received the Nobel prize in 1914. Not only did Laue's idea provide strong support for the view that X-rays were electromagnetic waves with definite wavelengths, but it simultaneously reinforced the hypothesis that the geometrical properties of crystals reflect an arrangement of atoms in a three-dimensional lattice. In addition, the discovery opened up two new and exciting interrelated fields of investigation: (1) the study of the spectra of X-rays from various target materials; (2) the study of the geometry of crystal structure—identifying the lattice arrangements and measuring interatomic spacing.

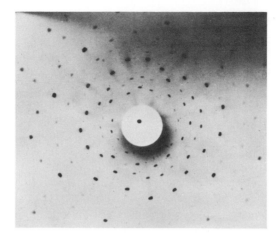

FIG. 34.2.1. Modern Laue photograph, showing diffraction spots produced after passage of a highly monochromatic X-ray beam through a crystal of sodium chloride. Note intense, undeflected central beam.

PROBLEM 34.1. From the descriptions given in this section of Laue diffraction and (in Chapter 33) of the scattering of α-particles by a thin metal foil, put together in your own words a statement of the similarities and differences between the observations in the two cases. How do you interpret the existence of a strong central beam emerging in each case? What differences seem to indicate fundamentally dissimilar interactions between matter and each of the two types of radiation?

34.3 BRAGG REFLECTION

To this day, Laue photographs play an important role in the study and determination of crystal structure (the spacing and three-dimensional arrangement of atoms in the crystal), but the interpretation of such photographs entails a somewhat more specialized and time-consuming geometrical analysis than we shall attempt in this text. We shall turn our attention to a related but considerably simpler series of experiments that were stimulated by Laue's success and were performed by the English physicists (father and son), W. H. Bragg (1862–1942) and W. L. Bragg (b. 1890).

In December 1912, W. L. Bragg published a short announcement in *Nature*.* Referring to the results of Laue and his colleagues, results that had been interpreted as due to interference maxima of waves *diffracted* by the regularly arranged atoms of the crystal, Bragg pointed out that:

"If this is so, these waves should be *regularly reflected* by a surface which has a sufficiently good polish, the irregularities being small compared with the [wave-

---

* *Nature*, **90,** 410 (1912).

length] of 10^{-9} cm. Such surfaces are provided by the cleavage planes of a crystal, which represent an arrangement of atoms ... in parallel planes, and the amount by which the centres of atoms are displaced from their proper planes is presumably small compared with atomic dimensions.

"In accordance with this, the spots in Laue's crystallographs can be shown to be due to partial reflection of the incident beam in sets of parallel planes in the crystal on which the atom centres may be arranged, the simplest of which are the actual cleavage planes of the crystal. This is merely another way of looking at the diffraction. This being so, it was suggested to me by Mr. C. T. R. Wilson that crystals with very distinct cleavage planes, such as mica, might possibly show strong specular reflection of the rays. On trying the experiment, it was found that this was so. A narrow pencil of X-rays ... was allowed to fall at an angle of incidence of 80° on a slip of mica about one millimeter thick mounted on thin aluminum. A photographic plate set behind the mica slip showed, when developed, a well-marked reflected spot as well as one formed by the incident rays traversing the mica and aluminum.

"Variation of the angle of incidence and of the distance of plate from mica left no doubt that the laws of reflection were obeyed. Only a few minutes' exposure to a small X-ray bulb sufficed to show the effect, whereas Friedrich and Knipping found it necessary to give an exposure of many hours. . . . By bending the mica into an arc, the reflected rays can be brought to a line focus . . . ."

The Braggs then seized on the idea that the reflection effect was not entirely a surface phenomenon. They suggested (early in 1913) that only a small portion of the energy of an incident wave front would be reflected at the first layer of atoms and that the front would continue into the crystal, with additional reflections occurring at each successive layer or plane of atoms (Fig. 34.3.1). The reflected waves from the successive layers would form parallel wave fronts traveling in the same direction. Whether these successively reflected waves interfere with each other (and with other reflected fronts) constructively or destructively must depend on the relation between the distance AE in Fig. 34.3.1 and the wavelength λ of the wave. The distance AE must, in turn, depend on the angle of incidence θ and the spacing d between the parallel atomic planes. Only small fractions of the energy of the emerging wave fronts would be reflected back into the crystal as the fronts progressed out through the atomic layer, and, in the case of constructive interference, a relatively strong reflected wave should be observed at an angle of reflection equal to the angle of incidence (specular reflection).

Let us formulate the theory of *Bragg reflection* in terms of the bow-wave model of specular reflection developed in Section 22.11. Figure 34.3.1 shows schematically what happens to one incident wave front, denoted by i. As it penetrates the crystal, this wave front forms reflected bow waves at each successive layer of atoms, as though the crystal were a stack of weakly reflecting, largely transparent, parallel mirrors separated by the spacing d of the atomic layers. The construction in Fig. 34.3.1 shows that the successive reflected wave fronts lag behind each other by the distance $AE = 2d \cos \theta$.

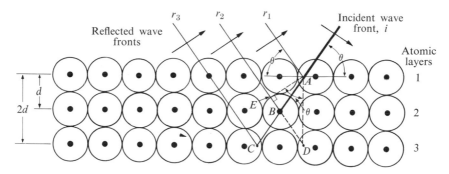

Fig. 34.3.1. Bragg reflection of an incident wave front i from successive parallel atomic layers (1, 2, 3, etc.) in a crystal. A small fraction of the incident energy is reflected at each layer to form parallel reflected wave fronts (r_1, r_2, r_3, etc.) all traveling in the same direction. The reflected wave fronts lag behind one another by a distance $AE = 2d \cos \theta$. In a sinusoidal wave train the reflected waves will interfere constructively if the distance AE is an integral number of wavelengths. (The decrease in width of line i is intended to imply successive decreases of incident wave intensity with reflections occurring at each atomic layer.)

PROBLEM 34.2. Show that the distance $AE = 2d \cos \theta$ in Fig. 34.3.1. [Construct BD as an extension of wave front r_2. Show that triangle ABD must be an isosceles triangle because of the law of specular reflection ($\theta_i = \theta_r$), and that the base AD of the triangle must therefore be perpendicular to the crystal planes and must have the length $2d$. The angle EAD is equal to θ. Why?] How might you construct a ripple-tank model of this phenomenon?

The reflected wave fronts r_1, r_2, r_3, etc., will interfere constructively only if the distance between them is an integral number of wavelengths λ; that is, if

$$n\lambda = 2d \cos \theta_n; \qquad n = 1, 2, 3, \ldots \tag{34.3.1}$$

Thus, for a particular wavelength of radiation λ_a and spacing d between atomic planes, a first-order constructive interference "line" would be observed at a particular angle of incidence and reflection such that:

$$\cos \theta_{1a} = \frac{\lambda_a}{2d}. \tag{34.3.2}$$

The reflected fronts for other wavelengths would interfere destructively at this angle. To observe the constructive reflection of another wavelength λ_b, it would be necessary to turn the crystal to a different orientation θ_{1b} with respect to the incident beam.

In other words, starting with the intense composite beam of radiation emerging from the X-ray tube, one can select a weaker beam reflected at a particular, glancing angle from a crystal plate. This final beam must be "monochromatic"; i.e., it must consist of X-rays of a very narrow range of wavelengths. By rotating the crystal plate so as to alter the angle of incidence (Fig. 34.3.2), one can obtain monochromatic

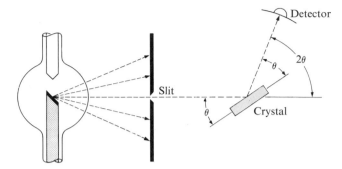

FIG. 34.3.2. Schematic diagram of X-ray crystal spectrometer. Each wavelength λ_a in the incident beam is reflected constructively at a particular angle θ_a, defined by Eq. (34.3.2).

beams of different wavelength—the original X-ray beam is separated into its component wavelengths just as visible light, in an analogous situation, is separated by a diffraction grating.

If the spacing d between atomic planes is known (or estimated from Avogadro's number, as in Section 33.9), it is possible to calculate, from Eq. (34.3.2), the wavelength of X-rays reflected to any particular angle θ. One can then study the character of the X-ray spectrum (wavelengths and intensities) emitted by different target materials in the X-ray tube under cathode ray beams accelerated through different voltages. On the other hand, selecting monochromatic X-ray beams reflected from the crystal plate (a device used in this manner is called a *crystal monochromator*), one can direct beams of known λ against other crystals, and study the structure and properties of these crystals by observing the angles of constructive interference, calculating d from a knowledge of λ and θ by use of Eq. (34.3.1).

The Braggs initiated this fruitful and exciting field of research, and their achievement was rewarded with the Nobel prize in 1915.

34.4 X-RAY SPECTRA

The Braggs, using a rock-salt crystal and an ionization chamber detector to compare intensities at different wavelengths, scanned the spectrum of X-rays from a platinum target. Whereas Laue and his associates had supposed the spectrum to be discrete, the Braggs showed it to be continuous, with several very intense bright lines superposed on the continuous background. Virtually simultaneously with the Braggs, H. G. J. Moseley (1887–1915), an associate of Rutherford's at Manchester, obtained the same results.

Several typical graphs of relative intensity versus wavelength are illustrated in Fig. 34.4.1. Such spectra, obtained with different accelerating potentials of the cathode beam and different target materials in the X-ray tube, reveal a systematic pattern of changes and relationships. In Problem 34.3 the reader is led to deduce the pattern from the information presented in Fig. 34.4.1. Answering the questions and noting down a list of the systematic effects will prove helpful in subsequent study.

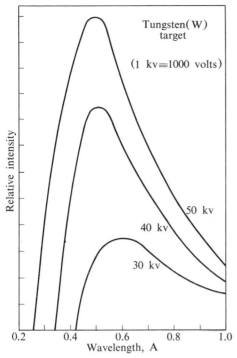

(a) Continuous X-ray spectrum from tungsten. *K*-lines do not appear until accelerating potential exceeds 69.5 kv. *L*-lines appear at about 1.1 A (to right of figure) at 11.5 kv.

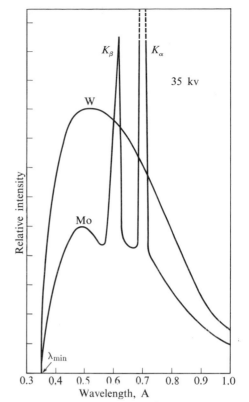

(b) Spectra of tungsten (W) and molybdenum (Mo) under 35-kv cathode beam. Note identical short wavelength limit (λ_{min})

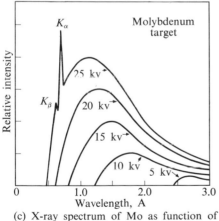

(c) X-ray spectrum of Mo as function of accelerating potential of cathode beam.

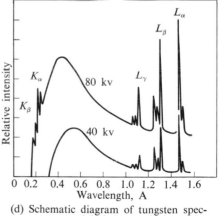

(d) Schematic diagram of tungsten spectrum at potentials below and above that necessary to excite the *K*-lines.

FIG. 34.4.1. Characteristics of X-ray spectra. Parts (a) and (b) are from *Introduction to Nuclear and Atomic Physics* (fourth edition), by Henry Semat. (New York: Holt, Rinehart, and Winston, 1962.) Part (c) from *Introductory Atomic Physics*, by Wehr and Richards. Part (d) from *Fundamentals of Modern Physics* by R. M. Eisberg (New York: John Wiley & Sons, 1961).

PROBLEM 34.3.   (a) Note that some of the spectra in Fig. 34.4.1 are continuous, while others have very intense bright lines labeled K_α, K_β, L_α, L_β, etc., superposed on the continuous spectrum. Under what circumstances do the bright lines seem to appear? (Some of Barkla's experiments on the absorption of X-rays by various materials had hinted strongly at the presence of intense lines. As a matter of fact, it was Barkla who introduced the K and L designations. The invention of the crystal spectrometer provided dramatic confirmation of his indirect conclusions.)

(b) When the bright lines are present, what differences exist between the spectrograms for different target materials?

(c) In each case the continuous part of the spectrum has a "short wavelength limit" beyond which no radiation is observed. What happens to the short wavelength limit as the energy of the cathode ray beam striking the target is increased?

(d) Do the short wavelength limit and the continuous spectrum seem to depend on the target material?

(e) At your present stage of knowledge, what interpretation would you place on the continuous portion of the spectrum and on the bright K and L lines? (Do not expect to be able to give a pat answer or even a "correct" one in some absolute sense. Be willing to speculate a bit in terms of the concepts you have been studying. If some of your ideas turn out to be incorrect, simply be prepared to modify them later on; seen in this light, subsequent discoveries and interpretations will have much deeper significance.)

It was Moseley who identified the bright lines of the X-ray spectra with Barkla's K and L radiation. Subsequently, more sensitive detectors revealed additional sets of lines (denoted M, N, etc.) at longer wavelengths.

Wavelengths of the K, L, M, ... lines are characteristic of the target element in the X-ray tube. Although the optical (visible) spectra of the elements are exceedingly complicated and differ markedly from one element to another, it is found that the X-ray spectra are not only relatively simple but are also very similar for different elements (Fig. 34.4.1). The wavelengths of the K, L, M, ... lines, however, decrease systematically with increasing atomic mass of the target element. Moseley was attracted to the study of this systematic variation and, in 1913 and 1914*, published an elegant set of experimental results that contributed significantly to clarifying the physical interpretation of the concept of "atomic number" of an element in the periodic system and also provided strong supporting evidence for Bohr's then newly developed theory of atomic structure. We shall return to these results after discussing Bohr's theory in Chapter 35.

34.5   CRYSTAL STRUCTURE AND X-RAY WAVELENGTHS

As indicated in Section 34.3, X-ray wavelengths were initially determined by measurements of angle of Bragg reflection from the principal cleavage planes of crystals such as rock salt. Spacing of atoms in these crystals was calculated from the best available values of density, atomic masses, and Avogadro's number, with

---

* The gifted young Moseley was killed at the battle of Gallipoli in 1915.

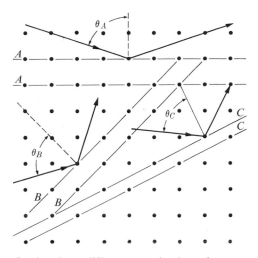

FIG. 34.5.1. Bragg reflection from different atomic planes in a crystal. Note that *rays* are sketched on this diagram, rather than wave fronts, as in Fig. 34.3.1. Planes such as *AA* are called principal planes. Note that planes *BB* and *CC* have successively smaller spacing than *AA*, and the corresponding Bragg angles also become smaller. The intensity of the reflection from planes *CC* is lower than that from *AA* because the *CC* planes contain fewer atoms per unit area.

full realization that the computed values would have to be changed as knowledge of the primary data—particularly Avogadro's number—improved. Even if absolute values were slightly in doubt, however, *relative* measurements of X-ray wavelengths could be made with very high precision. (Why?)

With monochromatic X-ray beams of known wavelength from the crystal spectrometer, it was possible to study the reflection of the rays from various crystals and to measure the spacing between different atomic planes within the crystalline structure (see Fig. 34.5.1). From a collection of such measurements, it is possible to deduce the geometrical structure of a crystal.

In 1916 Debye and Scherrer demonstrated the practicability of a simple and powerful modification of the techniques we have just described. Passing a narrow pencil of monochromatic X-rays through a *powdered* crystalline material, they photographed a diffraction pattern consisting of concentric rings, as illustrated in Fig. 34.5.2(b). The rings represent regions of constructive interference where a cone of rays intersects the photographic film after passing through the powder. Since the semi-apex angle of any cone of rays (ϕ in Fig. 34.5.2a) is twice the Bragg reflection angle for the set of atomic planes producing this reflection, the spacing between the planes can be calculated from measurements of ϕ and application of Eq. (34.3.1).

PROBLEM 34.4. Argue that ϕ, the semi-apex angle of the cone of rays in Fig. 34.5.2(a), must be twice the Bragg angle θ [Eq. (34.3.2)] for the set of atomic planes giving this particular cone of rays. [*Hint:* Take note of the angle 2θ in Fig. 34.3.2.]

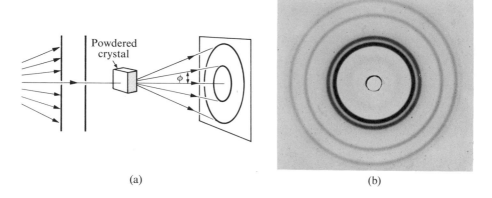

(a)   (b)

FIG. 34.5.2. (a) Narrow pencil of X-rays, formed by pinholes in lead plates, is incident
on a sample of crystalline powder. The thousands of tiny crystals are randomly oriented
with respect to the beam, and for some of these orientations the Bragg reflection condition
will be satisfied for a particular set of atomic planes in the crystal. Since all possible azimuthal
orientations of the crystals (around the axis formed by the beam) will be present, the constructively reflected rays form a conical surface. Each conical set of rays forms a circle on
the photographic film. (b) Debye-Scherrer photograph of diffraction of pencil of X-rays
on passing through aluminum. Photograph courtesy Professor B. E. Warren at M.I.T.

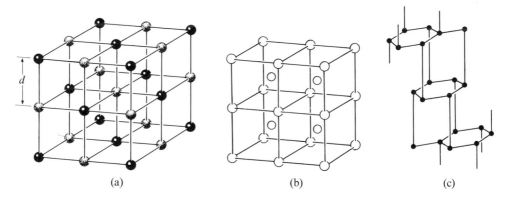

(a)   (b)   (c)

FIG. 34.5.3. Several examples of crystal lattices. (a) Simple cubic lattices of sodium
chloride (NaCl). (b) Body-centered cubic lattice of cesium chloride (CsCl). (c) Atoms of
carbon lying in parallel planes in graphite.

From measurements of spacing between various atomic planes, combined with
direct physical information regarding the shapes and symmetries of the natural,
macroscopic crystals, it is possible to deduce the details of the structure of each
different crystal lattice. Examples of several particularly simple structures are given
in Fig. 34.5.3. In their early investigations, the Braggs, for example, confirmed the
earlier assumption that Na and Cl atoms occupy alternate positions at the corners
of elementary cubes in the cubic lattice characteristic of rock salt. It is beyond the

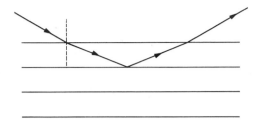

FIG. 34.5.4. Schematic diagram of refraction of a narrow beam of X-rays as it enters a crystal and is reflected from the second atomic plane. (Not to scale; actual effect is very much smaller than that illustrated.)

scope of this text to follow the geometrical analyses that lead to the deduction of lattice structure; the interested reader should consult references cited at the end of the chapter, or a treatise on X-ray crystallography.

Although early attempts to observe refraction of X-rays all led to null results, rapidly increasing precision of X-ray spectroscopy and crystallography after 1913 led to the discovery (1919) that X-rays were indeed refracted by crystals and that the index of refraction was very slightly *less* than unity; i.e., that propagation velocity of X-rays in a crystal was very slightly *greater* than the velocity of light in vacuum! (The index depends on the crystalline material and on the wavelength of the rays, but at wavelengths of the order of 2 to 3 A it is less than unity by the order of 10^{-5}.) The lower index implies that a ray, on entering a crystal, is bent very slightly *away* from the normal, as illustrated in Fig. 34.5.4.

PROBLEM 34.5. After the discovery of X-ray refraction, a number of investigators measured the index at various wavelengths by passing very narrow beams through the tips of prisms of glass, calcite, etc. In Fig. 34.5.5, sketch the path of the incident ray as it continues through the prism and emerges on the other side. In contrast, also sketch the path followed by a ray of light.

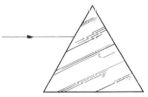

FIGURE 34.5.5

The bending of a ray away from the normal implies the existence of a critical angle of total reflection (see Section 22.12). Taking advantage of the total reflection phenomenon, Compton and Doan in 1925 observed the diffraction pattern formed when X-rays were reflected at *very* oblique incidence (less than 0.4°) from a ruled grating of speculum metal with 50 lines per mm. Such diffraction patterns make it possible to obtain an absolute measurement of X-ray wavelength without reference to crystal structure or use of prior estimates of Avogadro's number. Compton and Doan showed, for example, the wavelength of the K_α line of molybdenum to be 0.707 ± 0.003 A, and measurements of very much higher precision soon became available.

34.6 AVOGADRO'S NUMBER FROM MEASUREMENTS OF LATTICE SPACING

Once we have available an absolute value of an X-ray wavelength, based on the known spacing of lines on a ruled grating, it becomes possible to make an absolute determination of a crystal lattice spacing and, from this spacing, to evaluate Avogadro's number. For example: using the K_α line of molybdenum ($\lambda = 0.707$ A), we find that the first-order Bragg reflection angle from a cleavage plane of rock salt is 82.81°. From this measurement, we calculate the spacing d between principal atomic planes (Fig. 34.5.3) to be 2.82 A.

PROBLEM 34.6.   Verify the preceding result, taking cos 82.81° = 0.1254.

The density of rock salt is 2.165 gm/cm^3. Finding the volume of one mole, and remembering that one mole of NaCl contains $2N_0$ atoms (or ions) altogether, we can reverse the calculations made in Section 33.9 and calculate Avogadro's number from the interatomic spacing, obtaining the value $N_0 = 6.02 \times 10^{23}$.

PROBLEM 34.7.   Make the calculation just described and verify the quoted result.

In Section 33.8 we calculated N_0 from hypotheses concerning the significance of the Faraday (96,500 coul) in electrolysis, from the mass-spectrometric charge-to-mass ratio of hydrogen ions, and from the value of the elementary charge as determined in Millikan's experiment. Now we have obtained a completely independent value of N_0 from interpretations of the behavior of X-rays and from a number purported to represent the spacing between atoms in a crystal. Using modern values, we find our various calculations of N_0 agreeing to three significant figures! This provides an excellent illustration of the manner in which we frequently test scientific theories or conceptions by checking the network of reasoning, traversing it in various directions and demanding cross checks and internal consistency in quantitative as well as qualitative aspects.

PROBLEM 34.8.   Reviewing the hypotheses and tentative assumptions that have been made in the last few chapters concerning the structure of matter and the role of electricity in this structure, list the assumptions that you feel are confirmed and tied together by agreement among the different ways of calculating Avogadro's number. List assumptions that you feel are so far unconfirmed. (For example: do you feel that you have encountered any *direct* evidence that the charge carried by individual electrons is equal to the elementary charge determined in the Millikan experiment?)

34.7 INTERACTION BETWEEN MATTER AND ELECTROMAGNETIC RADIATION

When we described in Chapters 26 and 27 the development of the wave theory of the nature of light, we saw this conception evolve from observation of phenomena such as reflection, refraction, diffraction, dispersion, and polarization. All these phenomena involve interaction between electromagnetic radiation and matter, but they are in an important sense macroscopic interactions: Wavelengths of visible light (of the order of 5000 A) embrace thousands of atomic diameters, interacting with huge numbers of electrons, and producing well-smeared-out or averaged effects. Furthermore, our observations of the phenomena themselves do not admit of detection of instantaneous values of electric or magnetic fields, or of individual events of any kind; they are confined to observation (by eye, by photographic plates, or by other detecting devices) of *time average* values of intensity at various positions in space.

While the Maxwellian theory, visualizing light as a continuous electromagnetic wave, was very successful in accounting for macroscopic phenomena, it did not provide a successful model for explaining the origin of absorption or emission spectra of gases—phenomena that clearly involve individual atoms and the interaction of matter and radiation on a microscopic scale. Similarly, it provided no basis on which to account for a well-known aspect of the phenomenon of fluorescence: It had been observed that when a substance fluoresces under incident radiation (such as ultraviolet light), the "transformed" or emitted light invariably has a longer wavelength or lower frequency than the exciting radiation. (This observation is known as *Stokes' rule.*)

The discoveries of the 1890's added extensively to knowledge of various interactions on the microscopic scale. It was found that cathode rays incident on target materials produced X-rays; and that X-rays, possessing wavelengths of the order of atomic size, caused ionization of gases, ejecting electrons from individual atoms and molecules. Ultraviolet light was found to be particularly effective in ejecting electrons from metals—a phenomenon called the *photoelectric effect.*

All these microscopic phenomena played an important role in the "quantum revolution," the conceptual development that led to successful theories of atomic and molecular structure at the cost of abandoning certain deeply rooted preconceptions of classical physics. In this sequence, the photoelectric effect occupied a particularly crucial position.

34.8 LENARD'S EXPERIMENTAL METHOD

In Section 31.14 we referred briefly to the fact that Thomson, in support of his hypothesis that electrons were a universal constituent of matter, had shown that the charged particles ejected from metals by incident light have the same e/m as cathode rays. Other workers, including P. Lenard, obtained the same results independently. Lenard in particular, however, went on to make a systematic study of the photoelectric current*, using apparatus such as that illustrated schematically in Fig. 34.8.1. Two electrodes M and P are encased in a vacuum tube. (In Lenard's apparatus, electrode P was movable, and the electrode spacing could be varied from about 0.5 to about 4.0 cm.) The tube is fitted with a quartz or a mica window, Q, that transmits ultraviolet light (ordinary glass is virtually opaque to light in this range of wavelengths). Light, from a source such as an electric arc, is allowed to

---

* *Annalen der Physik*, **8**, 149 (1902).

pass through window Q and fall on the target M, which might be a bright plate of aluminum, platinum, zinc, or other metal. Lenard, in many of his experiments, also used a soot-coated electrode, making carbon the target material and greatly reducing the amount of reflected light, which otherwise bounces back and forth within the tube, causing a small amount of unwanted electron emission from plate P. If it is desired to shine monochromatic light on the target, a suitable filter F is interposed between the light source and Q.

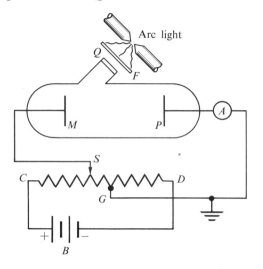

FIG. 34.8.1. Schematic diagram of tube designed for studying photoelectric current.

Electrode P is connected through a sensitive galvanometer or microammeter, A, to the midpoint G of the slide wire resistor CD. (Lenard actually made his electrical measurements with two separate electrometers, each connected to electrodes M and P, respectively.) If slide S is at point G, the potential difference between M and P is zero. If S is to the left of G, plate M is positive relative to P; electrons knocked out of M would be attracted back toward this electrode and retarded in their motion toward P. We shall adopt the convention of denoting this as a negative or "retarding" potential difference. Similarly, with slide S to the right of point G, emitted electrons would be repelled from M and accelerated toward P. We shall denote this as a positive or "accelerating" potential difference. When a photoelectric current, I, flows between the plates, its magnitude is registered by meter A.

34.9 LENARD'S OBSERVATIONS ON THE PHOTOELECTRIC EFFECT

Using three different light sources (an arc light with carbon electrodes, another with zinc electrodes, and a spark discharge between zinc spheres), Lenard made a systematic study of the influence of light intensity and of the potential difference between M and P on the photoelectric current. He reported the following observations.

(1) With a steady light source and a positive (accelerating) potential difference, the photoelectric current increased as P was moved toward M, indicating that ejected electrons had all directions of velocity and that more of them were being intercepted by P as it was brought closer to M. When P was about 5 mm from M, the current ceased to increase appreciably, indicating that most of the electrons were being intercepted. Further observations, described below, were made at this separation between the plates.

(2) Lenard then varied the light intensity in two ways: by changing the current through the arc and by moving the source to a greater distance from the window Q. In the latter case he could make use of the simple law that the intensity of a light beam from a small source varies inversely as the square of distance from the source. He found that the total photoelectric current under accelerating potential difference (i.e., the rate of liberation of charge from plate M) was always directly proportional to the intensity of the incident light (see Fig. 34.9.1).

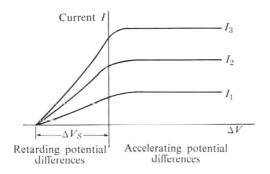

FIG. 34.9.1. Idealized diagram of curves obtained in observations of the photoelectric effect when monochromatic light is used (i.e., a filter plate F is employed in Fig. 34.8.1). The curves indicated are obtained at different intensities of incident light. Values of saturation current (I_1, I_2, I_3) are directly proportional to the light intensity. Stopping potential ΔV_S is independent of light intensity, and depends only on the frequency of the light and on the material of the electrode from which the photoelectrons are ejected.

(3) Lenard was impressed by the fact that this proportionality was obeyed down to extremely low light intensities—one three-millionth of the highest intensity used. He emphasized that there was "no indication whatsoever of the existence of a threshold value of light intensity." (A threshold value is one that must be attained by an excitation before it produces any observable effect.) It was reasonable to expect a threshold value of light intensity in the photoelectric effect on the ground that some minimum initial value of energy would be necessary to eject any electrons at all from the metal. (The intensity of light is a measure of the amount of energy propagated through a unit area parallel to the wave front in each second.) No threshold has ever been found for the photoelectric effect—if the light is capable of producing the effect at all, some electrons are always ejected, however faint the light!

(4) When slide S was moved to the left of point G in Fig. 34.8.1 and the potential difference given retarding values, the photoelectric current did not drop to zero immediately, despite the retarding effect. It decreased as the retarding potential became larger in magnitude, reaching zero at a potential difference ΔV_S of the order of two volts (see Fig. 34.9.1). We shall call ΔV_S the *stopping potential*. Lenard observed that the stopping potential was completely unaffected by the intensity of the incident light; it was altered only when a different type of light source was used, or when the material of plate M was changed.

(5) The fact that a photoelectric current I still flows (i.e., some electrons continue to reach plate P) even when a retarding potential is applied indicates that the electrons are ejected from electrode M with appreciable initial velocity and kinetic energy. The decrease in I as the magnitude of retarding potential is increased indicates that the ejected electrons have different kinetic energies, ranging from zero to a maximum value. It takes a retarding potential difference ΔV_S to stop the current; i.e., to prevent the most energetic electrons with velocities normal to emitting plate M from reaching collecting plate P. The maximum kinetic energy of ejected electrons must therefore be $e\,\Delta V_S$. Varying the incident light intensity by a factor of more than 1000 to 1, with everything else held constant, Lenard found that the stopping potential ΔV_S (i.e., the maximum kinetic energy of ejected electrons) did not change significantly!

> PROBLEM 34.9. The preceding paragraph asserts an interpretation of the effect of retarding potential differences and of the quantitative significance of ΔV_S. Explain the basis of these assertions in your own words. (Suppose that electrons are ejected from electrode M in various directions at various velocities. How does the electric field influence their motions? Sketch several possible trajectories for electrons with initial velocities perpendicular to M and at various angles to M. What relation do you see between this case and the ideas of projectile motion in Chapter 4? What is the justification for the assertion that the maximum kinetic energy is $e\,\Delta V_S$?) Why is it surprising that the maximum kinetic energy seems to be unaffected by the intensity of the incident light? It is clear that the intensity of the light does have *some* effect: an increase in intensity increases current I at any given potential difference ΔV. What does this imply so far as the effect on electrons is concerned? Lenard pointed out that it was very difficult to explain the observed photoelectric phenomena in terms of the classical Maxwellian wave theory of light. Explain his position in your own words.

34.10 EINSTEIN'S HEURISTIC MODEL OF THE MICROSCOPIC BEHAVIOR OF LIGHT

In the first of three classic papers that he sent to the *Annalen der Physik* in the year 1905, Albert Einstein (1879–1955) made a revolutionary suggestion aimed at accounting for certain aspects of the microscopic interaction between light and matter; among the aspects considered was the photoelectric effect. The paper was titled "Concerning an heuristic point of view toward the emission and transformation of light." It begins—in a manner highly characteristic of Einstein's general attitude and mode of thought—by pointing to a certain lack of symmetry and conceptual consistency in existing theories:

> ".... the total energy of a ponderable body must, according to the present conceptions of physicists, be represented as a sum carried over the energies of the atoms and electrons [that make up the body]. The energy of a ponderable body cannot be subdivided into arbitrarily many or arbitrarily small parts, while the energy of a beam of light from a point source (according to the Maxwellian theory of light or, more generally, according to any wave theory) is continuously spread over an ever-increasing volume.
>
> "The wave theory of light, which operates with continuous spatial functions, has worked well in the representation of purely optical phenomena and will probably never be replaced by another theory. It should be kept in mind, however, that the optical observations refer to time averages rather than instantaneous values. In spite of the complete experimental confirmation of the theory as applied to diffraction, reflection, refraction, dispersion, etc., it is still conceivable that the theory of light which operates with continuous spatial functions may lead to contradictions with experience when it is applied to the phenomena of emission and transformation of light [i.e., interactions on the microscopic scale].
>
> "It seems to me that the observations associated with blackbody radiation, fluorescence, the photoelectric effect, and other related phenomena . . . are more readily understood if one assumes that the energy of light is discontinuously distributed in space. In accordance with the assumption to be considered here, the energy of a light ray spreading out from a point is not continuously distributed over an increasing space, but consists of a finite number of energy quanta which are localized at points in space, which move without dividing, and which can only be produced and absorbed as complete units."

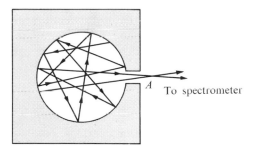

FIG. 34.10.1.   Schematic diagram of cavity containing blackbody radiation.

Einstein then goes on to present the theoretical analysis that provided the basis for his radically new conception. The analysis itself is beyond the scope of this text, but we can attempt a qualitative description of its background.

At the turn of the century one of the prominent unresolved problems of physical theory was that of the so-called *blackbody radiation*. Suppose that we have a block of metal (or of some other heat-resisting solid material) containing a cavity with a small opening (Fig. 34.10.1). If the walls are heated to sufficiently high temperature, the cavity becomes red or white hot, and a thermal equilibrium is established in which the walls absorb and re-emit electromagnetic radiation which propagates randomly in all directions within the cavity. Without significantly disturbing the equilibrium, a small fraction of the radiation is allowed to escape through the small opening at A, and the spectrum is analyzed by means of a spectrometer. It is found that the spectrum is continuous and that the distribution of energy among different frequencies depends *only* on the temperature of the enclosure and not at all on the material in the walls. Such equilibrium radiation is called blackbody radiation, and its spectrum is called the blackbody spectrum.

Recall that other spectra we have described, such as the emission spectra of gases and X-ray spectra, are profoundly characteristic of the substances with which they are associated and actually provide "fingerprints" for identification and detection of the emitting matter. Blackbody radiation, on the other hand, appears to be universal or fundamental, in the sense that its character depends only on temperature, and this universality attracted the attention of many leading physicists. Here, perhaps, was an instance of emission and absorption of radiation that provided a relatively simple starting point for a theory of microscopic interaction between electromagnetic radiation and matter. This hope was encouraged by the analogies that could be seen between the random, chaotic bouncing around of radiation in the cavity and the behavior of molecules of a gas. Perhaps a successful theory of blackbody radiation would be closely analogous to the kinetic theory of gases.

Efforts to derive the equation for the distribution of energy among the continuous frequencies of the blackbody spectrum were based on the classical theories of mechanics, thermodynamics, and electrodynamics. All such attempts failed to give a theoretical result in complete agreement with experimental observations.

In 1900 and 1901 the German physicist Max Planck (1858–1947) discovered an empirical equation that accurately fit the experimental data. He then discovered a theoretical derivation of this equation, but to achieve the derivation he found it necessary to assume that the charged particles, vibrating in the walls of the cavity and absorbing and emitting electromagnetic energy, could only take on *discrete* rather than continuous values of energy; i.e., Planck assumed that a vibrating atomic or subatomic particle (or "oscillator") could only take on values of energy that were integral multiples of a fundamental quantity of energy $\Delta\epsilon$. He found, furthermore, that for each oscillator of different frequency ν, the fundamental unit or *quantum* * of energy absorbed or emitted must be taken to be proportional to the frequency. Denoting the proportionality constant by h, we can describe Planck's assumption by saying that an atomic particle, oscillating at frequency ν, can only take on values of vibrational energy E such that

$$E = n(h\nu),$$

where $h\nu$ is the quantum of energy for the given frequency, and n is an integer. (In mks units, the numerical value of h is found to be 6.63×10^{-34} joule · sec.) Planck's hypothesis implied, for example, that a particle, oscillating at frequency ν,

---

* Quantum is the Latin word for "how much" or "how great."

could take on the energies $2h\nu$ or $3h\nu$ but could *not* have the energy $2.35h\nu$; that is, such a particle could only emit or absorb energy in whole quanta of size $h\nu$.

Planck's hypothesis led to the derivation of an equation agreeing perfectly with the observed blackbody spectrum, but this was done at the cost of abandoning one of the basic notions of classical mechanics—that a vibrating particle could take on continuous values of energy. Planck never went so far as to extend this idea of discreteness or "granularity" to the electromagnetic radiation itself. He continued to visualize the latter as perfectly continuous, in accordance with the Maxwellian wave theory.

It was precisely this issue that commanded Einstein's attention in the quotation cited above. If the energy of oscillating particles occurred in discrete quanta, why not the electromagnetic radiation being absorbed and emitted? Examining the blackbody radiation equation from this new point of view and developing a subtle analogy with formulas describing the thermodynamic behavior of ideal gases, he showed that one could think of the electromagnetic radiation itself as though it were a gas, consisting of a finite number of discrete quanta of different frequencies, ν, and of energy $h\nu$. We now refer to such localized "corpuscles" or quanta of electromagnetic radiation as *photons*.

34.11 APPLICATIONS OF EINSTEIN'S MODEL

As Einstein himself emphasized in the title of his paper, his model of the microscopic nature of light was essentially heuristic. He found it exceedingly useful in helping explain some of the phenomena we have described in preceding sections, but he did not pretend to offer an explanation of why light behaved in this fashion or how one might visualize a localized or "corpuscular" quantum of electromagnetic radiation that simultaneously exhibited properties of frequency and wavelength; nor did he attempt to describe any process by which such quanta are absorbed or emitted by atoms or electrons!

Pointing to the phenomenon of fluorescence, Einstein suggests that perhaps each incident photon, absorbed by fluorescent material, stimulates the emission of one or more photons, leading to re-emission of the energy that was absorbed. If each absorption and corresponding re-emission is an elementary process, independent of other incident photons, the law of conservation of energy requires that the energies of the emitted photons (and therefore their frequencies) be equal to or less than that of the incident photon. (The equality applies when the re-emission is of a single photon.) This prediction—that fluorescent radiation will in general have a longer wavelength or be "redder" than the stimulating radiation—is in accordance with the observation expressed in Stokes' rule (see Section 34.7). The agreement thus gives some support for Einstein's model of elementary processes in which light quanta (photons) are absorbed and emitted independently as whole units. Einstein then continues:

> "The usual conception, that the energy of light is continuously distributed over the space through which it propagates, encounters very serious difficulties when one attempts to explain the photoelectric phenomena, as has been pointed

out by Lenard in his pioneering paper. [Here Einstein refers to the work we have described in Sections 34.8 and 34.9].

"According to the concept that the incident light consists of energy quanta of magnitude $h\nu$, however, one can conceive of the ejection of electrons by light in the following way. Energy quanta (photons) penetrate into the surface layer of the body, and their energy is transformed, at least in part, into kinetic energy of electrons. The simplest way to imagine this is that a light quantum delivers its entire energy to a single electron; we shall assume that this is what happens. . . . An electron to which kinetic energy has been imparted within the body will have lost some of this energy by the time it reaches the surface. Furthermore, we shall assume that in leaving the surface of the body [i.e., escaping from the metal] each electron must perform an amount of work W_0, characteristic of the substance of which the body is composed. The ejected electrons leaving the body with the largest normal velocity will be those that were directly at the surface. The kinetic energy of such electrons is given* by

$$KE_{max} = h\nu - W_0. \tag{34.11.1}$$

"If the emitting body is charged to a positive potential difference relative to a neighboring conductor, and if ΔV_S represents the potential difference which just stops the photoelectric current [it follows that $e \, \Delta V_S$ must be equal to the maximum KE of the ejected electrons] and therefore

$$e \, \Delta V_S = h\nu - W_0, \tag{34.11.2}$$

where e denotes the electronic charge. . . .

"If the deduced formula is correct, a graph of ΔV_S versus the frequency of the incident light must be a straight line with a slope that is independent of the nature of the emitting substance. [Here was a suggestion for the performance of a new experiment to test the theory.]

"So far as I can see, there is no contradiction between these conceptions and the properties of the photoelectric effect observed by Lenard. If each energy quantum of the incident light, independently of everything else, delivers [all] its energy to a single electron, then the velocity distribution of the ejected electrons will be independent of the intensity of the incident light; on the other hand, the number of electrons leaving the body will, if other conditions are kept constant, be proportional to the intensity of the incident light. . . ."

Thus Einstein's hypothesis not only suggested an explanation of all of Lenard's paradoxical observations, but it also predicted that graphs of $e \, \Delta V_S$-versus-ν should be straight lines, differing in intercept along the ν-axis but all having the same slope, the slope being a universal constant identical with that arising in Planck's theory of blackbody radiation.

---

* We have altered Einstein's symbols in order to maintain a uniform notation throughout this text.

PROBLEM 34.10. Einstein's model implies that the intensity of a beam of mono-chromatic light is proportional to the *number* of photons arriving per unit area per second. Explain in your own words why it follows that the resulting photoelectric current should be proportional to the intensity of the incident light.

34.12 SUPPORTING EVIDENCE FOR EINSTEIN'S MODEL

Subsequent investigators (Millikan among them) showed that Einstein's prediction was correct, and that when experimentally measured stopping potentials were plotted as a function of the frequency ν of the incident light, the experimental points for different metals fell on straight lines as illustrated in Fig. 34.12.1. The lines all have the same slopes but possess different intercepts along the ν-axis.

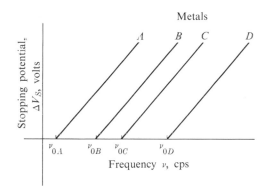

FIG. 34.12.1. Schematic diagram illustrating Einstein's prediction that stopping potential ΔV_S should be a linear function of the frequency ν of the incident light. The different lines show the behavior of different metals A, B, C, D. The slopes are identical, but the intercepts are properties of each particular metal.

PROBLEM 34.11. Argue from Eq. (34.11.2) that the slopes of the lines in Fig. 34.12.1 must be h/e. Compare this episode (Einstein's prediction of linear relation between ΔV_S and ν) with Dalton's prediction of the law of Multiple Proportions (Section 28.10). In what ways are these episodes similar? In what aspects do you feel they differ?

The intercepts ν_{0A}, ν_{0B}, etc., for different metals represent "threshold frequencies"; i.e., no electrons are ejected, even under intense illumination, by monochromatic light having a frequency less than the value ν_0 for the particular metal; then as the frequency is increased beyond ν_0 (farther toward the violet or ultraviolet), the ejected electrons are found to have larger and larger kinetic energies. Explain the existence of a threshold frequency in terms of Einstein's model: What is the connection between ν_0 and the quantity W_0 (called the *photoelectric work function* of a metal) in Eq. (34.11.2)? Show that the work function $W_0 = h\nu_0$. Why would no electrons be ejected by light of frequency less than ν_0? Visible blue or violet light is capable of causing readily observable photoelectric emission from metals such as sodium or cesium, while ultraviolet light of wavelength below about 2000 A is needed to excite photoelectric emission from platinum. How do you interpret these data?

PROBLEM 34.12.   The threshold frequency for gold is found to be 1.163×10^{15} sec^{-1}. Calculate the wavelength of this light; where does it lie in the electromagnetic spectrum? [*Answer:* $\lambda = 2580$ A] Under an incident radiation frequency of 1.757×10^{15} sec^{-1}, the stopping potential is found to be 2.46 v. What is the numerical value of h/e? [*Answer:* 4.14×10^{-15} v · sec.] Using the known value of electronic charge e, evaluate h and compare your result with the value given in Appendix A.

It is found experimentally that exceedingly low intensities of illumination are capable of exciting an observable photoelectric current. It can be calculated that under such intensities, if the incident energy were continuously spread over space and were distributed uniformly among the atoms in the surface layers of the metal, it might take a length of time on the order of a year before any electrons acquired enough kinetic energy to exceed the work function and escape from the metal. Yet it has been shown experimentally by Lawrence and Beams that (even at these low intensities) if there is a time lag between the incidence of light and the start of the photoelectric current, this time lag is less than 3×10^{-9} sec!

PROBLEM 34.13.   The preceding statements indicate a tremendous discrepancy between experimental observations and the predictions of classical theory. How does Einstein's model resolve this difficulty?

It was remarked earlier (Section 34.1) that in 1907, five years before the discovery of X-ray diffraction, Wien estimated the order of magnitude of X-ray wavelengths by invoking Einstein's model: When a cathode ray beam is incident on a target, it is assumed that the kinetic energy of electrons is converted into photons as the electrons are slowed down. Suppose that the electrons have been accelerated through a potential difference ΔV in the cathode ray tube and therefore have kinetic energy $e \Delta V$. If an electron of this energy is stopped in a single "collision" and all its energy is converted into a single photon of energy $h\nu$, we have that

$$h\nu = \frac{hc}{\lambda} = e \Delta V,$$

or that the wavelength of the photon is

$$\lambda = \frac{h}{e} \frac{c}{\Delta V}.$$

Since h/e is approximately 4×10^{-15} (see Problem 34.12), we have

$$\lambda = \frac{(4 \times 10^{-15})(3 \times 10^8)}{40,000} = 3 \times 10^{-11} \text{ m},$$

$$\lambda = 0.3 \text{ A,} \qquad \text{when } \Delta V \text{ is of the order of 40,000 v.}$$

As we have seen, this indeed turns out to be the correct order of magnitude of X-ray wavelength, and provides additional support for Einstein's model.

PROBLEM 34.14. Consider the continuous portions of the X-ray spectra illustrated in Fig. 34.4.1. In the light of Einstein's model, how do you account for the high frequency or short wavelength limit of such a spectrum? (Check one or two of the limits indicated on the graphs by utilizing a numerical calculation similar to that carried out above.) How do you account for the rest of the continuous spectrum? (Consider the fact that most electrons undergo numerous collisions before losing all their KE.)

34.13 COMPARISON OF ENERGIES ON A MICROSCOPIC SCALE: THE ELECTRON VOLT AS A CONVENIENT UNIT

Our discussion has brought us to a point at which we would do well to set the pattern of energy changes in various atomic phenomena in a more orderly perspective. First, however, it is convenient to adopt a small energy unit—one that will give us readily comprehensible numbers when measuring small quantities of energy. The joule and calorie have been useful in the macroscopic scale, but if we attempt to measure the energies of atoms or photons in these units, we shall be confronted with inconveniently small numbers which, in the denary notation, will have factors with large negative powers of ten.

A particularly convenient and widely used unit is the amount of work done when the fundamental corpuscle or quantum of electrical charge (1.60×10^{-19} coul) is accelerated through a potential difference of one volt. This amount of energy,

$$e \, \Delta V = 1.60(10^{-19}) \times 1 = 1.60 \times 10^{-19} \, j,$$

is called one *electron volt*, abbreviated 1 ev. In some cases we have occasion to deal with energies of millions or billions of electron volts, and we then use the nomenclature Mev and Bev, respectively. (The kinetic energies attained in modern high-energy particle accelerators are usually described in Mev or Bev.)

Thus, if the stopping potential in a photoelectric experiment is found to be 4.3 v, we say that the maximum kinetic energy is 4.3 ev; similarly, in a cathode ray tube with an accelerating potential difference of 35,000 v, the electrons acquire energies of 35,000 ev, and are sometimes referred to as "35,000-volt electrons" or "35 kilovolt (kv) electrons."

Suppose that we wish to calculate the energy of a photon of known frequency or wavelength. We have

$$E = h\nu = \frac{hc}{\lambda}. \tag{34.13.1}$$

If h, c, and λ are expressed in mks units, E is in joules. If we divide the result by 1.60×10^{-19}, we obtain E in electron volts.

PROBLEM 34.15. Using appropriate numerical values of h and c and taking proper account of units, show that if we express λ in angstroms and E in ev, the energy of a photon is given by

$$E = \frac{1.24 \times 10^4}{\lambda}. \tag{34.13.2}$$

TABLE 34.13.1

COMPARISON OF ENERGIES ASSOCIATED WITH VARIOUS
MICROSCOPIC PARTICLES AND PHENOMENA

Type of energy	Substance, particle or photon	Energy in electron volts, ev	Wavelength λ of photon of same energy, A
Average total energy of vibration of an atomic particle along one coordinate axis in a solid material (at ordinary room temperature)	—	~0.02	
Average total translational kinetic energy of a gas molecule at ordinary temperatures	—	0.04	
Average energy released per atom participating in a violent chemical reaction such as the explosion of TNT	—	~0.5	
First ionization potential—energy necessary to separate one electron from an isolated, neutral atom: ranges from about 4 ev for the alkali metals to about 20 ev for the noble gases	K Na Ag Pt Au H He	4.3 5.1 7.5 8.9 9.2 13.6 24.5	505
Photoelectric work function—minimum energy necessary to eject electron from surface of a metal: ranges from about 3 ev for active metals to 6 or 7 ev for less active ones	K, Na Ag Au Pt	~3 4.7 4.8 6.3	
Photons of various types of electromagnetic radiation	Far infrared Visible (sodium D lines) Ultraviolet X-rays	~0.02 2.1 6 Voltage of X-ray tube: order of tens of thousands	5890
Radioactive emanations	α-particles from U and Ra β-particles from many radioactive isotopes γ-rays from many radioactive isotopes	~4 × 10^6 to 6 × 10^6; i.e., 4 to 6 Mev* ~0.1 to 2 Mev* ~0.01 to 1 Mev*	

* The symbol Mev stands for million electron volts.

Then, for example, the energy of a photon with $\lambda = 4600$ A (blue light) is

$$E = \frac{1.24 \times 10^4}{4600} = 2.7 \text{ ev}.$$

What is the rate of change of photon energy per A of wavelength at a wavelength of 1000 A? Use calculus in your calculation. [*Answer:* $(dE/d\lambda)_{\lambda=1000} = -0.0124$ ev/A.]

Table 34.13.1 gives a summary of typical values of energy associated with various particles, photons, and physical changes. The reader is urged to assimilate the pattern of relationships and the relative orders of magnitude displayed. Problem 34.16 is designed to assist him in this study.

PROBLEM 34.16.   (a) Fill in the blanks in the last column of the table by calculating the corresponding values of λ in each instance.

(b) We associate the heating of a solid or gas with an increase in the kinetic (or "thermal") energy of the atoms of the material. Note the order of magnitude of such energies, as indicated in the first two entries of the table. Note also that photons of the same energy have wavelengths in the far infrared. Why do you suppose that infrared radiation is frequently referred to as heat radiation?

(c) The average translational kinetic energy of a gas molecule is given as a function of temperature by:

$$E = 1.29 \times 10^{-4}T, \tag{34.13.3}$$

where E is in ev and T is temperature in degrees Kelvin (or absolute), defined as Celsius temperature $+273$. At what temperatures would the average kinetic energy of gas molecules be in the range of energies of photons of visible light? [*Answer:* Temperatures of the order of 15,000°.]

(d) Note the enormous difference between the order of magnitude of energy per atom in a violent chemical reaction and the energies associated with radioactive disintegration. What implications do you see in this difference?

(e) The work function of any given metal is indicated to be systematically smaller than the ionization energy of an isolated atom of the same substance. What implications do you see in this difference?

(f) Why do X-rays cause ionization of gases while visible light does not?

(g) γ-rays do not themselves leave visible tracks in a cloud chamber, but a γ-ray photon may eject an electron from an atom, and the *electron* produces a visible track. Explain each of the several phases of the phenomenon in the vocabulary that has been developed.

34.14   THE WAVE-PARTICLE DUALITY

Radical though Einstein's proposed extension of Planck's quantum idea seems to be, it nevertheless, when viewed in perspective, falls into a continuous sequence of conceptual development that begins early in the nineteenth century with Dalton's rationalization of chemistry. Atomism, which prior to that time had been an influential philosophical speculation, began to achieve the status of validated physical theory. Matter was seen to be discrete or "quantized" in the form of atomic or molecular particles with distinct electrical and mechanical properties.

As this view toward matter was evolving, continuous fluid models of heat and electricity were simultaneously being discarded. By the middle of the century heat was being viewed as associated with the energy of random thermal motion of discrete atomic or molecular particles, and, as Einstein remarks in the quotations given above, the total thermal energy of a body was to be found by summing the individual energies of its discrete parts. By the end of the century there was strong supporting evidence for the idea that electrical charge was also "corpuscular" or quantized.

While these conceptual developments occurred in physics, a not-unrelated trend was evident in biology, where the concepts of the "cell" and the "gene" (as discrete entities in the structure of tissues and in the mechanism of heredity, respectively) reflected a pattern of atomistic thought and engendered revolutions as profound as those taking place in the physical sciences.

Planck's conception of the discreteness of energies assumed by oscillating particles and Einstein's extension of this idea to posit quantization in electromagnetic radiation itself are both clearly within the evolving pattern, viewed from this perspective. But consistency with prevailing trends does not necessarily imply a smooth and effortless transition. On the contrary, the new proposals posed at least as many questions as they answered.

The proposals of Planck and Einstein were both semiempirical, that is to say neither was derived from a prior body of law and theory that commanded confidence and carried conviction. Planck's was advanced as an *ad hoc* way of obtaining the blackbody radiation equation; Einstein's, through an analogy between radiation and ideal gas behavior, presented a way of accounting for several mystifying experimental observations of the interaction of matter and radiation.

Planck himself was reluctant to accept Einstein's extension of the quantum idea to electromagnetic radiation. As Gerald Holton describes Planck's reaction:

> ". . . similar to Dalton's repudiation of the work of Avogadro, Planck expressed grave doubts about Einstein's proposal. If the photon concept were accepted, Planck wrote in 1910, 'the theory of light would be thrown back by centuries' to the time of when the followers of Newton and Huygens fought one another on the issue of the particle versus the wave theory of light. All the fruits of Maxwell's great work were threatened . . . 'for the sake of a few still rather dubious speculations.'
>
> "It is of interest to note that the work of Thomas Young over a hundred years earlier, which revived and further developed Huygens' wave theory and later provided an essential basis for Maxwell's theory, was generally attacked at the time by proponents of the then current particle theory of light on the ground that the wave theory, as one critic put it, 'can have no other effect than to check the progress of science and renew all those wild phantoms of the imagination which . . . Newton put to flight from her temple.'"*

---

* G. Holton and D. H. D. Roller, *Foundations of Modern Physical Science*. Reading, Mass.: Addison-Wesley, 1958, pages 591, 592.

Not only does the photon concept seriously challenge classical electromagnetic theory; it precipitates troublesome physical questions such as the following:

(1) How or by what process are photons emitted or absorbed by electrons or other particles?

(2) Material particles appear to have a permanence that photons do not possess. Einstein's model suggests that the latter are created and destroyed in very unparticle-like fashion (while energy and momentum are presumably conserved). How is such appearance and disappearance of corpuscles to be interpreted?

(3) How can photons be "localized" and still possess wavelength and frequency? There is nothing periodic about a shower of bullets or raindrops or hailstones.

(4) If the continuous wave theory is being challenged, on what grounds do we connect photon wavelengths and frequencies by the familiar wave relation $c = \lambda\nu$?

(5) If photons are corpuscular and localized, how can they exhibit the phenomenon of interference which our macroscopic experience associates so firmly with continuous wave behavior?

If questions of this kind have coursed through the reader's mind in studying earlier sections of this chapter, he is in good company, since these were among the questions with which leading physicists greeted Einstein's model. But the model, applied to other situations, continued to generate impressively successful results. We shall see in the next chapter how in the hands of Niels Bohr it began to yield an insight into the bright line emission spectra of gases and into the K, L, M lines of the spectra of X-rays. In addition, by 1912, Einstein and then Debye had applied the quantum hypothesis to the development of a remarkably successful theory of the heat capacity of solids—a theory that accounts for the manner in which the heat capacity appears to decrease toward zero at very low temperatures.

Subsequent experience with the interaction between matter and X-rays and γ-rays added still other cases that could be understood only on the basis of Einstein's hypothesis. Thus the model came to be accepted and was eventually worked into the fabric of a more general theory—the modern theory of quantum mechanics.

We are confronted for the first time, in the sequence of scientific ideas considered in this book, with the paradoxical situation in which two irreconcilably different views or theories apply to different ranges or levels of a particular phenomenon. In the macroscopic phenomena of reflection, refraction, diffraction, etc., we adopt a model of light as a continuous wave; in microscopic interactions of short wavelength radiation with atomic particles we employ the photon concept.

This "duality" in point of view has been the focus of extensive philosophical and epistemological discussion during the past forty years, and it is surrounded by an extensive literature of books and articles. Various implications and interpretations are still unresolved and are subjects of discussion and even controversy.

In this short section we can hardly begin to give a definitive discussion of the philosophical problem posed by the conception of wave-particle duality. We can, however, indicate a few directions of thought. We have referred several times to our predisposition to view physical motions or changes in either wave or particle terms. The physicist Max Born, one of the architects of the modern mathematical theory of quantum mechanics, analyzes this predisposition in the following way.

"The ultimate origin of the difficulty lies in the fact (or philosophical principle) that we are compelled to use the words of common language when we wish to describe a phenomenon, not by logical or mathematical analysis, but by a picture appealing to the imagination. Common language has grown by everyday experience and can never surpass these limits. Classical physics has restricted itself to the use of concepts of this kind; by analyzing visible motions it has developed two ways of representing them by elementary processes: moving particles and waves. There is no other way of giving a pictorial description of motions—we have to apply it even in the region of atomic processes, where classical physics breaks down. Every process can be interpreted either in terms of corpuscles or in terms of waves, but on the other hand it is beyond our power to produce proof that it is actually corpuscles or waves with which we are dealing, for we cannot simultaneously determine all the other properties which are distinctive of a corpuscle or of a wave, as the case may be. We can therefore say that the wave and corpuscular descriptions are only to be regarded as complementary ways of viewing one and the same objective process, a process which only in definite limiting cases admits of complete pictorial interpretation."*

Our simple modes of speech themselves lead us into a trap. We are tempted to say on one hand that light *is* a wave or on the other that light *is* a stream of particles, and this positive use of the verb "to be," implying a concrete existence of a mode of behavior precisely similar to everyday experiences with macroscopic objects, makes us lose sight of the fact that we are reaching for analogies and comparisons. Our locutions would be clearer if we avoided talking of what light *is* and spoke more conservatively about how it *behaved* and what properties it *manifested* under various circumstances.

". . . whenever an observation of any sort is made, its *immediate* results will always be expressible in terms of familiar ideas of space and time, since these ideas have been developed out of human experience and any observation necessarily includes as its primary stage a certain experience by a human observer. But it does not follow that it will always be possible to construct a picture of the physical reality that causes these experiences in the same way that we picture everyday objects."†

It is in this sense that we speak of light as exhibiting essentially corpuscular properties in some contexts and essentially wavelike behavior in others.

---

* M. Born, *Atomic Physics*, seventh edition. New York: Hafner Publishing Co.,1962, page 99
  † Richtmeyer, Kennard, and Lauritsen, *Introduction to Modern Physics*, fifth edition. New York: McGraw-Hill, 1955, page 394

34.15 PROBLEMS

34.17. If monochromatic light is passed through "crossed" optical gratings (two gratings superposed with their lines perpendicular to each other) the diffraction pattern observed consists of a pattern of spots disposed as illustrated in Fig. 34.15.1. (Fainter spots falling farther out from the center are not shown.)   Account for the pattern exhibited in the figure. (The original beam of light is in the form of a thin pencil.)

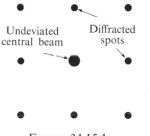

Undeviated   Diffracted
central beam   spots

FIGURE 34.15.1

34.18. Suppose that *nuclei* of atoms (stripped of their surrounding electrons) were to become fairly "close packed," as ordinary atoms seem to be in a solid. Making use of the estimated magnitude of nuclear size (see Section 33.12) calculate the expected order of magnitude of the density of matter in such a state. (If you use mks units, recalculate your result in tons per cubic inch to get a better sense of the significance of the result. There is reason to believe that certain stars consist of matter approaching this fantastic density.)

34.19. Suppose that ultraviolet light with a wavelength of 2000 A is incident on a gold electrode with a surface area of 1.0 cm^2. The intensity of the light is 10^{-7} watts (j/sec) per cm^2, and about 95% of the incident energy is reflected. Estimate the number of electrons ejected from the metal per second, making clear your idealizations and assumptions. If the collecting electrode effectively surrounds the emitting one, and if the potential difference is "accelerating" and is large enough to collect all the emitted electrons, estimate the expected order of magnitude of the photoelectric current in amperes. (Be sure to check whether or not electrons would actually be ejected from gold under the given circumstances. See Table 34.13.1.)

34.20. The energy necessary to decompose a molecule of silver bromide (AgBr) is about 1.0 ev per molecule. (Silver bromide is the photosensitive component of most ordinary photographic films.)   What is the threshold wavelength of photons capable of decomposing AgBr? [*Answer:* λ ~ 12,000 A.]   Why is photographic film sensitive to visible light but not to radio waves?

34.21. After publication of Einstein's suggestion of the photon model, various individuals tried to preserve the older conceptions by proposing modifications of classical theory. Among these efforts was one by J. J. Thomson [*Proc. Camb. Phil. Soc.*, **XIV**, 417 (1907)]. Thomson suggested that electromagnetic energy might be unevenly distributed over the wave front with regions of maximum energy relatively widely separated by areas of low or zero disturbance. This hypothesis led to the suggestion that at extremely low light intensities, when only a few maximum-energy regions would be present on any given wave front, ordinary diffraction patterns formed by slits or shadows of small obstacles might be modified in an observable way, perhaps by a fuzzing out of the pattern. The experiment was performed by G. I. Taylor [*Proc. Camb. Phil. Soc.*, **XVI**, 114 (1909)]:

"Photographs were taken of the shadow of a needle, the source of light being a narrow slit placed in front of a gas flame. The intensity of the light was reduced by means of smoked glass screens. ... The longest time [of exposure with very weak light] was 2000 hours or about 3 months. In no case was there any diminution in the sharpness of the pattern. . . . The amount of energy falling on one square cm of the plate is 5×10^{-6} erg/sec, and on the amount of energy per cubic cm of this radiation is 1.6×10^{-16} erg."

(a) Show that, from the point of view of Einstein's model, the given energy flux of 5×10^{-6} erg/cm$^2 \cdot$ sec corresponds to about 10^6 photons of visible light/cm$^2 \cdot$ sec (taking the average energy per photon to be about 2 or 3 ev).

(b) Show that this flux of photons implies that the average distance of separation between individual photons is of the order of 300 m. With an apparatus of the order of 1 m in length, it is extremely unlikely that more than one photon is present in the system at any one time! With modern counting equipment and photomultiplier tube detectors, Taylor's experiment can be repeated without waiting three months for a photographic exposure. All such experiments confirm his results. For example, a two-slit interference pattern formed by an intense beam of light is identical with one formed by light so weak that *only one photon* is likely to be passing through the slit system at one time. Closing either one of the two slits eliminates the interference pattern. What do you infer from the fact that an interference pattern is still formed under conditions of extremely weak illumination? How can the two slits be effective in producing an interference pattern when only one photon arrives at a time? [Do not expect to give or receive a pat answer to this question; the problem being posed lies at the heart of "modern" physics.]

SUPPLEMENTARY READING AND STUDY

On crystals in general:
  Crystals and Light, E. A. Wood. Princeton, N.J.: Van Nostrand Momentum Book No. 5, 1964

On X-ray spectra and diffraction:
  Physics of the Atom, M. R. Wehr and J. A. Richards. Reading, Mass.: Addison-Wesley, 1960, Chapter 6
  Introduction to Modern Physics, fifth edition, F. K. Richtmyer, E. H. Kennard, and T. Lauritsen. New York: McGraw-Hill, 1955, Chapter 8

On the quantum hypothesis and photoelectric effect:
  Physics of the Atom, op. cit., Chapter 3
  Introduction to Modern Physics, op. cit., Chapter 3
  Foundations of Modern Physical Science, G. Holton and D. H. D. Roller. Reading, Mass.: Addison-Wesley, 1958, Chapters 31, 32
  "Resource Letter QSL–1 on Quantum and Statistical Aspects of Light," P. Carruthers. *Am. J. Phys.*, **31**, 221 (1963)

CHAPTER 35

The Early Theory of Atomic Structure

35.1   INTRODUCTION

Among the products of imaginative inquiry into the laws of nature is the modern quantum theory—a theory that appears capable of accounting for the structure of atoms and molecules as well as their physical and chemical properties. We shall not be able to follow the evolution of quantum theory all the way to its present-day level of mathematical abstractness and complexity, but we can easily penetrate its first, semiempirical state of development and catch some glimpses of its implications and of its sharp break with classical physical ideas. In its early stages, with a greatly oversimplified model of atomic structure and an essentially heuristic view of the inter-action between light and matter, the theory yielded incomplete but nevertheless impressively fruitful results; and in its partial success it invited further elaboration and modification, pointed to those classical conceptions that would have to be altered or abandoned, and adumbrated the character of the new ideas that would replace the classical models.

In following this development we shall see how at least some of the puzzling questions we have raised in preceding chapters began to be resolved—in particular the Rydberg formula for the bright lines of the spectrum of atomic hydrogen (Section 27.8) and the connection between bright-line spectra and the structure of atoms.

35.2   SIGNIFICANCE OF h AS AN ATOMIC CONSTANT

In the years between 1905 and 1913, as physicists gradually became aware of the implications of the quantum ideas advanced by Planck and Einstein, it came to be recognized that the constant

$$h = 6.63 \times 10^{-34}\,\text{j} \cdot \text{sec}$$

must have a universal significance on the atomic scale—as do constants such as e, the fundamental quantum of electric charge, and m, the electronic mass.

It was noted, for example, that h has the dimensions ML^2/T, which are the dimensions of angular momentum. (See Sections 5.10 and 17.15 if review of basic concepts is required.) In 1912 the astrophysicist J. W. Nicholson of Trinity College,

Cambridge, influenced by Rutherford's recent proposal of the nuclear model, attempted to explain certain bright lines of the spectrum of the solar corona by means of an atomic model in which a ring of uniformly spaced electrons revolved around a positively charged nucleus.* In one of his calculations he noted that the total angular momentum of the ring of electrons came out to be about $25h$, and remarked:

> "If, therefore, the constant h of Planck has, as Sommerfeld has suggested, an atomic significance, it may mean that the angular momentum of an atom can only rise or fall by discrete amounts when electrons leave or return. It is readily seen that this view presents less difficulty to the mind than the more usual interpretation, which is believed to involve an atomic constitution of energy itself."

Nicholson was apparently very reluctant to accept Einstein's radical photon concept, and was trying to preserve as much as possible of the classical conception. His atomic model was not very successful, but his suggestion concerning discrete changes in angular momentum was to have further repercussions.

Another qualitative insight into the significance of h came from analysis of dimensions. As we have seen above,

$$h \text{ has dimensions } ML^2/T. \tag{35.2.1}$$

From Coulomb's law we note that the quantity ke^2 has the dimensions of force $\times$ length^2; therefore

$$ke^2 \text{ has dimensions } ML^3/T^2. \tag{35.2.2}$$

If we finally introduce the electronic mass m, we note that the combination

$$\frac{h^2}{mke^2} \text{ has dimensions } \left(\frac{ML^2}{T}\right)^2 \times \frac{T^2}{M^2L^3} = L. \tag{35.2.3}$$

That is, a quantity having dimensions of length has been deliberately constructed out of a combination of the fundamental atomic constants h, m, and e. If we substitute the appropriate numerical values, we find that

$$\frac{h^2}{mke^2} \sim 20 \text{ A}, \tag{35.2.4}$$

a length that is of the general order of magnitude of atomic dimensions! This lends further support to the speculation that h might have some connection with atomic structure.

PROBLEM 35.1.   (a) Substitute the mks values of h, m, k, and e into h^2/mke^2, and verify the numerical result quoted in Eq. (35.2.4). (b) Try to concoct a combination that has the dimensions of energy.

---

* *Monthly Notices Roy. Astron. Soc.*, **72**, 677 (1912).

Dimensional arguments and order-of-magnitude calculations such as the ones just illustrated frequently play an important role in the detective work of scientific research. In this instance they influenced the thinking of Niels Henrik David Bohr (1885–1962), a young Danish physicist who came to work with J. J. Thomson at Cambridge in 1911 and spent a year with Rutherford at Manchester in 1912–13. Bohr's first attempt at a quantum theory of atomic structure appeared in three issues of *Philosophical Magazine*, in July, September, and November of 1913* (Fig. 35.2.1).

FIG. 35.2.1. Niels Bohr (1885–1962). Photograph by H. &. H. Jacobsen, Copenhagen. Courtesy of *Physics Today*.

35.3   THE NUCLEAR MODEL AND THE QUANTUM HYPOTHESIS†

Bohr points to various ideas that moulded his line of thought by indicating that Rutherford's nuclear model "seems to be necessary in order to account for the results of the experiments on large-angle scattering of α-rays." He recognizes that, in such a model, classical theory requires that a revolving electron radiate electromagnetic energy:

".. . the electron will approach the nucleus, describing orbits of smaller and smaller dimensions, and with greater and greater frequency, the electron on the average gaining in kinetic energy at the same time as the whole system loses energy.** The process will go on until the dimensions of the orbit are of the same order of magnitude as the dimensions of the electron or those of the nucleus. A simple calculation shows that the energy radiated out during the process considered will be enormously great compared with that radiated out by ordinary molecular processes.

"It is obvious that the behavior of such a system will be very different from that of an atomic system occurring in nature. In the first place the actual atoms

---

* *Phil. Mag.*, **26**, 1; 476; 857 (1913).

† In this and the following sections we shall present Bohr's theory not precisely in its original sequence, but as a synthesis of the concepts evolved, clarified, and restated in Bohr's early papers. Bohr's notation will be changed to correspond to that used in this text.

** See Problem 18.18.

in their permanent state seem to have absolutely fixed dimensions and frequencies. Further, if we consider any molecular process, the results always seem to be that after a certain amount of energy characteristic for the systems in question is radiated out, the systems will again settle down in a stable state of equilibrium, in which the distances apart of the particles are of the same order of magnitude as before the process. . . .

"The way of considering a problem of this kind has, however, undergone essential alterations in recent years owing to the development of the [quantum theory of electromagnetic] radiation, and the direct affirmation of the new assumptions introduced in this theory, found by experiments on very different phenomena such as specific heats, photoelectric effect, Roentgen rays, etc. The result of the discussion of these questions seems to be the general acknowledgment of the inadequacy of the classical electrodynamics in describing the behavior of systems of atomic size. Whatever the alteration in the laws of motion of electrons may be, it seems necessary to introduce in the laws in question a quantity foreign to the classical electrodynamics; i.e., Planck's constant, or as it is often called, the elementary quantum of action. By the introduction of this quantity the question of the stable configuration of the electrons in the atoms is essentially changed, as this constant is of such dimensions and magnitude that it, together with the mass and charge of the particles, can determine a length of the order of magnitude required." [See Eq. (35.2.4).]

With this background of motivation, Bohr suggested a direct application of Einstein's photon hypothesis in the following manner:

(1) Abandon classical electrodynamics to the extent of assuming that at radii of atomic dimensions (order of several A) electrons can revolve in stable orbits *without* continuously radiating energy in the form of electromagnetic waves. Then, for example, with an electron in a circular orbit of radius r_1, the system of electron and nucleus would possess a fixed total energy $E(r_1)$ [see Problem 18.18]. The system is assumed to gain or lose energy *only* when electrons are transferred from one stable orbit or 'stationary state' to another. Thus if the electron is transferred to another orbit, r_2, the system must change energy by the amount $E(r_2) - E(r_1)$; the change corresponds to an absorption or emission of energy, depending on whether r_2 is greater than r_1 or less than r_1, respectively.

(2) Invoking Einstein's heuristic model, assume that electromagnetic radiation is absorbed or emitted in *transfer* of electrons from one orbit to another, and that such absorption and emission of energy by individual electrons is associated with absorption or emission of individual photons or radiation quanta of energy $h\nu$—as suggested by Einstein's heuristic explanation of the photoelectric effect. As in Einstein's theory, the law of conservation of energy is *not* to be abandoned, and it is required that

$$|E(r_2) - E(r_1)| = h\nu, \tag{35.3.1}$$

with the photon being emitted if $E(r_2) < E(r_1)$ or absorbed if $E(r_2) > E(r_1)$.

PROBLEM 35.2.   Interpret Eq. (35.3.1): Note, for example, that if this relation is valid, the frequency of absorbed or emitted radiation depends on the size of the energy "jump" between orbits and is *not* directly related to a frequency of revolution of the electron in an orbit.   What does classical theory say about frequency of radiation that should be emitted by a revolving electron?

PROBLEM 35.3.   We know it to be an experimental fact that the absorption and emission spectra of gases are *discrete* rather than continuous; i.e., only certain particular frequencies ν are observed.   If we try to couple this observed fact with the assumption embodied in Eq. (35.3.1), what seems to be implied concerning the radii of possible electron orbits?

35.4   DISCRETE ELECTRON ORBITS IN THE HYDROGEN ATOM

We indicated many times in preceding chapters that, regardless of other ramifications, a theory of atomic structure would be expected to have a close connection with bright-line absorption and emission spectra of gases, since all available evidence indicated that these spectra and their observed regularities are connected with the dynamical behavior of electrically charged particles in the atomic structure.   Furthermore, the simplest known spectrum is that of atomic hydrogen, consisting of series of lines described by the empirically discovered Balmer-Rydberg formula discussed in Section 27.8 [Eqs. (27.8.1) and (27.8.2)]:

$$\frac{1}{\lambda} = R_{\mathrm{H}} \left(\frac{1}{n_f^2} - \frac{1}{n_i^2} \right) \tag{35.4.1}$$

or, since $c = \lambda\nu$,

$$\nu = cR_{\mathrm{H}} \left(\frac{1}{n_f^2} - \frac{1}{n_i^2} \right). \tag{35.4.2}$$

If we multiply both sides of (35.4.2) by h and invoke Bohr's postulate, Eq. (35.3.1), we have the following statement:

$$h\nu = |E(r_f) - E(r_i)| = hcR_{\mathrm{H}} \left| \frac{1}{n_f^2} - \frac{1}{n_i^2} \right|. \tag{35.4.3}$$

Since only certain discrete frequencies ν are observed in the hydrogen spectrum, Eq. (35.4.3) implies that only certain discrete energy values or "levels" $E(r)$ are possible in the structure of the hydrogen atom.   How should one visualize this structure?   "General evidence indicates," wrote Bohr, "that an atom of hydrogen consists simply of a single electron rotating round a positive nucleus of charge e.   [This conclusion] is strongly supported by the fact that hydrogen, in the experiments on positive rays of Sir J. J. Thomson, is the only element which never occurs with a positive charge corresponding to the loss of more than one electron."

If, following Bohr's first analysis, we visualize the single electron as revolving in simple circular orbits around a massive nucleus of equal positive charge, we have from Problem 18.18 the total energy at any radius r:

$$E(r) = -\frac{ke^2}{2r}.\quad*$$ (35.4.4)

(The nucleus of the hydrogen atom, a particle with well-established charge-to-mass ratio and certain other properties, is called a *proton*.) If only discrete energy levels E_n are "allowed," it follows that the electron can occupy only certain discrete orbits or stationary states, with radii r_n satisfying the relation

$$E_n = -\frac{ke^2}{2r_n}.$$ (35.4.5)

Also, since each of the two terms on the right-hand side of Eq. (35.4.3) must be a quantity of energy, it is suggested that any particular energy level E_n might be related to the empirical Rydberg constant R_H by the equation

$$E_n = -\frac{hcR_H}{n^2},$$ (35.4.6)

where n is an integer: 1, 2, 3, ...

Recall that, in setting up the description of quantities of energy associated with the system in which one particle revolves around the other, we chose as a convenient zero reference level the condition of infinite separation between the particles. We must make sure that Eq. (35.4.6) is consistent with our earlier choice of the zero level. In Eq. (35.4.6), E_n becomes more positive as n increases; E_n tends toward zero as n becomes indefinitely large. Increasing values of n thus seem to be correlated directly with increasing values of radial separation r, and infinite separation corresponds to infinite n, without contradiction of our original choice of zero reference level. We can establish this correlation formally by combining Eqs. (35.4.5) and (35.4.6), and obtain

$$\frac{ke^2}{2r_n} = \frac{hcR_H}{n^2},$$

$$r_n = n^2\frac{ke^2}{2hcR_H}.$$ (35.4.7)

According to Bohr's hypothesis, the stationary state with $n = 1$, having the smallest allowed radius and the lowest (most negative) energy level, would be the "normal," "unexcited" state of the hydrogen atom. Under bombardment of elec-

---

* In arriving at this equation, we used the classical dynamical concepts of $F = ma$ and of kinetic and potential energy. We also implicitly assumed that the position, velocity, and centripetal acceleration of the electron could be continuously described in complete detail from instant to instant. In this context Bohr felt compelled to make very clear what aspects of classical theory he retained and what aspects he abandoned: "[It is assumed] that the dynamical equilibrium of the systems in the stationary states can be discussed by the help of ordinary mechanics, while the passing of the systems between different stationary states cannot be treated on that basis."

trons in a discharge tube or absorption of photons of incident radiation, the electron might be transferred to outer orbits with larger values of n, thus increasing the "size" of the absorbing atom and leaving it in an excited state. An electron in an excited state would tend to return to lower energy levels by emission of photons of radiation, ending up at $n = 1$, frequently referred to as the *ground state* of the atom.

To complete the solution of the problem, it is then necessary to discover some rational way of identifying the allowed orbits r_n. This in turn might lead to an expression for R_H in terms of known atomic constants; i.e., a theoretical prediction of the value of R_H which can be compared with the empirically known value, thus effecting a test of the entire theory.

35.5   ALLOWED ORBITS AND THE CORRESPONDENCE PRINCIPLE

Perhaps Bohr's most distinctive contribution to the theory we are describing was his discovery of an appropriate quantization rule—a way of specifying the allowed orbits or stationary states of the atom. This was achieved by a simple but subtle line of inductive reasoning: Since classical electrodynamics was known to yield valid and correct results for electrical charges accelerated along paths of macroscopic dimensions (oscillating electrical charges in sparks or radio antennae acted as sources of radio waves exactly as predicted by the classical Maxwellian theory), Bohr sought to formulate the new theory in such a way that it would merge continuously into classical theory as the electron moved out to very large orbits. That is, at very large values of n, when the electron moves in an orbit of macroscopic size, it must radiate very nearly classically, emitting frequencies of radiation essentially equal to the frequency f_n of orbital revolution. This requirement that quantum theory yield the same results as classical theory in the limit in which classical theory is known to be valid is frequently referred to as the *correspondence principle*.

Let us formulate an algebraic statement of the correspondence principle for the particular case of large circular electron orbits in the hydrogen atom (Fig. 35.5.1).

Since the Coulomb force imparts centripetal acceleration $r_n\omega_n^2$ to the electron (see Problem 9.18), we have the relation

$$\frac{ke^2}{r_n^2} = mr_n\omega_n^2, \qquad (35.5.1)$$

where m is the electron mass. Since the angular velocity

$$\omega_n = 2\pi f_n,$$

where f_n is the frequency of orbital revolution, we obtain

$$f_n^2 = \frac{ke^2}{4\pi^2 mr_n^3}. \qquad (35.5.2)$$

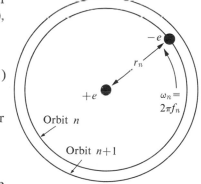

FIG. 35.5.1.   Successive large orbits corresponding to n and $n + 1$ in an H atom (n is, say, of the order of 100).

Substituting the expression for r_n in Eq. (35.4.7) into (35.5.2) gives

$$f_n^2 = \frac{1}{n^6} \frac{8h^3 c^3 R_H^3}{4\pi^2 m(ke^2)^2} .$$

(35.5.3)

PROBLEM 35.4.   Fill in the algebraic steps leading from Eq. (35.5.1) to (35.5.3).

The frequency of the photon emitted when the electron jumps from orbit $n + 1$ to orbit n is given by

$$\nu = \frac{E_{n+1} - E_n}{h} .$$

(35.5.4)

Let us examine the behavior of the energy difference $E_{n+1} - E_n$ as n becomes large. From Eq. (35.4.6), we have that $E_n = -hcR_H/n^2$, and therefore

$$\frac{E_{n+1} - E_n}{h} = cR_H\left[-\frac{1}{(n + 1)^2} + \frac{1}{n^2} \right] = cR_H\left[\frac{2n + 1}{(n + 1)^2 n^2} \right].$$

(35.5.5)

As n becomes large, the quantity $+1$ in the right-hand term of Eq. (35.5.5) becomes negligible, and the term in the brackets is more and more nearly equal to $2/n^3$. Thus, as n becomes large,

$$\nu = \frac{E_{n+1} - E_n}{h} \to cR_H \frac{2}{n^3} .$$

(35.5.6)

PROBLEM 35.5.   Note that the quantity $2cR_H/n^3$ appearing in Eq. (35.5.6) is equal to $1/h$ times the derivative of E_n with respect to n, where E_n is given by Eq. (35.4.6). Is this identity an accident or is there a fundamental connection between the two calculations? Explain your answer in some detail; do not ignore the fact that n represents successive *integers* and has no physical significance as a continuously variable quantity.

From Eq. (35.5.6) we see that the frequency of photons emitted in electron jumps between adjacent orbits at large n becomes more and more nearly equal to $2cR_H/n^3$. The correspondence principle demands that this frequency become more and more nearly equal to the *orbital* frequency f_n of revolution of the electron; that is, we require that

$$\nu \to f_n \text{ as } n \text{ becomes large.}$$

(35.5.7)

This suggests that we introduce the requirement that

$$f_n = \frac{2cR_H}{n^3} .$$

(35.5.8)

Then condition (35.5.7) will be automatically satisfied, and Eq. (35.5.8) becomes our means for introducing the correspondence principle formally into our algebraic derivation.

In Eqs. (35.5.3) and (35.5.8), we have two simultaneous equations in f_n and R_H. Eliminating f_n by substituting the latter into the former, we obtain

$$R_H = \frac{2\pi^2 m (ke^2)^2}{ch^3}. \tag{35.5.9}$$

Thus by introducing the correspondence principle we have established R_H entirely in terms of known universal constants! Now, having R_H, we can substitute it into (35.4.6) and (35.4.7) and evaluate both the allowed energy levels E_n and the allowed orbits r_n:

$$E_n = -\frac{2\pi^2 m (ke^2)^2}{n^2 h^2}, \tag{35.5.10}$$

$$r_n = n^2 \frac{h^2}{4\pi^2 mke^2}. \tag{35.5.11}$$

[Compare this result with the dimensional analysis calculation made in Eqs. (35.2.3, 4)!]

A remarkably simple result emerges when we evaluate the orbital angular momentum L_n for any allowed level

$$L_n = mr_n^2 \omega_n = 2\pi mr_n^2 f_n.$$

Substituting for r_n and f_n, the resulting expression reduces to

$$L_n = n\frac{h}{2\pi} \quad \text{or} \quad mr_n^2 \omega_n = n\frac{h}{2\pi}. \tag{35.5.12}$$

PROBLEM 35.6. Write out the algebraic steps that lead to Eqs. (35.5.9, 10, 11, 12); verify the stated results.

In the light of Eq. (35.5.12), which is by far the simplest relation that has emerged, we can say that application of the correspondence principle has led us to the result that angular momentum of allowed electron orbits is *quantized*; i.e., it can only have values that are integral multiples of $h/2\pi$; that is, the angular momentum of the electron can change by quanta or units of $h/2\pi$ in transitions from one stationary state to another. The quantity $h/2\pi$ is frequently denoted by the symbol $\hbar$, and is referred to as the *natural unit of angular momentum*. Bohr arrived at this quantization rule inductively by something like the process of reasoning we have outlined above, and then turned around and made it one of the primary postulates of his theory.

PROBLEM 35.7. Indicate some respects in which Nicholson's guess about the role of h in atomic structure (see quotation in Section 35.2) differs from the implications of Eq. (35.5.12) and from other aspects of Bohr's model.

PROBLEM 35.8. Review the preceding sections and assemble a list which summarizes in your own words all the assumptions or postulates which have been introduced into the Bohr theory as we have outlined it up to this point.

PROBLEM 35.9.   Instead of following the sequence of analysis used in this section, let us derive the final expressions for E_n and r_n [Eqs. (35.5.10, 11)] in an alternative way: Start with the quantization of angular momentum [Eq. (35.5.12)] as one of the primary postulates of the theory. Then introduce the other postulates, including that of photon absorption and emission in transitions between stationary states; introduce Eqs. (35.5.1) and (35.4.5) and derive expressions (35.5.10, 11) for E_n and r_n as well as the Rydberg formula, in the form

$$\frac{1}{\lambda} = \frac{2\pi^2 m(ke^2)^2}{ch^3}\left(\frac{1}{n_f^2} - \frac{1}{n_i^2}\right). \tag{35.5.13}$$

Show that the results satisfy the correspondence principle. (In the papers which followed his very first publication on the subject, Bohr usually presented his theory in the sequence outlined in this problem.)

35.6   INTERPRETATION OF THE HYDROGEN ATOM MODEL

Let us summarize the theoretical results obtained up to this point:

Radii of allowed orbits or stationary states:

$$r_n = n^2 \frac{h^2}{4\pi^2 mke^2} \tag{35.6.1}$$

$$= 0.52 \times 10^{-10} n^2, \quad \text{meters.}$$

Energy levels of stationary states:

$$E_n = -\frac{2\pi^2 m(ke^2)^2}{n^2 h^2}$$

$$= \frac{-21.76 \times 10^{-19}}{n^2}, \quad \text{joules.} \tag{35.6.2}$$

Wavelengths of photons emitted or absorbed in transitions between stationary states:

$$\frac{1}{\lambda} = \frac{2\pi^2 m(ke^2)^2}{ch^3}\left(\frac{1}{n_f^2} - \frac{1}{n_i^2}\right)$$

$$= 1.097 \times 10^7 \left(\frac{1}{n_f^2} - \frac{1}{n_i^2}\right), \quad \text{meters}^{-1}. \tag{35.6.3}$$

The integers denoted by n are referred to as *quantum numbers*.

PROBLEM 35.10.   Substituting the known values of h, e, m, k, c in mks units, verify the numerical results asserted in Eqs. (35.6.1, 2, 3). Compare Eq. (35.6.3) with the empirical formula given in Section 27.8.

Equation (35.6.1) yields the theoretical prediction that hydrogen atoms in the ground state ($n = 1$) should have an effective diameter of about 1.0×10^{-8} cm or 1 A. This result is in good agreement with atomic dimensions from entirely independent experimental data and interpretations.

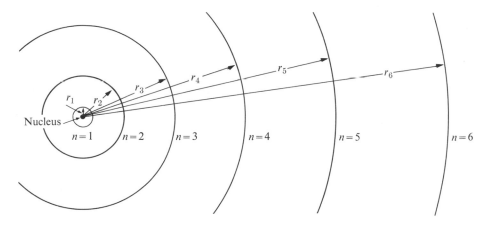

FIG. 35.6.1. Radii of the first few allowed orbits of the hydrogen atom as represented by Eq. (35.6.1).

It is not surprising that Eq. (35.6.3) should have the algebraic form of the Rydberg formula—recall how the latter was used to establish the pattern of the semiempirical analysis in Section 35.4—but a new level of insight has nevertheless been attained. The Rydberg constant R_{II}, which had hitherto been known only as a purely empirical, spectroscopic quantity, is now expressed in terms of universal constants m, e, h, and c, and its calculated value in Eq. (35.6.3) agrees to four significant figures with the spectroscopic value cited in Section 27.8!

Thus Bohr's model, although invoking radical departures from classical physical theory in the domain of atomic dimensions, provides a rational and coherent account of the various series of discrete lines in the spectrum of atomic hydrogen. The account is given in terms of an array of fundamental concepts that have played a role in helping clarify other physical phenomena such as cathode rays, α-particle scattering, photoelectric effect, etc. The success of this new juxtaposition of the concepts strengthens one's faith in their validity and at the same time leads one to regard the new theory as offering some measure of "explanation" of atomic structure and the origin of bright-line spectra.

Let us analyze the more detailed information contained in the cryptic equations summarized above. Equation (35.6.1) indicates that the allowed or quantized orbits of the electron form a pattern such as that illustrated in Fig. 35.6.1. The unexcited or ground state corresponds to orbit r_1 with a radius of 0.52 A, while the fifth level, for example, corresponds to an orbit with $r_5 = 25(0.52) = 13.0$ A. Bohr's model implies that electrons of an unexcited atom are transferred from orbit r_1 to larger orbits by absorption of energy—such energy perhaps being supplied by complex collision mechanisms in an electrical discharge, or by energetic molecular collisions associated with heating the gas to extremely high temperatures, or by absorption of photons of appropriate frequency from a beam of light traversing the gas. Electrons that have absorbed energy and have been "kicked" to outer orbits then "jump" back to inner ones, emitting photons of different energies, depending on the jump that

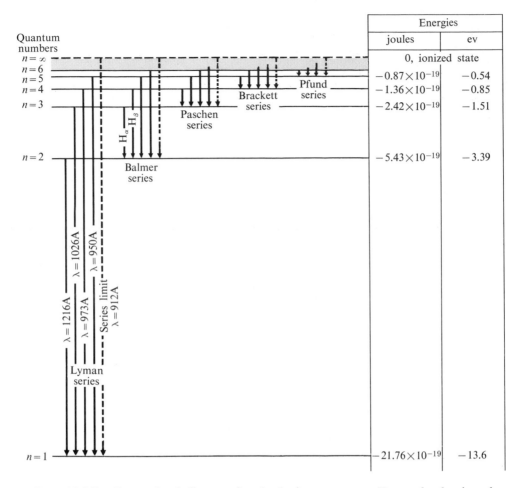

FIG. 35.6.2.   Energy level diagram for the hydrogen atom.   Energy levels given by Eq. (35.6.2).

occurs. The rudimentary theory we are presenting explicitly eschews any attempt to describe a "mechanism" for the transition of electrons from one orbit to another, or for the emission and absorption of photons. Questions regarding detailed aspects of interaction between charged particles and electromagnetic quanta (photons) were left for a much later and far more advanced inquiry.

Equation (35.6.2) gives the energy corresponding to each one of the allowed orbits, and these quantized or allowed levels are shown on an energy-level diagram, in which energy value, rather than orbital radius, is plotted along the vertical co-ordinate (Fig. 35.6.2). The energy levels get closer together as the orbits increase in size. Note that the ground state or lowest energy level is 21.76×10^{-19} j below the zero energy level associated with $n = \infty$, or infinite separation between electron and proton. (Infinite separation implies an ionized atom.) This energy corresponds to

$$\frac{21.76 \times 10^{-19}}{1.60 \times 10^{-19}} = 13.6 \text{ ev}$$

It is well established through direct experimental measurement that the ionization potential of the hydrogen atom is 13.6 v. (Ionization potentials can be found by measuring the potential difference through which electrons must be accelerated to produce substantial ionization of the gas in question. See Section 34.13 and Problem 34.16 for a review of this concept.)

Figure 35.6.2 gives an interpretation of the Rydberg formula, Eq. (35.6.3), for the wavelengths of the emitted spectral lines. Each line corresponds to a transition between two particular energy levels. The Lyman series is formed by jumps from various higher levels to the ground state, with $n_f = 1$. The Balmer series corresponds to jumps from higher levels to the second allowed level, with $n_f = 2$, etc.

Arrows showing jumps from orbit to orbit might also be superposed on Fig. 35.6.1 to illustrate the origin of the Lyman, Balmer, and other series of spectral lines. (Sketch a few such arrows to make sure you understand what is meant by this statement.) We shall not present such a diagram here, however, and our intention is to emphasize the following point: Despite the apparent success of the proposed model, it is a mistake to take it too *literally*—a mistake to insist that the electron must indeed be traveling in clearly defined circular orbits, a planet around a sun. The orbits invoked in our model are associated with the application of the Newtonian laws of motion and represent a fragment of classical physics arbitrarily retained in a context in which other classical conceptions have been abandoned.

It may be argued that the results of the theory are in striking agreement with observation, but let us remember that the observations do not deal directly with paths of motion of the electron; they concern only such *indirectly* observed properties as effective atomic size, total ionization energy, and differences between accessible energy levels (corresponding to discrete spectral lines). It is entirely conceivable that the detailed description of the behavior of the electron in the atom is very different from that assumed in the model, even though the model yields some correct end results.

As a matter of fact, as the theory was developed further it was found that not only was the visualization of circular orbits too great an oversimplification, but an extension to admit elliptical orbits was also inadequate. It proved necessary to develop a new mechanics, to abandon Bohr's initial attempt to retain a fragment of the older theory, and finally to accept the uncomfortable notion that it is *in principle* impossible to render a detailed description of a point-by-point, instant-by-instant orbital motion of the electron. In the modern quantum theory one is reconciled to a description that classifies, by means of integer numbers, the energy levels or steady states available to the electron, and describe its positions in any energy state only in terms of a fuzzy, statistical distribution in space rather than in terms of a sharply defined orbital path.

PROBLEM 35.11.   In the light of the preceding remarks, it is clear that Fig. 35.6.1 should be regarded only as a representation of the results of the simple model we have invoked rather than as a literal representation of the behavior of an electron in a hydrogen atom.   The representation does, however, agree with the overall "effective" atomic size at various energy levels.   These orders of magnitude will be useful in later discussions.   By use of a compass or a ruler, check whether the various orbits in Fig. 35.6.1 have all been drawn to the same scale, or whether the picture has been distorted.

PROBLEM 35.12.   In Chapter 31 we accepted the plausible hypothesis that the corpuscle or quantum of electrical charge (1.60×10^{-19} coul) as determined in Millikan's oil-drop experiments is a universal entity, and that this amount of charge is carried by the frequently observed particles (electrons) having $e/m = 1.76 \times 10^{11}$ coul/kg.   In no instance up to this point, however, have we been able to make a direct check of the latter hypothesis because we have encountered no cases (involving electrons) in which the numbers e and m appeared in our equations in any combination other than the already known ratio e/m.   What can be said about this hypothesis in the light of Eqs. (35.6.1, 2, 3) and the results described in this section?   Explain your reasoning carefully.   (See Problem 34.8.)

PROBLEM 35.13.   If a completely ionized hydrogen atom (a proton) captures an electron, it is conceivable that the latter may cascade toward the nucleus by transitions from one allowed energy level to the next one below it.   In such a case, what lines of the complete hydrogen spectrum would be emitted in the last four jumps?   (Larger jumps are, of course, perfectly possible, as illustrated in Fig. 35.6.2.)   What experimental evidence would you cite to support the view that, in the case of the hydrogen atom, the electron does *not* undergo transitions to an energy level at the nucleus; i.e., to a level with $n < 1$?

PROBLEM 35.14.   (a) It is observed experimentally that a line with $\lambda = 9500$ A exists in one of the spectral series of hydrogen.   Identify in Fig. 35.6.2 the transition associated with this line.

(b) In the numerology of line spectra it was known that the sum of the frequencies of the first Lyman line and the first Balmer line was equal to the frequency of the second Lyman line.   How is this explained in Fig. 35.6.2?   Point out some other analogous combinations.

35.7   THE SPECTRUM OF SINGLY IONIZED HELIUM

In 1896 the American astronomer E. C. Pickering had observed in the spectra of distant stars a series of lines very much like those of the hydrogen spectrum. The wavelengths of these lines satisfied the empirical formula:

$$\frac{1}{\lambda} = R_{\mathrm{H}} \left[\frac{1}{(n_f/2)^2} - \frac{1}{(n_i/2)^2} \right]. \tag{35.7.1}$$

This is a formula of the Rydberg type [Eqs. (27.8.2) and (35.6.3)], containing the constant R_{H} but differing from the original Rydberg formula in the utilization of half-integer numbers in the brackets.   As Bohr remarked in a later reminiscence: "These lines were therefore generally ascribed to hydrogen and were even thought by Rydberg to remove the apparent contrast between the simplicity of the hydrogen spectrum and the complexity of the spectra of other elements, including those of [sodium, potassium, etc.] whose structure comes nearest the hydrogen spectrum. This view was also upheld by the eminent spectroscopist A. Fowler who [in 1912], in laboratory experiments with discharges through a mixture of hydrogen and helium gas, had observed the Pickering lines. . . ."

In his first paper of 1913 Bohr pointed out that with the help of his proposed theory ". . . we can account naturally for these series of lines if we ascribe them to helium. A neutral atom of the latter element consists, according to Rutherford's theory, of a positive nucleus of charge $2e$ and two electrons." If we consider a singly ionized helium atom—one with a nuclear charge of $+2e$ and a single orbital electron—we are confronted with a hydrogenlike atom to which the entire analysis of the preceding sections applies *in toto*, except that wherever we have the expression ke^2 we should replace it with $2ke^2$ [since, by Coulomb's law, the force between the He nucleus and its single electron would be given by $k(2e)e/r^2$ and the total energy of the system by $E = -2ke^2/2r$].

As a result, Eq. (35.6.3) would be modified to become

$$\frac{1}{\lambda} = \frac{2\pi^2 m(2ke^2)^2}{ch^3}\left(\frac{1}{n_f^2} - \frac{1}{n_i^2}\right),\tag{35.7.2}$$

and, by changing the position of the 2 in $(2ke^2)^2$, we obtain

$$\frac{1}{\lambda} = \frac{2\pi^2 m(ke^2)}{ch^3}\left(\frac{2^2}{n_f^2} - \frac{2^2}{n_i^2}\right) - R_H\left[\frac{1}{(n_f/2)^2} \quad \frac{1}{(n_i/2)^2}\right]\tag{35.7.3}$$

in complete agreement with the original empirical formula (35.7.1). Thus the Pickering lines can be completely explained in terms of energy transitions of the single remaining electron in the singly ionized helium atom He^+. (Note that certain lines of this spectrum must be identical with hydrogen lines. Identify several such overlaps.)

In support of this interpretation, Bohr pointed out that the lines were not detected in ordinary helium tubes but were observed in Fowler's experiments under conditions of *strong* electrical discharge, when some ionization of the initially neutral atoms was to be expected. Fowler was thus encouraged to perform experiments with very highly purified helium. Showing that the Pickering lines were still observed under strong discharge and in essentially complete absence of hydrogen, he provided further evidence for Bohr's interpretation and thus additional support for the entire theory.

Aside from the fact that the Pickering lines are beautifully and simply explained as being associated with He^+, it is interesting to note that Bohr was led to another deep and important objection to the view that these lines are associated with hydrogen. He pointed out that in using the helium model one retained the concept of integral quantum numbers n (the 2, as we saw, enters the equation because of the charge $2e$ on the helium nucleus, and not through the introduction of nonintegral quantum numbers). If the lines were to be associated with hydrogen, however, it would be necessary to admit quantum numbers such as $\frac{1}{2}$, $\frac{3}{2}$, etc., thus allowing angular momenta that are nonintegral multiples of $h/2\pi$ in Eq. (35.5.12). Introduction of nonintegral quantum numbers *would not satisfy the correspondence principle* invoked in Section 35.5, and Bohr regarded this as a very serious objection to what might otherwise have been a very reasonable interpretation.

PROBLEM 35.15.   The next element after helium in the periodic system is the alkali metal lithium. It is plausible to assume that it has a nucleus with a charge of $+3e$ and three electrons. The doubly ionized lithium atom Li^{++} would have one electron and therefore a hydrogenlike structure. Write down the equation analogous to (35.7.3) that would be expected to describe the spectral lines of Li^{++} and interpret it in some detail. These lines have been observed in stellar spectra.

35.8 NUMBER OF EMISSION LINES

At the time Bohr proposed his theory it had been noted that only the first 10 or 12 lines of the Balmer series could be observed in laboratory discharge tubes, while as many as 33 lines of this series had been detected in stellar spectra or in the corona of the sun. Bohr was able to turn this curious discrepancy to good account:

"[This] is just what we should expect from the above theory. According to Eq. (35.6.1), the diameter of the orbit of the electron in the different stationary states is proportional to n^2. For $n = 12$ the diameter is equal to 1.6×10^{-6} cm [160 A], or equal to the mean distance between molecules in a gas at a pressure of about 7 mm mercury.* For $n = 33$ the diameter is equal to 1.2×10^{-5} cm [1200 A], corresponding to the mean distance of molecules at a pressure of about 0.02 mm mercury. According to the theory the necessary condition for the appearance of a great number of lines is therefore a very small density of the gas; for simultaneously to obtain an intensity sufficient for observation, the space filled with gas must be very great."

This combined condition of very small density and enormous volume is fulfilled in a stellar atmosphere, and the higher frequency lines then have sufficient intensity to be observed.

PROBLEM 35.16.   (a) Suppose that the density of a gas is increased by a factor of 8; what is the change in the average spacing of the molecules? In general, what must be the functional relation between the density ρ and the average molecular spacing?

(b) If 12 Balmer lines are observed at a pressure of 7 mm, about how many lines would you expect to observe if the pressure in the tube is 56 mm? [*Answer:* About 8 or 9.]

---

* A pressure characteristic of a discharge tube. The electron apparently cannot, on the average, move out to larger radii without becoming involved in the interference of neighboring atoms.

35.9 ABSORPTION LINES

In Section 27.5 and 27.6, we described the experimental observation of absorption lines and Stokes' very qualitative resonance model of their origin. It was noted that any successful theory of the structure of atoms would have to account not only for the existence of absorption lines but also for the fact that, while all the lines of the absorption spectrum are to be found in emission, there exist many emission lines that do not appear in the absorption spectrum (see Fig. 27.5.1).

To explain these phenomena, Bohr introduced the plausible assumption that an orbital electron can absorb an incident photon only if the photon has precisely the right energy (and therefore frequency) to transfer the electron from one stationary quantum state to another. (Note that this is the quantum analog of Stokes' classical resonance model described in Section 27.6.)

Given nonluminous atomic hydrogen (all atoms in the ground state) irradiated with light having a continuous spectrum, one would expect that only photons in the Lyman series could be absorbed and that no absorption lines in the Balmer series would appear. (No photons in the Balmer series have enough energy to excite any of the Lyman transitions, even the first one. Verify this prediction by examining Fig. 35.6.2.) Balmer absorption lines would be expected only if the gas were already excited and contained very many atoms initially present in the $n = 2$ state.

Thus, in general, the absorption spectrum of hydrogen with atoms in the ground state will show only spectral lines associated with transitions from the ground state ($n = 1$) to higher levels, while the emission spectrum of the same gas will show many additional lines associated with transitions from higher levels to states such as $n = 2$ and $n = 3$.

In connection with absorption spectra it had also been observed experimentally that above a certain frequency of incident light (i.e., above a certain incident photon energy) the absorption becomes continuous instead of discrete—all incident frequencies being absorbed. This is readily explained by Bohr's model. The highest-energy photon of the Lyman series just barely ionizes the hydrogen atom; i.e., it removes the electron from level $n = 1$ to the level corresponding to $n = \infty$. Still higher energy photons supply more energy than is necessary for ionization, and might conceivably impart the extra energy to the free electron in the form of translational kinetic energy. The translational motion (infinite radius of orbit) is not quantized, according to the correspondence principle, and can take on a continuous range of values.

Thus it is plausible that *any* photon with energy higher than the ionization energy can be absorbed, part of its energy being used to ionize the atom and the residue being conserved in the KE of the ejected electron. Thus the model readily accounts for the observation of a continuous absorption spectrum above the ionization frequency; we have described the photoelectric effect in gases in terms of the new vocabulary!

> PROBLEM 35.17. Calculate the kinetic energy that would be imparted to an electron ejected from the ground state in an H atom by an absorbed photon having $\lambda = 760$ A. See Section 34.13 and Problem 34.15. [*Answer:* 2.7 ev or 4.3×10^{-19} j.]

35.10 PHYSICAL INTERPRETATION OF THE "ATOMIC NUMBER" OF A CHEMICAL ELEMENT

Near the beginning of his second paper on the atomic theory (*Philosophical Magazine*, September 1913), Bohr makes the following statement:

"The total experimental evidence supports the hypothesis that the actual number of electrons in a neutral atom . . . is equal to the number which indicates the position of the corresponding element in the series of elements arranged in order of increasing atomic weight [as in Mendeléev's periodic table].   For example on this view, the atom of oxygen, which is the eighth element of the series, has eight electrons and a nucleus carrying eight unit charges."

In support of this statement, Bohr cites a paper by a Dutch physicist, A. van der Broek, in the *Physikalische Zeitschrift* for January 1913.   Van der Broek carefully examined all the available chemical and physical evidence (including the chemical researches of Soddy and Hevesy on the properties and atomic weights of the radioactive elements; the X-ray scattering measurements of Barkla; Thomson's mass spectrometric investigations; the α-particle scattering experiments of Geiger and Marsden), and demonstrated that everything fell neatly into place under the above hypothesis.   Bohr had apparently had the same idea independently while he was first working out his theory in 1912 and 1913 but, on consulting Rutherford, had encountered a cautious and conservative response.*

Within a period of a few months in 1913, however, several of the leading investigators in the field of atomic physics converged in their views and accepted the idea that the atomic number is identical with the net number of corpuscles of positive charge on the nucleus.   It might be interesting to follow this episode (at least insofar as it comes to view in the published literature) to see how an idea of this kind sometimes emerges before the scientific community.

An important part of the public exchange took place in the weekly English magazine *Nature*, a journal which is very much alive and widely read today.   *Nature* publishes a wide range of material—relatively short technical papers announcing new scientific discoveries, articles about events and ideas related to science, professional news items, society affairs, book reviews, letters of discussion on various scientific subjects.   Many a fascinating argument and polemic can be found in its pages.   (An approximately equivalent American publication is the weekly journal *Science*, published by the American Association for the Advancement of Science.)

Van der Broek put his hypothesis before the English audience in a short letter to *Nature* on 27 November 1913.   Here he emphasized the fact that the Geiger and

---

* See Bohr's reminiscences of Rutherford in *Rutherford at Manchester*, edited by J. B. Birks. New York: W. A. Benjamin, Inc., 1963, pages 117, 118.

Marsden α-particle scattering data for different elements fell on a much better straight line if the number of scattered particles [y, defined in Eq. (33.13.1)] were plotted against the square of atomic number rather than against the square of atomic weight, all other variables being held constant.

PROBLEM 35.18.   Review the discussion of Section 33.13 and explain the point of van der Broek's remark in your own words.

Soddy, then at the University of Glasgow, responded with a letter published on 4 December:

"That the intra-atomic charge of an element is determined by its place in the periodic table rather than by its atomic weight, as concluded by van der Broek, is strongly supported by the recent generalization as to the radio-elements and the periodic law. The successive expulsion of one α and two β particles in three radioactive changes in any order brings the intra-atomic charge of the element back to its initial value, and the element back to its original place in the table, though its atomic mass is reduced by four units."

(Soddy then went on to discuss the question of whether the nucleus contains positive charges only or whether its positive charge is a net value, with some positive charge neutralized by the presence of a smaller number of negative charges. This is a question regarding the structure of the nucleus itself; the modern subject of nuclear physics was being born. We shall not pursue this inquiry in the present text. The form of the questions raised by Soddy and van der Broek underwent many changes in subsequent years, as a vast new field of research evolved.)

The 11 December issue of *Nature* carried a letter which was signed E. Rutherford, one paragraph of which reads:

". . . The original suggestion of van der Broek that the charge on the nucleus is equal to the atomic number and not to half the atomic weight seems to me very promising. The idea has already been used by Bohr in his theory of the constitution of atoms. The strongest and most convincing evidence in support of this hypothesis will be found in a paper by Moseley in *The Philosophical Magazine* of this month. He there shows that the frequency of the X-radiations from a number of elements can be simply explained if the number of unit charges on the nucleus is equal to the atomic number [see Section 35.12 below]. It would appear that the charge on the nucleus is the fundamental constant which determines the physical and chemical properties of the atom, while the atomic weight, although it approximately follows the order of the nucleus charge, is probably a complicated function of the latter depending on the detailed structure of the nucleus."

A claim of priority and a note of irritation between old coworkers is apparent in Soddy's response appearing on 18 December:

"... I wish to take exception to Prof. Rutherford's statement 'that the strongest and most convincing evidence' in support of van der Broek's hypothesis will be found in Moseley's paper. The view had already been far more simply and convincingly established from the chemical examination of the properties of the radio-elements, notably by A. Fleck in this laboratory [Glasgow]. Moseley's conclusions are a welcome confirmation, by an independent method, for another part of the periodic table. It can only be described as the strongest and most convincing evidence if the prior chemical evidence is altogether ignored."

35.11 SHELL STRUCTURE OF ATOMS WITH MORE THAN ONE ELECTRON

The next atom after hydrogen in the periodic system is helium. According to the picture we have developed, the neutral helium atom must consist of a nucleus with charge of $+2e$ and two orbital electrons. Dynamically this system is far more complicated than the hydrogen atom. Not only is each electron attracted by the nucleus; the two electrons also *repel each other*. Taking all these interactions into account, applying quantum conditions, and working out possible stable orbits become a rather difficult problem; the difficulty is compounded in the multiplicity of interactions present in still more complicated atoms. (Recall that similar problems enter the detailed calculations of planetary orbits in the solar system. In this case, however, the planets are relatively far apart, and their attractions for each other introduce only relatively small "perturbations" into orbits whose characteristics are determined principally by the interaction between any individual planet and the sun. In atoms, where electrons are relatively closer together, the interactions between electrons are much stronger and play a more significant role than the interactions between planets in the solar system.)

In full awareness of these problems, Bohr set out in his second and subsequent papers to see what could be said about the structure of more complicated atoms, using the periodic table as a guide. He concluded that the two electrons of helium occupied, in the ground state, similar orbits, classified in the $n = 1$ quantum level and with radii about $0.6a_0$, where a_0 denotes the ground state radius of hydrogen. For the next atom, lithium, he concluded that two electrons should occupy an "inner shell," again with $n = 1$ and with radius about $0.36a_0$, while the third electron should be outside this shell in an $n = 2$ quantum level at a radius of $1.2a_0$. The atoms from lithium to neon seemed to be built up in sequence, as illustrated in Fig. 35.11.1, with each additional electron going into the outer ($n = 2$) shell. At the element neon, with 10 electrons altogether, the outer shell contains 8 electrons, and neon has properties similar to helium; it is a noble gas, very inactive chemically and with high ionization potential. The next element, sodium, has an eleventh electron starting a third shell, classified as an $n = 3$ level, at a larger radius.

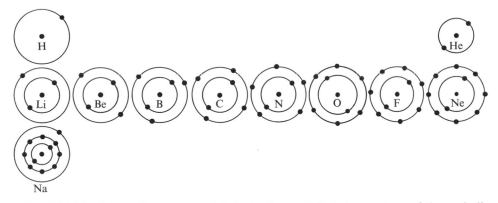

Na

FIG. 35.11.1. Schematic diagram of shell structures of first eleven atoms of the periodic system. The $n = 1$ shell is completed with 2 electrons, while the $n = 2$ shell is completed with 8 more. Filling of $n = 3$ shell begins with sodium. (Drawing is not to scale.)

We have seen in previous discussions (Chapters 28 and 29) that the elements H, Li, and Na are similar in chemical properties and behave as though they carry one unit of positive charge when their compounds are electrolyzed. This chemical and electrolytic behavior is consistent with the idea that one electron is lost to another atom when these monovalent elements enter chemical combination, and is restored when the elements are liberated. Furthermore, this behavior is consistent with the shell structure model, which indicates that each of the three different elements has a single outer electron that is relatively loosely bound. (Note that the outer electron is "held" by a force associated with only one unit of positive charge, since the effect of the rest of the nuclear charge is at least approximately canceled or screened by the inner electrons.)

PROBLEM 35.19. Refer to the periodic table (Table 29.11.1 or Appendix D) and fill in Fig. 35.11.1 up to potassium. Note that matters seem to get somewhat more complicated from there on.

PROBLEM 35.20. If the interaction between the two electrons in the inner shell is ignored to a first rough approximation, argue on the basis of Eq. (35.6.1) that the radius a of this shell should be of the order of

$$a \sim \frac{h^2}{4\pi^2 mZke^2} = \frac{a_0}{Z},\qquad\qquad (35.11.1)$$

where Z denotes the number of positive charges on the nucleus. If Z is identical with the atomic number, as Bohr suggested, what is the order of magnitude of the radius of the inner shell for the massive atoms near the end of the periodic system ($Z \sim 100$)? How does this number compare with Rutherford's estimate of the nuclear radius? [*Answer:* Order of 100 : 1.]

Thus, in its very incomplete and hazy way, the theory began to rationalize the chemical and physical properties of the elements. At least a semiempirical basis for the periodicity of chemical properties was emerging; the relative inertness of the noble gases seemed to be associated with the filling or completion of certain stable shells of electrons; hopefully an improved and more thoroughly developed theory would give a better explanation for the occurrence of the particular shell numbers 2, 8, 8, etc.

On the basis of these investigations, Bohr suggested that the optical spectra and chemical properties of the elements were determined by the energy levels and behavior of the outermost electrons:

". . . the ordinary line spectrum of an element is emitted during the re-formation of an atom when one or more electrons in the outer rings is removed. In analogy it may be supposed that the characteristic Roentgen radiation is sent out during the settling down of the system if electrons in inner rings are removed by some agency; e.g., by impact of cathode particles."

If the inner shells of electrons have essentially the same configuration (differing only in energy and radius with different nuclear charge), one might expect the X-ray spectra of elements to have very similar patterns, the frequencies of the lines changing systematically with nuclear charge. Bohr suggested that quantitative study of the X-ray spectra might supply a further test of the theory.

35.12   MOSELEY'S MEASUREMENTS OF THE X-RAY SPECTRA

Bohr had discussed his ideas about atomic structure with his friends at Manchester in 1912 and 1913, some months before his papers actually appeared in the *Philosophical Magazine*. These were the months in which von Laue, Friedrich, and Knipping, the Braggs, and Moseley had plunged into experiments on X-ray diffraction by crystals (see Sections 34.1–4). Motivated by Bohr's suggestions, Moseley undertook a systematic investigation of the *K* and *L* spectra of the elements. Table 35.12.1 presents a fragment of his final compilation of data. (Note the precision indicated by the number of significant figures retained in the data. This work was done within a year after the original discovery of the phenomenon of X-ray diffraction!)

Referring to the photographically recorded patterns of the spectral lines and to the above numerical data, Moseley wrote:

". . . We can confidently predict that in the few cases in which the order of atomic weights *A* clashes with the chemical order of the periodic system [note the sequence Co, Ni, Cu in Table 35.12.1], the chemical properties are governed by [the atomic number] *N*; while *A* is itself probably a complicated function of *N*. The very close similarity between the X-ray spectra of the different elements

TABLE 35.12.1

A PORTION OF THE TABULATED DATA FROM *The High Frequency Spectra of the Elements*, PART II, BY H. G. J. MOSELEY*

Element and symbol	Atomic mass, A	Atomic number, N	Wavelengths of spectral lines, A		
			K_α	K_β	L_α
Chromium, Cr	52.01	24	2.301	2.093	—
Manganese, Mn	54.94	25	2.111	1.818	—
Iron, Fe	55.85	26	1.946	1.765	—
Cobalt, Co	58.94	27	1.798	1.629	—
Nickel, Ni	58.71	28	1.662	1.506	—
Copper, Cu	63.54	29	1.549	1.402	—
Zinc, Zn	65.38	30	1.445	1.306	—
Yttrium, Y	88.92	39	0.838	—	—
Zirconium, Zr	91.22	40	0.794	—	6.091
Niobium, Nb	92.91	41	0.750	—	5.749
Molybdenum, Mo	95.95	42	0.721	—	5.423
Ruthenium, Ru	101.1	44	0.638	—	4.861
Palladium, Pd	106.4	46	0.584	—	4.385
Silver, Ag	107.88	47	0.560	—	4.170

* *Phil. Mag.*, Series VI, **27**, 703 (1914)

shows that these radiations originate inside the atom and have no direct con-nexion with the complicated light spectra and chemical properties which are governed by the structure of its surface."

Drawing on Bohr's model, Moseley conjectured that the K_α line might originate as follows: One of the two electrons in the $n = 1$ shell is ejected by impact of an electron in the incident cathode beam. The transition of an orbital electron from the $n = 2$ shell to the "vacancy" in the $n = 1$ shell would result in the emission of a photon corresponding to the K_α radiation. Similarly transition of an electron from the $n = 3$ shell to the $n = 1$ vacancy would result in the more energetic, shorter-wavelength photon of the K_β line. A transition from the $n = 3$ shell to a vacancy in $n = 2$ would account for the L_α line, etc.

To test these conjectures, Moseley examined the spectral data in the light of Bohr's theoretical equation for the hydrogen spectrum. (In the analysis outlined below, we use different symbols and a somewhat different arithmetical approach, but the logical content is identical with that of Moseley's paper.)

Let us rewrite Eqs. (35.6.2 and 3) for the energy levels and wavelengths of the spectral lines, taking into account the fact that the coulomb force on an electron in any given shell of a complicated atom is some function $f(Z)$ of the number of posi-tive nuclear charges Z, where, in accordance with Bohr's assumption, Z is identical with the atomic number. [If only one electron were present $f(Z)$ would simply be Z^2. Why? The noncommital $f(Z)$ leaves flexibility for accounting for influence of other electrons.] We then have

$$E_n = -\frac{2\pi^2 m(ke^2)^2 f(Z)}{n^2 h^2}, \qquad (35.12.1)$$

$$\frac{1}{\lambda} = \frac{2\pi^2 m(ke^2)^2}{ch^3} f(Z)\left(\frac{1}{n_f^2} - \frac{1}{n_i^2}\right) = R_H f(Z)\left(\frac{1}{n_f^2} - \frac{1}{n_i^2}\right), \qquad (35.12.2)$$

where $R_H = 1.097 \times 10^7 \text{ m}^{-1}$.

The K_α wavelengths of Table 35.12.1 vary systematically with the atomic number N, and are found to obey the following empirical equation with very high accuracy:

$$1/\lambda = 0.827 \times 10^7 (N - 1)^2 \quad \text{m}^{-1}. \qquad (35.12.3)$$

This empirical result suggests that, for the particular case of the K_α lines, the function $f(Z)$ in Eqs. (35.12.1 and 2) should be taken to be $(Z - 1)^2$. According to Moseley's interpretation of the Bohr model, the K_α line should be emitted in an electron transition from the level $n_i = 2$ to a vacancy in the ground level $n_f = 1$. On this basis, the numerical factor multiplying $f(Z)$ in Eq. (35.12.2) should be

$$R_H[(1/1^2) - (1/2^2)] = \tfrac{3}{4} R_H = 0.823 \times 10^7 \quad \text{m}^{-1}, \qquad (35.12.4)$$

and the theoretically predicted equation for the K_α wavelengths becomes

$$1/\lambda = 0.823 \times 10^7 (Z - 1)^2. \qquad (35.12.5)$$

The agreement between the empirical and predicted values is striking—the deviation being less than one-half of one percent! These results led Moseley to remark:

"It is at once evident that [$f(Z)$ increases in a regular manner] as we pass from one element to the next, using the chemical order of the elements in the periodic system. Except in the case of nickel and cobalt, this is also the order of atomic weights. While, however, [$f(Z)$ increases regularly], the atomic weights vary in an apparently arbitrary manner, so that an exception in their order does not come as a surprise. We have here proof that there is in the atom a fundamental quantity, which increases by regular steps as we pass from one element to the next. This quantity can only be the charge on the central positive nucleus, of the existence of which we already have definite proof."

(This was the evidence alluded to by Rutherford in the letter to *Nature* quoted in Section 35.10.)

The occurrence of the function $(Z - 1)^2$ in Eq. (35.12.3) can be explained, somewhat glibly, by arguing that, when there is a vacancy in the $n = 1$ shell, the net effective charge determining the energy change in transition from $n = 2$ to $n = 1$ is very nearly $Z - 1$, the total charge of the nucleus being reduced by one by the presence of the remaining electron in the $n = 1$ shell close to the nucleus.

This argument is a bit specious, however, since it does not work well for any of the other transitions. For example, the empirical equation of the L_α lines in Table 35.12.1 is

$$1/\lambda = 0.150 \times 10^7 (Z - 7)^2 \ \text{m}^{-1}. \tag{35.12.6}$$

In this case, interpreted as a transition from $n = 3$ to $n = 2$, it is not at all clear from an elementary point of view why the "screening" effect should be equivalent to that of 7 electrons, rather than the total of 9 which should be present in the first two shells.

PROBLEM 35.21.   (a) Check a few points to test how well empirical equations (35.12.3 and 6) represent the K_α and L_α data of Table 35.12.1. (b) Verify and explain the calculation made in Eq. (35.12.4).   (c) Calculate, from Eq. (35.12.2), the theoretical value of the numerical coefficient to be expected in Eq. (35.12.6). [*Answer:* 0.152×10^7.] (d) Make a summary list of the concepts and ideas that are supported by Moseley's results. What aspects do you feel remain in doubt?

The scientific community is rarely satisfied with indirect evidence, however, regardless of how persuasive it might be. Ever more direct evidence is invariably sought in support of fundamental conceptions to make sure that the "network" really does hold together. It was in this spirit that Foucault (see Section 26.14) measured the velocity of light in water, surely expecting that it would come out to be less than the velocity in vacuum. It was in the same spirit that Rutherford and Royds (see Section 32.7) trapped α-particles to give the final chemical proof of their identity with helium. In 1920 James Chadwick,* one of Rutherford's associates at the Cavendish Laboratory, set out to measure the nuclear charge as directly as possible. Making very precise measurements of α-particle scattering, he measured experimentally all the other quantities appearing in Rutherford's scattering formula [Eq. (33.13.1)], and from these observed values calculated the nuclear charge Ze. For copper he reported a value of $29.3e$; for silver $46.3e$; and for platinum $77.4e$. Compare these results with the respective atomic numbers: 29, 47, 78.

35.13   INADEQUACY OF THE EARLY THEORY

If, at this stage, the reader finds himself ambivalent with respect to Bohr's theory, impressed by its successes but perplexed by its arbitrary assumptions—the retention of classical mechanics where it happens to be convenient, the abandonment of classical electrodynamics, the unexplained and unpictured transitions between energy levels, the hardly intelligible emission and absorption of photons in these transitions—he is again in good company. No one was more sensitive to these gaps and loose ends than Bohr himself (although he also seems to have had a deep intuitive conviction that he had opened up the right path and that a more complete and satisfying theory would emerge as the path was followed to clearer altitudes). Before sending his paper for publication, Bohr consulted the master. In his reminiscences

* Later a Nobel prize winner for the discovery of the neutron.

in the volume *Rutherford at Manchester*, Bohr quotes Rutherford's first reaction to the atomic theory. A letter dated March 20, 1913 begins:

"I have received your paper safely and read it with great interest, but I want to look it over again carefully when I have more leisure. Your ideas as to the origin of the spectrum of hydrogen are very ingenious, and seem to work out well; but the mixture of Planck's ideas with the old mechanics makes it very difficult to form a physical idea of what is the basis of it. There appears to me one grave difficulty in your hypothesis, which I have no doubt you fully realise, namely, how does an electron decide what frequency it is going to vibrate at when it passes from one stationary state to another? It seems to me that you have to assume that the electron knows beforehand where it is going to stop."

About a decade was to elapse before physicists began to realize that it would be necessary to foreswear this kind of question.

Although some successful outcomes of Bohr's model were very striking indeed (and we have perhaps overemphasized these aspects by the prominence accorded them in the preceding sections), it was far from completely successful. There were many important problems that the theory in this form never successfully resolved:

(1) No convincing, *a priori* account could be given of the quantitative details of the shell structure of atoms beyond hydrogen.

(2) No resolution, within this framework, could be obtained for the question as to the propriety of using ordinary classical mechanics for the dynamical description of electron orbits. (This turned out to be one of the weakest aspects of the theory; it eventually had to be abandoned for an entirely new quantum mechanics, fundamentally and qualitatively different from classical mechanics in its formalism and interpretation.)

(3) The theory turned out to be incapable of giving a satisfactory account of the formation of molecules—particularly molecules formed by like atoms, such as H_2, O_2, N_2, etc.

(4) It was well known that some lines, even in a spectrum as simple as that of hydrogen, were very much more intense than others, indicating that some transitions occurred on the average very much more frequently (i.e., had a higher probability). Bohr's early theory afforded no way at all of calculating the probability of transitions and accounting for the relative intensity of spectral lines.

(5) The theory holds that the orbital angular momentum of an electron in the ground state of hydrogen is $h/2\pi$. An electron having angular momentum in such an orbit would form a current loop (see Section 24.12) and the system would behave as though it had a magnetic moment (i.e., were a small magnet with N and S poles, the axis of the "equivalent" magnet being oriented perpendicular to the plane of the orbit). Spectroscopic evidence indicates that the net orbital angular momentum of an electron in the ground state of hydrogen is *zero* rather than $h/2\pi$, in direct contradiction to the Bohr model.

Revisions of the theory were forthcoming; in the years following 1913 Bohr worked unflaggingly to extend, revise, and improve it. (He was awarded the Nobel prize in 1922.) Important additions were made by the German physicist Sommerfeld. At the Institute of Theoretical Physics, which he founded and directed at the University of Copenhagen, Bohr was host at one time or another to the ablest young theoretical physicists from all over the world. Among the visitors were names such as Heisenberg, Schrödinger, Dirac, Pauli, Born, Jordan, and many others who were the architects of the new quantum mechanics, fashioned successfully in the mid-1920's. Bohr's personality—his gentleness, consideration of others, and sense of humor, together with his deep and stimulating physical insights and his passionate concern with philosophy and epistemology—made the institute at Copenhagen a mecca for physicists. The tone he set can be sensed in the reminiscences appearing in the October 1963 *Physics Today*, a memorial issue dedicated to Bohr, who died in 1962.

To discuss the modern quantum theory and wave mechanics that made obsolete and replaced the model described in this chapter is beyond the scope of the present text; the interested reader will find descriptions at various levels in the supplementary sources. We elect to terminate here our story of inquiry into the structure of matter, an inquiry that has been successfully carried far beyond this point, an inquiry that will perhaps never end.

Our story has focused not only on what it is that we think we know, but on how we know it. What is the nature of scientific evidence? of scientific explanation? The knowledge we have described would not exist without discoveries of facts, phenomena, and relationships, but neither would it exist without the attendant creation of concepts and theories—creations that involve imaginative acts of intelligence and perception and are not themselves "facts" lying on the surface for all to behold. Time and again these abstract constructs have led to the recognition of relationships that lay close at hand but did not speak for themselves; time and again they led to the deliberate design of new experiments and the discovery of new facts.

But in many important cases the concepts have not proved to be immutable, and the theories have manifested only limited ranges of validity. Perhaps our story has made a little clearer the reasons why we now tend to be cautious about Faraday's optimistic conviction that scientific inquiry will lead to "fundamental knowledge not subject to change."

35.14 PROBLEMS

35.22. Examine Bohr's theory (as described in this chapter) in terms of the criteria of a good physical theory, as discussed in Chapter 12.

35.23. By algebraic analysis, confirm the assertion made in Section 35.7 that allowing half-integer quantum numbers in the case of the hydrogen atom would imply a violation of the correspondence principle.

35.24. Return to the X-ray spectra of Fig. 34.4.1:

(a) In the light of the Bohr-Moseley interpretation of the origin of the K- and L-lines, how would you account for the fact that the L-lines are excited at lower voltages than the K-lines? What would be the origin of the M-lines? Would you expect them to appear at lower or higher voltages than those which excite the L-lines? Why?

(b) What is the origin of the continuous spectrum forming the "background" on which the K- and L-lines are superposed? (Note that this is associated with the slowing down or "braking" of electrons in the incident cathode beam. Such radiation is frequently called *bremsstrahlung*, a German word for "braking radiation.")

(c) How do the theories and models we have used account for the existence of a sharply defined short-wavelength limit for the bremsstrahlung; i.e., why is there not simply a gradual dropping off of the intensity out to ever-shorter wavelengths?

(d) Summarize the aspects of X-ray emission which seem to be explainable only on the basis of the quantum concept.

PROBLEM FOR MORE ADVANCED WORK

35.25. As in the case of the moon and the earth (see Section 9.12), an electron in the Bohr model cannot revolve around the center of the proton; the two bodies must revolve around the common center of mass. This effect has been entirely neglected in the derivation carried out in this chapter. Show that a fully correct treatment leads to exactly the same expressions we have already obtained, except that the electron mass m is replaced in every expression by the "reduced mass" μ defined by

$$\mu \equiv \frac{m}{1 + (m/M)},$$

where M denotes proton mass. What effect does this have on the theoretically calculated value of the Rydberg constant R_H?

SUPPLEMENTARY READING AND STUDY

Rutherford at Manchester, edited by J. B. Birks. New York: W. A. Benjamin, Inc., 1963. (Reminiscences by Marsden, Darwin, Blackett, Bohr, and others. Reprints of a few of Rutherford's most important papers, and of the classic papers by Geiger and Marsden, Bohr, and Moseley.)

Foundations of Modern Physical Science, G. Holton and D. H. D. Roller. Reading, Mass.: Addison-Wesley, 1958, Chapters 34, 35

Three papers on the early development of Bohr's theory by C. E. Behrens in the *American Journal of Physics*, **11**, 60 (1943); **11**, 135 (1943); **11**, 272 (1943)

The Restless Universe, Max Born. New York: Dover publications, 1957

Explaining the Atom, S. Hecht. New York: Viking Press, 1954, Chapters 1–3

Physics of the Atom, M. R. Wehr and J. A. Richards. Reading, Mass.: Addison-Wesley, 1960, Chapter 4

Physics Today, **16**, 10, October 1963. A memorial issue following Bohr's death.

For descriptions of the ideas that have replaced Bohr's first theory see:

Mr. Tompkins Explores the Atom, G. Gamow. New York: Macmillan, 1944

Physics in My Generation, M. Born. New York: Pergamon Press, 1956

Atomic Physics and Human Knowledge, N. Bohr. New York: Science Editions, Inc., 1961

"What is matter?" E. Schrödinger. *Scientific American*, September 1953

"The Principle of Uncertainty," G. Gamow. *Scientific American*, January 1958

"The Quantum Theory," K. K. Darrow. *Scientific American*, March 1952

The Strange Story of the Quantum, B. Hoffman. New York: Harper, 1947

CHAPTER 36

The Special Theory of Relativity*

36.1 INTRODUCTION

In the section that precedes enunciation of the laws of motion in the *Principia*, Newton makes the following pronouncements:

> "I. Absolute, true and mathematical time, of itself, and from its own nature, flows equably without relation to anything external, and by another name is called duration. Relative, apparent, and common time is some sensible and external . . . measure of duration by means of motion, which is commonly used instead of true time, such as an hour, a day, a month, a year.
>
> "II. Absolute space, in its own nature, without relation to anything external, remains similar and immovable. Relative space is some movable dimension or measure of the absolute spaces, which our senses determine by its position relative to bodies, and which is commonly taken for immovable space . . . ."

Thus Newton was fully aware that a practical, operational description of motion is always given in a relative frame of reference: a frame in which positions are specified relative to other material objects—objects, such as a ship, the earth or the sun, that might themselves be in motion relative to still other objects. But he nevertheless supports his argument for the existence of a basic, "absolute" reference frame by appealing to a thought experiment:

> "For instance, if two globes, kept at a distance one from the other by means of a cord that connects them, were revolved about their common center of [mass], we might, from the tension of the cord, discover the endeavor of the globes to recede from the axis of their motion, and from thence we might compute the quantity of their circular motion. And then if any equal forces should be impressed at once on the alternate faces of the globes to augment or diminish

---

* *Note to teachers and students:* A substantial effort has been made in earlier portions of the text to prepare the reader for study of this chapter. Review of the following sections and problems will prove helpful at this point: Sections 4.2, 5.2, 9.11, 17.3–5, 17.9, 23.13, 23.14, and 27.14–20. Problems 1.20, 1.24, 4.11–13, 4.16, 4.22, 5.1, 5.2, 6.15, 6.16, 9.21, and 22.31.

their circular motions, from the increase or decrease of the tension of the cord, we might [infer the direction of the rotation]. And thus we might find both the quantity and the [direction] of this circular motion, even in an immense vacuum, where there was nothing external or sensible with which the globes could be compared."

Perhaps another way of emphasizing Newton's point is to note that if we start under circumstances in which the tension in the cord connecting the globes is zero and proceed ourselves to walk or rotate around the center of mass, the tension in the cord remains zero despite the relative motion. Furthermore, we might observe a finite tension in the cord when the circular motion relative to us happens to be zero, and we would then conclude that the system is rotating with respect to some more fundamental frame; i.e., the system seems to "know" whether it is rotating or not, regardless of its motion relative to us, the observer. Newton referred to this more fundamental frame as "absolute space," and recognized explicitly that there seemed to be no way of establishing position points in this space or of describing *translational* motion through it.

Although these conceptions first caused considerable controversy and debate both in theology and natural philosophy, they in time became weighted with Newton's tremendous authority and prestige and became deeply embedded in the unexamined subsumptions of eighteenth- and nineteenth-century science. It was not until 1883 that Ernst Mach (see Section 6.4) raised the question as to the possible influence of all the other ponderable objects of the universe—the suns, stars, and galaxies—on Newton's rotating globes in the "immense vacuum": Would there be tension in the cord in the absence of all other bodies in the universe? Would there be any difference between rotating the globes themselves or rotating the other objects of the universe around them?

These questions are not to be answered by direct observation and controlled experiment. The approach is made through careful analysis of concepts and construction of theory. The theory, in turn, is tested by the validity of its predictions, and the predictions might concern phenomena apparently far removed from those that first motivated the inquiry.

Early in the twentieth century, physics was led to final and unequivocal abandonment of Newton's ideas of absolute time and space. Although we shall not be able to carry the inquiry all the way to the answers to Mach's penetrating questions, we can readily develop some of the initial stages with their major results and conclusions. We begin with a careful look at how we go about measuring length and time in a single frame of reference.

36.2   LENGTH AND TIME IN A SINGLE FRAME OF REFERENCE: LOCAL SIMULTANEITY

Implicit in our operational definition of frames of reference in previous discussions has been the choice of a rigid set of coordinate axes consisting of physical objects along which we lay out a scale of positions by means of a rigid measuring rod.* We then proceed to observe displacements of physical objects, time intervals, velocities, accelerations, etc., in this frame of reference. Let us examine somewhat more intensively than we have done before the operations involved in measurement of time.

We first devise a unit of time, based on what we hope is a uniformly repeated periodic process such as the rotation of the earth, and we then construct clocks that appear to repeat the unit interval faithfully, as indicated by their agreement with each other and with the primary reference interval.† Clocks consist, for the most part, of devices governed by a periodic, oscillatory process such as the swinging of a pendulum, rotational oscillation of a balance wheel, vibration of a tuning fork, electromagnetic oscillation in an electrical circuit, or, at least in principle, of the regular bouncing back and forth of a sound or a light signal within a given space.

A given clock then measures what we shall describe as "local time"—time at the place in the frame of reference where the clock happens to be located. Thus we observe a particle to be located at position x_1 on our coordinate axis and *simultaneously* the hand of a clock very close by points to the number t_1 on its scale. We shall use the word "event" to describe this coincidence of positions of particle and hand on a nearby clock; for motion confined to one dimension along the x-axis, events would have as "coordinates" the ordered pair of numbers (x_1, t_1). In the conceptual structure we are developing, we are essentially forced to accept the idea of *local simultaneity* as a primitive, unanalyzable concept—the kind of thing we might be willing to describe as an "absolute." We have a deeply entrenched intuitive sense of what we mean by one or more occurrences taking place "here, now," and it is this primitive conception that we invoke in defining an event and asserting that a particle on the coordinate axis and the hand of a nearby clock occupy certain positions *simultaneously*.

This review of our most fundamental operations now leads us to the question of precisely what we mean by the concept of "there, now." How do we "synchronize" or establish an agreement between clocks located at widely separated points in our frame of reference? What is it that we mean when we say that two widely separated

---

* These deceptively simple words and phrases conceal a host of subtle but important philosophical-epistemological questions which we have neither time nor space to discuss in this chapter—questions as to the meaning of "straight line" in the context of description of physical phenomena, the role of Euclidean geometry in the structure of physical concepts, questions as to how we are to know whether a given system and measuring rod are "rigid," and so forth. The reader will find at least an initial entree into the huge literature on this subject in the following references: E. F. Taylor, *Introductory Mechanics.* New York: John Wiley & Sons, 1963, Chapters 1 and 2. P. W. Bridgman, *The Logic of Modern Physics.* New York: The Macmillan Co., 1927, Chapter 1 (paperback edition 1960). H. Reichenbach, *The Philosophy of Space and Time.* New York: Dover Publications, Paperback S443, 1957, Chapters 1–6.

† For a simple but penetrating discussion of some of the operational problems and conceptual difficulties arising in this context, see Henri Poincaré, *The Value of Science.* New York: Dover Publications, 1958, Chapter 2, "The Measure of Time." This chapter is also reprinted in A. B. Arons and A. M. Bork, *Science and Ideas.* New York: Prentice-Hall, 1964.

events, one occurring close by in our frame of reference and one occurring far away, took place simultaneously? As Bridgman states the question: How do we manage to spread time over space in a single frame of reference?

36.3 SPREADING TIME OVER SPACE IN A SINGLE FRAME OF REFERENCE: USE OF SIGNALS*

Our goal in spreading time over space is to achieve synchronization or "agreement" between widely separated clocks, as sketched in Fig. 36.3.1. A first, naïve approach that suggests itself is to construct clocks as nearly identical as possible in every respect, set the hands to identical readings (local simultaneity) when the clocks are together at point O, and then transport one clock to position A.

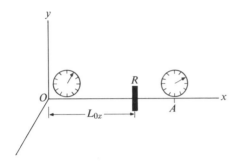

FIG. 36.3.1. How do we synchronize clocks at widely separated points O and A along the x-axis?

Such a procedure would be quite satisfactory in principle, provided that the very act of transporting the second clock did not affect its rate of operation. Prior to the development of the theory we shall discuss in this chapter, there seemed to be no conceivable reason why transport of a clock should affect the rate at which it ran, and the operational procedure suggested above was not even questioned. (Chronometers, capable of phenomenally uniform operation even under the influence of temperature changes and of accelerations encountered on a rolling and pitching ship, had been invented during the eighteenth century and were successfully used in navigation in all parts of the world.) Only in retrospect, after the development of the theory of relativity, did scientists realize that transportation of clocks at different velocities relative to each other would introduce discrepancies in their readings after the clocks were brought to a common point. We shall develop a better understanding of the details of this subtle problem later in the chapter; for the time being let us simply accept the *possibility* that transport of a clock might affect its rate of keeping time. Is there any way of getting out of this difficulty and giving a unique and unequivocal specification of a common time scale at separated points?

---

* For a more detailed discussion of the operational and conceptual problems raised in this and the following section see: P. W. Bridgman, *A Sophisticate's Primer of Relativity.* Middletown, Conn.: Wesleyan University Press, 1962, pages 13–67. Also: A. S. Eddington, *The Mathematical Theory of Relativity*, second edition, §11. London: Cambridge University Press, 1924 (paperback reprint 1963).

Let us try to establish synchronization by transmission of sound signals. First we wish to establish the velocity of sound, but we cannot do so by measuring the time interval elapsed in a unidirectional propagation of the wave; we do not have clocks synchronized at different positions. We can, however, take advantage of the trick of sending out a signal, returning it to its starting point, and measuring the elapsed time interval on a single clock: Suppose that in Fig. 36.3.1 we measure off the distance L_{0x} and place a sound reflector R on the x-axis as O indicated. We send out a sound pulse from O and observe its return after reflection from R. With a clock at O, we therefore observe two local events, the emission and return of the sound pulse, described by the numbers $(0, t_1)$ and $(0, t_2)$, respectively. We calculate the average velocity V of the sound pulse as $2L_{0x}/(t_2 - t_1)$.

We now set at zero the hand of the clock located at the origin and arrange to have the hand of the clock at A set at the reading $\overline{OA}/V$ (that is, the time it would take a sound signal to go from O to A at velocity V). Initially, neither clock is running. We arrange trigger mechanisms that start or stop the clocks on the arrival of sound pulses. We can start clock O when a sound pulse is emitted at the origin and start clock A when the sound pulse arrives at A. Having done this, we would be prepared to claim that clocks O and A are synchronized and have the same readings at the same time. In similar fashion we could synchronize any number of clocks positioned along the x-axis. Remember, however, that with the clocks widely separated, this is not a fact we can check simply by "seeing": i.e., by looking at the two clocks and appealing to our primitive sense of local simultaneity. Note also that, in making the assertion that the clocks are synchronized, we are implicitly assuming that the velocity of sound in one direction along the x-axis is exactly the same as the velocity in the opposite direction (or that the average value of V calculated in our velocity-determination experiment is applicable separately to propagation in either direction along the x-axis). We should like to believe that the facts of nature are indeed as simple as this, and much of our previous experience encourages this belief, but we must remember that things are not *necessarily* this simple and that we are at least temporarily relying on an assumption—a hope that must be tested empirically if at all possible.

PROBLEM 36.1. Another assumption implicit in the synchronization operation described above is that there is no wind blowing which would impart a velocity to the air relative to our frame of reference. Suppose a wind were blowing in the positive or negative x-direction. How would this affect our operational definition of synchronization? (Do not try to make a quantitative, algebraic analysis at this point; just try to develop a qualitative, verbal argument.)

PROBLEM 36.2. Suppose that, instead of using sound pulses, we elected to use light pulses in arranging to synchronize clocks at O and A in Fig. 36.3.1. Describe the sequence of operations in your own words and set up the corresponding simple algebraic expressions, denoting the velocity of light by the conventional symbol c.

PROBLEM 36.3. If from the very start we adopt the assumption that signal velocity (either sound or light) is the same in both the positive and negative x-directions, we can devise a simple way of synchronizing clocks at O and A in Fig. 36.3.1: We can establish the midpoint M between positions O and A and emit a signal from this point. Describe this method more completely in your own words: What initial settings would you make on the clocks at O and A to synchronize them with a clock at M that is started at zero when the signal pulse is emitted?

PROBLEM 36.4. (a)   In the light of these descriptions of clock synchronization, assess in your own words the meaning of an assertion such as "my book fell on the floor and *simultaneously* a taxi driver blew his horn in London." On what information would such an assertion have to be based?

(b) There are stars in our own Milky Way galaxy that are 10^5 light years away; that is, light emitted from these stars travels for 10^5 years before reaching the earth. What significance can be given to statements about events that might be occurring on such stars "now"?

36.4   SPREADING TIME OVER SPACE IN A SINGLE FRAME OF REFERENCE: TRANSPORTED CLOCKS

Bridgman, in his careful operational discussion of spreading time over space, suggests still another method that can be conceived of at least in principle—a hypothetical method of securing unique and unambiguous synchronization by transporting clocks, without recourse to propagation of sound or light signals.

Without having synchronized clocks positioned along the x-axis, we take the time scale given by the transported clock itself and calculate a value of transport velocity $\Delta x/\Delta t$, where Δx is a particular displacement and Δt is the corresponding time interval as measured on the transported clock itself. Such is the velocity measured on the speedometer of a car, and Bridgman refers to it as a "self-measured" velocity. He then goes on to describe the following operations:

"We specify, in the first place, that [a number of] clocks be transported from here to a distance by a single direct route [say along the x-axis in Fig. 36.3.1]. Along this route we shall transport clocks with different specified velocities. These are to be the self-measured velocities, which are uniquely determinable without further ado. When we have transported all our clocks, we shall presumably find that the various readings do not agree. We take the difference between the readings of the various clocks against some selected clock, perhaps the one transported with least self-measured velocity, and plot the difference of these readings against the self-measured velocity of the corresponding clock. We extrapolate these differences to zero self-measured velocity, and we set all of the clocks so as to agree with this extrapolated difference. By definition we have now set our clocks for zero velocity of transport. Such a method of setting a distant clock is unique and well defined, involving only actually performable physical operations, and therefore there seems to be no reason why we should not accept it."

We have now suggested three ways of distributing synchronized clocks along an axis of our frame of reference: synchronization by sound signals, by light signals, and by Bridgman's method of physical transport of the clock. Suppose we arrange three sets of clocks, each set synchronized by one of the above methods. Will the three sets agree with one another? This is not a question to which we can deduce an answer from prior knowledge or from theory—the question is one of physical fact; we must, in principle, appeal to experiment for an answer.

Although it is not practicable to set up experiments that verify agreement among these methods of clock synchronization *directly*, we shall see that all the *indirect* evidence we subsequently encounter—the way in which the network of theory and experimental observation hangs together without internal contradictions—leads to the conclusion that the different methods of synchronization must indeed agree, at least within the presently accessible range of physical experience. Not only do we have reason to believe that the different *methods* yield results in complete agreement with each other, but we also find that these methods appear to work identically for *all* "clocks" regardless of physical nature or type of construction. That is, we obtain, so far as we can tell, the same results whether we use mechanical clocks, electrical clocks, "light clocks" (based on bouncing a light signal back and forth between mirrors separated by a fixed distance), "atomic clocks" governed by regular oscillations associated with the structure of atoms or molecules, or "radioactivity clocks" based on the rate of decay of a radioactive material.

Since the transport method leads to the positioning of synchronized clocks along an axis of our frame of reference, we can proceed, in principle, to check whether or not the one-way or back-and-forth velocities of sound and light are identical in this system, as we assumed them to be in the synchronization methods described in Section 36.3. Experimentally verified agreement among the various methods of synchronization and among the multitude of different clocks shows that the two assumptions that played a crucial role in establishing synchronization (the assumption of uniqueness of the readings of transported clocks extrapolated to zero self-measured transport velocity and the assumption of the equality of back-and-forth velocities of sound and light signals) are fully consistent with each other, even though we cannot test each of the two assumptions *separately*. Such overall agreement and internal consistency support the conclusion that our assumptions have some connection with experimental facts and are something more than just arbitrary definitions or useful simplifying assumptions.

Finally, in light of the discussions of the last two sections, let us take explicit note of the fact that our operations for measuring time—in particular time at different locations—have become inextricably tied up with measure of space. Setting up a time scale throughout a given frame of reference involves much more than just the selection of a clock and the adoption of a unit of time; it involves prior definition of a scale of distance.

36.5   DETECTION OF A WIND BY USE OF SOUND SIGNALS

Sound waves move through air at a velocity V of about 1100 ft/sec.* In speaking of a wave velocity, we are referring to velocity *relative to the medium* through which

---

* The velocity varies with the square root of the absolute temperature, but in the following discussion we shall not concern ourselves with temperature variations.

the wave propagates. If a wind is blowing, moving the air at a velocity of 30 ft/sec relative to the ground, a sound pulse will still move at 1100 ft/sec relative to the *air;* relative to the ground, the pulse travels at 1130 ft/sec in the direction of the wind and at 1070 ft/sec against the wind. Exactly similar behavior is observed in surface ripples propagating on a stream of water.

One way of spreading time over space suggested in Section 36.3 was to utilize sound signals in still air, after determining the velocity of sound by means of a back-and-forth propagation and single clock located at the origin. What difficulties would arise in this method if the air were not still, but a wind of velocity u were blowing along the x-axis, as indicated in Fig. 36.5.1? With our frame of reference fixed relative to the ground, the sound pulse would travel more slowly from O to R and more rapidly from R back to O than it does in still air. Would the total time interval then remain the same as it is in still air? Let us calculate the elapsed time interval with and without wind and see whether the wind effect cancels out.

In the absence of wind, the elapsed time at O between the two events (emission of the sound pulse and return of the sound pulse) would be

$$\Delta t_0 = \underbrace{\frac{L_{0x}}{V}}_{\substack{\text{Time for pulse} \\ \text{to travel from} \\ \text{O to R}}} + \underbrace{\frac{L_{0x}}{V}}_{\substack{\text{Time for pulse} \\ \text{to travel from} \\ \text{R to O}}} = \frac{2L_{0x}}{V}. \tag{36.5.1}$$

With the wind blowing as shown in Fig. 36.5.1, the velocity of the sound wave relative to the ground will be $V - u$ while going from O to R and $V + u$ while returning from R to O. Therefore the total time interval for going and return will be

$$\Delta t = \underbrace{\frac{L_{0x}}{V - u}}_{\substack{\text{Time for pulse to} \\ \text{go from O to R}}} + \underbrace{\frac{L_{0x}}{V + u}}_{\substack{\text{Time for pulse to} \\ \text{return from R to O}}}.$$

Rearranging this equation, we obtain:

$$\Delta t = L_{0x} \left(\frac{V + u + V - u}{V^2 - u^2} \right) = L_{0x} \frac{2V}{V^2 - u^2} = \frac{2L_{0x}}{V} \cdot \frac{V^2}{V^2 - u^2},$$

$$\Delta t = \underbrace{\frac{2L_{0x}}{V}}_{\substack{\text{Time for pulse to travel} \\ \text{from O to R and back in} \\ \text{still air}}} \cdot \underbrace{\frac{1}{1 - (u^2/V^2)}}_{\substack{\text{Dimensionless factor} \\ \text{which is zero when} \\ u = 0}}. \tag{36.5.2}$$

Equation (36.5.2) reveals a somewhat surprising fact: The effect of wind velocity does *not* average out as the signal travels back and forth. The time interval Δt depends on u! Thus on measuring Δt and finding it to be different from $2L_{0x}/V$, we would conclude that there is a wind blowing—provided that we could measure Δt with sufficient accuracy. Note that Δt differs from Δt_0 only by the dimensionless factor in Eq. (36.5.2). This factor contains the *square* of the (usually) small quantity

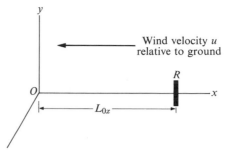

FIG. 36.5.1. Frame of reference fixed relative to the ground. Observer at O sends out signal to reflector R and measures time Δt between emission of signal and return of echo.

u/V rather than the first power. It is for this reason that the residual effect is frequently described as being of "second order"—the first-order term in u/V does not appear in the final result.

PROBLEM 36.5. Suppose that we had established the wind velocity u to be 30 ft/sec in the negative x-direction and the velocity of sound V relative to air as 1100 ft/sec. Make the relevant arithmetical calculations and describe how you would synchronize clocks located on the x-axis at $x = +10{,}000$ ft and $x = -10{,}000$ ft, respectively, with a clock located at the origin of the frame of reference.

PROBLEM 36.6. Suppose that we wish to use the measurement of Δt in Eq. (36.5.2) as a way of obtaining information about the wind velocity u. Investigate the accuracy with which it would be necessary to determine the values of Δt and $2L_{0x}/V$ in order to take advantage of Eq (36.5.2) and obtain a value of u/V which would be correct to about 10%. Assume that u/V is a small fraction; show that under these circumstances $[1 - (u^2/V^2)]^{-1}$ is very nearly equal to $[1 + (u^2/V^2)]$; then show that

$$\left(\Delta t - \frac{2L_{0x}}{V} \right) \simeq \frac{2L_{0x}}{V} \cdot \frac{u^2}{V^2}. \tag{36.5.3}$$

Suppose that u is of the order of 30 or 40 ft/sec, and that the distance L_{0x} is of the order of 100 ft. How accurately would Δt and $2L_{0x}/V$ have to be known in order to obtain values of u/V to the accuracy specified above? [*Answer:* to about $\pm 10^{-6}$ sec (one microsecond) in each value, or an accuracy of about $5 \times 10^{-4}\%$ of the magnitude of Δt.] Interpret this result, commenting on the problems that it poses if one were actually to attempt such an experiment with sound waves. What problems do you begin to anticipate if one were to attempt an identical experiment with light instead of sound?

36.6   SEARCH FOR THE LUMINIFEROUS ETHER AND THE ABSOLUTE FRAME OF REFERENCE

Fresnel, through his researches on the wave nature of light, had introduced into physics a far more concrete conception of a luminiferous ether than had ever been generated in the highly qualitative speculations of Newton, Huygens, or their eighteenth-century followers. The Maxwellian synthesis (see Sections 27.19 and 20) had sharpened this conception still further. In its successful prediction of the velocity of light from the electromagnetic properties (k_E and k_M) of the vacuum, it gave powerful support to the conception of an all-pervasive, intangible, supremely elastic ether—a medium for the propagation of electromagnetic waves; a medium *relative to which* the laws of electricity and magnetism take their simplest, most fundamental form; a medium through which material objects such as earth, planets, suns, and stars apparently whirl on their courses without encountering the resistance that would be offered by a material fluid; and, taking a cue from the mathematical order and symmetry continually being discovered in natural phenomena, a medium which is perhaps playing the role of Newton's absolute space and relative to which not only the laws of electromagnetism but also the laws of mechanics should, in principle, be expressed.

This was indeed a grandiose and inviting conception, and, as its significance came to be realized during the 1870's and 1880's, numerous ingenious and skillful experiments were constructed in efforts to detect evidence of the motion of the earth through the ether—to search for the absolute frame of reference.

Concerning the use of the word "absolute" in this context, Bridgman remarks:

> "The sort of tacit ideal that we have before us in using the word 'absolute' is itself not very definite, and may be one thing for the theologian or philosopher and another thing for the physicist. I think most physicists have in the back of their heads when using the word 'absolute' not something which cannot be specified in terms of physical operations, as did the theologian and philosopher, but something in which . . . the operations can be specified in terms which do not refer to accidental, temporary, local situations . . . . Thus if the existence of an all-pervading ether could have been established in some way, then velocity measured with respect to the ether would have been the sort of thing that the physicist would have been willing to call absolute. It is curious that there is a uniquely definable velocity, namely velocity with respect to the fixed stars, which is not felt to have the property of absoluteness implicitly wanted . . . ."

In its orbit around the sun, the earth has a tangential velocity of about 18.5 mi/sec or 30 km/sec. The direction of this velocity keeps changing, relative to the fixed stars, and at the end of every six-month interval the direction is opposite to what it was at the beginning of the interval. There is also an additional, but considerably smaller, tangential velocity associated with the diurnal rotation of the earth about its axis. If we could look down on the earth-sun system from a fixed frame of reference far above the north poles of the earth and sun, we would see the orbital and rotational motions of the earth as both having a counterclockwise direction.

Thus, regardless of how the entire solar system might itself be moving relative to the ether, any given position on the surface of the earth should be subjected to a periodic *variation* in its velocity relative to the ether—a variation that stems from the orbital and rotational motions. Furthermore, these variations in velocity relative to the ether should occur in the east-west direction, the north-south direction not being affected by the annual and diurnal motions.

PROBLEM 36.7. Verify the figures given above for the tangential velocity of the earth in its orbit around the sun. What fraction is this of the velocity of light? What is the tangential velocity (at your present latitude) associated with the diurnal rotation of the earth?

These visualizations of motion of the earth relative to the ether prompted a search for an "ether wind" by use of light waves in essentially the manner we described for sound in the preceding section. Maxwell, for example, remarked:

> "If it were possible to determine the velocity of light by observing the time it takes to travel between one station and another on the earth's surface, we might, by comparing the observed velocities in opposite directions, determine the velocity of the aether with respect to these terrestrial stations. All methods, however, by which it is practicable to determine the velocity of light from terrestrial experiments depend on the measurement of the time required for the double journey from one station to the other and back again, and the increase of this time on account of the relative velocity of the aether equal to that of the earth in its orbit would be only about one hundred millionth part of the whole time of transmission, and would therefore be quite insensible." [Note the discussion of this question in Problem 36.6.]

Because of these difficulties, Maxwell entertained little hope for a terrestrial test of the ether hypothesis, and turned his attention to astronomical evidence, proposing that highly refined observations of the eclipses of Jupiter's satellites (see the discussion in Section 26.2 of Roemer's determination of the velocity of light) might permit a detection of motion of the earth through the ether. In 1879 Maxwell's ideas came to the attention of the young American physicist, A. A. Michelson.

Michelson was not ready to give up the possibility of a terrestrial measurement and he had ideas as to how it might be executed. In 1887, with his colleague E. W. Morley at Case Institute of Technology in Cleveland, Michelson achieved what turned out to be one of the most crucial, precise, and convincing of many competing "ether wind" experiments. The Michelson-Morley experiment, now one of the most famous experimental observations in the history of physics, yielded essentially a null result—if there was an ether wind at all it must be less than one-sixth of the earth's orbital velocity (this was the uncertainty range of the initial experiment).

We shall not undertake a detailed discussion of the Michelson-Morley experiment in this text. It will suffice to say that the basic idea consisted of splitting a beam of light into two parts, one directed east-west and the other north-south, and reflecting the beams back to a common point, somewhat as in the experiment with sound waves suggested in Problem 22.31. Rather than attempting to measure the impossibly small difference in time intervals, Michelson and Morley superposed the light beams on their return to the origin so as to form an interference pattern, and searched for evidence of a difference between east-west and north-south velocities in the form of phase shifts of small fractions of a wavelength between the two beams.

The reader will find descriptions of the Michelson-Morley experiment in virtually any textbook on modern physics. The following three sources are suggested as a start: (1) Elementary discussion: B. Jaffe, *Michelson and the Speed of Light.* Garden City, N.Y.: Doubleday Anchor Book, Science Study Series S13, 1960. (2) College level text: M. R. Wehr and J. A. Richards, *Physics of the Atom.* Reading, Mass.: Addison-Wesley, 1960, Sections 5.3–5.5. (3) Historical discussion with many illuminating comments: R. S. Shankland, "Michelson-Morley Experiment." *Am. J. Phys.*, **32**, 16–35 (1964), and *Scientific American*, November 1964.

Subsequent refinements of the Michelson-Morley experiment, as well as of other methods, all gave similar null results. A recent experiment (*Physical Review Letters*, November 1958, pages 342–3) shows that if an ether wind exists it has a velocity less than one one-thousandth of the earth's orbital velocity.

The null results of the ether-drift experiments did not instantaneously overthrow the established points of view. Strenuous, in some cases even tortured, efforts were made to save the ether hypothesis. But additional *ad hoc* notions—such as the suggestion that the earth drags with it the ether in its immediate neighborhood—although they might explain one set of experimental observations, would be found to fail with respect to other sets, for example, astronomical ones. An interesting summary of the various efforts made to "save the appearances," and the ways these efforts failed, is to be found in W. K. H. Panofsky and M. Phillips, *Classical Electricity and Magnetism*, second edition. Reading, Mass.: Addison-Wesley, 1962, Chapter 15.

As time went by, it became more and more definitely clear that there seemed to be a "conspiracy" in nature against our detecting the notion of our frame of reference—the earth—relative to a universal ether. But if anything had engraved itself firmly on the consciousness of scientists since the advent of the seventeenth-century age of reason it was the idea that there is nothing special or favored or unique about the position of the earth in the physical universe. If incapability to detect motion relative to the ether is a fact in the earth frame of reference, the same incapability is to be expected in *all* frames of reference. This idea was to have revolutionary impact on our view of the seemingly most basic and unalterable physical concepts: space, time, mass, force.

36.7   VIEWING PHYSICAL PHENOMENA FROM DIFFERENT FRAMES OF REFERENCE: CLASSICAL THEORY

In order to follow the revolutionary conceptual changes referred to at the end of the last section, it is first necessary to sharpen our sense of how observers in two different frames of reference compare the numerical values with which they describe a given event or motion or other physical phenomenon. Such a connection between numbers applying to the same event but measured from two different frames is called a *transformation*. Let us examine the transformations we have been using implicitly in our system of classical or Newtonian mechanics.

Consider the two frames of reference S and S' sketched in Fig. 36.7.1, moving at uniform rectilinear velocity u relative to each other in the x-direction. We assume these to be frames of reference in which, in the absence of external forces, any material object is found to remain stationary or move in a straight line at uniform velocity. That is, we consider frames in which Newton's first law is obeyed without the *ad hoc* invention of fictitious forces—frames that we have previously characterized as "inertial" (see Section 9.11).

Let us imagine that we ourselves are observers in frame S and that we exchange notes with another observer in S'. Suppose that we each observe a particle at A moving parallel to the x-direction. We denote the velocity by v_x, and the S' observer uses the symbol v'_x. In previous calculations, we have employed a very simple connection between the numbers v_x and v'_x: If the particle moves in the positive x'-direction relative to S' at $v'_x = 30$ mi/hr, and if the relative velocity of the frames $u = 20$ mi/hr, we claim the velocity of the particle relative to us in frame S to be $v_x = 30 + 20 = 50$ mi/hr; that is, in general, the numbers v_x and v'_x have been connected by the transformation relations

$$v_x = v'_x + u; \qquad v'_x = v_x - u. \tag{36.7.1}$$

(For previous use of this idea, see Problem 4.22 and Section 17.3.) For a motion with a velocity component in the y-direction, we have claimed that

$$v_y = v'_y; \qquad v'_y = v_y. \tag{36.7.2}$$

Let us probe the origin of these simple transformations a bit more deeply by examining the connections between the two sets of position and time numbers characterizing an event in each frame of reference. Suppose an event occurs at A. In frame S we would say that it occurred at position x, y at instant t, while S' would specify position x', y' at instant t'. We assume that clocks have been synchronized and checked in each frame of reference by means of the techniques described in Sections 36.3 and 4, and that a simple connection between clock readings in the two frames is established by calling $t = 0$ the instant at which the origins O and O' pass each other. In every calculation and discussion we have carried out so far we have always tacitly assumed that, given the synchronization and clock setting

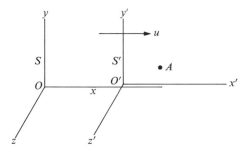

FIG. 36.7.1. Two inertial frames of reference. To an observer in frame S, frame S' appears to be moving in *positive* x-direction at velocity u. To an observer in S', frame S appears to be moving in the negative x'-direction at velocity u. The x- and x'-axes are meant to coincide, but are drawn with a slight separation for the sake of clarity. Clocks kept at the origins O and O' in each frame of reference are set to zero readings at the instant the origins pass each other.

just described, the two observers S and S' would agree in reporting the same numbers,

$$t = t', \qquad t' = t, \tag{36.7.3}$$

for the instant of occurrence of the event at A. Without inquiry and without careful operational investigation, we have been implicitly invoking the Newtonian concept of absolute time, "of itself, and from its own nature [flowing] equably without relation to anything external." We have assumed that time measurements were not mixed up with position measurements and that we could correct for the motion of one frame relative to other by taking into account the "wind" (either air or ether) in the frame of reference in which the wind was apparent. (In due course, we shall be forced to give up this inviting, but too naïve, conception.)

Comparing the other coordinates, we are led to the statements

$$y = y', \qquad y' = y, \tag{36.7.4}$$

$$x = x' + ut', \qquad x' = x - ut. \tag{36.7.5}$$

The last transformation emerges very simply from the fact that, in view of taking $t = 0$ at the instant the origins O and O' coincided, the distance $ut = ut'$ is the separation between the origins at the instant $t = t'$.

Let us verify that these transformations are consistent with the velocity relation in Eq. (36.7.1). Suppose we observe a displacement of a particle in the x-direction and the time interval in which the displacement occurs; we have in each frame of reference the coordinates (x_1, t_1), (x_2, t_2), etc., of the initial and final events characterizing the displacement. To calculate the velocity v_x relative to frame S we would take

$$v_x \equiv \frac{\Delta x}{\Delta t} = \frac{x_2 - x_1}{t_2 - t_1}. \tag{36.7.6}$$

To connect the S and S' numbers, let us make use of (36.7.3) and (36.7.5):

$$v_x = \frac{(x'_2 + ut'_2) - (x'_1 + ut'_1)}{t'_2 - t'_1} = \frac{x'_2 - x'_1}{t'_2 - t'_1} + u \frac{t'_2 - t'_1}{t'_2 - t'_1}.$$

Recognizing the next-to-last term as v'_x, we obtain

$$v_x = v'_x + u. \tag{36.7.7}$$

Thus our time and position transformations are entirely consistent with the intuitive composition of velocities invoked in Eq. (36.7.1).

Let us now try a similar calculation with the numbers that would characterize an acceleration in each frame of reference. To calculate an acceleration a_x relative to frame S, we would take the numbers

$$a_x \equiv \frac{v_{x2} - v_{x1}}{t_2 - t_1} = \frac{(v'_{x2} + u) - (v'_{x1} + u)}{t'_2 - t'_1} = \frac{v'_{x2} - v'_{x1}}{t'_2 - t'_1},$$

$$a_x = a'_x. \tag{36.7.8}$$

Thus, although velocities are *not* described by the same number in the two frames of reference (except when the velocity is perpendicular to the *x*-direction), the two observers get exactly the same number for an acceleration.

> PROBLEM 36.8. Starting with the definitions of v'_x and a'_x instead of v_x and a_x, follow algebraic procedures similar to those used in deriving Eqs. (36.7.7 and 8), and obtain the results $v'_x = v_x - u$; $a'_x = a_x$. Interpret the significance of this analysis. Show that, in general, $a' = a$, regardless of the direction of the acceleration. What significance do you see in this result?

> PROBLEM 36.9. If a light pulse is observed to have a velocity c in every direction in frame S, and if you assume the validity of the transformations developed in this section, what velocities would you expect the pulse to have in various directions relative to frame S'? [*Answer:* c in the y'-direction; $(c - u)$ in the positive x'-direction; $(c + u)$ in the negative x'-direction; if the pulse travels in the $x - y$ plane in a direction defined by an angle θ with the x-axis, it would have a velocity of magnitude $\sqrt{c^2 + u^2 - 2cu \cos \theta}$ in S', and would appear to move in the $x' - y'$ plane in a direction defined by $\tan \theta' = \tan \theta / [1 - (u/c) \sec \theta]$. Do you see any conflict between these deductions and the results of the ether-wind experiments described in Section 36.6?

36.8   THE CONCEPT OF INVARIANCE

The transformations examined in the preceding section summarize in a new way ideas that were implicit in all our earlier descriptions of motion. We frequently refer to them as *Galilean transformations*, and frames of reference in which they apply are called *Galilean frames*.

We have already pointed to the fact that observers at S and S' will use different numbers for the *x*-component of instantaneous velocity of a particle but will report identical numbers for acceleration. When a particular property is characterized by the same number in each of the two frames of reference, we speak of the property as being *invariant to the transformation*. Thus in the light of Section 36.7, the *y*- and *t*-coordinates of an event, the *y*-components of velocity, and the acceleration vectors are all invariant to Galilean transformation, while the *x*-coordinate of an event and the *x*-components of velocity (i.e., velocity in the direction of relative motion of the frames) are *not* so invariant.

These observations give us a deeper insight into the character of Newton's second law ($F_{net} = ma$). Acceleration being one of the quantities invariant to a change of frame of reference, we can set up our operational definitions of force and mass (as described in Sections 5.3, 5.4, or 6.4) and expect to get the same numerical results regardless of the inertial frame with respect to which we performed our experiments and calculations; i.e., force and mass are also invariant to Galilean transformation. If, contrary to experience, force were to be connected with velocity instead of acceleration, we would have an entirely different measure of force in each different frame.

Not only do we speak of various specific numerical properties as being invariant to transformation; we speak of such invariance for physical laws and principles as well. For example the law $\mathbf{F}_{net} = ma$ applies in each Galilean frame; not only the algebraic form of the expression but the numbers represented by each symbol remain the same when transformed to a new frame of reference. As another example, we draw from the discussions in Chapter 17 the conclusion that the law of conservation of momentum for a closed system is invariant to change of frame of reference. Our two observers in frames S and S' of Fig. 36.7.1 would measure different momenta and momentum changes of interacting particles, but they would both agree that momentum was conserved. In this example the momenta themselves are *not* invariant, but the *conservation relation* holds in each frame and is thus the invariant characteristic.

At the turn of the twentieth century, when ether-drift experiments had failed to give positive results, a number of investigators began to converge on the idea that no inertial frame of reference was "absolute" or privileged over any other—that the basic laws of physics had the same expression in each inertial frame of reference. The French mathematical physicist Henri Poincaré (1854–1912) expressed some of the implications forced by this conception.

> ". . . the laws of physical phenomena [are] the same, whether for an observer fixed, or for an observer carried along in a uniform movement of translation, so that we have not and could not have any means of discerning whether or not we are carried along in such a motion."

Poincaré referred to this assertion as the "principle of relativity."* It arises in his writings and lectures with increasing clarity in the years between 1895 and 1904. Neither Poincaré nor his contemporaries who groped toward similar ideas synthesized this principle into a new theory capable of clarifying the issues raised by failure to detect the electromagnetic ether; most of their efforts were directed toward trying to save the classical point of view by modification and adjustment of the older concepts. The explicit break with old conceptions, a bold reexamination of deeply held notions of space and time, and the incorporation of accumulated facts into a *new* theory began with a paper in the *Annalen der Physik* late in 1905. The paper was entitled "On the Electrodynamics of Moving Bodies." Its author was a 26-year-old German-born physicist—Albert Einstein.

36.9 ALBERT EINSTEIN (1879–1955)

Albert Einstein (Fig. 36.9.1) was born in Ulm, Germany, and received his schooling in Switzerland, obtaining a doctorate from the Swiss Federal Polytechnic Institute at Zurich in 1906. From 1902 to 1909 he earned his living as a patent examiner in the Swiss patent office. Within a period of a few weeks in 1905, he sent to the *Annalen der*

---

* For a recent discussion of Poincaré's important contributions to the evolution of the theory of relativity, see C. Scribner, Jr., "Henri Poincaré and the Principle of Relativity." *Am. J. Phys.*, **32**, 672 (1964).

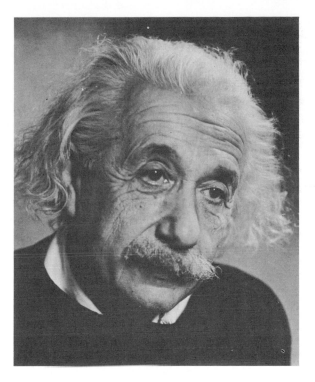

Fig. 36.9.1. Albert Einstein (1879–1955). Photograph by Fred Stein.

Physik three papers that have become classics of physical science. The first was the paper on the photon concept (see Chapter 34); the second was a mathematical analysis of Brownian motion that was then used by Perrin as the basis of his determination of Avogadro's number (see Section 33.8); the third paper, "On the Electrodynamics of Moving Bodies," enunciated what we now call the special theory of relativity.

The importance of these papers was rapidly recognized and appreciated. In 1913 Einstein accepted the post of professor of theoretical physics at the Kaiser Wilhelm Institute in Berlin—one of the highest academic positions in German physics. In succeeding years he became a world-renowned celebrity, and was accorded numerous honorary degrees and elections to scientific societies. In 1921 he received the Nobel prize in physics.

When Abraham Flexner was assembling the initial staff of the newly founded Institute for Advanced Study at Princeton in 1932, he persuaded Einstein to agree to spend six months of each year at the Institute. Toward the end of Einstein's first visit in 1932, Hitler came to power in Germany, and Einstein, under attack at home because of his Jewish extraction, never returned to his native land. In 1940 he became a citizen of the United States. At this time his colleagues enlisted his aid in calling President Roosevelt's attention to the military implications of the recently discovered phenomena of nuclear fission. His now-famous letter to the president helped generate administrative support for the wartime research and development that culminated in nuclear reactors and the atomic bomb.

Despite his fame, Einstein led a modest and secluded life, devoting himself to research to his last days. His extracurricular activities were for the most part in behalf of humanitarian causes, or in support of freedom of speech and conscience. He ranks, with Newton and Maxwell, among the great synthesizers of scientific thought.

36.10   EINSTEIN'S EXTENSION OF THE PRINCIPLE OF RELATIVITY

We have remarked previously that Newton's first law stands at the head of the laws of motion in the *Principia* as something of a proclamation of emancipation from Aristotelian views of motion. In a similar fashion, the introduction to Einstein's paper of 1905 is a proclamation of emancipation from the bondage of the ether concept and notions of absolute space and time:

"It is known that Maxwell's electrodynamics—as usually understood at the present time—when applied to moving bodies, leads to asymmetries which do not appear to be inherent in the phenomena. Take, for example, the reciprocal electrodynamic action of a magnet and a conductor. The experimentally observable phenomenon here depends only on the relative motion of the conductor and the magnet, whereas the customary conceptual view draws a sharp distinction between the two cases, in which either the one or the other of these bodies is in motion. For if the magnet is in motion and the conductor is at rest, we visualize that there arises in the neighborhood of the magnet an electrical field with a certain definite energy, producing a current at the places where parts of the conductor are situated. But if the magnet is stationary and the conductor in motion, no electric field arises in the neighborhood of the magnet. In the conductor, however, we visualize an emf, to which in itself there is no corresponding energy, but which gives rise—assuming equality of relative motion in the two cases discussed—to electric currents of the same path and intensity as those produced by the electric forces in the former case.*

"Examples of this sort, together with the unsuccessful attempts to discover any motion of the earth relative to the 'light medium,' suggest that the phenomena of electrodynamics as well as of mechanics possess no properties corresponding to the idea of absolute rest. They suggest rather that . . . the same laws of electrodynamics and optics will be valid for all frames of reference for which the equations of mechanics hold good. We will raise this conjecture (the purport of which will hereafter be called the 'Principle of Relativity') to the status of a postulate, and also introduce another postulate which is only apparently

----

* Note how similar is the tone of these remarks to that in the paper on the photon concept (see Section 34.10). These papers were submitted for publication within a few weeks of each other. In each instance Einstein indicates his concern over asymmetries in existing conceptual-theoretical views. Apparently holding a deep intuitive conviction regarding the role of symmetry in natural phenomena, he in each instance advances theoretical constructs aimed at removing the asymmetries from the theory.

irreconcilable with the former, namely, that light is always propagated in empty space with a definite velocity c which is independent of the state of motion of the emitting body. These two postulates suffice for the attainment of a simple and consistent theory of the electrodynamics of moving bodies based on Maxwell's theory for stationary bodies. The introduction of a 'luminiferous ether' will prove to be superfluous inasmuch as the view here to be developed will not require an 'absolutely stationary space' provided with special properties, nor assign a velocity vector to a point of the empty space in which electromagnetic processes take place.

"The theory to be developed is based—like all electrodynamics—on the kinematics of the rigid body, since the assertions of any such theory have to do with the relationships between rigid bodies (systems of coordinates), clocks, and electromagnetic processes. Insufficient consideration of this circumstance lies at the root of the difficulties which the electrodynamics of moving bodies at present encounters."

Thus Einstein makes the principle of relativity a basic postulate of his theory and adds the "apparently irreconcilable" postulate that the velocity of light in a vacuum has the same fixed numerical value of 3.00×10^8 m/sec relative to *any* frame of reference "for which the equations of motion hold good" (inertial frame). That is, the particular physical effect described as the velocity of light is asserted to be invariant to transformation from one inertial frame to another.

Let us examine some of the immediate implications of Einstein's assertion: (1) We saw in Section 36.7 that velocity v is *not* invariant to the Galilean transformation. If we simply substitute c for v, the Galilean transformations will not yield the result that $c' = c$ (see Problem 36.9). Thus the Galilean transformation is not consistent with the new postulate. (2) Suppose that a light flash is emitted from the origin at the instant that points O and O' (Fig. 36.7.1) cross each other. If, as Einstein suggests, the velocity of light appears to be the same in all directions to *any* given observer, each observer contends that, at later instants of time, the leading edge of the light pulse forms a sphere centered at *his* origin and that the other observer has moved over relative to the center of the sphere. Each observer will insist on his own contention and deny the argument of the other; there is no possibility of agreement between the two.

PROBLEM 36.10.   In order to visualize the assertion just made, sketch two separate pictures, each one illustrating the claim of one of the two observers. Note the symmetry or "reciprocity" of their points of view.

36.11   OPERATIONAL REEXAMINATION OF THE CONCEPT OF SIMULTANEITY

In our earlier discussion of synchronizing separated clocks (spreading time over space in one frame of reference) we noted that all the different methods at our disposal seemed to give concordant results—*including* the method of using light (or radio) signals. This gave uniqueness and internal consistency to the concept of simultaneity in a single frame, and we blithely assumed that comparison and *agreement* with observations in another frame of reference would be achieved simply by taking into account the effect of an ether wind with respect to any frame in which such a wind was apparent.

If we now accept the evidence implicit in the failure to detect an ether wind and elevate this failure to a generalization by adopting Einstein's postulate regarding the invariance of *c*, we note that each frame of reference has its own unique and reproducible system of defining clock synchronization and simultaneity, and that comparison between the two frames is possible *only* through the unique behavior of the velocity of light—the fact that it seems to be the same in all directions in each frame. As soon as we pursue this comparison, we see (as is already strongly suggested by the sketches made in Problem 36.10) that observers in frame S' will never agree that separated clocks in frame S have been properly synchronized; i.e., they will never agree that separated events said to be simultaneous by observers in S are indeed simultaneous. Conversely, observers in S will deny the validity of synchronizations carried out in frame S'. Let us carry out this comparison in more detail.

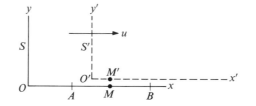

Fig. 36.11.1.   Light flash is emitted from M, midway between points A and B in frame S, in order to produce simultaneous events at A and B. Point M' in frame S' is coincident with M when flash is emitted.

An observer in frame S is located at the midpoint M of the line segment AB (Fig. 36.11.1). The location of this midpoint is determined by measurements with appropriate rods or scales along the x-axis and does not involve clocks or light signals. According to the ideas explored in Section 36.3 and Problem 36.3, if an observer at M wishes to cause events or actions to occur simultaneously at the separated points A and B, he sends out a light or a radio signal from M. Arrival of the signal causes switches to close at A or B, and, in accordance with his operational definition, the observer asserts that the switch actions occurred simultaneously since the signals originated at the midpoint M. In this fashion the observer in frame S would synchronize clocks located at A and B.

How does an observer in S' assess the synchronization of clocks at A and B? The observer in S' will agree that M is at the midpoint of AB because of the operational way in which the midpoint is established. (As will be shown, the observers will disagree on the *magnitude* of lengths such as AM or AB measured in specific units, but they will agree that, regardless of size, equal distances have been laid off on either side of M.)

Let us denote by M' the point (in frame S') which is coincident with M when the light flash is emitted. Since light appears to move at fixed velocity c relative to *each* observer, an observer in S' will claim that light emitted when points M and M' coincide travels at velocity c relative to *his* frame, and that frame S is additionally moving to the left at velocity u. Observer S' claims that point B is moving *toward* the advancing light pulse and point A is *receding* from the pulse traveling toward A. Hence observer S' contends that signals do not arrive at A and B simultaneously and that the clock at B must have been started ahead of the clock at A. Thus the observer in one frame will *always* contend that separated clocks in the other frame have not been correctly synchronized. This is identical with the statement that if S claims two events to have occurred simultaneously at A and B, S' will never agree on the simultaneity; he will always contend that the event at B occurred first.

Remember that this will hold for *all* clock synchronizations, not just the light signals, because, as we have pointed out repeatedly, all methods of synchronization and all clocks agree within the single frame of reference.

PROBLEM 36.11.   Suppose that an observer at M' synchronizes clocks at points C' and D' equidistant to the left and right of M'. What operation would he perform? How would an observer in S assess this synchronization; i.e., which clock would he contend was started first? [*Answer:* clock at C'.]

Thus if we accept the postulate of invariance of the velocity of light, we must accept as a consequence the relativity of simultaneity—simultaneity of events *separated in space* cannot be an "absolute," accepted and agreed upon in all frames of reference. Judgment of simultaneity is controlled by definitions and measurements made in each particular frame of reference, and there is no possibility of agreement between frames moving relative to each other.

36.12   LENGTH MEASUREMENTS AS VIEWED FROM DIFFERENT FRAMES OF REFERENCE

Suppose that a rod is at rest in frame S' (Fig. 36.11.1) and is oriented parallel to the x'-axis. Observers in S' can, at their leisure, mark the ends of the rod on the scale laid off along the x'-axis and read the length of the rod as indicated by these marks. Let us denote this length of the stationary rod by L'_{0x}. The length of an object at rest in the frame of reference is called a *proper length*.

An observer in S, wishing to measure the length of the same rod, must do so as it flies by him at velocity u. He cannot mark the ends of the rod along his x-axis scale at leisure but must do so *simultaneously*. Thus he uses clocks along the x-axis, synchronized as described above, and has his assistants agree to mark the ends of the flying rod at some predetermined clock reading.

How does the observer in S' assess this operation? In accordance with the argument developed in the preceding section, he contends that clocks toward the right (B in Fig. 36.11.1) were started in frame S before clocks toward the left (A).

Therefore, he contends, observers in S did not mark the rod ends simultaneously at all but marked the right-hand end (B) first. Before they marked the left end, their frame of reference had moved over toward the left, and the mark made at the left end of the rod was closer to B than it would have been had the marks been made simultaneously relative to S'. In this way, observers in S who try to measure a proper length along the x'-axis in S' will always obtain a value L_x which is *smaller* than L'_{0x}. Observers in two different frames of reference cannot agree on the length of a given rod.

Thus time becomes inextricably mixed up with the very operation of measuring the length of a moving object. If we had an identical rod stationary in frame S, we would obtain the same length as that recorded for the stationary rod in S'. But as soon as we try to measure the length of a *moving* rod, we must introduce a definition of simultaneity, and we will inevitably obtain a value shorter than the proper length; that is, the rod seems to *contract* when it is in motion relative to our frame of reference. It should be emphasized that the contraction referred to is not something we *see* by virtue of illumination of the whole scene by means of light but a value we *measure* by means of the scales and operations described above. In Einstein's interpretation, the contraction is entirely the result of operations of measurement and of the relativity of simultaneity forced on us by the apparent invariance of the velocity of light.

> PROBLEM 36.12.   Consider a rod at rest in frame S and having, in this frame, a proper length L_{0x}. Describe the operations which observers in S' must make to measure the length L'_x of this rod as it flies by along the x'-axis. How will an observer in S assess this measurement? (Show that he will argue that L'_x must be too short; make use of the result obtained in Problem 36.11.)

Note the *reciprocity* of the contraction effect revealed by the discussion in Problem 36.12. A proper length parallel to the x'-axis in S' is contracted for an observer in frame S; a proper length parallel to the x-axis in frame S is contracted for an observer in S'.

36.13   LENGTH MEASUREMENTS PERPENDICULAR TO THE DIRECTION OF RELATIVE MOTION

Let us examine the operation of measuring length in the y-direction, perpendicular to the direction of relative motion of our frames of reference. Do we encounter disagreement analogous to that associated with measurements in the x-direction? First we check the process of synchronizing clocks or establishing simultaneity along the y-axis.

Suppose that a light flash is emitted when points M and M' on the y-axes of our two frames of reference coincide (Fig. 36.13.1). Observers in frame S' elect to synchronize clocks at E' and F', equidistant from M', by means of this signal. To these observers, the rays of light reaching E' and F' are rays parallel to the y'-axis, since the light wave spreads out uniformly from M' so far as they are concerned.

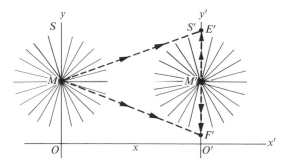

FIG. 36.13.1. Flash of light is emitted when points M and M' coincide. E' and F' are equidistant from M'.

To observers in frame S the light flash spreads out spherically from point M; frame S' appears to be moving over toward the right, and the S observers contend that the signals reaching clocks at E' and F' must have traversed the lines ME' and MF', respectively.

If the lengths ME' and MF' appear identical to observers in S, they will agree that the light signals arrived at E' and F' simultaneously (albeit they followed different paths from those assigned by observers in S'), and there will be no disagreement between the two frames regarding synchronization and simultaneity in the y-direction.

Here we raise a question regarding some of the most basic assumptions of the theory of relativity: On what grounds do we assume that observers in S will say that lengths ME' and MF' are equal? This is, of course, true if axis y' in the S'-frame appears to be perpendicular to axis x in the S-frame. But is it necessary that this perpendicularity obtain? Could not the perpendicularity be affected by the relative motion in some strange way, as are some of the other relations we have examined? This turns out to be a rather deep epistemological question, which is still discussed from time to time in current literature.

We shall not try to pursue the fine points of the discussion, but shall turn aside the question in the following way: First, there seems to be no apparent reason why the y'-axis should appear tilted either one way or the other to us who are in frame S. (Einstein points up our intuitive feeling about such matters by referring to "the properties of *homogeneity* which we attribute to space and time.") Second, our deductions from the theory must ultimately stand tests of internal consistency and agreement with experimental facts. This assumption does help generate a successful theory, and we adopt it accordingly.

The assumption of invariance of the perpendicularity of the Cartesian axes leads us to accept the assertion that $ME' = MF'$ in Fig. 36.13.1. As a consequence, we conclude that there will be no disagreement on simultaneity and clock synchronization along the y-directions. Furthermore, since the length contraction deduced in Section 36.12 arose because of disagreement as to simultaneity in the x-direction, we conclude that there will be no disagreement between the two frames of reference regarding length measurements in the y-direction. Thus, in the notation defined in the preceding section, we conclude that $L_y = L'_{0y}$ and $L' = L_{0y}$.

36.14   TIME DILATION

Suppose that the observer in S' sets up a "light clock" along his y'-axis (Fig. 36.14.1). That is, he places a mirror at position L'_y and bounces light back and forth between this position and the origin O'. The regular bouncing back and forth of the light signal is equivalent to the swinging of a pendulum or the oscillation of the balance wheel of a watch. Measured at the origin O', the time interval for the round trip $O'L'_y$ and L'_yO' is

$$\Delta\tau'_o = \frac{2L'_y}{c}. \tag{36.14.1}$$

(*Any* other clock would agree with this one and could be referred to in our discussion, but by invoking the "light clock" we have a simple way of relating the numbers used by the two observers.) Such a time interval is said to be a *proper time interval* in S' because it is a measure of the interval between two events (in this case the departure and return of a light signal) at the *same point* (O') in the given frame of reference. To the observer in S this is not a proper time interval since, if the departure of the signal occurred when O' and O coincided, O' has moved over along the x-axis by the time the signal returns; thus the departure and return of the signal at O' occur at different points along the x-axis, while occurring at the same point on the x'-axis.

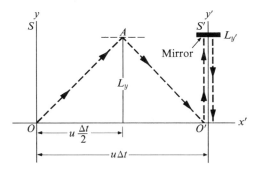

FIG. 36.14.1. A "light clock" with light reflected back and forth along the y'-axis is transported in frame S'. Light flash is emitted when O and O' coincide.

Observer S will claim that in going to the mirror and returning to O' the light moved at velocity c and followed path OAO' in Fig. 36.14.1—a longer path and therefore a longer time interval than is calculated by S'. Observer S invokes the Pythagorean theorem and calculates the total distance traveled by the light signal as follows: Δt denotes time taken (in frame S) for the light to travel distance OAO'. Therefore

$$OAO' = c\,\Delta t.$$

Also, since O' is displaced a distance $u\,\Delta t$ along the x-axis in this interval, we have

$$OAO' = 2(OA) = 2\sqrt{L_y^2 + [u^2(\Delta t)^2/4]}.$$

Therefore

$$c^2(\Delta t)^2 = 4\left[L_y^2 + \frac{u^2(\Delta t)^2}{4}\right].$$

Solving for Δt, we obtain

$$\Delta t = \frac{2L_y}{c} \cdot \frac{1}{\sqrt{1 - (u^2/c^2)}} \qquad (36.14.2)$$

PROBLEM 36.13.   Write out the algebraic steps that lead to Eq. (36.14.2).

Since observers S and S' agree that $L_y = L'_y$ (see Section 36.13), it follows that

$$\Delta t = \frac{2L'_y}{c} \frac{1}{\sqrt{1 - (u^2/c^2)}} = \frac{\Delta\tau'_o}{\sqrt{1 - (u^2/c^2)}}. \qquad (36.14.3)$$

Equation (36.14.3) compares clock readings or measurement of time intervals between events. Since $\Delta t > \Delta\tau'_o$, we find that observers in frame S will always obtain a larger value than observers in S' for the time interval between events occurring at a *fixed location in S'*. Another interpretation of this result is that observers in S will claim that a proper clock in S' runs systematically slow, relative to a clock in S, by the fraction $\sqrt{1 - (u^2/c^2)}$ if the clocks were both set to zero readings when origins O and O' coincided. (This phenomenon is called *time dilation*.) Remember, however, that it is not possible to compare the clocks without considering time intervals between specific events.

PROBLEM 36.14.   Using an analysis exactly parallel to that in Fig. 36.14.1 but reversed in point of view (i.e., the proper clock is located at the origin in frame S and measures a proper time interval $\Delta\tau_o$), show that S' will claim that

$$\Delta t' = \frac{\Delta\tau_o}{\sqrt{1 - (u^2/c^2)}}. \qquad (36.14.4)$$

Interpret Eqs. (36.14.3 and 4) in your own words. In what sense do the observers agree? In what sense do they disagree? How large must u be to produce a sizable difference between $\Delta t'$ and $\Delta\tau_o$? (Give some numerical examples.) What happens to the value of Δt calculated in one frame of reference as the proper clock in the other frame recedes at a velocity u approaching that of light? What do the equations say if you substitute a value of u greater than c? How do you interpret these indications? To what basic postulates or assumptions can you trace their source in the theory we have devised? (Do not assume that these last questions are susceptible to simple, pat answers.)

PROBLEM 36.15.   Unstable particles having a mass equal to about 207 times the mass of an electron have been found among the products of very energetic nuclear collisions. These particles are called *muons*, and are found to decay radioactively with a half-life of about 1.5 μsec (1.5 μsec $= 1.5 \times 10^{-6}$ sec) when they are essentially at rest relative to the observer; that is, half of the muons present at a given instant of time will decay during the next 1.5 μsec, half of the remainder will decay in the succeeding 1.5 μsec, etc. It has been observed that muons are produced not only in nuclear reactions induced artificially in the giant accelerators but also in the nuclear reactions that occur in the upper atmosphere when cosmic rays collide with atmospheric atomic nuclei. Muons produced under such circumstances have very high energies and velocities very close to that of light.

Consider a group of muons produced at an altitude of about 30 km above the surface of the earth. In our frame of reference, at rest relative to the earth, how long will it take a group of muons moving vertically downward to reach the surface of the earth? [*Answer:* about 10^{-4} sec or 100 μsec.] If the muons decayed during this time interval with the half-life cited above, what fraction of those produced at a height of 30 km would remain undecayed by the time they reached the surface of the earth? [*Answer:* virtually zero.] It is determined experimentally that about one-eighth of the initial number actually remain undecayed when they reach the surface of the earth. Regarding the known half-life of stationary muons as a "built-in decay clock" moving with the muons themselves and measuring a proper time interval in the muon frame of reference, what proper time interval is indicated by the fact that one-eighth of the original group remain undecayed? [*Answer:* $3 \times 1.4 = 4.5$ μsec.] Interpret these results. In what sense do they seem to provide experimental support for the concept of time dilation? Using the time-dilation equation, calculate the velocity u of the muons relative to the earth. Does the result make sense? [*Answer:* $u = 0.9990c$.] (See the next section for hints regarding numerical calculation.)

The phenomenon of time dilation is the basis of the so-called *clock* or *twin paradox* which has been the subject of considerable discussion and some controversy in recent years. We shall not have space for an analysis of this problem. The reader is referred to the booklet of selected reprints on special relativity (listed in the reference section at the end of the chapter) for a group of interesting papers.

36.15   NUMERICAL CALCULATIONS INVOLVING $\sqrt{1 - (u^2/c^2)}$

In many instances we shall wish to calculate values of $\sqrt{1 - (u^2/c^2)}$ when the ratio u/c is small relative to unity. In such circumstances it proves very convenient to expand the expression $[1 - (u^2/c^2)]^{1/2}$ by means of the binomial theorem:

$$\left(1 - \frac{u^2}{c^2}\right)^{1/2} = 1 - \frac{1}{2}\frac{u^2}{c^2} + \frac{1}{8}\left(\frac{u^2}{c^2}\right)^2 - \cdots \qquad (36.15.1)$$

If the ratio u/c is small, the third term of the right-hand side of Eq. (36.15.1) contains the number $(u/c)^4$ and is quite negligible relative to the second term. Dropping the third and so-called higher-order terms is equivalent to saying, for example, that

$$\sqrt{0.96} = (1 - 0.04)^{1/2} \cong 1 - \frac{0.04}{2} = 0.98. \qquad (36.15.2)$$

PROBLEM 36.16.   Verify numerically that 0.98 is indeed very nearly the square root of 0.96. Show that the third term in the expansion would contribute only an additional

0.0002 to the result. Using this expansion, evaluate some additional square roots such as $\sqrt{0.95}$, $\sqrt{1.04}$, $\sqrt{1.20}$, etc. When does the third term in the expansion begin to contribute more than 5% to the final result?

Occasionally (as in Problem 36.15) we confront situations in which the ratio u/c is close to unity and the radical itself is small. That is,

$$\sqrt{1 - (u^2/c^2)} = x, \tag{36.15.3}$$

where x is small relative to unity. If x is a known quantity and we wish to evaluate u/c, we proceed by squaring both sides of (36.15.3) and solving for u/c, or

$$1 - (u^2/c^2) = x^2,$$
$$\frac{u}{c} = (1 - x^2)^{1/2} \cong 1 - \frac{x^2}{2}. \tag{36.15.4}$$

PROBLEM 36.17. Evaluate u/c if it is known that $\sqrt{1 - (u^2/c^2)} = 0.06$. [*Answer:* $u/c = 0.9982$.]

The equations we have derived in preceding sections indicate that the reciprocal of $\sqrt{1 - (u^2/c^2)}$ will appear frequently in our algebraic expressions. Because of this it has become conventional to introduce a shorter notation, introducing the symbol γ:

$$\gamma = \frac{1}{\sqrt{1 - (u^2/c^2)}}. \tag{36.15.5}$$

Thus, if u/c is small relative to unity, we again invoke the binomial expansion:

$$\gamma = \left(1 - \frac{u^2}{c^2}\right)^{-1/2} = 1 + \frac{1}{2}\frac{u^2}{c^2} - \frac{3}{8}\left(\frac{u^2}{c^2}\right)^2 + \cdots,$$

$$\gamma \cong 1 + \frac{1}{2}\left(\frac{u^2}{c^2}\right). \tag{36.15.6}$$

This simple approximation is extremely useful even up to values of u/c as high as about 0.5.

36.16 NUMERICAL COMPARISON OF LENGTHS MEASURED IN DIFFERENT FRAMES OF REFERENCE; THE LORENTZ CONTRACTION

In Section 36.12 we presented a qualitative argument showing that if a rod lies parallel to the x-axis, the length measured in a frame of reference moving relative to the rod will always be shorter than the proper length. Now that we have established a numerical connection (Section 36.14) between time intervals measured in the two frames of reference, we can hope to establish a numerical connection between length measurements. We achieve this by visualizing a thought experiment in which observer S' measures the proper length L'_{0x} of a rod stationary in his frame by sending

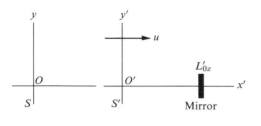

FIG. 36.16.1.   Observer S' places a stationary rod of proper length L'_{0x} on the x'-axis.   One end of the rod is at the origin O'.   A mirror is fixed at the other end located at $x' = L'_{0x}$.

a light signal back and forth along the rod and thus connecting the numerical value L'_{0x} with a proper time interval $\Delta\tau'_0$ measured on the clock located at O' (Fig. 36.16.1).

Observer S' starts his clock at O' when a light flash is emitted and stops it on return of the flash reflected from the mirror at the other end of the rod.   Since light moves at velocity c relative to him, S' claims that

$$\Delta\tau'_o = \frac{2L'_{0x}}{c}; \qquad L'_{0x} = \frac{c\,\Delta\tau'_o}{2}. \tag{36.16.1}$$

Observer S, assessing this experiment, argues that the light moved at velocity c relative to frame S and that S' moved over, relative to the light flash, while the measurement was being made.   Taking L_x as his unknown value of the distance between O' and the mirror at L'_{0x}, observer S argues that the time interval between the leaving of the light signal from O' and its return to O' is given by

$$\Delta t = \underbrace{\frac{L_x}{c - u}}_{} + \underbrace{\frac{L_x}{c + u}}_{}.$$

Time taken for light to get from O' to mirror while mirror is receding at velocity u.

Time taken for light signal to return from mirror to O' with O' moving toward light flash at velocity u.

Combining the terms on the right-hand side, we have

$$\Delta t = L_x\left[\frac{(c + u) + (c - u)}{c^2 - u^2}\right] = L_x\,\frac{2c}{c^2 - u^2} = \frac{2L_x}{c}\cdot\frac{c^2}{c^2 - u^2},$$

$$\Delta t = \frac{2L_x}{c}\cdot\frac{1}{1 - (u^2/c^2)}. \tag{36.16.2}$$

(Note how similar this analysis is to that which led to Eq. (36.5.2), but how different the point of view!)

Rearranging Eq. (36.16.2) to obtain an expression for L_x, the value given by observer S for the distance between O' and the mirror, we have

$$L_x = \frac{c\,\Delta t}{2}\,[1 - (u^2/c^2)]. \tag{36.16.3}$$

But from the relation between Δt and $\Delta\tau'_o$ in Eq. (36.14.3), we have

$$L_x = \frac{c\,\Delta\tau'_o}{2}\,\sqrt{1 - (u^2/c^2)}, \tag{36.16.4}$$

and from the relation between $\Delta\tau'_o$ and L'_{0x} in Eq. (36.16.1), we obtain

$$L_x = L'_{0x}\sqrt{1 - (u^2/c^2)}. \tag{36.16.5}$$

Equation (36.16.5) is the *quantitative* expression for the purely *qualitative* result we predicted in Section 36.12: A proper length in S' will always appear *shorter* when measured as it is flying by in frame S.

> PROBLEM 36.18.   Interpret Eq. (36.16.5).   How fast must a meter stick be moving past us if we are to conclude that it has a length of 0.5 m?

> PROBLEM 36.19.   Set up the situation which is the exact inverse of that in Fig. 36.16.1. (That is, the proper length is carried in frame S and is the distance between O and a mirror at L_{0x}.)   Using an analysis exactly parallel to the one above, show that under these circumstances observer S' concludes that the flying length L'_x is related to L_{0x} by
>
> $$L'_x = L_{0x}\sqrt{1 - (u^2/c^2)}. \tag{36.16.6}$$
>
> Compare Eqs. (36.16.5) and (36.16.6).   Note that they describe very different situations, but also note the *reciprocity* of the effect.

> PROBLEM 36.20.   In the light of the discussions carried out in this and preceding sections, what is your response to the question: "What is it that *really* happens to time intervals in moving systems, and what happens to lengths of moving objects?" The bear traps, of course, reside in the words "really" and "moving."   Do not feel that a pat answer is appropriate; this question is worth thought and discussion. (See references cited at the end of the chapter.)

During the 1890's the Irish physicist G. F. Fitzgerald and the Dutch physicist H. A. Lorentz had independently advanced the hypothesis that the null result of the Michelson-Morley experiment could be accounted for if the length of any material object contracted by the fraction $\sqrt{1 - (u^2/c^2)}$ in the direction of its motion through the ether.   That is, they suggested the possibility of an actual *physical* contraction in accordance with Eq. (36.16.5) in which L'_{0x} would represent the length of the object when it was stationary relative to the ether.   This effect came to be referred to as the *Lorentz-Fitzgerald contraction*, or frequently just as the *Lorentz contraction*. Einstein's reexamination of the operational definitions of length and time yields exactly the same algebraic formula, but accords it a very different interpretation. We still refer to the numerical relations summarized in Eqs. (36.16.5) and (36.16.6) as the Lorentz contraction, but we no longer regard this as a physical shortening in the sense proposed by Lorentz and Fitzgerald.

36.17   SYNCHRONIZATION OF CLOCKS IN ONE FRAME OF REFERENCE AS VIEWED FROM THE OTHER

Let us return to the question of disagreement on synchronization of clocks, a problem discussed qualitatively in Section 36.11.   We now undertake a quantitative inquiry.   Suppose that observers in S' synchronize clocks (i.e., start them simul-

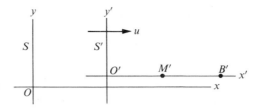

FIG. 36.17.1. Observers in frame S' start clocks at O' and B' simultaneously (for frame S') by arrival of a light flash from midpoint M'. Point B' is located at coordinate position x' so that length $O'B' = x'$, a proper length in frame S'.

taneously) at O' and B' by means of arrival of a flash of light emitted from the midpoint M' (Fig. 36.17.1). What will observer S say about this synchronization? He will contend that the clock at O' was started first, ahead of the one at B'. How far ahead? We can now calculate his view of the discrepancy: S will measure the proper length x' in the S'-frame as having the length $x'\sqrt{1 - (u^2/c^2)}$ in his own frame [Eq. (36.16.5)], and he will contend that the lengths $O'M'$ and $M'B'$ are each $(x'/2)\sqrt{1 - (u^2/c^2)}$. S will also claim that since B' is moving toward the right with velocity u while the light flash is traveling in the same direction with velocity c, it will take the light a time interval

$$\frac{x'}{2(c - u)} \sqrt{1 - (u^2/c^2)}$$

to get from M' to B'. Similarly, he will claim that O' is moving toward the light flash, and the time taken for the signal to get from M' to O' will be

$$\frac{x'}{2(c + u)} \sqrt{1 - (u^2/c^2)}.$$

Thus S will contend that the clock at O' was started ahead of the clock at B' by a time interval

$$\Delta t = \frac{x'}{2} \sqrt{1 - (u_2/c_2)} \left(\frac{1}{c - u} - \frac{1}{c + u} \right)$$

$$= \frac{x'}{2} \sqrt{1 - (u^2/c^2)} \left[\frac{(c + u) - (c - u)}{c^2 - u^2} \right]$$

$$= \frac{x'}{2} \sqrt{1 - (u^2/c^2)} \left(\frac{2u}{c^2 - u^2} \right) = \frac{x'u\sqrt{1 - (u^2/c^2)}}{c^2[1 - (u^2/c^2)]},$$

$$\Delta t = \frac{x'u}{c^2} \frac{1}{\sqrt{1 - (u^2/c^2)}}, \qquad (36.17.1)$$

where x' is a proper length in frame S'. Observers in S' claim that clocks at O' and B' were started simultaneously, but observers in S contend that clock at O' was started *first* by the amount Δt. The failure of synchronization calculated by observer S depends on x'; that is, on how far apart the clocks are in x'! This is the quantitative description of the effect that we were able to predict only qualitatively in Section 36.11. We have arrived at the quantitative result through a step-by-step analysis of the operations of measuring length and time in the two frames of reference.

PROBLEM 36.21. Set up an argument inverse to that given above: Show that when clocks at O and x are synchronized in frame S, observers in S' will contend that the clock at x was started *first* and is ahead of the clock at O by the amount

$$\Delta t' = \frac{xu}{c^2} \frac{1}{\sqrt{1 - (u^2/c^2)}} . \tag{36.17.2}$$

36.18   THE LORENTZ TRANSFORMATION

Suppose that observers at O and O' start their clocks when the origins pass each other. Such an initiation of clocks at the same position involves only the primitive concept of local simultaneity and causes no difficulty. Some time later an event occurs, as indicated in Fig. 36.18.1. Observers in S' say the event occurred at co-ordinated position (x', y') and at instant t' as measured by a clock at x' synchronized with the clock at O'. If observers in S use the numbers x, y, and t to describe the same event, how are these numbers related numerically to x', y', and t'?

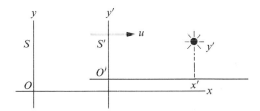

FIG. 36.18.1. Event occurs with space-time coordinates (x', y', t') in frame S'. We seek the corresponding space-time coordinates (x, y, t) of the event relative to frame S.

Note that this is exactly the same question as the one raised in Section 36.7. At that point the analysis led us to the Galilean transformations. Let us investigate the transformations that stem from the new theory in which we have abandoned the notions of ether and absolute time and space and have asserted the invariance of c.

As we argued in Section 36.13, we expect no discrepancy or disagreement about length measurements in the y-direction. Therefore we expect observers in the two frames of reference to agree on the y-coordinates of the event, giving the simple transformation

$$y = y'; \qquad y' = y. \tag{36.18.1}$$

Concerning the time of occurrence of the event, observers in S argue as follows: The clocks in S' have been running slow all the time. If any clock in S' reads a proper time interval t', the corresponding interval measured by our clocks would be

$$t = \frac{t'}{\sqrt{1 - (u^2/c^2)}},$$ (36.18.2)

as required by Eq. (36.14.3). If clocks at O' and x' had been properly synchronized, expression (36.18.2) would give the correct time of the event. But the clocks at O' and x' were *not* correctly synchronized (says S); the clock at x' was started *later* than the clock at O' by the amount indicated in Eq. (36.17.1), and therefore the reading on the clock at x' is too small by this amount. If the clock at x' reads the value t' for the event, the corresponding reading on a clock in our frame of reference would be

$$t = \underbrace{\frac{t'}{\sqrt{1 - (u^2/c^2)}}}_{} + \underbrace{\frac{ux'}{c^2\sqrt{1 - (u^2/c^2)}}}_{}$$ (36.18.3)

Correcting t' for time dilation; i.e., for the fact that clocks in S' have been running slow as indicated by Eq. (36.14.3).

Correcting for fact that reading on clock at x' is too low, since it was started *after* clock at O' by this amount. (Clocks at O and O' were started simultaneously on passing each other.)

To compress our notation, let us adopt the symbol

$$\gamma \equiv \frac{1}{\sqrt{1 - (u^2/c^2)}},$$ (36.18.4)

as suggested in Section 36.15. Equation (36.18.3) then becomes

$$t = \gamma\left(t' + \frac{ux'}{c^2}\right).$$ (36.18.5)

PROBLEM 36.22. Making use of the result obtained in Problem 36.21, carry out an analysis inverse to that developed above, and show that observers in S' will say that

$$t' = \gamma\left(t - \frac{ux}{c^2}\right).$$ (36.18.6)

What about the connection between x and x'? Having started clocks at O and O' when the origins crossed, observers in S' will contend that the position of the event along the x-axis relative to point O is given by $x' + ut'$, where x' is its location relative to O', and ut' is the distance O' has moved over along the axis since the origins crossed. Observers in S will claim that the event took place at coordinate position x, the distance from the origin to x being a proper length in their reference frame. In accordance with Eq. (36.16.6), observers in S' will measure this distance as the contracted length x/γ. Thus to observers in S' the numbers $x' + ut'$ and x/γ are two ways of expressing the same distance. Therefore we write

$$x/\gamma = x' + ut', \qquad x = \gamma(x' + ut').$$ (36.18.7)

This is the manner in which the number x must be related to the numbers x' and t'.

Similarly, observers in S will say that the event was located at a distance $x - ut$ from the origin O', where x is its distance from O and ut is the distance O' moved over along the x-axis after the origins crossed. Also, observers in S will say that this distance can be calculated as x'/γ, since x' is a proper length in the prime frame. Therefore we have the relation that connects x' with x and t,

$$x' = \gamma(x - ut). \tag{36.18.8}$$

Let us assemble the transformations we have derived.

For S values in terms of S' values

$x = \gamma(x' + ut')$ (36.18.7)

$y = y'$

$t = \gamma\left(t' + \dfrac{ux'}{c^2}\right)$ (36.18.5)

For S' values in terms of S values

$x' = \gamma(x - ut)$ (36.18.8)

$y' = y$

$t' = \gamma\left(t - \dfrac{ux}{c^2}\right)$ (36.18.6)

These connections among the respective numbers (x, y, t) and (x', y', t') describing the space-time coordinates of an event from two different frames of reference are usually called the *Lorentz transformations*. A short time before Einstein derived these relations from the relativistic point of view (Einstein's derivation is somewhat different in form from the one we have presented here), H. A. Lorentz had discovered that these are the transformations that leave Maxwell's electromagnetic equations unaltered in shifting from one frame of reference to another; that is, he showed the Maxwell equations to be invariant under this transformation, whereas they are *not* invariant under the Galilean transformation.

PROBLEM 36.23. Note how the Lorentz transformations satisfy a "correspondence principle" (see Section 35.5 for definition of the term); that is, they reduce to the classical Galilean transformations when the velocity u is very small relative to c. Why is this significant? Would any other behavior be acceptable in the new theory? Why or why not?

PROBLEM 36.24. If our calculations are internally consistent, we should be able to combine Eqs. (36.18.5) and (36.18.7), eliminating x' and solving for t' so as to obtain (36.18.6), or eliminating t' and solving for x' so as to obtain (36.18.8). Verify that this is indeed the case.

From the Lorentz transformations we should be able to work back to the time-dilation [Eq. (36.14.3)] and length-contraction [Eq. (36.16.5)] equations: A clock retaining a fixed position x'_1 in frame S' measures a proper time interval $t'_2 - t'_1$; from Eq. (36.18.5), we have

$$t_2 - t_1 = \gamma\left(t'_2 + \frac{ux'_1}{c^2} - t'_1 - \frac{ux'_1}{c^2}\right) = \gamma(t'_2 - t'_1), \tag{36.18.9}$$

corresponding to Eq. (36.14.3).

If observers in frame S wish to measure a proper length $x_2' - x_1'$, flying by in frame S', they must mark the ends simultaneously at some instant t_1 according to their synchronization. From Eq. (36.18.8) we have

$$x_2' - x_1' = \gamma(x_2 - ut_1 - x_1 + ut_1) = \gamma(x_2 - x_1),$$

$$x_2 - x_1 = \frac{x_2' - x_1'}{\gamma}, \qquad (36.18.10)$$

corresponding to Eq. (36.16.5).

PROBLEM 36.25. Derive in a similar fashion the relations corresponding to Eqs. (36.14.4) and (36.16.6).

PROBLEM 36.26. Return to Problem 36.15 and note that from the point of view of a frame of reference moving with the muons one might say, "Of course the time taken for the descent was only 4.5 μsec. The distance was not 30 km at all; it was only $30\sqrt{1 - (u^2/c^2)}$ km, and the velocity of descent was very nearly c." Does this argument check out numerically? What significance do you see in the fact that the two divergent points of view agree on the same final numbers?

36.19 THE TRANSFORMATION RELATIONS FOR COMPONENTS OF VELOCITY

Let us apply to the Lorentz transformations exactly the same procedure we used to derive the Galilean velocity transformation, Eq. (36.7.7). From Eqs. (36.18.5) and (36.18.7) we have for a particle undergoing displacement Δx in time interval Δt

$$\Delta x = \gamma(\Delta x' + u\,\Delta t'); \qquad \Delta t = \gamma\left(\Delta t' + \frac{u\,\Delta x'}{c^2}\right),$$

$$v_x \equiv \lim_{\Delta t \to 0} \frac{\Delta x}{\Delta t} = \lim_{\Delta t' \to 0} \frac{\Delta x' + u\,\Delta t'}{\Delta t' + (u\,\Delta x'/c^2)} = \lim_{\Delta t' \to 0} \frac{(\Delta x'/\Delta t') + u}{1 + (u/c^2)(\Delta x'/\Delta t')},$$

$$v_x = \frac{v_x' + u}{1 + (uv_x'/c^2)}. \qquad (36.19.1)$$

By exactly similar procedures, we obtain the full set of relativistic velocity transformations:

$$v_x = \frac{v_x' + u}{1 + (uv_x'/c^2)}, \qquad (36.19.1) \qquad\qquad v_x' = \frac{v_x - u}{1 - (uv_x/c^2)}, \qquad (36.19.3)$$

$$v_y' = \frac{v_y'}{\gamma[1 + (uv_x'/c^2)]}, \qquad (36.19.2) \qquad\qquad v_y' = \frac{v_y}{\gamma[1 - (uv_x/c^2)]}. \qquad (36.19.4)$$

PROBLEM 36.27. Complete the derivation of the above set of velocity transformations.

It is frequently convenient to express velocities as fractions of the velocity of light rather than in meters per second, etc. For this purpose, we divide both sides of

(36.19.1) by c, obtaining

$$\frac{v_x}{c} = \frac{(v'_x/c) + (u/c)}{1 + (u/c) \cdot (v'_x/c)}.$$

(36.19.5)

Suppose that frame S' is receding from S at a velocity u equal to half the velocity of light, and that a particle in S' has a positive velocity v'_x equal to three-fourths the velocity of light. In the Galilean transformation we would calculate the particle to be moving relative to frame S at a velocity

$$v_x = \tfrac{1}{2}c + \tfrac{3}{4}c = \tfrac{5}{4}c,$$

or faster than the velocity of light. What prediction do we obtain from Eq. (36.19.5)?

$$\frac{v_x}{c} = \frac{\tfrac{3}{4} + \tfrac{1}{2}}{1 + \tfrac{1}{2} \cdot \tfrac{3}{4}} = \frac{10}{11}.$$

(36.19.6)

According to the new theory, the velocities "add up" to only ten-elevenths that of light. This is an entirely new view of the composition of velocities.

PROBLEM 36.28. Interpret the velocity transformation relations: (1) Do they obey the correspondence principle and reduce to the classical transformations in the limits of low velocities? What does "low" mean in this context—low relative to what? Is it only u that has to be low or is it v also? (2) Suppose that a particle is stationary in S' (that is, $v'_x = v'_y = 0$). What velocity does it have relative to frame S according to the equations? Suppose that a particle is similarly stationary in frame S, what velocity do the equations give it relative to S'? Do these results make sense? (3) What significance do you see in the fact that the value of v_y is connected not only to v'_y but to the value of v'_x as well?

PROBLEM 36.29. Verify that light traveling at $v'_x = c$ in frame S' will be calculated as traveling at velocity $v_x = c$ relative to frame S. (This result should not be surprising, since this requirement was built into the theory with the initial hypothesis concerning the invariance of c.) Verify that for a light pulse propagating in the negative x'- direction (that is, $v'_x = -c$), the transformation equation gives $v_x = -c$.

PROBLEM 36.30. In frame S' an electron is observed moving along the y'-axis with velocity v'_y very nearly equal to c. What value for the velocity of the electron is obtained by observers in S? Use a diagram to interpret the results. [*Answer*: $v_x = u; v_y = c/\gamma; |v| = c$.] Note that the velocity does not appear to be parallel to the y-axis in frame S. This phenomenon is called *aberration*.

36.20 INDUCTION OF A NEW DYNAMICAL LAW

Our development of the relativistic theory has so far been entirely *kinematic*. We have evolved a description of motion alone, without reference to laws that govern changes of motion or the behavior of material particles. We are therefore in a stage of development quite analogous to the stage at which Newton confronted classical theory—it is necessary to undertake some inductive guesswork in order to discover the basic dynamical laws. "For," as Newton remarks in the preface to the *Principia*, "the whole burden of philosophy seems to consist in this—from the phenomena of motions to investigate [by induction] the forces of nature, and then from these forces to demonstrate [by deduction] the other phenomena . . . ." Our inductive guesses must ultimately stand the test of yielding predictions in agreement with stubborn experimental facts.

It quickly becomes apparent that the Newtonian laws of motion are not likely to help us: The relativistic velocity transformations, Eqs. (36.19.1–4), indicate at a glance that acceleration will *not* be invariant to transformation from one frame to another, as it was in the Galilean case [Eq. (36.7.8)], but will depend in a complicated way on the relative velocity u. Thus a scale of force that we set up in one frame of reference in accordance with the operational definitions of Chapter 5 would probably not be of much use to us in another frame, and there is also no assurance that we shall be able to characterize each particle by a single number referring to the invariant, intrinsic property that we called "mass." We shall not try to explore the dead end to which this investigation would carry us, but shall turn directly to the points of view that are fruitful in leading to the formulation of a new "relativistically valid" dynamics.

We have already hinted at these points of view in the discussion of the conservation laws in Chapters 17 and 18. We saw that the law of conservation of momentum was in many ways more fundamental than the ideas embodied in Newton's second and third laws, and, as a matter of fact, was known and used well before publication of the *Principia*. We shall approach our inductive investigation from the point of view of the Einstein-Poincaré principle of relativity, assuming that observation of a law of conservation of momentum is not an accident of our terrestrial frame of reference but a general regularity satisfied in all frames. We imply by this choice that a conservation law is perhaps a more significant and more fundamental statement than one such as $F_{net} = ma$ that involves the definition of an additional concept, namely force. As suggested by our previous experience, we shall define momentum of a particle as the product of velocity and some other number m, characteristic of the particle and analogous to the mass number m_0 of Newtonian mechanics. We shall insist, as we have previously, that our new theory obey the correspondence principle: It must reduce, in the limit of low velocities, to the classical theory which we know to be successful and "correct" in that range of experience. Thus, if it turns out that m is a property more complicated in some way than the mass m_0 of Newtonian mechanics, we shall impose the condition that m must approach m_0 at low velocities, etc.

As an heuristic device to assist our detective work, let us consider a specific dynamical situation in which material particles interact (collide) in a simple, known way, and let us examine this collision from different frames of reference. We shall deliberately introduce a high degree of symmetry into this thought experiment and appeal to the symmetry in making our analyses.

Consider the situation sketched in Fig. 36.20.1(a). In frame of reference Σ we arrange a symmetrical, glancing collision of two identical particles A and B moving

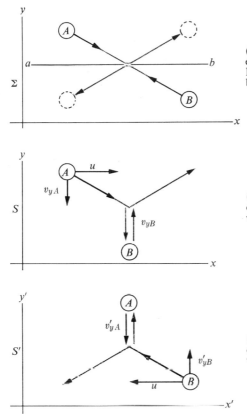

(a) Identical particles A and B moving at equal speeds undergo a glancing collision. Line ab, parallel to x-axis, bisects the angle between the trajectories.

(b) Collision in (a) viewed from a frame of reference in which x-component of velocity of particle B is zero.

(c) Collision in (a) viewed from a frame of reference in which x'-component of velocity of particle A is zero.

Fig. 36.20.1. Viewing a highly symmetrical collision of identical particles from different frames of reference.

at equal speeds. We orient the axes of Σ in such a way that line ab, parallel to the x-axis, bisects the angle between the trajectories of the particles. Let us assume the collision to be elastic so that the x-components of velocity remain unchanged while the y-components are reversed in direction but unchanged in magnitude.

Now suppose that we view the collision from a frame of reference in which the x-component of velocity of particle B is zero (Fig. 36.20.1b). In this frame, particle B would be observed moving parallel to the y-axis with velocity v_{yB} and would bounce back after collision with this velocity reversed. Body A would be observed as having an x-component of velocity denoted by u and a y-component v_{yA}, reversed on collision.

Similarly, if we observed the same collision from a frame S' moving with body A, the collision would have the appearance illustrated in Fig. 36.20.1(c).

Because of the symmetry specified in the initial frame of reference, the situation in parts (b) and (c) of the figure must also be symmetrical, the roles of A and B

being simply exchanged. Because of this symmetry we are led to say that

$$|v'_{yA}| = |v_{yB}|. \tag{36.20.1}$$

Note, however, that we have been left with an open question concerning the connection between v_{yA} and v_{yB}. The y-components were equal and opposite in frame Σ, but they are not necessarily so in S. The velocity transformations make it possible for us to investigate this problem. According to Eq. (36.19.2), observers in frame S would say that

$$v_{yA} = \frac{v'_{yA}}{\gamma[1 + (uv'_{xA}/c^2)]}. \tag{36.20.2}$$

Since $v'_{xA} = 0$, this reduces to

$$v_{yA} = v'_{yA}/\gamma = v'_{yA}\sqrt{1 - (u^2/c^2)}, \tag{36.20.3}$$

and we can now establish a connection between v_{yA} and v_{yB} in the *same frame of reference:* Combining (36.20.1) and (36.20.3), we obtain

$$|v_{yA}| = |v_{yB}|/\gamma = |v_{yB}|\sqrt{1 - (u^2/c^2)}. \tag{36.20.4}$$

Note the effect of changing the frame of reference from Σ to S: While the particles appeared to approach each other with equal and opposite y-components of velocity in frame Σ, the y-components no longer appear to be equal in frame S; the y-component of velocity of particle A appears to have a *smaller* magnitude than the y-component of velocity of particle B. The difference arises because of the presence of velocity component u, possessed by body A but not by body B; i.e., because of the different velocities relative to the new frame of reference.

Let us examine the collision from the point of view of frame S. We assign to each particle a property denoted by m_A and m_B, respectively, which, when multiplied by velocity, will give a measure of our *redefined* concept of "quantity of motion" or "momentum" and investigate what characteristics the m numbers must have if this product is to be conserved in the collision. For body A the product is changed by the amount $2m_A|v_{yA}|$ in the positive y-direction, while for body B the product is changed by the amount $2m_B|v_{yB}|$ in the negative y-direction. If the observer in S is to find the product conserved, we must have the relation

$$2m_A|v_{yA}| = 2m_B|v_{yB}|. \tag{36.20.5}$$

It is immediately apparent that this condition *cannot* be satisfied by assigning equal numerical values to m_A and m_B (even though the particles were postulated to be identical in frame Σ), because Eq. (36.20.4) indicates that $|v_{yA}|$ is not equal to $|v_{yB}|$ but is somewhat smaller. The only change in shifting from frame Σ to frame S is a change in velocity of the particles relative to the frame of reference. Thus if we are to preserve a relativistic conservation law that is formally like the conservation of momentum in classical mechanics, we must allow the number m to depend in some appropriate fashion on the relative velocity of the particle; to satisfy Eq. (36.20.5) we would have to assign m_A a value sufficiently greater than m_B to cancel the effect of Eq. (36.30.4).

36.21   THE MASS–VELOCITY RELATION

We now take the next step in our inductive guesswork: What connection between m_A and m_B would make the conservation relation [Eq. (36.20.5)] "work"?
From Eq. (36.20.4), we have that

$$|v_{yB}| = \gamma|v_{yA}|,$$

and substituting this into (36.20.5), we obtain

$$m_A|v_{yA}| = m_B\gamma|v_{yA}|,$$

$$m_A = \gamma m_B = \frac{m_B}{\sqrt{1 - (u^2/c^2)}}. \qquad (36.21.1)$$

Thus the conservation relation would hold in the new frame of reference S if the
m numbers assigned to the identical particles depended on u in the manner specified
by Eq. (36.21.1). Let us investigate the implications of this relation, particularly
any connection it reveals between our relativistic m numbers and the ordinary
mass of Newtonian mechanics.

Consider what happens to our view of the phenomenon in frame S (Fig. 36.20.1b)
if the y-velocity components v_{yA} and v_{yB} are visualized as becoming very small
relative to c while the component u remains large. Particle B appears to be moving
at ordinary (or nonrelativistic) velocity. Under these circumstances we invoke the
correspondence principle and require that we be able to characterize the momentum
of particle B by the product $m_{0B}v_{yB}$, where m_{0B} is the ordinary, intrinsic, invariant
mass number of classical theory. We call this quantity the *rest mass* of the particle.
Particle A, on the other hand, has a high velocity component u, and the presence
of this component affects the relative values of v_{yA} and v_{yB} as required by Eq. (36.20.4).
Thus, to satisfy the conservation relation, we would still have to assign m_A the value

$$m_A = \frac{m_{0B}}{\sqrt{1 - (u^2/c^2)}}. \qquad (36.21.2)$$

With v_{yA} and v_{yB} small relative to u, the magnitude of the total velocity of particle A
relative to particle B is very nearly equal to u itself. Thus the quantity u that appears
in (36.21.2) is very nearly the relative velocity of the two identical particles. Furthermore, our assumption that the particles are identical implies, among other things,
that their rest masses must be identical; i.e., that $m_{0A} = m_{0B}$. On this basis we
would rewrite Eq. (36.21.2) as

$$m_A = \frac{m_{0A}}{\sqrt{1 - (u^2/c^2)}}. \qquad (36.21.3)$$

Our whole pattern of reasoning from symmetry, from analogy to classical mechanics, from the particular heuristic device of the thought experiment in Fig. 30.20.1
leads us to the following inductive generalization of Eq. (36.21.3): This relation
suggests that we should redefine our classical concept of mass, assigning a given
particle moving at instantaneous velocity v in a particular frame of reference a mass
number m that is directly proportional (1) to the classical "rest mass" m_0 of the par-

ticle in the given frame of reference (as defined in Chapters 5 and 6) and (2) inversely proportional to $\sqrt{1 - v^2/c^2}$, where $v = |\mathbf{v}|$, the absolute value of the velocity. That is, we drop the subscript referring to a particular particle and adopt as a general specification for the mass number m of a particle the relation

$$m = \frac{m_0}{\sqrt{1 - v^2/c^2}}. \tag{36.21.4}$$

This is the mass–velocity relation of the special theory of relativity. It indicates that our extended, redefined conception of "inertial mass"—the conception which preserves conservation of momentum—confronts us with a relativistic property, dependent on the velocity of the particle relative to us in our own frame of reference and not the old, reassuring, "intrinsic" property of classical mechanics. This change in view hardly encourages our persistence in holding the old Newtonian and nine-teenth-century notion of inertial mass as measuring "quantity of matter," whatever "matter" might mean.

We have in a sense "derived" the mass–velocity relation by our sequence of in-ductive reasoning, but we have certainly not demonstrated its validity or the validity of the sequence of inductions. The theory stands or falls on its correspondence with observable facts.

Relation (36.21.4) is one of the aspects of relativity theory subject to direct ex-perimental confirmation. The inertial mass of electrons, protons, and other atomic and subatomic particles can be determined as a function of u after acceleration to high velocities (the earliest observations were on the masses of beta particles ejected at various velocities in radioactive decay), and Eq. (36.21.4) is found to be obeyed to the highest experimental accuracy so far attained.

A specific example of comparison between theory and experiment is illustrated in Fig. 36.21.1. The solid line, a graph of Eq. (36.21.4) with m/m_0 plotted against v/c (note the convenience of using dimensionless coordinates), represents the theo-retical prediction. The crosses and dots show the results of experimental measurements

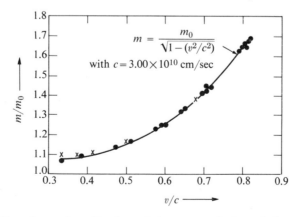

FIG. 36.21.1. Experimental verification of the mass–velocity relation. Solid curve, the graph of Eq. (36.21.4), represents the theoretical prediction. Crosses and dots show ex-perimental values of m/m_0 for β-particles of different velocities v.

on β-rays. We shall not describe the experiments in detail but will simply outline the basic idea: (1) The velocity of a particular group of beta particles emitted from a radioactive substance is determined by the crossed electric and magnetic field technique [see Problem 24.24 and Eq. (31.11.5)]. (2) The momentum of these β-particles is then determined by measuring the radius of curvature of their circular motion in a uniform magnetic field [see Eq. (24.11.1)]. From these two measurements, it is possible to calculate the charge-to-mass ratio e/m as a function of β-particle velocity v. In the light of experience with the electromagnetic theory (experience that we shall only assert and not analyze here), electrical charge is successfully treated as a relativistic invariant; that is, the electronic charge e shows no evidence of changing with respect to different frames of reference. Thus, if we divide the electronic charge-to-mass ratio $e/m_0 = 1.76 \times 10^{11}$ coul/kg, obtained in experiments with low-velocity electrons, by the values of e/m obtained for β-particles of various high velocities, we should have values of m/m_0 to plot against v in Fig. 36.21.1. The crosses in Fig. 36.21.1 are such values observed by Bucherer in 1909, and the dots represent more recent data.

PROBLEM 36.31. It is important to develop some sense for the numerical properties of Eq. (36.21.4); the reader should ask himself some questions and work out some numerical illustrations. For example: What must the velocity of a particle be in order to affect the mass a sensible amount, say 5%? What is the mass of an electron (in rest masses) when it has a velocity of $0.999c$? Replot the graph of Fig. 36.21.1 to obtain a better sense of the shape of the curve in the neighborhood of small values of v/c and for values between 0.9 and 1.0.

PROBLEM 36.32. Return to the operational definitions of mass developed in Chapters 5 and 6. (These definitions establish the concept we have now designated m_0.) On what grounds was mass regarded as an intrinsic, invariable property in classical physics? Describe in your own words how the point of view was changed in the analysis carried out in this section. In the light of these analyses, try to anticipate how one might proceed to redefine the concept of force in the new context. Would your redefined quantity be invariant to transformation of frame of reference?

36.22 THE EQUIVALENCE OF MASS AND ENERGY

Let us examine the implications of the mass–velocity relation, Eq. (36.21.4), in more detail in the region of small values of v/c:

$$m = \frac{m_0}{\sqrt{1 - (v^2/c^2)}}. \tag{36.22.1}$$

Expanding this relation for small values of v/c (see Section 36.15), we obtain

$$m = m_0\left(1 + \frac{1}{2}\frac{v^2}{c^2} - \cdots\right), \tag{36.22.2}$$

$$m = m_0 + \frac{\frac{1}{2}m_0 v^2}{c^2} - \cdots \tag{36.22.3}$$

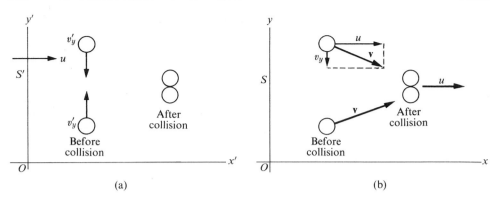

(a)   (b)

FIG. 36.22.1. Inelastic collision of identical particles viewed from two different frames of reference.

Examine the second term on the right-hand side of (36.22.3): This is the classical kinetic energy of the particle divided by c^2. Thus the total inertial mass of the particle, when it is moving relative to us at low velocity v, appears to be the sum of two terms: the rest mass m_0 and an *additional* inertia given by KE/c^2. This suggests that the addition of energy to a system increases the total inertial mass of the system or that quantities of energy, which in classical physics were not detectably associated with inertial properties, must be considered as possessing inertial mass.

Let us test the consistency of the preceding analysis from a rather different point of view. We observe a perfectly inelastic collision of two identical particles from two frames of reference, as illustrated in Fig. 36.22.1. In frame S' the particles approach each other head-on with velocities v'_y, collide inelastically, and stop as shown in Fig. 36.22.1(a). The total momentum is zero initially and remains zero throughout the interaction. In frame S, from which S' appears to be moving to the right at velocity u, the same inelastic collision appears, as shown in Fig. 36.22.1(b). The particles approach each other obliquely with velocities $\mathbf{v}$, and after inelastic collision continue moving to the right with velocity u. The x-component of velocity $\mathbf{v}$ is also equal to u.

In frame S the apparent mass of the particles before collision is given by $m_0/\sqrt{1 - (v^2/c^2)}$. Let us denote the rest mass of the combination of the two particles after collision by M_0 and investigate the relation between M_0 and m_0: Is M_0 simply equal to $2m_0$?

After collision the apparent mass of the combination of the two particles is given by $M_0/\sqrt{1 - (u^2/c^2)}$. For horizontal momentum to be conserved in frame S we have the relation

$$\underbrace{\frac{2m_0u}{\sqrt{1 - (v^2/c^2)}}}_{\substack{\text{Total horizontal component of}\\\text{momentum before collision}}} = \underbrace{\frac{M_0u}{\sqrt{1 - (u^2/c^2)}}}_{\substack{\text{Total horizontal momentum}\\\text{after collision}}}. \tag{36.22.4}$$

Since $v^2 > u^2$, it is clear from Eq. (36.22.4) that if momentum is to be conserved

M_0 must be greater than $2m_0$! Let us examine this indication in more detail. As $u \to 0$, $v_y \to v'_y$, and we have

$$\frac{2m_0}{\sqrt{1 - (v'^2_y/c^2)}} = M_0. \qquad (36.22.5)$$

By evaluating the limit as $u \to 0$, we discover the relation between M_0 and m_0 for the head-on collision of Fig. 36.22.1(a). Equation (36.22.5) says that the total apparent inertial mass before inelastic collision is equal to the total rest mass after collision; i.e., total mass is conserved in the event but *rest* mass is *not* conserved. The rest mass actually *increases*.

Let us evaluate the increase in rest mass:

$$M_0 - 2m_0 = 2m_0 \left(\frac{1}{\sqrt{1 - (v'^2_y/c^2)}} - 1 \right). \qquad (36.22.6)$$

For the region of small values of v'_y/c, this becomes

$$M_0 - 2m_0 = 2m_0 \left(1 + \frac{1}{2} \frac{v'^2_y}{c^2} - \cdots - 1 \right),$$

$$M_0 - 2m_0 = \frac{2(\frac{1}{2}m_0 v'^2_y)}{c^2} - \cdots \qquad (36.22.7)$$

Equation (36.22.7) indicates that, at relatively low velocities, the total rest mass increased by an amount equal to the total classical KE before collision divided by c^2. In other words, the kinetic energy, which seems to be associated with the inertia of the moving bodies before collision and which is zero after the inelastic collision, is directly related to the increase in rest mass of the system. If we multiply Eq. (36.22.3) through by c^2, we obtain

$$mc^2 = m_0 c^2 + \tfrac{1}{2}m_0 u^2 - \cdots \qquad (36.22.8)$$

All the quantities in Eq. (36.22.8) have the dimensions of energy. Einstein suggested the interpretation which is now famous for the confirmation to be found in the phenomena of nuclear physics: mc^2 is to be interpreted as the *total* energy to be associated with a particle of apparent inertial mass m; $m_0 c^2$ is the energy associated with the rest mass. If in a particular phenomenon the total rest mass of a system increases or decreases (i.e., the energy associated with rest mass is increased or decreased), energy in one form or another is absorbed or liberated. For example, the splitting up of a uranium nucleus is accompanied by a decrease in total rest mass and the appearance of an equivalent amount of kinetic energy of the fragments.

36.23 THE RELATIVISTIC WORK–ENERGY THEOREM

We can carry out a check on the internal consistency of the calculations and interpretations made in the last section regarding the mass–energy equivalence by setting up another analysis, one that parallels the development of the work–kinetic energy theorem in Section 18.4. In order to do this we must first redefine the concept of force in a manner consistent with our new theory. This is done by taking the force acting on a particle to be defined as the time rate of change of momentum imparted to the particle:

$$\mathbf{F}_{net} = (d/dt)(m\mathbf{v}). \tag{36.23.1}$$

This definition reduces to the classical second law of motion in the limit of low velocities. Coupled with the third law, it assures us that interacting particles, even at relativistic velocities, will impart equal and opposite momentum changes to each other in a closed system; thus definition (36.23.1) is consistent with the requirement that momentum be conserved in a closed system.

Let us now imagine that we impart a net force, $\mathbf{F}_{net}$, to a particle (located at $s = 0$ and having an initial velocity $v = 0$), and accelerate the particle to a final velocity v at position s. Let us denote the work done on the particle by the symbol $E - E_0$ (final minus initial energy), and evaluate the integral

$$E - E_0 = \int_{\substack{s=0 \\ v=0}}^{\substack{s=s \\ v=v}} F_{net}(s)\, ds = \int_{\substack{s=0 \\ v=0}}^{\substack{s=s \\ v=v}} \left[\frac{d}{dt}(mv)\right] ds. \tag{36.23.2}$$

Adopting exactly the same mathematical strategy used in Section 18.4, we invoke the chain rule of differentiation to convert the derivative with respect to t into a derivative with respect to s:

$$\frac{d}{dt}(mv) = \frac{d}{ds}(mv)\frac{ds}{dt} = v\frac{d(mv)}{ds}. \tag{36.23.3}$$

Thus, to evaluate the integral in (36.23.2), we must find an antiderivative with respect to s of $v\, d(mv)/ds$. There are many ways of evaluating this antiderivative, but it happens that everything reduces to particularly simple form if we express m and v in terms of γ. First let us note that $v\, d(mv)/ds$ can be expressed as a derivative of $(mv)^2$ if we multiply and divide by $2m$:

$$v\frac{d(mv)}{ds} = \frac{2(mv)}{2m}\frac{d(mv)}{ds} = \frac{1}{2m}\frac{d(mv)^2}{ds}. \tag{36.23.4}$$

Now, in terms of γ, we have $m = m_0\gamma$, and

$$\gamma \equiv \frac{1}{\sqrt{1 - (v^2/c^2)}}; \quad 1 - \frac{v^2}{c^2} = \frac{1}{\gamma^2}; \quad v^2 = c^2\left(1 - \frac{1}{\gamma^2}\right). \tag{36.23.5}$$

When we use the last two relations, Eq. (36.23.4) becomes

$$v\frac{d(mv)}{ds} = \frac{1}{2m}\frac{d(mv)^2}{ds} = \frac{1}{2m_0\gamma}\frac{d}{ds}\left[m_0^2\gamma^2 c^2\left(1 - \frac{1}{\gamma^2}\right)\right]$$

$$= \frac{m_0 c^2}{2\gamma}\frac{d}{ds}\left[\gamma^2\left(1 - \frac{1}{\gamma^2}\right)\right] = \frac{m_0 c^2}{2\gamma}\frac{d}{ds}(\gamma^2 - 1), \tag{36.23.6}$$

$$v\frac{d(mv)}{ds} = \frac{m_0 c^2}{2\gamma}\cdot 2\gamma\frac{d\gamma}{ds} = m_0 c^2\frac{d\gamma}{ds}. \tag{36.23.7}$$

Therefore (36.23.2) becomes

$$E - E_0 = m_0 c^2 \int_{\substack{s=0 \\ v=0}}^{\substack{s=s \\ v=v}} \left(\frac{d\gamma}{ds}\right) ds$$

$$= m_0 c^2 [\gamma]_{v=0}^{v=v} = m_0 c^2 \left[\frac{1}{\sqrt{1 - (v^2/c^2)}}\right]_{v=0}^{v=v},$$

$$E - E_0 = m_0 c^2 \left[\frac{1}{\sqrt{1 - (v^2/c^2)}} - 1\right] = mc^2 - m_0 c^2. \qquad (36.23.8)$$

Equation (36.23.8) reinforces the suggestion made in the preceding section that mc^2 should be regarded as the total energy E associated with the particle when it possesses velocity v relative to our frame of reference. It also reinforces the hypothesis that the quantity $m_0 c^2$ represents a quantity of energy associated with the rest mass of the particle. Whether these numbers actually behave as energy quantities —in the sense of being conserved in various transformations as are the more familiar analogous quantities of classical mechanics—is a question for experiment to decide. The inductive calculations made in this and the preceding section do not prove anything in themselves; they only suggest possibilities that must be tested.

36.24 EXPERIMENTAL VERIFICATION OF THE MASS–ENERGY RELATION

The prediction of the mass–energy equivalence and the possibility of the conversion of rest mass into other forms of energy (or vice versa) was one of the most dramatic results of Einstein's theory. These predictions have been confirmed quantitatively, with great precision, in a variety of ways, a confirmation which culminated in the design and construction of atomic bombs and nuclear reactors. We shall discuss here only two very brief examples.

Since, in Eq. (36.23.8), the energy E tends to infinity as $v \to c$, the energy-conservation concept implies that, with finite energy supply, we cannot accelerate a material particle to a velocity equal to that of light; i.e., that the velocity of light constitutes an *ultimate speed* which may be approached, but not reached or exceeded, in processes involving material particles. This prediction is experimentally confirmed by the data represented in Fig. 36.24.1. Electrons are accelerated in a high-energy accelerator through various potential differences ΔV, and their velocities are measured after acceleration. The experimental values of velocity are observed to level off and approach c as ΔV increases to very large values, instead of showing the indefinitely increasing velocity $v^2 = 2e\,\Delta V/m$ predicted by classical theory.

The most direct confirmation of the mass–energy relation is provided by nuclear transformations, in which it is possible to observe net changes in rest mass and the appearance of equivalent amounts of kinetic energy of the resulting particles. When the metallic element lithium is bombarded with energetic protons, it is found that two α-particles are formed in accordance with the reaction

$$_3^7\text{Li} + {}_1^1\text{H} \to {}_2^4\text{He} + {}_2^4\text{He}. \qquad (36.24.1)$$

Rest mass m_0 in atomic mass units				
7.01822	1.00814	4.00387	4.00387	

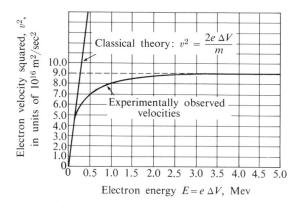

FIG. 36.24.1. Graph of v^2 versus $e \Delta V$ for electrons (charge e) accelerated through potential difference ΔV. Straight line shows graph that would be expected from classical theory. Curve shows experimentally measured velocities squared. Experimental values level off, approaching c^2 and confirming the relativistic prediction that c is an ultimate speed.

The combined kinetic energies of the two α-particles is found to be over 50 times greater than the KE of the bombarding protons. Note the following comparisons of rest masses:

$$\text{Total rest mass of reactants} = 7.01822 + 1.00814 = 8.02636$$
$$\text{Total rest mass of products} = 4.00387 + 4.00387 = 8.00774$$
$$\text{Decrease in rest mass for each event, } \Delta m_0 \qquad\qquad = 0.01862$$

The rest mass of the system decreases, and the conservation law we are proposing associates this decrease in rest mass with the enormously increased KE of the products. Let us calculate the rest mass decrease in energy units by evaluating $c^2 \, \Delta m_0$:

$$\underbrace{\frac{0.0186 \times 10^{-3}}{6.02 \times 10^{23}}}_{\Delta m_0 \text{ in kg}} \cdot \underbrace{(3.00 \times 10^8)^2}_{c^2} = 2.78 \times 10^{-12} \, \mathrm{j} = 17.3 \text{ Mev}.$$

(See Section 34.13 for definition of electron volt as a unit of energy.) Thus, if our interpretation is correct, the α-particles formed in this reaction should have a combined energy of 17.3 Mev in excess of the energy of the incoming proton. It is observed experimentally that the α-particles each have energies of about 8.7 Mev when the incoming protons have energies of about 0.25 Mev—an excellent confirmation of our hypothesis.

PROBLEM 36.33. Show that the total rest mass of an electron corresponds to 0.51 Mev and that 1 atomic mass unit corresponds to 931 Mev. What energy would be released (in Mev) if a proton rest mass were entirely converted into KE of other particles?

PROBLEM 36.34. It is asserted that the enormous energy release of the sun (this was a great puzzle to nineteenth-century scientists, who calculated that the sun could last no more than about one million years running on the energy of known chemical reactions) can be accounted for by a succession of nuclear reactions that have the net result of combining protons to form helium nuclei. Consider the relevant rest masses and determine whether or not you would expect energy to be released in such a sequence.

PROBLEM 36.35.   In the Cambridge electron accelerator, electrons can be accelerated to energies of about 6 billion (that is, 6×10^9) electron volts. What is the total inertial mass of electrons of this energy? What is their velocity? [*Answer:* $m \cong 12{,}000$ electron rest masses; $v \cong 0.9999999935c$.]

Just as Mayer and Joule in the 1840's recognized that units of heat and work represent different ways of measuring a quantity (energy) that is conserved in physical changes, relativity theory recognizes inertial mass as being part of the same conservation scheme; i.e., units of mass and units of energy are different measures of a conserved quantity, one that can manifest itself in a variety of forms. Thus in relativity theory we frequently refer to "mass-energy" or the "law of conservation of mass-energy," referring to the unification of view that the theory reveals.

In the theory of relativity we take as fundamental physical laws those regularities which seem to be invariant to transformation from one inertial frame of reference to another. In the development we have carried out to this point these regularities are indicated to be

       (1) The constancy of the velocity of light,
       (2) The conservation of momentum,
       (3) The conservation of mass-energy.

Note that these regularities are not "derived" or "proved." These are *inductions,* drawn from particular cases, just as Newton induced the laws that constituted his theory of mechanics and gravitation. The inductions become the primary postulates of the theory. The theory as a whole is acceptable only because it appears to "work"; its analyses and predictions agree with observed physical facts to the best accuracy of observation available at the present time.

36.25   THE WAVE–PARTICLE DUALITY

After development of the mass-energy concept, Einstein himself was quick to point out that we must associate inertial mass with energy in any form and that we must therefore expect electromagnetic energy (i.e., light) to have inertial properties. In 1924 the French physicist Louis de Broglie used this idea as a point of departure for a rather startling hypothesis based on purely theoretical speculations. Although de Broglie's detailed analysis involves a rather elaborate analytical treatment, we can boil down its essence to the following very simple sequence:

Recall that a photon of light is defined by its quantum of energy $h\nu$. In the light of the mass-energy equivalence, the inertial mass of a photon should be given by

$$m = \frac{E}{c^2} = \frac{h\nu}{c^2}. \tag{36.25.1}$$

(*All* of this inertial mass is associated with the electromagnetic energy; the *rest* mass is zero. If the rest mass were not zero, the energy would be infinite, since photons have velocity equal to *c*.) Since photons have velocity *c*, the momentum *p* of a photon must be given by the product *mc*, and from Eq. (36.25.1) we have

$$p = mc = \frac{h\nu}{c} \qquad (36.25.2)$$

Since c/ν is equal to λ, the wavelength associated with photons of frequency ν, Eq. (36.25.2) becomes

$$p = \frac{h}{\lambda}; \qquad \lambda = \frac{h}{p}. \qquad (36.25.3)$$

That is, the wavelength associated with photons of frequency ν can be regarded as the quotient of Planck's constant and the momentum of the photons.

De Broglie's speculation runs as follows: Light exhibits a wave-particle duality, manifesting a wavelike behavior in time average values on a macroscopic scale and a corpuscular (photon) behavior in the emission and absorption of light on the micro-scale. Might matter (entities with nonzero rest mass) exhibit an analogous duality in a reverse sense, corpuscular on a macroscopic scale and wavelike on the micro-scopic? If so, might not Eq. (36.25.3) apply to electrons, say, as well as photons? What would it mean to say that electrons with momentum $p = mv$ were associated with a "wavelength" h/mv? (Note that, in this inductive guesswork and reasoning by analogy, there is no attempt to spell out just what is "waving" any more than Young and Fresnel tried to identify what was waving in their wave model of light, or any more than Einstein tried to draw a concrete picture of a photon.)

The most characteristic manifestations of wave behavior are interference and dif-fraction. If electrons exhibit a wavelike behavior, it might possibly be detected experimentally through the formation of some kind of diffraction pattern. What is the order of magnitude of wavelength one would have to contend with?

PROBLEM 36.36.(a)   Verify that electron beams formed in cathode ray tubes under potential differences of the order of 1000 v (Chapter 31) are not relativistic; that is, that the electron velocity is not large enough to justify correcting for relativistic effects under these circumstances. Is this consistent with the graph shown in Fig. 36.24.1? (b) Show that the momentum of an electron accelerated through a potential difference ΔV is given by $\sqrt{2me\,\Delta V}$ and that, according to Eq. (36.25.3), we then have

$$\lambda = \frac{h}{\sqrt{2me\,\Delta V}}. \qquad (36.25.4)$$

(c) Substitute the numerical values of the constants, and show that for accelerating potentials between 100 and 1000 v, λ would lie between about 1.2 and 0.38 A.

The predicted wavelengths, calculated in Problem 36.36, are similar in order of magnitude to the wavelengths of X-rays, and fall in the range of values equal to

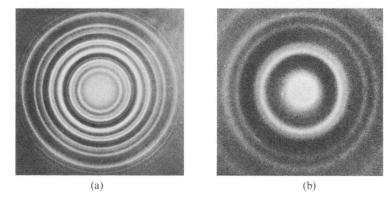

(a)   (b)

FIG. 36.25.1. Electron diffraction pattern. (a) Polycrystalline SnO_2. (b) Gold.
Part (a) from *Theory and Practice of Electron Diffraction*, by G. P. Thomson and
W. Cochrane (London: Macmillan & Co. Ltd., 1939). Part (b) from *Wave Mechanics of the Free Electron*, by G. P. Thomson (New York: McGraw-Hill, 1930).

atomic spacings in crystals.   Thus, if such wavelengths are indeed associated with
a beam of electrons, a crystalline material should act as a diffraction grating for the
electron beam, just as it acts as a diffraction grating for a beam of X-rays.

In 1925, G. P. Thomson (son of J. J. Thomson) put these ideas to direct experimental
test by performing an experiment exactly analogous to the Debye-Scherrer experiment with X-rays described in Section 34.5. A narrow beam of electrons was passed
through a very thin metal foil (such a foil consists of a multitude of very small,
randomly oriented, metallic crystals, and is in this sense similar to the crystal powder
utilized by Debye and Scherrer), and a diffraction pattern such as that illustrated
in Fig. 36.25.1 was observed. Note how similar it is to the X-ray pattern shown in
Fig. 34.5.2.

The diffraction pattern implies that electrons are deflected in the crystal and form
regions of darkness or "destructive interference" (absence of electrons) and regions
of brightness or "constructive interference" (presence of electrons). If values of λ
are calculated from the diffraction pattern (making use of the known spacings in
the crystal lattice), these values are found to agree precisely with the values predicted by de Broglie's formula.

About the same time that Thomson performed his experiments, Davisson and
Germer at the Bell Telephone Laboratories observed constructive and destructive
interference patterns in electron beams reflected to various angles after incidence
at the surface of a nickel crystal. The apparent wavelengths determined in these
experiments also agreed with the de Broglie formula. In the years following the experiments of Thomson and of Davisson and Germer, it was shown that similar
diffraction effects were exhibited not only by electrons but by atoms and molecules
as well.

The concept that material entities could exhibit wavelike properties played a profound role in the evolution of the modern theory of quantum mechanics during the
years 1926 and 1927. We cannot pursue these particular developments, but we can

readily show that the wave-particle concept is consistent with the atomic model first visualized by Bohr.

Recall that each orbital radius of an electron in the hydrogen atom is associated with a particular velocity and therefore a particular linear momentum $mv = mr\omega$. According to de Broglie's formula, the electron should have an effective wavelength

$$\lambda = \frac{h}{mr\omega}. \tag{36.25.5}$$

As the electron revolves in a particular orbit, its "waves" or "wave trains" can presumably interfere either constructively or destructively. A destructive interference would imply removal of the electron from the given region; constructive interference would imply presence of the electron in a steady state. For heuristic purposes, without specifying what the waves "are," we can imagine the waves interfering as sketched in Fig. 36.25.2.

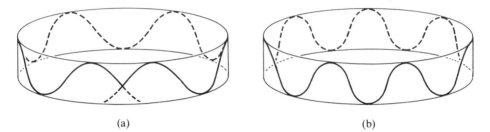

(a)   (b)

Fig. 36.25.2. Constructive and destructive interference of a wave train repeatedly overlapping itself in a circular orbit. (a) Wave moves around a narrow channel in one direction under circumstances such that overlap is *not* crest-to-crest and trough-to-trough; i.e., overlap is not constructive. Wavelength does not fit into circumferential path an integral number of times. (b) A different wavelength in the same channel. If the wavelength fits into the circumference an integral number of times, the overlap continues to be constructive all the way around the circumference.

In this wave train, which repeatedly overlaps itself in motion of the electron in a circular orbit, constructive interference occurs if the wavelength fits into the circumference of the circle an integral number of times. That is, if

$$2\pi r = n\lambda, \qquad n = 1, 2, 3, \ldots \tag{36.25.6}$$

If we substitute Eq. (36.25.5) for λ, we obtain

$$2\pi r = n\,\frac{h}{mr\omega},$$

$$mr^2\omega = n\,\frac{h}{2\pi}. \tag{36.25.7}$$

Equation (36.25.7) is exactly Bohr's quantum condition, Eq. (35.5.12). Thus we could develop the entire Bohr model of the hydrogen atom with the concept of the de Broglie wavelength as a starting point. As we saw in Chapter 35, this model is only partially successful; the concept of the de Broglie wave is not in itself enough to establish a better theory. As has been remarked previously, in order to develop a theory more nearly consistent with known facts of atomic and molecular behavior, it proved necessary to abandon the elements of classical mechanics retained in the Bohr model and develop an entirely new mechanics of microscopic phenomena. Discovery of the de Broglie relation was only an initial step in this direction; the rest of the path must be followed in more advanced presentations.

SUPPLEMENTARY READING AND STUDY

The impact of the unsettling conceptions of the theory of relativity on both the popular and professional imagination has been such that a huge literature is available at every level, from the most popular to the most technical. It would be impossible to give anything resembling a comprehensive reading list. The author merely cites here some of the sources that he personally has found illuminating and useful, publications which are in addition to the references already cited in the body of the chapter.

Original sources, including a translation of Einstein's epoch-making paper of 1905:
The Principle of Relativity. Papers by Lorentz, Einstein, Minkowski, and Weyl. New York: Dover Publications, Paperback S81, 1958

Popularizations of the relativity concepts and their background:
Relativity. The Special and General Theory, Albert Einstein. New York: Crown Publishers, Bonanza Paperback, 1961. This is Einstein's own presentation.
Relativity for the Million, M. Gardner. New York: The Macmillan Co., 1962. A lucid and conceptually sound explication.

Biographical material and commentaries:
Albert Einstein, Philosopher-Scientist, 2 volumes, P. A. Schilp (editor). New York: Harper, 1959, Harper Torchbooks, 502, 503
Ideas and Opinions, Albert Einstein. New York: Crown Publishers, 1954

Epistemological discussions:
The Logic of Modern Physics, P. W. Bridgman. New York: The Macmillan Co., 1961
A Sophisticate's Primer of Relativity, P. W. Bridgman. Middletown, Conn.: Wesleyan University Press, 1962
Concepts of Space, Concepts of Force, Concepts of Mass, M. Jammer. Cambridge, Mass.: Harvard University Press, 1954, 1957, 1961 (respectively)

Text presentations at freshman–sophomore college level:
Einstein's Theory of Relativity, M. Born. New York: Dover Publications, Paperback S769, 1962
Electromagnetism and Relativity, E. P. Ney. New York: Harper & Row, 1962
Introductory Mechanics, E. F. Taylor. New York: John Wiley & Sons, 1963
The Feynman Lectures, Volume I, R. P. Feynman, R. B. Leighton, M. Sands. Reading, Mass.: Addison-Wesley, 1963, Chapters 10, 15, 16, 17

Bibliography and reprints of useful journal articles:

"Resource Letter SRT-1 on Special Relativity Theory," *Am. J. Phys.*, **30,** 462 (1962)

Special Relativity Theory: Selected Reprints.   Published for the American Association of Physics Teachers.   Available from American Institute of Physics, Department BN, 335 East 45th St, New York, N.Y.   (Contains copy of Resource Letter SRT-1.)

Films particularly useful in conjunction with this chapter:

Frames of Reference, issued by the Physical Science Study Committee

Time Dilation, issued by Educational Services, Inc.

The Ultimate Speed, issued by Educational Services, Inc.

Matter Waves, issued by the Physical Science Study Committee

FUNDAMENTAL PHYSICAL CONSTANTS*

Name of quantity	Symbol	Best current value	Value for ordinary computation (3 significant figures)
Velocity of light in vacuum	c	$(2.997925 \pm 0.000003) \times 10^8$	3.00×10^8 m/sec 186,000 mi/sec
Universal gravitational constant	G	$(6.670 \pm 0.015) \times 10^{-11}$	6.67×10^{-11} n · m^2/kg^2
Coulomb's law constant	k	$(8.98759 \pm 0.00002) \times 10^9$	9.00×10^9 n · m^2/coul^2
Planck's constant	h	$(6.6256 \pm 0.0005) \times 10^{-34}$	6.63×10^{-34} joule · sec
Boltzmann's constant	k	$(1.38054 \pm 0.00018) \times 10^{-23}$	1.38×10^{-23} joule/°K
Faraday's constant	F	$96,4870 \pm 16$	96,500 coul
Avogadro's number	N_0	$(6.02252 \pm 0.00028) \times 10^{23}$	6.02×10^{23}/mole
Universal gas constant	R	8.3143 ± 0.0012	8.32 joules/mole · °K 0.0821 liter · atm/mole · °K
Molar volume of ideal gas at STP	—	22.4136 ± 0.0030	22.4 liters
Absolute zero of temperature	—	$273.16°K$	$-273°K$
Mechanical equivalent of heat	J	4.1868 ± 0.0004	4.19 joules/cal
Electron charge	e	$(1.60210 \pm 0.00007) \times 10^{-19}$	1.60×10^{-19} coul
Electron rest mass	m_e	$(9.1091 \pm 0.0004) \times 10^{-31}$ $(5.48597 \pm 0.00009) \times 10^{-4}$ amu	9.11×10^{-31} kg
Proton rest mass	m_p	$(1.67252 \pm 0.00008) \times 10^{-27}$ $(1.00727663 \pm 0.00000024)$ amu	1.67×10^{-27} kg
Neutron rest mass	m_n	$(1.67482 \pm 0.00008) \times 10^{-27}$ $(1.0086654 \pm 0.00000013)$ amu	1.67×10^{-27} kg
Hydrogen atom rest mass	m_H	$(1.67343 \pm 0.00008) \times 10^{-27}$ $(1.00782543 \pm 0.00000024)$ amu	1.67×10^{-27} kg
Proton-electron mass ratio	m_p/m_e	1836.12	1840
Radius of first Bohr orbit in hydrogen	a	$(5.29167 \pm 0.00007) \times 10^{-11}$	5.29×10^{-11} m 0.529 A

* Adapted from "New Values for the Physical Constants, as Recommended by the NAS–NRC," *Physics Today*, February 1964. All values are based on the physical scale of atomic masses with $C^{12} \equiv 12.00000000$ amu.

DATA ON THE SOLAR SYSTEM*

Body and symbol		Mass (earth = 1)	Mean distance from sun		Sidereal period, days	Mean diameter	
			km	miles		km	miles
Sun	☉	329,390	—	—	—	1,390,600	864,100
Mercury	☿	0.0549	58×10^6	36.0×10^6	87.97	5,140	3,194
Venus	♀	0.8073	108	67.1	244.70	12,620	7,842
Earth	⊕, ♁	1.0000	149**	92.9**	365.26	12,756	7,926
Mars	♂	0.1065	288	141.7	686.98	6,860	4,263
Jupiter	♃	314.5	778	483.4	4332.59	143,600	89,229
Saturn	♄	94.07	1426	886.1	10759.20	120,600	74,937
Uranus	♅	14.40	2869	1782.7	30685.93	53,400	33,181
Neptune	♆	16.72	4495	2793.1	60187.64	49,700	30,882
Pluto	♇	—	5900	3666.1	90885	—	—
Moon	☽	0.01228	38×10^4†	23.9×10^4†	27.32	3,476	2,160

* Adapted from the *Handbook of Chemistry and Physics*, Chemical Rubber Publishing Co., Cleveland, Ohio.
† Distance from the earth.
** Called the "astronomical unit," 1 AU.

MISCELLANEOUS TERRESTRIAL DATA

Standard atmospheric pressure	$1.013 \times 10^5 \ \text{n/m}^2$
	$14.70 \ \text{lb/in}^2$
Velocity of sound in dry air at STP	$331.4 \ \text{m/sec}$
	$1089 \ \text{ft/sec}$
	$742.5 \ \text{mi/hr}$
Acceleration due to gravity; g = standard value	$9.80665 \ \text{m/sec}^2$
Approx. 45° lat. at sea level	$32.1740 \ \text{ft/sec}^2$
Sea level at equator	$9.78049 \ \text{m/sec}^2$
Radius of earth: equatorial	$3963 \ \text{mi}$
polar	$3950 \ \text{mi}$
Mass of earth	$5.983 \times 10^{24} \ \text{kg}$
Mean density of earth	$5522 \ \text{kg/m}^3$
Mean orbital velocity of earth	$29,770 \ \text{m/sec}$
Mean angular velocity of rotation of earth	$7.29 \times 10^{-5} \ \text{rad/sec}$
Earth magnetic field (about 40° lat.)	$5.7 \times 10^{-5} \ \text{weber/m}^2$

ARITHMETICAL CONSTANTS: $\pi = 3.1415926$; $\epsilon = 2.718282$

CONVERSION FACTORS

Length
  1 meter: 3.281 ft, 39.37 in.
  1 inch: 2.540 cm
  1 mile: 1609 m, 1.609 km
  1 Angstrom unit: 10^{-8} cm, 10^{-10} m

Volume
  1 liter: 0.2642 gal (U.S.), 1.000×10^3 cm^3

Speed
  1 meter/sec: 3.281 ft/sec, 3.6000 km/hr, 2.235 mi/hr
  1 mi/hr: 1.467 ft/sec, 0.4470 m/sec

Force
  1 newton: 1.000×10^5 dynes, 0.2247 lb
  1 pound: 4.448 n

Mass
  1 kilogram: 2.205 lb, 0.0685 slug
  1 pound: 0.4536 kg, 0.0311 slug
  1 atomic mass unit (physical scale): 1.65980×10^{-27} kg

Energy
  1 joule: 1.000×10^7 ergs, 0.2389 cal, 2.389×10^{-4} kcal
  1 calorie: 4.186 joules
  1 electron volt: 1.602×10^{-19} joule, 1.074×10^{-9} amu
  1 atomic mass unit (physical scale): 1.492×10^{-10} joule; 931.478 Mev
  1 Btu: 251.996 cal, 778.26 ft · lb, 60.2 joule
  1 calorie/gram: 1.80 Btu/lb

Electric charge
  1 coulomb (absolute): 2.998×10^9 statcoul (esu)

GREEK ALPHABET

A	α	alpha	I	ι	iota	P	ρ	rho
B	β	beta	K	κ	kappa	Σ	σ	sigma
Γ	γ	gamma	Λ	λ	lambda	T	τ	tau
Δ	δ	delta	M	μ	mu	Y	υ	upsilon
E	ϵ	epsilon	N	ν	nu	Φ	ϕ	phi
Z	ζ	zeta	Ξ	ξ	xi	X	χ	chi
H	η	eta	O	o	omicron	Ψ	ψ	psi
Θ	θ	theta	Π	π	pi	Ω	ω	omega

ALPHABETICAL LIST OF THE ELEMENTS*

Element	Symbol	Atomic number, Z	Atomic weight	Element	Symbol	Atomic number, Z	Atomic weight
Actinium	Ac	89	[227]	Hafnium	Hf	72	178.49
Aluminum	Al	13	26.9815	Helium	He	2	4.0026
Americium	Am	95	[243]	Holmium	Ho	67	164.930
Antimony	Sb	51	121.75	Hydrogen	H	1	1.00797
Argon	A	18	39.948	Indium	In	49	114.82
Arsenic	As	33	74.9216	Iodine	I	53	126.9044
Astatine	At	85	[210]	Iridium	Ir	77	192.2
Barium	Ba	56	137.34	Iron	Fe	26	55.847
Berkelium	Bk	97	[249]	Krypton	Kr	36	83.80
Beryllium	Be	4	9.0122	Lanthanum	La	57	138.91
Bismuth	Bi	83	208.980	Lead	Pb	82	207.19
Boron	B	5	10.811	Lithium	Li	3	6.939
Bromine	Br	35	79.909	Lutetium	Lu	71	174.97
Cadmium	Cd	48	112.40	Magnesium	Mg	12	24.312
Calcium	Ca	20	40.08	Manganese	Mn	25	54.9380
Californium	Cf	98	[249]	Mendelevium	Md	101	[256]
Carbon	C	6	12.01115	Mercury	Hg	80	200.59
Cerium	Ce	58	140.12	Molybdenum	Mo	42	95.94
Cesium	Cs	55	132.905	Neodymium	Nd	60	144.24
Chlorine	Cl	17	35.453	Neon	Ne	10	20.183
Chromium	Cr	24	51.996	Neptunium	Np	93	[237]
Cobalt	Co	27	58.9332	Nickel	Ni	28	58.71
Copper	Cu	29	63.54	Niobium	Nb	41	92.906
Curium	Cm	96	[245]	Nitrogen	N	7	14.0067
Dysprosium	Dy	66	162.50	Nobelium	No	102	
Einsteinium	Es	99	[253]	Osmium	Os	76	190.2
Erbium	Er	68	167.26	Oxygen	O	8	15.9994
Europium	Eu	63	151.96	Palladium	Pd	46	106.4
Fermium	Fm	100	[255]	Phosphorus	P	15	30.9738
Fluorine	F	9	18.9984	Platinum	Pt	78	195.09
Francium	Fr	87	[223]	Plutonium	Pu	94	[242]
Gadolinium	Gd	64	157.25	Polonium	Po	84	[210]
Gallium	Ga	31	69.72	Potassium	K	19	39.102
Germanium	Ge	32	72.59	Praseodymium	Pr	59	140.907
Gold	Au	79	196.967	Promethium	Pm	61	[147]

ALPHABETICAL LIST OF THE ELEMENTS (*Continued*)

Element	Symbol	Atomic number, Z	Atomic weight	Element	Symbol	Atomic number, Z	Atomic weight
Protactinium	Pa	91	[231]	Tellurium	Te	52	127.60
Radium	Ra	88	226.05	Terbium	Tb	65	158.924
Radon	Rn	86	[222]	Thallium	Tl	81	204.37
Rhenium	Re	75	186.22	Thorium	Th	90	232.038
Rhodium	Rh	45	102.905	Thulium	Tm	69	168.934
Rubidium	Rb	37	85.47	Tin	Sn	50	118.69
Ruthenium	Ru	44	101.07	Titanium	Ti	22	47.90
Samarium	Sm	62	150.35	Tungsten			
Scandium	Sc	21	44.956	(Wolfram)	W	74	183.85
Selenium	Se	34	78.96	Uranium	U	92	238.03
Silicon	Si	14	28.086	Vanadium	V	23	50.942
Silver	Ag	47	107.870	Xenon	Xe	54	131.30
Sodium	Na	11	22.9898	Ytterbium	Yb	70	173.04
Strontium	Sr	38	87.62	Yttrium	Y	39	88.905
Sulfur	S	16	32.064	Zinc	Zn	30	65.37
Tantalum	Ta	73	180.948	Zirconium	Zr	40	91.22
Technetium	Tc	43	[99]				

* The atomic weights, based on the exact number 12 as the assigned atomic mass of the principal isotope of carbon, are the most recent (1961) values adopted by the International Union of Pure and Applied Chemistry. For artificially produced elements, the approximate atomic weight of the most stable isotope is given in brackets.

Trigonometry

E.1 Radian measure. Familiar angular measure, in degrees, is established by subdividing the angle contained in a full positive turn around vertex O into 360 equal parts. This defines an arbitrary unit, and angles measured in such units are said to have a dimension, just as measurements of length have dimension and units. An alternative way of measuring angles is by means of a ratio or dimensionless, "pure" number. Angle α in Fig. E.1.1 intercepts arcs of length s_1 and s_2 on circles of radius r_1 and r_2, respectively. In each case the fraction of circumference intercepted is the same; therefore

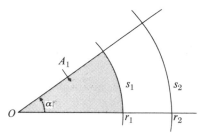

FIG. E.1.1. Angle α intercepts arcs of length s_1 and s_2 on circles of radius r_1 and r_2.

$$\frac{s_1}{2\pi r_1} = \frac{s_2}{2\pi r_2} \quad \text{or} \quad \frac{s_1}{r_1} = \frac{s_2}{r_2}. \quad \text{(E.1.1)}$$

Another way of viewing the problem is to note that the area of sector A_1 is the same fraction of the total area of the circle as the intercepted arc s_1 is of the circumference. That is,

$$\frac{s_1}{2\pi r_1} = \frac{A_1}{\pi r_1^2} \quad \text{and} \quad \frac{s_1}{r_1} = \frac{2A_1}{r_1^2} = \frac{s_2}{r_2} = \frac{2A_2}{r_2^2}. \quad \text{(E.1.2)}$$

Thus any particular angle α is associated with a unique, dimensionless number defined by the ratio s/r or $2A/r^2$, and we can use this number as a measure of the angle itself. We take

$$\alpha \equiv \frac{s}{r} = \frac{2A}{r^2}, \quad \text{(E.1.3)}$$

and say that α is being measured in *radians*. Since, for a complete turn, $s = 2\pi r$, the complete angle is 2π radians. Therefore 2π radians $\backsimeq$ 360° (read the symbol $\backsimeq$ as "equivalent to" or "corresponds to"), and 1 radian $\backsimeq$ 57.3°. Angles such as 10 radians or 573° would correspond to more than one full turn, etc. The student should learn to recognize $\pi/6$, $\pi/4$, $\pi/3$, and $\pi/2$ as angles of 30°, 45°, 60°, and 90°, respectively.

[*Note:* Rigorous mathematical treatment of these concepts requires arithmetical definition of the number π and of arc length and sector area. No attempt has been made in the preceding paragraph to establish such definitions. Use is simply made of the student's previous, intuitive geometrical knowledge. Individuals interested in pursuing these ideas more rigorously should consult a text on calculus.]

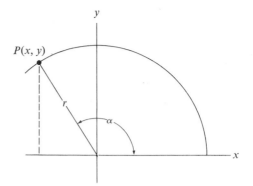

FIG. E.2.1. Trigonometric functions of angle α are defined in terms of coordinates of point $P(x, y)$ and radius r.

E.2   Trigonometric functions. For any particular angle α, ratios such as y/r, x/r, x/y (Fig. E.2.1) have fixed numerical values. (The x and y are Cartesian coordinates, and may assume positive or negative values; the radius r is taken as an inherently positive quantity.) We can therefore think of any one of these ratios as being a function of the angle α. These ratios are given names as follows:

$$\text{sine } \alpha = \sin \alpha = \frac{y}{r}, \tag{E.2.1}$$

$$\text{cosine } \alpha = \cos \alpha \equiv \frac{x}{r}, \tag{E.2.2}$$

$$\text{tangent } \alpha = \tan \alpha \equiv \frac{y}{x}. \tag{E.2.3}$$

The functions have the domain $-\infty < \alpha < +\infty$, and take on positive and negative values depending on the coordinates x and y. From the definitions it follows, for example, that $\sin 0 = 0$; $\sin \pi/2 = +1$; $\sin \pi = 0$; $\sin 3\pi/2 = -1$; etc. The absolute value of the sine and cosine functions can never exceed unity. Graphs of the various functions are sketched in Fig. E.2.2. The reader is advised to connect the graphs with the definitions given above either by actually plotting them or by visualizing the arithmetical behavior of (E.2.1, 2, 3) as α passes through a sequence of values, both positive and negative.

The graphs illustrate the assertion that any one of the trigonometric functions has a unique value for a particular angle α. The inverse, however, is not unique, as illustrated in Fig. E.2.2(a): an infinite number of angles have a sine equal to $+\frac{1}{2}$. When we wish to find an angle α, whose sine is some particular number, we must sort out from the infinity of possible answers the one relevant to our particular problem.

E.3   Tables and triangles. The graphs in Fig. E.2.2 are called *periodic*; the functions repeat the same pattern over and over again at intervals or periods of 2π. A more careful examination of the graphs reveals that the whole story of numerical values assumed by any one function is actually told in a shorter interval—the quarter period between $\alpha = 0$ and $\pi/2$. In any other quarter period the same values are repeated in a decreasing sequence or with negative sign, etc. The values of sine, cosine, and

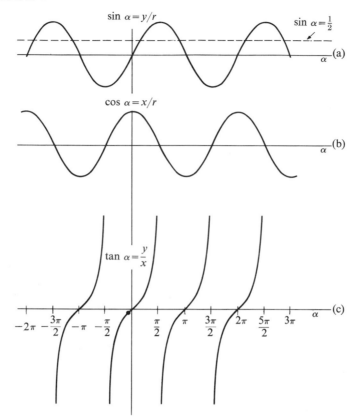

Fɪɢ. E.2.2. Graphs of $\sin \alpha$, $\cos \alpha$ and $\tan \alpha$ versus α.

tangent for a few special angles are easily calculated from geometrical properties, but the values for other angles must be computed by more advanced mathematical methods. (These methods consist of "expanding" the functions in terms of converging infinite series. Consult a calculus text for details.) The table at the end of this section has been computed in this fashion, and, in giving values of the functions for angles between 0 and 90° ($\pi/2$ radians), gives complete information for all other angles as well.

It is useful to recall how to evaluate the functions of the simple angles given in Fig. E.3.1. Using definitions E.2.1, 2, 3:

$$\sin 45° = \frac{1}{\sqrt{2}} = \frac{\sqrt{2}}{2} \qquad \sin 30° = \frac{1}{2} \qquad \qquad \sin 60° = \frac{\sqrt{3}}{2}$$

$$\cos 45° = \frac{1}{\sqrt{2}} = \frac{\sqrt{2}}{2} \qquad \cos 30° = \frac{\sqrt{3}}{2} \qquad \cos 60° = \frac{1}{2}$$

$$\tan 45° = 1 \qquad \qquad \tan 30° = \frac{1}{\sqrt{3}} = \frac{\sqrt{3}}{3} \qquad \tan 60° = \sqrt{3}$$

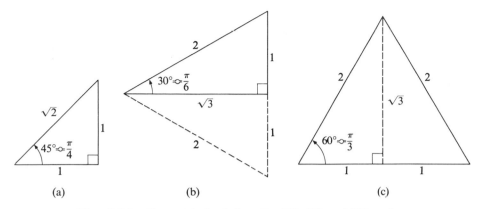

FIG. E.3.1. Geometrical relations for 30°, 45°, and 60° angles.

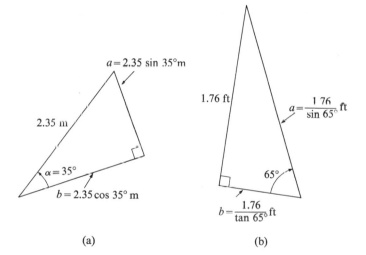

FIG. E.3.2. Calculating the sides of right triangles.

Availability of the tables makes it very easy to perform numerical calculations involving angles and sides of right triangles (Fig. E.3.2).

For a general triangle (Fig. E.3.3), we have

$$c^2 = (b \cos \alpha - a)^2 + (b \sin \alpha)^2,$$
$$c^2 = b^2 \cos^2 \alpha - 2ab \cos \alpha + a^2 + b^2 \sin^2 \alpha,$$
$$c^2 = a^2 + b^2(\sin^2 \alpha + \cos^2 \alpha)* - 2ab \cos \alpha,$$
$$c^2 = a^2 + b^2 - 2ab \cos \alpha . \qquad (E.3.1)$$

Equation (E.3.1) is called the Law of Cosines.

FIGURE E.3.3

* $\sin^2 \alpha + \cos^2 \alpha = 1$; see Eq. (E.4.1).

NATURAL TRIGONOMETRIC FUNCTIONS

Angle					Angle				
De-gree	Ra-dian	Sine	Co-sine	Tan-gent	De-gree	Ra-dian	Sine	Co-sine	Tan-gent
0°	.000	0.000	1.000	0.000					
1°	.017	.018	1.000	.018	46°	0.803	0.719	0.695	1.036
2°	.035	.035	0.999	.035	47°	.820	.731	.682	1.072
3°	.052	.052	.999	.052	48°	.838	.743	.669	1.111
4°	.070	.070	.998	.070	49°	.855	.755	.656	1.150
5°	.087	.087	.996	.088	50°	.873	.766	.643	1.192
6°	.105	.105	.995	.105	51°	.890	.777	.629	1.235
7°	.122	.122	.993	.123	52°	.908	.788	.616	1.280
8°	.140	.139	.990	.141	53°	.925	.799	.602	1.327
9°	.157	.156	.988	.158	54°	.942	.809	.588	1.376
10°	.175	.174	.985	.176	55°	.960	.819	.574	1.428
11°	.192	.191	.982	.194	56°	.977	.829	.559	1.483
12°	.209	.208	.978	.213	57°	.995	.839	.545	1.540
13°	.227	.225	.974	.231	58°	1.012	.848	.530	1.600
14°	.244	.242	.970	.249	59°	1.030	.857	.515	1.664
15°	.262	.259	.966	.268	60°	1.047	.866	.500	1.732
16°	.279	.276	.961	.287	61°	1.065	.875	.485	1.804
17°	.297	.292	.956	.306	62°	1.082	.883	.470	1.881
18°	.314	.309	.951	.325	63°	1.100	.891	.454	1.963
19°	.332	.326	.946	.344	64°	1.117	.899	.438	2.050
20°	.349	.342	.940	.364	65°	1.134	.906	.423	2.145
21°	.367	.358	.934	.384	66°	1.152	.914	.407	2.246
22°	.384	.375	.927	.404	67°	1.169	.921	.391	2.356
23°	.401	.391	.921	.425	68°	1.187	.927	.375	2.475
24°	.419	.407	.914	.445	69°	1.204	.934	.358	2.605
25°	.436	.423	.906	.466	70°	1.222	.940	.342	2.747
26°	.454	.438	.899	.488	71°	1.239	.946	.326	2.904
27°	.471	.454	.891	.510	72°	1.257	.951	.309	3.078
28°	.489	.470	.883	.532	73°	1.274	.956	.292	3.271
29°	.506	.485	.875	.554	74°	1.292	.961	.276	3.487
30°	.524	.500	.866	.577	75°	1.309	.966	.259	3.732
31°	.541	.515	.857	.601	76°	1.326	.970	.242	4.011
32°	.559	.530	.848	.625	77°	1.344	.974	.225	4.331
33°	.576	.545	.839	.649	78°	1.361	.978	.208	4.705
34°	.593	.559	.829	.675	79°	1.379	.982	.191	5.145
35°	.611	.574	.819	.700	80°	1.396	.985	.174	5.671
36°	.628	.588	.809	.727	81°	1.414	.988	.156	6.314
37°	.646	.602	.799	.754	82°	1.431	.990	.139	7.115
38°	.663	.616	.788	.781	83°	1.449	.993	.122	8.144
39°	.681	.629	.777	.810	84°	1.466	.995	.105	9.514
40°	.698	.643	.766	.839	85°	1.484	.996	.087	11.43
41°	.716	.658	.755	.869	86°	1.501	.998	.070	14.30
42°	.733	.669	.743	.900	87°	1.518	.999	.052	19.08
43°	.751	.682	.731	.933	88°	1.536	.999	.035	28.64
44°	.768	.695	.719	.966	89°	1.553	1.000	.018	57.29
45°	.785	.707	.707	1.000	90°	1.571	1.000	.000	∞

E.4   Various relations among trigonometric functions

(1) The Pythagorean theorem gives a relation among x, y, and r in Fig. E.2.1: $x^2 + y^2 = r^2$. Dividing by r^2 and using the definitions of sine and cosine, we have

$$\frac{x^2}{r^2} + \frac{y^2}{r^2} = 1, \qquad \sin^2 \alpha + \cos^2 \alpha = 1. \tag{E.4.1}$$

(2) From definitions of sine, cosine, and tangent, we have

$$\tan \alpha \equiv \frac{y}{x} = \frac{y/r}{x/r} = \frac{\sin \alpha}{\cos \alpha}. \tag{E.4.2}$$

(3) Relations among the functions of α and $-\alpha$ follow from the illustration given in Fig. E.4.1:

$$\sin(-\alpha) = \frac{y_2}{r} = -\sin \alpha, \tag{E.4.3}$$

$$\cos(-\alpha) = \frac{x_2}{r} = \cos \alpha, \tag{E.4.4}$$

$$\tan(-\alpha) = \frac{y_2}{x_2} = -\tan \alpha. \tag{E.4.5}$$

(4) From the geometrical relations shown in Fig. E.4.2, we have

$$\sin\left(\alpha - \frac{\pi}{2}\right) = \frac{y_3}{r} = -\frac{x_1}{r} = -\cos \alpha, \tag{E.4.6}$$

$$\cos\left(\alpha - \frac{\pi}{2}\right) = \frac{x_3}{r} = \frac{y_1}{r} = \sin \alpha, \tag{E.4.7}$$

$$\sin\left(\alpha + \frac{\pi}{2}\right) = \frac{y_3}{r} = \frac{x_1}{r} = \cos \alpha, \tag{E.4.8}$$

$$\cos\left(\alpha + \frac{\pi}{2}\right) = \frac{x_3}{r} = -\frac{y_1}{r} = -\sin \alpha. \tag{E.4.9}$$

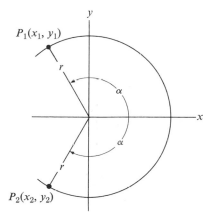

FIG. E.4.1. Angles α and $-\alpha$: $x_1 = x_2$; $y_1 = -y_2$.

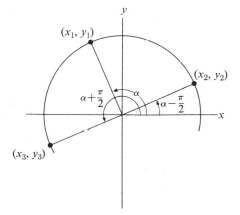

FIG. E.4.2. Angles $\alpha - (\pi/2)$; α; $\alpha + (\pi/2)$. Geometrical relations: $x_2 = y_1$, $x_3 = -y_1$, $y_2 = -x_1$, $y_3 = x_1$.

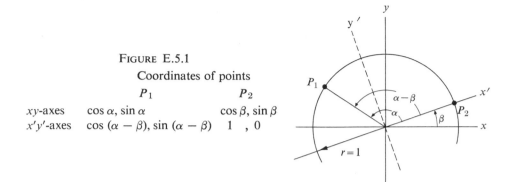

FIGURE E.5.1

Coordinates of points

	P_1	P_2
xy-axes	$\cos \alpha,\ \sin \alpha$	$\cos \beta,\ \sin \beta$
$x'y'$-axes	$\cos (\alpha - \beta),\ \sin (\alpha - \beta)$	$1\ \ ,\ \ 0$

E.5   Functions of $(\alpha + \beta)$ and $(\alpha - \beta)$.   In Fig. E.5.1 we show angles α, β, and $(\alpha - \beta)$ with points P_1 and P_2 lying on a circle of unit radius. The coordinates of these points are expressed in terms of α and β in the xy-system of axes and in terms of $(\alpha - \beta)$ in the $x'y'$-system. Making use of the formula for the distance between two points [Eq. (3.1)], we have in the xy-system:

$$(P_1 P_2)^2 = (\cos \alpha - \cos \beta)^2 + (\sin \alpha - \sin \beta)^2$$

$$= \cos^2 \alpha - 2 \cos \alpha \cos \beta + \cos^2 \beta + \sin^2 \alpha - 2 \sin \alpha \sin \beta + \sin^2 \beta$$

$$= 2 - 2 \cos \alpha \cos \beta - 2 \sin \alpha \sin \beta . \qquad \text{(E.5.1)}$$

[The last step utilized Eq. (E.4.1).]
    In the $x'y'$-system:

$$(P_1 P_2)^2 = [1 - \cos (\alpha - \beta)]^2 + [0 - \sin (\alpha - \beta)]^2$$

$$= 1 - 2 \cos (\alpha - \beta) + \cos^2 (\alpha - \beta) + \sin^2 (\alpha - \beta)$$

$$= 2 - 2 \cos (\alpha - \beta). \qquad \text{(E.5.2)}$$

Equating the right-hand sides of (E.5.1) and (E.5.2), we have

$$\cos (\alpha - \beta) = \cos \alpha \cos \beta + \sin \alpha \sin \beta. \qquad \text{(E.5.3)}$$

If we now take $\beta = -\beta'$ and substitute into (E.5.3):

$$\cos (\alpha + \beta') = \cos \alpha \cos (-\beta') + \sin \alpha \sin (-\beta'),$$

and from Eqs. (E.4.3, 4):

$$\cos (\alpha + \beta') = \cos \alpha \cos \beta' - \sin \alpha \sin \beta'. \qquad \text{(E.5.4)}$$

Using Eqs. (E.4.9) and (E.5.3), we have

$$-\sin (\alpha - \beta) = +\cos \left(\frac{\pi}{2} + \alpha - \beta\right) = \cos \left(\frac{\pi}{2} + \alpha\right) \cos \beta + \sin \left(\frac{\pi}{2} + \alpha\right) \sin \beta$$

$$= -\sin \alpha \cos \beta + \cos \alpha \sin \beta;$$

$$\sin (\alpha - \beta) = \sin \alpha \cos \beta - \cos \alpha \sin \beta. \qquad \text{(E.5.5)}$$

By substituting $\beta = -\beta'$, it immediately follows that

$$\sin (\alpha + \beta') = \sin \alpha \cos \beta' + \cos \alpha \sin \beta'. \tag{E.5.6}$$

If $\beta' = \alpha$, we have, from (E.5.4) and (E.5.6):

$$\cos 2\alpha = \cos^2 \alpha - \sin^2 \alpha, \tag{E.5.7}$$

$$\sin 2\alpha = 2 \sin \alpha \cos \alpha. \tag{E.5.8}$$

Summarizing the relations obtained in Section E.5:

$$\sin (\alpha \pm \beta) = \sin \alpha \cos \beta \pm \cos \alpha \sin \beta,$$

$$\cos (\alpha \pm \beta) = \cos \alpha \cos \beta \mp \sin \alpha \sin \beta,$$

$$\sin 2\alpha = 2 \sin \alpha \cos \alpha,$$

$$\cos 2\alpha = \cos^2 \alpha - \sin^2 \alpha = 1 - 2 \sin^2 \alpha = 2 \cos^2 \alpha - 1.$$

Propagation Velocities of a Small-Amplitude Transverse Pulse on a String and of a Longitudinal Pressure Pulse in a Fluid

F.1 Transverse pulse on a stretched string. Consider the idealized situation in Fig. F.1.1: The end of a stretched string is given a transverse particle velocity v_y and is kept in motion at that velocity. A "kink" propagates along the string at velocity V. To the right of the kink, the string is yet undisturbed. To the left of the kink, all particles of the string have acquired transverse velocity v_y, as the kink passed them at succeedingly later instants of time. This part of the string retains a straight-line shape, inclined at angle θ to the original unperturbed orientation.

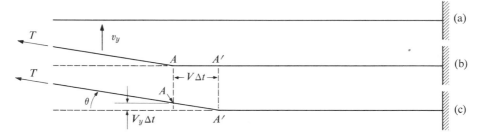

FIG. F.1.1. String is under tension T. End of string is given transverse velocity v_y and is kept in motion at that velocity. "Kink" at point A, A', etc., propagates along string at velocity V.

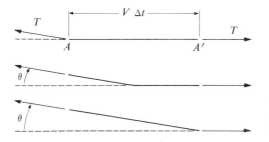

FIG. F.1.2. Force diagram of section AA' of string at three successive instants as kink propagates from A to A' during interval Δt.

Figure F.1.2 shows several successive force diagrams of the section AA' of the string during the time interval Δt. The net force in the y-direction is constant throughout the interval and is given by

$$F_{y\,\text{net}} = T \sin \theta - 0. \tag{F.1.1}$$

The impulse-momentum theorem [Eq. (17.7.2)] requires that

$$F_{y\,\text{net}} \, \Delta t = \Delta(m v_y). \tag{F.1.2}$$

In moving from A to A', the kink travels a distance $V \Delta t$. If we let μ denote the mass per unit length of string, the section AA' has a mass $m = \mu V \Delta t$. This mass "enters the wave" or "passes through the kink" and acquires a transverse velocity v_y. Thus the initial momentum of the section $V \Delta t$ is zero, and the final momentum is $\mu(V \Delta t)v_y$. Substituting into Eq. (F.1.2), we have

$$(T \sin \theta) \Delta t = \mu(V \Delta t)v_y. \tag{F.1.3}$$

Now we shall introduce some powerful, simplifying approximations: Let us assume that the deflections of the string are kept quite small; that is, θ is assumed to be a very *small* angle. Then horizontal deflections of points on the string are negligible; we can consider the horizontal forces on section AA' as being almost perfectly balanced; and $\sin \theta$ is very nearly equal to $v_y \Delta t / V \Delta t = v_y/V$, since the slant distance AA' in Fig. F.1.1(c) is negligibly different from the horizontal distance $V \Delta t$.

With this approximation, Eq. (F.1.3) becomes

$$\frac{Tv_y}{V} \cdot \Delta t = \mu(V \Delta t)v_y,$$

$$V^2 = \frac{T}{\mu}; \qquad V = \sqrt{\frac{T}{\mu}}. \tag{F.1.4}$$

Equation (F.1.4) predicts that wave velocity increases as the string tension is increased and decreases as the string becomes more massive. These predictions are readily checked by simple experiments.

Note that the propagating wave disturbance is actually at the kink itself. No variations propagate along the straight portion of the string to the left of the kink unless the motion is reversed, and another kink or curvature is introduced. Only if a section of string is *curved* is there a net force causing it to accelerate toward or away from the axis and to convey disturbances to adjacent portions of the string.

F.2   Longitudinal pressure pulse in a fluid. To ensure a simple geometry and avoid problems associated with the spreading out of the pulse in space, let us imagine a compression pulse traveling in a tube of cross-sectional area A, as shown in Fig. F.2.1.

In a time interval Δt, the leading edge of the pulse travels a distance $V \Delta t$, and encompasses a mass of fluid $\rho_0 A V \Delta t$. The mass of compressed fluid emerging from the trailing edge of the pulse occupies a volume $A(V - v_x) \Delta t$, since the pulse has advanced a distance $V \Delta t$ but the fluid behind it has been advancing a distance $v_x \Delta t$. We assume that the pulse has attained a steady state and is not changing its form or accumulating mass in the region of the pressure change. Then the mass entering the leading edge in time Δt must be equal to the mass leaving the trailing edge, and

$$\rho_0 A V \Delta t = \rho A (V - v_x) \Delta t,$$

$$\rho_0 V = \rho(V - v_x). \tag{F.2.1}$$

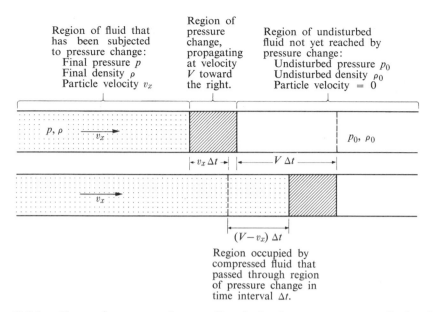

Region of fluid that has been subjected to pressure change:
Final pressure p
Final density ρ
Particle velocity v_x

Region of pressure change, propagating at velocity V toward the right.

Region of undisturbed fluid not yet reached by pressure change:
Undisturbed pressure p_0
Undisturbed density ρ_0
Particle velocity $= 0$

p, ρ v_x p_0, ρ_0

$\leftarrow v_x \Delta t \rightarrow$ $\leftarrow V \Delta t \rightarrow$

v_x

$(V - v_x) \Delta t$

Region occupied by compressed fluid that passed through region of pressure change in time interval Δt.

FIG. F.2.1. Change in pressure from undisturbed value p_0 to constant final value p propagates through fluid in a tube of uniform cross section A. Compressed fluid behind region of pressure change acquires particle velocity v_x toward the right.

We now draw a force diagram (Fig. F.2.2) of the fluid in the region $V \Delta t$, subjected to the pulse during the time interval Δt, and apply the impulse momemtum theorem:

$$F_{x \text{ net}} \Delta t = \Delta(mv_x). \tag{F.2.2}$$

The initial momentum of this fluid is zero, and the final momentum after reaching pressure p and acquiring particle velocity v_x is $mv_x = \rho_0(AV \Delta t)v_x$. Therefore

$$(pA - p_0A) \Delta t = \rho_0(AV \Delta t)v_x,$$

$$p - p_0 = \rho_0 V v_x. \tag{F.2.3}$$

Eliminating v_x from Eqs. (F.2.1) and (F.2.3) gives

$$V^2 = \frac{p - p_0}{\rho - \rho_0} \cdot \frac{\rho}{\rho_0}. \tag{F.2.4}$$

The density of a fluid is not, in general, a unique function of the pressure. The density

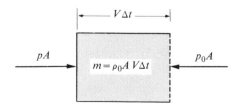

$\leftarrow V\Delta t \rightarrow$

pA

$m = \rho_0 A \, V \Delta t$

$p_0 A$

FIG. F.2.2. Force diagram of section of fluid of mass $\rho_0 VA \Delta t$, passing through pressure pulse in time interval Δt.

can change in a variety of ways when pressure is applied, depending on whether heat is simultaneously allowed to flow in or out or whether heat flow is precluded (adiabatic process). In sound waves, the pressure variations take place so rapidly that heat flow from warmer compressed regions to cooler expanded regions within the wave is negligible. Thus sound waves involve almost perfectly adiabatic changes; under these circumstances the pressure is a well-defined function of the density for any given fluid.

The velocity of sound, which we shall denote by V_0, is defined as the velocity of very small pressure disturbances; that is,

$$V_0^2 \equiv \lim_{\substack{p \to p_0 \\ \rho \to \rho_0}} \left[\frac{p - p_0}{\rho - \rho_0} \cdot \frac{\rho}{\rho_0} \right] = \left(\frac{dp}{d\rho} \right)_{\text{adiabatic}} . \tag{F.2.5}$$

It must be carefully emphasized that neither of the preceding derivations constitutes a dynamic analysis showing that a wave disturbance must necessarily propagate in a given medium. Neither do these derivations inform us as to how waves are generated, what determines their shape, under what circumstances the propagation is steady, etc. We have assumed on the basis of previous experience that nearly steady propagation does indeed occur, and we have used this *a priori* knowledge to discover how propagation velocity might depend on properties of the medium if our restrictive assumptions are satisfied. A far more illuminating analysis of wave phenomena begins without these assumptions, applies the laws of mechanics and discovers the conditions which govern all aspects of wave propagation in the given medium. Such analyses are to be found in more advanced texts on wave motion

Electrical Field Strength

G.1 Electrical field strength at point P near a uniformly charged plane of unlimited extent.

The symbol σ denotes charge per unit area; D denotes distance of P from the plane.

We set up an axis of symmetry by dropping a perpendicular from P to the plane at point O, and we divide the plane up into circular ribbons or strips centered at O as shown in Fig. G.1.1. The charge carried by the circular strip is $2\pi\sigma r\,\Delta r$, and all chunks of the strip are a distance $z = \sqrt{r^2 + D^2}$ from P. By Coulomb's law, a point charge $2\pi\sigma r\,\Delta r$ would produce a field

$$\Delta E = \frac{2\pi k\sigma r\,\Delta r}{z^2},\qquad (G.1.1)$$

at a distance z, but in the distribution in Fig. G.1.1, each patch of charge on the strip contributes a force directed at an angle θ to the line PO, perpendicular to the plane. Each individual contribution must be multiplied by $\cos\theta = D/z$ to obtain the component parallel to PO. (By symmetry, the components perpendicular to PO cancel each other out.) Therefore the net contribution, ΔE, to the field at P is perpendicular to the plane and is given not by Eq. (G.1.1) but by

$$\Delta E = \frac{2\pi k\sigma r\,\Delta r}{z^2}\cos\theta = \frac{2\pi k\sigma\,Dr\,\Delta r}{z^3},\qquad (G.1.2)$$

where $z = \sqrt{r^2 + D^2}$, and $\cos\theta = D/z$.

To obtain the total resultant field at P, we must evaluate the limit of the sum of all these contributions as the Δr's are made indefinitely small. Since the plane is of unlimited extent, the range of integration is from $r = 0$ to $r = \infty$. Therefore

$$E = 2\pi k\sigma D \int_0^\infty \frac{r}{(r^2 + D^2)^{3/2}}\,dr.\qquad (G.1.3)$$

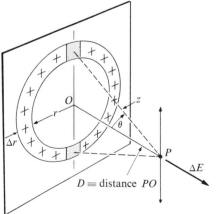

FIG. G.1.1. Plane carries uniformly distributed positive charge σ coul/m². Circular ring shown in diagram has area $2\pi r\,\Delta r$ and carries charge $2\pi\sigma r\,\Delta r$. At point P, electrical forces from elements on opposite sides of the ring cancel each other in the direction parallel to the plane and add in the direction perpendicular to the plane. Total field at P due to charge on ring is denoted by ΔE.

Consider the function

$$\frac{1}{(r^2 + D^2)^{1/2}}.$$

Using methods of differentiation (including the chain rule) developed in Chapter 8, the derivative of this function is found to be $-r/(r^2 + D^2)^{3/2}$. Therefore an anti-derivative of the integrand in (G.1.3) is $-1/(r^2 + D^2)^{1/2}$, and

$$E = 2\pi k\sigma D\left[-\frac{1}{(r^2 + D^2)^{1/2}}\right]_0^\infty = 2\pi k\sigma D\left[0 + \frac{1}{D}\right] = 2\pi k\sigma. \quad (G.1.4)$$

Equation (G.1.4) indicates that the electrical field strength around a charged plane of *unlimited* extent is *uniform*; it does not decrease with increasing distance from the plane! If the plane is positively charged, the field is directed away from the plane; if negatively charged, the field is directed toward the plane.

G.2   Electrical field strength at point P outside a uniformly charged spherical shell of radius R.   The symbol σ denotes charge per unit area; D denotes distance of point P from center of sphere.

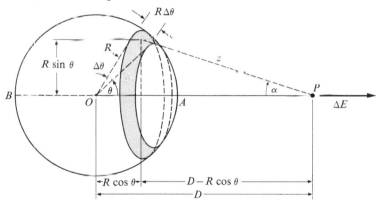

FIG. G.2.1.   Field at point P outside uniformly charged sphere.

We set up an axis of symmetry around the line PO, dividing the charged shell into strips, as shown in Fig. G.2.1. The width of the strip is $R\,\Delta\theta$ and its radius (perpendicular to PO) is $R\sin\theta$. Thus the area of the entire strip is $(2\pi R\sin\theta)R\,\Delta\theta$, and the charge carried on it is $2\pi\sigma R^2\sin\theta\,\Delta\theta$. The contribution of each individual chunk of the strip to the field at P must be multiplied by

$$\cos\alpha = (D - R\cos\theta)/z$$

to obtain the component parallel to PO, and, by symmetry, the contributions perpendicular to PO cancel each other. Therefore, when we apply Coulomb's law, the total contribution of the strip to the field at P is directed radially outward along

PO (assuming positive charge), and has the magnitude

$$\Delta E = \frac{2\pi k\sigma R^2 \sin\theta \, \Delta\theta}{z^2} \cdot \frac{D - R\cos\theta}{z}, \tag{G.2.1}$$

or

$$\frac{dE}{d\theta} = \frac{2\pi k\sigma R^2 \sin\theta (D - R\cos\theta)}{z^3}, \tag{G.2.2}$$

where z is the *magnitude* of the distance from P to the charged strip.

From the diagram, we also have the geometrical relation

$$z^2 = R^2 + D^2 - 2RD\cos\theta. \tag{G.2.3}$$

Since z and θ are related to each other, we must express ΔE entirely in terms of one or the other quantity in order to carry out the integration. In this analysis we make the choice of eliminating θ and carrying out the integration with respect to z. To do this we shall need an expression for dE/dz instead of $dE/d\theta$ as in (G.2.2). From the chain rule, we have

$$\frac{dE}{d\theta} = \frac{dE}{dz}\frac{dz}{d\theta}. \tag{G.2.4}$$

Taking the derivative with respect to θ of each side of (G.2.3), we obtain

$$2z\frac{dz}{d\theta} = 2RD\sin\theta,$$

$$\frac{dz}{d\theta} = \frac{RD\sin\theta}{z} \tag{G.2.5}$$

and solving (G.2.3) for $(D - R\cos\theta)$:

$$D - R\cos\theta = \frac{D^2 - R^2 + z^2}{2D}. \tag{G.2.6}$$

Solving (G.2.4) for dE/dz and making use of (G.2.2), (G.2.5), and (G.2.6):

$$\frac{dE}{dz} = \frac{dE/d\theta}{dz/d\theta} = \frac{2\pi k\sigma R^2 \sin\theta}{z^3} \cdot \frac{z}{RD\sin\theta} \cdot \frac{D^2 - R^2 + z^2}{2D}$$

$$= \pi k\sigma \frac{R}{D^2}\left(\frac{D^2 - R^2 + z^2}{z^2}\right);$$

$$\Delta E = \pi k\sigma \frac{R}{D^2}\left[\frac{(D + R)(D - R)}{z^2} + 1\right]\Delta z. \tag{G.2.7}$$

Equation (G.2.7) expresses, entirely in terms of z, the contribution of the shaded strip to the field at point P. If we wish to find the total field strength E, we must carry out the integration of (G.2.7) from $z = D - R$ (point A in Fig. G.2.1) to $z = D + R$ (point B):

$$E = \pi k\sigma \frac{R}{D^2} \int_{z=D-R}^{z=D+R} \left[\frac{(D + R)(D - R)}{z^2} + 1 \right] dz \tag{G.2.8}$$

$$= \pi k\sigma \frac{R}{D^2} \left[-\frac{(D + R)(D - R)}{z} + z \right]_{D-R}^{D+R}$$

$$= \pi k\sigma \frac{R}{D^2} [-(D - R) + (D + R) + (D + R) - (D - R)]$$

$$= \frac{k4\pi R^2 \sigma}{D^2} . \tag{G.2.9}$$

Since $4\pi R^2$ is the surface area of the sphere, the quantity $4\pi R^2\sigma$ is the total charge q carried by the sphere. Equation (G.2.9) thus becomes

$$E = \frac{kq}{D^2} , \tag{G.2.10}$$

which is precisely the expression we would obtain if q were all concentrated at a point at the center of the sphere. Thus we have proved that a uniformly charged sphere behaves as though its charge were concentrated at the center. This is the famous theorem that Newton proves for the gravitational case in the *Principia*.

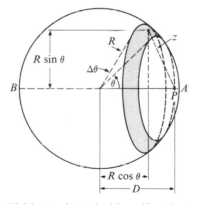

FIG. G.3.1. Field at point P inside uniformly charged sphere.

G.3 Electrical field strength at a point P inside a uniformly charged spherical shell of radius R.   If we take point P inside the spherical shell, as shown in Fig. G.3.1, the equations of Section G.2 are completely unchanged, and (G.2.7) represents the contribution of the shaded strip to the field at P. But in evaluating the integral to obtain the total field strength E, we note that the limits of integration are slightly different from those of the preceding section. At point A, we must take $z = R - D$ instead of $D - R$, since z represents the *magnitude* of the distance from P to the charged strip, and a negative value of z would not have physical meaning in this formulation. At point B, $z = R + D$ as before.

Instead of (G.2.8), the expression for E then becomes

$$E = \pi k \sigma \frac{R}{D^2} \int_{z=R-D}^{z=R+D} \left[\frac{(D + R)(D - R)}{z^2} + 1 \right] dz \tag{G.3.1}$$

$$= \pi k \sigma \frac{R}{D^2} \left[- \frac{(D + R)(D - R)}{z} + z \right]_{R-D}^{R+D}$$

$$= \pi k \sigma \frac{R}{D^2} [-(D - R) + (R + D) - (D + R) - (R - D)];$$

$$E = 0. \tag{G.3.2}$$

Since this result does not depend on D, the electrical field strength is shown to be zero at *all* points inside a uniformly charged sphere.

Image Formation by Thin Lenses

[The following material is not meant to be a complete, textual presentation. This is an outline or a set of study notes, designed to guide a reader through the sequence of concepts and relationships. It is best utilized by sitting down with pencil and paper at hand, working carefully through every step of the outline, answering the guiding questions, filling in the omitted steps, sketching *new* diagrams, working the problems, interpreting the results, and performing relevant experiments. A list of useful supplementary references is given at the end of the Appendix.]

H.1   The focal length of a thin lens.   Consider a particularly simple form of lens (called plano-convex), as shown in Fig. H.1.1. Let us examine the refraction of a ray which enters the lens parallel to the principal axis. Since the ray is normal (angle of incidence $= 0$) to surface 1, no refraction occurs at this surface. The ray is refracted at surface 2, being bent toward the principal axis. The coordinates have been so positioned as to place the center of curvature of surface 2 at the origin O. Thus the length OA is equal to the radius of curvature R, and the line OA is normal to the surface 2 at A (why?); θ_1 is the angle of incidence of the ray at surface 2; θ_2 is the angle of refraction. The problem is to find where the ray crosses the principal axis and to generalize the results into a prediction as to where other rays will cross. Other rays are described by different values of b. From the point-slope form of the

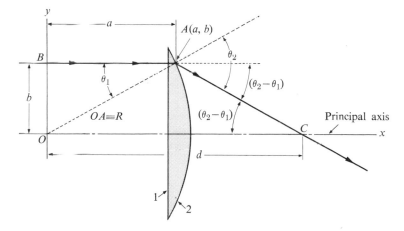

FIG. H.1.1. Plano-convex lens; principal axis of lens superposed on x-axis of coordinates. Center of curvature of convex surface at O. Diagram shows refraction of a ray BAC which enters the lens from the left, parallel to the principal axis. The distance of this incident ray from the principal axis is denoted by b. The plane surface of the lens is denoted by 1; the convex surface by 2; R denotes radius of curvature of surface 2. The angle of incidence of ray BAC at surface 2 is θ_1. Note that $b = R \sin \theta_1$ and that either b or θ_1 gives information about the distance of the incident ray from the principal axis.

equation of a straight line (Chapter 3), the refracted ray, AC, is represented by the equation:

$$y - b = -\tan[(\theta_2 - \theta_1)](x - a) \qquad \text{(H.1.1)}$$

Let d denote the value of x at which $y = 0$, then

$$d = a + \frac{b}{\tan(\theta_2 - \theta_1)}. \qquad \text{(H.1.2)}$$

This defines the point at which the refracted ray crosses the principal axis. Let us examine how this position changes with θ_1; that is, with the distance of the incident ray from the axis. From Fig. H.1.1:

$$a = R\cos\theta_1, \qquad b = R\sin\theta_1. \qquad \text{(H.1.3)}$$

Combining Eqs. (H.1.3) and (H.1.2), we have

$$d = R\left[\cos\theta_1 + \frac{\sin\theta_1}{\tan(\theta_2 - \theta_1)}\right]. \qquad \text{(H.1.4)}$$

Equation (H.1.4) indicates that d depends on θ_1 and that, in general, each refracted ray will cross the axis at a different distance d from the origin O. More careful examination, however, shows that this broad generalization is somewhat misleading and that a very important bundle of rays relatively *close* to the axis is converged through very nearly the same point.

Let us examine the form taken by Eq. (H.1.4) when the incident ray is close to the axis; that is, b is small, and therefore θ_1 and θ_2 are also small.

Since the cosines of small angles are very close to unity, and since the sines and tangents are very nearly equal to the values of the angles themselves (measured in radians), Eq. (H.1.4) becomes, to a very good approximation,

$$d \cong R\left[1 + \frac{\theta_1}{\theta_2 - \theta_1}\right] = R\left[1 + \frac{1}{(\theta_2/\theta_1) - 1}\right]. \qquad \text{(H.1.5)}$$

The θ_2 and θ_1 are related to each other by Snell's Law. Denoting the index of refraction of the glass relative to air by n, we write out the relation between the sines of θ_1 and θ_2, and then show that, for small angles, Eq. (H.1.5) becomes

$$d = R + \frac{R}{n - 1}. \qquad \text{(H.1.6)}$$

Interpret Eq. (H.1.6) carefully. Note that b, θ_1, and θ_2 have disappeared and that d depends only on *constants* R and n. What does this tell you about the refraction of rays lying close to the axis but nevertheless at different distances from it?

The effect we have just described is called *focusing*, and the distance $(d - R)$ is denoted by the symbol f and is called the focal length of the lens. The point at which the bundle of rays (incident parallel to the principal axis) is converged is called a principal focus or focal point.

If both surfaces of the lens are curved, the algebraic derivation becomes somewhat more complex, but the final result is identical with that obtained above. Any lens will have *two* principal foci (why?). Describe what will happen to light emitted from a point source at either focal point after passing through the lens. If the lens is "thin," the distance $(d - R)$ can be described simply as the "distance of the principal focus from the plane of the lens" (why?). How would you *measure* the focal length of a lens by direct experiment if you were not in a position to calculate it from a knowledge of R and n?

Describe in words, without algebraic analysis, the location of the principal foci of a *diverging* lens, by sketching what happens to a bundle of incident rays parallel to the principal axis. Also sketch the cone of converging rays, incident on the lens, that will emerge as a bundle parallel to the principal axis.

H.2   The formation of images by thin lenses.   In the language of geometrical optics, the term "real object" is used for anything that emits or reflects light intercepted by a lens. Each point of the object is thought of as a point source which emits light rays in all directions. A cone of these rays may be intercepted by a lens, refracted, and caused to converge or diverge, depending on the geometry of the system.

(In the following discussion the symbol $\updownarrow$ will be used to denote converging lenses and the symbol $)($ to denote diverging lenses.)

It is a convention of geometrical optics to draw diagrams in such a way that the light intercepted by the lens always comes from the left. Consider the sketches shown in Fig. H.2.1, in which P and Q denote any two points on the object. In H.2.1(a), the cones of rays from these points are shown to be converged to P' and Q' by a converging lens. In Fig. (b) the cone of rays is shown to be diverged so that, to the right of the lens, it appears to come from P' instead of from P. The primed points, if such clear-cut intersections exist, are called *image points*, and the entire collection of image points forms an *image* of the object.

The first questions which must be asked are: Does a lens converge (or diverge) cones of light from object points to clearly defined image points? If it does, what are the locations of the image points? Do the image points occupy the same relative

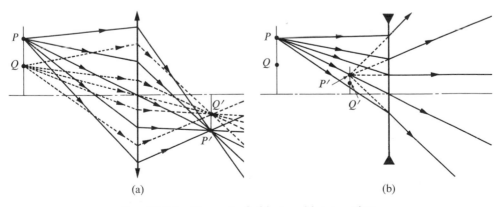

(a)   (b)

FIG. H.2.1. Concept of object and image points.

positions to each other as do the corresponding object points? The answers to these questions can be obtained by pursuing the same kind of geometrical-algebraic inquiry developed in Section H.1. We shall not carry out the analysis, but will simply assert the results: If the object points are relatively close to the principal axis so that the rays make small angles with the axis (such rays are called "paraxial"), all the rays in the cone from an object point are converged (or diverged) to (or from) very nearly the same point. If object points P, Q, etc., lie in the same plane perpendicular to the principal axis (as sketched in Fig. H.2.1), the image points P', Q', etc., lie very nearly in another plane perpendicular to the principal axis.

Image points formed by the *convergence* of light *after* emerging from a lens [Fig. H.2.1(a)] are called "real." Such points appear to be sources of light themselves. You can stand to the right of $P'Q'$ and look at the image sitting there in empty space. (Be sure to do this when you perform the experiment.) If you place a screen in the plane $P'Q'$, it reflects the incident light in all directions and you see the image projected on the screen.

Image points such as P' in Fig. H.2.1(b) are called "virtual." This word is descriptive of the fact that the diverging cone of rays to the right of the lens does not actually originate at P': it only appears to do so. The image we see in a mirror is of a similar character. Such images cannot be projected on screens.

This description of image formation is idealized. In reality, all the rays in a cone from an object point are not focused at a single image point, but are brought close together in a slightly fuzzed-out volume of space in the neighborhood of what we would like to think of as the image point. Furthermore, different colors of light are not brought together in the same region. All the effects which conspire to fuzz out the region of focus are called "aberrations." Take careful note of the fact that aberrations are not due to imperfections such as departure from spherical shape or lack of smoothness of the lens surfaces. They stem from the inherent impossibility of perfect focusing by a perfect spherical lens. Practically, it turns out that the effect of aberrations can be very significantly reduced by making "compound" lenses which consist of combinations of individual lenses of different radii of curvature and different indices of refraction. Such lenses in cameras, microscopes, and other optical instruments produce fine, sharp images, but it is well to remember that this is simply a matter of degree and that aberrations are never completely eliminated.

H.3   The location, by geometry, of images formed by thin lenses. Given the general statements about the formation of images asserted in Section H.2, it is a very simple matter to locate the images by means of geometrical diagrams. All we need do is utilize the definitions of the principal foci as developed in Section H.1. An illustration is given in Fig. H.3.1, where A and A' are the principal foci of the converging lens.

Consider the cone of rays emanating from the object point P. Among this infinity of rays is one (PD) which is parallel to the principal axis. Draw the ray. By definition of focal point A', this ray is refracted so as to pass through A'. Draw DA' and extend the line indefinitely. In the cone of rays from P is one which passes through focal point A and is intercepted by the lens at E. By definition of focal point A,

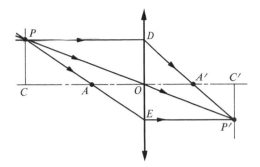

Fig. H.3.1. Geometrical location of image point by construction of principal rays (converging lens).

this ray must be refracted so as to emerge from the lens parallel to the principal axis. The two rays so far drawn intersect at P'. Since all other rays in the paraxial cone also intersect at P', the image point is established.

Its position can be checked by a third ray PO. This ray passes through the center of the lens where the opposite surfaces are very nearly parallel to each other. It is therefore not appreciably refracted. (Part of the idealization implied by the term "*thin* lens" is that the ray is also not appreciably *displaced* from its original path, as it would be in passing through a thick pane of glass.) The ray PO extends through the previous intersection P'.

The three rays drawn in Fig. H.3.1 are called the *principal rays*. Be able to define them in your own words by describing how each one is drawn and specifying what idealizations and limitations are involved. Describe in similar fashion the principal rays for a diverging lens. In all subsequent problems, image locations are to be established by diagrams like that in Fig. H.3.1. The appearance of the diagrams will be very different from one situation to another, but the definitions of the principal rays are the unchanging tools applicable to each case.

PROBLEM H.1. Redraw Fig. H.3.1 two or three times, moving the object PC farther to the left in each case. Observe what happens to the location of P'. Get a feeling for the geometry of the changes. The situation being dealt with is essentially that of a lantern slide projector; PC is the slide and the projection screen is at $P'C'$. Where must you put the slide to obtain a large image? A small image? Where will the screen be in each case?

PROBLEM H.2. Place the object PC between A and O and draw the ray diagram, carefully using the definitions of the principal rays. Do not just copy Fig. H.3.1. The diagram changes drastically, and the image is now *virtual*. This situation is exactly the one which obtains when you use a simple magnifying glass. Ask yourself some questions about this case in the manner suggested in the preceding problem. What happens when the object is placed at A? Look through a simple magnifying glass and relate what you see to things you have worked out and discussed in this problem and in problem H.1.

Figure H.3.2 presents a diagram closely analogous to that of Fig. H.3.1, except that the lens is diverging: Note that ray PD emerges from the lens as though it originated at principal focus A. Ray PE is the one which is originally directed toward

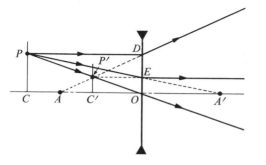

FIG. H.3.2. Geometrical location of image point by construction of principal rays (diverging lens).

principal focus A'; it emerges parallel to the principal axis. Ray PO, as before, passes through the lens essentially undeviated. Note that the image is *virtual*.

> PROBLEM H.3. Redraw Fig. H.3.2 for a few different positions of the object, ascertaining what happens to the image position as the object is moved closer to or farther away from the lens. What happens if the object position lies between A and O? Is it ever possible to obtain a real image with the basic situation presented in Fig. H.3.2?

Consider the following situation: We take a second lens (either converging or diverging) and insert it somewhere between O and C' in Fig. H.3.1. This lens intercepts a cone of rays converging toward P' and changes their direction. The effect is sketched in Fig. H.3.3.

The point P', which would have been the real image point of P formed by the first lens, is said to constitute a "virtual object" for the second lens. From the infinity of rays in the converging cone, one can again select three principal rays and determine the position R' of the image formed by the second lens. The principal rays are shown by heavy lines in Fig. H.3.3. Here we have a case of formation by a second lens of a real image of a virtual object. (If the second lens had been inserted to the right of C' in Fig. H.3.1, P', the real image formed by the first lens, would have become a real object for the second lens and the diagram of Fig. H.3.1 would simply have been repeated.)

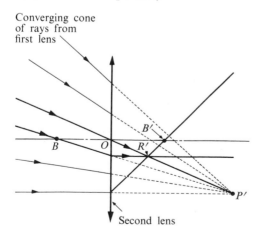

Converging cone of rays from first lens

Second lens

FIG. H.3.3. Light from first lens, off to the left of the diagram, is converging to form real image at P' but is intercepted by a second lens. B and B' are the principal foci of the second lens. Instead of intersecting at P', rays are caused to converge at R'. P' is called a "virtual object point" for the second lens.

PROBLEM H.4.   Replace the converging lens in Fig. H.3.3 by a diverging lens, and determine the resulting image position. Repeat the problem, placing P' closer to lens than B', instead of farther away as in Fig. H.3.3. Note that in one case the final image is real, while in the other case it is virtual.

H.4 Analytic geometry of image formation by thin lenses.   The procedures in Section H.3 were purely *geometrical*. A very powerful element would be added to our description of image formation if we could obtain an *algebraic* description which would give us a complete arithmetical analysis of the whole problem, and the ability to predict locations and character of images by arithmetical procedures.

In this particular instance we have an excellent opportunity to use our knowledge of the analytic geometry of a straight line in a powerful way.

Let us adopt the following conventions, illustrated in Fig. H.4.1:

(1) We introduce a Cartesian coordinate system in which the x-axis coincides with the principal axis of the lens and the y-axis is contained in the plane of the lens L.

(2) Rays of incident light, as always, pass through L in the positive x-direction; i.e., from left to right.

(3) Rays of light arriving at L parallel to the axis are deviated through the focal point to the right of the lens if the lens is converging, and are deviated so as to appear to be coming from the focal point to left of the lens if the lens is diverging. We denote the coordinates of these focal points by $(f, 0)$. Thus: (a) f is positive for a converging lens, and (b) f is negative for a diverging lens.

(4) We denote the coordinates of the object point P by $(-s, b)$. Thus: (a) If $s > 0$, this implies that P lies to the left of L and constitutes a real object point. (P might be either an actually luminous point or a point on a real image formed by a preceding lens.) (b) If $s < 0$, this implies that P lies to the right of L. This would correspond to the virtual-object cases illustrated in Fig. H.3.3 and Problem H.4.

(5) We denote the coordinates of the image point P' by (s', b').

The conventions outlined above are illustrated in Fig. H.4.1 for the special case of a converging lens with real object.

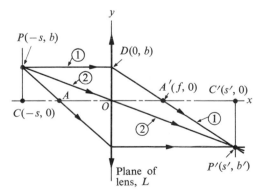

FIG. H.4.1. Conventions adopted for analytic representation of image formation by a thin lens.

In every case of image formation there will be, within the cone of rays reaching the plane L, the following two rays:

(1) A ray parallel to the principal axis. Its equation is

$$y = b. \tag{H.4.1}$$

The equation of this ray after it emerges from the lens is

$$y = -\frac{b}{f}x + b. \tag{H.4.2}$$

[Be sure to derive Eq. (H.4.2). This involves a straightforward application of the slope-intercept form of the equation of a straight line.]

(2) A ray passing, essentially undeviated, through the center of the lens at O. The equation of this ray before and after emerging from the lens is

$$y = -\frac{b}{s}x. \tag{H.4.3}$$

PROBLEM H.5.   For a diverging lens, draw a figure corresponding to Fig. H.4.1. Remember that f is now taken as negative, and the point $(f, 0)$ is the focal point to the left of the lens. Verify the fact that Eq. (H.4.2) still correctly represents the equation of the emerging ray (1).

PROBLEM H.6.   Verify the fact that Eqs. (H.4.2) and (H.4.3) correctly represent rays for the case of virtual object, as in Fig. H.3.3.

By definition, the image point P' (s', b') is located at the intersection of the emerging rays described by Eqs. (H.4.2) and (H.4.3) (that is, at $x = s'$; $y = b'$), and we obtain from (H.4.2) and (H.4.3):

$$\frac{-b}{s}s' = -\frac{b}{f}s' + b, \tag{H.4.4}$$

$$b' = -\frac{b}{s}s'. \tag{H.4.5}$$

Rearranging Eqs. (H.4.4) and (H.4.5) gives

$$\frac{1}{s} + \frac{1}{s'} = \frac{1}{f} \quad \text{(Gaussian lens equation)}, \tag{H.4.6}$$

$$\frac{b'}{b} = -\frac{s'}{s}. \tag{H.4.7}$$

Another rearranged form of Eq. (H.4.6) is

$$s' = \frac{sf}{s - f}. \tag{H.4.8}$$

Equation (H.4.6), the Gaussian lens equation, was used and popularized by the German astronomer and physicist Karl Friedrich Gauss.

Equation (H.4.8) is not a different equation. It is just a rearrangement of Eq. (H.4.6) which helps us interpret the algebraic properties of s'. Note that if f is positive (converging lens) and if $s > f$ (that is, if the object is to the left of focal point A), s' is positive; i.e., the image is located to the right of the lens. If $s < f$ (that is, if the object is between A and O), s' is negative, implying that the image is located to the *left* of the lens. Compare these results with your geometrical work in Problems H.1 and H.2. Note carefully that positive values of s' are associated with real images and negative values with virtual images, and that this association becomes part of our *interpretation* of the algebraic properties of s'.

Interpret Eq. (H.4.7) carefully; it contains a great deal of information. For example, Eq. (H.4.7) says that a real image formed by a convex lens is always *inverted* relative to the object. It also says that a virtual image is erect relative to the object. Equation (H.4.7) also gives information about the relative *sizes* of object and image. Be sure to extract all these interpretations in your own words.

A remarkably simple form of the lens equation can be obtained if we define the following quantities:

$$z = s - f, \qquad (H.4.9)$$

$$z' = s' - f. \qquad (H.4.10)$$

(Interpret these definitions on a diagram and in your own words. They simply assign numbers to object and image positions by measuring distances to the right or left of the respective principal foci.)

Combine Eqs. (H.4.9) and (H.4.10) with Eq. (H.4.8) so as to eliminate s and s', and show that the deceptively messy combination actually reduces to

$$zz' = f^2. \qquad (H.4.11)$$

Equation (H.4.11) is known as the *Newtonian lens equation*. Many texts and workers in the field use this equation in preference to the Gaussian form.

PROBLEM H.7.   Reexamine your geometrical diagrams in Problems H.1, H.2, and H.3 in the light of Eqs. (H.4.6) and (H.4.7). Verify that the equations predict all the image effects you discovered geometrically. Remember our convention that $f < 0$ for a diverging lens.

PROBLEM H.8.   Reexamine Fig. H.3.3 and Problem H.4 in the light of Eqs. (H.4.6) and (H.4.7). Verify that the equations predict all the image effects you discovered geometrically. Remember the convention that $s < 0$ for a virtual object.

For supplementary references on image formation by thin lenses, see:

Physics, Physical Science Study Committee. Boston: D. C. Heath, 1960, Chapter 14

Physics for Students of Science and Engineering, R. Resnick and D. Halliday. New York: Wiley & Sons, 1960, Chapter 42

University Physics, F. W. Sears and M. Zemansky. Reading, Mass.: Addison-Wesley, 1964

Index

ABCDE698765